Geography of

NORTH AMERICA

GEORGE J. MILLER
Indiana University

ALMON E. PARKINS
Late of George Peabody College for Teachers

BERT HUDGINS
Wayne University

THIRD EDITION

NEW YORK · JOHN WILEY & SONS, INC.

LONDON · CHAPMAN & HALL, LIMITED

PREFACE

To the Third Edition

In a comparatively short period of time white man has moved into and taken possession of North America. In his endeavor to satisfy his wants he has striven to make the most effective use of his resources, chief among which are those of the natural setting in which he is placed. In his occupancy of the land he has been guided, consciously or unconsciously, by his human desires and the natural conditions. His occupancy of the continent and his utilization of the natural resources available to him are the central theme of this book. What are the natural assets of the land he has occupied? What use has he made of those assets? What opportunities are still available to him? What are some of the social, political, and economic outcomes of his endeavor to utilize his resources and attain a higher standard of material well-being? These are but a few of many questions that may properly arise. Such a study involves consideration of physical features such as climate, relief, soils, minerals, etc., and native plant and animal life as elements of the natural environment. We believe that these features should receive sufficient consideration in a textbook to enable the student to evaluate their relationship to the cultural landscape. Some students have a tendency either to forget the earth upon which man lives in their enthusiasm to describe what man does, or forget man in their enthusiasm to describe the natural landscape.

Types of "geographical regions" appear to be about as numerous as authors, and most of such regions are little used by the average citizen. As an outgrowth of many years of class work with hundreds of beginning students we have found the units used in this book convenient for an introductory study. They are regions in common use, and hence of particular significance, since the great majority of students will study the geography of North America as a part of their training in general education. Only a few will become specialists in the geographic field, and to such students the book will serve as an introductory course. Since the book is designed as a basic textbook—not a treatise—it has been our purpose to present only the more general and basic materials, leaving the more detailed presentation and study to the instructor and student. It may be considered as the starting point for a study of the continent.

The usual statistical appendix has been omitted, since such material is readily obtainable from government and other sources. Furthermore, students should receive training in the use of original source material. As an aid in starting a working library we recommend the accompanying selected list of references. We follow the practice of assigning all these references and expect them to have been studied by the time the course is completed.

We wish to acknowledge our indebtedness to many individuals and government bureaus whose work has been drawn upon freely in the preparation of this book. Without the splendid work of the late Dr. O. E. Baker and his colleagues, the discussion of agriculture in the United States would be inadequate indeed. Other specific acknowledgments are made throughout.

We are also especially indebted to various departments of the Canadian Government, particularly the Bureau of Statistics, which has supplied a large amount of material, maps, and diagrams; to Dr. R. L. Gentilcore who read all the manuscript on Canada and contributed constructive criticism in the preparation of numerous maps; to Dr. Erwin Raisz and to Dr. A. K. Lobeck for permission to use the physiographic maps of Alaska and of North America. We also owe much to many who have used the second edition in their college classes and who have aided by giving constructive suggestions; also to many of our students who have contributed to this edition by selecting parts of the text not clear to them and suggesting what was needed. Further criticisms and suggestions are invited.

GEORGE J. MILLER
BERT HUDGINS

March, 1954

Selected List of References

A given publication is listed only once, though it may contain material on several of the divisions shown. Magazines carry a vast amount of material of great value, but very few such references are listed.

GENERAL

1. United States Government Publications. (Lists should be obtained from at least the following departments.)

   1. Department of Commerce.
   2. Department of Agriculture.
   3. Department of State.
   4. Department of the Interior.
   5. War Department.
   6. Navy Department.
   7. Government Printing Office. (Copies of catalogs of government publications.)

2. United Nations Publications, New York, N. Y.
3. *Energy Resources of the World*. Government Printing Office, Dept. of State, 1949.
4. *Goode's School Atlas*. Rand McNally, Chicago, 1949.
5. V. C. Finch and G. T. Trewartha, *Elements of Geography*, McGraw-Hill, New York, 1949.
6. N. A. Bengtson and W. Van Royen, *Fundamentals of Economic Geography*. Prentice-Hall, New York, 1950.
7. Dorothy Good, "Some Recent Studies of Population," *Geographical Review, 35*, p. 122, 1945.
8. G. T. Trewartha, *An Introduction to Weather and Climate*, McGraw-Hill, New York, 1949.
9. T. S. Lovering, *Minerals in World Affairs*. Prentice-Hall, New York, 1943.
10. G. E. Pearcy, "Air Transportation—World Coverage," *Jour. of Geography, 28*, p. 105, 1949.
11. A. N. Strahler, *Physical Geography*, Wiley, New York, 1951.
12. G. W. Robinson, *Soils: Their Origin, Constitution and Classification*. Wiley, New York, 1951.
13. H. M. Kendall, R. M. Glendinning, and C. H. MacFadden, *Introduction to Geography*. Harcourt, Brace, New York, 1951.
14. J. C. Weaver and F. E. Luckermann, *A World Statistical Survey of Commercial Production: A Geography Source Book*. Burgess, Minneapolis, 1950.
15. W. E. Pratt and Dorothy Good, *World Geography of Petroleum*. Princeton University Press, Princeton, 1950.

16. Edwin Raisz, *Atlas de Cuba*. Harvard University Press, Cambridge, 1949.
17. J. L. Jones and P. W. Bryan, *North America*. E. P. Dutton, New York, 1949.
18. A. M. Bateman, *Economic Mineral Deposits*. Wiley, New York, 1950.
19. C. E. Landon, *Industrial Geography*. Prentice-Hall, New York, 1947.
20. J. R. Smith and M. O. Phillips, *North America*. Harcourt, Brace, New York, 1940.
21. J. R. Smith and M. O. Phillips, *Industrial and Commercial Geography*. Holt, *New York, 1946*.
22. P. E. James and H. V. B. Kline, *A Geography of Man*. Ginn, New York, 1949.
23. O. W. Freeman and H. F. Raup, *Essentials of Geography*. McGraw-Hill, New York, 1949.
24. D. H. Davis, *The Earth and Man*. Macmillan, New York, 1948.
25. G. L. White and G. T. Renner, *Human Geography*. Appleton-Century-Crofts, New York, 1948.
26. Guy-Harold Smith (Editor), *Conservation of Natural Resources*. Wiley, New York, 1950.
27. William Vogt, *Road to Survival*. William Sloane Associates, New York, 1948.
28. G. Renner, L. Durand, Jr., C. Langdon White, and W. B. Gibson, *World Economic Geography*. Crowell, New York, 1951.
29. William Van Royen, Oliver Bowles, and others, *Mineral Resources of the World*. Prentice-Hall, New York, 1952.
30. *Strategic Materials Surveys*. U. S. Government Printing Office, Washington, D. C., 1952.
31. *Resources for Freedom*. U. S. Government Printing Office, Washington, D. C., 1952.
32. *A Water Policy for the American People*. U. S. Government Printing Office, Washington, D. C., 1950.

MAGAZINES

1. *Journal of Geography*. A. J. Nystrom & Co., 3333 Elston Ave., Chicago, Ill. (Official Publication of the National Council of Geography Teachers.)
2. *Economic Geography*. Clark University, Worcester, Mass.
3. *Geographical Review*. American Geographical Society, New York, N. Y.
4. *Focus*. American Geographical Society, New York, N. Y.
5. *Annals of the Association of American Geographers*. Central Office, Map Division, Library of Congress, Washington, D. C.
6. *Commercial America*. Philadelphia Commercial Museum, Philadelphia, Pa.
7. *Commerce Reports*. U. S. Dept. of Commerce, Washington, D. C.
8. *Americas*. Pan-American Union, Washington, D. C.
9. *National Geographic Magazine*, Washington, D. C.
10. *Canadian Geographical Journal*. Canadian Geographical Society, Montreal.
11. Trade magazines such as those for petroleum, coal, and iron industries.
12. Many general magazines such as *U. S. News*, *Fortune*, and *Foreign Affairs*.

UNITED STATES

1. U. S. *Yearbooks of Agriculture*. Government Printing Office, Washington, D. C.
2. *Statistical Abstract of the United States* (an annual). Government Printing Office, Washington, D. C.
3. *Census of the United States*. Government Printing Office, Washington, D. C.
4. G.–H. Smith (Editor), *Conservation of Natural Resources*. Wiley, New York, 1950.
5. H. F. Otte, *Industrial Opportunity in the Tennessee Valley and Northern Alabama*. Columbia University Press, New York, 1940.
6. H. H. Bennett, *Soil Conservation*. McGraw-Hill, New York, 1943.

7. *Minerals Yearbook.* U. S. Government Printing Office, Washington, D. C.

8. A. J. Wright, *United States and Canada.* Appleton-Century-Crofts, New York, 1948.

9. C. L. White and E. J. Foscue, *Regional Geography of Anglo America.* Prentice-Hall, New York, 1943.

10. O. W. Freeman and H. H. Martin, *The Pacific Northwest.* Wiley, New York, 1942.

11. Loyal Durand, "The American Dairy Region," *Jour. of Geography, 48,* p. 1, 1949.

12. *Fishery Resources of the United States.* U. S. Senate Document No. 51, 79th Congress, 1st Session, Washington, D. C., 1945.

13. R. E. Ward, "Northern Great Plains as Producer of Wheat," *Economic Geography, 22,* p. 231, 1946.

14. T. R. Carskadon and R. Modley, *United States: Measure of a Nation.* Macmillan, New York, 1949.

15. W. H. Haas and others, *The American Empire.* University of Chicago Press, Chicago, 1940.

16. U. S. *Yearbook of Agriculture,* Government Printing Office, Washington, D. C.
    1. *Soils and Men,* 1938.
    2. *Climate and Man,* 1941.
    3. *Science in Farming,* 1943-1947.
    4. *Grass,* 1948.
    5. *Trees,* 1949.

17. *Investigation of National Resources,* Hearings Before a Subcommittee of the Committee on Public Lands, U. S. Senate, 80th Congress, 1st Session, Government Printing Office, Washington, D. C., 1947.

18. J. A. Guthrie, *The Economics of Pulp and Paper.* State College of Washington, Pullman, 1950.

19. C. E. Kellogg, *The Soils that Support Us.* Macmillan, New York, 1941.

20. *Mineral Resources of the United States,* by the staffs of the Bureau of Mines and Geological Survey, Public Affairs Press, Washington, D. C., 1948.

21. Fairfield Osborn, *Our Plundered Planet.* Little, Brown, Boston, 1948.

22. Walter R. Ingalls, "The Great Lead and Zinc Mines," *Mining and Metallurgy, 27,* September, 1946.

23. Franklin C. Erickson, "The Broken Cotton Belt," *Economic Geography, 24,* October, 1948.

24. Thomas Russell Smith, *The Cotton Textile Industry of Fall River, Massachusetts; A Study of Industrial Localization.* King's Crown Press, New York, 1944.

25. Terry Ramsaye, "Rise and Place of the Motion Picture," *Annals of the American Academy of Political and Social Science, 254,* November, 1947.

26. United States Department of Interior, Bureau of Reclamation, *How Reclamation Works,* Washington, 1947; *The Columbia River,* Washington, 1947; *Central Valley (California) Project Studies,* Problems 1-7, Washington, 1945.

27. A. E. Parkins and J. R. Whitaker, *Our National Resources and Their Conservation.* Wiley, New York, 2nd Ed., 1939.

28. C. F. Korstian and L. M. James, *Forestry in the South.* Dietz Press, Richmond, 1948.

29. E. A. Ackerman, *New England's Fishing Industry.* University of Chicago Press, Chicago, 1941.

30. W. F. Thompson, *The Effect of Fishing on Stocks of Halibut in the Pacific.* University of Washington Press, Seattle, 1950.

31. P. K. Whelpton, *Forecasts of the Population of the United States,* 1945-1975. Bureau of the Census, Government Printing Office, Washington, D. C., 1947.

32. L. A. Stoddard and A. D. Smith, *Range Management.* McGraw-Hill, New York, 1943.

33. J. Russell Smith, *Tree Crops, A Permanent Agriculture without Plowing.* Devin-Adair, New York, 1950.

34. Ralph H. Brown, *Historical Geography of the United States*. Harcourt, Brace, New York, 1948.
35. Erich W. Zimmermann, *World Resources and Industries*. Harper, New York, 1951.
36. *Atlas of Pacific Northwest Resources and Development*. J. K. Gill Co., Portland, 1953.
37. *Economic Subregions of the United States*. U. S. Government Printing Office, Washington, D. C., 1953.

ALASKA

1. G. W. Gasser, "Agriculture in Alaska," *Arctic Journal of the Arctic Institute of North America. 1*, p. 75, 1948.
2. W. A. Rockie, "A Picture of Matanuska." *Geographical Review, 82*, p. 353, 1942.
3. L. J. Palmer and C. H. Rouse, *A Study of the Alaska Tundra*. Research Report 10, Fish and Wild Life Service, Government Printing Office, Washington, D. C., 1945.
4. W. A. Rockie, "What of Alaska?" *Soil Conservation, XI*, p. 147, 1946.
5. H. F. Bain, *Alaska's Minerals as a Basis for Industry*. Information Circular 7379, Bureau of Mines, Washington, D. C., 1946.
6. G. Sundborg, *Opportunity in Alaska*. Macmillan, New York, 1945.
7. K. H. Stone, *The Matanuska Valley Colony*. Bureau of Land Management, Department of Interior, Washington, D. C.
8. S. R. Tompkins, *Alaska*. University of Oklahoma Press, Norman, 1945.
9. *Proceedings of the Alaskan Science Conference*. National Academy of Sciences, Bull. National Research Council, No. 122, Washington, D. C., 1951.
10. *Mid-Century Alaska*. U. S. Government Printing Office, Washington, D. C., 1951.

CANADA

1. Publications of the Canadian Bureau of Statistics and Geographical Bureau of Information. Numerous departments issue publications of great value.
2. *The Canada Yearbook*. King's Printer and Controller of Stationery, Ottawa. A *must* in a reference library.
3. Griffith Taylor, "Future Population in Canada," *Economic Geography, 22*, p. 67, 1947.
4. Trevor Lloyd, "The MacKenzie Waterway," *Geological Review, 33*, p. 415, 1943.
5. C. W. Johnson, "Relative Decline of Wheat in the Prairie Provinces of Canada," *Economic Geography, 24*, p. 209, 1948.
6. Griffith Taylor, *Canada*. Dutton, New York, 1945.
7. J. L. Robinson and M. J. Robinson, *The Geography of Canada*. Longmans, Green, Toronto, 1950.
8. *Province of Newfoundland: Statistical Background*. Dominion Bureau of Statistics, Ottawa.
9. A. W. Currie, *The Geography of Canada*. Macmillan, Toronto, 1945.
10. *Canadian Provinces* (a series, with one bulletin for each province). Canadian Geographical Society, Ottawa.
11. W. D. Albright, "Past, Present, and Future of the Peace," *Canadian Geographical Magazine, XVI*, p. 127, 1938.
12. *Native Trees of Canada*. Dominion Forest Service, Bull. 61, King's Printer, Ottawa, 1949.
13. *Reindeer in Canada*. Lands and Development Service, King's Printer, Ottawa, 1949.
14. *Canada Today*. Bank of Montreal, Montreal, 1949.
15. S. C. Hudson and others, *Types of Farming in Canada*. Dept. of Agriculture, Farmer's Bull. 157, King's Printer, Ottawa, 1949.

16. B. V. Gutsell, *Introduction to the Geography of Newfoundland*. Geographical Bureau of Information, Ottawa, 1949.
17. *Canada* (published annually). Dominion Bureau of Statistics, Ottawa.
18. *Canadian Frontiers of Settlement* (a series of nine volumes). Macmillan, Toronto.
19. D. F. Putnam (and others), *Canadian Regions, A Geography of Canada*. Dent and Sons, Toronto, 1952.

MEXICO AND MIDDLE AMERICA

1. R. R. Platt et al., *The European Possessions in the Caribbean Area*. American Geographical Society Map of Hispanic America, No. 4, New York, 1941.
 2. M. Santillan, "Synopsis of the Geology of Mexico," *Bull. of the American Association of Petroleum Geologists, 20* (4), 1936.
 3. R. de C. Ward and C. F. Brooks, "The Climates of North America," *in* W. Koppen and R. Geiger, *Handbuch der Klimatologie, 2*, Part J, Berlin, 1936.
 4. S. Chase and M. Tyler, *Mexico: A Study of Two Americas*. Macmillan, New York, 1944.
 5. H. C. Herring, *Mexico, the Making of a Nation*. Foreign Policy Assn., New York, 1942.
 6. C. L. Jones, "Production of Wealth in Mexico," *Annals of the American Academy of Political and Social Science, 208*, 1940.
 7. E. N. Simpson, *The Ejido, Mexico's Way Out*. University of North Carolina Press, Chapel Hill, 1937.
 8. N. L. Whetten, *Rural Mexico*. University of Chicago Press, Chicago, 1948.
 9. C. Senior, *Democracy Comes to a Cotton Kingdom: The Story of Mexico's La Laguna*. League For Industrial Democracy, New York, N. Y., 1940.
10. M. Covarrubias, *Mexico South: The Isthmus of Tehuantepec*. Knopf, New York, 1946.
11. N. S. Haynes, "Mexico City: Its Growth and Configuration," *American Jour. of Sociology, 50*, 1945.
12. J. Biesanz and M. Biesanz, *Costa Rican Life*. Columbia University Press, New York, 1944.
13. S. Tax, "Ethnic Relations in Guatemala," *American Indigena, 2*, 1942.
14. Great Britain, Colonial Office, *Agriculture in the West Indies*. Colonial Report, No. 182, London, 1942.
15. J. G. Leyburn, *The Haitian People*. Yale University Press, New Haven, 1941.
16. W. A. Roberts, *The French in the West Indies*. Bobbs-Merrill, Indianapolis, 1942.
17. F. Ortiz Fernández, *Cuban Counterpoint, Tobacco and Sugar* (trans. from Spanish by H. de Oniz). Knopf, New York, 1947.
18. C. Schuchert, *Historical Geology of the Antillean-Caribbean Region, or the Lands Bordering the Gulf of Mexico and the Caribbean Sea*. Wiley, New York, 1935.
19. A. H. Verrill, *West Indies of Today*. Dodd Mead, New York, 1931.
20. G. F. Deasy and P. Gerhard, "Settlements in Baja California: 1768-1930," *Geographical Review, 34*, 1944.
21. R. Redfield, *The Folk Culture of Yucatan*. University of Chicago Press, Chicago, 1941.
22. C. O. Sauer, "Aboriginal Population of Northwestern Mexico," *Geographical Review, 31*, 1941.
23. O. Lewis: "Social and Economic Changes in a Mexican Village: Tepoztlan, 1926-1944," *America Indigena, 4*, 1944.
24. D. D. Brand, "Dividivi and Sesame in Mexico," *Economic Geography, 17*, 1941.
25. Preston E. James, *Latin America* (Revised Edition). Odyssey, New York, 1950.
26. Howard F. Cline, *"The United States and Mexico*. Harvard University Press, Cambridge, Mass., 1953.
27. Charles Curtis Cumberland, *Mexican Revolution*. University of Texas Press, Austin, 1952.

CONTENTS

North America—The Continent

CHAPTER 1

The Continent
and Man

In examining a continent the geographer is concerned with a description of its major natural features and with its present and potential value to man. The natural features provide the setting, but man decides what will be done in that setting. In other words, the natural setting does not determine what man *will* do but places limits on what he *may* do, as his technical knowledge evolves. We must, therefore, consider both the geographical environment of man and man himself. His decisions may bring economic prosperity and happiness, or he may destroy the natural resources available to him, and may even destroy himself and the society of which he is a part.

The fitness of a continent or a region as a home for man may be measured by the number of people it can support and, if it has long been occupied, by the number it does sustain. The number it is sustaining can readily be determined by a census. But to determine the ultimate possible population with any degree of certainty is a difficult, if not an impossible, task because of the many factors involved. Besides, many of these factors are variable.

Since no continent is, at present, supporting all the people it can, that is, since no continent has reached the saturation point, a time factor is involved, and time in the future. Since the normal increase over a period of years is slight, the time involved is long, a matter of many, many centuries.

Besides the time factor, there are both natural environmental and human factors. Among the natural environmental factors are:

1. The degree of productivity of the soil. This is largely based on the topography of the land, on the climate, and on man, of course, who must manipulate the soil.

2. The length of the growing season, the amount of insolation, and the amount and seasonal distribution of rainfall.

3. The healthfulness of the region.

4. The power and mineral resources.

5. The natural conditions for transportation.

3

Whereas the climatic factors are fairly constant over even long periods, the resources may become depleted or even exhausted. Man cannot change the climate (except in very local situations, and then only slightly), but he may permit the soil to wear out or be destroyed by erosion and gullying. Coal, oil, gas, metallic minerals, and even some non-metallic minerals may be exhausted. On the other hand, man may by drainage and irrigation make non-productive lands productive and, by careful treatment of the soils, may increase their fertility. He may discover how to utilize materials previously considered worthless. He may improve on the natural transportation facilities, deepen harbors and rivers, excavate canals, bore tunnels, and construct bridges.

The human factors are highly variable. Man is constantly improving his methods and techniques in the utilization of natural resources. The most variable of all human factors, the most uncertain, are man's standards of living and his social ideals and practices. Resources and their utilization concern the production of consumers' goods, and the standards of living affect consumption. Both, therefore, are involved in estimating the number of people a given area may support.

MAN IN NORTH AMERICA

American civilization is transplanted European civilization modified, to some extent, by adaptations to the American natural environment. Europeans brought with them experiences and techniques in the utilization of resources and unbounded human energy that enabled them to reach on the North American continent, within two or three centuries, economic and social developments that had taken Europeans thousands of years to evolve.

In a few regions on the North American continent the Indian had made much advance, as in central Mexico, in and about the Mexican basin, in Yucatan and the lands to the south, in what is now the United States Southwest, central New York, and the mountain valleys of the south. But in most parts of North America there were no barriers to protect a nascent civilization from hostile marauders or to check the wandering habits of the people. Apparently, judging from a world-wide study of evolving civilizations, an increasing population is the dynamic factor, the urge, that forces man into a more advanced type of land utilization. Accompanying this is an advance in culture. There is little doubt that in time the majority of the Indian tribes of North America would have developed an advanced civilization, but it would have taken many thousands of years. A small percentage of the Indians of Mexico and Central America have participated actively.

since about 1820, in the development of Latin North America, but it is to the white man that we owe the present-day advance in the United States and Canada, i.e., in English America.

The Areas of Moderate to Very Dense Population. When migrants spread over a continent, as the Europeans and their descendants did in the exploration and settlement of North America, they tend to select the regions best suited to supply them the necessities of life, and surpluses, with the least expenditure of human energy. How well they succeed depends greatly on their experience in pioneering, on their utilization of resources, and on the extent of their knowledge of the continent. Before the survey of the continent is fully completed excellent opportunities are likely to go unclaimed. As the explorers and exploiters gain in experience in their new environments, their degree of utilization increases; and, as the demands on the environment become greater (with increasing population density), the science of production and conservation advances and the environments yield more and more. This makes a still larger population possible. This has been the process and the condition in North America up to the present, at least. The continent has had an evolving civilization, and the curve of population growth (see Fig. 3) has always had an upward trend. The advances have been most rapid in English North America. Since the migrants to the continent came from the east, the eastern section has the older settlements and the larger population. The southeastern quarter of English America has by far the most people of the continent (Fig. 1). In this most densely settled area live more than four-fifths of the people of the United States and nearly two-thirds of Canada's population. Here are the largest number of cities and the largest cities of these two countries. In Canada the most densely settled area is the Great Lakes-St. Lawrence Lowland. This is the industrial section of Canada.

The largest aggregation of people on the whole continent is to be found about the mouth of the Hudson in what we may call the geographic New York area. The center of population of the United States is in southeastern Illinois, but the center of greatest density of population is this small area within a 15-mile radius of the city of New York. From this New York center northeastward to Boston and southwestward to Philadelphia is the most densely settled area, for its size, on the continent.

Why this great concentration of people? Largely because it is here that natural conditions have, since the earliest period of occupancy of the region by Europeans, been highly favorable for man to make a living, through commerce, manufacturing, transportation, and financial transactions. Some of the natural environmental conditions that have favored man's work here are: location on the shores of the North Atlantic, which has, since the settlement of the Americas, been the busiest of oceans; close and relatively easy contacts with the great inte-

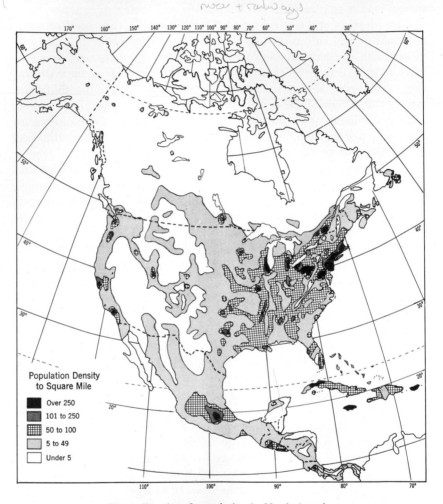

Fig. 1. Density of population in North America.

rior of the continent; proximity to the great coal and oil (oil is nearing exhaustion) fields of the northern Appalachians; and a large amount of water power. The present-day activities are, of course, based to some degree on developments in the past. Men and women have flocked to this center from both home and abroad. Nearly all of the millions of immigrants that have come to America, chiefly to improve their economic conditions, have entered through the ports of this area.

Factories, docks, banks, customs houses, steamboats, and railways are not, however, the only elements in the cultural landscape. Here for more than a century man has practiced intensive agriculture, and extensive agriculture for two centuries before this. The farmers are producing far more to the acre than the farmers of most other sections of the United States. Yet so many are the urban dwellers and so few the farmers of this manufacturing-commercial area that the area is "parasitic." Both men and machines must be fed by other regions. Even the farmers producing specialties in foods purchase a large part of their food elsewhere, and the dairymen import much of the concentrated feed supplied to their cattle. In this relationship of man and factories to food and raw materials, transportation plays an active part.

Each of the other more densely populated sections in eastern United States and Canada, shown on Fig. 1, has similar advantages for manufacturing and commerce. Some centers like Pittsburgh, Cleveland, Detroit, and Chicago have become world famous as manufacturers of some special type of commodity.

The most densely settled area of Mexico is about the capital city, Mexico, D.F. As in most Latin American countries, the capital city is the most populous in the realm, for it is both a political and a social center. Here live, for a part of the year at least, a large percentage of the wealthy landowners, and with each is a retinue of servants. Mexico, D.F., is not without its factories. Here, too, are many of the headquarters of the companies (a great number of them foreign) that operate mines, factories, and other large enterprises.

The plateau of central Mexico has many attractions for the farmer. It has moderate rainfall and mild temperatures the year round over a large area. The mountainous character of the surface greatly restricts the area suitable for cultivation, but there are productive valleys; and the low standard of living of a large part of the rural population makes it possible for a few acres of cultivated land per farm to sustain a large family.

The Areas of Low Population Density in the United States. Western United States (westward from the 100th meridian, approximately), is sparsely settled, though its area is nearly half that of the United States.

Man and his works are very unevenly distributed in the West. He lives, as a rule, where water is available. Taking the region as a whole, water is scarce. In the Pacific Northwest, west of the mountains, rainfall is both abundant and fairly well distributed seasonally. Elsewhere rains fall mostly on the mountains, and from here man directs it, by irrigation works, upon valley and piedmont lands. The irrigated acreage is very unevenly distributed, and, hence, the population is widely scattered. Cultivation, in general, is intensive. The population density on the irrigated lands is, therefore, greater than in the average rural community in the humid sections of the United States. Irrigation farming, mining, grazing, lumbering, commerce, transportation, and some dry- and humid-land farming are the occupations that sustain the people in this land of little rainfall. The sparsity of population in a large part of this vast area is due primarily to aridity.

Although the lack of water restricts the number of people engaged in agriculture, it has little effect on the population that earns, or might earn, its living from mining. Mining companies in some locations are put to great expense to provide water for their operations, particularly in the concentration and separation of the metals. Few mineral deposits, however, are unworked because of a lack of water.

That an ocean location offers superior advantages for people to make a living is evidenced by the fact that four of the six larger cities of the West are Pacific Ocean ports, with factories and commercial ties that extend to many lands on the shores of the great ocean, some of them also to the Atlantic. California and Washington have densities of population like those of the Midwest.

Areas of Low Population Density in Mexico and Canada. Types of land utilization similar to that of the arid United States West support the people of Mexico in the area of thin population. Living, however, is on a far lower scale of existence. A large fraction of the population of northern Mexico and southern Yucatan is almost as untouched by modern civilization as in the days of Cortez. Here and there irrigation works on a large scale have been set up, and in northern Yucatan commercial farming of henequen supports part of the population. But most of the people live by rather primitive agriculture.

Canada has the bulk of the unoccupied land of the continent. The thinly settled areas form a narrow fringe scarcely more than 100 miles wide along a part of the northern border of the United States. The remainder of the scant population of this vast country, which is larger in square miles than the United States, is less than 2 people to the square mile.

This small population and the vast area of unoccupied land are not because man is a recent arrival, for some of the oldest settlements in English North America were made (by the French) in Maritime Canada, along the St. Lawrence, and on the shores of the Great Lakes. Environmental, geographic, and historical conditions and circumstances have conspired against man's establishing himself in large numbers in Canada.

Canada's proximity to the United States is a factor of no small influence in checking Canada's growth. The United States to the south, with a more genial climate, cheap lands, democratic institutions (Canada was a French and later a British colony until 1867), and greater reputation as a home for the poor, landless, and persecuted drew to its shores the vast bulk of Europeans who crossed the Atlantic to find a home in North America. Some manufacturing and intensive agriculture in parts of the St. Lawrence Plains, extensive agriculture in Maritime Canada and the Prairie Plains, grazing, fishing, lumbering, mining, and fur collecting are now the sustenance activities of the people of Canada.

A Comparison of the Continents. North America, after more than three centuries of occupancy by Europeans and their descendants, has come to have some 200,000,000 people. In area, population, and population density, it is third in rank among the continents. These statistical comparisons may be read from Table I.

TABLE I

A COMPARISON OF THE CONTINENTS

Continent	Area in Square Miles (000 omitted)	Population* (000 omitted)	Density (per square mile)
North America	9,360	206,000	22.0
South America	6,825	104,000	15.2
Europe	3,774	532,000	140.9
Asia	16,495	1,285,000	77.9
Africa	11,530	187,000	16.2
Australia	2,975	7,700	2.6
Antarctica	5,363		
Total	56,322	2,321,700	

* Estimates.

Although North America falls far short of being as populous as Asia or Europe, its people have made great progress in the utilization of its rich store of resources and the establishment of civilization. Its youthfulness is a factor in its favor. For a long time to come, man will find here wonderful economic opportunities, superior to those of most other continents, for the acquisition of these things for which he has ever been seeking—peace, a home and its comforts, wealth, and influence. North

America today is the most advanced of the continental colonies of Europe.

THE FUTURE POPULATION OF NORTH AMERICA

Curves of Population Growth.   Many students of population phenomena find curves of population growth of great value in projecting trends into the future. In Fig. 2 are presented the population curves for the United States, England and Wales, Europe, and the world, covering the period from 1700 to 1930. Note that the vertical units—ordinates— differ in value in the curves. It should be noted, also, that the curves assume a common form. There is first a period of slow growth, followed by a period of rapid growth; and all the curves, by 1930, begin to show a decrease in the rate of slower growth. They begin to show a veering to the right, a tendency to establish a plateau. There is every reason, backed by some experimentation, for believing that all nations will eventually reach a stationary stage in their population growth when their people become so numerous as to approach, or arrive at, the limits of the sustenance power of their environment. Sustenance includes both the products of the soil raised within the country and the output of the mines and factories which are exchanged with other peoples for sustenance products. How many hundreds or thousands of years in the future it will be before the limits of sustenance of a given country are reached, only time can tell.

In the portions of the curves shown in Fig. 2 and marked "hypothetical," many changes in the indicated trends may occur.

We may consider a composite of these curves the normal curve form of population growth.

Another conclusion we draw from these curves (backed also by much other evidence) is that the vertical swing of the curve, the total growth in population, is roughly proportional to the size of the areas involved and their store of resources. It should be noted that the ordinate units (value of the units the same), the vertical range, of the curve of population growth of Europe are far less than those for the world; and that the curve for England and Wales would have a far lower vertical range than that for the United States if both were reduced to the same value for ordinate units.

The Population Curve of North America.   From a study of these curves we are led to believe that the population curve for North America up to the present (if complete data were available for its construction) would, in most respects, resemble that for the United States in form, but its vertical range (if the same units of value were used) would, of course, be greater. *The ultimate population of the world will be limited by the amount of food that the lands and waters of the world can be made to produce and the average per capita consumption of this food.* For a region, country, or con-

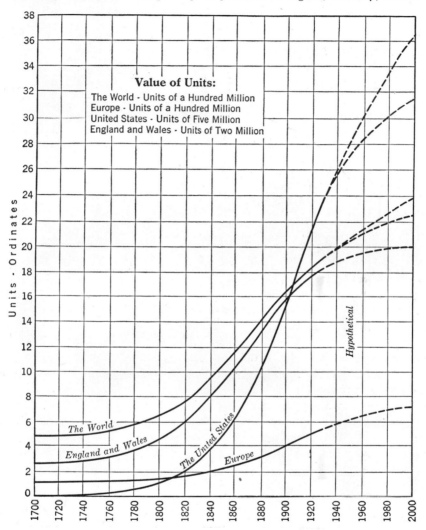

Value of Units:
The World - Units of a Hundred Million
Europe - Units of a Hundred Million
United States - Units of Five Million
England and Wales - Units of Two Million

Fig. 2. Population curves for the world, England and Wales, the United States, and Europe. The dotted portions of the curves are hypothetical. The curve for North America is similar to that for the United States. *Parkins.*

tinent the limits of population are set not alone by the area's ability to produce foods, but also by the resources that favor manufacturing and the exportation of fabricated products for food grown elsewhere. With

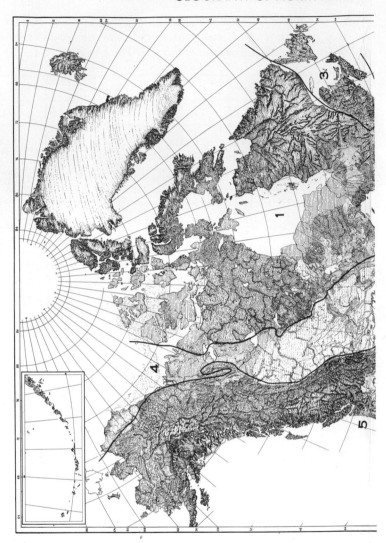

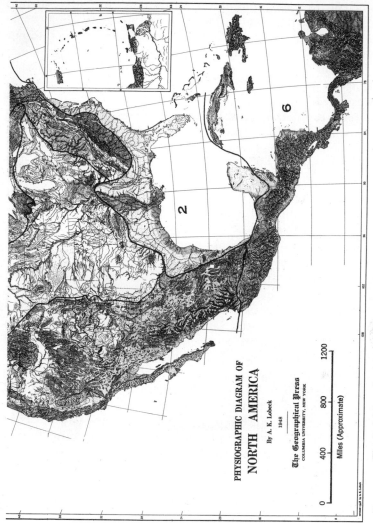

Fig. 3. Major physiographic provinces of North America. *Courtesy, A. K. Lobeck.*

1. Canadian Shield   3. Appalachian Highlands   5. North American Cordillera
2. Atlantic Plain   4. Interior Plains   6. Antillean Mountain System

PHYSIOGRAPHIC DIAGRAM OF
NORTH AMERICA

By A. K. Lobeck

1948

The Geographical Press
COLUMBIA UNIVERSITY, NEW YORK

0   400   800   1200

Miles (Approximate)

cheap, efficient transportation and an abundance of power, there is hardly a limit to the population that manufacturing areas may come to support. The limit to manufacturing is the size of the market. In our attempts to get some conception of North America's ultimate population and the limits to which its population curve will rise, both the food-producing ability and the industrial ability of the continent must therefore be considered.

Surface Features Affecting Land Utilization.   Plains have always been the seats of dense population groups and the centers of advanced civilizations. The plains of China, the Indus, the Tigris and Euphrates, and the Nile all hold prominent places in history because the people that occupied them have been prosperous and have made valuable contributions to developing world civilization. In North America today, it is almost wholly the plains lands that are occupied by the farmers of the continent. Here soil tends to be deep, leaching and slope wash are at the minimum, and there are few obstructions to the movements of man and the use of machinery.

North America has large areas of plains; the Great Central Plain from the Arctic to the Gulf of Mexico, the Atlantic Slope, the Coastal Plains of Central America (see Fig. 3), and the large river plains like those of the Yukon, Willamette, Sacramento, and San Joaquin. Unfortunately, parts of the plains areas have adverse climatic conditions. The intermontane plateaus that stretch from the Bering Sea to the Isthmus of Tehuantepec, in the western part of the continent, have surface features that offer few obstacles to their use for agriculture; but most of this entire area is too arid or too cold for profitable farming.

Mountain areas, in contrast to plains, do not lend themselves to widespread agriculture and are as a rule but thinly peopled. Agriculture is confined for the most part to the valleys and basins, and it is largely the area and fertility of these that determine the number of people. The slopes unsuited to tillage are likely to be clothed with forests, even if the foothills and plains about are arid; and mountain pasture lands may be utilized by cattle and sheep herders. Minerals and water power may also concentrate people at scattered points; and, if the mountain regions possess beauty of scenery, tourists and students of nature are attracted. Because of the healthful, bracing air of such regions, health resorts are established in them. Yet none of these methods of utilizing the land resources offers favorable conditions for a dense population.

When the mountain areas of the continent are added to the large tracts that are too cold and the other large tracts that are too arid for farming, there remains probably not more than a third of the continent that may be considered ideal (relatively) for agriculture. One is surprised at the vastness of the area that is limited in its value to man because of adverse physiographic and climatic conditions. Yet the other continents, except possibly Europe, are in no way superior to North America in this respect. A comparison of the production of some of the crops of the continents supports this generalization.

A Comparison of the Continents in Agriculture. Although younger historically than either Europe or Asia, with an area only a little more than half that of Asia, and with a population much less than a third of that of Europe and a sixth that of Asia, North America ranks remarkably well in the production of farm crops. Only the widest generalization and conclusion may be made in such comparisons, for latitude positions and other conditions greatly affect the kinds of crops grown, and many data are not reliable.

North America leads the continents in the production of corn, oats, sugar, and cotton, surpasses Asia in wheat, corn, sugar, cotton, and oats, and produces almost as much wheat, more oats, and almost as much rice as Europe. Corn is the outstanding crop of North America, and rice of Asia; and in these crops each leads the world. Can the corn crop of North America offset the rice crop of Asia? Is not the slight lead that Europe has over North America in wheat and rice more than compensated in North America's vastly superior production of corn and cotton? These questions must be answered by the student to his own satisfaction. Since North America is one of the "younger" continents it is likely to continue to hold a prominent rank in agricultural production.

Population Based on Agriculture. It has previously been pointed out that the ultimate population of a continent where economic existence is based on agriculture alone will be limited by the amount of food that the continent can produce. And as we have pointed out, the food-producing power of North America is based, so far as nature determines, on the area of land that has favorable climatic and topographic conditions. Man is an important factor, of course, since the amount of food that may be produced depends on his experience and technical skill in making nature "work" for him. In Europe, for example, for hundreds of years before about 1840 the average yield of wheat was 10 to 12 bushels to the acre. After Liebig's epoch-making experiments and discoveries in the chemistry of agriculture became known and utilized in soil improvement, the yield of wheat was gradually increased until, in countries like Britain and Belgium, the average is about 30 to 35 bushels, and many fields produce 50 to 60. There is, of course, no reason for thinking that improvements are at an end. The checking of soil erosion, careful selection of seed, careful adaptation of crop to soil and climate, breeding of new varieties of plants, introduction of new plants, better methods of tillage, more careful application of manures and fertilizers, improvements in the application of water to irrigated lands, and many other methods and practices recognized as improvements by agricultural experts, if applied to all the lands in North America to which they are applicable, will greatly increase yield and establish permanent agriculture. So far most of our farming has been exploitive. A hundred years ago the farmers of Europe and America had no conception of the great improvements that science would make, and did make, in the century following. We, at present, have no idea of the developments during the century to come. Yes, centuries to come, for there is every reason to believe that man will continue on and on for thousands and thousands and millions of years as the dominant form of life on this globe, and we feel confident that he will ever need to go to the soil for his sustenance.

In trying to form an estimate of the productive power of the agricultural lands of North America, we, of course, have limitations. We tend to form our judgments on the basis of present-day methods and practices of agricultural production.

Subsequent chapters present fairly complete discussions of the potentialities of all the countries and regions of the continent. The population possibilities are far from being uniform over the continent. The United States will always dominate by sheer numbers, but both Canada and Latin North America are capable of supporting many more people. From data available it seems probable that the continent can ultimately sustain 500,000,000 to 600,000,000 people by agriculture, practicing methods of land utilization now known, and maintaining a high-level standard of living. Although these estimates must be based on many variables, they give us an idea of the terms in which to think in evaluating the continent. Other resources, such as minerals, may be produced and exported either in the crude or fabricated form, in exchange for food.

CLIMATE AND HUMAN OCCUPANCY

It is probable that climate and weather exert a greater influence on man than any other elements in his natural environment. Soil is largely a product of climate and weather processing, and its productive value to man is dependent on climate and weather. Climate is commonly described as the mathematical mean of the weather, that is, of the conditions existing from day to day. All the elements of weather and climate—temperature, pressure, winds, and moisture—are measurable by

nches. From the Gulf of Mexico northward in the eastern
th America, there is a decreasing amount of rain. On the
, from about the parallel 23° southward in Mexico and

specially devised instruments, and the measurements are expressed in
mathematical terms. Averages and means are therefore easily determined. However, this is an oversimplification of the meaning of climate.
Data must be given for extremes as well as means, for departures from

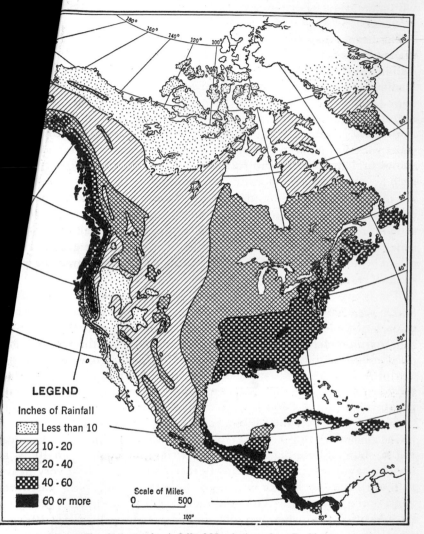

Fig. 6. Annual rainfall of North America. *Parkins.*

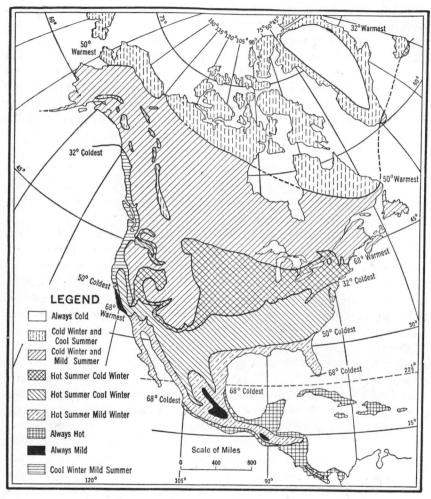

Fig. 4. Temperature regions of North America. *Parkins.*

Central America, there is an increasing amount. It is significant that
a large part of the continent has rainfall sufficient to produce useful
vegetation. These facts of rainfall distribution are phases of geography.
The explanation of these facts belongs, strictly speaking, to meteor-

the normal as well as for the normal, and for seasonal, monthly, or
daily as well as annual ranges. Man tends to adjust his activities to
the averages or means of weather and climate; yet it is the extremes of
heat and cold, excessive falls of rain or unusually long droughts, and
unseasonable frosts that often spell success or failure to his economic

activities. In this chapter, only the main outstanding characteristics of
the climate of the continent are presented, details being left to subsequent chapters.

Some Major Factors Affecting Climate.   The location of North America
in latitude and its latitude extent are among the important factors in
its geography, determining the angle at which the sun's rays strike the
land surface throughout the year, and thus its solar climate; determining what winds blow across the land, and thereby influencing both the
areal and the seasonal distribution of rain. How unlike present conditions would man's life be if the continent extended from the equator
to 50° N.! The longitude extent is one of the factors that affect the
amount of rainfall of the interior; but more important are the surface
features—altitude, and distribution of mountains and plains, the rela-

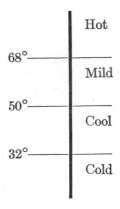

Fig. 5. Four types of months. The vertical line may be thought of as a thermometer
scale showing monthly averages. *Parkins.*

tion of the prevailing winds to ocean currents, and the location of storm
tracks.

Temperature Conditions of the Continent.   Except in the most general
way, maps of so-called climatic zones have little value, for zones are
the resultants of solar control, and the effect of solar control is so modified by other conditions that some visualizing device must be used that
contains as many of the factors controlling climate as may be conveniently shown on a map. We shall contine to talk about the tropics, the
temperate regions, the polar or frigid zones, but always with a feeling
of the inadequacy of the age-old terms to express climatic conditions.
So also must sea-level isothermal maps be discarded, for man carries
on his activities on the surface of the earth and geography is a study
of man's activties as adaptions or adjustments to the natural environ-

ment. Maps of mean annual ten___
ing the geography of regions, ex___
isothermal maps of the warmest a___
winter, and surface temperature-___
devices.

The Temperature-Region Map.   Te___
major elements of climate, and its sea___
itability of the continent. The simplifi___
4, shows surface temperatures groupe___
bounded by selected isotherms, the 32___
month, and the 32°, 50°, and 68° for the ___
isotherms are, after all, but one set that n___
ward with the sun. On the map, the 32°, ___
shown in their January and July positions. ___
such a way that the temperature conditions ___
are indicated, the coldest and warmest mon___
characteristics of the winter or summer season___
are the areas between the isotherms. This arran___
nine temperature regions for the world. Beca___
extent of North America, its latitude position and ___
series of regions is found in this continent.

The Types of Months.   The nine regions are ___
four types of months: cold, cool, mild, and hot. Th___
of each of these types is indicated by Fig. 5, which___
as a thermometer scale showing monthly means wit___
50°, and 68°. A month with a mean temperature ab___
ered a *hot* month. If the mean lies between 50° and ___
mild; between 32° and 50°, *cool;* and below 32°, *cold.* T___
peratures of January and July at any place determine t___
region in which that place falls.

The Annual Rainfall.   The map of annual rainfall of N___
Fig. 6, shows a long, narrow strip bordering the Pacific fr___
60° N., having 60 inches of rain. Bordering this section of___
rain are strips, each with decreasing amounts, lying to the___
Most of the western highland and mountain area and the G___
have less than 20 inches, but some of this section has less than___
scant), and some more than 20. The southeastern third of the ___
has 20 inches or more, and the southeastern quarter of the Unite___

[1] These three temperatures have ecological significance. The 68° isotherm___
coldest month is the approximate poleward limit of the palm; the 50° isotherm___
warmest month is the poleward limit of tree growth; and the 32° isotherm mar___
frost line.

ology. However, a brief summary of certain causal factors, such as winds, highlands, lowlands, and major water bodies, will help in understanding the rainfall distribution.[2]

North America north of 30°–35° N. latitude, is in the belt of the *Westerlies.* South of 25°–30° the *Northeast Trades* prevail. Northern Mexico and southwestern United States form an area that is debatable ground between the *Westerlies* and the *Northeast Trades.*

The west wind off the Pacific gives the very heavy rainfall on the Pacific Slope. The air, laden with moisture, is adiabatically cooled as it moves up over the Coast Range and again over the still higher Cascade-Sierra Nevada Range, and rain falls. The air descending on the eastern slope is warmed and becomes moisture-absorbing rather than moisture-giving. East-facing slopes (leeward) of these mountains, therefore, have less rainfall than west-facing (windward), yet are not so dry as the leeward lands at lower altitudes because the clouds that precipitate the moisture on the windward slopes are carried over beyond the crests of mountain ridges before the air begins its descent.

Most of the plateau between the Pacific ranges and the Rockies lies much below the level of the mountains to the west; it is therefore a region of low precipitation. The driest sections lie just to the east of the highest portion of the Pacific ranges.

There is rain on the Southern Rockies because many mountains stand even higher than the High Sierras. The Northern Rockies, although lower in altitude than the Southern Rockies and the still lower mountains of Idaho and northern Oregon, have moderate rainfall, chiefly because the Pacific ranges northward from 45° are less of a barrier to Pacific Ocean air than the mountains farther south. East of the Rockies, the eastward-moving air descends, is warmed, and becomes moisture-absorbing.

Since the eastern half of North America, north of 25° N., lies at a lower altitude than the western mountains and plateaus, how is it that the *Westerlies* bring rain to it and spread this rain copiously over a large area?

The low-pressure air masses, great eddies of air moving eastward and northeastward, largely from the Pacific, a few from the Gulf of Mexico and the Carribean, across North America in the belt of the *Westerlies,* give rain to the continent north of 30° to 35° N. latitude. Air moves into these low-pressure eddies from all points of the compass and is gradually forced upward. This upward-moving air is cooled by expansion, and moisture is precipitated. In the western half of North America,

[2] For a more complete discussion of climate see Trewartha, *An Introduction to Weather and Climate,* McGraw-Hill, 1949.

the rain-giving winds are moving from the Pacific to the Low. In the eastern half, the winds from the Gulf and the Atlantic bring the moisture. The Rockies, in a rough way, act as a great divide in the movement of the moisture that comes from the oceans and falls as rain. A Low on the western border of the Great Central Plain, to a large degree, draws in dry winds from the west; but if this Low is well developed it may affect the movement of air 800 miles or more to the east and southeast, even as far as the Gulf of Mexico or the Atlantic. Moisture-laden air starts from these bodies of water toward the center of the Low. While this air is moving northwestward the Low is moving eastward, and, by the time Gulf and Atlantic air gets to the Low center, the Low center has traveled several hundred miles from the western margin of the Great Central Plain. Much of the western margin of the Great Central Plain is, therefore, semiarid. Some of the water that falls as rain in Iowa, for example, has probably not come directly from the Atlantic or the Gulf. Part of it is reevaporated moisture from previous rains.

Low temperature, and thus limited capacity of the air for holding moisture, is the chief reason for the scant rainfall of the Arctic Slope. On the other hand, the high moisture capacity of the air in the tropical region of North America and the *Trade Winds* (for the most part) give moderate to very heavy rainfall in southern Mexico, Central America, and the West Indies. Windward slopes have the heavier rainfall. Some of the summer rain in Middle America comes from the northward-moving *Doldrum* belt.

Seasonal Distribution of Rainfall.   The seasonal distribution of rainfall is of vital importance to the farmer. Thirty inches of rain, with a large fraction coming in frequent gentle showers during the growing season, may provide more moisture for crops than 50 inches occurring largely during the late fall and winter. Figures 7 and 8 show the winter and summer distribution of rainfall. In winter the eastern and most of the western margins of the continent have more than 6 inches and the interior, from the Arctic to central Mexico, is dry. In summer a large part of the continent has more than 6 inches, including much of the Plains area. Except for relatively small areas the whole continent receives a moisture supply in the spring and summer. However, some areas (Fig. 7) are arid. A composite map of topography, heat, rainfall, and native vegetation indicates that nearly all the plains and lowlands, and many of the highlands, have sufficient heat and summer moisture for the growing of vegetation of value to man. This includes the Arctic tundra, grassland pastures, and forest lands. This favorable seasonal distribution is an important factor in man's use of the continent.

Climatic Regions of North America. Figure 9 shows the major climatic regions of North America as developed by Dr. Trewartha. Climatic regions are largely a combination of temperature and rainfall regions, but seasonal distribution of rain and the rate (known or probable) of evaporation are given due weight. Therefore, isotherms and isohyets constitute, for the most part, the boundaries of the regions, and the names of the regions express both rainfall and temperature conditions. It will be noted that the climates of the continent include nearly all types, ranging from the humid tropical rainforest to polar ice cap to hot deserts. Continental interior climates, as usual, are characterized by extremes, but a large proportion of the continent, especially the eastern half, has warm summers and a supply of moisture. The large area having a microthermal climate (Dcf) produces forest, and the polar area

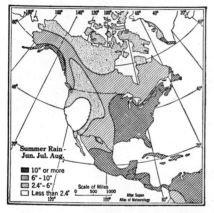

Fig. 7.

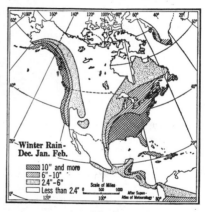

Fig. 8.

(ET) produces vegetation suitable for reindeer and caribou pasture. The climates of the west coast range from polar, microthermal, mesothermal, tropical and subtropical desert, to tropical savanna. This great variety of climates enables man to produce a great variety of products. It is probable that the continent is capable of producing any vegetative growth that man utilizes in any other part of the world. Suppose you could wave the "magic wand" and change the climate of the continent, what changes would you make? Suppose you could cut down the western highlands to an altitude of 1000 feet, how would the climates of North America be changed? Would conditions be more, or less, favorable to man?

MINERAL RESOURCES AFFECTING OCCUPANCY

Europe, the United States, and southern Canada are probably the best known geologically; yet in the United States new deposits of useful

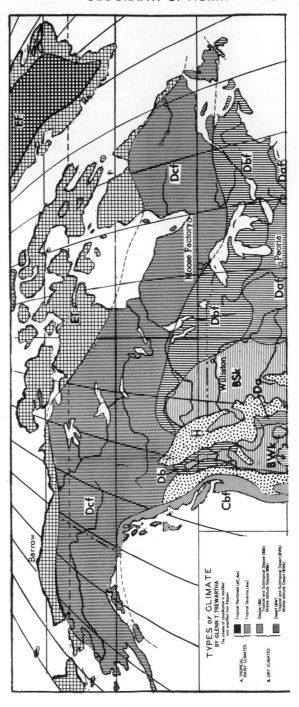

TYPES OF CLIMATE
BY GLENN T. TREWARTHA
The scheme of classification is modified
and simplified from Köppen

A. TROPICAL
RAINY CLIMATES

Tropical Rainforest (Af, Am)

Tropical Savanna (Aw)

B. DRY CLIMATES

Steppe (BS)
Tropical and Subtropical Steppe (BSh)
Middle latitude Steppe (BSk)

Desert (BW)
Tropical and Subtropical Desert (BWh)
Middle latitude Desert (BWk)

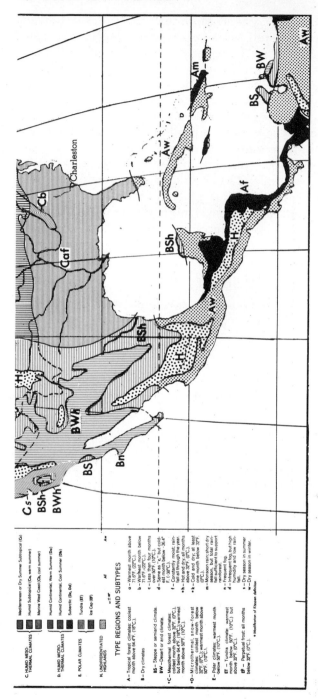

Fig. 9. Climatic regions of North America. The scheme of classification is modified and simplified from Köppen. *After Goode's School Atlas, Courtesy, G. T. Trewartha and Rand McNally & Co.*

minerals are being found every year. More than two-thirds of Canada is yet to be examined in detail for minerals, and few geologists have ever worked systematically in the regions to the south of the United States, or in Africa, Asia, and much of Australia. All mineral reserves are of importance to man. The more critical are probably those used for power, the baser metals, and many non-metallic minerals. Only a few, those used for power, are considered here.

The coal resources of the world are probably the best known, yet the available data are little more than estimates. North America has more than half the world's reserves. Only in North America and Europe is coal mined on a large scale. The normal coal production of India and Japan are small compared with U.S.S.R., Great Britain, or United States. The average world production is approximately 1,750,000,000 tons, of which North America produces 600,000,000 tons, Asia about 120,000,000, Europe 590,000,000, Australia and Africa 23,000,000 each. See Table II.

TABLE II

COAL RESERVES OF THE CONTINENTS

	Probable Metric Tons (000,000,000 omitted)	Per Cent of World
North America	2844	51.0
South America	34	0.6
Europe*	619	11.1
U.S.S.R.	1525	27.3
Asia*	297	5.3
Africa	222	4.0
Australasia	34	0.6

Source, "Energy Resources of the World," by U. S. Dept. of State.
* Excluding U.S.S.R.

Petroleum reserves are difficult to estimate, but data available indicate a world reserve of some 95 billion barrels. More than half is in Asia and a little less than a third in North America (Table III). The production in North America, however, is on a huge scale, especially in the United States. North America also has very large resources of other hydrocarbons such as bituminous shales and natural gas.

Reliable estimates of natural gas reserves for the world are not available, and comparable production data are several years old (Table IV). In 1950 the United States production was approximately 220,000 million cubic yards, and its reserves were estimated to be 6900 billion cubic yards. Canada has very large reserves.

TABLE III

PETROLEUM RESERVES BY CONTINENTS *

	Reserves, Barrels (000 omitted	Per Cent of World
North America	28,723,000	30.1
South America	10,650,000	11.2
Europe	6,207,000	6.5
Asia	49,446,000	51.9
Africa	183,000	0.2
Australasia	500	
	95,208,500	99.9

Source, World Oil, Feb. 1951.
* Estimates vary widely and change yearly. Compare with Fig. 26.

TABLE IV

NATURAL GAS PRODUCTION BY CONTINENTS*

	Millions of Cubic Meters	Per Cent of World
North America	69,219	86.9
South America	4,819	6.1
Europe †	2,581	3.2
Asia †	1,047	1.3
U.S.S.R.	2,000	2.5
Africa	8	—
Australia	—	—
	79,674	100.0

Source, "Energy Resources of the World," by U. S. Dept. of State.
* Data for 1937.
† Excluding U.S.S.R.

In considering the population of the future in North America, we think chiefly of coal, petroleum, and gas as power resources. To these must be added water power. North America holds third rank among the continents in potential water power, but its ratio of developed to potential ranks first, and it has large reserves for future use (Table V). The significance of the tremendous power resources of North America derived from the utilization of coal, natural gas, petroleum, and water power is realized only when considered in comparison with human power, the power now characteristic of the tropics, the East, and to some extent of many of the countries of Europe. Engineers have found that the energy stored up in 2 pounds of coal, used in an engine of 10 per cent efficiency and expended through a day, will do the work of 1 man, and that the energy output of an average workman is about ⅕ horsepower. On this basis the average daily output of coal mines in the United States is equal to the energy of 1,900,000,000 men. Add to such estimates the human energy equivalent of petroleum, natural gas, and water power produced in North America daily, and the high standard of living and material comforts attained by man are understandable.

Power resources, next to the potential ability of a country to produce foods, are the most important elements of the environmental bases of population. In coal, petroleum, gas, and water power North America has power resources that give it an advantage over any other of the continents.

TABLE V

WATER-POWER RESOURCES BY CONTINENTS*

	Potential (millions of kilowatt-hours)	Per Cent of World	Developed (millions of kilowatt-hours)	Per Cent of Potential
North America	458,688	11.6	73,644	21.6
South America	444,800	11.3	3,029	0.7
Europe †	361,472	9.2	64,125	17.7
Asia †	557,632	14.2	22,752	4.1
U.S.S.R.	465,600	11.8	6,900	1.5
Africa	1,615,864	41.0	542	‡
Australasia and Oceania	34,056	0.9	1,566	4.6
	3,938,112	100.0	172,558	4.3

* From "Energy Resources of the World," by U. S. Dept. of State.
† Excluding U.S.S.R.
‡ Less than 0.05 per cent.

Among the more valuable metallic minerals used in the great industries of today are iron ore, copper, zinc, and bauxite. (See succeeding chapters.) Since North America has a large part of the world's supply of these and of nickel, sulfur, and phosphate; a large share of the power resources of the world; large areas of almost virgin agricultural lands producing their share of the world's agricultural products and capable of several times the present output; and some of the largest stands of timber to be found in any continent (with the possible exception of Asia), both mining and manufacturing will contribute effectively to maintenance of the future population.

POPULATION AND NON-AGRICULTURAL RESOURCES

Owing to its wide range of latitude, great variety of climates, minerals, and native vegetations, the North American continent is nearly self-contained and can long remain so. But it may be a good policy to exchange the products of mines and factories either in the crude or fabricated form for foodstuffs produced in other countries. Britain has been exporting coal, power, and labor for more than a century, and has sustained a population far larger than the British farmers can feed. Every country tends, as its population increases in numbers and density, to advance in its economic evolution from the plucking, gathering, and collecting stage in the exploitation of the resources to extensive agriculture, intensive agriculture, manufacturing, and mining. But for a country to become active in manufacturing it must possess power resources—coal, oil, gas, water power. Only a few countries in the world have the environmental requisites for manufacturing. Fortunately for North America, these more useful minerals are in great abundance. It is evident that our continent will have an abundance of power for manufacturing for centuries to come.

It seems possible that the manufactures of North America—only as the products to be exchanged for food produced in other continents are considered—may expand our sustenance space, so that North America may ultimately come to have (or support) twice the estimated 500 to 600 millions. This we may consider as the environmentally or physically possible population of North America, with man using the types of utilization of resources now known. Whether such a population is desirable, or whether these limits will ever be reached, and how long it will take to reach the ultimate, depend on man himself.

SOME HUMAN FACTORS

Since the beginning of the existence of the human race the curve of the world's population has probably had in general an upward trend. We can hardly avoid such a supposition. The historical glimpses we have of scores of nations throughout the many thousands of years of their known existence indicates that growth in population is a normal condition. Adam Smith, the English economist of the eighteenth century, saw a relationship between economic well-being and rate of growth of population. The most decisive mark of prosperity of a country, he writes, "is the increase in the numbers of inhabitants." And again, "No species can ever multiply beyond the means of its subsistence." For more than a century countries that passed through the Industrial Revolution or that were drawn into the great world-wide maelstrom of commercial relations have experienced a rapid increase in population. All or nearly all the advanced nations of the world have suffered a decline in their rate of increase, i.e., their curve of population is tending toward the horizontal.[3] Civilization apparently carries in its wake, after the effect of the first flush of prosperity wanes, a decrease in the rate of births—and so great a decrease that, though the death rate is greatly reduced through the advance of medical science and improvements in sanitation, there is an actual decline in population growth over a long period. The rising standards of living are important factors in this decline. Ricardo wrote that "a taste for the comforts and enjoyments of life is excellent security against a superabundant population."

At no time in the history of the world has the general public in civilized lands enjoyed so many comforts and so much prosperity. Education now is provided for the masses. Life has lost the drabness that characterized man's living in the earlier centuries. Man on a low plane of existence seems to be governed in his sexual life by the laws of the animal world, but, as his educational and cultural attainments advance and his standards of living are raised, the rate of propagation declines. Intellectual prudence rather than physiological imprudence rules. Fear in the minds of parents of their inability to provide for a large family on the social and economic plane that they desire serves to restrain the birth rate. The parents of each generation desire to give their offspring the best and to save their children from the hardships the parents experienced. Social practices and ideas thus are regulating factors. Perhaps the world may some time see the working out of Herbert Spencer's belief that "in proportion as individual or a community becomes perfected in civilization, in the same proportion the race inclines to run out." There is no telling whither we are headed, whether toward a stronger or a weaker race, a weaker which eventually may not be able to reproduce itself.

The problem of population growth involves two phases of man, the physical and the mental. Through superior intellect man has established dominion over all other forms of life and has learned to utilize many of, and possibly most of, the forces of nature. There is little reason for doubting that the advances in the future will be even greater than in the past. As population increases, man will find new resources and new ways to utilize them, and democracy will see to it that the benefits are more evenly distributed than at present. How these easier conditions will affect the physical man and this, in turn, the growth of population in North America cannot be foretold. It seems to be a law of nature that progress and development, physical and mental, come only through work, the conquest of adversity, and success in the struggle against physical and mental inertia.

[3] The rapid rate of increase in the United States since World War II may be only temporary.

Some are likely to be too optimistic as to the efficacy of science to solve the problems of human existence in the centuries to come. Medical science can greatly reduce the toll of disease, reform our diet, and establish standards of sane living. But will people listen to its teaching? Food, produced by nature, is certain to remain a limiting factor in the population of the world. There is little hope that man will ever be able to thrive on a daily ration of compressed, synthetic tablets carried about in a single pill box. If we may judge from the past, he will continue to eat carbohydrates and proteins and will demand spinach for roughage, and all these will be produced more cheaply by Dame Nature's plant, by sunlight, rain, and soil, than in a chemical factory.

The resources of the North American continent—soil, climate, minerals, water, native vegetation, and natural transportation conditions—and their degree of utilization condition the continent's sustenance power; but many human factors will determine whether the sustenance possibilities will ever be levied upon by a thousand million or more people. Trends observable in many population phenomena today lead many to think that we will come to have a stationary population before we reach even half that number.

QUESTIONS, EXERCISES, AND PROBLEMS

1. The *Statistical Abstract* gives normal temperatures for selected stations in the United States. Select ten or more widely distributed stations and, from a study of the data for these stations, determine in what temperature regions they are.

2. Data for normal monthly precipitation may also be obtained from *Statistical Abstract*. Select six or more stations in various parts of the country and construct graphs showing the seasonal distribution of rainfall.

3. If it were possible to make changes in the physical environment of North America, what changes would you suggest to increase the usefulness of the continent to man? Consider changes in the varieties and distribution of mineral resources, in surface features, navigable rivers, temperatures and rainfall, and location.

4. What part of the continent would have the denser population today if North America had been settled from the Pacific instead of the Atlantic?

PART II

The United States and Alaska

CHAPTER 2

The United States as a National Unit

In the United States lives a people under conditions that are far superior to those of any like area of the earth. The natural environment has provided opportunities which enabled a capable people, in a short period, to attain a high stage of prosperity and evolve a nation that ranks among the first. Its past history is largely a record of man's exploitation of superb natural resources. Static conditions, or relatively permanent adjustment, have not yet been attained in many activities. The process of human evolution, by which man finally makes the most complete use of the natural assets of his environment, is still in progress. Absolutely permanent adjustment, of course, will never occur with a progressive people. The people of the United States are still profiting chiefly by using the superabundant natural gifts of the most richly endowed political unit of the world. They still seem to be unaware that many of their resources are being exhausted. They produce and destroy with little regard for the future. The future alone can record whether the country wields as great an influence in the world and makes as great contributions to the advancement of human welfare as the countries of Europe. Though material resources that assure opportunities for maintaining high standards still exist, the day of free land—"Uncle Sam is rich enough to give us all a farm"—has gone. Forests and soils are being depleted rapidly, mineral production is on a huge scale and the date of exhaustion is in sight for some minerals, and population is increasing at a high rate. *It is the principal purpose of this chapter to provide an over-view of the United States as a nation by considering some of the major aspects of its development and some of the opportunities available to future generations; and, perhaps, to awaken an appreciation of "Our Own United States."* More detailed discussion of sections of the country follows in succeeding chapters.

A Region and Its People.   People everywhere live in a given area or regional environment, *and their opportunities depend upon (1) the size of the region, (2) the natural resources of the region, and (3) the number and ability of people competing for participation in those resources.* Such regions may be political, physiographic, geographic, natural, etc., and the opportunities

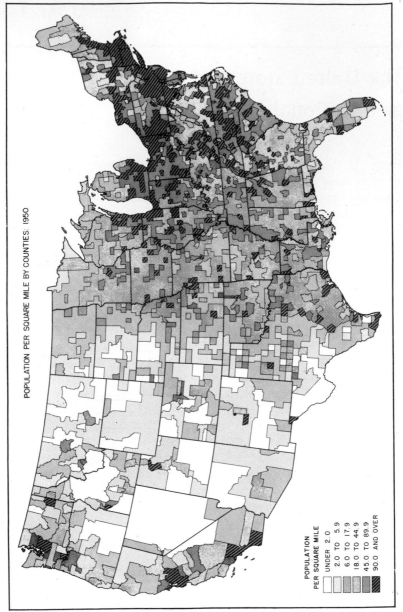

Fig. 10. Distribution of population. *Courtesy, Bureau of the Census.*

offered may be few or many. Perhaps the cycle in which man modifies his environment in order that he may make the most of opportunities available, and the environment modifies man in turn, *ad infinitum,* holds as a general principle. Possibly the operation of such a principle accounts for the present degree of social and intellectual attainment of the more advanced peoples. However, there are so many modifiying factors, both within and without a given environment, that the general principle cannot be considered an immutable law. Certainly, what man does is influenced greatly by the environment in which he lives; but it is equally certain that not all racial stocks produce the same results in the same or in a similar environment. It is interesting to contemplate the results that would ensue if Germans were substituted for Chinese or the Englishman for the Mexican. When people migrate to a new environment they take with them qualities that may have been acquired through centuries of ethnic experiences. These qualities are brought to bear upon the new environment and, in turn, may be altered considerably. It is probable that the United States people are now undergoing such a change and that the qualities which may cause them to wield a beneficent or a malignant influence in future world affairs are now being evolved. Hence, the stage of human evolution—the human factor—must always be recognized in any geographical study.

Material Progress of a Nation.   For our purpose we are considering here a political unit—a nation—that stands as an individual entity among the nations of the world. It has been a land of abundance, of rapid growth in population, of rapid industrial development, and a land in which the stress of overpopulation, with the accompanying era of stringent economy and narrow margin between a comfortable living and poverty, has not yet been felt seriously. This difference in well-being has caused the flow of humanity from the older parts of the world to the newer and chiefly to the United States. In a very short period the material progress of the nation has been phenomenal. Within its bounds live less than 7 per cent of the world's population. However, of the world's production, that relatively small population produces one-third of the coal; one-third of the iron ore and half the steel; more than one-third of the pig iron; about three-fourths of the motor vehicles; more than three-fifths of the petroleum; three-fifths of the Indian corn; two-fifths of the cotton; and similar proportions of several other important products. Of the world's resources and material development, the United States has four-fifths of the coal reserves; a quarter of the iron reserves; more than half the telephone instruments; nearly one-third of the railroad mileage; more than half the radio sets; etc. It has become the leading nation in agriculture, mining, manufacturing, commerce, transportation, wealth, and standard of well-being of its people. Within a large, un-crowded, and richly endowed area, its people have made the greatest progress in material things.

Factors Favoring Material Evolution.   What has made possible the great material progress of the United States in such a comparatively short time? Many factors—geographic, economic, ethnic, political—have influenced its growth, chief of which are the following:

1. An area of more than 3,000,000 square miles, which is larger than Australia and about four-fifths as large as all Europe with its multidinous nations each struggling with its environment and with other countries to attain greater opportunities for its people.

2. Great variety of climates, ranging from tropical to cold winters and hot summers, from winter rains, to well-distributed summer rains, from aridity to excessive rainfall, from weather uniformity to frequent changes, from long to short growing seasons, and, on the whole, healthful and invigorating over most of the country.

3. Extensive area of varied soils of high average fertility.

4. Large proportion of lowland plains accessible to the coast; the lesser mountain range on the Atlantic side; few isolated physiographic regions, a condition favoring unity.

5. Abundant, accessible minerals of high quality, especially the more important ones, such as coal, iron, copper, and petroleum.

6. Abundant forests of the most useful types of wood.

7. Long sea coast with numerous good harbors readily accessible to the rich hinterland.

8. Location in the northern midlatitudes across the narrowest major ocean from the progressive nations of Europe, and occupation of the choice section of the North American continent.

9. A population derived chiefly from the north European racial stock, which is noted for its initiative, energy, and intelligence, and which has contributed most to the welfare of the world.

10. A strong, stable government which has fostered and protected individual initiative, general education, and scientific research, aided in industrial development, and protected from invasion.

UTILIZING THE LAND

Agricultural land is probably the most important natural resource that man possesses in that it may provide food and clothing. It was man's desire for new lands, with the greater opportunities for human well-being, that brought European settlers to North America. The first settlers were confronted by a broad expanse of forest-covered terrain, much of which provided poor soils when the forests were cleared away. Production of food under those pioneer conditions was a strenuous task, and even the optimum reward must have been discouraging. Later the tide of migrating man swept on westward to the vast, gently rolling, grassland plains. At first he ignored them, as his ancestral experiences had implanted in him the idea that crops could be produced only on forest land—on land which produced only grass, never! When this erroneous idea was finally abandoned settlement spread rapidly over the fertile, level prairies of the interior; and some of the more hardy souls pressed

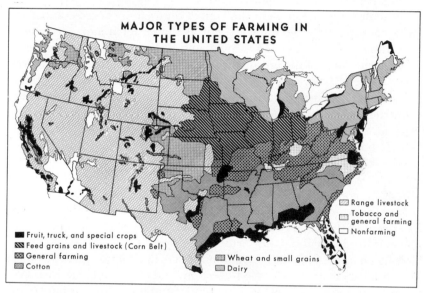

Fig. 11. Types of farming. *Courtesy, Bureau of Agricultural Economics.*

ever onward to the far Pacific, lured there at first by the gold but later to culivate, to irrigate, to mine, and to harvest the products of the forest and of the sea. Thus, from the primitive agriculture of the early New England farmer on his boulder-strewn and forest-bordered clearing to the far-flung expanse of field on field that now spreads out across the interior plains, and on to the Pacific, has gone man in his effort to produce more and still more. Today those lands, pioneered but a few years ago, are being utilized on a scale never before approximated in the history of the world; yet an *intensive* utilization has been reached in only very limited areas.

Importance of Agriculture.   Agriculture is man's most important industry, because it provides for his fundamental needs. The nation that can feed, clothe, and shelter its people in comfort is as nearly independent as a nation can become. However, man *desires* far more than his mere necessities. To supply his *desires,* he produces for others and builds up a complex system of interchange of products. Many of our largest manufacturing industries, especially those of food and clothing, depend quite as much upon the producer of crops as upon the financier who provides the capital, the miner who supplies coal for power, or the captains of transportation who carry the raw materials and the finished goods. In fact, most of the commercial and industrial prosperity of America is rooted in the land, whether that land is used for crops, grazing, forests, mining, transportation systems, or cities.

Agricultural production in the United States now exceeds that of any other country. Reliable data are not available for major agricultural countries like U.S.S.R., China, India, and Pakistan. However, estimates indicate the value of the products of U.S.S.R. is about three-fourths that of the United States; that of China about half to two-thirds; and that of Pakistan and India combined, less than half. The production of all other countries is small in comparison. The United States is also the leading exporter of agricultural products. The value of its exports since World War II has been larger than that of all other countries combined, yet those exports were only a small part of its production. Of the world's aggregate crop production the United States now produces about 61 per cent of the corn, 40 per cent of the cotton, 35 per cent of the oats, 20 per cent of the wheat, 21 per cent of the flaxseed, 12 per cent of the barley, 6 per cent of the sugar, and 38 per cent of the soybeans. Taking grains alone, it produces about a quarter of the world's total crops. Machine-farming on large acreages, with a minimum of hand labor, great advances in technology of acre yield, seed selection, and processing, has increased production faster than world consumption, and the cultivable land of the United States has not yet reached its productive capacity even by the use of improved methods.

SOILS A BASAL ASSET

The earth's surface is covered by a layer of loose material consisting of sand and clay ranging in thickness from a mere film to many feet. In a few places where rocks outcrop it is absent. This material constitutes what soil specialists call the parent material of the soil. The upper or surface layer of this material is converted into soil, the true soil, by the action of various forces, the most important of which is that of organic life, mainly plant life. It is evident that if the soil is producd by the action of the plant, the plant must begin to grow on the parent soil material before it is converted into soil.

On the basis of important and significant characteristics the soil of the United States may be divided into two great groups, pedalfers and pedocals. In general the soils of the eastern half of the United States are pedalfers and those of the western half are pedocals. The *pedalfers* include all soils in which not only is there no accumulation of calcium carbonate, but also such calcium carbonate as may have been present in the soil material has been entirely removed from the true soil layer by the time the soil becomes well developed. In addition, these soils when well developed have a subsoil that is heavier in texture than the surface soil. They are also more or less acid in reaction. The *pedocals* include all soils which, if they have been well developed as soils, have acquired at some depth or at some level in their vertical section a layer in which calcium carbonate has accumulated in greater proportions than in the layers of the soil above it or in those of the soil material below it. In addition, the surface soils are neutral or alkaline in reaction, or in other words they are not acid. The most important members of the group are dark in color, but some of them may be light.

The soils of each of these major groups may be subdivided into smaller groups in which all members have a number of important characteristics in common. The pedalfers may be subdivided into four well-defined subgroups: (1) Podzols, (2) Gray-Brown Podzolic Soils, (3) Red and Yellow Soils, (4) Prairie Soils. The distribution of the two major groups as well as of the subgroups within the United States is shown on the map, Fig. 12.

Podzol Soils.   Podzol Soils in their natural condition, before being cultivated by man, wherever they occur, have developed under a forest cover. The forest trees may be of many kinds, but in most parts of the world they contain at least a mixture of narrow-leafed trees, or conifers. In the forest these soils are covered with a layer of organic matter consisting of leaves, twigs, and other forest debris. This layer may range from a few inches to a foot or more in thickness. It is brown, sometimes quite dark in the lower part, and may be woven together, especially in the lower part, into a kind of mat by fine roots coming up into it from the soil beneath or by filaments of fungi and other plants growing within it. Beneath this layer, which is usually called raw humus, is a layer that ranges in thickness from a very thin film up to a foot or more of gray material which may or may not be mixed with organic matter in the upper inch or two. The lower part may be nearly white. This material is loose and powdery or sandy and, therefore, without what is called structure. This layer is called the podzolized layer. Beneath the light-colored layer lies a brown to dark coffee brown or faint reddish brown layer which may be soft and light in weight or may be indurated into a stonelike body. When indurated it is usually darker in color than when loose. The transi-

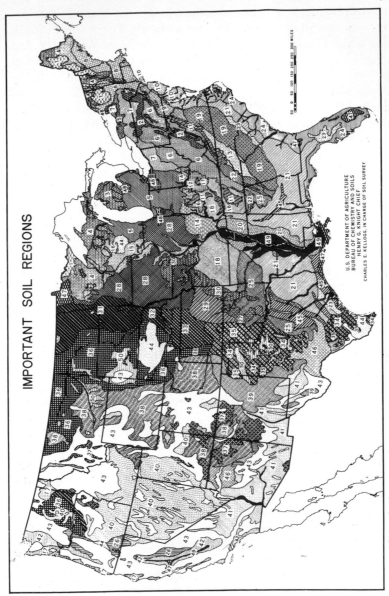

Fig. 12. Soil regions of the United States. *Courtesy, Bureau of Agricultural Economics, Bureau of Plant Industry, Soils, and Agricultural Engineering.* The map is schematic. Each soil region outlined includes associated soils developed under a relatively uniform environment. The names in parentheses refer to the more extensive or representative soil series in the respective regions.

Fig. 12 (*Continued*)

Podzols. The profile consists of a very thin organic layer above a gray leached layer which rests upon a dark-brown or coffee-brown horizon. The Podzol is developed usually under a coniferous forest in a cool moist climate. Its inherent productivity for crop plants is low. The figures below refer to area numbers on the map.

1. Rough stony land, including areas of shallow Podzols.
2. Chiefly loams and silt loams, developed from sandstones and shales of the plateau and mountain uplands. Includes the Leetonia and the Dekalb soils.

Gray-Brown Podzolic Soils. The profile has a rather thin organic layer over grayish-brown leached soil which overlies a brown horizon. The soils are generally acid, at least in the surface. These soils develop in a moist and cool-temperate climate under a deciduous forest and are inherently more productive than the Podzols.

3. Dominantly sands and loamy sands, developed on glacial drift. (Roselawn, Kalkaska.)
4. Dominantly loams and clay loams, developed on glacial drift. (Hermon, Ontonagon.)
5. Dominantly loams and silt loams, developed on calcareous glacial drift. (Miami, Crosby, and Honeoye—Ontario associations.)
6. Brownish yellow silty loams or stony loams with hilly relief developed on sandstones and shales. (Muskingum, Zanesville, Westmoreland.)
7. Loams and silt loams, developed on acid glacial drift, composed of sandstones and shale material. Some of these soils are imperfectly drained. (Canfield, Volusia, Lordstown.)
8. Dominantly stony and gravelly loams, developed on glacial drift. (Gloucester, Troy.)
9. Loams and silt loams, developed mostly on the crystalline rocks of the northern Piedmont. (Chester, Manor, Penn.)
10. Largely sandy loams developed on the sands and clays of the northern Coastal Plain. (Sassafras, Collington.)
11. Chiefly brown silt loams, developed on limestone. (Hagerstown, Maury, Frederick.)
12. Shallow soils developed on interbedded limestone and calcareous shales. (Fairmont, Lowell.)
13. Loams and stony loams from granitic material with hilly to mountainous relief. (Ashe, Porters.)
14. Silt loams with heavy clay subsoils, developed on Illinoian glacial till. (Gibson, Cory, Clermont, Rossmoyne.)
15. Silt loams, developed largely from loess. (Clinton, Fayette.)
16. Imperfectly drained grayish silt loams with silty clay loam subsoils, developed from acid glacial drift. (Spencer.)
17. Largely loams and silt loams with yellowish subsoils, developed from sandstones and shales. (Melbourne.)
18. Grayish yellow to reddish silt loams and cherty silt loams, developed from cherty limestones. (Clarksville, Dickson, Baxter.)

Red and Yellow Soils. This group of soils consists of two general types of profiles which are very intimately associated. Both have thin organic layers. The profile of the Red soil is a yellowish brown leached layer over a red horizon; the profile of the Yellow soil is a grayish-yellow leached layer over a yellow horizon. Both developed under the forest in a moist, warm-temperate climate. Generally the yellow profile

Fig. 12 (*Continued*)

is more pronounced under the coniferous forest and the red under the deciduous forest. The inherent fertility of the Yellow soils is generally relatively low and that of the Red soils, medium.

19. Dominantly brownish red clay loams and gray sandy loams, developed largely from crystalline rocks of the southern piedmont. (Cecil, Durham, Appling, Georgeville, Davidson.)

20. Yellow to light brown silt loams, developed on loess. (Memphis, Grenada.)

21. Dominantly gray to yellow sandy and fine sandy loams, with some sands and fine sands, developed from Coastal Plain materials. (Norfolk, Ruston, Orangeburg.)

22. Largely brownish red to red silt loams and clay loams, developed from limestone. (Dewey, Decatur, Fullerton.)

23. Grayish yellow to light brown sands and fine sands of the Coastal Plain. (Norfolk sands.)

24. Grayish fine sandy loams, with some gray or black loams, developed in the flatwoods area of the Coastal Plain. Includes areas underlain by coralline limestone. (Coxville, Leon, Portsmouth.)

25. Grayish yellow to reddish fine sandy loams and silt loams, developed from sandstones and shales. A considerable portion is hilly and stony. (Hartsells, Hanceville, Conway.)

26. Red soils of the north Pacific slopes. (Aiken, Sierra, Sites.)

Prairie Soils. The profile of the Prairie Soil grades from a very dark brown or dark grayish brown surface through brown to lighter colored parent material at a depth from 2 to 5 feet. It is developed in a moist temperate climate under a tall-grass prairie. Inherent fertility for crop plants is high.

27. Reddish brown soils of variable texture, developed on sandstones, shales, clays, and sands. (Zaneis, Renfrew.)

28. Dark brown silt loams with yellowish brown subsoils, developed on glacial drift and loess. (Carrington, Tama, Clarion, Marshall.)

29. Dark brown to reddish brown silt loams and clay loams, developed from limestone and calcareous shales. (Summit, Crawford.)

30. Dark brown or grayish brown silt loams, having heavy subsoils or claypans. (Cherokee, Parsons, Grundy, Putnam.)

Northern Chernozem. The profile has a black or dark grayish brown surface soil grading below into light-colored material which is calcareous at 2 to 6 feet. It is developed in a temperate to cool, subhumid climate under tall and mixed grasses. Inherent productivity is high.

31. Black loams, silt loams, and clay loams, developed on calcareous glacial drift and associated lacustrine deposits. (Barnes, Bearden, Fargo.)

32. Dark grayish brown loams and silt loams, developed from loess. (Moody, Holdredge.)

33. Dark grayish brown silt loams with claypans developed from loess. (Crete, Hastings.)

Southern Chernozem—Dark Brown Soils. The profiles have dark brown to reddish brown surface soils underlain by brown or red horizons, grading below into light-colored material which is calcareous at 3 to 6 feet. These soils develop in a warm, subhumid to semiarid climate under a mixed tall- and short-grass prairie.

34. Heavy or moderately heavy dark brown soils, developed from calcareous materials. (Pullman, Abilene, Victoria.)

35. Predominantly red and brown sandy loams and sands, developed largely from unconsolidated calcareous sands, silts, and sandy clays. (Amarillo, Miles, Duval.)

Northern Dark Brown (Chestnut) Soils. The profile grades from a dark brown surface soil into a whitish calcareous horizon at a depth from 1½ to 3 feet. These soils develop under mixed tall and short grasses in a temperate to cool semiarid climate.

36. Dark brown soils developed on unconsolidated, calcareous sands, silts, and clays. (Scobey, Rosebud, Keith, Walla Walla.)

37. Dark brown soils, developed upon heterogeneous material associated with mountainous and plateau terrain.

Brown Soils. A brown surface soil grading at a depth, ranging from 1 to 2 feet, into a whitish calcareous horizon. The profile is developed in a temperate to cool, semiarid climate under short grasses, bunch grasses, and shrubs.

38. (Northern) chiefly brown loams, developed largely on unconsolidated sands, silts, and clays. (Joplin, Weld.)

39. (Southern) chiefly light brown to gray fine sandy loams to silty clay loams of smooth relief, developed largely on limestone or unconsolidated sands, silts, and clays. (Uvalde, Reagan.)

Sierozem and Desert Soils. Grayish and reddish soils, closely underlain by calcareous material. These soils develop in an arid climate under short grass and desert plants.

40. (Northern) gray and grayish brown soils of variable texture, developed largely on loess and alluvial fan material. (Ritzville, Portneuf.)

41. (Southern) gray, brown, and reddish soils of variable texture, developed largely on alluvial fans. (Reeves, Mohave.)

Soils of the Pacific Valleys.

42. Includes a number of variable zonal, azonal, and intrazonal soils which are too intimately associated to separate on a schematic map. These soils are developed under a range of climatic and geological conditions. (San Joaquin, Fresno, Hanford.)

Intrazonal and Azonal Soils. These soils may possess one of two general types of profile (*a*) The profile may express a local condition as drainage or parent material rather than the zonal profile of the region; (*b*) the profile may be too immature to express a zonal type.

43. Rough and mountainous (azonal).

44. Largely azonal sands, some of which are associated with bogs. (Valentine sand, dune sand, etc.)

45. Black (or brown) friable soil underlain by whitish material excessively high in calcium carbonate. These soils develop under a prairie vegetation and are known as Rendzinas (intrazonal). (Houston, Sumter.)

46. Shallow stony soils from limestone (azonal). (Valera, Ector.)

47. Marsh, swamp, and bog (intrazonal). (Carlisle, Pamlico, Rifle.)

48. Soils largely intrazonal, developed upon lake plains. (Brookston, Maumee, Vergennes.)

49. Alluvial soils (azonal). (Huntington, Sharkey, Columbia, Cass.)

50. Rough broken land, including Pierre soils.

tion from the gray to the brown layer is usually quite abrupt. The brown layer is darkest in color at the top and becomes lighter with depth. It ranges in thickness from a few inches to more than a foot.

These soils in the United States develop mainly in regions of cool climate, abundant moisture, a humid atmosphere, and forest vegetation. When cleared and put into cultivation, they are somewhat unproductive because they have been rather thoroughly leached by the heavier rainfall and also because the leaching has been hastened by the organic matter which has been carried down through the surface soil or the gray layer. This organic matter is always acid in reaction and partly because of this tends to rob the gray layer of the materials which produce high productivity in soils. By careful cultivation, the growth of grass, by fertilizers and manures, man is able to change these soils after he begins to cultivate them into good productive soils, more productive than they were in their virgin condition. By the growth of grasses and the grain crops, all of which belong to the grasses as family groups, these soils are improved, provided that man does not take anything away from them. When he removes crops from them, he must supply materials that he has removed, but by adding more than he removes he may easily convert these soils into productive ones.

Gray-Brown Podzolic Soils.   Figure 12 shows that the Gray-Brown Podzolic Soils occur in the eastern United States from the Atlantic Coast westward to western Indiana and northern Missouri, and are bounded on the north by the region of Podzols and on the south by the Red and Yellow Soils.

These soils are Podzolic Soils, but they have not been developed as far in podzolization as the true Podzols. In virgin condition they were developed under a forest cover of deciduous trees such as oak, maple, and beech. The surface of these soils is covered by a layer of organic matter which has been derived from the forest leaves and other debris. This layer, however, is not so thick as that overlying the Podzols and is not so thoroughly woven together into a mat or compact layer. It also rarely amounts to more than 3 inches in thickness, most of which consists of loose material. It is underlaid by a thin dark-colored layer of mineral soil which may or may not be present in the Podzols. The thin dark-colored layer, usually 3 inches or less in thickness, is underlaid by a pale yellowish or light brown layer, corresponding to the gray layer in the Podzols.

In virgin condition these soils are more productive than the Podzols, partly because they are less acid and partly because they have been leached of their constituents less than the Podzols. In that part of the region of Gray-Brown Podzolic Soils lying west of the Alleghenies and also in considerable areas east of the Alleghenies, these soils have developed from limestone materials, but even in such cases they have become relatively poor soils because they have been podzolized, though not converted into true Podzols. They also are acid in reaction regardless of their development from limestone material. They are more productive, however, than the surrounding Gray-Brown Podzolic Soils developed from materials which do not contain lime.

These soils are more productive than the Podzols and may be easily converted into productive soils by proper management. The most important factors in their management are the growth of grass and the application of manures and fertilizers. These soils like the Podzols have a low content of nitrogen, phosphoric acid, lime, and potash—or, in other words, practically all the constituents required for high productivity in a soil—but the deeper material contains higher percentages of these constituents; and, when grass is grown on them, this material is brought in greater or less extent upward and stored in the surface soil. When the growth of grass is aided by the application of fertilizers, productivity is greatly improved.

Red and Yellow Soils.   The southeastern part of the United States is covered by a group of soils which is designated as Red and Yellow Soils, or more properly as the Red and Yellow Podzolic Soils. They have a section or profile, as we usually say, very much like that of the Gray-Brown Podzolic Soils. The surface layer is light in color, and the subsoil is stronger in color and heavier in texture; or, in other words, it has more clay. The surface soil is generally yellowish and the subsoil deeper yellowish-brown or red. Whether it is yellowish-brown or red depends partly upon the character of the material from which the soil developed and partly on the drainage of the soil.

These soils have been more thoroughly leached of their lime, potash, soda, and phosphoric acid and also of their organic matter than have the other Podzolic Soils. They have, therefore, a very low content of these constituents and to that extent are less productive in their natural condition than the other soils described. Because of their sandy texture, however, they warm up in the spring very early, they are easily cultivated, and they will absorb the rainfall to a greater extent than the other soils. Because of their sandy clay subsoils, they will hold a considerable amount of moisture and allow plant roots to develop in them thoroughly and obtain this moisture. Their physical characteristics, therefore, so far as they depend on the texture of the soil material, are favorable to production of many crops and especially of cotton. When fertilized or manured they may be converted into highly productive soils, but they require more fertilizers and manures than the soils of either of the two groups already described. They are somewhat too sandy over considerable areas, though not everywhere, for the luxuriant growth of grass, and they do not have a rich supply of organic matter which favors a high production of corn. The climate is too warm also for the growth of wheat and barley, but oats may be grown in winter. The climate favors the growth of cotton, however, if fertilizer is used, and many of the important forage crops when grown with fertilizers may be produced in good quantities.

Prairie Soils. The Prairie Soils occur in the central part of the United States as shown by Fig. 12. They are dark in color, the best of them being black. The black layer ranges in thickness from 6 to 8 inches up to 2 feet or slightly more. The surface soil is usually as heavy in texture as the subsoil, differing in this respect, therefore, from all groups of the Podzolic Soils. No clay material or lime or other constituent in any important quantity has been taken out of the surface soil and into the subsoil, as in the Podzolic Soils. In considerable areas, to be sure, this has taken place in the Prairie Soils, but such Prairie Soils are designated as degraded Prairie Soils; or, in other words, they have begun to be podzolized. The true Prairie Soils, however, are not podzolized and, therefore, have not been leached extensively of their materials. They have a fair-to-good supply of all the constituents which bring about high productivity in soils. The climate in which they occur also has abundant rainfall and sufficiently long growing season to produce good yields of the grain crops. They may be described as simple soils so far as the processes of development are concerned. Nothing has happened to them except the accumulation of a large amount of organic matter which gives them their dark color.

This organic matter supplies them with a high percentage of nitrogen, when that has been released by proper decomposition, which promotes high productivity. The presence of this organic matter and also of a good percentage of lime which has combined with the organic matter that holds it in place and bars leaching by water has given these soils a good structure. They are granular in structure, as we usually say; or, stated in another way, they are friable and have a good crumbly structure, and when cultivated can be brought into good tilth readily.

These soils are highly productive for most of the grain crops, and especially for corn and oats. They are productive also for grass and for such crops as alfalfa and clover and many of the forage crops. They are not so productive for tree fruits, such as apples and peaches and pears, as the lighter-colored soils, because they were not developed under a forest cover and, therefore, many kinds of trees do not grow so well on them as on the better of the Podzolic Soils. They are, however, highly productive

agricultural soils and do not require the use of fertilizers in order to produce fair-to-good crops. Even the poorer soils, those in which podzolization
has begun, are more productive than any of the Podzolic Soils.

Chernozem Soils. The soils so far described constitute the members of
the pedalfer group. The Chernozem Soils constitute one of the groups of
the *pedocals*. The Chernozem Soils are typically black. They are even
blacker than the Prairie Soils. In the United States these soils, as shown
by the map, occur in a belt running from north to south. They occur also
in Canada in a belt which runs northwestward from the northern part of
the United States. In Canada and in the northern part of the United
States,these soils are black. As we come southward in the United States
they become less black but still have a very dark color well into the High
Plains region of Texas and a dark brown color southward to their
southern limit on the coast of the Gulf of Mexico. In the soil section they
are very much like the Prairie Soils, except that in the subsoil there is a
layer which contains a very high percentage of calcium carbonate; sometimes this is mixed with other salts like gypsum and various small
percentages of salt which are usually designated as alkali salts. However,
these salts do not usually occur in the Chernozem Soils in sufficient
amount to interfere with the growth of plants. Where gypsum occurs, it
generally lies below the layer of maximum calcium carbonate accumulation. Normally the surface soils do not have calcium carbonate, but
they are not poor in lime. Like the best of the Prairie Soils, these soils contain enough lime to combine with the organic matter and hold it in
place, preventing it from being taken out in solution by rainfall. They
also have a highly granular structure in the surface soil, causing them to
work well under cultivation. The rainfall of the area in which they are
found is somewhat low, however, for maximum crop production, and
severe droughts occur at times. They are productive for wheat and other
small grain crops, especially barley, the quality of the grain being very
high. In the United States and in other parts of the world where they
occur, they produce most of the wheat that enters into the international
wheat trade of the world. They are not highly productive for corn; not
because the soils are not good for corn but because the moisture supply is
not sufficient for that plant. They are productive soils for grass, however.
In the southern part of the belt in which they occur, they are productive
soils for cotton. When the rainfall is high, they produce large crops
without the use of fertilizers; when the rainfall is low, they will not
produce large crops even with fertilizers.

Dark Brown Soils. West of the belt of Chernozem Soils lies a belt of
Dark Brown Soils. Aside from their dark brown rather than black color,
they are very much like the Chernozem Soils in their characteristics.

They differ, however, from the Chernozem Soils in having a less thick
dark-colored layer which in the Chernozem may range up to 2 or 3 feet.
In the Dark Brown Soils this layer is rarely more than 1 foot in thickness.
These soils, however, are granular in structure like the Chernozem Soils.
They have a good supply of calcium, which permits organic matter to
stay in the soil rather than to be leached out, and the supply of organic
matter is large enough to furnish a fair to good supply of nitrogen as it
decomposes. Like the Chernozem and the best of the Prairie Soils, the
iron and alumina and clay have not been taken out of the surface soil and
carried into the subsoil. In some places where it is thought that the
climate has become more moist than formerly, the Chernozem Soils have
become degraded, as it is often described; or, in other words, they have
become slightly podzolized like the Prairie Soils. In rare cases or possibly
never have the Dark Brown Soils been podzolized.

The Dark Brown Soils are adapted to the growth of wheat, barley, and
grass, but are less productive, not because they are less fertile, but
because they have a lower moisture supply than the Chernozem Soils.
They can be used, nevertheless, for the production of wheat and barley if
the moisture supply is conserved. The region in which they occur, however, is subjected to droughts, and the farmers on them must take into
consideration the possibility of such occurrences at relatively frequent
intervals.

Brown Soils.   West of the belt of Dark Brown Soils is a belt of Brown
Soils, lying along the foot of the Rocky Mountains and extending eastward to the western edge of the Dark Brown Soils. The area of distribution
is shown on Fig. 12. These soils, like the Dark Brown Soils, the Cher-
nozems, and the Prairie Soils, developed also under a grass cover, but the
cover was not so dense as in the other soils nor did it cover the surface of
the ground in a continuous sod or grass cover. The grass was distributed
in bunchlike areas, although it was not a typical "bunchgrass." The grass
growing on these soils is a short grass similar to that growing on the Dark
Brown Soils, but it has been too light to supply as much organic matter
in the surface soils as is found in the Dark Brown Soils.

On the surface there is a thin layer, usually from a fraction of an inch
to 3 inches in thickness, of loose, usually sandy, material. It is light in
color. This is underlaid by a firm, claylike, brown material, which breaks
into clodlike masses, but is soft and friable when moist. This layer ranges
up to a foot in thickness but is usually somewhat less. The lower part of
this layer contains a high percentage of calcium carbonate identical with
the layer in the Dark Brown Soils and the Chernozem. Beneath the layer
of accumulated calcium carbonate is a parent material which may vary
in character depending upon the character of the underlying geological

formation. These soils contain high percentages of the constituents of soil productivity except nitrogen, and a moderate percentage of that constituent. They do not have a granular structure like the Prairie, Chernozem, or Dark Brown Soils. They are highly productive soils under irrigation but are not good for dry farming. They occur mostly in regions where the rainfall is insufficient for growing crops without irrigation and where there is only a relatively small amount of water for irrigation purposes. They are, however, irrigated in Colorado along the Platte River and certain other streams, also in western Nebraska, Wyoming, Montana, and various other places in the West, but organic matter added by growing crops that will enhance it, or in some other way, is advantageous.

Gray Soils. In the desert part of the United States the soils are designated as Gray Soils. They are very light in color because of the low percentage of organic matter which they contain. The low percentage of organic matter is due to the absence of a grass cover. They developed under a thin cover of scattered bushes, and this kind of vegetation does not add organic matter to the soils. The surface soil is often gravelly, but not too gravelly for cultivation. There is a thin layer of loose material like that overlying the surface of the Brown Soils. Beneath the loose material is a firm layer, grayish, or, in the southwestern part of the United States, slightly reddish in color. It is similar to the corresponding layer in the Brown Soils but contains less organic matter. The same layer may contain calcium carbonate in considerable quantities, and the lower part of the layer contains high percentages. In other words, the zone or layer of calcium carbonate accumulation lies close to the surface in these soils.

These soils are productive for crops under irrigation but cannot be used for dry farming. The percentage of organic matter, as already stated, is low, but what is present decomposes and delivers its nitrogen to the soil rather rapidly. If the method of cultivation under irrigation provides for the restoration of organic matter, these soils may be used for a long time without fertilizers other than such as are added in roots of plants or by plowing under organic matter of any form.

THE PROBLEM OF SOIL EROSION

In the preceding discussion we have seen the rapid expansion of agriculture in the United States and the vast acreage of highly fertile soils available for man's utilization. Thus far only one thought has guided the exploitation of its agricultural land, *viz.*, to get more land under cultivation so as to produce bigger and bigger crops. The people have assumed that soils were inexhaustible and that the United States had an abundance of good land for every person who wanted to cultivate it. The expressions, "It will last as long as I want it" and "There is plenty more," are typical of the sentiment that has prevailed. The careless waste of cultivable land has been similar to the waste of many other natural resources. It is probable that such an attitude is the reaction of a people to a new land endowed with rich natural resources that appeared to them as limitless. However, the time has come when not only must soil erosion be stopped but reclamation of eroded lands must also become a fixed

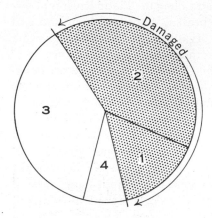
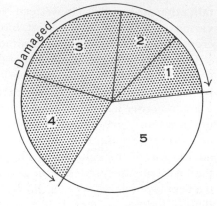

A. Extent of Erosion in Total Area
　　Damaged
  1. Ruined or nearly ruined—14.8%
  2. Erosion moderate or started—40.7%

　Not Damaged
  3. Grassland, forest, marsh, swamp, etc.—36.8%
  4. Mountains, deserts, etc.—7.6%

B. Erosion Damage to Cropland
  1. Ruined for cultivation—10.8%
  2. Damaged severely—10.8%
  3. Half or all of topsoil removed—21.7%
  4. Erosion started—21.7%
  5. In good condition—35%

Fig. 13. The problem of soil erosion. Out of our total area (*A*) of 1,905,000,000 acres, approximately 1,057,000,000 acres have been ruined or damaged by erosion. Of our good cropland of 460,000,000 acres, some 300,000,000 acres are ruined or damaged.

policy. Destructive methods have already ruined, or severely damaged, 100,000,000 acres of good cropland and removed half to all the topsoil from another 100,000,000. See Fig. 13. Soil studies thus far made show that under some conditions of soil, slope, and cultivation as much as 7 inches of soil are removed in 8 years, and that twenty-one times as much plant food is removed from the soils of the country annually as is used by the growing crops. Many of these huge annual losses can and must be prevented.

Fig. 14. Agricultural regions of North America. The United States is divided into a humid eastern half and an arid or semiarid western half except for the higher mountain elevations and the North Pacific Coast. Each subdivision or region is characterized by a distinctive crop system or crop combination due primarily to climatic differences. In the humid East these regions have been determined by a leading crop, except for the subtropical coast where climate and low wet lands are determinants. In the drier West the names reflect the strong climatic influence of topography and of the Pacific Ocean. *Courtesy, O. E. Baker and* Economic Geography.

Fortunately, great progress in soil conservation has been and is being made. Continued cooperation of government and farmer can solve the problem.

AGRICULTURAL REGIONS[1]

It is axiomatic that not all land is equally suited to the raising of the same crop. In an area as large as that of the United States and located in midlatitude, divergence in agricultural and pastoral industries is to be expected. Many factors determine the differences that now exist or may develop in such a large area. Among the more important geographic factors are (1) climatic differences, (2) varying proximity to markets, (3) topographic differences, and (4) differences in the chemical and physical characteristics of the soil. The influence of factor 4 is most striking in small areas such as a township or county, and the influence of the others in larger areas. See Fig. 14.

Other significant factors that may exercise a controlling influence in some areas include government subsidies, tariffs, introduction of new crops and development of more favored competing areas, more efficient methods of farming and marketing, and new types of machinery such as the combine, harvester, and cotton-picking machine. An interesting current example is the rapid spread of the soybean and machinery for handling the crop. This new crop is now crowding cotton in the Delta region of southeastern Missouri where handpicking still prevails and where large soybean mills are well established.

The East vs. the West.   In general, the United States is divided about equally into an eastern humid half, characterized by the cultivation of grains, tame hay and pasture, and the production of shelter-fed livestock; and an arid or semiarid western half, characterized by wild hay, pasture and grazing, irrigation, dry farming, and very limited humid-type agriculture. Local sections in California, the north Pacific Coast and the northern Rocky Mountains are exceptions, but they are relatively small. The transition belt between the eastern and western halves corresponds approximately to the 100th meridian West and to an average annual rainfall of 25 inches in southern Texas and 15 inches along the Dakota-Canadian border. The agricultural regions in the eastern humid half extend, in the main, east and west, corresponding closely to latitude, and are determined chiefly by temperature and the leading crop. Those of the western arid and semiarid half extend north and south and are based primarily upon the rainfall, topography, altitude, and soils. The eastern

[1] For a more detailed discussion of agriculture, see Chapters 5, 8, 12, and 16.

humid half produces fully 85 per cent of the total value of all crops and has a like proportion of the crop acreage. In the East "corn is king," and in the West hay is the leading crop, though forage secured by grazing nearly equals it in value. More than five-sixths of the land in crops is in the eastern humid half of the country, and nearly two-thirds is in the triangular-shaped area extending from eastern Ohio to north central North Dakota and central Texas. This triangular region includes only about a quarter of the area of the country, yet it produces three-fifths of the hay, four-fifths of the corn, and three-fourths of the wheat and oats. No similar area of the world offers equally favorable conditions for corn culture, and it is probable that few, if any, other regions are as suitable for the production of small grains and hay.

The Arid and Semiarid West. This extensive area of scant precipitation is a land of high mountains and plateaus and has an average elevation of more than 4000 feet; hence altitude, scant rainfall, and soils are the principal factors determining its subdivision into agricultural regions. Except in the humid north Pacific region, and in the irrigated and dry-farming sections, 2000–4000 acres are needed to support a family. In the irrigated sections 80–120 acres are required, and in the dry-farming sections 640 acres or more. The total value of all the crops of this area forms only a small fraction of the total for the United States. The current character of the agriculture is shown by the fact that hay and forage constitute more than a quarter of the value of the crops; wheat, and fruits and nuts about a fifth each; with much smaller proportions for vegetables, oats, and barley. More than three-fifths of the crop acreage is in the Great Plains regions of dry farming and grazing.

The scant rainfall throughout nearly the whole area limits most of this area to the grazing industry. From the western Dakotas, Nebraska, and Texas to the Pacific Coast are more than 700 million acres of range land. Other important range areas occur in central Texas, in the Flint Hills of Oklahoma and Kansas, and in the Arbuckle Mountains of Oklahoma. Sheep are raised in the more arid and cattle in the less arid sections. In areas of seasonal grazing sheep are commonly moved to the foothills in spring and fall and to the mountains in summer. Cattle are likewise grazed during the summer in the mountain ranges, pastured on hay or cropland on spring-fall range, and fed during the winter months. Here are produced about two-thirds of the sheep of the United States and more than a quarter of the cattle. Goats are the major livestock on the brush-covered, rough range of the Edwards Plateau of Texas. In the cool, moist north Pacific region, dairying is the most important livestock industry. In the vast mountain and plateau country between the north Pacific Coast and the Great Plains, grazing is likely to remain the leading activity.

Much of the region provides only scanty pasturage, as it is so dry that 50–100 or more acres are required to maintain one steer. Crop production on an intensive scale is impossible except by irrigation, and because of insufficient water only a very small fraction of this area can ever be irrigated. Approximately 20,400,000 acres are now irrigated in the entire West, and more than half of this area is in California, Colorado, and Idaho. These three states also have half of the undeveloped irrigable acreage for which water is available in present irrigation systems. Projects under development will increase the irrigated acreage in the arid areas. In some sections feed production by irrigation and livestock grazing on the dry lands has been coordinated.

Dry farming appears to offer limited possibilities in competition with the humid East. At most, it is an effort to make the best of an unfavorable climate. It consists essentially of cultivating semiarid lands in such a manner as to accumulate and conserve the moisture received during 1 or more years, and taking a chance that there will be sufficient moisture to produce a crop once in 2 or 3 years. If conditions prove favorable, profit may result, as the land is relatively cheap and the investment small. Thus far, it has proved disappointing in the solution of dry-land problems, and as a means of providing for a large agricultural population it is not promising.

The Spring-Wheat Region. This nearly flat to gently rolling area with fertile black soils, within which lies the famous Red River Valley, is characterized (1) by spring-grown cereals—wheat, oats, barley, flax— with wheat as the dominant grain, and (2) by an extensive type of agriculture. Most of its products are shipped to distant markets, and very little is consumed on the farm where grown. Livestock and cultivated hays are relatively unimportant, though corn for forage and the dairy industry are now entering the region. Fields of corn may now be seen in the northern stronghold of spring wheat. The potato and soybean are crops rapidly growing in favor and competing with spring-grown cereals. Little spring wheat is grown outside this area. Its crop constitutes more than 20 per cent of the total wheat crop of the United States, and more than 85 per cent of the spring wheat. More than four-fifths of the area is in farms; nearly seven-tenths is improved, and more than half is in crops. About half the spring-wheat acreage of the United States is in the Spring-Wheat Region, where two-fifths of the crop acreage is devoted to its culture, and most of the remainder is in the adjoining Great Plains region. Nearly nine-tenths of the total crop of North America is produced in the Canadian and United States sections of this area. A lesser but important producing center is located in the subhumid sections of Washington and Oregon. The principal factors in evolving the distinguishing type of agriculture in this region have been (1) the low rainfall of 15–25 inches, coming chiefly in the spring and summer; (2) long, cold winters of comparative idleness; (3) short, hot summers favorable to ripening and harvesting of grains; (4) fertile prairie soils; and (5) the distant consuming markets.

The Hay and Dairying Region.   This northern region, extending from Minnesota to Maine, with its cool, moist summers, its poorly drained podzolic glacial soils and many swamps, and its relatively large proportion of rough lands, is preeminently a land of hay, pasturage, and silage of high quality. Half or more of the improved land in nearly every county of the region produces these crops. Less than a third of the area is improved, and only about a fifth is devoted to crops. The large production of hay and the excellent pasturage are the bases for a well-developed dairy industry which finds a ready market for its milk, butter, and cheese in the scores of large cities within or adjacent to the region. Near urban centers the major product is fluid milk; butter and cheese predominate at greater distances from market. Much of the grain and other concentrates which comprise a part of the heavy feed ration are produced on the dairy farms, but large quantities are imported from other regions. Other crops, such as fruits, sugar beets, potatoes, beans, corn, and small grains, occupy a leading position in local districts but are relatively small factors in the agricultural economy of the region as a whole.

On the northern margin is an extensive deforested area, parts of which are suited to agriculture and are being settled slowly. However, much of this section is best suited to the growth of forests and should be used for that purpose.

The Corn Belt.   The Corn Belt probably produces more food to the square mile than any area of like extent in the world. More than nine-tenths of its area is in farms, more than three-fourths is improved, and more than three-fifths is in crops. The warm, moist climate and rich prairie soils make the region peculiarly well adapted to corn and associated meat production. Nearly two-fifths of the crop acreage is devoted to that cereal, and the annual crop contributes half the value of all crops. More than half the corn crop of the United States is produced in this region, and it is also the center of the beef-cattle and hog-raising industries, where about a quarter of the cattle and more than two-fifths of the hogs are produced or got ready for market. Other important crops are hay, oats, soybeans, and wheat, which provide a desirable system of rotation—hay and oats along the northern margin and hay and wheat along the southern. Abundant spring and summer rains, a long, warm growing season, and great extent of exceedingly rich dark brown silt loams spread over a level or gently undulating plain are the basal geographic factors that have contributed toward making the Corn Belt a superior agricultural region. The stage of general prosperity and progress of its farming people is indicated by the widespread use of modern conveniences such as the automobile and telephone. The fine homes with grass-covered lawns, large, well-kept barns and outbuildings, fields of excellent crops enclosed by wire fences, herds of high-grade domestic animals, farm machinery, hard-surfaced highways, railroads, telephone lines, motor vehicles make up a striking cultural landscape. From 60 to 90 per cent of the farms have telephones; many have radio-receiving sets; one-half to three-fourths of the farms have automobiles; and two-fifths of the total number of automobiles on farms in the United States are in the Corn Belt. A similar ratio holds in the use of modern farm machinery. All this reflects the tendency of the United States farmer to utilize modern mechanical equipment, and the degree of rural progress and prosperity attained.

Corn and Winter-Wheat Belt. On the south the Corn Belt blends into the Corn and Winter-Wheat Belt and the Hard Winter-Wheat Region with no sharp line of demarcation. The three regions have more than seven-tenths of the winter-wheat acreage of the United States, nearly half being in the second and third. The Hard Winter-Wheat Region of western Kansas, Oklahoma, Texas, and eastern Colorado is by far the more important. Growing wheat on a large scale is the major farm enterprise, but there is a large total acreage of sorghums. Other minor crops include barley, oats, alfalfa, and sweet clover in the eastern portion and on the flat lands along the streams. The northern limit of winter wheat corresponds in general with the mean winter isotherm of 20°, and its southern limit with the mean isotherm of 72° for the month just before harvest. Though winter wheat occupies about 30 per cent of the crop acreage in the Corn and Winter-Wheat Belt, corn exceeds it in value. Cattle and swine are also produced in large numbers, but they are relatively less important than in the Corn Belt.

The Cotton Belt. Cotton is king of crops in the Cotton Belt, and corn is the leading cereal. More than two-fifths of the cropped land is devoted to cotton culture—this is a region where only about a fourth of the entire area produces cultivated crops of any kind. However, the intensity of cotton culture varies greatly within the Cotton Belt. In some specialized areas a third to more than half the farm land may be devoted to cotton, such as the Delta areas of Louisiana, Mississippi, Missouri, and Arkansas; and the Corpus Christi and High Plains areas of Texas. In other sections little cotton is grown, or it is grown as part of a more general type of farming economy which may include peanuts, tobacco, pasture, livestock, and dairying. The only other cotton-producing areas that may be considered of importance are found in the irrigated lands of California, New Mexico, and Arizona. Unlike corn, cotton is distinctly a cash crop, and all except part of the seed leaves the farm upon which it is grown. Prosperity, therefore, soars or wanes with the price of cotton and size of the crop. As noted, very little cotton is grown in the United States outside of this belt. Its northern limit has 200 frost-free days and a mean summer temperature of 77°; the southern limit has 11 inches of autumn rainfall—more than that amount injures the lint and seriously interferes with picking. Scant rainfall limits cotton growth on the west, except by irrigation. Cotton is grown on all well-drained types of soil, but the larger crops are produced in normal years upon the dark-colored clay lands, especially those rich in lime, and upon the red, brown, and black bottom lands. Both the climate and the soil of the Cotton Belt are particularly well suited to the growth of cotton and are the principal geographic factors that have made this the world's largest cotton region, and cotton

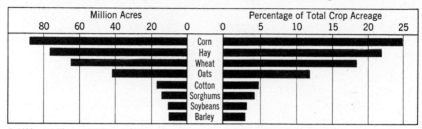

Fig. 15. Principal Crops of the United States. These eight crops occupy nine-tenths of the acreage of all crops. The United States produces about three-fifths of the world's corn, more than two-fifths of the cotton, more than one-third of the oats and soybeans, and one-fifth of the wheat.

the largest commercial crop of the United States and a large export commodity. Other factors favoring the extensive culture of cotton are (1) a large world demand and limited areas favorable to its culture, (2) the fact that cotton growing provides employment from early spring to early winter, (3) the fact that the crop is sold directly for cash instead of indirectly through livestock as is corn, and (4) mechanization of production.

Subtropical Coast. This hot, moist coastal lowland region extends from South Carolina to Texas. The warm winds from the warm Gulf of Mexico and oceanic waters exercise a controlling influence on its climate and agriculture. It is characterized by a subtropical climate, sandy soils, and extensive areas of poorly drained land, rather than by any leading product. Agriculture is subtropical in character and varies from growing of rice, sugar cane, winter vegetables, and citrus fruits to cattle ranching. Only about a fifth of the area is in farms, only 8 per cent is improved, and only 6 per cent produces crops.

Cropped Land and Leading Crops. The acreage devoted to crops is an index of the distribution of agriculture. Though crops are produced throughout the humid eastern half of the United States where five-sixths of the crop acreage is located, the north central section is by far the most important. The triangular section lying between north central North Dakota, central Texas, and eastern Ohio contains nearly two-thirds of the cropped land, and, though it embraces only about a quarter of the United States, it produces four-fifths of the corn, three-fourths of the wheat and oats, and three-fifths of the hay. Cotton is the only other important crop produced outside this section, whose geographic advantages

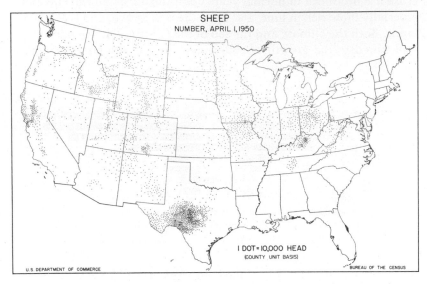

Fig. 16. More than three-fifths of the sheep are in the West, largely because they can graze on arid lands better than any other domestic animal, and also because they are less subject to disease in arid climates than in humid.

for the growth of small grains and hay are equaled by few other parts of the world. It is superior to any other equal area for the production of corn.

Corn, hay, wheat, oats, cotton, sorghums, soybeans, and barley are the principal crops of the United States (Fig. 15). These crops occupy more than nine-tenths of the acreage and constitute nearly seven-tenths of the value of all crops produced. They also constitute a large proportion of the world's production.

Livestock. The production of livestock is a major phase of American agriculture. About two-thirds of the crop acreage produces food for domestic animals, and, in addition, more than 149 million acres of plowable land and 940,000,000 acres of non-plowable land, public lands, and forest lands, are used for this purpose. Domestic animals consume essentially all the feed produced on unimproved land, two-thirds of that on improved land, and fully four-fifths of all that produced by wild and tame vegetation in the country. The humid East produces most of the

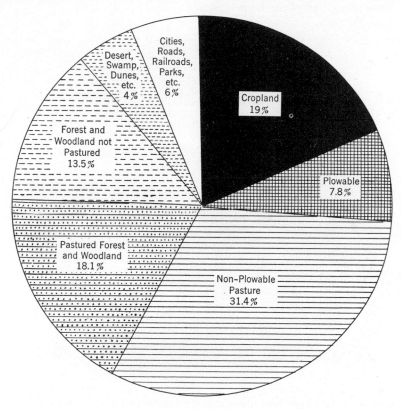

Fig. 17. Use of land in the United States. The total land area of the United States is 1,905,000,000 acres. Approximately 19 per cent of the land area is used for crops; about 40 per cent for pasture and grazing exclusive of pastured forest land; and 32 per cent is in forest and cut-over land, more than half of which is used for pasture. The area of the pasture land physically suitable for crops is less than half as large as the present cropland, but it is poorer land and cannot be used for crops under present economic conditions.

food and most of the cattle and swine; the drier lands of the West produce most of the sheep. Cattle are more evenly distributed than either swine or sheep, being most abundant in the Corn Belt, the Hay and Pasture Region, and the Corn and Winter-Wheat Belt. Swine are intimately associated with the production of abundant fattening food, hence two-fifths are in the Corn Belt and another fifth in the Corn and Winter-Wheat Belt. Sheep are better adapted to the rougher and more arid lands than are other domestic animals; they can go for days or even weeks without water when the pasture is succulent; they can be handled in large bands owing to their herding instinct; hence three-fifths are raised in the western half of the United States. (Fig. 16.)

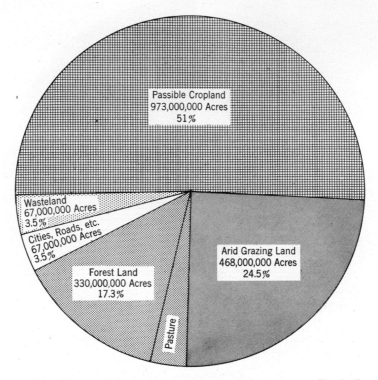

Fig. 18. Potential uses of land under extreme population pressure. Physically, 51 per cent of land area of the United States is suitable for crops, nearly 25 per cent for grazing only, and 17 per cent is best suited to forests and grazing. However, it is likely to be many generations—if ever—before it will be economical to produce crops on all the land physically suitable. Yet the estimate is an approximate measure of our resources.

Potential Agricultural Area and Population.   How to provide food that is adequate both in quantity and quality to meet the needs of an increasing population is one of the serious problems confronting every nation that endures during any extended period. Many nations must turn to an outside source of food supply; a few have an abundance of potentially productive lands within their borders. The chief agricultural uses that any nation makes of its land are for crops, pasture, and forest. Nearly one-fifth of the land area of the United States produces harvested crops; about two-fifths produces pasture; and nearly one-third is occupied by forest and cut-over land, more than half of which is pastured. See Fig. 17. However, the value of the harvested crops produced on the one-fifth so used is immensely greater than the value produced on the seven-tenths devoted to pasture and forest. For many years the United States met its food requirements for consumption and export by bringing new land under cultivation. The peak of agricultural land supply in proportion

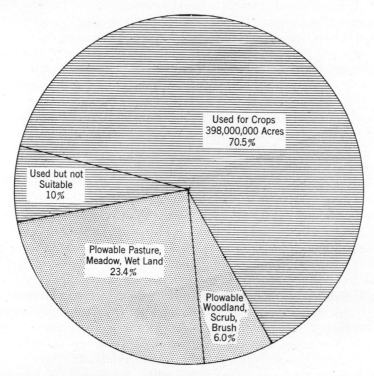

Fig. 19. Potential cropland in farms. If 64,000,000 acres of plowable land are reserved for pasture the potentially good cropland in farms is approximately 460,000,000 acres.

to population was passed many years ago, and the future will show a continually increasing scarcity of such land. Nearly all the land suitable for crops, pasture, or forest has long since been appropriated; hence an increase in food supply must come either (1) from increased yield per acre, or (2) at the expense of pasture and forest area. It seems certain that both means may be utilized to advantage.

The United States has about 973 million acres physically capable of producing crops, about 398 million of which are now used. See Fig. 18.

It is, however, idle to assume that the maximum will ever be so used or, at least, until the need is extreme and cost of utilization is of little consideration. Such figures have value only as indicators of maximum potentiality. It is more realistic to think in terms of lands now in farms (Fig 19). Out of some 564 million acres, 398 million are used for crops even though some 40 million acres are very poor land and not economical to use. There are about 166 million acres of unused plowable land in farms. These consist of pasture, wet lands, meadow, woodland, scrub and brush lands. It appears probable that at least 64 million acres of this land should be reserved for pasture. This leaves a potential of good plowable cropland in farms of about 460 million acres. Further drainage and irrigation of land not in farms will add considerably to the potential productive capacity of the country. It has been estimated that a population of 170,000,000 can be cared for without seriously altering the standard of living, by adding to crop acreage and yield, by improved pasturage, mechanization, and technology. These changes have been in progress for many years. Beyond that number of people, both the standard of living and crop yield an acre must be materially altered. Such alterations are now in progress. If the acre-yield is increased until it equals that of western Europe, and a European standard of living is accepted in the United States, about 300,000,000 people can be provided for. It is likely that for many decades the reality will be between these two population estimates, as standards of living and acre-yield slowly change.

These estimates, however, assure us that the United States has the land resources capable of maintaining a considerably larger population than it now has, on a living level far above that of western Europe. The United States possesses agricultural advantages both geographic and non-geographic that are superior to those of any other nation. Among these are (1) great extent of highly fertile and varied soils on nearly level or gently rolling plains, (2) varied and highly favorable agricultural climate over the fertile plains, (3) a healthful and stimulating climate, (4) an excellent transportation system, (5) excellent home markets and accessibility to foreign markets, especially those across the narrow Atlantic in western Europe, (6) a highly developed system of agricultural education and government aid, both state and national, and (7) a strong, stable government.

MINERALS AND POWER

Next to the products of the soil, modern, complex, human life—called "civilization"—depends for its material success upon the application of mechanical power to machinery. The application of power to the machine has made it possible for man to rise far above primitive living. Such application has increased his productive capacity tremendously. It is probable that the energy output of the United States is more than 300 times its population. In any nation the critical elements are (1) agricultural lands, (2) minerals, (3) manpower. The use of agricultural land is the measure of the capacity to provide food and clothing; the use of minerals is th measure of the capacity for industry, transportation, and communication; and manpower is the measure of the capacity to utilize effectively the resources at hand. Any nation that has abundant agricultural land, abundant and varied minerals, and abundant and intelligent manpower is in a very strong position. Industrial development requires

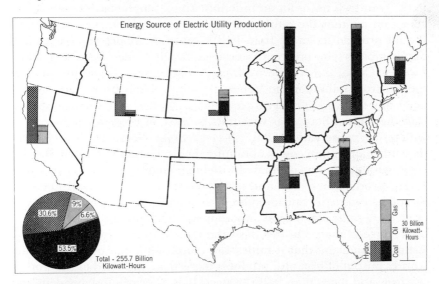

Fig. 20. Energy source of electric utility production. Note and explain the variation in the source of energy.

extensive use of minerals—coal, water, oil, gas, iron, copper, and others. The United States has nearly all the important minerals. Sources of power are also widespread, which together with man's utilization of coal, water, oil, and gas are well illustrated by the sources of energy for electric utilities (Fig. 20). Only a few minerals are of such vital significance that they need to be considered here.

Iron. Of all mineral derivatives, iron may be considered the indispensable one, though its use is well-nigh inseparable from that of coal, which is needed for its production and as one source of power to drive the machinery made from it. It is the most important of all metals to man— probably more than all other metals combined. The iron-ore deposits of the United States are both widespread and of high quality compared with much of the iron ore that is used in western Europe. It is fortunate, indeed, that the best and most cheaply mined ore is tributary to the Great Lakes, over which it may be transported, at low cost, to those centers in the central and eastern states where the presence of good coal fosters manufacturing and the development of great consuming markets. Within the country's borders is located about a quarter of the known metallic iron of the world, and the United States has sufficient coking coal with which to smelt the iron. Though the higher-grade ores would be exhausted within a generation were it possible to maintain the present rate of production, the vast amount of lower-grade ore assures a supply ample to the country's needs for an indefinite time. On the basis of 40–50 per cent iron content the estimated reserves of nearly 5,400,000,000 tons should provide for more than half a century. At present the United States imports some ore from Venezuela, Brazil, Chile, Canada, Norway, Sweden, Cuba, and Northern Africa. As high-grade ores decline more of the ores from Labrador and Venezuela will probably be used. It now appears that the world's reserves are sufficient to meet all human needs and that the United States has within its bounds, or readily available to it, with proper conservation, all it will ever require. National advantage will depend chiefly upon cost of obtaining the iron, and the United States is in a favorable position compared with other countries.

The production of iron and steel is often spoken of as a barometer of industrial prosperity and an index of the stage of modern material development, because of the basal importance of iron and steel in the activities of "civilized" man. On this basis the United States should rank high. Estimates indicate that it mines and consumes about one-third of the world's output of iron ore; produces more than one-third of the world's pig iron and more than half the steel. It is as nearly independent and self-sufficing as any nation can be, and is likely to remain so.

Coal.   Machine power makes possible the difference between modern and primitive man. It makes possible our cities, our railroads, our manufacturing industries and extensive commerce, our great churches and schools, and much of our recreation and pleasure. In fact, our whole modern social and industrial fabric depends upon it. Coal is still the major source of that power (Fig. 22) and hence is fundamental to our well-being, as it is impossible to imagine a social and economic system, such as we now possess, depending upon the unaided labor of man. However, oil, water, and natural gas are becoming increasingly important as sources of power, and coal is declining relatively.

To meet its requirements, the United States produces nearly two-fifths of the world's coal, an annual tonnage which is nearly twice that of any

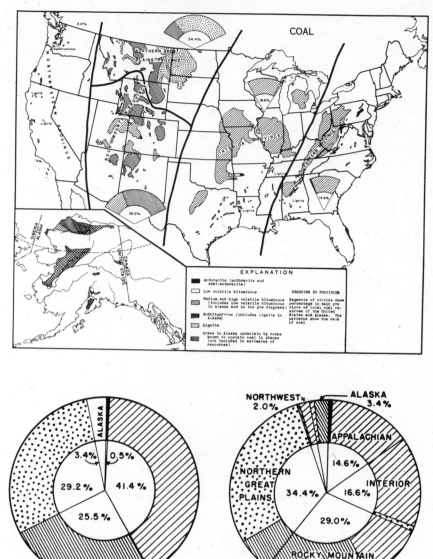

Fig. 21. Coal is well distributed throughout the country and is our chief source of energy, though declining in relative importance. Nearly all the high-grade coal is east of the Mississippi where more than nine-tenths of the total annual output is mined, and where it is of greatest usefulness. Reserves of the United States are enormous, constituting more than two-fifths of the known coal of the world. *Courtesy, U. S. Bureau of Mines.*

other country. Measured in heat or power units, the ratio in favor of the
United States is very much greater, as a large proportion of European
production is low grade. For the future the United States has more than
two-fifths of the known coal of the world. Nearly all the coal of high grade
is east of the Mississippi River, where it is of maximum usefulness and
where more than nine-tenths of the annual output is now mined, chiefly
in Pennsylvania, West Virginia, Illinois, and Kentucky. Even though the
present rate of production of all grades is considerably increased, the
supply is sufficient to last many centuries (Fig. 23). The high-grade coals,
however, will be gone in much less time if production is confined almost
exclusively to them as at present.

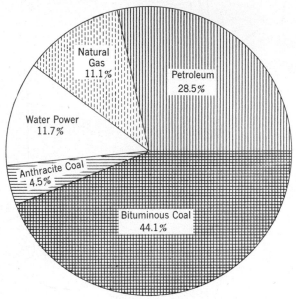

Fig. 22. Energy sources of the United States. Three-year average.

Water Power.   Water is the most permanent and constant source of
power (Fig. 24), as coal, oil, and gas are exhaustible. Present utilization
in the United States is about 18.5 million kilowatts, and resource available, at mean flow, is calculated to be 84.8 million kilowatts. It is significant (1) that the larger amount probably would turn all the wheels of the
country's present industries, and (2) that more than two-fifths is in the
Pacific states, which are poorly endowed with good coal for their industries and railways. However, these resources undoubtedly would be of
greater value if a larger proportion were located east of the Mississippi.
It is clear that coal and water assets provide power adequate for all future
needs.

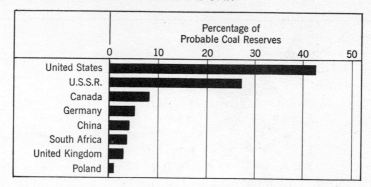

Fig. 23. Coal reserves of the world. The large coal reserves—mechanical energy—of the world are held by a few countries. The dominance of United States and U.S.S.R. is evident in the diagram. Eight countries have more than 95 per cent of the world's coal.

Petroleum.   Petroleum has become a commercial necessity. It serves chiefly as a source of power, light, and lubricants, though scores of other refined products are derived from it. It is even conceivable that future national leadership in the air and on the sea may be determined by the

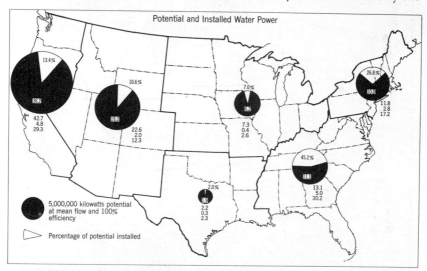

Fig. 24. Distribution of water power in the United States. Two-thirds of the potential water power of the United States is in the Pacific and Mountain sections, and more than half of the developed power is in the eastern sections. The potential power available at mean flow is 84.6 million kilowatts. *Note:* Read figures beside circles as follows: The Southeast has 13.1 per cent of potential water power, based on mean flow and 100 per cent efficiency, and 5,000,000 kilowatts installed January 1, 1949, which is 30.2 per cent of the total installed in the United States.

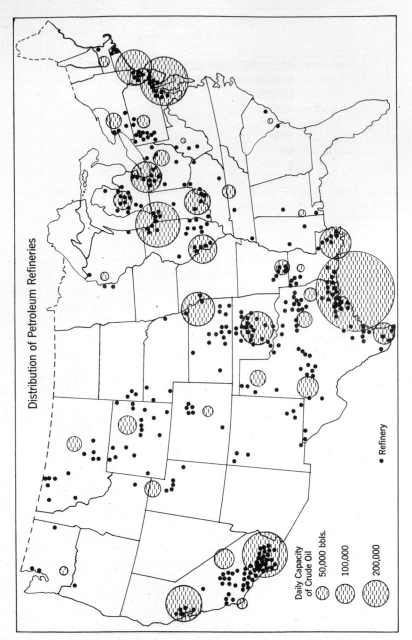

Distribution of Petroleum Refineries

Daily Capacity
of Crude Oil

50,000 bbls.

100,000

200,000

• Refinery

Fig. 25. Distribution of petroleum refineries.

possession of fuel oil, kerosene, gasoline, and lubricating oil, since their efficiency for navigation purposes is greatly in excess of that of coal or its products.

Since the discovery of petroleum in western Pennsylvania in 1859, United States production has grown to enormous size. For several decades thereafter Pennsylvania led, but new fields were located and opened, and production spread to Ohio, West Virginia, Kentucky, Indiana, and Illinois; to the midcontinent field of Texas, Oklahoma, and Kansas; on westward to the California field, and to the Rocky Mountain Area. At various times many of these states have led in production, but now Texas is far in the lead. Peak production has attained nearly 2.25 billion barrels in a single year, although the average annual production rate is smaller.

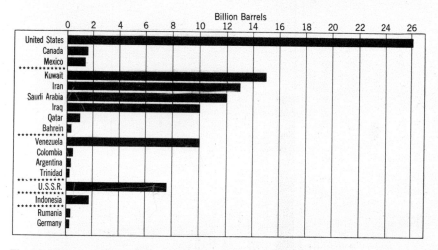

Fig. 26. Major petroleum regions of the world. Estimated proven reserves, as of January, 1951, were approximately 102 billion barrels, with half in the Middle East. How does this distribution affect international political and economic relations?

Outside the principal producing regions most of the refineries are located in the major manufacturing belt, from Illinois to New Jersey (Fig. 25). Well over a hundred thousand miles of pipe line convey the products of the oil and natural gas industry to refineries and consuming markets.

The United States has produced about two-thirds of the world's output, the maintenance of which ratio seems improbable. Even though other regions of the world have large known resources of liquid petroleum, those of the United States still exceed the reserves of any other country (Fig. 26). However, estimates indicate that some of the major fields in the United States are near exhaustion of proven reserves (Fig. 27). Texas has by far the largest reserve. Based on proven reserves and

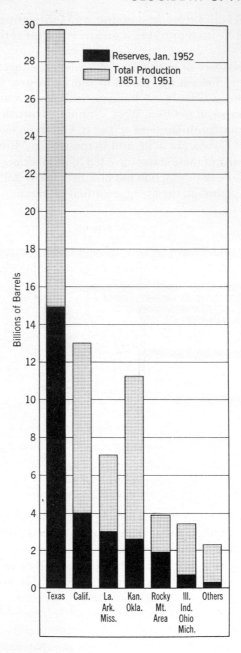

Fig. 27. Estimated crude petroleum reserves and cumulative production.

present methods of production resources will be practically exhausted within a half century, as the country is producing, exporting, and consuming at a suicidal rate. Every effort is being made to locate and develop new fields such as the Williston Basin, the Gulf of Mexico, and other continental shelf areas.

As exhaustion of liquid hydrocarbons approaches and prices become higher, the United States must turn to its large reserves of oil shales and increase greatly the recovery from wells, which is now scarcely half of the oil present. However, it is clear that a substantial advantage will lie with the nation possessing the cheapest liquid oil.

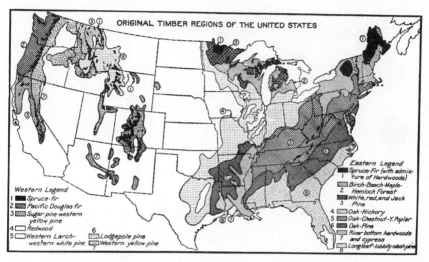

Fig. 28. Original forest lands. Much of the United States originally carried forests of highly useful timber. *Courtesy, U. S. Forest Service.*

HARVESTING OUR FORESTS

The Passing of Our Virgin Forests.   To the early explorer and settler America appeared like a vast, unbroken forest. To him a future shortage of timber must have seemed impossible. Nearly half the area now within the United States was forested at that time (Fig. 28). To the pioneer the trees were a serious handicap and had to be removed for agriculture and settlement. Fully 200,000,000 acres were cleared for this purpose, and three-fourths of the timber removed was wasted, as there was no market. Later the demand for lumber led to rapid exploitation of the virgin forests. The fine northern forests extending from New England to Minnesota—the land of the stately white and Norway pines—were among the first to be attacked. The excellence of their timber and their location on the Great Lakes waterways and near the centers of large population favored rapid removal.

The central hardwood forest occupied large areas of agricultural land, and little now remains except on rough mountain and hilly tracts, or in farmers' woodlots. The southern forest is now falling before the advance of the lumberman. It is here that the United States secures most of the yellow pine, four-tenths of the softwood, and three-fifths of the hardwood saw timber produced annually. In addition the South now exceeds the North in pulpwood production, nearly all of which is from pine. Scores

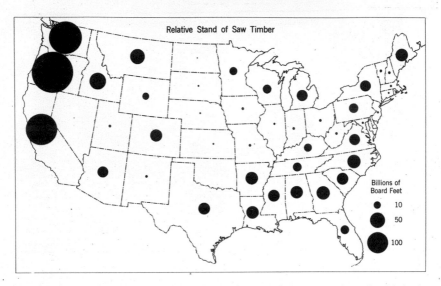

Fig. 29. Relative stands of saw timber. Three-fourths of the present forest land is in the East and one-fourth in the West, but the West carries most of the remaining saw timber. About half the standing saw timber is in the Pacific Coast States.

of pulp and paper mills have been erected or enlarged since about 1930 (Fig. 33). The Rocky Mountain forests are located in scattered areas, difficult of access and remote from markets, and hence have been exploited but little. However, they do not constitute a large timber resource. The Pacific Coast forests, with their Douglas fir, redwoods, spruce, cedar, yellow pine, and giant sequoias, are among the finest in the world. The warm summers, mild winters, heavy rainfall, and deep soil of this region make ideal conditions for tree growth. At present it supplies 45 per cent of the annual production of softwood saw timber. Here still stands half the remaining saw timber of the United States, of which more than a third is Douglas fir. Exploitation of these splendid forests is now progressing rapidly. Today about two-thirds of the original forested area has been cut-, culled-, or burned-over, and fully three-fifths of the timber is gone.

Production and Depletion.   The forests have been removed like coal from a mine, with little thought of a new crop. The pressing problem is to increase growth to meet the demand for saw timber, which constitutes 80 per cent of the forest drain. The United States is the largest wood consumer in the world, and the demand for wood is increasing in spite of all "substitutes." This enormous demand has produced a destructive drain upon forest resources (Fig. 31). Today only about two-fifths of the origi-

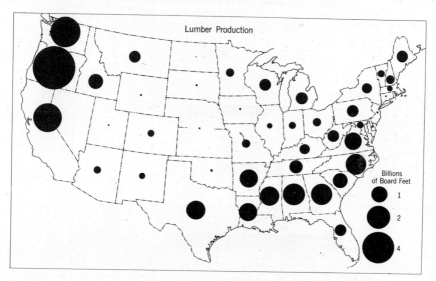

Fig. 30. Lumber production. The Pacific Coast states produce 45 per cent of the soft-wood timber and the South about 40 per cent of the softwood and 60 per cent of the hardwood timber.

nal supply of timber remains; only about one-sixth of the original forested area carries virgin timber; only about one-eighth, second-growth saw timber; about one-sixth, cordwood; and one-tenth is unproductive. Nearly two-thirds of the remaining stand of saw timber is west of the Great Plains, with half in the Pacific Coast states, and about one-fifth in the Gulf and south Atlantic section (Fig. 29). These sections are now supplying home needs and a small surplus for export. Since nearly half is consumed in the northeastern quarter of the country, a long haul and high cost are involved. In the North, fir, spruce, hemlock and pine supply three-fourths of the pulpwood, where cut-over land and small trees are utilized, where water power is available, and where the markets are nearby. The United States also produces a large share of the world's naval stores, chiefly from southern forests.

Nearly seven-tenths of the timber of all kinds consumed in the United States is softwood—pine, fir, spruce, hemlock—and the softwood saw timber is being removed about one and three-fourths times as fast as it grows (Fig. 31). The annual rate of forest depletion from all causes, measured in cubic feet, nearly balances the growth. However, this ratio of growth to drain is deceptive since the growth figures include small poles and saplings, and the drain of saw timber is more than half again as great

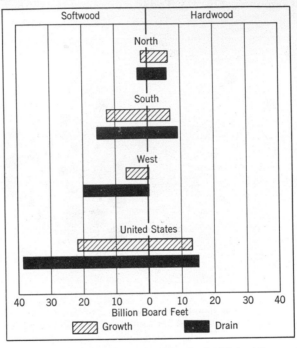

Fig. 31. Annual growth and drain of saw timber in the United States. *Courtesy, U. S. Forest Service.*

as saw-timber growth, which is needed for human use. Though many economies can and should be practiced, though numerous substitutes for wood may be found, many new uses for wood are being developed and the demand continues. In the last analysis, there is one real solution to the forest problem: trees must be grown, and the mining of the forests must cease. Approximately two-thirds of the original forest land is still available, and estimates indicate that at least 61 billion board feet of saw timber annually will be needed within the next 5 to 8 years. If intensive forestry comparable to that of Scandinavia, Germany, and France is practiced, the 624 million acres of forest land can produce all that the nation is ever likely to need. In addition the forests of Alaska may be utilized. Thus far the United States has followed a policy of immediate profit rather than one of provision for future need. The best welfare of the country demands a complete reversal of this policy.

Public and Private Forests.   Probably because of the popular belief that the forests were inexhaustible, the Federal Goverment was slow in becoming an active leader in conservation. Federal funds were appropriated for forest investigations as early as 1876, but nothing was accomplished. The first reserves were created in 1891, but no National Forest was so designated until 1905, when a forest policy was definitely established for the

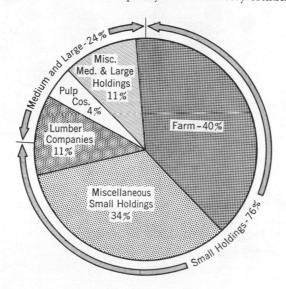

Fig. 32. Distribution of private commercial forest land by class of ownership. *Courtesy, U. S. Forest Service.*

first time. Additional areas have since been set aside or purchased until the total area of the National Forests has grown to 123 million acres (net). To this may be added about 38,000,000 acres set aside by states and local units such as counties, schools, municipalities, and 54 million acres administered by various Federal agencies other than the Forest Service. Only part of this area is productive forest land. Private commercial forests contain about 345 million acres, or nearly three-fourths of the total for the United States. More than three-fourths of this area is held by more than 4 million owners, such holdings averaging about 62 acres (Fig 32). This makes establishment of a sound forest policy and management extremely difficult. A vast program of education appears to be essential if these lands are to be utilized to the fullest. Many large holders, particularly those engaged in forest industries, endeavor to practice good forestry methods, but there is no uniformity. Extensive areas are held by absentee owners. Vast areas must be planted and protected from fire and disease, and growing tree crops on private lands must be encouraged if future needs are to be met.

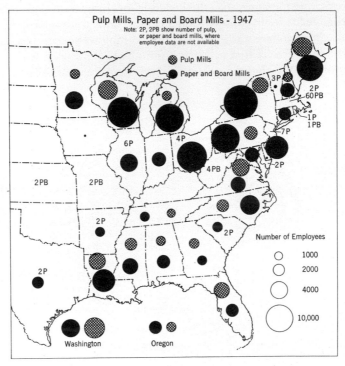

Fig. 33. Pulp mills, paper and board mills. Most of the mills are located in the North Atlantic and Great Lakes States, however, the South now exceeds the North in pulpwood production. Rapid expansion in the South is now underway.

MANUFACTURES

Growth.   Agriculture is fundamental; mining and manufacturing are secondary. This was strikingly true in the development of the United States until comparatively recent times. For many years, cheap land was abundant, population was small, and anyone could have a farm by winning it from the forest or prairie. The numerous opportunities for the individual to gain ample reward independently were unfavorable to the factory system of manufacturing, which requires regularity of routine labor for others. During the colonial period manufacturing was insignificant. Only cotton and iron manufactures had made much progress by 1830. Though the country began to feel its manufacturing power before the beginning of the Civil War, only since about 1870 has its people really discovered and begun to utilize their great resources. Those varied and abundant resources, in a land of large size, have led to manufacturing on an immense scale by huge industrial organizations unequaled in any other country. Here again, the country expresses itself in the superlative. Thus far it has gone on by exploiting natural resources while the population has been rapidly increasing—a process that cannot continue indefinitely. Clearly there must be an elimination of waste, an increase in production, technology, and efficiency, or a decrease in rate of population growth, or opportunities will vanish and the people will be obliged to seek homes in other lands, like many of those of European countries.

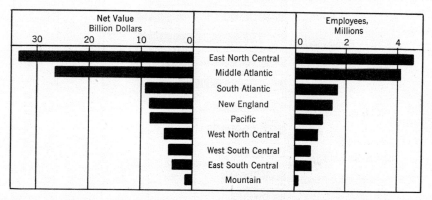

Fig. 34. Manufactures by sections (1951). The East North Central (Great Lakes) and Middle Atlantic sections produce about three-fifths of the net value of the manufactures, and have nearly the same proportion of manufacturing employees.

These requirements now seem assured. Farms, forests, mines, and factories are completely dependent on one another for their fullest development. Their abundant products provide for transportation and commerce and for a prosperous people. Since the United States possesses all the fundamentals of national prosperity—power, agricultural land, raw materials, labor, capital—it appears certain that the conversion of raw materials into finished products and their sale in domestic and foreign markets will enable the country to maintain its high standard of living, provide abundantly for its people, and continue manufacturing progress far beyond that of any other nation. At present the only possible serious competitor appears to be U.S.S.R.

Present Position.   United States is the leading manufacturing nation of the world. The total net value of its products reaches the huge sum of

$102,000,000,000 (1951) (which is a fair value measure of the significance of the manufacturing process [2]); and 15,600,000 people are employed in its mills and factories. Probably not less than five times that number of people are directly or indirectly dependent upon them. Among the major industrial groups, machinery and food products are responsible for more than a quarter of the net value and engage a like proportion of the country's manufacturing employees. These are followed in order by transportation, primary metals, chemicals, metal and textile mill products. These

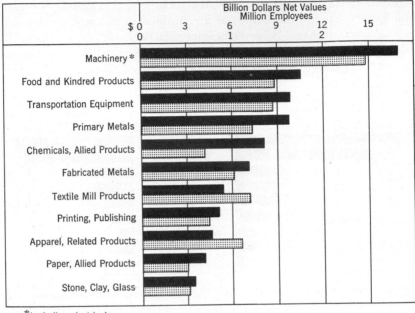

Fig. 35. Manufactures of the United States by major industrial groups (1951). By the measures used, machinery and food products lead all other groups of manufactures. The first seven groups account for three-fifths of all manufacturing employees and two-thirds of net value of manufactures of the United States. The diagram shows large diversification and many other smaller groups differing from each other by small margins. Does this diagram display weakness or strength?

seven groups account for three-fifths of the employees and two-thirds of the net value of the manufactures of the United States. They occupy a commanding position in American industry. In addition, many other groups (Fig. 35) give employment to several million people and produce many billions of dollars worth of goods. This indicates great diversification and industrial strength.

[2] The terms "net value" and "product value" are suggested and here used in place of the cumbersome forms—"value added by manufacture," and "value of manufactured product." However, both forms will be found in this book. Which is preferable?

DISTRIBUTION OF MANUFACTURING

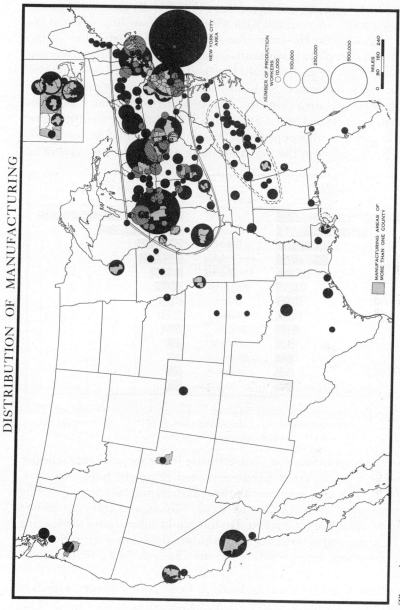

FIG. 36. The major manufacturing belt contains only about one-tenth of the area of the country, but it has about half the population, and more than seven-tenths of the employees and net value of products. With one exception, it contains the first ten leading industrial cities. The secondary belt, extending from Virginia to northern Alabama, has more than one-third of all manufacturing employees outside the major belt.

Distribution of Manfacturing.   It is interesting to note that the Great Lakes states now exceed the Middle Atlantic, measured by either number of employees or net value of products (Fig. 34). By each measure the Great Lakes states are credited with a little more than 30 per cent of the total for the country. However, the major manufacturing belt of the United States occupies a comparatively small strip of country extending from southern Maine and central Maryland westward to Iowa and Missouri. Portland, Baltimore, St. Louis, and Milwaukee may be taken as the end cities of this strip (Fig. 36). This small strip contains about one-tenth of the area of the United States; has more than seven-tenths of the employees and net value of products; has half the population; and, with one exception, contains the first 10 leading industrial cities. Out of 53

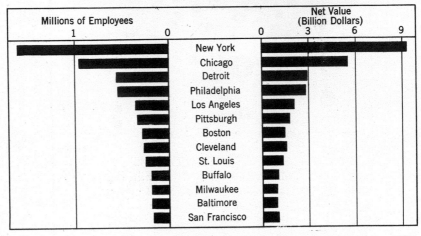

Fig. 37. Standard metropolitan industrial areas. New York, Chicago, Detroit, and Philadelphia are the four outstanding manufacturing centers of the United States. All are ocean, lake, or river ports.

standard metropolitan areas, four-fifths are in the major manufacturing belt and only 2 such areas, producing a net value of 1 billion or more, are outside. Here are essentially all the industrial organizations operating on a huge scale. New York, Pennsylvania, Illinois, and Ohio are leading states; and New York, Chicago, Detroit, and Philadelphia the leading cities. In many respects the region resembles the Ruhr-Rhine-Belgium section of western Europe where industry has reached a high stage of concentration.

A secondary manufacturing belt has been taking shape. This belt extends from Virginia to northern Alabama. More than a third of all manufacturing employees of the United States, outside the major belt, are in this new secondary belt. The reasons for the great concentration in the major manufacturing belt are largely geographic, as this region is especially favored in its natural-resource equipment, possessing (1) abundant, accessible power in the form of coal, oil, gas, and water; (2) great variety and abundance of agricultural raw materials produced within or readily accessible to it—cotton, livestock, cereals; (3) great variety, abundance, and accessibility of important minerals—iron, coal, oil, copper; (4) excellent home markets which are both a cause and an effect of the industrial development, and accessibility to foreign markets; (5) excellent transportation facilities by railways, inland waters, and by sea; (6) abundant skilled labor and ample capital; and (7) the momentum of an early start.

Among other factors which favor industrial development in the United States, which are shared by this region but in which it has no superior advantage over some other sections, should be mentioned: (1) a healthful, invigorating climate; (2) self-sufficiency in food supply; (3) a strong government assuring stability and giving assistance; (4) a standard of education for the masses far above that of other countries; (5) a consuming population having a high standard of living; and (6) a capable, energetic people derived from the progressive stocks of industrial Europe. Taken as a whole, these constitute the industrial assets of the United States.

TRANSPORTATION AND COMMUNICATION

The facilities for transportation and communication and the use made of them are indices of the material development of a country and the general level of prosperity of its people, as they are both the cause and the effect of industrial progress. Chief among such facilities are railroads, highways, waterways, motor cars, telegraph, telephone, and postal service. Though the United States has only about 6 per cent of the world's population, it has approximately

1. 30 per cent of the world's railroad mileage.
2. 57 per cent of the world's telephone instruments.
3. 72 per cent of the world's automobile passenger cars, trucks, and buses.
4. 38 per cent of the world's highway mileage.
5. 31 per cent of the world's broadcasting stations.
6. 51 per cent of the world's radio sets.

Although definite world data are not available, it is certain that the United States has a very large proportion of the world's telegraph and civil aviation service. In the distribution and use of these facilities the United States excels any of the principal nations having a large population, but is exceeded in a few cases by countries having a small population.

Railroads. The eastern half of the country is provided with a close network of railroads so that no productive area is far from transportation facilities; the western half, which is drier and less productive, is crossed by several trunk lines. Thousands of miles of navigable rivers are available, but the total freight carried by rivers is small compared (1) with that moved by the railroads, or (2) with the possibilities of rivers as carriers when the population is as static and as dense as that of western Europe. There are many reasons why railroads meet the demands of modern industry more effectively than rivers and canals: (1) Railroads may reach the resource to be developed and the industrial center to be served, and a network of facilities may be provided to any section by building branch lines. (2) Through shipments are obtainable on railroads to every important part of the country, and even to the door of the industrial establishment, thus reducing truckage and handling costs to the minimum. (3) Railway transportation is much faster. (4) Railways operate throughout the year, whereas many rivers are closed to traffic by ice and some by low water during part of the year. (5) Railroads can readily meet the shipping needs by varying the size and frequency of trains, thus controlling the cost.

Waterways. The total freight-tonnage on all United States rivers exceeds 200,000,000, more than three-fifths of which is on the Mississippi, Ohio, and Monongahela. This means that, taken as a whole, rivers are important carriers. Though the tonnage carried by all rivers is highly significant in the transportation system no one river carries a strikingly large amount. In contrast with rivers, the Great Lakes provide the greatest inland waterway of the world whether measured by extent or volume of traffic. The total tonnage (United States) carried on them annually is more than half as large as the combined tonnage of the Atlantic, Gulf, and Pacific Coasts, whereas the tonnage passing through the Sault Canal is more than four and one-half times that of the Panama Canal. Because of the economies possible in handling such a large volume of bulk cargo—iron ore, coal, grain, pulpwood—it is probable that the freight rates on the Lakes are lower than for any unsubsidized water service in the world. It is proposed to open the Great Lakes to the sea by deepening the St. Lawrence route to permit the passage of ships of 27-feet draft from Lakes to tidewater. The arguments of the proponents of this plan remind one of the extravagant claims advanced at various times in the past when the building of sundry other canals was being considered. The arguments of the opponents are equally vigorous, and the two groups make clear the influence of geographic location and resources in the development of sectionalism—the Middle West demanding a cheap water outlet, and the

North Atlantic region being desirous of retaining the Middle West as a part of its hinterland. The evidence available at present appears to favor the construction of the proposed waterway.[3] With the exhaustion of high-grade iron ore in the Lake Superior region, completion of the St. Lawrence Seaway might prevent profound changes in the location of the iron and steel industry.

Highways and Airways.   Motor vehicles for the land and ships for the air are revolutionizing our concepts of transportation. Though their use has grown with great rapidity many people are still thinking in terms of canals and "improved" rivers. This is especially true when funds for such projects are to be taken from the public treasury. Highways now reach all parts of the country. The more than 3 million miles of highways is more than a third of the world's total and averages about 1 mile for each square mile of area. Half our highways are already surfaced for all-weather use. Over these highways travel more than 40 million passenger cars, buses, and trucks, providing a service unequaled in any other part of the world.

Travel, and transport of mail, express, and freight by airplane are well established. This service is now a routine part of the United States transportation system. A network of more than 68,600 miles of trunkline airways, largely equipped with all modern devices to assure safety and service, serves the country today. Over these routes scheduled operators fly nearly 340,000,000 revenue miles a year and carry more than 13,000,000 passengers. In addition to passengers, air service now carries a high tonnage of express, freight, and mail. This far exceeds the airplane service of any other country, yet the development of such service is probably in its infancy.

FOREIGN TRADE

Nature of Trade and Conditions Giving Rise to It.   Commerce, or trade, is the movement of products from regions of surplus to those of deficiency. Such movement may be over comparatively short distances, as from farm to adjacent city, or may be over great distances, as between countries located on opposite sides of the earth. Trade depends primarily upon the wants of people, the ability of those people to pay for the thing wanted, and the ability of other people to produce and transport it or have it transported. The conditions that result in a surplus in one region and a deficiency in another may be geographic, ethnic, economic, or political,

[3] "An Economic Appraisal of the St. Lawrence Seaway Project," *Industry Report on Domestic Transportation,* Department of Commerce, Bureau of Foreign and Domestic Commerce, 1947.

differences in geographic environment being the more important factors. Among the differences giving rise to commerce are the following: (1) differences in climate, e.g., tropics *vs.* midaltitudes; (2) differences in soil, mineral, forest, and other natural resources, e.g., coal, petroleum, lumber;

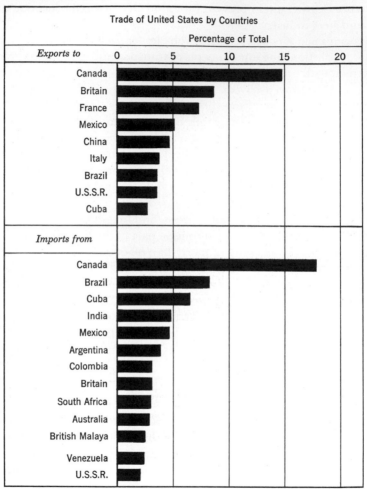

Fig. 38. Trade of the United States with principal foreign countries. Canada is the best customer and sells far more to the United States than any other country, measured by percentage of value.

(3) differences in availability of markets, e.g., fresh vegetables *vs.* cotton, silk, or wheat; (4) differences in relief, e.g., between highlands and lowlands; (5) differences in the stage of cultural development—"civilization"—and in specialization, e.g., a manufacturing people *vs.* an agricul-

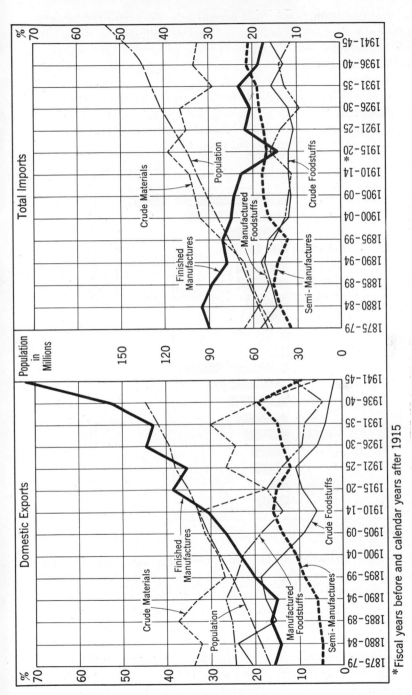

Fig. 39. Changing character of the foreign trade of the United States as shown by percentage of value. The population increase has been accompanied by a decrease in exports of foodstuffs and crude materials and an increase in manufactured products. At the same time importation of finished manufactures has decreased, semi-manufactures have increased slightly and crude materials have increased greatly.

tural one, and the distinctive artistic wares of the French or the lacquer wares of the Japanese; (6) differences in political policies which result in tariffs, rebates, subsidies, etc. The differences in climate, soil, topography, and other natural resources within the United States give rise to an enormous domestic trade, and the same conditions produce a large surplus that enters foreign trade. It is this surplus with which we are especially concerned here.

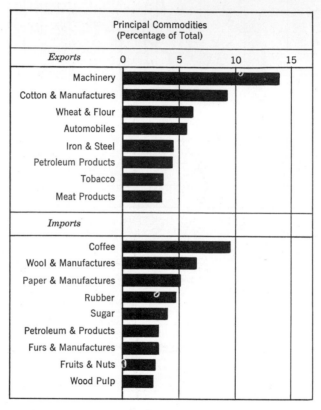

Fig. 40. Trade of United States by principal commodities.

Development of United States Foreign Trade.   Foreign commerce was a vital factor in the early colonial period. The hinterland of the colonist was largely untraversed and undeveloped; hence he looked outward across the ocean to the markets of the more developed "mother countries" whence he came. For many years he sent his produce, chiefly raw materials, to Europe and other parts of the world, and imported manufactured wares. During the colonial period and for many years following the Revolutionary War, American ships carried most of the trade, averaging from four-fifths to nine-tenths up to 1830 and about two-thirds at the beginning of the Civil War. The loss of vessels during the Civil War; the rapid expansion westward and the development of agricultural lands and vast mineral and forest resources after the war, and the consequent opportunity for investment at home; the change from sailing to steel steamships; and the repeal by Congress of laws that favored American shipping led to a rapid decline to less than one-tenth in 1890. Not until 1900 did the total value of foreign trade exceed $2,000,000,000. The more complete development of natural resources, the expansion of manufacturing to surplus production, a corresponding demand for foreign raw materials, and the stimulus of two world wars have renewed interest in foreign trade and a United States merchant marine (Fig. 38). Today the export trade is more than twice that of any other country and imports are second in value to those of Great Britain. This ratio is due in part to the devastating effects of World War II, especially in Europe; greatly increased price of goods; and loans and gifts to war-stricken countries.

The Character of the Trade.   The changing character of United States trade since about 1900 is shown in Fig. 39, a change which reflects the extent of the internal development of the United States. The relative decline in exports of raw materials and foodstuffs has been accompanied by an increase in exports of manufactures and in growth in population. At the same time, crude materials and semimanufactures have come to constitute a major proportion of the imports, and finished manufactures a minor percentage. The United States has entered upon an era of greater economic maturity—manufacturing its own raw materials, as well as those imported, and seeking a foreign market for the finished products. Machinery is the leading export, and cotton and cotton manufactures rank second. These are followed closely by wheat and flour, and automobiles. Principal imports are coffee, wool and woolen manufactures, paper and manufactures, rubber, and sugar. Canada is the chief market and supplies more imports than any other country.

Commercial Gateways.   Foreign trade now follows well-established routes through comparatively few ports of outstanding importance (Fig. 41). These gateways have attained their prominent positions because of their superior geographic and economic conditions, such as (1) a large, highly productive and easily accessible hinterland having a large population, and (2) good harbors possessing extensive and well-equipped dockage facilities. Since the highly productive area of the country lies east of the Mississippi directly tributary to eastern ports, and since most of the trade is transatlantic, the Atlantic Coast gateways handle nearly three-fifths of the total commerce, and combined with those of the Gulf Coast nearly three-fourths. More than two-fifths of the trade flows through the New York customs district. Other important eastern gateways are Boston, Philadelphia, Baltimore, and Norfolk. Galveston and New Orleans compete for leading position on the Gulf Coast and handle three-fourths of the trade. San Francisco, Seattle, Portland, and Los Angeles are the leading Pacific Coast ports, but the total trade of the Pacific Coast is less than half that of the Gulf Coast.

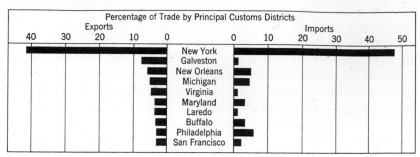

Fig. 41. Trade of United States by principal customs districts. The New York district handles more than two-fifths of the total exports of the country and nearly half the imports.

The preeminent position of the port of New York in overseas commerce is due to a number of influencing factors: (1) It has access to the rich hinterland previously mentioned, principally through the Hudson-Mohawk route by easy grades, but also by rail via the southern routes. (2) It has an excellent harbor open throughout the year with a developed waterfront of more than 350 miles, measured around piers and heads of slips, and a total potential frontage, including shore line, of 995 miles. (3) It is on the main transatlantic trade route over which most of the trade flows. (4) It is the financial center of the country. (5) It has all types of facilities needed in handling foreign trade on a large and expeditious scale.

Commercial Future. The future development of overseas trade depends very largely upon the same factors that make possible the leading position of the country in agriculture, mining, manufacturing, and transportation, which have been discussed elsewhere in this chapter. With a rich endowment of essential natural resources, with intensive production yet to be attained, and with good, well-equipped harbors accessible to that richly endowed hinterland, it seems reasonably certain that the United States will continue to hold a large share of the world's trade.

SUMMARY

With a great extent of level, varied, and fertile arable land; a healthful, invigorating climate highly favorable to abundant food production of high quality and great variety; an abundance of all essential minerals high in quality and readily accessible; an abundance of commercially available mechanical power; superior transportation and communication facilities; good harbors favorably located in relation to productive area and to principal world markets; a topography that favors unity rather than sectionalism; an ethnic stock derived from the most progressive peoples of the world; an educational system that tends to raise the general ability of the masses to a high level; a strong, stable government that rests upon the will of the governed and functions for their welfare, the United States offers a home to man in which he should be able to live on a high standard and contribute to the welfare of the world and the advancement of the human race more effectively than have the people of any other land. Of such a country one should be proud to be a citizen, and such an appreciation should come from knowledge of the opportunities for human well-being offered. "Our Own United States" continues to be the land of opportunity for better living, primarily because of the abundant natural resources available to man. The use he makes of them depends upon himself—the human factor.

PROBLEMS

1. Will the United States wield as great an influence in human welfare of the world in the future as Europe has in the past?

2. Are geographic or human factors most important in the development of a nation?

3. Can the United States maintain twice its present population with the same standard of living?

4. Have the agricultural or the power and iron resources been most important in the development of the United States?

5. Will the large water-power resources of the North Pacific States make them the leading manufacturing section of the future?

6. If Europe were organized as a single nation, would it be a better home for man than the United States?

7. Has agriculture or manufacturing wielded a greater influence in the development of the United States?

8. Can the United States maintain its position as the leading agricultural and manufacturing nation of the world?

9. Had wiser British policy prevailed in our colonial period and the present United States area remained in the British Empire, what effect might it have had on the status of Great Britain and the Empire?

CHAPTER 3

The Physiographic Regions of the Northeastern States

Topography Related to Human Activity. The Northeastern States are considered to be that group east of the Hudson-Champlain Depression—New England, together with New York, Pennsylvania, and New Jersey. The Census Bureau and the Department of Agriculture deal with this division in their statistical reports on the United States by sections, thus giving some justification for our use of the Northeastern States as a unit for study. But of far greater importance is the fact that here the northern colonies of early American history were located, and here began a differentiation of economic activities that distinguished them from the southern colonies. Here also today one finds a congestion of population, intensification of manufacturing and agriculture, great wealth, and some of the greatest educational institutions of the country, as well as great diversity in economic activities and in cultural landscapes, rural and urban.

The dominating elements of the natural environment of the Northeastern States that have tended to set them off as a unit is their location on the North Atlantic near to natural trade routes connecting them with the mother countries of Europe; and their rough and broken surface features. To the student of the geography of this section, the physiography forms the background for a scientific study of the distribution and character of human activities and accomplishments. Coastal plain, outwash plain, alluvial plain, lake plain, flat plateau, rolling plateau, dissected plateau, glaciated mountain area, glaciated igneous rock, glaciated sedimentary rock—all of these have their characteristic natural and cultural landscapes. Minerals and their related industries, coal power, water power, the location of traffic lines, the distribution and nature of harbors, and various economic activities, even the fishing industry also have a definite relationship to the physiography of the land. Thus, in order that the student may the better localize and interpret the diverse human activities and the cultural landscapes, attention is called to a brief consideration of the physiographic divisions of the Northeastern States.

Physiographic Divisions, Provinces, and Sections. The major physiographic divisions of the United States represented in the northeastern states are the Atlantic Plain, the Interior Plains, and the Appalachian Highlands. To the southeast and extending from Cape Cod through New Jersey is the Atlantic Plain, and to the northwest bordering the lakes is the Interior Plain. By far the greatest part of the Northeastern States lies within the Northern Appalachian Highland division (Fig. 42).

These major physiographic divisions are further subdivided into provinces and sections. Only the Embayed section of the Coastal Plain province is representative of the Atlantic Plain. Likewise only the Eastern Lakes section of the Central Lowlands province is representative of the Interior Plains. The larger provinces of the Appalachian Highlands are as follows:

1. New England province.
2. Adirondack province.
3. Appalachian Plateau province (Alleghany section).
4. Appalachian Ridge and Valley province.
5. Piedmont province (Piedmont Upland and Triassic Lowland).

From the standpoint of geologic age the Appalachian Highlands may be divided into three portions: (1) The Adirondacks, which belong to the Laurentians of Canada, and some of the most ancient of lands, and consist of granites, crystalline limestones, and schists. (2) The Older Appalachians (yet younger than the Laurentians) include the New England province, the Piedmont, and Triassic Lowland. They are composed of old rocks such as granite schists and slates. (3) The Newer Appalachians consist of the Allegheny Plateau, the Ridge and Valley section, and the Great Appalachian Valley. Here the rocks are limestones, sandstones, and shales. It will be noted that the Older Appalachians and Adirondacks occupy the larger part of the area towards the north and east, whereas the Newer Appalachians dominate the area in the south and west.

The Atlantic Coastal Plain. The Atlantic Coastal Plain includes Cape Cod peninsula, Nantucket and Martha's Vineyard, Long Island, and all of New Jersey southeast of a line from New York Bay to Trenton.

Cape Cod peninsula and the three islands just named have been the scene of glacial deposition, their surface features being characterized by morainic hills (knob and kettle type), mostly of sand, and outwash plains of sand and gravel.

The outlines of Cape Cod and the glacially deposited islands to the west have undergone some changes since glacial times. Waves and alongshore currents have built barrier beaches and bars across the mouths of bays, and on the eastern coast of Cape Cod a vast amount of till has been removed and carried northward and northwestward around the end of the glacially deposited Cape Cod peninsula, forming an intricate series of hooked spits with enclosed lagoons and marshes. The wind has also been

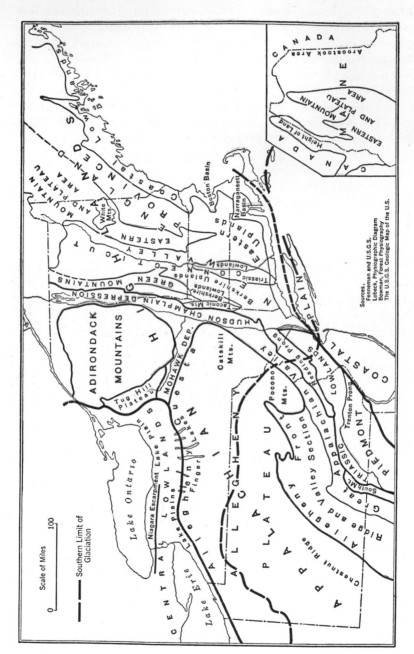

Fig. 42. The physiographic regions of the Northeastern States. Boundaries mainly from Fenneman's Monograph.

active on Cape Cod, and much of the low surface of the sandy spits has been built up by sheets of sand and dunes, the dunes huge billows of sand. Provincetown is built on the southern side of a newly formed spit (Fig. 43).

The inner edge of the Coastal Plain in New Jersey is marked by the Fall Line that extends in a fairly direct line from near New Brunswick, near the mouth of the Raritan River, to Trenton, and on along the Delaware River to Delaware Bay. The Fall Line lies in a lowland. To the northwest the lowland is carved in shales and sandstones, farther on trap caps several isolated ridges; to the southeast the lowland, which stands slightly lower, is cut out of limestone deposits. The two parts form the Inner Lowland of New Jersey. About 90 per cent of the population of

Fig. 43. Bridge over Cape Cod Canal. *Photo by Miller.* This sea-level canal, 12 miles long, excavated across the narrow strip of land between Buzzards Bay and Cape Cod Bay, shortens the distance from Boston to New York by boat. The route around Cape Cod is dangerous at times.

New Jersey lives on this inner Lowland. Here are most of the large cities, most of the factories, and most of the railroad lines of the state. It is a part of that great thoroughfare that connects New York and Philadelphia, undoubtedly the most traveled strip of country in the United States today. Along this Inner Lowland passed the trails of the Indians in pre-Columbian days. Post roads traversed it in colonial times. In the softer limestone was dug the Delaware-Raritan Canal, to be paralleled only a few years later by one railroad line, and later by many. To the southeast of the Inner Lowland is the thinly settled New Jersey Coastal Plain.

Drowning of the eastern coast of the Northeastern States brings ocean waters to the edge of the New England Plateau from Cape Cod northward. Farther south, this process, for the most part, gives origin to Buzzards Bay, Narragansett Bay, Long Island Sound, New York Bay, the swamps of eastern New Jersey, and Delaware Bay. Because ocean vessels may tie up at wharves on the edge of the old land at New York and Philadelphia, commerce moves around both ends of the Coastal Plain area of New Jersey. It is not, therefore, a transit region, and there is not the demand for modern roads and railroads that there is over the lowlands on its inner border.

About three-fifths of the area of New Jersey is in the Coastal Plain; yet a much smaller fraction, relatively, of the agricultural products of the state comes from there than from the other sections, for the soil is for the most part sandy and loamy and has been so thoroughly worked over by the waves and currents during its deposition that the percentage of soluble material is low. The surface is a plain sloping southeastward toward the ocean. The inner portion of the plain is highest, and here west-flowing streams have dissected the land. The lower courses of the east-flowing rivers are drowned and, therefore, have marshy borders and enter shallow marshy bays and lagoons, separated from the ocean by barrier beaches. There are no large cities on the Coastal Plain in New Jersey except Camden, and that is geographically a part of Philadelphia. Along the east coast are many resort towns. Long Beach and Atlantic City are the largest, their importance being due to the excellent bathing facilities and the nearness to large population centers.

Along the railroads that have direct connections with the large manufacturing cities, particularly in the marl belt near the western border, there are truck gardens, for the soil is easily worked, aerates well, drains well, is warm, and when well fertilized is suited to the growing of crops that do not demand rich soil for profitable yields. Large areas too sandy and too distant from shipping points to be profitably farmed are undeveloped, and are covered with forests of pine. In such sections one finds people living in isolation and poverty, in striking contrast to the wealth to be found in the Inner Lowland.

The Lake Plains.   The Lake Plains of the Central Lowland occupy that small part of the states of New York and Pennsylvania which borders on the Great Lakes. They extend from the Thousand Islands exit of Lake Ontario southward and westward, along the lake shores, sometimes having a width of about 50 miles in New York State but narrowing to less than 10 miles on the Erie shore in Pennsylvania.

These plains are lacustrine in origin, in the main—that is, they are areas covered by former extensions of the Great Lakes when the St. Lawrence outlet was blocked by ice and the lake waters rose to higher levels and covered larger areas than the present lakes: The otherwise uniform slope of the plains towards the bordering lakes is broken by stream erosion, and by numerous kames, elongated gravelly hills known as drumlins, old beach lines, and other evidences of glacial deposition. The only major feature of the surface of the Lake Plains resulting from the rock structure in the province is the steep, northward-facing Niagara Escarpment which begins in New York east of Rochester as a low bluff and extends westward increasing in elevation to more than 200 feet where it was cut by the Niagara River to form Niagara Falls. This escarpment is due to erosion of the resistant Niagara limestone and its dipping southward.

The Lake Plain in New York joins the Mohawk Depression toward the east and marks one of the important outlets of the glacial lakes which followed immediately a recession of ice to expose this low route leading to the Hudson River and the sea, while the lower St. Lawrence was still blocked. Man has taken advantage of this low route for building the Erie Canal, railroads, and highways, which have been so important in linking the interior with the eastern seaboard.

The New England Province. The New England province as a whole is an upland or plateau sloping southward, as the trend of the rivers indicates. The highest parts are in the north and west, the upland surface here reaching 2000 feet or more, with a few mountain peaks attaining heights of 3000–6000 feet. Crystalline rocks are the basal formation, and outcrop in various parts of the province, the larger areas being found in southern Maine, the White Mountains, Rhode Island, and the Green-Hoosac Mountain range. The whole province was once peneplained, later tilted and slightly warped, dissected, the dissection being more pronounced in the north than in the south, and lastly glaciated. The less resistant rock areas have been worn into basins. Above the general level of the plateau are a few residuals or monadnocks which owe their height more to their location on stream divides than to superior hardness. Long before the erosive forces had formed the peneplain there had been warping, close folding, and faulting, so that many of the igneous and sedimentary rocks were metamorphosed into schists, gneisses, slates, marbles, and conglomerates. Limestones, shales, and sandstones, however, are to be found in some parts.

There are several recognizable subregions of the New England province. The Eastern Mountain and Plateau area is a broad upland which reaches its greatest height and development in the White Mountains but which also has, above the general level, Mount Katahdin, Saddleback, and other peaks in Maine. This upland extends southward through New Hampshire, across Massachusetts, and dies out in northern Connecticut (Fig. 44).

The Green Mountain region, represented in Vermont by the Green Mountains, in northern Massachusetts by the Hoosac Mountains, and farther south, extending into Connecticut, by a broad plateau surface, forms a western mountain section. The core of the Green Mountains in Vermont is a very ancient rock, but on the western flank there are marble deposits, derived from folded and metamorphosed limestones, that have long been quarried. The well-known Barre granite region lies on the eastern flank of the mountains.

Fig. 44. A landscape in the New England Upland of central Massachusetts. *Courtesy, Berkshire Chamber of Commerce.* In this scene the slopes are gentle and the land is generally farmed or pastured everywhere. Higher wooded hills may be seen in the distance.

The Green Mountains are highest in central Vermont to the north of Rutland, and, although they are barriers to transportation and communication in some sections, they are crossed in northern Vermont by two river valleys of low gradient; and in southwestern Massachusetts and northern Connecticut the ascent to the crest from either east or west is gentle. The Hoosac Mountains proved a barrier to canal making, and the builders of the first railroad from Boston to Albany had to construct the famous Hoosac Tunnel to avoid steep grades. The Mohawk Trail, a famous automobile road, crosses the Hoosac Mountains at an elevation of more than 2000 feet. In the days when Vermont was being taken up by settlers from both New England and New York, the New Yorkers, recognizing the effectiveness of the Green Mountains as a political boundary, strove to include western Vermont, west of the mountains, within its jurisdiction; this brought on a broader warfare in which the "Green Mountain Boys," who fought to make Lake Champlain the western boundary, were victorious.

Between the Eastern Mountain and Plateau area and the Green Mountains lies the broad valley of the Connecticut. This valley is partly due to warping, but the structural form has been further deepened and widened by stream and glacial erosion. During late geologic times the southern end of the Connecticut Valley in Massachusetts and Connecticut was warped below the level of the sea, and sand and mud were deposited. Sheets of igneous rock were intruded into these sedimentary rocks. Later the whole was elevated, faulted, tilted, and eroded; and today this lower valley is a lowland, the Connecticut Lowland, with ridges capped with igneous rock forming conspicuous features of the landscape.

Fig. 45. A landscape in the Berkshires near Cheshire, Massachusetts. *Photo by Bartlett Hendricks.* These hills have rock cores, but glaciation is much in evidence in the form of sand and gravel. Boulders are commonly seen. The hills are wooded, and agriculture is confined to the valleys.

Along the western border of the New England province is a third mountain subregion, the Taconic Mountains, a part of the Newer Appalachians. This is a much-eroded, folded mountain region. There are ridges of varying lengths of hard rock, separated by valleys carved in limestone. Between the Taconic ridges and the Green-Hoosac Mountain region [1] is another depression, floored with limestone. It is called by some the Berkshire Lowland (Fig. 45).

The Connecticut Lowland, the Berkshire Lowland, and the Lake Champlain Lowland, together with the Boston Basin and the Narragansett Basin, have the best agricultural lands in New England and, in

[1] All the hill and mountain land of Berkshire County, western Massachusetts, is called the Berkshire Hills or the Berkshires.

the westward expansion of the New England people, were taken up by farmers before the bordering uplands.

Effects of Glaciation.   No agency in the physiographic history of New England has exerted a more profound influence on human geography than the glacier. The main topographic features sketched in the preceding pages were little affected by the southward-moving ice, but most of the minor surface features owe their origin to glacial processes. Although there are bare ridges and ledges here and there in New England, most of the land is mantled with morainic material of fluvio-glacial deposits. In many parts of New England, particularly in southeastern New Hampshire and eastern Massachusetts, drumlins are common. Most of the islands of Boston harbor are drumlins. Some of these drumlins have been cleared and are tilled, but most of them are too stony for any use except as forests or pasture lands.

In general, the soil is thin on the upland hills, ridges, and mountains, and on these areas of thin soil one finds most of the abandoned farms, the increasing number of which has attracted the attention of so many students and writers for three-quarters of a century or more. To most students the abandoned-farm phenomenon is only a natural economic adjustment to the opening of the Middle West and the shifting of New England interests from agriculture to manufacturing. After the Revolutionary War, for 40 or 50 years, land in southern New England was scarce and many farms were established on the uplands where general farming and domestic economy did not demand an intimate contact with markets. The hill towns and hill farms were at their zenith about 1820-1830, and many farms were taken up that would not have been had there been easy access to the West. The upland farmers were "marginal" farmers, who succeeded when there was little competition; but, when the canal and railroads brought the products of the cheap lands of the Middle West to eastern markets, they were forced to better lands or to the cities. Many farms were worn out by one-crop agriculture, erosion, and excessive leaching. The farmers on the betters lands of the valleys and lowlands likewise felt the pressure of cheap western products but adjusted themselves to the new order by intensifying their agriculture. Other factors also led to the abandonment of farms. The railroads, when built in New England, avoided the hill lands. The more progressive of the young men and women left the isolated, primitive rural districts for the greater opportunities and comforts to be found in the rapidly growing cities, and preferred to remain there. Many families, because of better wages in the factories, abandoned the farms, and many farms were lost on mortgages. The Civil War hastened the movement. Many families were broken up by the loss of the male workers. Some veterans purchased homesteads in the West. Prices of farm products were low, and credit was difficult to secure. The abandonment of the hill farms is no more striking than the decadence of the hill towns; both are due to about the same causes.

Since probably as much as 75 per cent of the material of the drift has on the average not been moved more than 50 miles, it is the local bedrock that determines largely the mineral composition of the soil in any section. (See Fig. 46.) New England has little of the limestone and felds-

Fig. 46. A pile of boulders taken from a field in New England. Much of the mantle rock in the Northeastern States consists of glacial clay, sand, gravel, and boulders from which the soil has been derived. Agriculture required not only that forests be cleared from lands but that stones be removed because they interfered with tillage. This accounts for numerous rock piles at edges of fields, in gullies, and other out-of-the-way places, as well as the use of boulders for making fences. *Photo by Hudgins.*

pathic rocks from which the best glacial soils are derived. The soil is everywhere made up mainly of crystalline material and is surprisingly uniform over large areas, because there is great uniformity in the bedrock. In mechanical composition the soils vary from loam to stony loam. Scattered rocks and boulders of large size in many sections make the use of farm machinery difficult.

The rough topography and the thin soils of northern New England protected the forests here from the early onslaught experienced in those portions of the United States having good agricultural lands. New England, in the three centuries since the founding of Plymouth, has furnished pioneer farmers for the vast agricultural area to the west, from the Atlantic to the Pacific. Some have migrated 3000 miles, crossing deserts and mountain ranges, yet they are only now invading a few of the north-

ern valleys of New England with the plow. The lumberman still dominates the economic life of the north, and if a sensible forestry is followed
he will continue to hold his own.

Glacial lakes are numbered by the thousands in New England (Fig.
47). There are probably more than 1000 in Connecticut, and an even

Fig. 47. A landscape in western Massachusetts. *Photo by Arthur Palme.* A typical glacial
landscape of New England—rounded hills, undrained depressions, marshes, and lakes.
Agriculture is possible on much of the lowland and slopes.

Fig. 48. Bridge over the Merrimack River at Lawrence, Massachusetts. In the background are factories localized by water power.

greater number in Maine. Only a few are large enough to be shown on
small-scale maps. Lakes add greatly to the scenic beauty of the landscape, are admirable natural reservoirs for municipal water supply, furnish sites for summer homes, are storage basins that serve to regulate the
flow of streams, and are thus of particular benefit to factories using water
power (Fig. 48).

The sea interests have been benefited by glaciation, a partial compensation for the meager opportunities in agriculture. Ice scouring has been a factor in harbor making along the rock coast from Salem northeastward, and the "Banks" of northeastern North America, thought to be due to glacial deposition, favor the fishing industry. The glaciers of the the Ice Age, therefore, affected all the major economic interests of New England—agriculture, lumbering, fishing, manufacturing, and commerce.

The Adirondack Province. Similar in many respects to northern New England in its physiographic conditions and economic interests is the Adirondack province, an outlier of the Laurentian Plateau of Canada. The region long remained unsettled and little visited by whites, even after the surrounding lowlands had fine farms. But because of its proximity to the great cities to the south and to the long-traveled routes on the east, south, and west, and because of its wildness, beauty of scenery, and excellent fishing and hunting, it has become in recent decades a great playground. It can now be traversed along many routes; hotels and club houses are numerous; and there are many beautiful summer homes on large estates. Forests cover most of the surface and are held by large lumbering companies and hunting clubs, or by the state as forest reserves. The bedrock is largely crystalline limestone and several forms of granite. The whole was thoroughly glaciated, as the rounded surfaces, scoured basins and valleys, ice-molded hillocks, and morainic deposits show. There are a few high peaks, Mount Marcy having an altitude of 5344 feet, and Whiteface about 4900.

Newer Appalachians. In the Middle Atlantic States the Newer Appalachians are represented by the Allegheny Plateau and the Great Appalachian Valley, and the Older Appalachians by the Piedmont Plateau.

The Allegheny Plateau. The Allegheny Plateau, the eastern edge of which is the Allegheny Front, varies in width from 125 to 200 miles. The western edge has no definite name, but is represented nearly everywhere by a low, yet distinct, escarpment from central Ohio northeastward, the location of which is indicated on Fig. 42.

The Catskill Mountains, overlooking the Hudson Valley, are on the dissected edge of the Allegheny Plateau at its northeastern border. The horizontal stratified rocks—shale below, sandstone above, and conglomerate on the summits of many of the ridges and peaks—have many joints along which erosion has been rapid, giving rise to numerous valleys. Within the shales and sandstones are rocks of varying hardness outcrop along the valleys, and thus rapids are numerous in the channels of the streams, and ledges on the valley sides. Not being suited to agriculture, the region supports a scantier population than the nearby lowlands, but the beauty of the scenery and the proximity to New York City have brought a lucrative tourist and resort business in recent decades. One of the main ranges of the Catskills, a dissected ridge extending northwest and southeast, has a length of about 35 miles. The higher peaks vary in height from 3800 to 4200 feet.

The Allegheny Front sweeps across Pennsylvania from the southern boundary northeastward, in a broad curve as far as the forks of the Susquehanna. From there northeastward, its outline is not so regular. From the southern border to central Pennsylvania, the continuity of the Front is unbroken except by small stream valleys with separating spurs. Seen from the plains to the east, it looks like a serrated mountain ridge. It is still known to many as the Allegheny Mountains. The West Branch and the North Branch of the Susquehanna, as well as their tributaries, pierce the Front from central Pennsylvania eastward by deep, broad valleys, and along these valleys the easiest routes to the plateau are found.

The surface of the plateau is thoroughly dissected, especially near the major drainage lines. Here the valleys are deep and the slopes so steep that many areas have been left in forest, or, if tilled, have suffered greatly from soil wash and gullying. On the large interstream areas, the land is gently rolling; such surfaces are found just west of the crest of the Allegheny Front. The rocks of the plateau lie practically horizontal or only gently warped, as in Chestnut Ridge and Laurel Hill in southwestern Pennsylvania.

The Appalachian Valley.   Most of the Appalachian Valley province is a series of limestone and shale plains separated by numerous, long, even-crested ridges that have in general a northeast-southwest trend, roughly paralleling the Allegheny Front and the western edge of the Piedmont Plateau. These ridges are composed of sandstone and conglomerate, the same formation occurring in several ridges. The strata in the ridges stand at a steep angle, showing that they are parts of great folds. The ridges are pierced at intervals by water gaps of streams that flow at right angles to their general trend. There are unbroken stretches of ridges of 20–40 miles, and some single ridges, like the Kittatinny Mountain, extend for 200–300 miles. This particular ridge was the first of the barriers to be met by the westward-moving settlers from Philadelphia in the early eighteenth century. Beyond this "Endless Mountain," the settlers on their way to western Pennsylvania met with many other barriers. Along the Pennsylvania Railroad from Harrisburg westward to the Allegheny Front west of Altoona, one may count ten or twelve separate ridges.

Some of the limestone plains of the Appalachian Valley province are almost entirely enclosed by ridges, the only low-gradient route for ingress and egress being along the drainage line. Such plains are known to physi-ographers as canoe-shaped valleys. Some of the ridges have a zigzag course.

The eastern portion of the Appalachian Valley province, lying to the southeast of the Kittatinny Mountain, is a long limestone lowland, gen-erally known as the Great Valley. In southern Pennsylvnia and Mary-land, it is called the Cumberland Valley; and in eastern Pennsylvania, the Lebanon Valley. It continues on northward to the St. Lawrence Lowlands. It is known as the Wallkill or Kittatinny Valley in Northern New Jersey, and as the Hudson Valley and Champlain Lowland farther north.

Fig. 49. The Mohawk Valley as a traffic route. *Courtesy, New York Central Railroad*. Here one sees hard-surface highways, railways, telegraph and telephone lines, as well as the river which forms the way for the Erie Canal, now known as the New York State Barge Canal. The Mohawk route offers the lowest grades and altitudes of any of the passes across the Appalachian Highlands.

The Appalachian Valley province throughout its extent in the North-eastern States offers excellent opportunities for agriculture, and where ready access is had to markets supports a dense rural population.

The Mohawk Depression.   Cutting across the Appalachian Highlands between the Adirondacks and the Allegheny Plateau is the Mohawk Valley, which connects the Hudson Valley with the eastern Lake section of the Central Lowland in western New York. This valley is a great thoroughfare between the Great Lakes and tidewater at Boston or New York, and is, like the New York-Philadelphia thoroughfare discussed previously, an inner lowland carved out of the softer strata that skirt the southern border of the Adirondacks. It is an area of prosperous farms and thriving cities and is traversed by hard-surface roads, the New York State

Barge Canal-Erie Division, several railroads, and telegraph and telephone lines. It and the Hudson River Valley form the lowest route across the Appalachian Highlands, from the Canadian border to Central Alabama (Figs. 49, 50, and 51).

The Piedmont and the Various Prongs.   The Piedmont Plateau in Pennsylvania and New Jersey covers only a small area and is unlike the piedmont in the southern states in that metamorphosed igneous rock has a smaller surface exposure than sedimentary rocks. The Blue Ridge extends northward into southern Pennsylvania as a ridge, but dies out near Carlisle. This is known as the Carlisle Prong (South Mountain). In southeastern Pennsylvania the crystallines outcrop over a much larger area but terminate northward near the Delaware River at Trenton. This is called the Trenton Prong. A tongue of the crystallines of New England crosses the Hudson Valley to the north of the Palisades, in northern New

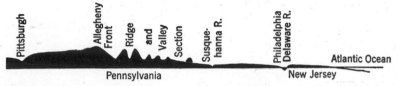

Fig. 50. Profile of land features from Pittsburgh to Philadelphia. (Vertical scale about fifty times horizontal.)

Jersey, and extends into Pennsylvania in a narrow belt on to Reading. This is called the Reading Prong. Another less distinct tongue of the crystallines of New England underlies Long Island Sound and outcrops on Manhatten Island, where it offers solid rock foundations for tall buildings in New York, but renders construction for subways and buildings very expensive. This is called the Manhattan Prong.

Between these prongs lies a lowland similar in geologic history, bedrock, and surface features to the Basin of Minas in Nova Scotia and the Connecticut Lowlands. The lowland of Pennsylvania is a repetition of the lowland of Connecticut; drowning, and possibly some glacial erosion, has placed a portion of it beneath Long Island Sound; but in northern New Jersey its surface, as earlier shown, forms a part of the Inner Lowland. Trap ridges and isolated hills occur in the lowland of the middle Atlantic states as in the Connecticut. The Palisades of the Hudson and the trap ridges of northern New Jersey and about Gettysburg represent the largest exposures of these igneous rocks. At Gettysburg trap ridges and hills figured largely in the Union defenses that broke the strength of Lee's invading army.

The sandstones and shales of the lowland in Pennsylvania were deposited in troughs in the Piedmont Plateau. These rocks weather into a gravelly-to-sandy-loam type of soil locally known as the Indian red soils. The Piedmont soils are known as "gray lands" and are quite distinct from the "red lands" of the lowland.

Within the Piedmont crystalline rocks in southeastern Pennsylvania, in Lancaster County, is a large area of limestone, similar in age to the limestones of the Appalachian Valley province.

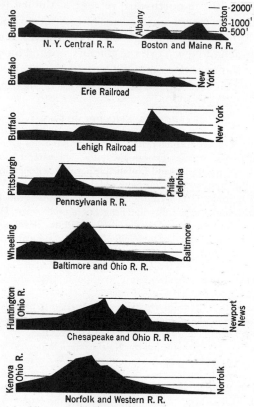

Fig. 51. Profiles of some transappalachian railroads. (Vertical scale about 140 times the horizontal.) The New York Central route is far superior to the others in the adjustment to surface features. Between Albany and New York the route is practically at sea level.

Glaciation in Pennsylvania and New Jersey. The effects of glaciation in Pennsylvania and New Jersey are not so far-reaching as in New York and New England, for only a small portion of these states was covered by ice. Long Island, as previously explained, owes its surface features and soils to the ice work. A lobe pushed southward down the Hudson Valley to the south shore of Staten Island. Northeastern and northwestern Pennsylvania were ice-covered, as was all of New York except a small area about the headwaters of the Allegheny River, the higher lands of the Allegheny Plateau retarding the southward movement. The Adirondacks and the northern edge of the Allegheny Plateau in New York suffered much erosion. River channels in the edge of the plateau were widened and deepened into long, narrow lakes, the Finger Lakes. Numerous drumlins were deposited on the level lands to the north of these lakes, and, in the northward retreat of the ice front, a series of glacial lakes of large extent, antecedents of Lakes Erie and Ontario, were formed, so that the soil of much of northwestern New York is lacustrine in origin. In much of New York the glaciers worked on softer rock than in New England; hence thin soils and bare ledges are less frequently met with, the Adirondacks and parts of the Catskills being exceptions.

EXERCISES AND PROBLEMS

1. It is the belief of geographers that New York has been greatly benefited in its growth in population, industries, foreign and domestic commerce, and business in general, in comparison with Boston and Philadelphia, by the closer contact it has with the great interior of our country. Show the truth or falsity of this belief. What is the physical basis of this easier contact? Work out graphs of population growth of these cities, of growth in foreign commerce, of railroad mileage, of manufactures. Data may be secured from the *Statistical Abstract*. Acquaint yourself also with the development of transportation lines to the interior. Which of these cities has the best local environment favoring growth? May not the difference in growth be due to the greater enterprise of the New Yorkers, past and present? Or is it a question of adjustment to opportunities? Is degree of enterprise a measure of the extent of natural opportunities with which man has had contact?

2. It is estimated that the railways to the west and south from New York City now carry a greater volume of shipment annually than do the railways which follow the Hudson-Mohawk Depression. Verify and account for this fact.

3. Where are the "playgrounds" of the Northeastern States? What physical features make them suited to such use and not to agriculture? Write to the various advertising bureaus of the railroads for booklets describing the attractions of the various "playgrounds." Try to determine what attractions are based on geography.

4. Compile a list of all the effects of glaciation on the economic, commercial, and social life of the people living in the glaciated portion of the Northeastern States.

5. The text states that a depression of the coastal regions of these states has been of great value to New York and Philadelphia as ports. What would have been the consequences if the coastal lands, instead of being depressed, had been elevated, say about 400 feet above the present position?

CHAPTER 4

Manufacturing
in the Northeastern States

FACTORS OF LOCALIZATION

The northeastern group of states is the greatest manufacturing section of the country. Here manufacturing began early under the encouragement of numerous water-power sites, a dense population supplying labor and markets, and rough stony lands that did not encourage extensive agriculture. Although this section comprises only 5.5 per cent of the land area of the United States, it had 27 per cent of the population in 1949. At the same time, this section had 40 per cent of the wage earners engaged in manufacturing in the country, and it accounted for 37 per cent of the net value of manufacturing (Table VI).

TABLE VI

MANUFACTURING IN THE NORTHEASTERN STATES COMPARED
WITH THAT OF TOTAL UNITED STATES

	United States	Northeastern States	Northeastern States Per Cent of U.S.
Area in square miles (land only)	2,973,000	162,000	5.5
Population	150,697,000	39,470,000	27..
Wage and salary earners	15,000,000	5,500,000	40.
Net value of manufacturing	$74,425,800,000	$27,604,400,000	37.

Practically every type of industry is represented in these states. Indeed, the variety of product, from the lady's wrist watch to the giant locomotive, from the coarsest cotton to the finest silk, from the deadliest and most powerful chemicals to perfumes, is one of the outstanding characteristics of this industrial development. *What are the natural advantages that make this group of states the greatest manufacturing section of the country?*

The Power Resources of the Northeastern States. The abundance of power resources and fuel is one of the outstanding advantages. Water power has all along been one of the factors that tended to localize factories. In colonial days, nearly every rapids and falls in southern New England, along the Hudson and Mohawk Valleys, in northern New

Jersey, and in southeastern Pennsylvania, had beside it a factory of some sort—sawmill, gristmill, carding mill, fulling mill, or blast furnace—or perhaps several factories, the power generally being supplied by an over-shot water wheel. The numerous power sites in the glaciated portion of these states gave an opportunity for wide dispersal of factories in the early days when they were all small and required only a small stream of water for power. The power sites to be used first were near the coast, where the waters of the plateau fall over the edge of the plateau, the Fall Line. About these power sites, in time, great industrial cities grew up: Fall River, Providence, New Bedford, and others. The power sites in the inte-rior are largely at boulder dams in the postglacial channels of the streams, at the edge of filled preglacial valleys where the course of the postglacial stream departs from that of the preglacial, and where streams flow from more resistant to less resistant rocks. The forest cover, the numerous glacial lakes and marshes, and a rainfall of 30–50 or more inches fairly evenly distributed throughout the year all tend to give the rivers flowing from or in the glaciated area a fairly constant flow.

Water Power of New England.   New England industries and public utilities are now utilizing nearly to the limit the power of the rapids and falls which they have harnessed; indeed, the power actually developed and used in New Hampshire, Vermont, Massachusetts, Rhode Island, and Connecticut (Table VII and Fig. 24) is in excess of the estimated available low-water horsepower, as determined by the usual method em-ployed by the United States Geological Survey. Many a factory uses steam power to supplement water power and tide it over the low-water season.

The wide distribution of power sites tended to give the colonial fac-tories a wide distribution, and thus to make for "democracy" in the industrial world; but as large machines came to be built, as well as large factories equipped with a great variety of large machines, many a small mill beside small rapids or falls lost out, and industries came to be con-centated at the larger power sites. Fortunately for some small power sites, the railroad came with coal, and a steam plant was used to supply the power needed for factory expansion; but this was not until about the middle of the nineteenth century. Even large plants at medium-sized power sites were checked in their expansion. The expansion of the tex-tile mills at Waltham, Massachusetts, is a typical example. The first com-plete cotton factory of the state was built at Waltham in 1814, utilizing the power of the small Charles River. By 1820 the power capacity of the falls had been reached, and the company purchased a site on the Merri-mack where the water has a fall of 32 feet. Here Lowell grew up, and came to have, in a short time, 33 mills. Before the invention of the dynamo-motor the factory utilizing water power had to be located at the falls, rapids, or dam, and thus the number of factories that could be secured by a power site was limited.

The installed capacity of the water wheels of Maine is 369,000 kilowatts. Most of the falls occur in the rivers where they flow down the eastern slope of the Eastern Mountain and Plateau area to the New England Upland. The numerous large lakes of the region are admirable natural storage basins. The Kennebec, Penobscot, and Androscoggin Rivers in Maine have large water-power developments used in the pulp, paper, and textile industries located there. The Merrimack River furnishes a large part of the power for the industries at Manchester, New Hampshire; and Lowell, Lawrence, Holyoke, Turner's Falls, Massachusetts, Vernon, Vermont, and numerous other industrial towns take a large part of their power from the Connecticut River and its tributaries. On the flanks of the Green Mountain region, from northern Vermont far into Connecticut, are numerous power sites.

The Deerfield River on the east slope in Massachusetts, alone, has plants that develop 58,000 h.p. Between 1800 and 1850, 27 paper mills were built on the borders of the Berkshire Valley on the west slope, all using water power. At the town of Lee alone, there were 18 mills; but, when the heavy Fourdrinier paper machines, which turn out sheets of paper miles long and which demand a great amount of power, came to be used, many of the small paper mills had to be abandoned. Abandoned power sites, with their picturesque overshot water wheels, and moss-covered factories beside a half-filled mill pond, were and still are in some parts of New England only a little less common than abandoned farms. Both represent adjustments to changing economic conditions.

Water Power of New York.   On the Hudson, Black, and Oswego Rivers in New York are many large power plants. The numerous streams descending from the mountain and plateau borders of the Hudson and the Mohawk early furnished power for the gristmills, sawmills, and oil mills. Most of the larger sites have come to be utilized only lately. About the falls of the Genesee where the water power was used early in the nineteenth century to grind the wheat grown in the nearby region, Rochester grew up. The great industrial development here has far outrun the power resources of the falls, and coal is brought from the coal fields of Pennsylvania. The largest power plants in New York state today (except those at Niagara Falls) are at Spier Falls and Glens Falls on the Hudson, where 38,000 hp and 40,000 hp, respecitvely, are developed. At Cohoes, where the Mohawk falls 103 feet in a series of rapids as it enters the Hudson Valley, and at Little Falls, where there is a fall of 245 feet in a half mile, are important power plants. The Mohawk system alone has a potential water power of approximately 180,000 hp. less than half of which is developed. The most important power sites in North America are about Niagara Falls, although the "lion's share" of the power goes to Canada. On the United States side of the falls the plants have more than 560,000 hp capacity. The output is used locally in many plants, particularly in the electric chemical industries, and is distributed widely over western New York.

Power in Pennsylvania and New Jersey.   The small power sites in both Pennsylvania and New Jersey were used early, as in New England and New York. Today there are large developments on the lower Susquehanna with immense turbines from which electricity is furnished to Philadelphia, Baltimore, Washington, and many smaller cities. The latest power development is just over the southern boundary of Pennsylvania in Maryland—the giant Conowingo with 11 turbines, the total capacity of which is about 360,000 hp. Many other sites are utilized on the Susquehanna, but, since most of Pennsylvania lies outside the glaciated area and has mature topography, the flow of the streams is not so regular as in New England. The Allegheny, Monongahela, and Youghiogheny all have much potential power. Hydroelectric plants are replacing the old water wheels. There are several plants now in operation along the Monogahela, and the resources of the Allegheny are about to be utilized.

New England and New York, both coalless, have made the most of their water-power resources; but Pennsylvania, rich in coal and still producing oil and gas, has had good reasons for its belated utilization of its water-power resources.

Superpower Systems.   In order to make the greatest possible use of the power potentialities of the many electric plants in the Northeastern States or in a part of these states, both steam and water, great "superpower" systems, are being developed in which all the larger power plants and stations are to be connected so that electricity may be transferred from one plant or station to one or more of the others. These are not to be great monopolies but coordinated systems, each plant maintaining its identity but being able, if necessary, to secure electricity from other generating plants or dispose of its excess, and thus to meet the varying local demands. A great saving will result in the greater possibility of keeping the plants running at their full capacity all the time, and thus fewer plants will be needed. It is planned to have a closer coordination of electric and steam plant. The steam plants are to be run when excess demands call for their assistance. Early in 1924, 11 electric-power manufacturing companies, operating in Ohio, Pennsylvania, Virginia, West Virginia, and Maryland, agreed to organize their power plants into a superpower system to be known as the Coal Field Super-Power Group. This system can readily be connected with the power group being developed in other parts of the Northeastern States and even with the ones in use in the South.

Summary of Power Resources. The water-power resources of the Northeastern States are shown in Table VII.

TABLE VII

DEVELOPED AND UNDEVELOPED WATER POWER OF THE
NORTHEASTERN STATES IN 1947
(in thousands of kilowatts)

State	Developed			Undeveloped	Total Potential
	Utilities	Industrials	Total		
Maine	246	122	368	2,448	2,817
New Hampshire	233	50	283	393	676
Vermont	161	15	175	303	478
Massachusetts	164	56	221	110	331
Rhode Island	3	10	13	—	13
Connecticut	87	18	105	94	200
New York	1,155	72	1,227	2,738	3,965
New Jersey	7	3	10	105	115
Pennsylvania	422	3	425	2,332	2,757
Total	2,478	349	2,828	8,523	11,351
Total for U. S.	14,971	985	15,956	77,130	93,086

It is shown that the developed power in the Northeastern States is 2,828,000 kilowatts. The power employed from all sources in the utilities and industries is more than four times this amount. Hence the potential water power (11,351,000 kilowatts), if completely developed, would not quite be enough to turn the wheels of all industries in these states. Coal, oil, and gas furnish most of the power for the many hundreds of industrial plants; and much of the coal, oil, and gas is furnished by the state of Pennsylvania.

The Coal Resources. In eastern Pennsylvania is the only important anthracite coal field now being worked in the world. From beneath an area of about 478 square miles, more than 50,000,000 tons of anthracite are mined annually, mainly from the mines along the Wyoming Valley from Wilkes-Barre through Scranton on to Carbondale and in a detached area of irregular shape from Hazleton southwestward to Shamokin and Pottsville. Reliable sources place the original reserve at 21,-000,000,000 tons, one-third of which has been mined. Anthracite was first discovered in the Wyoming Valley in 1762, but it was fully half a century later before it was mined on a commercial scale. In 1820 only

365 tons were taken out; about 1840 it began to be mined on a large scale for fuel in blast furnaces. Most of the anthracite mined today is for domestic use, although many steam boilers in factories are heated with it in Philadelphia, New York, and other nearby cities. A large percentage of homes, even as far west as the Great Lakes region, are heated by anthracite.

In western Pennsylvania, there are about 14,000 square miles of coal lands, the annual output from which has been about 500,000,000 tons from 1940 to 1952, and the estimated available supply yet in the ground more than 100,000,000,000 tons. Pennsylvania produces about 23 per cent of the bituminous output of the country, and Pennsylvanian coal runs the larger portion of the factories of the Northeastern States, although coal from Ohio, West Virginia, and Maryland gets to some of them. The railroad is the chief distributing agent, carrying coal directly to the coal yards of cities, to factories, or to the seaboard for shipment by water. New England receives from 14,000,000 to 15,000,-000 tons by coastwise vessels each year. A small amount is exported, and much used for bunkers. Canada gets 25,000,000 tons a year, mainly from Lake Erie ports by vessel. Coal from the northern Appalachian fields is transported as far west as the Pacific Coast and southward to the Gulf Coast. About 40 per cent of the total output of Pennsylvania is used within the state in coke making, on the railroads, and in the mines and factories. The abundance of coal enables western Pennsylvania to turn out many products, such as heavy machines, glass, and special steels, which could not be manufactured in sections where coal is scarce.

About half the bituminous coal of Pennsylvania comes from the Pittsburgh seam, a bed which is about 6 feet thick, having an areal extent of some 2500 square miles, and furnishing one of the best coals produced in America. It is hard, for bituminous, does not break up readily, and hence stands long-distance shipping and frequent transshipping. It gives 36-38 per cent of volatile matter in gas plants, makes excellent coke, and gives good results in furnaces in houses and factories. Much of the bituminous coal of Pennsylvania is obtained by drift mining, the outcrop occurring in the borders of the deep valleys that dissect the Allegheny plateau. The beds are very regular in thickness and quality of coal, are generally free from shale, and are practically horizontal. The larger part of the coal is mined by machinery. The mining of bituminous coal is therefore much easier than that of anthracite, which occurs in steeply inclined beds that have been folded and faulted. Some deposits of anthracite are reached only by deep shafts, and machines are little used. This is the chief reason for the high price of anthracite coal in comparison with bituminous.

Many explorers had made mention of the coal deposits of western Pennsylvania before the Revolutionary War. The British garrison at Fort Pitt, shortly after the French vacated Fort Duquesne, used coal for fuel. The pioneer farmers used it, many shiploads being floated down the Monongahela, and even the Ohio, before 1800. Commercial mining began shortly after 1820. Only 3080 tons of coal were mined in the United States in 1820; 286,000 in 1830; and only 1,850,000 in 1840. The output of the United States today is nearly one hundred times that of 1850. Until about 1850 Pennsylvania produced nearly all the commercial coal of the country.

Petroleum as a Raw Product, Fuel, and Power Resources. Western Pennsylvania and southwestern New York were, up to about 1895, the greatest petroleum-producing section of the country. In fact, the petroleum industry of the world had its birth in this region and it was here that the methods of drilling, pumping, transporting, and refining of petroleum, now in use the world over, were developed. The French explorer Charlevoix made mention of oil on the upper Allegheny. The Indians and early pioneers collected oil for medicinal purposes from the surfaces of the small streams. The first shipment from Pennsylvania went to New York City some time before 1850. It was bottled and used for medicine, the price received being $275. Various attempts were made to collect the oil on a commercial scale from the surfaces of creeks and ponds, but without success. Colonel Drake of New York made the first attempt (1859) to secure a larger supply by sinking a shaft, and then a pipe, to the "pool" from which the surface oil evidently came. This was a new venture, for nothing was known of the stratigraphy of oil deposits and little of well drilling. Fortunately the oil pool was reached at a depth of only 69.5 feet and oil came within 10 feet of the surface of the ground in the pipes. In the first 4 months, 2000 barrels were pumped from the well. This success of Colonel Drake incited others to drilling, and in a few months there were scores of wells. The drillers gained in experience, and deeper holes were attempted. A gusher was struck at a depth of 400 feet in 1861. In 1860 the production was nearly 500,000 barrels, and by 1861 more than 2,000,000 barrels. The supply soon came to exceed the demand, and prices fell. Before there could be much demand, uses had to be found for the oil, lamps invented to burn it, and refineries provided to prepare it for use. Until the development of the internal combustion engine and the era of the automobile, kerosene was the chief product the refiners made.

Eventually other fields were opened up, about 1885 in Ohio, 1890 in West Virginia; and by 1865 California was producing about 1,000,000 barrels a year. In the meantime the oil wells of Pennsylvania and New York declined. In 1920 Pennsylvania was producing only 7.1 per cent of the petroleum of the country, and in 1950 about two-thirds of 1 per cent. The many refineries established to handle the product of the Pennsylvania oil wells are now refining oil from every field east of the Rockies. Oil is the basis of a large refining industry producing kerosene, gasoline, and many by-products; but oil has also been, like natural gas, much used as fuel in the factories and has therefore been a factor in the localization of industries.

The Abundance of Natural Gas. Natural gas, called "the most perfect fuel nature furnishes us," was found in most oil pools and escaped from many wells. The first gas well was sunk in 1879. Since about 1890 gas has been widely used as fuel in iron and steel mills, and in the manufacture of glass, porcelain, and cement. It is a common domestic fuel in both country and city in western Pennsylvania. Natural gas has served to localize many factories. Being a cheap fuel and easily handled, it enabled gas-using factories to produce their products at low cost. Manufactured gas (coal gas) is sold for several times the price of natural gas.

Abundance of cheap coal, petroleum, and natural gas have for about half a century or more been important factors in encouraging industries in the Northeastern States, some parts, of course, being more favored than others. New England has been the least benefited, western Pennsylvania the most. Coal is used in all parts of this group of states, but oil and gas mainly where they are produced. New England has its water power to compensate for its lack of mineral fuel deposits and has specialized in products that require little fuel in their manufacture.

Since about 1940 the relative importance of coal as a source for fuel and power has decreased in the United States with an increase in the use of petroleum and natural gas. However, since petroleum and natural gas are more rapidly exhausted, the future will bring an increase in the importance of coal, as well as a dependence upon nuclear energy. The Northeastern States appear to be fairly well equipped for future sources of power.

Sources of Raw Products. Many of the raw products needed in manufactures occur in limited quantities and in great variety in the Northeastern States. The coniferous and hardwood forests (Fig. 20) have long supplied (now only a small part of the needs) raw material for saw and planing mills, pulp and paper mills, furniture factories, shipbuilding plants, and box and cooperage factories, as well as bark for the large tanning industry (Fig. 52).

Herring, cod, mackerel, oyster, and other fisheries off the coast furnish raw products for the canning, drying, smoking, and for the fish-oil and fertilizer factories. The canning industry uses vegetables from New Jersey and Long Island, berries from widely scattered areas, and peaches from northwestern New York, southern New England, and other sections. Grape juice and wines from the grapes of the Finger Lakes and

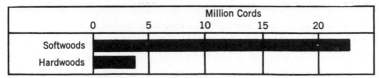

Fig. 52. Kinds and amounts of pulpwood consumed in the United States in 1951.

Lake Ontario vineyards are well known over most of the eastern United States. Butter, cheese, and condensed milk are some of the products of the dairies. The wheat fields, although far surpassed by those of the Middle West, still furnish some raw material for the flour mills. New York and New Jersey still supply small amounts.

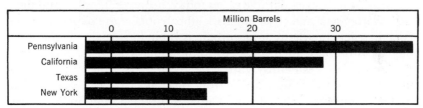

Fig. 53. Production of Portland cement in the United States by leading states in 1950.

From the widespread clay deposits the numerous brick yards secure their material, and the pottery works at Trenton once depended entirely upon local supplies of clay. The shale and limestone of the Lehigh Valley are the basic materials used in cement making. In this valley the first Portland cement of the United States was made about 1890; and today, even though cement making has become widely distributed, the Lehigh Valley is still the leading cement section of the country (Fig. 53). The proximity of many large cities in need of cheap and serviceable fireproof building material to the Lehigh cement section is another factor in the prominence that the cement industry holds in these states. The Hudson Valley also has cement plants utilizing local deposits of clay and limestone.

The Indians obtained brine from the salt springs of central New York, and ever since the arrival of the white man salt making has been an important industry of Onondaga County. It was an important factor in the early growth of Syracuse. Salt deposits have been struck by boring at many points in central and western New York. Brine pumped from Tully to Solvay near Syracuse is used, with limestone, in the manufacture of immense quantities of soda and allied products.

There are many other minerals of considerable commercial value which are directly or indirectly associated with manufacturing. In New England there are at present few minerals produced other than granite, slate, marble, limestone, basalt, and sandstone. Some of the granite and marble quarried is worked up into finished forms, cut, smoothed, and polished, at the quarries, but stone cutting and polishing is an industry in many towns and cities. Talc occurs in northern New York and Vermont. Graphite, used in the making of lead pencils and crucibles, is found near Lake George, New York. The gypsum of central New York is manufactured into plaster of Paris and other wall finishes. Mineral pigments—red, brown, and yellow ochre, green shales, and slates, and red iron ore—are ground for paints. Feldspar is utilized in the pottery industry. Indeed, in no other section of the United States is so great a use made of the products of the mine and quarry.

The great industries of these states today, however, textiles, and those utilizing iron, steel and other metals, leather, rubber, and paper and pulp, depend largely or wholly upon products brought into the section from other parts of the United States or from foreign countries. Most of the iron ore that makes Pennsylvania the greatest pig iron and steel-producing state of the Union comes from the Lake Superior region, with smaller quantities imported from Cuba, Venezuela, and other sources. Zinc and lead do occur in New Jersey but only in small quantities. The hundreds of plants turning out automobiles, steam and gas engines, locomotives, dynamos and motors, railroad coaches and cars, stoves, tools, builders' hardware, machines for use in the textile, woodworking, paper, leather and shoe industries, firearms, plumbers' supplies, and a thousand other products are using metals that have been directly or indirectly secured from other parts of United States and from foreign countries.

All the cotton and silk, and nearly all the wool used in the widely distributed and varied textile industries comes from outside these states. Most of the hides come from the slaughter houses of the North Central States or are imported from temperate South America, Australia, or elsewhere. More and more the pulp and paper industry is dependent on Canadian forests, and the woodworking industries on lumber brought from the South, the Pacific Coast, Canada, or the tropics. The necessity for importing so many and so much of the raw materials handicaps the industries but slightly if at all, for the factories and their reputation are already well established, power is plentiful and relatively cheap, and numerous and direct traffic lines give this section superior advantages in collecting raw materials and distributing the finished products. All the seaports of the Northeastern States were important commercial centers before they became industrial centers, and commerce today absorbs the energies of a large part of their people.

Strategic Location for Manufacturing.   The position of these states on the border of the greatest commercial ocean, the Atlantic, is of supreme advantage. As a result of the sinking of the coast line and the formation of indentations that project back into the continent, the four largest cities, Boston, New York, Philadelphia, and Baltimore, although on the edge of the Appalachian belt, are on the ocean. Fortunately, the coastal plain that guards the eastern border of the old land from Cape Cod southward is dissected by estuaries, and these cities have every access to the world-ocean traffic routes. The contact that the Northeastern States enjoy with the ocean through the many harbors, and their position between the ocean and the great "heart" of America, the Great Central Plain, make them the greatest transit region of the American continent.

Equally important are the low passes of the Northern Appalachians, the lowest of which is the Hudson-Mohawk Depression that opens out upon the Lake Plains of western New York (Fig. 42).

The commercial contact with the Great Central Plain was not obtained without effort on the part of the northern seaboard cities, for the natural tendency of the trade was to move southward with the currents of the Mississippi and its tributaries and make New Orleans the great emporium of the Central Plain. Not only did the eastern seaboard cities struggle against geography to turn the traffic eastward, but they struggled also with each other. Although all benefited from this struggle, the one most favored by natural traffic lines benefited most.

Struggle for Commerce of Interior.   In the first phase of the struggle for the control of the commerce of the Middle West, roads were built. In road building, Baltimore had the advantage as to distance, and, moreover, it was assisted by the National Government in building the National Pike from Cumberland, Maryland, to Wheeling, West Virginia, and beyond. Pennsylvania built the Philadelphia-Pittsburgh Pike; and New York, a road from Albany to Buffalo. All these were well traveled; along them moved as many of the products of the Middle West and the manufactures of the East as could stand high freight charges.

In the second phase of the struggle canals were dug. Boston, recognizing the great barrier the Hoosac and Taconic Mountains offered, made only a feeble attempt to get to the Mohawk Lowland.

Baltimore, financed by Maryland, started the Chesapeake and Ohio Canal and in time built it as far west as Cumberland, Maryland. Further progress was stopped by the Allegheny Front and the building of the Baltimore and Ohio Railroad, which was started in 1828. Philadelphia, assisted by Pennsylvania, pushed the Pennsylvania Canal and Portage Railroad to Pittsburgh, but not until long after New York had completed the Erie Canal along the Hudson-Mohawk Depression and across the Lake Plains to Buffalo. In canal building, New York led all

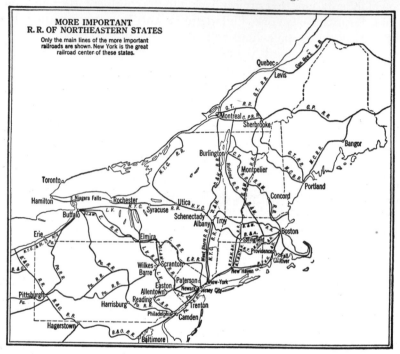

Fig. 54. Most of the more important railroads of these states connect the larger ports with the great northern interior. The greatest rail thoroughfare lies between New York and Philadelphia.

the rest and was the first to get its artificial water line across the Highlands to the great productive interior. Moreover, at Buffalo the Erie Canal connected with the Great Lakes, which led a thousand miles back into the Great Central Plain. Canals were built to connect the Ohio River with Lake Erie, and thus the commerce of nearly all of Illinois, Indiana, and Ohio, as well as the states to the north, flowed eastward through the Erie Canal. Thus an immense area, rapidly being settled and developed, was made tributary to New York. The beginning of the leadership of New York dates from the opening of the

Erie Canal in 1825. The Erie Canal is the only one of the great state canal systems built in the early part of the nineteenth century that survived railroad competition. In 1918 at a cost of more than $110,000,-000, the State of New York enlarged this canal, Erie Division, New York State Barge Canal System, to float boats drawing 10-11 feet of water. This gives a water route, 490 miles long, from New York to Buffalo, that has a capacity of 20,000,000 tons a year. The annual movement of freight in 1951 was, however, only 5,211,000 tons.

In railroad building, the third stage in the stampede for interior commerce, New York led also. In fact, one of the first railroads of the country was in eastern New York, near Albany. Before 1842, railroad communication between Albany and Buffalo was established, and shortly after, the Erie Railroad, the first trunkline in America, connected New York with Lake Erie in an almost direct line across the Allegheny Plateau along river valleys. In 1855 New York, because of these successes in

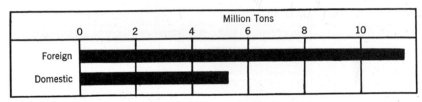

Fig. 55. Comparative tonnage of United States merchant vessels employed in foreign and domestic trade in 1951.

laying out traffic lines, had drawn to itself a large part of the traffic of the upper Mississippi Valley and the Lakes region. The route from Buffalo to Albany and down the Hudson to New York was developed for both water and rail and thus dominated as a traffic line. As railways became developed to the west and south from New York, the Hudson-Mohawk route has declined relatively in the traffic between New York and the interior, but the volume remains great. The railroads, however, also gave Boston, Phiadelphia, and Baltimore an opportunity to get a share of the interior trade. There are several well-known railroads that cross the Northern Appalachian region, the Baltimore and Ohio, the Boston and Albany, the New York Central, the Erie, the Lackawanna, the Lehigh Valley, and the Pennsylvania (Fig. 54).

For the reasons indicated above, this group of states may well be called the "bridge states." The eastern approaches to the "bridge" are the New York, Massachusetts, Delaware, and Chesapeake bays which lead to the Atlantic and thus to the world ocean. At the western approach are the Great Lakes, the Ohio River, and the numerous rail-

roads that span the continent. In fact, most of the commerce and trade
of the immense area that extends from the Middle Atlantic seaboard
nearly to the Pacific crosses the Northern Appalachian region. The factories of this region, therefore, can draw raw materials from a vast area
both in America and in the world at large, and manufactured goods
have access to a wide market (Figs. 55, 56, and 57).

The Abundant Labor Supply.   The great number of workmen available, skilled and unskilled, because of the dense population, is another
important factor in the localizing of industries in the Northeastern States.
In 1950 the population density of New England as a whole was about
135 to the square mile, and that of the Middle Atlantic states 275; the
population densities of the chief manufacturing states were about 225
for Pennsylvania, 285 for New York, 350 for Connecticut, 555 for New
Jersey, 548 for Massachusetts, and 675 for Rhode Island. These are
high densities for a section as young in its industrial development as is

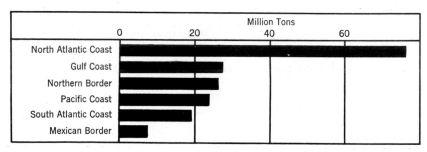

Fig. 56. Foreign trade vessels entered and cleared by customs districts in the United
States in 1950.

the Northern Appalachian region. Nearly all the better lands have been
taken and are being tilled intensively, land values are high, rents are
high, "free goods" are scarce, and the factory offers about the only opportunity to feed the thousands who work with their hands. The North
Atlantic ports are the chief immigrant-receiving stations of the country.
The number of immigrants and alien passengers entering the United
States from 1820 to 1950 was about 58,000,000, most of them coming
to the Northern Appalachian states. Since most of the immigrants who
come seeking work have not the means to begin commercial enterprises
or farming, they seek employment in the factories in these cities. The
whole foreign-born population of New York City in 1950 numbered
over 2,000,000, the total population being 7,835,000; Boston had about
180,000 white foreign-born in the total population of 790,000. Newark
had over 90,000 out of a total population of 437,000. Philadelphia, be-

ing less important as an immigrant port, had over 290,000 in the total of 2,064,000.

There are several other factors of long standing that have contributed, and are contributing, to make this a great manufacturing region. During the colonial period the Appalachian barrier tended to hold the people near the seaboard, thus checking the natural tendency toward expansion, and forced them into more intensive utilization of the resources. The limited area suitable for agricultural expansion in New England, the large area of hilly and mountainous land, and the thin and patchy soil limited the agricultural opportunities and forced men and women into various other economic fields. The fisheries and the

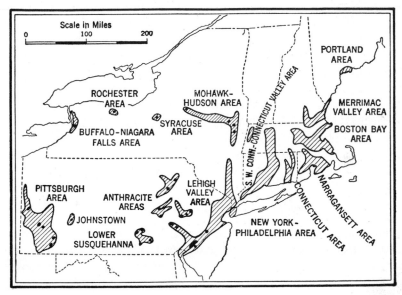

Fig. 57. The more important manufacturing areas in the Northeastern States. Although manufacturing is the dominant activity of the northeastern states, the manufacuring areas form but a small part of the total area of these states.

merchant marine offered some outlet for the economic activities of the people, but always many were engaged in manufacturing. Manufacturing was also stimulated by the high cost of European goods which had to be carried 3000 or more miles in small and slow ships.

From early colonial times the manufacturers of the Northeastern States have had skilled craftsmen from whom to select their workmen. In coming to a pioneer environment where civilization by necessity was "stripped of its non-essentials," there was naturally some economic retrogression. There were complaints that many workmen had abandoned their trades for agriculture, yet many of those migrating had been reared for generations in the atmosphere of the workshop of the city and were not so easily attracted to the land as were their descendants in the following generations. But the factories rarely suffered because of scarcity of labor.

In 1650 Boston is reported as having skilled craftsmen in many trades. In Philadelphia there were shoemakers, coopers, wool combers, potters, tanners, felt makers, brick makers, blacksmiths, silversmiths, and many others.

The industries of many parts of the Northeastern States are old enough to have passed into the more advanced stages of manufacturing in which the artistic is emphasized. Quality is recognized as more desirable in manufacture than quantity. The conception of careful workmanship is a tradition carried over from one generation to the next. In an old manufacturing region there is likely to be greater wealth, more refined surroundings, better schools, and more art than in new industrial areas. The Pittsburgh environment, with its huge blast furnaces and its great factories that demand an enormous amount of power, will probably never, in spite of its art museums and beautiful architecture, develop workmen—like those of eastern Pennsylvania, New Jersey, New York, and New England, particularly New England—that take pride in producing articles of beauty. It has taken nearly three centuries to develop the eastern environment in which are manufactured most of the artistic commodities displayed in today's "exclusive" shops.

The Financial Center of the United States.   Money with which to start factories has always been easier to obtain in these states than in other sections. The greatest money-lending regions of the world are those in which commerce and manufacturing have long been prominent. The capital of the north Atlantic seaboard cities has financed the enterprises of the whole country. The profits of capitalists and the savings of millions of well-paid workmen have always been available for investment in legitimate manufacturing enterprises in the Northeastern States.

The Leading Manufacturing Regions.   Although the great majority of the people of the Northeastern States are connected in one way or another with manufacturing, the industrial regions occupy only a small part of the total area of these states. Moreover, these regions are widely scattered, being chiefly near the sea, along natural lines of transportation, or near sources of power.

The Boston Bay Region and Its Industries.   The Boston Bay region is the oldest manufacturing area in the United States and in some ways

is the "mother" of other New England regions, since the success of industries in this area led to their establishment in others. Boston has also
given financial assistance to many other manufacturing sections outside
New England.

The high cost of imported manufactured goods in colonial days, due
to the heavy freight rates and enormous profits sought by importers,
and the necessity of adding to the meager returns from farming led the
people to try their hand at providing themselves with clothing, implements, and other articles that we class as manufactured goods. Industrial development, however, encountered the difficulties usually experienced in new countries. The abundance of cheap land led some good
craftsmen to abandon trades they had spent years to learn; yet, through
government encouragement, in various ways there was a steady though
slow growth in manufacturing. For a century or two these manufactures were almost wholly carried on in the home—household industries—and were small in total volume; yet ideals of good craftsmanship
and skill were being developed. The relative abundance of power was
also a favorable factor in the early periods; but since about 1850, because of the increase in both number and size of industrial plants, large
quantities of coal have been consumed, for the demands for power have
exceeded the quantity supplied by water power. In many plants at
waterfalls, coal is used to supplement water power during the dry
seasons.

The most important industry in the Boston area today is the making
of shoes and other leather goods. Boston, Brockton, Lynn, Salem, Weymouth, Beverly, and Worcester are the more important shoe-manufacturing towns. Boston, Brockton, and Weymouth specialize in men's
shoes, and Salem, Lynn, and Beverly in women's shoes. The factories
of Haverhill on the Merrimack and of Newburyport, which specialize
in the making of women's slippers, have close trade relations with the
industry in the Boston area.

The shoe industry in Massachusetts is very old. The first skilled shoemakers came to the Massachusetts Bay Colony from England in 1629,
and by 1650 the industry was well established. Many farmers made the
shoes for their households, and there were itinerant shoemakers who
made and repaired shoes; but in most of the large towns, by 1650,
shoemakers had set up small shops, popularly known as "ten footers,"
where shoes were repaired or made to order for people or for stores.
Standardization in size, as we have it today, came after a machine which
was invented for turning out gun stocks was applied to the making of
shoe lasts. Americans have always been among the leaders of the world
in devising machines for the shoe industry. In 1809 and 1810 several

machines were devised for fastening heels to shoes. It was easy to adapt the sewing machine, patented by Howe in 1846, to the sewing of the "uppers" of shoes, but not for sewing soles to uppers, and a machine for this purpose was devised by Blake in 1858, and later improved by McKay. Machines of this type are still in use in the industry, and

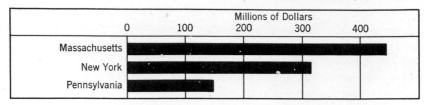

Fig. 58. Leading states in the manufacture of leather footwear and leather cut stock, in terms of the value of the product shipped. This industry is spreading westward and southward, but Massachusetts is likely to hold the leading place for some time. Most of the more expensive shoes come from Massachusetts. One-half of all leather footwear manufactured in the country comes from the Northeastern States.

shoes made on them are known to the trade as the McKay type. At present nearly 50 per cent of the shoes made in Massachusetts are classed in the trade as the McKay.

A welt machine with a curved needle, invented in 1862 by Destary and later improved by Charles Goodyear, has given origin to another type of shoe, known in the trade as the welt or Goodyear. Extreme spe-

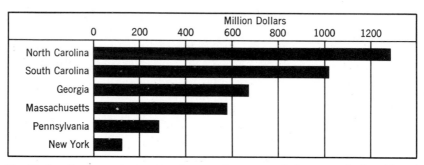

Fig. 59. Leading states in the manufacture of cotton goods, in terms of value shipped. A great advance in this line has been made since about 1900 in the Southern States. The bulk of the product from the South, however, consists of broad woven fabrics and yarns.

cialization, great skill, and numerous machines—in some factories a score or more of different machines are used in the making of a shoe— enable American manufacturers to turn out shoes that are in demand the world over. Shoes are manufactured in about a hundred or more towns in Massachusetts, New Hampshire, and Maine. About 25 per cent of the total for the United States, in quantity, are produced in

Massachusetts alone (Fig. 58). Associated with the making of shoes are a few tanneries and many leather goods factories and plants engaged in the manufacturing of rubber shoes. The manufacturing of India-rubber goods began at Roxbury (now a part of Boston) in 1833, but the industry did not have the greatest growth until the discovery of a method of hardening rubber by sulfur and heat, by Goodyear of Connecticut in 1839.

The textile industry in the Boston area, although not so important as in other parts of the Northeastern States, dates from the colonial period (Fig. 59). In 1656 the Colonial Assembly required each family to spin 3 pounds of woolen yarn each week for 30 weeks each year, under heavy penalty, and in 1640 the magistrates were directed to fur-

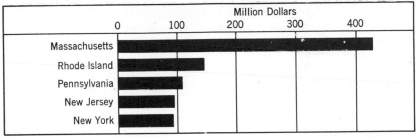

Fig. 60. Leading states in the manufacture of woolens and worsteds in terms of value of product shipped. The dominance of the Northeastern States in this type of textile manufacture is well shown by the graph.

ther the growing of flax, and to provide spinning wheels that the boys and girls might learn to spin wool, flax and cotton. As a result of these efforts, New England by 1700 was exporting manufactured cloth to the southern colonies and elsewhere. The climate of New England was well adapted to the production of wool and favored the growing of flax; and, through the active commerce with the West Indies and India, cotton was supplied the spinners. The first cotton mill in America, it is claimed, was built at Beverly in 1788. Francis Cabot Lowell, after a visit to the textile mills in England, set up the first successful loom at Waltham in 1814. But the Merrimack Valley and the Narragansett Bay region have far outstripped the Boston Bay area in the textile industry.

The excellent harbor on which Boston is located, the numerous radiating railroad lines, and the long-time interest in ocean carrying are the chief reasons for the importance of its commerce. Many of the products imported go to the factories of the Boston Bay area and other manufacturing districts of New England. Since World War I, Boston has become one of the most important wool markets of the world, to which buyers come from all parts of the United States and even from Europe. The numerous steamship lines bring wool from all the leading overseas wool-producing countries, and the railroads bring it from the Rocky Mountain states and elsewhere in the United States (Fig. 60). The manufacturers of goods using wool, therefore, find in Boston a great variety from which to select.

The manufacture of chocolate and cocoa products from imported cacao beans is one of the important industries. So also is the preparation of tea, coffee, coconut, and other imported products.

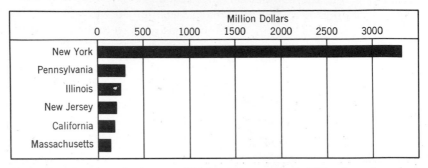

Fig. 61. Leading states in the manufacture of women's and children's ready-to-wear clothing in 1947 (value of product shipped). The dominance of New York State is due largely to great output of jobbers engaging contractors who do not produce in the so-called contract factories. This is made possible by the large labor supply of the New York City metropolitan area. The Midwest and the Far West are increasing in this business.

The making of women's and children's ready-to-wear clothing, which may be considered as the secondary manufacture of textiles, uses large numbers of foreign laborers who work for comparatively low wages. An excellent market for these goods is found in the northeastern section itself (Fig. 61).

The list of minor industries is very large, as one might expect in a region so long engaged in manufacturing. At one time there were iron furnaces at Lynn and Braintree, the one at Lynn having been erected in 1643. Here, for a century or more, agricultural implements and tools, and hardware used in shipbuilding were made. The iron ore came from the glacial ponds and bogs and was smelted by charcoal burned in the nearby forests. There are many foundries and machine shops in which shoemaking and textile machinery is made and repaired, besides the great variety of job work necessary in this machine age. Most of the work in metals is in small metal goods and jewelry, electrical apparatus, and copper and brass. Waltham has one of the largest watch factories in the world, and, it is claimed, turns out about a million watches a year.

The Merrimack Valley Area.   Textile manufactures, which dominate in the Merrimack Valley area, had their beginning in the city of Lowell. A Waltham, Massachusetts, company purchased a power site at Pawtucket Falls on the Merrimack about 1820, and erected a large cotton mill, about which the village, and later the city, of Lowell grew up. The mill village was a model in its day. Up to 1840 the mill hands, except a few dyers and calico printers who had been secured in England, were American girls from the nearby villages and farms, in whom the com-

Fig. 62. The Osgood Mill at North Andover, Massachusetts. *Courtesy of M. T. Stevens & Sons Co.* Many mills located by water power still exist in New England. Those at North Andover and Lawrence on the Merrimack River are particularly noteworthy in that they represent the center of the woolen goods industry in the country.

pany had a much greater interest than it did in the French Canadians who later made up a large portion of the workers, or in the Europeans who came still later. Many other mills were later built in Lowell, and at one time the city was so dominant in cotton manufacturing as to be called the "Spindle City" and the "Manchester of America"; but the water power at Pawtucket Falls became insufficient to meet the needs of the expanding industry. Mills were accordingly built at Lawrence and Haverhill, at Nashua and Manchester and elsewhere in New Hampshire, and at Biddeford and Lewiston in Maine. Lowell has been surpassed by Fall River and New Bedford in cotton manufacturing because the latter two cities, being seaports, can secure cheaper coal than Lowell or any of the Merrimack River cities. It probably is still true that no other river in America supplies power to as many spindles as does the Merrimack. The low cost of building dams, particularly in comparison with those on the Connecticut River, was of particular importance in attracting mills in the early decades of the nineteenth century (Fig. 62).

Haverhill and Newburyport, as previously stated, are interested in the manufacture of shoes, and the shoe industry also dominates at Manchester, New Hampshire. But woolens and worsted goods are by far the leading products of the factories at Lawrence. This city produces about an eighth of the wool manufactured in the United States, in value, and a third of the total for Massachusetts. Most of the small cities of southern New Hampshire and southwestern Maine manufacture shoes and woolen and worsted goods, and not a few still have an interest in woodworking, being the nearest of the New England cities to the forests in the north.

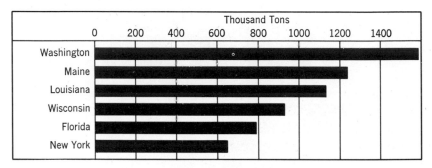

Fig. 63. Leading states in woodpulp production. Western and Southern as well as the Lake States are important in this industry, yet the combined Northeastern States are still important producers. It was only after 1940 that Maine lost leadership to the State of Washington.

Pulp mills are widely scattered in northern New England, being located at falls on the rivers, which, because of the many glacial lakes in their basins, furnish clean water and have a fairly regular flow (Fig. 63).

The wide range of metal manufactures is seen in the making of locomotives at Manchester, needles in some towns, and silverware at Newburyport. Foundries and machines shops, as in the Boston Bay area, are numerous. At Portland, Maine, there are many foundries and machine shops, some textile mills and shoe factories, and plants for canning and preserving vegetables and fruits.

The Narrangansett Bay Region. Although the manufactures of the Narragansett Bay area are varied, the textile industries predominate. At Pawtucket, on the Blackstone River, Samuel Slater built his first cotton mill of 250 spindles in 1793. During the latter half of the eighteenth century there had been many epoch-making inventions in textile manufacture in England, by Kay, Hargreaves, Arkwright, Compton, Cartwright, and others, but Parliament had prohibited the exportation of any of the machines or even the drawings of them. Samuel Slater, who had worked several years in textile-machine factories and had made himself familiar with the parts and operation of the Arkwright spinning machines, migrated to America and, with the help of Rhode Island capital, built the first modern cotton mill in America. About all that Rhode Island offered as an inducement to the industry was capital and a limited amount of water power. Wool was obtained from Rhode Island or Massachusetts flocks. Cotton, for a few years after the completion of the Pawtucket mill, was brought from India or the West Indies, Providence being the port of entry. Success from the first met this new venture, and the textile industry soon began to draw much of Rhode Island capital into it. From Pawtucket the textile industry spread up the Blackstone, every waterfall or rapids becoming the site of a textile town, even on into southern Massachusetts. Pawtucket, Central Falls, and Woonsocket today are the larger textile centers. The valley of the Pawtuxet River, to the southwest of Providence, also has many textile towns, and the industry has expanded on into eastern Connecticut along the Quinebaug and other branches of the Thames. The chief cities in the latter valley are New London, Norwich, and Willimantic, Connecticut, and Webster, and Southbridge, Massachusetts.

In this expansion along streams, state lines were no barriers to the textile manufacturers in their zeal to find power sites. The limited amount of water power at many falls or rapids has somewhat retarded factory growth in comparison with that at ocean ports like New Bedford and Fall River which receive western Pennsylvania coal from the Delaware and Chesapeake Bay shipping points. All the early mills were erected at power sites on the river, the later ones near the sea. Power, therefore, has been an important factor in localization, although the shore climate has had some attractions. There is a surprising concentration of spindles in southern Massachusetts. Bristol County, which contains the three large textile cities of New Bedford, Fall River, and Taunton, has about 7,500,000 spindles, or more than one-fifth of the total for the United States.

The Narrangansett Bay region manufactures both cotton and wool goods (woolens and worsted). New Bedford, Fall River, and Pawtucket are predominantly cotton towns. Providence produces some wool goods, as do also many of the towns in the Quinebaug Valley. Pawtucket's interests are largely in cotton and silk, but Woonsocket, although producing these goods, is most active in the manufacturing of woolens and worsteds. The manufacture of goods from wool dates from colonial days, and many mills have developed from early carding and fulling mills; but the worsted industry in America dates from the 1860's when a tariff on imported worsteds was passed by Congress and skilled workmen from Europe were brought to America. The manufacture of worsted calls for large plants and costly machinery. The industry is widely scattered in the Northeastern States; besides the cities already mentioned—Lawrence, Manchester, and Woonsocket—woolen mills are found at Fitchburg, Worcester, and many smaller places.

Most of the textile mills of the Narrangansett Bay area are complete in themselves and perform all the processes from raw products to finished goods, but there are plants given over exclusively to spinning, weaving, bleaching, dyeing, or finishing. Associated with this great activity in textile manufactures are foundries and machine shops.

The manufacture of jewelry ranks next to that of woolens and worsteds at Providence, in value of product and value added by manufacture. Like many of the industries of the Northeastern States, and particularly of New England, this industry is an old one, dating from about 1780. "Gold filling" was invented by Dodge of Providence in 1794, and the manufacture of silverware was begun soon after the Revolutionary War. Skill in workmanship and a reputation for good wares have kept Providence in the lead in jewelry manufacture.

Diversified Industries of the Connecticut Areas.   Since late colonial days Connecticut has been producing clocks, watches, tinware, small metal goods, and "Yankee notions." When transportation was still in its primitive stages in America, peddlers with push carts visited the farmers along the waysides of Connecticut and other nearby states and supplied them with much-needed household articles. In the early part of the nineteenth century, Connecticut clocks and other articles were sold in the farming communities and small villages and cities of the Northeastern States and even the Middle West and the South. Today something like 1200 articles are manufactured in Connecticut.

The textile mills are widely scattered in Connecticut and in the Connecticut Valley in Massachusetts. The manufacture of silk began in 1732. Mansfield had a factory in 1758. Cheney Brothers began the manufacture of spun silk at South Manchester in the 1840's. Today South Manchester in Connecticut and Northampton in Massachusetts are the leading centers. The dominant reasons for the localization of silk factories in these towns are early interest in the making of textiles, the presence of skilled textile workers, clean water, and water power. The activity of New England in the carrying trade with India and the Far East in the colonial period made the securing of raw silk at low prices possible.

There was a small woolen factory at Hartford in 1788; today, mills are found at Hartford, Norwich, Rockville, and many small towns on streams that furnish water power. Danbury, in western Connecticut, is interested in the making of hats and caps and the machinery for manfacturing these articles. The mills at Pittsfield in western Massachusetts began when sheep were numerous on the Berkshire Hills. The large amount of water power available at Hadley Falls at Holyoke, where the Connecticul falls 60 feet in 1½ miles as it descends from the crystalline uplands to a broad valley, gives the city a decided advantage in

Fig. 64. Plant of the Colt's Manufacturing Company at Hartford, Connecticut. *Courtesy, Colt's Manufacturing Company.* This plant has been producing firearms for more than a century. Here the Browning machine gun and automatic rifle were invented and manufactured. Here also Vicker's machine guns and automatic pistols and revolvers were produced for use in World War I. The plant has also turned out washing machines, tableware, electrical goods, radio parts, and various articles made of Bakelite and phenolic compounds.

the making of pulp and paper. It was not until about 1849 that the engineers felt competent to harness a large falls. A dam 1017 feet long was constructed that year, and a large amount of water power, 40,000 hp in all, was developed along the numerous canals that led away from the river above the falls. Cotton goods were the first manufactured products of Holyoke, many small power sites being utilized; but today Holyoke leads all cities of the United States in the manufacture of fine paper. Holyoke, with its large plants equipped with large pulp grinders and Fourdrinier paper machines, was soon able to outstrip the numerous smaller plants at small water-power sites on the slopes of the Berkshires. At one time the Housatonic River Valley in Massachusetts had more than a score of plants; one town, Lee, had 18; but the smaller plants have not succeeded in competition with the larger, and now there are fewer pulp and paper mills than formerly but a greater output.

The southwest Connecticut and Connecticut Valley region, however, is most active in the manufacture of firearms, brass and bronze, clocks and watches, plated ware, cutlery, and metal "specialties" of various sorts, as earlier stated. At New Haven, Bridgeport, Hartford, and New Britain in Connecticut, and Springfield in Massachusetts, foundries and machine shops are the leading plants, and metal goods are manufactured at many other industrial centers (Fig. 64).

Rogers Brothers began the making of cutlery in 1847 at Meriden, and this led to the establishment of "plating" plants at Waterbury, Norwich, and Hartford. The making of brass buttons at Waterbury led to the plants turning out brass, bronze, and copper products, which industry is very active in the Naugatuck Valley today. Hartford at one time was one of the leading cities of the country in the manufacture of bicycles. It now manufactures automobile bodies and accessories. Firearms led the foundries and machine-shop products of Springfield; and firearms and sewing machines those of Bridgeport. The manufacture of firearms at Springfield dates from the Revolutionary War period, an arsenal having been established here by the Continental Congress. Springfield small arms have long been famous.

There seems to be no outstanding geographic reason for the prominence of small metal goods in the industries of this region. Before the Revolutionary War, the manufacture of pig iron and iron goods was active, the ore being obtained from deposits in northwestern Connecticut. The lack of coal for fuel and power has forced New England in general to an intensification of manufactures in the competition with western Pennsylvania. Many important inventions have been made in this region and these have contributed greatly to the interest in manufacturing. Connecticut clock makers have long been noted for their ingenuity. Eli Terry was a famous maker of wooden clocks; Jerome in 1837 conceived the idea of using brass wheels; and at Thomaston for many decades the famous Seth Thomas clocks have been manufactured. It was in this region that Howe and Wilson devised the sewing machine, and here Charles Goodyear, after many years of thought and experimentation, perfected the process of vulcanizing rubber, and Colt began the manufacture of Colt firearms. Eli Whitney, whose cotton gin made cotton the leading textile fiber of the world, was a Connecticut Yankee. From no other region in the United States have inventers taken out so many patents. Thus, all along, the boys of this region have had schooling in ingenuity. Many fortunes have been made by perfecting some article in great demand, and this in itself has been inducement enough for men to become inventors and manufacturers of the articles devised.

Still another factor, non-geographic, that was of great importance was the Joint Stock Act, adopted by the Connecticut Legislature in 1837, whereby men with small capital were permitted to pool their holdings and thus join forces in manufacturing. This act has since been adopted by all the states of the United States, by Great Britain, and by most other manufacturing countries.

The Connecticut region has always had good transportation facilities, as good as any in America, a good supply of labor, and much capital. Its metal manufactures call for little raw material and little coal, but much skill.

The Mohawk-Hudson Area.   The industrial area along the Mohawk owes its development to several factors. Shortly after the valley was settled, small mills for sawing lumber, grinding grain, and pressing flax seed were set up along the numerous small streams that flow down the slopes of the bordering uplands; but these, after engineers had gained experience in building large dams, were overshadowed by the large developments at Little Falls, Cohoes, and elsewhere. And when manufactures outgrew the available water power, railroads began to bring coal to the factories from both the anthracite and the bituminous regions of Pennsylvania. Since the opening of the Erie Canal in 1825 the cities have had the best of transportation facilities to collect raw materials and get their products to buyers. The earliest railroads of New York were constructed westward from Albany. Although the Barge Canal, with its 12 feet of water and locks 310 feet long and 45 feet wide, and its annual capacity of 20,000,000 tons, is far from being used to its capacity, it forces the railroads to give minimum rates to the factories.

Troy is famous for its shirts and collars; and Cohoes, near the mouth of the Mohawk, is the greatest center in the United States for the manufacture of knit goods. Schenectady has large locomotive works and is the home of the General Electric Company, one of the largest manufacturers of dynamos, motors, and electrical appliances in America. Among the other industries at Schenectady are those producing hosiery and knit goods, hardware, paints and varnishes, fire engines, and agricultural implements. Carpets and knit goods are made at Amsterdam, and cotton and woolens at Utica and Johnstown, and Gloversville manufactures most of the gloves worn in the United States. Rome, on the divide between the Hudson River and Lake Ontario, produces brass and iron goods.

The Industries of Syracuse.   Syracuse, farther west on the border of the Lake Plains, ranks high among the manufacturing cities of the state.

Many of the factories are supplied with hydroelectric power from Niagara Falls. The principal products of its factories are automobiles, foundry and machine shop products, ready-made clothing, iron and steel products, typewriters, sewing machines, shoes, and agricultural implements.

The Syracuse region early became known to Europeans because of the salt deposits. Long before the Revolutionary War, the Indians evaporated brine and sold salt to the whites at Albany. In 1795 the state purchased the salt lands of Onondaga County from the Indians and encouraged the production of this most necessary article. Onondaga salt had a wide market until the opening of great deposits in Michigan. The salt deposits since about 1920 have become the basis of a large chemical industry, the largest plant in America for the production of soda-ash being at Solvay, a suburb of Syracuse. The method of manufacture is called the Solvay process.

The Industries of Rochester.   Flour milling was the first industry at Rochester, the abundant water power of the Genesee—there are three cataracts with 96-, 36-, and 83-foot drops, respectively—being used to furnish the energy. After 1825 the Erie Canal gave ready acess to eastern markets. Flour milling is still active, but the city's largest industry today is the making of men's clothing which finds a market over most of the United States. The making of shoes and leather goods holds second rank, and foundry and machine shop products third. Rochester is widely known as the "Kodak" city. In the manufacture of photographic apparatus and supplies, moving picture supplies, meteorological apparatus, and optical goods such as telescopes, opera and field glasses, it probably holds first rank among the cities of the world. It also manufactures much electrical apparatus and machinery.

The Buffalo-Niagara Falls Area.   The industries of Buffalo, in the Buffalo-Niagara Falls area, owe their development largely to their being at the eastern terminus of the Great Lakes, near the coal, oil, and gas fields of western Pennsylvania, and to their having excellent transportation facilities to the eastern markets by way of the Erie (in past) and Barge canals and the numerous railroads.

Commerce is one of the chief activities of Buffalo, this city being a distributing center for the manufactures of the East seeking western markets, and for the products of the forest, field, and mine on their way to the East. This close touch with producing regions and markets gives the industries of Buffalo a decided advantage. Its chief plants are flour- and gristmills, linseed-oil plants, slaughtering and meat-packing plants, mills turning out lumber and timber products, shops making cars and railroad equipment and repairs, and laboratories making patent medicines, chemicals, and soaps. There are also copper smelters and refineries, petroleum refineries, drydocks and shipyards, and a large steel plant of the Lackawanna Iron and Steel Company.

Tonawanda, to the north, the eastern terminus of lake navigation, is an important lumber center; and at Niagara Falls there has grown up, since the construction of several hydroelectric plants, an important electrochemical industry. Chemicals are the chief manufactured products of the city of Niagara Falls. At many of the smaller towns in northwestern New York and at some of the larger cities—mainly outside the Buffalo-Niagara Falls area—there are large plants for canning and preserving fruits, making wine, and bottling grape juice, the raw materials coming from the nearby fruit region.

The Varied Industries of the New York-Philadelphia Area. The area that lies between New York City and Philadelphia, inclusive, is the most important manufacturing section in the United States, judged from the value of the output of the factories and the value added by manufacture. More than one-sixth of the manufactured products of the country, in value, comes from this area. It is not a region producing large quantities or a variety of raw products. There is little or no water power, no coal, oil, or gas. Its chief asset is its location near the center of the habitable coast of North America on the western border of the most important commercial ocean, the Atlantic, at the eastern termini of the best traffic routes across the Appalachian Highlands, and near large deposits of excellent coal. The output of its factories is varied. Indeed, it would be difficult to think of many articles not manufactured in this region.

The Importance of the New York City Area. Chief among the manufacturing cities of this area is New York. Although commerce is one of the major activities of the city of New York, the output of the factories in 1947 amounted to $5,501,000,000.[1] This was about 57 per cent of the total of the State of New York, and 7 per cent of the output of the factories of the United States. The output of the factories of New York City in 1947 was greater than that of all the factories of the United States in 1880. The Erie Canal and later the railroads gave access to the interior of the United States, the large number of immigrants who landed at the port of New York, and the expansion of overseas commerce that have made New York City, since the middle of the nineteenth century, the largest manufacturing center of the United States.

The most important industry is the making of men's and women's clothing, representing more than a quarter of the total output of the fac-

---

[1] The foreign commerce of the port of New York, which includes parts of New Jersey and New York State, in 1947 was 16,700,000 tons, or nearly 30 per cent of the total for the United States.

tories of the city in value, or in value added by manufacture. This industry is carried on largely in small shops, and its importance is due largely to the abundant supply of foreign labor and the large market. Other related products are millinery and lace goods, fur goods, men's shirts, silk goods, and men's furnishings.

In the printing and publishing of newspapers, magazines, and books, New York leads the cities of the country. Among other industries and plants are slaughtering and meat packing, bakeries, confectionery and ice cream plants, and foundries and machine shops.

The Industries of Northern New Jersey.   The cities of northeastern New Jersey, on or near the Hudson River and the bays—Upper New York, Newark, and Raritan—are really a part of geographic New York, and their growth is due to many, if not most, of the same causes. Farther south, toward Philadelphia, the cities share many of the advantages for growth that have made Philadelphia the third manufacturing center of the United States in value of product. The narrow strip of territory between the Hudson and the Delaware in New Jersey has about four-fifths of the people of that state and nearly all the manufactures.

In value of product the five leading types of manufactures in this area are refining the copper and oil, building ships, making of silk goods, and slaughtering and meat packing; but, based on value added by manufacture, the list of products in order of importance is ships, silk goods, refined oil, rubber tires, rubber goods, and leather.

There are large shipyards at Elizabeth, Bayonne, Jersey City, and Camden, at which both wooden and steel ships are constructed. Paterson, the "Lyons of American," owes its prominence chiefly to the success of early attempts at the manufacture of silk cloth and floss, which was first begun here about 1840. Coal fields are near, and also excellent markets, but the raw silk was imported from the Far East or Mediterranean regions. Until about 1940 there were about 800 plants in New Jersey interested in all phases of the manufacture of silk and rayon including dyeing and finishing. The outbreak of war in Europe in 1939 and later with Japan handicapped this industry because it stopped the cheap source of raw silk. Rayon manufacture continues, but it tends to shift to the southern states in proximity to the raw resource, cotton. Elizabeth and Bayonne have immense petroleum-refining plants, which at Elizabeth cover more than 800 acres, with distilleries and refineries, laboratories, tanks, and warehouses, at which crude oil from all the fields of the United States east of the Rocky Mountains, even from Oklahoma and northern Texas, is separated into scores of products for home consumption or export. Bayonne has immense docks for receiving crude petroleum from foreign fields or loading the tank vessels with export product. The advantages for overseas shipping and the proximity to large domestic markets are undoubtedly the chief geographic reasons for the localizing of oil refining on the shores of New York Bay and connecting waters. Not a drop of crude oil is produced in New Jersey.

Advantages in the importation of crude rubber from Brazil and from the very important sources of supply in the East Indies, the large local markets, access to large, more distant markets, and activity in the chemical industry are all favorable to the production of rubber tires and rubber goods.

The tanning industry at Newark dates from about 1770, when hides derived from local slaughtering houses were tanned with oak and hemlock bark from New Jersey forests. Now hides may be imported readily or secured from the slaughtering houses of New Jersey or New York or Chicago; but the tanbark must come largely from the distant forests of the Appalachian Highlands or be imported. Much tanning extract is now used.

The refining and smelting of copper, which stands first among the industries, when value of product is considered, is carried on chiefly at Camden and Newark. It probably had its beginning in the treatment of the copper ores mined in the Piedmont in the state; but the refineries and smelters today treat large quantities of ore from the western states as well as from Mexico, Bolivia, Peru, Chile, and elsewhere. Pennsylvania furnishes the fuel. The state still produces small quantities of copper ore; and zinc, once very important in its output, is now mined, although in small quantities, at Franklin Furnace. Platinum, nickel, gold, silver, zinc, and lead are also treated in New Jersey metallurgical works, the more important of which are at Elizabeth. The manufacture of iron began in 1674, with ores mined near Shrewsbury. The interest in this industry is attested by the fact that one of the inventors, at Newark, devised a machine for making nails, made several improvements for locomotives, and discovered a method of making malleable iron. Magnetite is still mined in small quanities, and several cities have iron and steel works.

The above types of industries are only a few of the more important. Numerous foundries and machine shops, as well as textile factories, are to be found in all the cities. Camden manufactures cotton and worsted goods; Passaic, woolens and worsteds; New Brunswick, hosiery. The Singer Sewing Machine plant at Elizabeth is one of the largest, if not the largest, in the world. Felt hats have long been made at Newark, and Orange and Jersey City refine both cane and beet sugar, and raw sugar coming mostly from Europe and the West Indies. The clay deposits near Trenton gave an early impetus to the pottery industry, although ball and flint clays and kaolin are now imported from other states or from overseas. Many brick plants in northeastern New Jersey find a good market in New York City and other urban centers. Pennsylvania coal supplies the great heat necessary in the manufacture of pottery at Trenton, brick in many cities, and glass at Glassboro and Millville, which are on the Coastal Plain in southern New Jersey near large deposits of sand suitable for the making of glass.

Philadelphia and Vicinity.   Philadelphia has a slight advantage in manufacturing over New York in having easier access to both anthracite and bituminous coal fields. The first canals and canalized rivers constructed in Pennsylvania connected Philadelphia with the Schuylkill and Lehigh coal fields. The Lehigh River was improved about 1822, and soon after "arks" loaded with coal floated down to the state's metropolis by way of the Delaware. Franklin, as early as 1770, advised the construction of a canal along the Schuylkill, but nothing was done toward utilizing this water route until 1822 when $1,000,000, a tremendous sum for that day, was appropriated, and coal began to move downstream in 1825. The Pennsylvania Canal, which was completed in 1830 and in operation only about two decades, and the Pennsylvania Railroad, constructed in the 1850's, put Philadelphia in touch with the bituminous fields of western Pennsylvania. Philadelphia is also an ocean port, but its contact with the great North Atlantic trade route is not so close as that of New York, nor does it have so low a land route across the Appalachian Highlands. It was chiefly this better route across the Highlands that enabled New York to forge ahead of Philadelphia in the last century or more in population growth, and eventually in growth of manufactures.

As in Boston, Providence, and some cities of Connecticut, many of the present-day industries of Philadelphia and the nearby towns had their start in colonial days. The manufacture of hosiery and knit goods was begun by German colonists shortly after 1680, hand looms being used. "Germantown woolens" were well known throughout the Middle Atlantic settlements. The first active manufacture of iron in the state was at Pottstown, some 30 miles from Philadelphia in the Schuylkill Valley, probably as early as 1716. The woolen industry of the city was greatly aided during the Revolutionary War by the large orders given for uniforms for the Continental Army. Carpet weaving was begun in 1774.

In value of product, sugar refining is an important industry in Philadelphia. This city, like all Atlantic ports, possesses good facilities for the importation of raw sugar, and can command a large domestic market. In value added by manufacture, this industry ranks very low.

The weaving of woolen goods, carpets and rugs, and cotton goods and silks, and the making of men's and women's clothing all rank high among the industries and owe their importance to their long standing among the industries of the city and to the good transportation facilities for collecting raw materials and distributing the manufactured articles. Cramp's shipyard and the Federal Government yard at League Island, at which many of the vessels for the United States Navy are built and equipped, are famous. Philadelphia's yards launched many of the finest of the clipper ships in the decades when these swift vessels made America famous on the world's oceans. The Baldwin locomotive works have for decades been producing the best of American locomotives. (Fig. 65). Their superiority over foreign makes is indicated by the large orders from all parts of the world where railroads are opening up undeveloped regions to

Fig. 65. Airplane view of the 488-acre plant of the Baldwin locomotive works at Eddystone, Pennsylvania, near the city of Philadelphia. *Courtesy, Baldwin Locomotive Company.*

world commerce. Thus Philadelphia makes its contribution to both sea and land transportation. Stetson hats, Disston and Keystone saws, the Saturday Evening Post, and Philadelphia tools typify other leading industries.

The leather industry is very old but received its greatest growth about the time of the Civil War, when the decline of the forests of New York made an imperative call for another source of tanbark, and Pennsylvania ridges with their dense oak forests were able to supply the demand. By 1880 Pennsylvania had one-fifth of the tanneries of the United States. Although the Northern Appalachian forests have long since been depleted of their tanning materials, the use of tanning extracts and a monopoly of a chemical tanning formula have enabled Pennsylvania to hold its lead among the states. Philadelphia is the leading city.

Chester, to the southwest of Philadelphia on the Delaware, has rolling mills and steel works and shipbuilding, and has long been interested in the textile industry, the making of cotton and worsted goods and artificial silk.

The valley of the Schuylkill, when coal was the chief fuel used in iron making in Pennsylvania, was before about 1870 the seat of an active iron industry.

Industrial Symbiosis in Eastern Pennsylvania.   There are plants in eastern Pennsylvania making iron and steel castings, builders' hardware, iron pipes, and textile-mill machinery. These call for male laborers, whereas the numerous factories employed in producing knit goods or in dyeing and finishing textiles give work to the more delicate hands of women. Most of the workers, male and female, are foreigners. This "symbiosis" in industrial types is repeated in nearly every one of the cities in or near the anthracite regions of the state. Scranton, in the Lackawanna Valley in the Wyoming field, is interested in producing locomotives, mining machinery, and many other iron and steel products, and also woolens, cottons, laces, and buttons. Wilkes-Barre, also in the Wyoming field, has machine shops, forged axle and wire rope works, and also silk and lace mills. Allentown in the Lehigh Valley, which leads out of the Lehigh coal fields, has iron furnaces, rolling mills, foundries, shoe factories, and cement plants, and also silk and knitting mills. Bethlehem has the great Bethlehem steel works which produce armor plate, steel rails, machinery, and castings of many sorts. In the city and nearby towns there are cement plants, brick yards, and automobile works, as well as silk mills and ribbon factories. Easton, also in the Lehigh Valley at its junction with the Delaware, produces cement, pig iron and steel, pneumatic tools, mining and hydraulic machinery, chemicals and paints, and also silk goods, cotton yarn, and hosiery. Hazleton manufactures mining machinery, pumping machinery, pianos, and other products demanding the labor of men; and also silk, hosiery, knit goods, overalls, and other goods which may be made by women and children. At Norristown, Harrisburg, Steelton, and other cities, the same conditions as to labor demands exist.

Smaller Industrial Centers in Pennsylvania.   The industries of Lancaster and York bear a closer resemblance to those of New England than to the industries of the cities just discussed. Lancaster has a watch factory, a linoleum plant, a toy factory, and plants producing small metal goods, such as jeweler's tools, padlocks, and ball bearings. The textile products are cotton and silk. York makes agricultural implements, tobacco and cigarettes, paper products, a wall finish of excellent quality, leather goods and textiles, as well as a few heavy articles, such as ice-making machinery, sawmill equipment, chain and wire.

Altoona, at the eastern foot of the Allegheny Front near a low gap in this mountain wall, is a small industrial center standing quite alone in a large area of agricultural and forest lands. It is largely the creation of the Pennsylvania Railroad, which has here its largest shops. It is near the eastern edge of the bituminous coal area. Other industries are silk mills, and iron works and brick yards the localization of which is due to nearby deposits of clay, as well as fuel.

Iron and Steel in the Pittsburgh Area. The industrial region of western Pennsylvania is dominated by Pittsburgh, the "Iron City"; and the industries of most of the cities of the area are but reflections of those of the major city. The abundance of fuel—coal, oil, natural gas—with a few raw materials such as glass sand and iron ore, or easy access to iron ore, have from the first been factors favoring the localization of the iron and steel industry. The position of Pittsburgh, at the junction of the Monongahela and Allegheny rivers and at the head of the Ohio, enables it to collect raw materials by water from the north and south, the rivers having been improved for some distance from Pittsburgh—91.5 miles on the Monongahela. In the settling of the Ohio Valley, Pittsburgh was the port of embarkation for the flatboat journey down the Ohio, and afterwards the farmers looked to the city to fill their needs for manufactured goods. Until the completion of the Pennsylvania Canal and Portage Railroad and, later, the Pennsylvania Railroad, transportation across the Highlands was so expensive that Pittsburgh or the surrounding region was called upon to produce most of the manufactured goods used in the Ohio Valley. An iron furnace was erected near Uniontown about 1790, using local iron ore and charcoal. Hollow ware and other articles needed on the frontier were made. By 1806 the manufacture of iron was well begun. The first rolling mills were built in 1812. Iron came to dominate the industrial life of the city after about 1825. The greatest development followed the use of Connellsville coke and, later, the use of the rich ores of the Lake Superior region. It has been found that coal other than that at Connellsville will make coke suitable for iron smelting, and that the southern Lake ports are as well located for the meeting of iron ore and fuel as the forks of the Ohio; yet the large amount of money invested in blast furnaces and steel mills that would have to be sacrificed if plants were moved enables Pittsburgh to hold its place as the greatest iron-producing city in America. From the industrial nucleus at the forks of the Ohio, city after city has grown up along the Allegheny and Monongahela, along the Ohio, and even along Beaver River northward toward Lake Erie. Johnstown on the Concmaugh, to the east of Pittsburgh, has a coal, iron, and steel industry. Most of the ore comes from Lake Superior.

About one-third of the factories of the city of Pittsburgh are engaged in producing iron and steel and products of steel works and rolling mills; the total value of the products of blast furnaces, steel plants, foundries, and machine shops is one-half the total for the city. Nearly all the iron products of the Pittsburgh area are "heavy" iron and steel goods, in which the amount of material, rather than the amount of skill or labor, largely determines the value. The Westinghouse air brakes have been furnished by Pittsburgh to a large part of the railroad cars of America, and Westinghouse electrical apparatus is well known. Some work is done in brass, bronze, and copper. The making of glass dates from 1797, the industry being first localized here because of the abundance of glass sand; its later expansion was due to the large stores of natural gas, which is both a cheap and an ideal fuel in glass making. The city being a railroad center, there is a call for locomotives, cars, and general railroad repairs.

Trends and the Future of Manufacturing in the Northeastern States. From the beginning of American history, trade has been of primary importance in manufacturing in the Northeastern States, and freight costs, today, remain an important factor in the lives of the people. At an early date, fishing stimulated sea trade, which in turn supported industry. As the West developed its lands and resources the Northeastern States developed its industries not only to supply the West but also to enter worldwide markets. With the impetus of an early start, cities grew and population density became great; hence to a large extent the people of this section today live by selling manufactured products made of imported raw materials.

Since about 1910 some of the industries of the Northeastern States have shown a tendency to shift to other sections of the country. The cotton-textile industry as well as silk and rayon manufacturing have advanced in the southern seaboard states and declined in the northeast. The steel industry, the boot and shoe industry, and others have tended to move westward. This does not mean that manufacturing has ceased or even that it may in the future come to an end in the Northeastern States, for this section remains the great manufacturing center of the nation. Some abandoned industrial plants are in evidence and some cities have been hard hit by a decrease in population. However, with new products and improved processes, some of the old textile centers have partially adapted themselves to the change, but the question arises, "Can the Northeastern States retain sufficient industrial activities so as to increase in numbers and prosperity and maintain a standard of living in accord with the future increases in the remainder of the nation?" To arrive at an understanding of the problem it is necessary that one examine the events, and conditions which apply to them.

The causes for this shift in industry are numerous, but important among them are: (1) longer hours, lower wages, and no labor troubles among the workers, mainly in the South, (2) lower land values, taxes, and rents elsewhere, (3) improved markets in the South and West resulting from growth in population, and (4) nearness to sources of bulky raw materials. On close examination it is noted that some of these causes are not necessarily lasting ones. As industrial plants move to new sections, land values rise, also taxes and rents. Labor unions follow the workers, and in general there is a tendency to standardize wages, hours, land values, rents, and taxes throughout the land. Thus from the causes mentioned it would seem the shifting of industries would come to an end eventually.

Another factor of importance is that skilled labor and management tend to remain in the original centers. Thus those manufactured products that require skilled labor and have high value compared to their weights, so as to stand higher freight rates, become a specialty in the northeastern states. The cotton-textile industry illustrates this point in that the product of the southern mills consists of a large volume of common woven goods and outing flannels, whereas that of the northeastern mills includes laces, print-cloth and the more highly technical fabrications.

Perhaps the most important change in industries of the Northeastern States is the development of the steel industry since 1940 in the embayed section along the Atlantic seaboard, as at Morrisville, Pennsylvania, on the Delaware River above Trenton, as well as that farther south at Sparrows Point, Maryland, on Chesapeake Bay. The growing importance of importation of special quality ores from Labrador, Quebec, Venezuela, Cuba, Mexico, and a few other sources favor these locations because the land haul of this bulky commodity to inland steel centers is thus eliminated.

The future of northeastern manufacturing cannot be predicted with any degree of certainty because of the many factors involved, but some geographic conditions are favorable for its maintenance and are thus worthy of consideration. The efficiency of labor is stimulated by a climate in the Northeastern States not generally equaled in other sections of the country.[2] The proximity to superpower development anticipated from the mighty St. Lawrence is favorable. Also the front-door position of the Northeastern States on the North Atlantic trade route gives the section an advantage in general shipping rates from and to important foreign lands. Finally, the dense population of a highly developed people in this section is in itself a large market for manufactured products. Transportation facilities and freight rates will continue to be an important factor since a large part of the raw materials of industry must be imported.

[2] Ellsworth Huntington, *Civilization and Climate*, Yale University Press, 1915.

QUESTIONS, EXERCISES, AND PROBLEMS

1. Is it environment or man that has made the northeastern states the greatest manufacturing region in the United States? What are the natural environmental conditions? Did the Europeans who settled this section bring with them European inheritances and experiences that contributed to the great industrial development?

2. Is it environment or man that keeps New England a manufacturing section?

3. Make a list of 25 of the largest cities of the United States. What percentage of the total number is in the northeastern states? What percentage of the total population of the 25 urban groups is in the urban groups of these states?

4. How are New England manufactures affected by the lack of local coal deposits?

5. Make a detailed study of New York as a type port. Consider depth of water, extent of shoreline, protection from winds and waves, contact with interior United States and the world oceans, government improvements and aids to navigation, warehouses and facilities for transfer of cargoes, and other items.

6. Many of the large manufacturing companies operating in these states publish excellent booklets that will furnish much basic material for the working out of excellent type studies. The following is a list of possible studies that are typical of the industries of these states: The Pennsylvania Railroad, the Hammermill paper mill, the Baldwin locomotive works, the Connellsville coke region, the Douglas shoe factory, the Arlington mills, Lawrence, Mass. Each of these may stand as a type of industry. Emphasize geographic relationship.

7. What contribution to the settlement and the economic and commercial life of the United States has the coal of Pennsylvania made?

8. The petroleum industry had its start in Pennsylvania. Trace out the far-reaching influences that petroleum has had in the past, and has today, on American social and economic life.

9. Make a list of certain types of industries that are migrating or have migrated from New England to some other section of the United States. Give the major causes and effects in each case.

10. How have climate and geologic forces and processes given the Northeastern States large resources of water power? Consider each section of these states separately.

CHAPTER 5

Agriculture
in the Northeastern States

THE DEVELOPMENT OF AGRICULTURE

Agricultural Adjustments. American agriculture, even as practiced today in the northern half of the United States, owes much to the farmers of colonial days and later. Along with the European colonists who founded Plymouth, New Amsterdam, and the other colonies came seeds and livestock and a knowledge of agricultural methods.

In the new environments in America, new adjustments had to be made, and this problem has ever been uppermost in the history of American agriculture. The fairly dependable oceanic climate of northwestern Europe offered few problems in crop adjustment to climate, in comparison with the fickle continental and littoral climate of northeastern United States. In the westward expansion of the agricultural frontier from the shores of the Atlantic, the farmers had to adapt their crops and methods of tillage to every grade of soil from gravelly and sandy to stiff clay, and to soils of every origin; to climates of the lowlands and of the highlands; to long growing seasons and short growing seasons; and in addition to constantly changing economic conditions as cities grew and transportation was improved. Naturally, they made many mistakes, but the trying conditions called for, and no doubt developed, ingenuity and adaptability, two cardinal virtues of the character of the people of the United States.

Tillage was formerly wasteful. New lands were constantly being opened up, and there was thus no pressure on the farmers to utilize the agricultural resources of any field or any region to the utmost. Agriculture, for 2 centuries or more, was largely migratory, a fact which accounted for the general lack of attention to soil erosion and depletion, and slowness of American people to adopt land and forest conservation methods. Each farmer migrated from old communities to new, and he migrated with his tillage on his own farm from field to field. "Summer fallowing" was common, instead of a carefully thought-out scheme of crop rotation. On many farms, even the manures were not used.

147

For nearly 2 centuries there was little attempt to evolve new varieties of crops suited to American conditions, and there were, with the exception of corn, peas, beans, pumpkins, and the grape, no food plants that had been developed from American plants. Native grasses have been utilized for fodder. Flint claims that the extensive and practical cultivation of natural grasses originated in North America, or at least was introduced here long before it was in England. Fortunately for the experimenters, this development took place in the hay and fodder region where conditions are most favorable. Timothy is an American grass, so named after Timothy Hanson, who was much interested in its propagation and who took seeds of this grass from New York to the Carolinas and even to England.

Not until improved transportation broadened the markets for the farmers and the commercial regime was ushered in was there a change from general cropping. Each community produced, for the most part, all the crops it needed, rather than crops that represented climatic and soil adjustment.

The Evolution of Agricultural Implements and Machines. The implements of colonial days were crude, handmade, and mostly of wood. The early plows, which were of wood, merely "disturbed" the soil and did not turn it over. The first farming in the Massachusetts Bay colonies, as in the other settlements, was largely "planting" and not real agriculture, for there were not enough plows to go around. The agricultural machinery age in the United States began about 1830. For several decades thereafter nearly all the patents granted were taken out by men from the northeastern states, and nearly all the agricultural-implement factories were in these states, no doubt a response to the rapid expansion of the farm area by the opening of the Middle West and the creation of a shortage of farm labor.

In the decades following 1900 the Northeastern States did not keep pace with the other sections of the country in percentage growth in value of farm machinery. The reason for this slow growth has sometimes been given as increased attention, in the Northeastern States, to dairying and gardening, where great applications of machinery were not made at first. The large areas of the Middle Atlantic states and the West were particularly applicable to machine work, and people adopted machines in a large way. However, since 1940, machines have been devised and used in all phases of work in dairying and gardening, so that between 1940 and 1950 the increase in value of farm machinery in New England was 70 per cent, and that for all other sections of the country was only about 60 per cent.

The Livestock Industry in the Northeastern States.   In colonial days the northeastern section had many breeds of cattle, each colony having imported its own special favorites from its own mother country. There were breeds from Holland, Scotland, England, Sweden, and Denmark. Cattle were brought from England to Plymouth in 1624. In the selection of sites for new settlements, the presence of land suitable for cow pastures was an important item. The marshlands along the coast and those of the filled glacial lakes fed many herds.

There were really no pure breeds at this time, for scientific breeding was unknown even in Europe. Each county or region developed a strain peculiar to itself, in most cases the result of accidental rather than artificial selection. In most parts of the Northeastern States, oxen were used

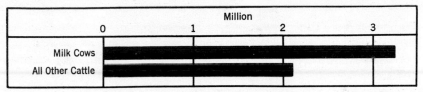

Fig. 66. Cattle on farms in Northeastern States in 1952. (The dominance of milk cows indicates the importance of dairying.)

quite generally on the farms until about 1840. On the hill farms of New England they were in favor much later, as they were cheaper than horses and thrived better on the sparse grass of the hills. The building of turnpikes and the introduction of agricultural machinery made a demand for a much speedier animal, and the horse came into general demand.

The Dominance of Dairying Today.   Most of the herds of the Northeastern States today are dairy cattle—about 3,240,000 out of a total 5,389,-000 (Fig. 66). Commercial dairying began even before the Revolutionary War. Near some of the cities there were herds of 50–100 cows or more; with increasing urban population and improved transportation, the dairy farms increased in number. Farms within 200–300 miles of the cities now furnish milk and cream, generally through milk dealers who prepare, bottle, and distribute the product in the cities. Along some railroads, milk express trains are run. Electric cars and auto trucks are prominent in this transportation. In the parts of these states beyond the 5- to 8-hour run to some city, creameries and cheese factories turn the raw product of the dairies into butter, cheese, and processed milk—more concentrated and less perishable forms than the sweet or raw milk (Fig. 67).

Dairying will continue to be an important type of farming in the Northeastern States, and must increase. As a result of "better babies" and health campaigns, the per capita milk consumption is increasing. Nearly 77 per cent of the population of the Middle Atlantic states and more than 76 per cent of that of New England live in cities, and the urban population is increasing. Milk production must increase, therefore, within the sustenance area of the large cities. This may be accomplished by an expansion of the area devoted to dairying, by extending the radius from which milk is now drawn, by speedier transportation facilities, and by the selection of better breeds of dairy cattle.

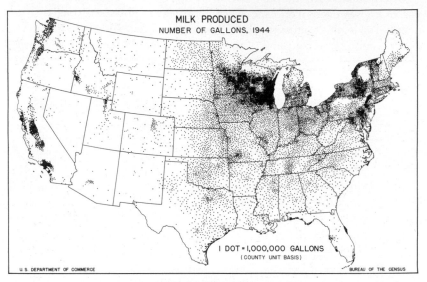

Fig. 67. New York and Pennsylvania were the greatest dairy states before about 1910. Wisconsin, Minnesota, and Iowa now exceed New York in the number of dairy cows, and Wisconsin and Minnesota exceed New York in the amount of milk produced. Since 1930 there has been a general increase in production of dairy products in all parts of the country, but the greatest increase was in the North Central States.

On some dairy farms, only the roughage is raised, the concentrated foods being imported from the grain-growing states of the Middle West. This practice may be extended. Many pastures are not now producing the maximum fodder because of continued cropping. Some pastures have been grazed continuously, it is claimed, for more than a century. Many could be improved by selecting a better variety of grass (Fig. 68).

A special type of dairy farming is to be found in some parts of the Northeastern States—the preparation of certified milk, often prescribed by physicians for delicate babies and even for mature invalids. There is a relatively limited market for this product, yet undoubtedly the profits are greater in its preparation than in the production of the common sort of milk. The dairy equipment is costly, for great care must be exercised in making and keeping the milk pure and clean.

The Sheep Industry of the Northeastern States.   On January 1, 1952, there were some 31,725,000 sheep in the United States, but less than 500,000 in the Northeastern States. From 1910 to 1952 the sheep of New England declined from 431,000 to 57,000. There was a time when a sheep was considered a necessary animal on most farms, the wool being in demand for the making of clothing. Since 1800 the number has been

Fig. 68. A typical dairy farm in New England. *Courtesy, Berkshire Hills Conference.* There are a great number of large dairy farms in New England with extensive barns and equipment, but perhaps a large bulk of total dairy products comes from the many small dairy herds consisting of from 8 to 15 head of cows.

declining gradually. Many breeds have been imported and tried. The Leicester, which originated in England in 1755, was one of the earliest to be tried out, but it did not become popular in New England until about 1860. The first merinos were brought from Spain to Massachusetts about 1801. Because of their fine wool they were in much demand, and by 1811 nearly 20,000 had been introduced. Western wool, however, brought about a decline in the number of merinos in the Northeastern States. The Dorset, a mutton variety, is now in favor with sheep raisers who specialize in the production of "hot house" lambs. The lambs, born early in the winter, are fattened by forced feeding and extra care and are ready for market in 60 days.

The increasing density of population and the intensification of agriculture do not necessarily mean the passing of the sheep industry from

the Northeastern States, for Great Britain has more than 300 sheep to
100 cattle, in comparison with about 13 sheep to 100 cattle in the Northeastern States. If sheep raising has a place in the farm economy of England, where manufacturing so completely dominates the activities of
men, it certainly has a place on the farms of the Northeastern States.
Sheep raising primarily for wool is a thing of the past; but the production
of mutton with wool as a by-product should prove profitable, although
Americans are not mutton eaters to the extent that the English are. The
stony hillsides of the Northeastern States may well be utilized for sheep
raising. Large-scale production will undoubtedly prove most profitable.
Abandoned farms of the hill lands may be combined, and large ranges
thus provided. The production of "hot house" lambs is another intensive
form of the industry.

Contributions to Fruit Growing. Europe furnished America its first
apple, pear, and peach trees, and the first of other varieties of fruit; yet
the orchard fruits of today are more distinctly American creations than
are the many grains and vegetables discussed elsewhere in this chapter,
for the transplanted fruit has been modified in the new environment and
hundreds of entirely new varieties have been developed.

The first orchard of New England was on Governor's Island in Boston
Harbor, from which there were picked on October 10, 1639 "ten fair
pippins." From eastern Massachusetts, seeds or nursery products were
carried by Indians and whites to other parts of New England and even
New York. In western New York, the earliest apples were probably
grown from seed brought by the Jesuits. The propagation of orchard
fruits has always been an important work of farmers and nurserymen. A
farm with a valuable orchard was much prized, and no farm was complete unless it had an orchard. A knowledge of fruit tree propagating and
grading was one of the many accomplishments of most of the ingenious
New England and New York farmers.

Apples for the first century or two in America were raised chiefly for
cider and for fresh fruit. Their storage in bins and root-houses extended
the season of consumption. There was little commerce in them, because
of poor transportation. Improved transportation gave growers a market
and made apple growing profitable. For a time there was a boom in
many parts of these states in apple growing; but overplanting glutted the
markets, some investments failed to pay, and orchards were cut down to
make way for other crops or were neglected. Only those sections with
best transportation facilities survived as producers. New demands have
developed since about 1930. Cold storage now gives us fresh apples the
year round, and food specialists have quite convinced the public that
the apple has a high food value.

Apple Growing Today.   Apples are raised today quite generally over the northeastern states except in the undeveloped Adirondacks and northern New Hampshire and Maine. There are about 17,000,000 apple trees in these states out of a total of 65,000,000 in the United States (Fig. 69).

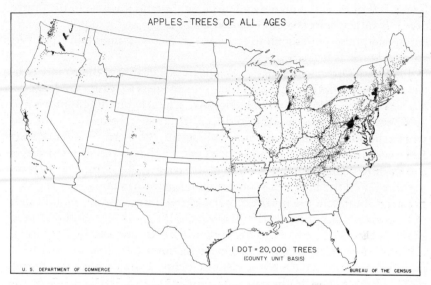

Fig. 69. Apple trees in the United States.

Massachusetts and Maine produce Baldwins for the New England markets. The more important commercial sections are northwestern New York, southern Pennsylvania, and western Maryland. New York for many years led all other states in apple production, but since about 1919 it has held second place to Washington, which has had a phenomenal growth in the number of bearing trees and production since 1909. Climatic conditions could hardly be better for fruit raising than they are in western New York near the southern shore of Lake Ontario where the largest orchards are located. In some parts of Maryland and Pennsylvania, slopes are selected to take advantage of air drainge.

The invasion of eastern markets by western-grown apples naturally leads one to a consideration of the future of this competition. With geographic conditions so favorable for the eastern growers, markets near, and excellent transportation facilities to these markets, it is surprising that western-grown apples can be sold on eastern markets while thousands of bushels of eastern apples of commercial quality rot in the orchards. The West has one great advantage in the relative ease with which

diseases and pests are controlled, the great distances between the irrigated oases tending to check migration. But a 2000-mile freight bill must
reduce materially the returns to the westerner. The success of the western grower undoubtedly lies more in the methods of marketing than in
any geographic factors. In the West, in the Yakima and Hood River Valleys, for example, the apple is the leading money crop, whereas in the
East it is the chief crop on only a few farms. Should the East in the future
take advantage of its favored location and climate and adopt better marketing methods, it is difficult to see how the West can maintain a place in
eastern markets for its apples.

The Peach-Growing Industry.   Peach trees, because of their more delicate response to spring heat and their sensitiveness to winter cold, are restricted in their distribution to sections where early budding is prevented
or where air drainage tends to reduce the damage from late frosts, and
where the winter temperatures are moderate. Western New York near
Lake Ontario, from the standpoint of production to the square mile, is
the leading peach-growing section of these states. Extreme winter temperatures and the high range of spring temperatures make peach growing unprofitable in the northern parts of these states and the highlands
of Pennsylvania. Since nearly 80 per cent of the peaches of the United
States are grown south of the Mason and Dixon Line and in California,
it is evident that the peach is a crop for sections that have warmer temperatures than most parts of these states. Pennsylvania among the Northeastern States leads in the number of bearing and non-bearing peach
trees, with New York second. Pennsylvania also leads in production, but
New Jersey is second. The New England states produced only 268,000
bushels in comparison with 5,700,000 bushels in the Middle Atlantic
states and 68,000,000 bushels in the United States.

The apple and peach regions also produce pears, cherries, bush fruits,
and strawberries. New York ranks fourth in cherry production after
Michigan, California, and Washington, respectively. New York also
ranks fourth in production of pears after California, Washington, and
Oregon.

Rank in Grape Growing.   Although the production of grapes is small
in comparison with that of California, New York is the leading grape-
producing state east of the Pacific Slope. The southern shore of Lake
Erie in both New York and Pennsylvania and the slopes about the Finger
Lakes of central New York produce more than 95 per cent of the output
of the vineyards of the Northeastern States. Large bodies of water tend
to retard the spring warming of the air and ground and thus delay the
budding until the danger of late frosts is at the minimum. The grape of
the United States, except the varieties grown in California which are

from the European *vinifera,* is an American product. During the era of agricultural experimentation which characterized the colonial period, the European grape was tested out, but fungus and the insect *Phylloxera* blighted all attempts, and the grape enthusiasts were forced to develop the wild grape of the forests which was indigenous to a moist climate. The grape in Europe grows on well-drained soils or in regions of summer drought. The first well-known American grape developed was the Catawba. Its history began about 1802. The Concord was evolved in 1849. The names Niagara, Concord, Early Ohio, Delaware, and others attest to the American origin of the grapes grown in eastern United States.

The Development of Gardening.   Practically all the vegetables now grown in United States truck gardens were also grown in colonial days from seeds imported from Europe. The Indians were raising beans, peas, melons, and pumpkins when the Europeans reached North America. These were probably developed from wild plants. From both of these sources, American and European, plant breeders developed a large number of varieties that are adapted to various forms of home gardening and commercial truck gardening, to the different climates found in America, and to the various tastes or whims of consumers.

A garden, like an orchard, has always been considered a necessity on most farms in these states. Not until the rise of the manufacturing city did commercial truck gardening become an important industry. The Northeastern States produce about one-fifth of the total for the United States measured by value. For commercial truck produce the leading five states are California, Florida, New York, Texas, and New Jersey, in the order named. Commercial gardening today is stimulated by the excellent markets offered by the numerous large cities. About every city there are market gardens, well-drained sandy land being much preferred because it is more easily worked and is warmer, and therefore matures plants more rapidly, than heavier soils. The terrace lands of the Connecticut, the outwash plains of Long Island, and the sandy lands of the Coastal Plains are the leading truck-garden areas. There are few other sections of the world where truck gardening has been intensified to such a degree as in parts of these states. Coldframes, hotbeds, and greenhouses are common equipment in many sections. The greenhouse makes year-round production possible.

Potato growing is practiced in many parts of these states other than Maine. Maine is, however, the leading potato-producing state in the Union, followed by Idaho in second place and New York third (Fig. 70).

Types of Farming in the Northeastern States.   The farmers of the Northeastern States, like the farmers of other parts of the world, tend to adjust the type of crop they raise to the natural environmental conditions, the market demands, and effective competition from the outside. As for climatic conditions, all of this section, except northern New England and the Adirondacks, lies in the continental Hot Summer and Cold Winter temperature region (Figs. 4 and 9). Since the section lies near the northern border of the temperature region the hot months are few—one or two above 68°. In the coastal sections easterly winds bring in ocean air, and ocean air and the prevailing high relative humidity moderate the temperatures somewhat. Northern New England has a growing season of 90 to 120 days; the remainder of the section more than 120. There is

Fig. 70. Harvesting potatoes near Caribou, Aroostook County, Maine. *Courtesy, Maine Development Commission.* The potato does best in cool lands where summer temperatures do not exceed 65° F., where moisture is plentiful, and where soils are loose and easily worked. These conditions are found in much of the northernmost county in Maine—Aroostook.

a deficiency of sunlight, the areas receiving only approximately 50 per cent of that possible. The rainfall is moderate yet quite sufficient for all types of crops. Soil and topography have been discussed previously. Although the farmers of the last century or more, since the development of the railroad, have had a close contact with ready markets, they have had to compete (as suggested above) with the farmers of more distant sections who have utilized cheap virgin lands and who have commercial contact with this section by cheap, efficient transportation (Fig. 71).

Figure 71 shows in detail the types of farming which have been adjusted largely to the conditions listed above. It will be noted that specialized dairy farming is the most widespread of any type, and in it, dairying represents more than 40 per cent of all farm products. Note also that dairying is carried on in combination with other farming. Outside of the dairy, fruit and specialty crops, much of the combination types of farming in the Northeastern States is of the nature of self-sufficiency farming. This is most interesting for a section so long settled, and having adequate

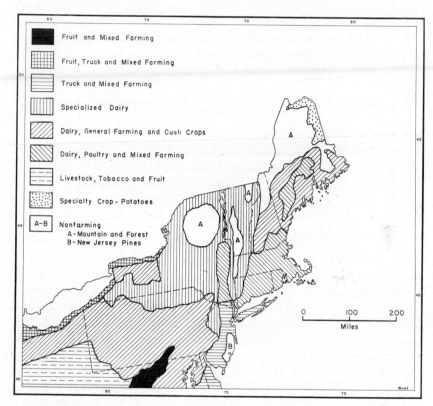

Fig. 71. Types of farming in the Northeastern States. In a mixed-farming region several types of farming are carried on, none dominant. In regions of general farming there are several distinct sources of income on the same farm, none dominant. *Adopted from Bureau of Agricultural Economics, 1950.*

transportation facilities to ready markets. Under such environmental conditions one would expect commercial farming. A self-sufficient farm is one on which the products used by the family is 50 per cent or more of the total value of farm products. Some of the self-sufficient farms are occupied by retired farmers, business men, and professionals, and are located generally in the rough and remote sections of the country.

The map shows that several types of intensive farming are practiced. Besides dairy farming there is truck farming, fruit raising, and the raising of many crop specialties like potatoes and poultry. Where are these?

The active tourist and resort business in this section, as a whole, enables a small percentage of the farmers to earn part of their sustenance by taking boarders and lodgers. If the returns from boarders, lodgers, and campers represent 50 per cent or more of the total the farm is known as a boarding or lodging farm. This business is active chiefly in the summer. A small percentage of the farmers who have small holdings work part time in the forests or factories, and their wives and children do the daily routine work on the farms, largely specialty farms.

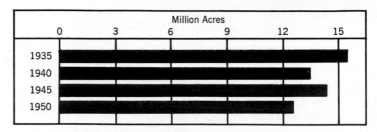

Fig. 72. All land in farms in New England 1935–1950 inclusive.

The Northeastern States in Comparison with Other Sections. The Northeastern States section is usually thought of as a great manufacturing region. Elsewhere it is shown that, although this section is not a great agricultural region, in comparison with the North Central States or the South, it holds an important place in the history of American agriculture because it was for two centuries or more the experimental area for a good part of the nation, for garden, orchard, and field crops imported from Europe. In statistical comparison made with other sections of the country—North Central, South, and West—involving totals for these sections, the Northeastern States often show up poorly. This is chiefly because of the small area of these states. New England occupies only 2.2 per cent of the total area of the country; the Middle Atlantic States, 3.4 per cent; and both only 5.6 per cent in comparison with 25.3 per cent for the North Central group, 29.8 per cent for the South, and 39.3 per cent for the West. Although the density of population of this group of states is far greater than that of other major groups, only 27.2 per cent of the total population of the country lives in northeastern United States, in comparison with 32 per cent in the South and 30 per cent in the North Central area. Another fact should not be lost sight of in comparing the agricultural activities of various sections: only a small part of the population of many of these states is engaged in agricultural production. Only 8.4 per cent of the population of Rhode Island is rural, 10.6 per cent of Massachusetts, 17.2 per cent of New York, 17.4 per cent of New Jersey, 32.2 of Connecticut, 33.5 per cent of Pennsylvania, 42.4 per cent of New Hampshire, and about 65 per cent of both Maine and Vermont. Taking this section as a whole, almost one-fourth of the population is rural (Figs. 72 and 73).

When these facts are given full consideration, it is easy to show that the northeastern region, besides being the greatest manufacturing section of the United States, ranks exceedingly high in agriculture. This section, which has only 5.6 per cent of the area and 14 per cent of the

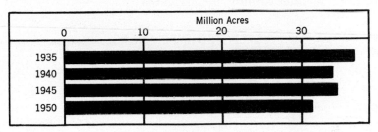

Fig. 73. All land in farms in New York, New Jersey, and Pennsylvania, 1935–1950 inclusive.

rural population of the United States, produces about 7.6 per cent of all field and orchard crops, vegetables, and farm gardens, 16 per cent of the truck crops (in value), 10 per cent of the fruits and nuts (in value), and 26 per cent of the horticultural products of the United States. It has 15 per cent of the acreage of hay and forage of the country, 9 per cent of the livestock on farms, and 13 per cent of the dairy cattle. And yet only 26 per cent of the total area of New England, and 46 per cent of the Middle Atlantic states, is in crops and pasture. Evidently the farmers of this section of the United States are contributing their quota and more to meeting the demands the nation makes on the holders and operators of the soil.

Agriculture today in many parts of the Northeastern States is in the intensive stage, as previously suggested, yet only a beginning has been made in intensification. Intensive agriculture, fully developed, means the continuous use of the soil during the growing season, the growing of high-profit-yielding crops, the employment of labor the year round, and a handling of the soil such that there will be no depletion. Intensification at present, in most of these states, is represented by the production of special crops or products, as orchard fruits, garden truck, small fruits, to bacco, potatoes, onions, cranberries, dairy products, nursery stock, garden and flower seeds, and greenhouse products. In only a few of these have the farmers an appreciation of the degree to which intensification may be carried. In the production of orchard fruits and the marketing of the products, the eastern farmer has much to learn from the western. Much of the truck gardening is little more than single-crop farming, with little appreciation of the need of a carefully thought-out rotation scheme. Dairying, although not using the land to produce the most profitable crops, is an all-year-round industry. As carried on in most parts of these states, it depends upon the grain states for its concentrated foods. Undoubtedly, the ideal intensive agricultural unit is the farm of general or diversified agriculture, an early type, which is represented by the agriculture of Lancaster County, Pennsylvania.

SELECTED TYPE AREAS

Agricultural Adjustments in Plymouth County, Massachusetts

It is fitting that we begin the study of agricultural types in the Northeastern States with a consideration of the oldest farming section of the North, Plymouth County. Here on the shore of Cape Cod Bay, the Pilgrims landed in December, 1620. The next spring they began the planting of maize in small plots, which the Indians had used for this pioneer cereal. Maize soon became the staple crop. In addition to supplying the needs of the colony, it was sold to the fishing villages up and down the coast. Wheat also was sown, and likewise a variety of vegetables. As time went on, horses, cattle, sheep, and hogs were introduced, and thus was established one of the nuclei of the livestock industry of the North.

Selection of Lands. To the little agricultural settlement on the shores of Cape Cod Bay, as population increased by natural increment and by immigration, lands were added and the pioneers began in earnest their conquest of an inhospitable agricultural environment. For the most part, only the best lands were used. Areas of thin soil, sandy ridges, mucky or boggy lands were left in their natural state. On the better lands, forests of white pine, oak, beech, maple, hemlock, and other trees had to be removed, and some farms had literally to be reclaimed by the removal of tons of erratic boulders an acre.

The conditions that prevailed in Plymouth County are fairly typical of many parts of the Northeastern States; yet under these seemingly adverse conditions has developed an honest, upright, enterprising, painstaking type of citizen to whom credit must be given for most of the great progress that has been made in agriculture, and in other fields as well, in the North from New England to the Pacific. The New England environment has put its stamp on the people who have labored long and honestly to gain a livelihood. The New Englander of the old school may have been provincial and conservative, but he was the sort needed to give solidarity to a developing civilization in the American environment, most phases of which tend toward economic superficiality in the development of the resources.

Farm Activities.   The early New England family was large, often numbering a dozen or more. The necessity of feeding and clothing so many persons, coupled with the shortness of the growing season, the climatic limitations for many crops, and the patchy distribution of the deep soils on most farms, forced the head of the family, as well as the mother and older children, into habits of work and economy. Each household was an economic unit in which farm implements, furniture, and clothing were manufactured during the long winter months. Leather was tanned, cut, and sewed into harness, shoes, and boots. Many houses had forges and anvils near the chimneys at which iron was heated and hammered into nails, runners for sleighs, tires for wheels, and straps for plows. Clothing was made from wool grown, spun, and woven at home. Such conditions no doubt tended to develop the mechanical ingenuity that is characteristic of so many Americans, and aided greatly in the development of manufacturing in New England at a later date.

The fields were planted or sown mostly to supply crops. Gardens, and orchards of apples, pears, and cherries were planted on nearly every farm. The system of tillage was similar to that prevalent in England at that time, and this system continued in use down to the middle of the nineteenth century. Indeed many of the farms of Plymouth County remained in possession of descendants of the original families until that date. Until the coming of the railroad about 1840, when access was had to the growing industrial centers, there was little to force the farmers to change from this system of general farming to special crops and intensification. Migration to the better agricultural sections of the Lake states and the constant drift to the cities, as they expanded in industries and trade, kept the rural population nearly stationary in density. The great age of the communities, the meager though sufficient returns from the lands, and the constant migration of the younger and more venturesome and progressive from the farm kept the rural people conservative. There is nothing quite so fixed as an agricultural community after it has once reached the limits of its areal expansion of cultivated lands and its markets have become fixed.

Some Economic Adjustments.   The growth of cities made increasing demands for agricultural products, but the urban population was small in comparison with the rural. In 1700 Boston had a population of about 7000, whereas the population of New England was 105,000. By 1763, when New England had grown to 510,000 people, Boston's population was between 15,000 and 20,000 and there were few other urban groups. Poor roads restricted the sustenance area of the cities to lands within a 40- or 50-mile radius. Coast towns, however, had much larger commercial areas.

From 1840 to 1860 was a prosperous period for the farmers of Plymouth County and other parts of New England. The railroads opened up new markets, but new dangers arose. Gradually there came an increasing flood of products from the rich plains of the Middle West, as railroads reached farther west. These came to compete with those raised with much toil on the scanty, patchy soils that had already been producing for a century or two. The railroads also expanded the markets for the manufacturers of New England, the factories grew in size and multiplied in number, and the drift of laborers to the cities increased. Many farms were abandoned outright; others were unworked. In 1880 there were 86,000 acres of improved land in Plymouth County, out of a total of 194,787 acres of farm lands; but in 1910 there were only 50,200 acres improved and 137,000 acres in farms. In 1950 there were only 105,860 acres in farms and 34,560 acres in crops. Figure 72 shows the change in acreage in improved farm land in New England since 1850 and 1860.

Since about 1920 many farms have been purchased as country homes, the suburban trains and the automobile making it possible for the office man to live 25, 50, or more miles from his work. Some farmers, who were more adaptable to changing conditions than others and were able to weather the adverse times and hold on, have enlarged their acreage by purchasing adjoining farms; yet in many parts of New England farms have been divided into 10–15 acre plots and sold to European immigrants who grow berries, poultry, and garden truck by intensive methods, the women and children furnishing most of the labor, although the man of the family, who generally is a factory worker, assists at spare times. Now there are few abandoned farms to be found in this part of New England. One finds, on all the better soils, well-kept farms that have an air of prosperity, refinement, and contentment about them.

Present Conditions.   Although general farming continues on many farms and the system of colonial days is little changed, corn, hay, oats, barley, beans, and potatoes being raised, there has been a decided improvement in most communities. Dairying has become an active industry on the larger farms, milk and cream being shipped to Boston and other industrial centers. Potatoes and garden truck come from the lighter soils;

and since about 1910 the bogs, which for more than 300 years were considered worthless, have been improved to grow cranberries. Some years more than two-thirds of the cranberries poduced in the United States come from Massachusetts.

Bog reclamation is generally done by companies who lease the land or buy it outright. The cost of improving a bog is high. Unimproved bog or muck land sells for $25–$100 to the acre, bearing cranberry land for $100 or more. If the muck land is forested, the trees are cut and the roots dug out. If the muck is thick, some of it must be removed. Ditches 2 or more feet deep are excavated, to drain the lands in wet weather or to irrigate them in dry seasons. Only such bog lands as may be drained and irrigated are improved. Water is wanted especially in the fall, to protect the berries from frost, for the harvest runs into late September and even later, and for this reason bog lands along streams are in greater demand. Over the surface of the muck, a 3-inch layer of sand is spread. This makes the land firm, and in this the plants are set about 3 feet apart. It takes 3 years for the plants to reach bearing age. A thin layer of sand is applied each year; this reduces the cost of weeding and makes the gathering of the berries easier. At nearby packing houses the berries, with bits of the vines, are cleaned, sorted, and packed in barrels. The usual crop is 50–60 barrels per acre. Many of the laborers in the bogs are for the most part a floating type of worker.

The Camden Trucking Area

The Camden Area. There are few areas in the United States where crop adaptation and adjustment of systems of tillage to soil conditions have reached the perfection found in the Camden area of New Jersey. This is chiefly the result of the age of the region (the Swedes having planted the first colony here in 1637), the nearness to large markets, the excellent transportation facilities, and the high land values of the improved farms. As in all agricultural sections of the United States near large cities, the transportation facilities are excellent at present. Camden is the center of numerous steam and electric lines; ferry lines connect the city with Philadelphia; and small boats ply upon the lower courses of the river and give many farmers ready access to the wharves of Camden, Philadelphia, and nearby towns.

The area lies on the western margin of the Coastal Plain and borders the Delaware River. Bordering the Delaware are terracelike tidal flats which extend back into the westward-flowing streams some 5 or 6 miles. Some of the tidal marshland has been reclaimed by diking. Most of it

can be reclaimed, but concerted action is necessary. Inland from this
tidal area are remnants of two higher-level terraces that border the western edge of the marine-deposited Coastal Plain. The highest part of the
Coastal Plain in the Camden area, 130–200 feet above sea level, lies
about 12–15 miles east of the Delaware River, and, from this broad crest
8–12 miles wide, the land slopes westward with a gradient of 3–5 feet to
the mile, but eastward much more gently. Beneath the general level the
streams have cut valleys 100 or more feet deep, reaching tidewater level
some 7 or 8 miles from their mouths. The streams have been at work long
enough to develop broad, swampy flats in their lower courses, through
which they flow in ill-defined channels.

In their lithologic makeup the soils have been derived—the mother
material—from marine beds of sand, sandy clay, gravel, greensands, and
marl or glauconite. The mother soil material on gentle slopes in a deciduous forest environment has become gray-brown in color. There is little
iron, alumina, or lime in the upper portions of the mature soils. The sods
are only slightly acid. Soil students class these soils in the Gray-Brown
Podzol group. (See full discussion in Chapter 2.)

On the deep, well-drained, warm, sandy soils are truck gardens of
20–40 acres. Tillage with light equipment is possible. Here are grown
such early vegetables as tomatoes, asparagus, peas, beans, sweet potatoes, and sweet corn. Asparagus, sweet potatoes, and early Irish potatoes are generally grown on ridges thrown up by the plow. Berries
are also a large crop. The heavier sandy loam grows medium late vegetables, as Irish potatoes, tomatoes for canning, cabbage, peppers, beans,
peas, corn, general farm crops, and such orchard fruits as apples,
peaches, and pears. On the heavier soils are general farm crops and
dairying. Here the farms are, as a rule, 100–160 acres.

Types of Farming.   At present there are several types of farming:
trucking alone; a combination of general farming and trucking; and fruit
raising or dairying. Dairying is important in many sections, especially on
those farms where the land is suited to the growing of hay or where there
is natural pasturage. The 6-months' growing season and the tempering
influence of the waters of Delaware Bay and the Atlantic (when the wind
is from the east) favors, as does the soil, the growing of fruits and vegetables. The rainfall is about 46 inches and is well distributed during the
growing season. Droughts are uncommon. The driest year on record had
36 inches of rainfall.

Present Conditions.   Since about 1940 the number of large farms has
declined and the number of small farms has increased. The area of farm
land is only about two-thirds that of 1920. The following data present
pertinent facts about land utilization for Camden County, New Jersey.

	Acres		Acres
Total land area	141,400	Corn acreage	2,160
All land in farms	33,390	Hay crop	1,640
Average size of farms	35.9	Area in potatoes (Irish and	
Land in crops	23,850	sweet)	1,690
Plowable pasture land	2,320	Land in orchard fruits	2,290
Area in vegetables	4,890	Woodland (total)	6,950

Diversified Farming in Lancaster County, Pennsylvania

Lancaster County, in southern Pennsylvania and bordering on the Susquehanna, is partly a Piedmont, with soil derived from schists and gneiss, and partly a limestone county. Its fame as the leading agricultural county of Pennsylvania rests mainly on the limestone soils which cover more than a third of the area.

Environmental Factors. About half the area of the county is lowland, limestone plains, and bottom lands; the remainder is upland plateau, and hills of meta-igneous rock, the typical Piedmont rock, which stands from 200 to 600 feet above the limestone lowlands. The limestone lowlands extend east and west across the county. In the upland sections the streams have cut deep valleys, making some of it too rough for cultivation. The gradient of the streams is for the most part low, for they have been long at work, and a rainfall of 40 inches or more, well distributed throughout the year, makes them perennial, particularly those fed by underground water in the limestone area. The valleys in some parts are deep, and thus some of the land is too rough for cultivation. Gristmills were established in the early days at a few points along the streams, particularly on the borders of the lowlands.

The area has always had, since its settlement, the advantage of the best transportation. The first long turnpike of Pennsylvania, the Philadelphia-Pittsburgh Road, passed through the city of Lancaster. The low relief, deep soil, and easily excavated rock of the limestone plain were the chief factors that led the engineers to lay out the eastern section of the Pennsylvania Canal through Lancaster, and this canal was soon paralleled by a railroad. With Philadelphia but 60 miles distant, and Baltimore about the same, excellent railroad connections to the East, and numerous small manufacturing cities within the county itself, all connected by excellent roads, the farmers have always had accessible markets. But they have been, since about 1850, on a fairly direct railroad line, the Pennsylvania, to Pittsburgh and the North Central States, and have had the competition of farmers of the Middle West to meet. These are the leading physical and economic factors to which man has adjusted his agriculture in Lancaster County.

Agricultural Adjustments.   The first settlers, Swiss Mennonites who secured land from William Penn, came in 1710. They were followed by Germans, French, English Quakers, and Scotch-Irish. The Swiss and Germans selected farms on the limestone lowlands; the Scotch-Irish, by necessity and in some cases perhaps by choice or lack of foresight, settled on the crystalline uplands in the southern part of the county.

During the entire history of the Lancaster section, general farming has been the rule. In the early decades it was extensive, becoming more and more intensive as larger markets developed, better transportation facilities were provided, and land values advanced. The majority of the farmers during most of the agricultural history of the country have been careful, painstaking husbandmen. Livestock has always had a fairly important place on the farms. Barnyard compost and careful rotation of crops have always been leading factors in the maintenance of soil fertility. The natural fertility of the limestone soils has favored the farmer; long leaching, however, makes the liming of the soils necessary. Corn, wheat, and tobacco are the chief crops used in the three-, four-, or even six-year rotation schemes. Fertilizers are freely used. The money crops are varied: potatoes, wheat, tobacco, fruit, vegetables, dairy products, and beef cattle.

Wheat and corn were the chief field crops in the early decades. Spelt was the form of wheat raised for fully a century, then came several varieties of wheat. Tobacco has long been raised and is the chief money crop on most farms, and varieties peculiar to Lancaster County conditions have been developed. There is a prevalent local belief that the soil and climate of the section is the chief factor in giving the quality and flavor to the tobacco, and that any variety will, if planted in the section, in a few years take on the character of the Pennsylvania tobacco. The limestone soils produce as high as 2500 pounds of tobacco an acre, whereas many fields in crystalline rock produce only about 900 an acre. The tobacco is used chiefly for cigar filler and binder. As in other parts of the United States, only a small part of each farm is devoted to tobacco raising, the patches varying from 2 to 20 acres.

There are few commercial apple, pear, or peach orchards. Dairying is important on some farms, but on others not enough cows are kept to supply the families with milk, cream, and butter. Winter fattening of cattle has long received much attention, the lean cattle being purchased at the stockyards in Lancaster. From 100 to 400 carloads are received daily during part of the fall. The roughage and most of the grains used are grown on the farms of Lancaster County. About 82 per cent of the total area is farm land, and 60 per cent of the total is in crops. Lancaster is one of the wealthiest counties in the state, the average value of land and buildings to the farm being $20,500.

Diversified Agriculture on the Allegheny Plateau

Clearfield County in central Pennsylvania may be taken as a type agricultural area of the Allegheny Plateau where the urban population is small but where numerous railroads give access to many markets.

Physical and Economic Setting.   Although located to the west of the Allegheny Front, most of the land lies at the headwaters of the west branch of the Susquehanna and, therefore, is deeply dissected. The valley flats in the northeast corner of the area lie only 850 feet above sea level, whereas the watersheds between the tributaries have elevations of 1700–2500 feet or more. The land is, therefore, steeply rolling to hilly.

Flat to gently rolling land is found on the narrow floodlands and the broader interstream areas. In the north where sandstones and conglomerates outcrop, the surface is wild and picturesque. Here the land is poor; the slopes are steep and consequently stony, or have thin soils. This portion is little used for farming, being held by lumber companies and hunting clubs. About 60–75 per cent of the county, however, is underlaid by shales and sandstones that bear workable coal seams, hence coal mining serves to give employment to some urban dwellers. The largest city has a population of about 11,500; the second in size, about 9000; numerous small villages ranging from a few hundred people to 2000. These cities furnish a limited local market for certain products of the farms, but coal mining and the revenue that comes to some of the farmers from coal leases detract seriously from agriculture.

The sawmill towns of the early nineteenth century furnished a small market for some products but apparently affected the general run of farmers but little. After the coming of the Pennsylvania Railroad in 1869, there was a decline in agricultural activities in the southern part of the county, due to an increased attention to lumbering and mining; and mining is still a factor interfering with a better and more active utilization of the agricultural resources.

Present Conditions.   Today less than a fourth of the total area is in farms, and the cropland is about one-eighth and the pasture land about one-twentieth of the total area. The farmer has therefore made only a beginning in land utilization. Agriculture is diversified, the average annual rainfall of 44 inches and the growing season of 120–150 days permit almost any crop of the cool temperate zone. Besides the field crops common to northern United States, nearly every farm grows vegetables for home supply and for the local market, and has a small orchard with apple, plum, and cherry trees, a berry patch, dairy cows and beef cattle, and pigs. There are no large truck gardens, only a few young commercial apple orchards, and, except near the towns, no large dairies. Some poul try is found on every farm. It is evident, then, that the farmers still have much to accomplish before they can derive the maximum advantage from their agricultural opportunities. Diversified farming calls for a complete equipment. The farms are large, outbuildings numerous, often including a silo, and the farm machinery is varied, consisting of wagons, plows, cultivators, harrows, rollers, seeders, binders, and mowers. The houses are well built and well kept. More than 88 per cent of the farms are operated by the owners.

The Fruit Region of Northwestern New York

Early Importance. The date when fruit growing began in northwestern New York is unknown, for when American settlers entered the section just after the Revolutionary War they found that the Indians had for many years collected apples of European varieties. It is thought that seed had been planted by the French missionaries who visited the Indians about the middle of the seventeenth century. The American settlers brought apple seeds and stock, and there were bearing orchards west of the Genesee River by 1800. The Erie Canal and the railroads to Buffalo, New Yory City, and Boston opened up larger markets for the apple growers of northwestern New York. Commercial apple growing dates from 1860, and grape culture from about 1865 or 1870. Since these dates vast orchards of apples, peaches, pears, and cherries, besides large vineyards of grapes and many hundreds of acres of small fruit, have been set out, and the region has become the most important temperate-zone fruit region east of the Rockies. New York before about 1930 led all states in the production of apples but now holds second place. In few other places in the United States have the trees retained their vigor as in New York. There is certain to be a decline in the apple crop, however, unless more planting is done.

Wheat and corn were the first crops raised by the American settlers, and the Genesee section before 1840 was celebrated as a wheat region. Before the opening of the Erie Canal in 1825 wheat was grown mainly for local consumption, for contact with the larger markets was had only by ox-wagons. The cost of transportation to New York City by this means was three times the price of the wheat. Flour mills were erected in 1820 at the falls of the Genesee River at Rochester, and flour was shipped to Canada by way of Lake Ontario, and to Buffalo and the East after the opening of the Erie Canal. With the settlement of the cheap prairie lands of Illinois, and later of Minnesota and Dakota, the area of commercial wheat growing was expanded greatly, and although the Genesee region continued to produce about as many bushels as formerly, relatively its output was, and is, so small that people no longer think of it as a wheat-growing section. The yield to an acre is greater now than in the wheat regions of the Middle West and greater than it was 75 years ago, a testimony of the careful tillage practiced.

Physical Factors. Monroe County, which we are taking as a type area of northwestern New York, has a variety of soils. Most of them are lacustrine in origin; even the glacial deposits, in most instances, were deposited in glacial lake waters. Crop adaptation to soil is a problem that the careful farmer has attempted to work out. Glaciated land, because of the great variety of soils generally found on even a small farm, offers exceptional opportunities for experimentation. The large industrial population of Rochester gives an admirable market for the products of intensive cultivation. Another factor influencing agriculture, particularly fruit growing, is the retarding influence of lake winds, previously noted, on the spring temperatures, tending to delay budding until danger from late frosts has passed. The farmers of northwestern New York, therefore, are operating under many favorable conditions. The air of comfort, refinement, and prosperity that is seen on every hand is evidence that they have actively developed the advantages of their environment. Nearly all the land of Monroe County outside of Rochester is in farms, and about 82 per cent of the farm land is improved (cropland and plowable pastures).

The fine sandy and sandy loam and muck soils are used for garden truck, early potatoes, nursery stock, small fruit, peaches, and cherries. Grapes are also grown on this soil near Lake Ontario. For apples and pear orchards, loam soils are generally selected; and the clay loams and heavy clays are used for growing grains and grass.

Diversified farming is the rule; but fruit growing, truck gardening, potato growing, and dairying are special forms to be found, rarely more than one on any one farm, throughout the county.

QUESTIONS, EXERCISES, AND PROBLEMS

1. Make a statistical comparison of the agriculture of two counties in Pennsylvania, one well over on the Allegheny Plateau (Indiana or Somerset County) and another on the Piedmont (Chester County). The latest Census Report will supply data. The selection of the items is left to teacher and students.

2. What tendencies toward intensification of agriculture are in evidence in the northeastern states? What are some of the probable causes of this tendency?

3. Make a graphic comparison of the changes from 1850 to 1950 in number of farms, acres of land in farms, and improved land in farms in New England, the Middle Atlantic, East North Central, West South Central, and Pacific States. Volume 1, *Census Report*, 1950, will supply data. Discuss the graphs.

4. Compare changes in percentage of total land area on farms and of improved land on farms in United States, New England, the Middle Atlantic, West North Central, South Atlantic, and Mountain States. Write your conclusions.

5. What portions of the United States and other parts of the world contribute to the food supply of New York? How has improved transportation affected the area of New York's sustenance space? Trace out the development of improvements affecting transportation.

6. What natural conditions, climatic and topographic, have been taken advantage of in fruit raising in the Northeastern States?

7. Does California or New York possess the better natural conditions for drying fruit? Which one will be likely to win out in the struggle if natural conditions dominate?

CHAPTER 6

The Fishing Industry
in the Northeastern States

Introduction. In 1784 the Massachusetts House of Representatives voted to have hung in the session room a "representation of a codfish . . . as a memorial of the importance of cod fishing to the welfare of the Commonwealth." It hung there until 1895, when, after a careful investigation of its history and in accordance with a vote, it was removed to the new chamber, where it may be found today, "an emblem significant of the hardiness, courage, and faith of those who dare and defy. . . ."

Fishing was the first American industry, antedating even the first settlements. Indeed, it was chiefly the fisheries off northeastern North America that led to its settlement. Within 6 years after the discoveries of the Cabots, the ships of the French fishermen from Dieppe and St. Malo visited the banks of Newfoundland. By 1517, vessels of many nationalities—French, Portuguese, Spanish, and English—to the number of 50 and, by 1577, 315, had crossed 2000 miles of stormy sea to take the cod.

The first fishing voyage to the coast of which is now the Northeastern States was made by Gosnold in 1602. He named Cape Cod as a memorial to the "luck" he had near its stormy shores. His glowing accounts of the richness of the fisheries and the evidence he presented interested several merchants and fishermen. In 1607, cabins, a storehouse, and a small fort were built near the mouth of the Kennebec River as a base for fishing on the Maine coast. The first ocean vessel launched in America was built here and subsequently made several voyages across the Atlantic.

Before the Leyden Pilgrims landed at Plymouth, English, French, and Dutch fishermen had become fairly well acquainted with the northeastern coast of the United States. During the 6 years before 1620, 26 vessels had fished on the coast with great success; and by 1624 from 40 to 50 vessels from England visited the fisheries yearly, and fully 250 sails, employing 5000 persons, operated on the Newfoundland banks. Fishermen, therefore, opened the way across the trackless ocean for settlement, and fish was the first natural resource of the American continent to be exploited by Europeans.

Many of the early settlements of New England were planted to exploit the fisheries, and fish on more than one occasion kept the colonists from starvation. Fish, furs, and timber were the first products carried to Europe to purchase the necessities that could not be had in America. The very nature of the industry, as carried on in the early days, bred democracy, for the fish were free for the taking, and, until large vessels came to be built, almost anyone, or at the most a small group of men, could provide themselves with the necessary appliances. The colonists, therefore, opposed all attempts on the part of the English Crown or the colonizing companies to establish fishing monopolies; and, no doubt, it was this same spirit of democracy, bred by nearly two centuries of free life on the sea in the fisheries and in ocean trade, combined with the fact that the sea was the chief basis of their economic existence, that led the New Englanders to defy the British Government in its attempts at the enforcement of the Navigation Acts of 1672 and 1696, the Molasses Act, the Sugar Act of 1764, and other acts that had for their aim the destruction of American fisheries and commerce. Within a month after the passage of the last of these acts the Revolutionary War began.

Perhaps most important of all is the fact that fishing encouraged the establishment of sea trade and manufacturing in New England history. Whale fishers who rounded the Horn in an oceanwide search for their quarry, discovered the possibilities of trade in the Pacific and with the Orient. Their ships became the connecting link between the eastern United States seaboard and the Pacific, and yielded large profits. Manufacturing in New England was stimulated because fishing expeditions demanded supplies, and returning vessels brought back raw materials to support industries. Pork and salt-meat packing, biscuit manufacture, clothing and brass industries, and the making of barrels, hoops, kettles, and salt, all began for the purpose of supplying the trading vessels. Returning ships brought sugar, metals, and many other products which stimulated manufacturing. Sugar started the refining and distilling industries, hides supported shoe manufacturing, gold and silver went into the jewelry industry, and various fibers, but mainly cotton and wool, supported textile manufacturing. The fact that New England was lacking in many raw materials from the home land did not hinder manufacturing. Returning vessels from all parts of the earth took care of that. Capital from the fisheries, and water power, were put to use at home. Thus fishing, sea trade, and manufacturing were intimately related, each supporting the others.

For two centuries, or more, a young man in New England had few opportunities open to him, other than those related to the sea. Fisheries were dominant. However, there has been a decline in relative importance of fishing in the economic history of New England, the extent and nature of which is reserved for later discussion.

Environmental Conditions Favoring Fishing.   We have seen the ill effects of glaciation on agriculture in New England. The meager opportunities in agriculture kept many people in the fisheries. Many of the earliest settlements were made by fishermen, it is true; but had the land offered the inducements that it did farther south, the hard life of the fisherman would have been abandoned by many for the easier and safer life on the land. Many a farmer was forced into winter fishing that he might have food enough to meet the needs of his large family. The long, cold winters gave the farmer a long "off season" for fishing; and the short, mild summers restricted the variety of crops.

The high latitude of the region and the cool Labrador Current gives cool waters, the natural habitat of a large number of edible fish known to Europeans and Americans. Fish from cool or cold water undoubtedly have firmer flesh and are more palatable than those from warm water; moreover, there is less danger of putrefaction, an important factor in localization before ice came to be used so generally. Ice was not used by vessels to preserve fish on the journey from the banks to the markets until about 1840. Now it is considered a necessity.

Geologic forces, previously described, gave New England many excellent harbors for the sheltering of vessels, the curing of fish, the mending of nets, and the repairing of vessels. From Cape Cod Bay northward the coast is rocky, with deep inlets, rocky headlands, islands, and sheltered coves. Southward, even to the tip of New Jersey, the shore is sandy, with shallow bays, sounds, and many lagoons. There are thus two distinct habitats for shore-loving fish. The broad continental shelf with its many "banks" brings deep-sea fish that summer near the ocean's bottom near enough to the surface to be caught readily. The nearness of the New England fishermen to the Bay of Fundy, Nova Scotia, the Gulf of St. Lawrence, the Newfoundland Banks, and even Labrador extended the area of fishing grounds. The fishermen of maritime Canada, until the last 50 or 100 years, have never been numerous enough to offer much competition, and in all these fishing grounds New England fishermen have had an advantage over those of Europe because of the shorter distance to the home markets.

The New England fishermen have always had cheap material for building their vessels and, most fishermen being adept in the use of ship carpenter's tools, built boats during leisure times. Little capital was needed, therefore, to enter the fishing industry. The vessels were staunchly built, seaworthy, and expertly handled. The nearness of some fishing grounds to the home ports had many advantages. The voyages were short. Small vessels were used. Vessels, in case of a storm, could reach a harbor readily and thus reduce the risk of life and property, and for that reason insurance rates were low. Fishing could be pursued by many as a spare-time occupation, and many fishermen were aided by the women and children in the curing of the fish. Until the invention of net-making machines, the women made many of the nets. Fishing, especially inshore fishing, was somewhat of a family affair.

The Earnings of the Fishermen.   Fishing has never been a very "gainful" occupation. Until the large companies came into existence and success became a matter of expensive equipment, few fortunes were made. The love of the sea, the possible chance ȯf a good season, lack of knȯwledge of other industries, the "chains of habit," and pure inertia have kept many on the fishing grounds. In the early days, before the dominance of manufactures in the economic life of the people, the traditions of the family and the education of the children were confined chiefly to nautical affairs. By the age of ten many a boy had entered upon his period of apprenticeship. "He aspired to the position of skipper of a schooner, possibly owner of the craft he was to command, and it was his ambition that led him, summer and winter, to face the storms of the Atlantic in preference to the fields and forests of the Middle West."

When agriculture, lumbering, commerce, and fishing were the leading occupations, the returns from fishing compared favorably with those of the others; but as new and rich agricultural lands opened up in the Middle West, the Great Lakes forests began to be exploited, manufactures developed in the East, and economic life became complex, fishing became one of the less gainful occupations. The high price of fish since the 1930's has increased the income of the fishermen to some degree; but the catch is declining relatively, because the waters are being overexploited. In 1950 there were in the United States a little fewer than 150,-000 fishermen. The value of the product was $320,000,000, making an average gross return of approximately $2100 a worker. With reduction for interests on investments, depreciation, overhead charges, and other items, the returns must have been low indeed.

The Value of the Fisheries.   In total value of product and income per man, the fishing industry has not, particularly in the last century, compared favorably with other industries. The product of the fisheries of the United States and Alaska in 1950 was $330,000,000, that of minerals $11,855,000,000, and that for net value of manufactures $90,000,-000,000. The value of the catch of fish by Massachusetts in 1950 was about $39,000,000, but the output of the factories of that state in net value was about $2,000,000,000. New England fisheries in 1950 yielded

$58,000,000 worth of products, and those of the Middle Atlantic States $27,000,000.

The strategic importance of the fisheries in the past and their influence in the development of overseas commerce, however, far transcends their economic value to the nation. Naval and merchant craft are now little more than mechanical engines on which a boy from the farm, the factory, or the machine shop is as much at home as one sailor-bred. Before they assumed this character, however, the fisheries were the nurseries for seamen. Besides being considered the "cornerstone of New England prosperity," the fisheries furnished men for the first navy; and in the Revolu-

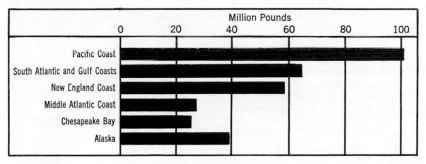

Fig. 74. Value of fisheries of Alaska and the United States by sections, 1950.

tionary War and the War of 1812 most of the privateers were manned by fishermen. Bounties were provided from time to time by local, state, and national governments to encourage the fisheries.

For a considerable time Alaska led in the value of the products of the fisheries of the United States. After about 1920 New England was a leader, but in 1950 the Pacific Coast held first place, the South Atlantic and Gulf coasts second place, New England third place, and Alaska dropped to fourth place among the fishing regions of the country (Fig. 74).

The Haddock.   This is a bottom-feeding "banks" fish belonging to the cod family. It much resembles the cod in its habits of feeding and spawning, and is caught with the same type of gear. It is marketed as "haddock on ice" or, if dried and smoked in the Scotch fashion, as "finnan haddies" or Finland haddock.

The Cod.   Of the deep-sea fish, the cod, until the Civil War, was by far the most important. For more than two centuries the history of the New England fisheries was little more than the history of cod fishing. To many a New Englander, even today, the cod is the best of food fish.

Many diplomatic battles have been fought and treaties made with France, Britain, and Canada in the interest of the cod fishermen of New England.

The cod lives for most of the year in salt water that ranges in temperature from 35° to 45°, and on a rocky or stony bottom at a depth of about

Fig. 75. A familiar scene along the waterfront at Gloucester, Massachusetts. *Courtesy, Gloucester Chamber of Commerce.* In the foreground are seine boats used in mackerel fishing. In the background are "bankers" and "draggers" used on the fishing banks. Landings of cod, herring and other fresh ocean fish at Gloucester (since 1944) have totaled more than 210,000,000 pounds annually.

120 fathoms. It is sometimes taken at a depth of 250 fathoms, and in the spawning season it moves into shoal waters near the shore.

The stony banks on the continental shelf of the Gulf of Maine, the Grand Banks of Newfoundland, and other smaller banks, and the rocky submerged ledges and islands from Cape Cod northward are the best cod-fishing grounds in the world. The most celebrated fishing grounds in the Gulf of Maine are Georges Bank, Middle Bank, Flippenies Bank, Jeffreys Ledge, Cashes Ledge, Blatts Bank, Grand Menan, Gormans Banks, Seal Island Grounds, and Browns Bank. The cold Labrador Current keeps the water temperatures low and brings in fresh supplies of food.

Sometime during the spawning season, October to April, the cod, both female and male, move into shoal water, and each female extrudes eggs to the number of 2,000,000-5,000,000. After being fertilized by the male, these float to the surface, where the sun hatches them in 12 to 21 days, and the small fry begin their struggle for existence. The cod attains a weight of 4–5 pounds in 3 years, and many ultimately weigh 50–70 pounds, although most of the cod caught weigh 15–30 pounds. The cod is a predatory fish, and a voracious eater, devouring any life small enough to swallow.

The craft used in fishing for the cod vary from small sailboats manned by 2 men who cast their lines near the shore on the lee side of rocky head-lands, to sailing schooners or auxiliary schooners operated by a crew of 15 to 30 men, which resort to the deep-sea banks and are, therefore, called "bankers.' The typical "banker" today is about 120 feet long, has a depth of 10 or 12 feet, and a 25-foot beam. The mainmast rises about 85 feet above the deck, with a topmast above this, 45 feet long. It may spread 2000 square yards of canvas. It has a gasoline engine of 75–100 hp and is roomy enough to give comfortable quarters to 15 to 30 men, besides having space for an ice house, general storerooms, and the storage of 300–400 barrels holding the catch (Fig. 75).

Winter fishing is laborious and accompanied by many hardships. Hauling in a mile or more of wet trawl from water near the freezing point on a winter day in a chilling wind and heavy sea is an occupation most people shun. Besides, the fishermen are subject to many dangers. Most of the time, when the catch is on, the dories are a mile or more and even several miles, from the schooner on the open sea. Strong winds and the high seas may make it difficult to reach the mother ship. A dense fog may set in, and the dory may become lost at sea with limited amounts of water and provisions. Then may come days and nights of constant rowing to reach land or the "lanes" of the ocean frequented by trans-ocean liners. The trawler operates both summer and winter, but winter fishing is more disagreeable.

Comparative statistics showing the trend of the cod fisheries are diffi-cult to obtain. Since 1940 there has been a decline, due probably to over-fishing of the waters, in spite of the admirable work the fish hatcheries are doing to maintain an adequate supply. In 1947 the Federal Govern-ment spent $1,500,000 in the United States and Alaska in the propaga-tion of food fish. More than 1,218,000,000 fry and 1,346,000,000 eggs were planted.

Codfish may be purchased on the markets as fresh cod (iced or frozen), dried cod, "fish flakes" in cans, pickled cod, or salted boneless cod in the shape of bricks. Only about 60 per cent of the "codfish" bricks are cod-fish, for hake and haddock are often sold under the name of cod.

Mackerel Fishing. Until about 1750, mackerel was used chiefly for bait; then the exporters began to send this fish, which they considered

very inferior, to the West Indies to feed the slaves on the sugar plantations. The West Indies had long been taking the inferior grades of fish.
After about 1820 the industry advanced rapidly. The catch of mackerel
fluctuates greatly. It was low in 1910, and again in 1921. It rose to a high
in 1939, declined again, then rose to another high in 1947. One year the
catch may be 113,000,000 (1939) pounds, the next year 55,600,000, and
the third year it may drop to 37,800,000. In 1950 it was less than 100,-
000,000 pounds. Such uncertainty is extremely discouraging to mackerel
fishermen; yet, with full equipment on hand and the possible chance of a
very prosperous year, they hang on. Some years, some vessels on a trip of
several weeks may not catch sight of a single school of mackerel.

The mackerel is the "mystery fish" of the deep-sea fisheries. It is a
warm-water fish and migrates northward with the northward movement
of the sun. It reaches Cape Hatteras about April 1, and the New England coast early in June. Another body reaches the shores of Nova Scotia
about July 1. With the coming of the winter it starts southward. Its destination is unknown to man. It is a surface-swimming fish, sometimes
moving in vast schools that spread over several square miles, and again at
times traveling in small detached groups. A small school may yield only
a few barrels, a large one several hundred barrels. A mackerel schooner
is in most respects like the cod-fishing schooner. The mackerel fishermen
use a purse seine, which when open is a net 200 feet wide and a half mile
or more long. When closed about a school of mackerel it is like a huge
purse.

Herring Fisheries.   The herring family, of which the leading varieties
are the true or common herring, shad, alewife, and menhaden, is the
most important of the commercial fish of the world. The common herring
has been for centuries the food of rich and poor alike on the coast lands
of the cooler parts of both the Atlantic and the Pacific. It is sold frozen,
fresh, pickled, dried, or smoked. The herring is caught in deep water
off the coasts of Newfoundland, eastern Canada, and New England,
and on the banks; but more often within the 3-mile limit in bays and
inlets, where it resorts to spawn. Here it is caught as it moves near the
surface of the waters in great schools. The young are taken on the Maine
coast, canned in oil, and sold as sardines.

The Rosefish.   Until 1935, the rosefish was scarcely known in the market. Before 1928 less than 100,000 pounds were landed annually, but in
1936 the catch totalled 15,000,000 pounds and ranked third in species
taken by New England fishermen. The increase in production of this species has been rather regular. It headed the list in species in the total
United States catch in 1947. It is a ground fish found on muddy banks

and around rocks below 50 fathoms, everywhere in the Gulf of Maine. It is a year-round resident and has a range of temperature tolerance that resembles that of the cod (33°–50° F), hence the habitat extends northward off Nova Scotia and the adjacent islands. It is a comparatively small fish (1–3 pounds) with bony structure and a large head; hence the edible portion forms a low percentage of the total weight. For this reason shipping charges have prohibited its export, either to the interior or to foreign markets. With the growth of the practice of filleting, rosefish have become an important commercial item in the fisheries, because the head and bony parts can be cut away and only the edible portions need stand shipping costs.

With the irregularity in numbers of haddock, the large off-shore trawlers have turned to the rosefish. At present the favorite fishing grounds for rosefish are the bank below 50 fathoms just off Cape Cod, and Browns Bank off the southern tip of Nova Scotia. No doubt other areas will be tried as the demand for fish increases.

The Less Important Fisheries.   Shad and alewife are caught in great numbers in nearly every inlet, bay, and river mouth from Florida to Maine, inclusive. They are anadromous, ascending the coast rivers to spawn, traveling hundreds of miles, in some cases, from the ocean where not checked by dams. They have about abandoned some rivers because of water-power dams, chemicals discharged by industrial plants, sewage of cities, and muddy water from newly opened ditches. The rivers of Maine, Connecticut, Pennsylvania, and New Jersey furnish most of the catch from the Northeastern States. Many of the New England rivers have been stocked with shad fry. Through the activity of the many state fish hatcheries of some of these states, working in conjunction with the United States hatcheries, attempts are being made to prevent the extermination of this fish. The alewife is considered superior to the sea herring as food, but not so good as shad. Like the shad, it is caught in large quantities in the lower courses of the rivers by means of pound nets, wires, gill nets, and seines.

The menhaden is little used for food but is valued commercially for its oil and as a fertilizer, and as bait for cod and other ground fish caught by the hand line or trawl. Thousands of barrels are used by the cod fishermen in a single season for bait. The fish is taken by means of the purse seine, as it swims in schools numbering thousands of individuals, swimming in closely packed, unwieldy masses, helpless as flocks of sheep . . ." The extracting of menhaden oil was begun about 1850 on the coast of Maine. For many years, fisher-farmers operated hand presses, three or four families often forming a neighborhood company. The first factory was built in Maine in 1864. Now there are factories to be found in many coast towns from Maine to Florida, and since 1930 there has been a tendency for the industry to shift to the states south of New England.

Lobster Fisheries.   The lobster is an inshore fish whose habitat is clear water on rocky bottoms, mainly from Cape Cod Bay northward. It lives at various depths. In the spring the mature lobsters migrate into shallow waters where they spawn, and here they remain most of the summer, returning in the fall to the deep water, 100 fathoms or more. The lobster was caught in colonial days for food, but not until the middle of the last century was it an article of commerce.

Oysters.   The sandy coasts of New Jersey, Long Island, Connecticut, Rhode Island, and Cape Cod provide annually about $10,000,000 worth of oysters, although the industry belongs more to Delaware and Chesapeake Bays than to these sections. In New England the industry is of recent development.

Big Business Goes Into Fishing.   Fishing in New England and Newfoundland waters has, up to about 1930, largely been an individual or partnership enterprise. The trim, fast-sailing fishing schooners are disappearing gradually, replaced by efficient steam trawlers on which machinery is doing much of the drudgery formerly performed by hand. All these developments call for far greater capital than formerly, for ships and for marketing facilities. Sonic depth finders—some trawlers are so equipped —give the exact location of the banks, and radio telephones enable the skipper and the crew to keep in close touch with the home port. Accidents and sickness are reported. A radio receiver on board gives the latest market prices, weather forecasts, and general happenings. Machinery makes a smaller crew possible. The schooner's crew usually numbers 15 to 20 men. The steam trawler requires only about 7.

The trawl is a huge conical bag 150 or more feet long, drawn through the water aft of the trawler that steams 2 or 3 miles an hour. When not trawling the vessel's speed is about 15 knots. The casting of nets is more frequent, and thus more contacts are had with the schools of fish than was the cast with the sailing or auxiliary schooners. Cleaning machinery enables the crew on board to take care of 5000 or 6000 pounds of fish in some 45 minutes. Steam trawlers often land 300,000 pounds of cod, haddock, or halibut in a single trip, cleaned and iced ready for the market. The increased production of fish has forced the fish dealers to seek more extended markets and also to extend the marketing over more months in the year. A quick-freezing process has lately been devised by which the iced fish when landed at the docks are prepared for distant shipments or for storage which may last months. Marketing methods have been improved greatly.

The new type of fishing boat is still in the experimental stage. A standardized type will undoubtedly soon evolve which will become as common as the trim schooners which have dominated the North Atlantic fishing banks for a century or so.

Though the fishing industry declined, relative to other industries in the Northeastern States from 1850 to 1925, it is important to note that the business has never ceased to exist. In fact it still plays an important part in the economy of the section. With changes in national economic conditions, technical advances in the industry, and the substitution of fish for high-priced meat as food, there are reasons to expect a considerable revival of the fishing industry.

QUESTIONS, EXERCISES, AND PROBLEMS

1. A successful fisherman is he who knows best the habits of fish. What practical biological knowledge is essential to the cod fisherman? To the mackerel fisherman?

2. How have geologic forces and processes prepared the coastal districts and waters of New England and eastern Canada for the fisherman?

3. What advantages does the Chesapeake Bay region possess over the Maine coast for the oyster industry?

4. Make a list of species of fish that did not enter the industry in early New England fishing but that have become important in the catch since about 1930. Explain why this is true in each case.

5. From the *Statistical Abstract* of the United States or other sources, get data to show the trend in cod fishing in the last decade. Do the same for mackerel.

CHAPTER 7

The North Central Section —
An Inland Empire

Here in the interior of the continent lies a great domain with natural assets surpassing those of several of the principal nations of the world. It is endowed with practically all the essentials for industrial sovereignty —a self-sustaining empire. White man has occupied it only a very short time, but in that brief period he has brought it to a commanding position in the nation. Politically he has divided it into a dozen states. However, utilization of the natural resources has tended to develop common interests among those states—empire unity. *What are its natural assets? To what extent has man utilized those assets? Has he made the best use of them? Does the region offer opportunities for further extensive development by man? Can it provide adequately for many more people?* In our consideration of these questions let us first examine the section as a whole and then by smaller units.

A Great Plains Region. Plains have always been important in the economy of man, and humid, temperate ones particularly so. Such plains have been the great producing areas for most of the world's people, as they possessed a stimulating climate, and provided an abundance of well-watered, adequately heated, fertile lands; their low relief favored easy communication with all parts; many possessed rich deposits of the most useful minerals, and were accessible to the ocean. The north central portion of the United States is part of the vast Great Central Plain which extends from the Gulf of Mexico to the Arctic and from the western to the eastern highlands. Fully 1,250,000 square miles of this great inland plain is susceptible of high development. The north central humid section of this plain in the United States, here being considered, is nearly as large as the combined area of the British Isles, France, Germany, Belgium, Netherlands, Denmark, Switzerland, Austria, and Czechoslovakia. It now maintains less than a fifth as many people as there are in the countries named, though it rivals them in the natural assets within it, or tributary to it and unrestricted by artificial barriers such as political boundaries. The whole section is of low relief (Fig. 76), with only minor elevations here and there which offer no serious obstruction to intercourse throughout its extent. The low relief, navigable rivers, Great

Lakes, and low passes through the eastern highland by way of the St. Lawrence and Oneida-Mohawk Depressions permit access to the Atlantic—the world's chief commercial ocean. Similar low relief and navigable rivers provide equally easy access to gateways at the south on the Gulf of Mexico. These eastern and southern gateways are of special significance, since the eastern United States and Europe are the principal outside markets for the agricultural and other products of the central plains.

Fig. 76. Between the lofty mountain and plateau area in the West and the comparatively low Appalachian Highland in the East lies a broad expanse of level to gently rolling plain, except where broken by the Ozark uplift. *Courtesy, Bureau of Agricultural Economics.*

A Propitious Climate.   The climate is of even greater significance than the surface, soil, and gateways. It is of the continental type, with hot summers and cold winters but with precipitation sufficient for agricultural purposes. Weather changes are frequent, due to the passage of cyclonic areas, and provide frequent showers. The rainfall decreases westward from 40 inches in eastern Ohio to 20 inches at the 100th meridian, but increases in the proportion that falls during the spring and early summer months, thus extending the productive area far westward. Throughout the entire North Central Section from 20 to more than 80 per cent occurs during the warmer half of the year when it is of greatest benefit to crops. The diurnal distribution approximates the ideal since from 45 to more than 65 per cent of the warm-season precipitation occurs at night. This increases the amount that enters the ground, reduces loss from evaporation, and provides for the maximum number of sunshine hours for crop growth. The region is also favored with 50 to 70 per cent of the amount of sunshine possible (Fig. 79). The growing season varies from 190 days in the south to 100 days in the north, favoring the growth of a great variety of agricultural products.[1]

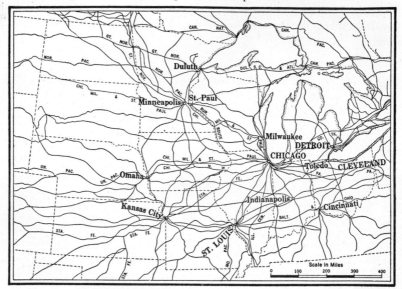

Fig. 77. Principal railroads in the North Central States. The railroad mileage in this group of states is more than two-fifths as large as that of Europe, and constitutes nearly two-fifths of the total in the United States.

A Land With Copious Resources. The North Central Section offers greater opportunities as a home for man than any other region of the United States. Here are agricultural and grazing lands of the richest; here is power—coal, oil, natural gas, water; here are iron, copper, lead, zinc, cement-making materials, forests; here is a healthful, stimulating climate; here are the Great Lakes and America's great rivers; here is about 30 per cent of the population of the United States—a progressive, capable people maintaining a stable government; here is one of the world's most richly endowed areas—the making of a great inland empire. Though a casual examination will reveal somewhat divergent physiographic, climatic, agricultural, and other industrial units, such as the Corn Belt, Spring-Wheat Area, etc., yet all are so closely related, so integrated, that common interests are being clearly recognized for the whole area and the evolution of sectional consciousness is in progress.

---

[1] For further discussion of climate, see Chapter 1.

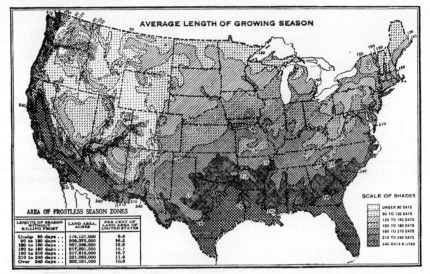

Fig. 78. More than 90 per cent of the United States has a growing season longer than 90 days. The season ranges from an all-year tropical condition in southern Florida to less than 90 days in the western highlands where high altitude and aridity favor rapid radiation at night. The powerful influence of the mild westerly winds from the Pacific carries a growing season of more than 200 days northward along the coast through Washington, and the lesser influences of cyclonic winds from the Atlantic extend a similar growing season northward to Chesapeake Bay. *Generalized from Atlas of American Agriculture, U. S. Department of Agriculture.*

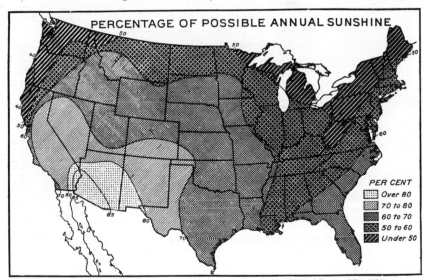

Fig. 79. The principal agricultural regions of the United States receive from 50 to 70 per cent of the possible amount of sunshine. (See Fig. 14 for agricultural regions.) *Courtesy, U. S. Department of Agriculture.*

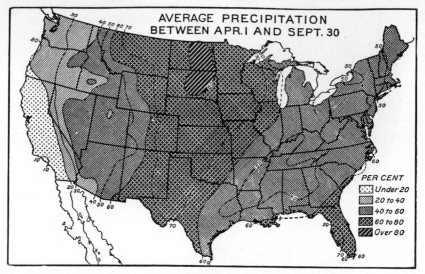

Fig. 80. Where the total annual rainfall is small its seasonal distribution is of great importance. Throughout most of the Great Plains region from 70 to more than 80 per cent occurs during the warmer half of the year when it is of greatest benefit to crops. During the same period from 50 to more than 70 per cent occurs throughout the eastern agricultural region. Compare with Figs. 6–9. *Courtesy, U. S. Department of Agriculture.*

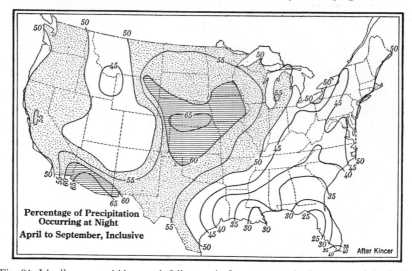

Fig. 81. Ideally we would have rainfall occur in frequent, gentle showers at night during the growing season, and have abundant sunshine during the daylight period. It is significant that 40 to more than 65 per cent of the total warm season precipitation occurs at night over principal agricultural regions of the United States. Compare with Figs. 6–9, and 78–81, and formulate a statement of the significance of the relations shown. *After Kinser, Atlas of American Agriculture.*

PHYSIOGRAPHIC REGIONS

Major Regions.   Though the North Central Section is essentially a plain of low relief, the great variety of soils, the character of the old and new glaciated surfaces and the unglaciated areas, rocks of varying geological age, and small variations in relief produce divergencies sufficient to warrant the consideration in this discussion of at least two major physiographic regions—the Lake region and the Central Low Plains. These regions may in turn be further subdivided when limited areas and greater details are considered. *The boundaries, however, are zonal rather than lineal in most places.* The regions of human use are not delimited by the physiographic boundaries, and the process of man's adjustment to what —at least theoretically—will be the most appropriate boundaries for selected types of activities is still in progress. Conceivably, the time may come when man will find the activity that can best be carried on in each unit. However, such an ideal adaptation is far in the future and will not be determined by physiographic features alone, nor are they likely to be the most important determinants (Fig. 82).

The Lake Region.   No marked topographic feature separates the Lake region from adjoining lands, yet this region is readily recognized as a physiographic unit. Its distinctive surface features are due to recent glaciation and are characterized by moraines, lacustrine plains, swamps, and thousands of lakes. It was originally forested, and a large portion of the north is still occupied by native forests or cut-over lands, although most of the south has been cleared for agricultural purposes. A southern extension of the Canadian Shield, a forested and slightly rugged mass of ancient rocks, projects into northeastern Minnesota, northern Wisconsin, and the upper peninsula of Michigan. These rock masses were somewhat subdued by glacial erosion and nowhere take on the character of mountains. The chief resources of the Upper Lake Region are its forests, iron ore, and copper, which have been exploited extensively by man. Agriculture on the cleared lands is slowly extending into the northern region but is dependent upon the lumbering and mining communities for a market. Agriculturally, most of the Lake region lies in the Hay and Dairying Region, but the Corn Belt extends into the southern portion. The southern portion also has most of the papulation and many large cities, and is one of the most important manufacturing and commercial sections of the United States. Much of the region's importance is due to the Great Lakes as well as to the great resources of minerals, forests, and soils, as few other areas of the world possess such superior opportunities for inland transportation. In the early days the Great Lakes carried the explorer, fur trader, and settler in canoe or sailing craft; today steel vessels that rival the largest ocean freighters in size annually carry a freight tonnage more than three-fourths as great as the combined tonnage of Atlantic, Gulf, and Pacific ports of the United States. The principal products carried are iron ore, coal, and grain. Many commercial and industrial cities such as Chicago, Detroit, Cleveland, Buffalo, Toledo, Milwaukee, and Duluth have grown up along the lake shores.

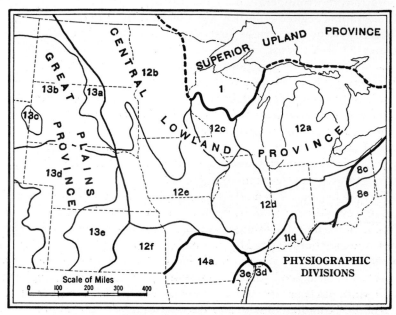

Fig. 82. Physiographic provinces and sections of the north central states. *After Feneman, Ann. Assoc. Am. Geog., Vol. VI.* The sections are named as follows:

3*d*. East Gulf Coastal Plain.	12*d*. Till Plains.
3*e*. Mississippi Alluvial Plain.	12*e*. Dissected Till Plains.
8*c*. Allegheny Plateau (glaciated).	12*f*. Osage Plains.
8*e*. Allegheny Plateau (Conemaugh).	13*a*. Missouri Plateau (glaciated).
11*d*. Western (unnamed, but part of Interior Low Plateaus).	13*b*. Missouri Plateau (unglaciated).
	13*c*. Black Hills.
12*a*. Eastern Lake.	13*d*. High Plains.
12*b*. Western Lake.	13*e*. Plains Border.
12*c*. Wisconsin Driftless.	14*a*. Springfield-Salem Plateaus.

The Central Low Plains.   This region of low plains extends south and west from the Lake Region and, as Dr. Feneman has aptly stated, "is in the main bounded by lands which are either not low plains or not plains." [2] To the south and east are the Ozark Plateau and the western

---

[2] "Physiographic Boundaries within the United States," *Ann. Assoc. Am. Geog.*, 4, p. 109.

plateaus of the Appalachian system. On the west the boundary is more indistinct, especially in Kansas and Nebraska. Along the western boundary the glacial drift is thin, and loess is distributed over both glaciated and unglaciated lands. To the west are the high, semiarid grazing lands of the Great Plains (or Plateau), and to the east the more humid, fertile prairies adapted to agriculture. As the name implies, the surface of the region, as a whole, is gently undulating plain, though in a flat country low hills may become quite conspicuous features locally. With the exception of limited areas such as the Driftless Area, essentially all the surface is covered by glacial drift older than that of the Lake Region. Upland lakes and swamps are rare, the moranic hills or ridges are comparatively low, and the slopes are gentle. Though the region as a unit possesses great uniformity, the differences between glaciated and unglaciated areas, between recent and old glaciation, and between the work accomplished by altering agencies that toiled upon these surfaces through the thousands of years since glacial times afford a considerable variety of soils. These contrasts in relief and soil, together with native vegetation, afford bases for subdividing the region into, at least, the Forested Glacial Plains of Ohio, Indiana, and southern Illinois, which were originally timbered, and where the glacial surface is dissected into hills only along the streams; the Prairie Plains, a vast, native grassland country extending westward to the high Great Plains; and the Driftless Area of southwestern Wisconsin and adjoining states, with its poor, light soils derived from the underlying sandstone, and fertile clay loam soils derived from limestone.

The Driftless Area.   An area of about 15,000 square miles in southwestern Wisconsin, and extending into adjoining states, was not covered by ice at any time during the glacial period. It is essentially a dissected plateau similar in many respects to west central Kentucky. Along its morainal contact with the Lake Region, glacial outwash material fills many of the valleys, forming extensive plains above which rise numerous native rock hills resembling the buttes so common in the West. Numerous picturesque cliffs, crags, pinnacles, and curiously formed "needles" and "chimney rocks," formed by caps of limestone on the easily eroded sandstone, are common and striking features. There are also many sink holes and caves. Weathering has produced a mantel of residual soil varying from sand, to sandy loam derived from sandstone, to clay-loam derived from the limestone. The sandstone-derived soils are poor, and the average value of farm land is about a fifth less than in the adjacent glaciated sandstone area. Land values in the glaciated limestone area of Wisconsin are about twice those of the glaciated sandstone and two and a half times those of the unglaciated sandstone; the unglaciated limestones of the southwest have been so efficiently utilized for pasture, hay, forage, and dairying that land values are less than a tenth below those of the glaciated limestones. The uplands of the Driftless Area in Minnesota carry a heavy cover of fertile loess and are highly productive.

COHERENCE IN THE SECTION

The differences in soil and relief are not nearly so important in the major use that man has made of the section's resources as might be inferred from the contrasts drawn. The "human-use regions" overlap and cross the physiographic regions indiscriminately. Far more important is climate. This is well shown in the present distribution of agricultural regions. Most of the Corn Belt, much of the Corn and Winter-Wheat Belt, and essentially all of the Spring-Wheat Area, lie within the Central Low Plains, and their limits are not determined by physiographic features. The major regions or subdivisions are not separated by marked features. Neither are these independent economic units. Instead they are distinctly interdependent, each having a variety of interests but specializing in one or more. The leading product of one unit may find its chief market in another, or entirely outside the North Central Section. For its successful development, each region depends quite as much upon the outside, as a market for its products and a source of goods not produced by it, as upon its own resources. Often a region produces only raw material that finds its market elsewhere, e.g., the Spring-Wheat Region and the Lake Superior iron region (Upper Lake Region).

Together, the divisions of the North Central Section produce the essentials for sound economic development and a surplus to exchange for commodities produced elsewhere. With coal, water, petroleum, and natural gas as power, much of the raw material is converted into finished products. Within the region, many manufacturing, mining, and commercial centers are developing. With this development is growing a more insistent political demand for cheaper outlets to the sea, such as the proposed Great Lakes-St. Lawrence, and Lakes-to-Gulf canal projects. The influence of the inland location is felt through the competition of the Panama Canal, which favors the eastern and western coasts, and through increased freight rates on railways.

INDUSTRIAL DEVELOPMENT

Relative Position of North Central Section. In addition to its leading position in agriculture, the North Central Section is one of the most important manufacturing, commercial, and mining regions of the United

States (Table VIII). It possesses a remarkable combination of geographic and economic factors favorable to industrial development. Its great extent of well-drained and fertile lands of low relief produces huge quantities of agricultural raw materials. It has a healthful, stimulating climate; a great variety of metallic and non-metallic mineral resources— coal, iron, copper, lead, zinc, petroleum, natural gas, cement materials, building stone, salt, gypsum, clay; considerable water power; superior transportation facilities on the Great Lakes, thousands of miles of navigable rivers,[3] a close network of railways (Fig. 77); and thousands of miles of

TABLE VIII

COMPARATIVE INDUSTRIAL POSITION OF THE NORTH CENTRAL STATES IN PERCENTAGE OF THE UNITED STATES

1. 37.5 per cent of the net value of manufactured products.
2. 34.1 per cent of manufacturing employees.
3. 39.4 per cent (value) of power used in manufactures.
4. 6.0 per cent of lumber produced (board measure).
5. 91.8 per cent (tons) of iron ore.
6. 46.1 per cent (tons) of pig iron.
7. 40.7 per cent (tons) of steel ingots and castings.
8. 49.1 per cent (net value) of flour and grain mill products.
9. 65.2 per cent (employees) of meat-packing products.
10. 3.8 per cent (tons) of copper.
11. 24.7 per cent (tons) of bituminous coal.
12. 45.0 per cent (tons) of lead.
13. 16.1 per cent (tons) of zinc.
14. 18.6 per cent (value) of all mineral products.
15. 46.1 per cent (tons) of salt.
16. 50.0 per cent (employees) of the 20 leading metropolitan manufacturing centers.
17. 22.0 per cent (employees) of petroleum refining.
18. 81.8 per cent (net value) of motor vehicles and parts.
19. 83.8 per cent (net value) of agricultural implements and tractors.

highways that are being improved rapidly. The section produces nearly two-fifths of the total product-value of manufactures of the country and uses more than one-third of the power employed in manufacturing; it produces one-fifth of the value of all mineral products, more than four-fifths of the iron ore, one-tenth of the copper, about one-fourth of the lead and zinc, more than half the salt, nearly two-fifths of the clay products, and more than two-fifths of the pig iron and steel. Utilization of its varied mineral resources and farm products has resulted in a rapid and extensive development of manufacturing and commerce, and the growth of many industrial centers, especially along the shores of the Great Lakes,

---

[3] Little used at present, but of high potential value.

or at focus points on its navigable rivers. It now has 14 of the 25 leading manufacturing cities, and both Buffalo and Pittsburgh, located just outside the area, owe much of their industrial growth to the development of the North Central Section.

Natural Resources Affect Civic Attitude. The varied economic resources and consequent diversity of human interests have long shown their influence in a lack of unity in politics in contrast with the unity of New England. In the past, political leaders have been unable to agree among themselves as they represented people engaged in diverse occupations. On the one hand are the manufacturing and commercial interests inclusive of the wage-earner who depends upon them, and on the other the agricultural interests. Today the farmer is both a laborer and a capitalist, and modern financing methods have led all groups to invest their funds in a great variety of enterprises. Though mercenary group interests still dominate, yet out of these conditions is slowly arising a realization that the interests of all human activity groups are closely integrated, and that the success of one depends upon similar success of the others. Neither the farmers nor the dweller in the densely populated city can prosper without the other. Practical attainment of such a unity concept will go far toward the most effective development of the section and of the country as a whole.

PROBLEMS

1. Can the North Central States maintain a population as large as that now maintained on any equal contiguous area in Europe?

2. Can the North Central States ever equal the North Atlantic States in material development?

3. Will manufacturing become of greater importance than agriculture in the North Central States?

4. To what extent do physiographic regions influence man's activities?

5. Can the handicap imposed by an inland location be overcome?

Agriculture
in the North Central Section

Agriculture the Leading Industry. Agriculture is the most widespread and the leading industry, though more people are engaged in the numerous other industries and professions carried on in the region. Three-fifths of the population at the last census was classed as urban. The rural population declined from 61.4 per cent in 1900 to 39.1 per cent in 1950; the actual *farm* population is probably slightly more than half the percentage classed as rural by census reports. This decline is, undoubtedly, continuing. From the standpoint of the farmer, the decrease is economically desirable as it increases his market in the centers where manufacturing, commerce, and mining are developing. With large farms and the use of machinery, to which the surface of the region is excellently adapted, he will be able to produce sufficient food to meet all demands for considerable time to come.

Agriculture is now more fully developed in the North Central Section than in any other portion of the country. The broad expanse of arable land is well tilled, there are extensive improvements, and the average returns are relatively high. About four-fifths of the land area of the North Central Section is in farms. A large part of the present unimproved land is capable of producing crops or pasture and now constitutes a reserve. The section has nearly half the total value of farms and buildings and of automobiles and trucks on farms, one-third of the farms with running water, nearly three-fifths of those with telephones, two-fifths of those with electricity, in the United States. Seven-tenths of its farms are operated by owners and part owners. This section produces more than nine-tenths of the soybeans, nearly three-fifths of the wheat, four-fifths of the corn, nearly seven-tenths of the swine, three-fifths of all livestock, and similar ratios of other products. Farms have been increasing in size and now average about 200 acres each. More than 100,000 exceed 500 acres. Table IX illustrates the relative agricultural importance of the north central section, the preeminent food-producing region of the United States. No other agricultural region of the world equals it in production or in the economic well-being of its farm people (Fig. 83).

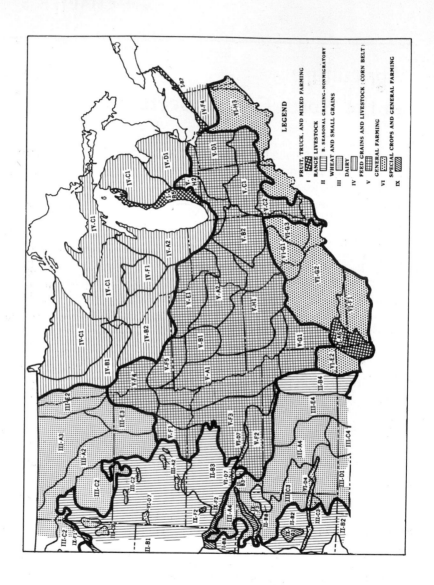

LEGEND

I   FRUIT, TRUCK, AND MIXED FARMING

II RANGE LIVESTOCK
    B. SEASONAL GRAZING—NONMIGRATORY

III WHEAT AND SMALL GRAINS

IV DAIRY

V   FEED GRAINS AND LIVESTOCK (CORN BELT)

VI GENERAL FARMING

IX SPECIAL CROPS AND GENERAL FARMING

Fig. 83. Types of farming in the North Central Section. Agricultural enterprises in the subregions are significant, in addition to the dominant enterprises of the major region. Courtesy, Bureau of Agricultural Economics.

I-A6. Fruit, poultry, and dairy.
1-B5. Fruit, truck, dairy, and poultry.
I-B7. Fruit, truck crops, and dairy.
II-A2,3,4,8. Seasonal grazing—non-migratory.
III-A2,3,4. Specialized wheat.
III-C2,3,4. Wheat and range livestock.
III-D1. Wheat, grain sorghums, and range livestock.
III-E2,3,4. Wheat and general farming.
IV-A2. Specialized dairy.
IV-B1,2. Dairy and livestock.
IV-C1. Dairy, hay, and potatoes.
IV-D1. Dairy and cash crops.
IV-F1,4. Dairy and general farming.
V-A1,2. Cattle feeding and hogs.

V-B1,2. Cash corn, oats, and soybeans.
V-C1, 2. Hogs and soft winter wheat.
V-D1. Livestock, dairy, soybeans, and cash grain.
V-E1. Hogs and dairy.
V-F1,2,3,4,5. Livestock and cash grain.
V-G1. Livestock, cash grain, and dairy.
V-H1,2. Livestock and pasture.
VI-D4,7. Livestock and special crops—irrigated.
VI-E2. Livestock and cash grain.
VI-F1. Livestock, truck, and cotton—small-scale.
VI-G1,2,3. Dairy, livestock, and poultry.
VI-H3. Livestock and tobacco.
IX-F1,2,3. Sugar beets, dry beans, and livestock—irrigated.
IX-G1. Dry beans—non-irrigated.

The process of crop adjustment to physical and economic conditions is never completed because all the influencing factors are variables. In attaining the present stage of land use, man has been influenced profoundly by the natural setting in which he was placed. As Elliott has so aptly stated, the "tendency of farmers to adjust their organizations and practices to their environmental conditions is merely an attempt, on their part, to get a maximum utilization of the resources at their command. They are consciously or unconsciously seeking to economize on their resources by producing those commodities which will give them a maximum of return for the resources used. In doing so, they necessarily depend upon obtaining from others commodities and services which they themselves are at a comparative disadvantage in producing. The inevitable consequence of such a development is that farmers in different regions will follow different lines of production." [1] The same basic principle of human occupance of the land and maximum utilization of the resources has been set forth lucidly by Holmes: "Each region tends to utilize its productive resources by producing those commodities from which it will realize a maximum of value for the resources used and to exchange these products for those in which its productive advantage is comparatively less, drawing these latter products from regions in which their production means maximum utilization of resources." [2] Since land resources and economic conditions vary widely in the North Central Section there is a similar wide variation in the use made of the land. As a result we have cash-grain regions such as the Spring-Wheat and Winter-Wheat Regions, the Corn Belt, Dairy Region, etc.

Premier geographic conditions have made possible a rapid and extensive agricultural development, such as the great expanse of level land suited to large-scale use of labor-saving machinery, manifold variety of soils of high average fertility, abundant summer rains falling in frequent gentle showers, high summer temperatures and long growing season, a stimulating and healthful climate in which to live, excellent home markets in the rapidly growing urban centers, access to eastern and to foreign markets, and superior transportation and marketing facilities.

Leading Crops.   A great variety of crops are now produced, but the fertile soils, large expanse of level land, labor supply, and available markets favor extensive rather than intensive agriculture. The temperature and rainfall are highly favorable to wheat throughout the entire section, and to corn, in the central and southern parts. Though the section is dominantly a cereal country, most of the farm area is devoted to produc-

[1] F. F. Elliott, "Types of Farming in the United States," U. S. Dept. of Agr., 1933, p. 1.

[2] C. L. Holmes, "Economics of Farm Organization and Management," U. S. Dept. of Agr., p. 47.

tion of feed and livestock and to dairying (Fig. 83). Farm animals occupy a prominent position in the agricultural economy practiced in the North Central Section. The wheat areas in such states as Michigan, Illinois, Wisconsin, and Minnesota have decreased, and production of stock feed and dairying have come in. The leading crops of the section are corn, wheat, hay and forage, soybeans, and oats. Other important crops include rye, barley, potatoes, flax, fruits, sugar beets. As shown in Table IX, a large share of the leading crops of the United States is produced in this section.

TABLE IX

COMPARATIVE AGRICULTURAL POSITION OF THE NORTH CENTRAL SECTION
IN PERCENTAGE OF UNITED STATES

1. 82.6 per cent of total land area is in farms.
2. 198 acres average size of farm.
3. 47.5 per cent of total value of farms and buildings.
4. 51.7 per cent of total value of farm machinery.
5. 35.2 per cent of all farms operated by owners and part owners.
6. 43.2 per cent of all automobiles and trucks on farms.
7. 58.0 per cent of all tractors on farms.
8. 57.6 per cent of all farms with telephones.
9. 40.0 per cent of all farms with electricity.
10. 57.6 per cent of all wheat (bushels) produced.
11. 79.0 per cent of all corn (bushels) produced.
12. 46.8 per cent of all hay (tons) produced.
13. 49.0 per cent of total value of all livestock on farms.
14. 39.1 per cent of population is rural.
15. 60.0 per cent of all dairy and livestock farms.
16. 33.1 per cent of all farms with running water.
17. 31.6 per cent of farm population.
18. 81.6 per cent of all oats (bushels) produced.
19. 93.7 per cent of all soybeans (bushels) produced.
20. 41.5 per cent of all cattle (number).
21. 68.7 per cent of all swine (number).
22. 70.0 per cent of its farms are operated by owners and part owners.

WHEAT

Wheat, the Principal Food Crop. There are two major wheat regions, spring wheat at the north and winter wheat farther south. Between these two great wheat-producing areas and overlapping into each is the Corn Belt. Out of an annual wheat production of 1,250,000,000 bushels in the United States, 750 million come from this section. It has been estimated that 5 to 6 billion bushels of wheat are required annually to feed the wheat-eating population of the world. On this basis the North Central States produce 12–15 per cent of the world's requirements, making this section one of the world's great producers of high-quality foods.

The Red River Valley.   The Red River Valley, celebrated for its high-quality wheat, is the heart of the spring-wheat region. Throughout this region, extending westward from central Minnesota into North Dakota and northward into Canada, the traveler is confronted by mile upon mile of almost level plains carrying a fertile, heavy, black clay-loam soil. Highways, straight as an arrow for many miles, lead off toward the horizon and apparently fade out to infinity. Here and there a group of trees,

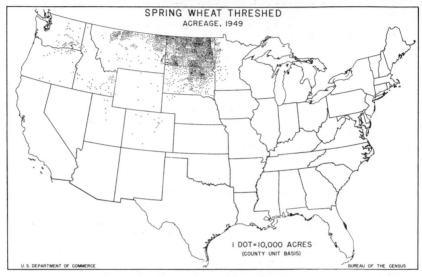

SPRING WHEAT THRESHED
ACREAGE, 1949

1 DOT=10,000 ACRES
(COUNTY UNIT BASIS)

U.S. DEPARTMENT OF COMMERCE   BUREAU OF THE CENSUS

Fig. 84. The Spring-Wheat Region.

forming a windbreak about a farm home, or a ribbon of foliage along a stream breaks the view. During the harvest season of the late summer, thousands of acres of golden-colored grain, falling before the battery of modern harvesting machines, confront the eye. Still later, the night sky is lighted by dozens of burning straw piles that send up their flames like beacons on a seemingly endless plain. This is the land that produces the high-grade, hard, spring wheat. However, the spring-wheat region is not confined to the Red River Valley proper. It extends to the southern bend of the Minnesota River in Minnesota, south to the Missouri in South Dakota, and westward to the high plains of northwestern North Dakota, where it is limited by scant rainfall. This region produces more than three-fourths of the spring wheat of the United States (Fig. 84).

Conditions are almost ideal for the growth of a superior grade of breadmaking wheat. Most of the region is covered by glacial soils or by lacustrine deposits of fine black soils varying from clay loams to heavy, black, sticky clay, or "gumbo" (Fig. 12). Most important, however, is climate. The ideal conditions for wheat are commonly considered to be a long, cool, wet spring, favoring "tillering," followed by a warm, sunny, dry harvest period. The climatic conditions are almost ideal. Most of the rain comes in spring and early summer, followed by a dry and sunny fall for the maturing and harvesting of the grain. The dry, warm, ripening period is largely responsible for the large, glossy kernel, rich in nitrogen and protein, that makes the product of this region a choice flour wheat superior to the softer grains grown in cooler and moister areas. Approximately half the rain comes from March to June, and much of the winter snow melts and enters the ground, thus providing the moisture needed early in the spring. The western limit of spring wheat is practically the mean annual rainfall line of 15 inches.

For many years, wheat has been the dominant crop. It is well known that the practice of growing one kind of crop year after year will ultimately cease to yield a profit. Yet it is difficult to bring about a change. A change from a single crop to mixed farming is much easier in sections east and south where rainfall is more abundant and the growing season longer. However, in a region having a short growing season with a small margin of rainfall safety, and located long distances from market, such a change is difficult, and is commonly accompanied by much economic distress which is reflected frequently in political dissatisfaction. There is a human tendency to cling to what has been tried, especially when the chief money crop is involved. The tendency to look to the government for the solution of geographic and economic problems is a natural result. This was illustrated by the rise of the Non-Partisan League in North Dakota and its extension to adjoining states, as Minnesota and South Dakota, and by a coalition with labor and the Democrtic Party. The astuteness of the political leader who can capitalize this discontent, offer a panacea, make this combination between the capitalist-farmer and urban laborer, and be elected to office must at least command respect. This mental state is not difficult to understand, considering the high freight rates to distant markets, and a high price for commodities purchased. With a small margin of safety in rainfall, a decrease of a few inches during the growing season means a large crop loss, more economic distress and more political determination.

Wheat, and still more wheat, remains the dominant idea. With 30–60 per cent of the crop acreage devoted to its culture, prosperity waxes and wanes with the yield and price. This is reflected in the sale of new machinery, automobiles, clothing, groceries, and the whole gamut of produce needed by the farmer. Yet, as previously noted, a change is slowly taking place. The problem of selecting suitable crops for diversification is difficult. Hay and other forage crops (such as corn) and potatoes are being tried northward into the moister parts of the Red River Valley. The drier portions in the West are still in the agony of being reborn, and a possible new life may be found in a decrease of wheat acreage and a partial return to forage crops and livestock.

The Land of Winter Wheat. Winter wheat, unlike spring wheat, is sown in the fall and attains a substantial growth during that season. It readily survives the cold of a moderate winter, especially where amply

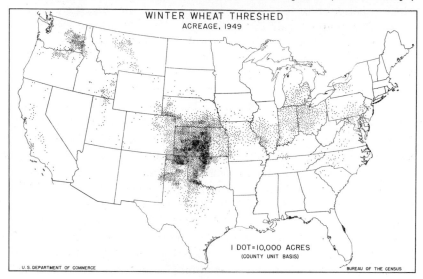

Fig. 85. Most of the winter wheat is grown in the Hard Winter-Wheat Region, the Corn and Winter-Wheat Belt, and the Corn Belt. The southern boundary follows closely the isotherm of 72° for the month preceding harvest (June 15). Wheat grown south of this line is subject to severe damage from rust. The northern boundary follows, in general, the mean winter isotherm of 20°.

covered with snow. During the cool of early spring, it tillers more abundantly than spring wheat and sends forth many stalks, each of which bears a head of grain, hence the yield is larger than that of spring wheat. The harvest season comes in June and early July, and requires the importation of much labor. A floating class of laborers handles much of the wheat during the harvest season. These laborers, together with their harvesting machinery, start their trek in Texas and Oklahoma and move northward into Kansas, the Dakotas, and Canada as the harvest season advances.

The principal producing area (Fig. 85) is central Kansas, extending northward into Nebraska and southward into Oklahoma. This area produces the high-grade, hard winter variety. A minor winter-wheat area, producing softer wheat, extends through Illinois, Indiana, southern Michigan, Ohio, Pennsylvania, Maryland, and Delaware. The limits of the region of densest production are determined by climate rather than by surface or soil. The climate is not the best in the world for wheat, but wheat is the most profitable crop to grow in such a climate. The region of greatest production has a rainfall of 15–30 inches and a growing season of 150–220 days. The northern boundary is essentially the mean winter temperature line of 20° which extends from southern Wisconsin across northern Iowa and northwestward across North Dakota and Montana. Very little winter wheat is grown north of this line, yet the larger yield that may be obtained has led a number of Minnesota and Dakota farmers to "take a chance" on winter wheat. There appears to be an increasing number who are taking that "chance," and consequently winter wheat is spreading into the southern part of what has long been known as the spring-wheat region. Beyond the western boundary, which is determined by low rainfall, better returns may be obtained by utilizing the grasslands for pasture. The eastern limit is determined by heavier rainfall, which makes corn and livestock production more profitable. Toward the south, where high temperature and high humidity and rainfall stimulate fungus diseases of wheat, where the soils are more leached than in the north, and where a rainy harvest is very unfavorable, wheat comes into competition with cotton.

Winter wheat constitutes more than three-fourths of the total wheat crop of the United States. More than half the winter wheat comes from the north central section, mostly from the Kansas-Nebraska-Oklahoma hard-wheat area. Few states east of the Mississippi River produce more wheat than they consume, and their surplus is not nearly equal to the consumption east of the river. Some of their wheat is exported, and other wheat is brought in from the West to meet the requirements. Winter wheat, as a whole, is now on an export basis, and since the United States produces a surplus for the markets of the world, marketing of this surplus brings into relief the influence of inland location and transportation rates.

Wheat is a cash crop, and the dominant one in the hard-winter-wheat-producing area. Here the farmer depends almost entirely upon it for his money income. In central Kansas, from 60 to more than 80 per cent of the crop acreage produces wheat, and three-fourths of the farmers of that state grow the crop. Other products—oats, corn, rye, butter, eggs—are produced for home consumption. Hence, here as in the spring-wheat region, prosperity is governed by the returns upon the wheat crop.

The wheat farmer of the Kansas-Nebraska-Oklahoma area who considers the future and contemplates diversification is confronted with the problem of finding suitable rotating crops. The number available is distinctly limited by the small rainfall. His substitutes are forage crops— hay, millet, corn, kafir, milo, and other sorghums, etc.—hence the raising of livestock. Though non-geographic factors, such as rail and water freight rates, tariffs, and increased wheat consumption may direct his efforts in coming years, it seems likely that the wheat acreage will be decreased somewhat and forage crops and livestock increased relatively. The farms are also likely to remain large, as the level land is favorable to the use of machinery, and the small rainfall limits the crops to comparatively low yields an acre. Limited as it is by climate, the area is likely to continue to be a producer of wheat for bread and livestock for meat.

UNIT AREAS IN THE WHEAT REGION

Studies of several small unit areas, even though such studies are in the nature of an "overview," aid in amplifying the more generalized treatment. Since a brief discussion of any large region must be on broad lines, many details that show the intimate adjustments of man to the land are necessarily omitted. However, it is the sum of these detailed relationships that characterize the whole. Numerous reasons may determine the selection of such unit areas for study, e.g., because they are representative of a much larger area; because they represent the highest type of all-round development; because they typify the growth of a selected industry; because they represent the evolution of an urban or a rural community. The unit areas discussed in succeeding pages have been selected from widely separated parts of the north central section as representative of (1) rural and (2) rural-urban communities in which one or more phases of human interests predominate. However, none of these areas possesses outstanding leadership in any particular field of human endeavor. In this respect each is typical rather than exceptional. Essentially the same form of organization has been followed in the discussion of each unit so as to facilitate comparisons.

TRAILL COUNTY, NORTH DAKOTA[3]

The Red River Valley has long been famous for its fertile soils and high-quality spring wheat. Traill County, North Dakota, bordering the Red River of the North and lying midway between Fargo and Grand Forks, is a representative section. All of the county, except a few square miles of glacial moraine, lies within the limits of glacial Lake Agassiz.

[3] See a more detailed study of the Red River Valley by J. R. Schwendeman in *Economic Geography*, July and Oct., 1944; Jan. and Oct., 1945.

winter wh...
cent, and i...
The firs...
principally...
acquiring la...
recent years...
of large area...
sus the farms...
1000 or more...

Fig. 87. Diagrammatic r...

owners and part own...
number of seasons wit...
checked settlement, bu...
ily since the advent of...
every quarter-section ex...
the soil is poor and the p...
regions, the farm and th...
city population has incre...
Hutchinson, which now...
county. The attraction...
greater social and educati...
chinery in large-scale farr...

it as early as 1880. Ten y...
farms, and the maximum a...
declined in relative impor...
the crop land was devoted...
companied by (1) an increa...
oats, barley, rye, corn, cultiv...
(2) an increase in the numbe...
a trend toward greater dive...
The continuous growth of w...
yield and an excessive grow...
may be produced in favora...
Conditions have fostered cro...
the cultivation of which redu...
able return for the season in c...
change is coming the producti...
grain growing still dominate...
portance, though there are no...
horses and poultry, to the sq...
horses is declining and that of...
The wheat lands are usually...
from two to eight plows being u...
done in the early spring, and t...
Harvesting time is a very busy s...
larger farms to see five or more...
field, each cutting a swath of 7 c...
and threshed from the field, an...
way. Today the combine is displ...
scene. Many operators of the lar...
outfits, but threshing on the smal...
farm to farm. Most of the wheat...
Minneapolis and Duluth.
Barley now ranks next to whea...
devoted to it. Flax is a close secon...
ranking next in order. The short g...
duction of corn for grain, and it is...
that form more efficient use can be...
Oats are a very important stock...
maturing type—60-day oats—whi...
prevalent in the last half of July. B...
ever since the days of early settlem...
Flax became an important crop...
poses, as the sale of seed yielded an i...

The northwestern two-thirds is covered by a glacial river delta which was formed in Lake Agassiz and which has a gently sloping, level-to-slightly-ridgy topography. The lower lake bed to the east is nearly flat and is poorly drained. Numerous ditches have been excavated to carry off the excess water during wet seasons. The area as a whole presents a very flat to gently undulating prairie landscape broken only by groves

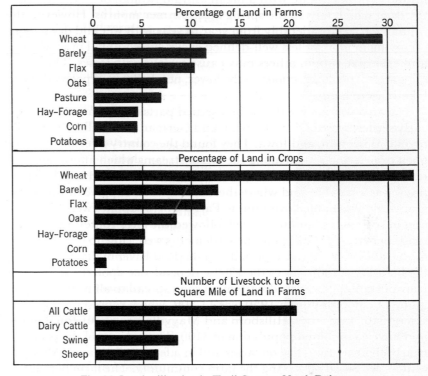

Fig. 86. Land utilization in Trail County, North Dakota.

of trees forming windbreaks about the farm homes, or a narrow belt along some of the streams. The soils are of lacustrine, glacial, or alluvial origin. The lacustrine deposits, which cover most of the region, consist chiefly of fine silt and clay-loam derived from glacial till, laid down in the quiet waters of Lake Agassiz and later weathered under very deficient drainage conditions. They carry a high percentage of humus and are dark-colored to black.

The winters are long and cold (average 8°) and the summers are cool (average 66°) but have a growing season of 130 days and sufficiently hot periods to be very favorable to the growth of hardy cereals. Extremes of

ment. The present farm population averages about 12 to the square mile, and, under the prevailing conditions of climate, soil, and general economy, there is little indication that this average will increase materially in the immediate future.

Surface and Soils. Physiographically, the area is in the Great Plains. Its gently undulating surface slopes very uniformly downward toward the east and is intersected by three relatively narrow and shallow valleys. The present local elevation differences are due primarily to wind action and stream erosion. The maximum range in elevation is only about 400 feet, and this is due in large part to the general westward rise common to the Great Plains. The area contains four physiographic regions which differ in their adaptability to agricultural uses, viz., (1) the prairies, (2) the Arkansas River Valley, (3) the valleys of the Ninnescah and Little Arkansas Rivers, and (4) the sand hills or dune areas. In general, the soils are brown in color and residual, alluvial, or aeolian in origin.

The prairie region occupies most of the county and has a gently undulating surface with broad, gently sloping ridges that rise scarcely 20 feet above the adjacent depressions. It has numerous low-gradient, short, intermittent streams that flow in indistinct valleys. Along the western margin are areas of sandy, dunelike hills. The soils over most of the high prairies vary from silty loam to clay-loam and are somewhat heavy. They are best adapted to small grains, especially wheat. They are also good corn lands, but are not so good in dry years as the sandy loams. The principal crops in the prairie region include wheat, sorghum, oats, hay, corn. More than 85 per cent of the hay-producing land grows alfalfa, and some 9000 acres produce clover seed.

The Arkansas Valley bisects the northeastern quarter of the area (Fig. 87) and is a broad, shallow trench. It is 5-10 miles wide and 10-50 feet below the upland, but in places the valley and prairie blend so completely that there is scarcely any line of demarcation. The city of Hutchinson is situated in this valley trench, with South Hutchinson just across the river. The flat-bottomed valley is occupied to a depth of 100 feet or more by alluvial sand, gravel, and clay carried from the Great Plains and Rocky Mountains. These materials are good retainers of moisture absorbed from the winter snow and the rain, and serve as a water reservoir to supply wells and crops. Wheat, corn, alfalfa, and numerous feed crops are grown on the loams and sandy loams. The fine sandy loam is very good truck and corn land and is the best soil for apples. The valley has many large commercial orchards of apples, pears, and peaches, a few of which contain several hundred acres.

The Little Arkansas River Valley is 1–3 miles wide and crosses the northeastern corner of the area. It is a shallow sand- and clay-filled trench similar to the Arkansas Valley. On the south it merges into a sand-dune upland, and on the north into rolling prairies. The North Fork of the Ninnescah River and its tributaries have cut narrow valleys in the southern and western parts of the area. These flat-bottomed valleys are ¼–1 mile in width and 20–100 feet below the bordering hilly prairies. In the southeast, the river and its tributaries have cut down to the Red Beds, producing a more rolling and eroded surface. Here the soils are reddish brown clay and very difficult to cultivate, as they are too hard when dry and too sticky when wet. Though some crops are produced, much of this section is used for pasture and the population is sparse. In most other parts of this physiographic region, the soils are good and produce crops similar to those of the prairie region.

The principal dune regions are located chiefly north of the Arkansas Valley and in the northwestern and western parts of the county. The sand hills are 10–30 feet high and have numerous small marshy areas between them. They are rarely cultivated, but the coarse grass provides a poor grade of pasture for herds of cattle.

A Variable Climate.   Since the county is in the transition belt between the humid and semiarid portions of the country the climate wields a large influence in its material development. The growing season of 180–190 days is usually hot in midsummer, with a mean temperature of 77° and a maximum of 109°. Periods of very high temperatures may last for several days, and 100° may occur frequently. There are also occasional periods when strong, hot, dry winds sweep over the plains, and crops are likely to be damaged seriously; but these winds do not occur frequently during any one season. The average winter is mild (34°), but some winters are very severe, with strong, cold winds, and an absolute minimum temperature of −24° has been recorded. Winter cold, however, does little damage to crops.

As a part of the Great Plains, the area suffers the precariousness of rainfall that characterizes that region, though to a somewhat lesser degree. The mean annual rainfall of 28 inches is adequate when it comes at the right time. The average rainfall for the growing season is 18.7 inches but varies from 11.6 inches to 26.7 inches. This variability gives some seasons in which the precipitation is far below normal, or fails to come at the time when it is of the greatest value for a mixed-farming, humid type of agriculture. Normally there is sufficient to prevent a complete crop failure during any dry season, but the considerable seasonal fluctuations and high temperatures, combined with strong winds and high evaporation, maintain the element of uncertainty, and produce large variations in crop yield. With a small rainfall margin of safety, a comparatively small drop below normal converts the region from a humid to a semiarid condition. Hence, "good and bad years" follow closely the amount and distribution of rainfall and summer heat. The winter snowfall of 21 inches is particularly significant in such an area of pervious soils, as most of the moisture enters readily. It is common practice to keep the fields rough and trashy in winter to prevent the snow from blowing away. Old straw is commonly spread upon the sandy soils to keep both snow and soil from drifting and to add mulch.

Agriculture. Agriculture is the dominant industry of the region (Fig. 88). All the land area is in farms; more than three-fourths of the farm land is in crops and nearly one-fourth is pastured. Many farmers, especially on the heavier loam and clay loam soils, specialize in one or

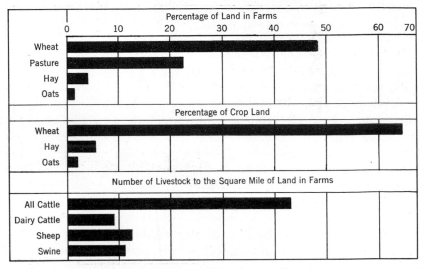

Fig. 88. Land use in Reno County, Kansas.

two crops, producing them on an extensive scale. The land is preeminently one of cereals, especially small grains, with more than two-thirds of the cultivated land devoted to their culture. Wheat occupies a dominant position, as more than three-fifths of the cropland is devoted to it. All other cultivated crops are insignificant in comparison. Wheat is likely to retain its relative place in the agricultural system because it can be marketed at any time, is well adapted to the soils, is better suited to large-scale farming methods with a minimum of labor than other available crops, and is probably a more certain crop under the climatic conditions than any of the other small grains. The broad expanse of level plains is highly favorable to the use of modern machinery.

Conservation of moisture is always a necessity, hence the wheat lands are commonly plowed or listed from the middle of July to late September and worked down level with a mulch surface. Early working is preferable, as the soil is then in the best condition. Hard winter wheat is grown, and the seeding extends from September 15 to November 1. June is harvest time, and the yield averages 16 bushels an acre, though it varies considerably from season to season.

Sorghum, oats, hay, and corn are all grown, but the acreage of each is relatively very small. Corn is grown principally for grain and is produced chiefly on the sandy loams where mulching by cultivation reduces evaporation most effectively. The average yield of 15–20 bushels, compared with 50–60 bushels on the best soils in good years, indicates the sensitiveness of the crop to seasonal fluctuations in weather. Failure of rain to come at the right time—even if it comes at some other time—results in serious damage to the corn, as evaporation from the growing plant under hot winds is excessive. The corn land is commonly prepared by listing. Though this method has serious defects it has compensating advantages, as the trench and ridge produced lessen soil drift under the strong winds, and retain the snow—when the ground has been prepared in the late fall —and the moisture derived from its melting. The seed is planted in the bottom of the lister trench and the soil brought in about the growing plants by cultivation until the ground is again essentially level and the crop has reached a height sufficient to prevent soil drift. The corn and oat crops are produced chiefly to feed farm animals. The oat yield is usually small, as the prevalent dry weather retards germination in the spring and the strong winds blow the soil away from the roots of the young plants. Other minor crops include kafir, milo, rye, barley, Sudan grass, sweet clover, and cowpeas, and are grown for fodder or pasture, but the acreage of each is small. Kafir is well adapted to the dry seasons and to the soils, is one of the most certain crops, and is likely to increase in importance as a rotating crop.

Hay and forage crops rank next to wheat in acreage. Alfalfa is the dominant cultivated hay crop though it is difficult to get started on account of the strong winds and dry soils. A fourth of the acreage devoted to hay crops produces a coarse, wild, nutritious grass, which is cut from meadows along the smaller streams and wet, low areas among the sand hills. These crops are used for winter feed for farm animals and for fattening cattle.

The raising of livestock is of secondary importance as this is a land of wheat and other small grains. Many swine are produced in connection with general farming; but there are few large droves, and the total number is small compared with that of a corn belt county. Four-fifths of the cattle are of the beef type, and some are raised by most farmers. A few specialize in cattle, but there is practically no "cattle ranching," as such is known farther west, though the sand-hill country supports many head. Large numbers of cattle and several thousand sheep are imported each winter and fattened on corn, cowpeas, alfalfa, corn fodder, and wild hay. They are marketed chiefly in Kansas City. This is the most important phase of the livestock industry. About a fifth of the cattle normally maintained on the farms is for dairy purposes, and the products are principally for home consumption. Any surplus is marketed in the village or city centers, especially at Hutchinson, where there is a large creamery that purchases milk from an extensive territory in this part of the state. Main and branch lines of four large railroad systems cross the area and provide good transportation facilities to all the large markets, such as Kansas City, Chicago, Omaha, and Denver. Most farms are less than 6 or 8 miles from a railroad shipping point, but there are some in the northwestern part of the area that are 10–12 miles away.

Living conditions in the farm home of today are in striking contrast to those of only a few years ago. Modern machinery has relieved man from much of the heavy drudgery as well as increasing production per man-hour. Even though they are located on the margin of the humid area of the country more than a third of the farm homes have running water. Ninety-five per cent have automobiles, 80 per cent have radios, nearly 70 per cent have telephones, and more than 60 per cent are supplied with electricity. With diversification, increased efficiency, and greater income has come a higher standard of living.

Urban Centers.   The county has 13 urban centers within it, varying in population from 100 to 33,500. More than four-fifths of the urban population lives in Hutchinson, which contains three-fifths of the inhabitants of the county. Railroads radiate from it in many directions, and it is the chief distributing and shipping point for a large part of western Kansas. Wheat is brought here from a large territory, and cleaned, graded, and reshipped to other milling centers for export. The city has 60 or more manufacturing establishments, closely related to the resources of the region and to the needs of the people of the vicinity. Most of the enterprises are small, but several have products valued at more than $1,000,000 annually. Among its industries are grain elevators, flour mills, salt, straw-board, and soda-ash factories. Industries of the other towns are confined principally to creameries or milk-receiving stations, and the handling of grain.

Summary.   The gently rolling Plains country about Hutchinson, with its generally fertile soils, is primarily a grain-producing area. It lies in that border region where a variable climate makes agriculture very precarious, though total crop failure rarely occurs. When rainfall is sufficient and properly distributed, and strong, hot, dry winds are not too frequent, prosperity reigns; but a succession of seasons with unfavorable weather may convert this area to a semiarid land, and sweep away the gains of good years. This is a region where man presses his humid agricultural system into the margin of the semiarid—a climate and soil to which small grains, especially winter wheat, are better adapted than most other crops—but where small returns must be expected part of the time. Even though the handicaps may appear severe, the average production is large; and the growth of cereals and feed crops with the raising and fattening of livestock is likely to continue to be the type of husbandry best adapted to conditions. Unfavorable weather in such a region produces not only poor crops and "bad years," but also human discontent which is reflected frequently in state and national politics. Because of the numerous "issues" or "movements" that have arisen in the Middle West, it may be called the "emotion region of the United States," and Kansas may be taken as the center. However much such a statement should be qualified, it is worthy of note that most of the "movements" originating in Kansas were associated with agriculture in the western two-thirds of the state. That the reasoning of its people on national problems should be different from that of people living in the manufacturing East is to be expected, since the outlook on life in the two regions is influenced by strikingly different natural environments. Who can say which is right and which is wrong? May not the greatest good ultimately come from a mutually better understanding of the conditions under which each group of people lives?

CORN AND MEAT

The Primacy of the Corn Crop. Corn is both the pioneer and the premier American crop. It was one of the first crops grown on American farms, if not the first. It was being produced in America when the colonists first settled in Massachusetts and Virginia, and it was the Indian who taught the colonists how to grow it. In 1609 the Virginia colonists had 30–40 acres in corn; in 1614, 500 acres, and in 1631 a surplus was produced for export. As the people migrated westward, corn was one of the principal crops carried with them. This westward movement of corn growing began immediately following the Revolutionary War and spread into the Northwest Territory, Tennessee, and Kentucky. By 1839 it was well across the Mississippi River. The introduction of the steel plow, especially adapted to the breaking of the prairie, and later the advance of the railroad into the region, hastened the expansion of the corn area over the prairies. Its most intensive culture became established in what has become known commonly as the corn belt, an area extending from central Ohio to southeastern South Dakota and thence southward along the Missouri River, occupying parts or the whole of the states of Ohio, Indiana, Illinois, Iowa, Nebraska, Kansas, and Missouri. This large area, except in the East, consists of fertile, well-drained prairie or bottom lands, easily worked (Fig. 12).

Climate and Corn. Though corn is widely grown in the United States, being produced in every state and on three-fourths of the farms of the country, the principal producing area is limited to the central part of the country (Fig. 89). The principal limiting factors are rainfall, temperature, and length of growing season, though soil plays its part. The largest yields

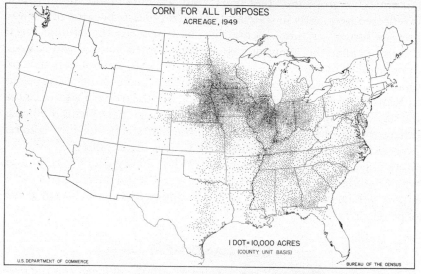

Fig. 89. The distribution of corn.

are obtained in well-drained, fertile, loamy soil of high humus and available nitrogen content and well adapted to the use of the labor-saving machinery. The climatic bounds of the Corn Belt are "a mean summer temperature of 70° to 80°, a mean night temperature exceeding 58°, a frostless season of over 140 days, and an annual precipitation of 25 to 50 inches, of which 7 inches occurs during July and August." [4] Essentially, no corn is grown where the average summer temperature is less than 66° or where the average summer night temperature falls below 55°. Low summer temperatures, therefore, are the principal limiting factors at the north; the western limit is practically the mean summer rainfall line of 8 inches. July is the critical month, and the rainfall of that month is very closely related to the yield. The combination of these ideal conditions of

[4] Finch and Baker, "Geography of World Agriculture," U. S. Govt. Printing Office, 1917, p. 29.

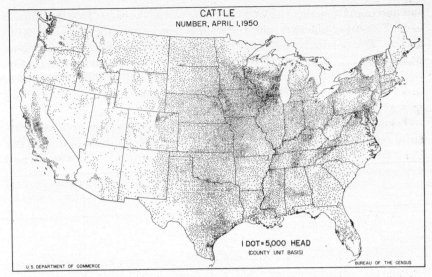

Fig. 90. Beef cattle exceed slightly dairy cattle in number, but their value is a little less. Nearly half the total number of beef cattle in the United States are in the Corn Belt and the Great Plains Region.

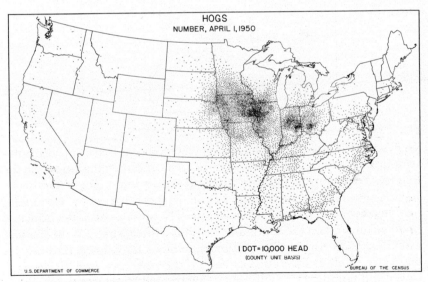

Fig. 91. More than two-fifths of the swine are in the warm, rich Corn Belt where they average more than 100 to the square mile. The Cotton Belt and Corn and Winter-Wheat Belt have about one-fifth each.

soil and climate makes the Corn Belt the world's greatest food-producing area. Few other places possess these ideal conditions, and none are as extensive. The northern and southern limits of corn grown for grain are now practically reached, though early maturing varieties and growth for forage or green fodder may extend its culture still farther north. The warm, moist conditions of the South produce a large vegetative growth but low-quality grain.

Related Crops.   Corn is not the only crop grown in this great agricultural region. In fact, it is grown on less than half of the croplands in the Corn Belt. More than half the agricultural land grows hay, soybeans, and

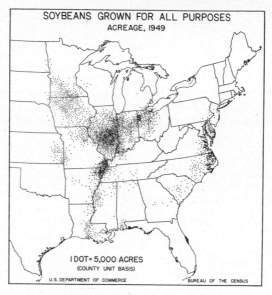

Fig. 92. Distribution of soybeans.

small grains. These may be harvested when labor is free from corn cultivation; they supplement corn as stock feed; and they maintain the soil fertility. Temperature, moisture, and soil are the important factors determining the choice of such crops. In the northern part of the Corn Belt, from northwestern Indiana to northeastern Nebraska, oats is the principal small grain, and on the south and east it is winter wheat. West of a line extending from Kansas City, Missouri, to Sioux City, Iowa, crossing the other two small-grain sections, alfalfa is the chief hay; and, to the east, clover and timothy. This selection is determined largely by the moisture supply to the east and west of this line. Soybeans are also a major crop in Illinois, Iowa, and Indiana. The Corn Belt is, therefore, a large producer of spring oats, clover, timothy, alfalfa, winter wheat, and soybeans.

The relative importance of this production is shown in Table X. Closely related to the production of these crops is the raising of hogs, beef cattle, and poultry.

Importance of Corn.   Corn is the leading crop of the United States. Its value in 3 out of 4 years is greater than the total value of wheat and cotton, and usually double the value of either. A hundred million acres is devoted to it, and it is grown on three-fourths of the farms in the United States. It is typically an American crop, as the United States produces about three-fifths of the world's crop, more than three-fifths of which is produced in the Corn Belt. As a food producer it is prolific, as it yields twice as much grain and, inclusive of forage, more than three times as much food to the acre as either oats or wheat. Directly and indirectly, it is the chief food source of the people of the United States. However, outside the South, less than 10 per cent is used directly as human food.

TABLE X

PROPORTION OF SELECTED PRODUCTS OF THE UNITED STATES PRODUCED IN THE CORN BELT STATES

1. 82.8 per cent of soybeans.
2. 66.2 per cent of corn.
3. 54.3 per cent of hogs.
4. 80.5 per cent of oats.
5. 31.7 per cent of all chickens and turkeys.
6. 23.5 per cent of all wheat.
7. 27.2 per cent of all cattle.
8. 27.2 per cent of hay.
9. 26.2 per cent of milk cows.
10. 24.1 per cent of total net value of manufactures.

Corn, swine, and cattle are intimately related (Figs. 89, 90, 91, 95). The regions of densest swine and corn production are practically identical, except where corn is sold as grain. The sale of corn as grain is usually determined by nearness to large markets, such as Chicago, where it is manufactured into starch, cornmeal, glucose, or other corn products. Beyond a radius of 150–200 miles from that center corn goes to market "on the hoof," as in such concentrated form it can better stand the cost of transportation. Two-thirds of the corn, four-fifths of the soybeans and oats, about one-quarter of the wheat, all cattle, milk cows, and more than half the swine are produced in the Corn Belt. Great numbers of cattle and sheep are brought in from the Western grassland plains and fattened for the market. Livestock on farms alone consume more than four-fifths of all of the corn crop. Scarcely a quarter of the crop goes out of the county in which it is grown, and less than 1 per cent finds a foreign market, a condition that is in striking contrast to wheat marketing.

The Present and Future of the Corn Region.   For many years the efforts of the Corn Belt farmer have been directed toward producing larger and larger crops. Ideal geographic conditions and a hungry world population able to pay for high-quality food have fostered his efforts. The world demand for corn-fed beef, pork, and other corn products have made corn the most profitable crop that could be produced in the Corn Belt. Land values rose rapidly to high levels during World War I, along with prices of products. Modern conveniences were added to farm homes, and many other improvements were made. At the close of the war, prices of corn products declined more rapidly than the commodities purchased by the farmer. At the same time, the cost of moving his products remained high. High-priced farm property, increasing ratio of debt to property value, declining price and demand for Corn Belt products in Europe, relatively high freight rates, and large production combined to produce a decrease in rural population and much economic distress. During World War II prices again rose to a high level and have been sustained artificially by government subsidies. The North Central Section has now developed strong secitonalism finding expression as an agrarian *bloc* in American politics. In this respect the history of the Corn Belt is not unlike that of other sections of the United States in which the people have in the past reflected the dominant interest of their environment or do so today. Perhaps another epoch will see an adjustment of production to consumption and a counter-balancing influence brought about by the further development of manufacturing and trade. It seems probable that climate and soil will continue to make the present types of products the most profitable ones to produce in the Corn Belt.

A CORN BELT UNIT

Adair County situated about 50 miles southwest of Des Moines and 75 miles east of Omaha and Council Bluffs, may be taken as a typical agricultural area in the Iowa portion of the Corn Belt. It lies on the watershed between the Missouri and the Des Moines Rivers. This watershed extends from the northwest corner of the county to its center, where it bears eastward, and where a branch divide extends southward. Numerous small ridges radiate from these principal divides, but as a whole the surface is gently rolling with broken belts along the numerous streams which reach practically all parts of the area. No marshes, ponds, or lakes worth mentioning exist. The "rougher" lands occur in the southwestern and southeastern parts, but the range in elevation for the county is very small, being less than 250 feet, and the extensive development of highways on the sectional plan divides it into a nearly uniform checkerboard

Fig. 93. Agricultural pattern in Monona County, Iowa, and a small rural community center. *Courtesy, U. S. Production and Marketing Administration.*

pattern. Nearly all the soil is of glacial origin but modified by wind, streams, and other weathering agencies. Over the more elevated surfaces rests a mantle of loess, and, on the lowland, alluvial soils representing wash from the uplands.

The climate is characterized by long, warm summers and moderately cold winters, with extremes rarely prolonged sufficiently to injure crops

or livestock seriously. Temperatures for the three summer months average 72°, and for the three winter months 22°. With a growing season of
165 days; an average annual rainfall of 33 inches, seven-tenths of which
comes in the spring and summer months; with rich soils on a land of low
relief; and with good transportation facilities to markets, the area
presents conditions highly favorable to agricultural development.

The first settler came in 1849. Other settlers soon followed in rapidly
increasing numbers, and the county was organized in 1851. Most of the
early immigrants came from eastern states, and 95 per cent of the present
inhabitants are native-born. There are a few hundred of German and
Scandinavian origin. The population is wholly rural, as there are only 7
small vilages, 3 of which are on the county boundary lines. The largest
village is Greenfield, with a population of 2000, located near the center
of the county. The farm population averages about 13 to the square mile
of farm land, and the total population, including the villages, averages
23. As in many other rural districts, the population decreased during the
last census decade. Today the county's 569 square miles of gently undulating surface, covered by dark brown to black fertile loam soils, presents
a panorama of well-kept farm homes and other buildings, and well-tilled
fields enclosed by mile upon mile of barbed-wire fence modified in part
by woven-wire bases where required to confine the thousands of swine
that are raised annually and fattened upon the chief crop—corn. Nine-
tenths of the homes have radios and telephones, nearly half have electricity, one-quarter are provided with running water, and there are more
automobiles than farms. Practically the only areas not cultivated are the
more broken sections which are kept in permanent pasture, and farm
woodlots. The woodlands and the other unimproved lands in farms constitute a very small part of the entire area of the farm land. Telephones
and rural mail service reach all parts of the area, and modern farm machinery and other equipment are in common use. It is preeminently a
farming area with a few small rural villages serving the local needs of a
farm population.

Production of Feed Crops.   Farming has been the dominant industry
since the arrival of the first settler and is likely to remain so. In the early
days the livestock was herded on the open range, often by contract, and
only the cultivated fields were fenced. As the population increased the
fenced areas came to occupy an ever-increasing proportion of the land
area, and the open ranges were largely taken up by the late 1870's and
early 1880's. Flax was used frequently as a breaking crop in the early
days, but its growth was practically discontinued in the decade following
1900. The original type of agriculture—livestock and feed crops—has
continued to increase in importance. This type has as its basis the raising

of livestock, especially hogs and beef cattle, and to a smaller extent sheep, horses, and mules, and the production of food crops chiefly supports the animal industries. Some grain, principally wheat and corn, is marketed. Oats, barley, rye, sorghum, mixed grains, soybeans, sweet clover, timothy, clover, alfalfa, and prairie grass comprise essentially all the crops utilized for animal sustenance.

Adair County is truly a part of that "land where the tall corn grows," as more than 43 per cent of its cultivated land is devoted to corn. During the summer months the landscape resembles one continuous corn field dotted at frequent intervals by groves of trees, in the midst of which are

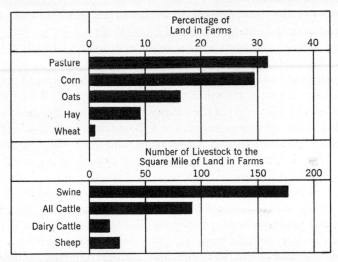

Fig. 94. Agricultural practice in Adair County, Iowa. Most crops of Adair County are produced for stock food. Corn acreage is nearly twice that of any other crop. Nearly a third of the land in farms is devoted to pasture.

set a fine home and excellent farm buildings equipped with most modern conveniences. Even though corn may be grown on the same land for several years in succession, the average yield is about 40 bushels an acre. Corn lands are commonly plowed in the fall if time is then available, but much of the acreage is not prepared for the crop until spring. The planting is done during the first half of May with automatic planters, and the corn is cultivated three or four times during the season. The matured ears are "snapped," by hand or machine, from the stalks in the fall and stored in cribs for feeding. Some corn is now cut by machinery for silage or for fodder-feeding during the winter.

Oats rank next to corn, and are produced chiefly as food for animals. Only occasionally is there a surplus for market. They are sown in the latter part of March if the season is favorable, but more commonly during the first half of April, and are thus "out of the way" before corn-planting time.

Hay crops rank next to oats and are produced in considerable variety. Practically the entire production is fed on the farms of the county.

Wheat is not considered a profitable crop under normal conditions. Most of the wheat is of the winter variety and is sown in the latter part of September. The spring variety is sown about the same time as oats. Nearly all the threshing is done from the shock in the field, but some wheat is stacked to be threshed later.

Barley, rye, and soybeans are minor crops used primarily as stock food. Potatoes for family use are grown in small patches on most farms. Nearly every farm maintains an apple orchard, and there are some peach, plum, pear, and cherry trees, and various small berry fruits to supply the home needs.

Production of Livestock.   Swine, cattle, and sheep are the principal animals raised. There are more than 98,900 swine, 52,000 cattle, and 14,400 sheep on the farms of the county. Chickens are also produced on all farms and the surplus products are disposed of in local markets. Practically every farmer raises and fattens swine, and the average farmer markets from 50 to 60 a year. Many of the swine produced are purebred or very high-grade stock.

Cattle are nearly all of the beef type, and this type has about twice the monetary value of swine. Most of the cattle are raised locally, but some feeders are imported for fattening. The herds range in size from 25 to 30 on a quarter-section farm, to 100 or more. Dairy cattle are only a sixth as numerous as the beef type, and, though dairying is considered only an incidental farm industry it provides a substantial farm income yearly. The cream is separated on the farm and sold to creameries, such as the cooperative creamery at Greenfield from which the butter is shipped to distant markets.

Sheep are of much less importance than cattle or swine and are raised more generally in the rougher lands of the southeastern and western parts of the county. Markets for cattle, swine, sheep, and other livestock are readily accessible at Omaha, St. Joseph, Kansas City, Des Moines, and Chicago.

Adair County is a typical agricultural area specializing in meat-producing livestock, and stock-food crops. Ninety-eight per cent of its total area is in farms. Its farms average 175 acres in size, and, inclusive of buildings, represents an average investment of about $19,500. Nearly three-fifths of its farm land is operated by owners and part owners.

HAY AND FORAGE—DAIRYING

Importance of Hay and Forage. Hay and forage constitute one of the most important crops produced in the United States. The term includes a great variety of both cultivated and wild grasses, of which timothy, clover, alfalfa, and prairie are the leading ones. Most of the prairie hay and alfalfa are grown in the drier western portion of the North Central Section; the others thrive best in the more humid and cooler eastern portions. The growth of hay and forage is not restricted by geographic con-

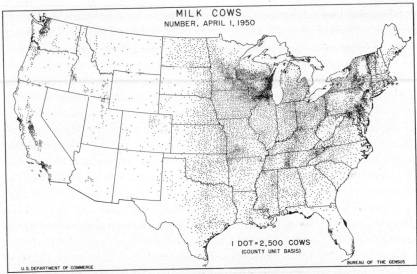

MILK COWS
NUMBER, APRIL 1, 1950

1 DOT = 2,500 COWS
(COUNTY UNIT BASIS)

U.S. DEPARTMENT OF COMMERCE   BUREAU OF THE CENSUS

Fig. 95. Distribution of milk cows. Nine-tenths of the dairy cattle are in the eastern part of the country, mostly in the cool Hay and Dairy Region and in the adjacent eastern and northern margin of the Corn Belt.

ditions as are many other crops and hence is widespread, being adapted to climates ranging from hot to cold and humid to arid, and also to a great variety of soils. Abundant moisture during the growing season, with little rain and much sunshine during the curing period, and well-drained clay soil are conducive to successful production. Its selection as a major crop in a given area is the joint result of geographic and economic factors. The large amounts required for stock feed make it the second most important crop in the North Central States, where nearly half the crop of the United States is produced. These states have half the dairy cattle, and produce four-fifths of the butter and cheese. As population increases there is a tendency to increase the acre yield. Under present conditions, permanent agriculture has its most substantial basis in the production of forage crops and livestock, which means a system of general farming. Such a system is enduring because (1) legumes constitute many of the forage crops and add nitrogen to the soil; (2) the decaying fine roots of grasses provide nourishment for nitrogen-fixing bacteria, add humus to the soil, and serve to keep it in excellent tilth; (3) animal manure is unexcelled by any artificial fertilizer; and (4) the system tends to maintain economic stability. From the standpoint of value, dairy cattle comprise the most important type of livestock on the farms of the United States today.

Specialization in the North. The northern region has passed through several periods of agricultural development and has attained a more advanced stage than have most other parts of the North Central Section. The exploring-hunting stage was followed by pastoral husbandry, when the pioneer settlers pastured a few cattle and sheep in the forest lands. Then came specialization in grain growing, as transportation facilities, such as railroads, canals, and lakes, became available for marketing the crops; and finally came the system of mixed farming in which hay and forage and dairying became dominant, a system associated with a denser population than normally exists at the other stages named. A number of geographic, economic, and human factors have fostered, in Wisconsin, Michigan, Minnesota, and the adjacent northern edge of the Corn Belt, especially Illinois and Iowa, the development of hay and forage and the dairy industry. This development is in contrast with that of the wheat regions and of the corn belt in which one crop dominates agricultural economy. Among these influencing factors are the long winters, the cool, moist summers with moderately long growing and grazing season, which discourage the growth of grain in competition with more favorably endowed areas, but encourage dairying; abundant rain in frequent showers during the growing season but with little rain and much sunshine during the curing period; slight injury from drought; heavy snow cover which prevents serious loss from freezing; a glacially derived surface containing much hilly morainic land, many lakes and swamps, soils ranging from silts to sand and gravel not well suited to the growth of corn and other cereals; a fairly large population with a constant city demand for dairy products; a large population of north-European human stock familiar with the dairy industry.

Near city centers of dense population where modern rapid transportation facilities have been provided by railroads and trucks, a large proportion of the dairy products go to market as milk; and at more distant points the milk is condensed or converted into butter and cheese, which can better stand the cost of transportation.

Wisconsin the Leading State.   Wisconsin is the leading dairy state. Its commercial milk is made into cheese and butter or is condensed. Its cheese output is nearly half that of the entire country. Of the United States production of American cheese the state supplies about two-fifths; brick and Münster nearly nine-tenths; Limburger nearly half; Swiss nearly two-thirds; Italian more than half; and nearly two-thirds of other varieties. Minnesota exceeds Wisconsin in the production of butter and is now the leading butter state, but Wisconsin ranks third, being exceeded

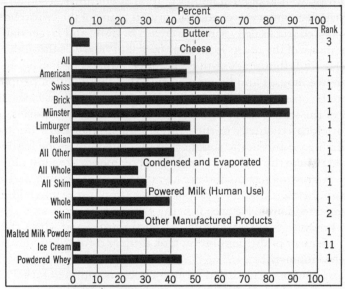

MANUFACTURED DAIRY PRODUCTS 1946
Wisconsin Production as a Percent of the United States Total

Fig. 96. Wisconsin dairy products in percentage of United States total. *Courtesy, Wisconsin Crop Reporting Service.* Wisconsin leads in the manufacture of dairy products except butter, powdered skim milk, and ice cream.

by Iowa. The adjacent northern portion of Illinois, near the large city markets, likewise has a highly developed dairy industry. The leading position of Wisconsin is due to a combination of geographic, economic, and human factors. Its geographic and economic advantages are no better than exist elsewhere, but the influence of scientific research and able leadership has been profound. The contributions and far-sighted campaign of education among a people ancestrally, and in many cases personally, trained in dairying, and living in a physical environment highly conducive to the industry, have wielded a large influence in producing a stable agricultural system.

Dairying is well distributed over Wisconsin except in the forested, sparsely settled north and in the central region of poor, sandy soil. Dairy manufactures have become one of the leading industries. More than four-fifths of the farm income is derived from livestock and livestock products, and more than half the income comes from milk alone. The entire crop system is built around livestock, and dairying ranks first as a source of farm income in nearly every county of the state. As one traverses the leading dairy areas over the hard-surfaced highways he is impressed by the general appearance of substantial prosperity prevailing. In that cultural landscape he sees a gently rolling country of fenced fields of feed crops, well-kept farm homes and farm buildings, a silo on nearly every farm, a creamery or cheese factory on many of the crossroads with heavily loaded trucks delivering the cream or milk, and larger dairy factories in many of the towns located at frequent intervals throughout the region. He finds thousands of those homes equipped with every modern convenience, houses and barns electrically lighted, and a people who appear to be operating their industry on a modern business basis. Three-fourths of the state's dairy establishments are cheese factories. These plants are located chiefly in the central and east central sections near Lake Michigan, and in the rougher, unglaciated limestone lands of the southwest, where the nights are cool. The creameries are most abundant in the corn-growing section and are an adjustment to summer and winter dairying; cheese is mainly a response to summer dairying. The chief American cheddar cheese area is in the eastern lake shore section where the pioneer New Yorkers transplanted the industry and where the large German element in the population took it up and contributed to its successful development.

The production of so-called foreign cheese is confined largely to the two chief areas, of which Green County, in the Driftless limestone southwest, and Dodge County, in the glaciated limestone soils and 30 miles northeast of the first area, are the respective centers. The Green County area is a Swiss settlement, and the brick cheese of the Dodge County area was originated by a young Swiss.

MICHIGAN FRUIT BELT

A narrow belt along the western side of the lower peninsula of Michigan is one of the most important fruit-producing regions of the United States, chiefly because of the climatic influence of Lake Michigan. This belt produces great quantities of grapes, peaches, pears, apples, and small fruits. In these border counties is produced nearly seven-tenths of the total value of all fruit of the state, which is nearly four times that for the entire state of Wisconsin, located on the windward side of the Lake. The value of the fruit produced in Oceana County in Michigan is seventeen times that of Sheboygan County, directly across the lake in Wisconsin; and that of Berrien County, Michigan (in the extreme southwest) is

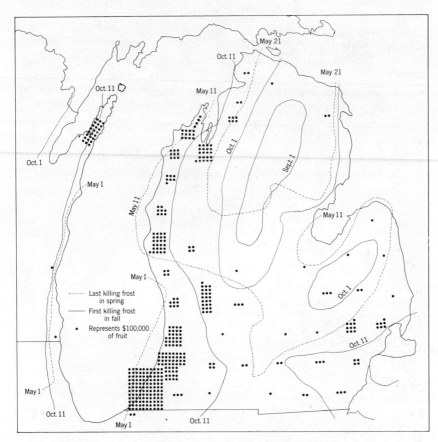

Fig. 97. Lake Michigan and the westerly winds are powerful factors in modifying the climate of western Michigan, and in influencing the kinds of crops produced and the recreation industry. In this narrow belt along the leeward Lake Michigan shore is produced nearly seven-tenths of the total value of all fruit grown in Michigan, and nearly four times that for the entire state of Wisconsin situated on the windward side of the lake.

three times that of all the Wisconsin counties bordering the lake, and more than one-fifth greater than that of the enire state. Door County, which receives the moderating influence of Green Bay from the west and Lake Michigan from the east, is the only Wisconsin County that compares favorably with Michigan counties along the eastern shore of the

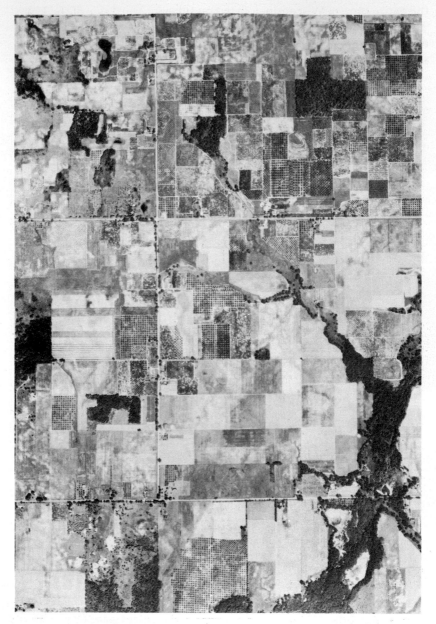

Fig. 98. Part of the Michigan fruit belt with Lake Michigan bordering the area on the left. *Courtesy, U. S. Production and Marketing Administration.*

lake (Figs. 97 and 98). The relative positions of Michigan and Wisconsin in fruit production does not imply, of course, that Wisconsin cannot produce fruit.

Climate, Lake Michigan, sandy-loam soil, and nearness to large city markets are the principal factors that have influenced the development of the Michigan fruit belt. The potency of Lake Michigan in raising the temperature and moisture content of the westerly winds, and in retarding early spring growth, is much greater in Michigan than in Wisconsin. This influence extends some 20 miles or more inland from its leeward shore and may be summarized as follows: (1) In spring the cool westerly winds from the lake retard plant growth until the danger from frost is past, and in autumn the relatively warm winds delay the first killing frosts until the more tender trees are ready for the winter. (2) A growing season of about 160 days prevails along the Michigan shore nearly to the northern extremity of the lower peninsula but decreases rapidly in length toward the northern interior. This gives the northern lake shore as long a growing season as the southern interior of the state. However, the length of the growing season is not greater than on the Wisconsin side. (3) The winter temperatures are much milder along the Michigan shore than in Wisconsin, and the extreme minimum temperature is never as low. The critical temperatures of −15° to −20°, which kill the buds, seldom occur on the Michigan shore but occur nearly every winter on the Wisconsin side. (4) The extreme summer temperatures are 6° to 10° lower on the Michigan shore than in the interior of the state. This is a large factor in the development of an extensive summer-resort business as well as in the production of fruit. (5) The snowfall of the Michigan shore counties is 10 inches to 20 inches greater than in the interior of the state or on the Wisconsin side. The percentage of winter cloudiness and summer sunshine is also greater than in Wisconsin, both of which favor fruit growing. The moist winters, which reduce the loss from "winter killing," and the delayed springs are probably the two most important climatic factors favoring the leeward shores of Lake Michigan as a fruit region.

Extensive areas of muck lands, lying in depressions among the glacial gravel and sandy hills, have been developed for production of truck crops. Large tonnages of vegetables are now being grown for canneries. Practically all of this type of land utilization is well inland from the lake, and the climatic influence of the lake is of little or no significance.

OTHER CROPS AND LIVESTOCK

Although there is crop and livestock specialization in the various agricultural regions previously described, these regions produce a large variety of other important agricultural products. The chief major producing sections of barley, rye, potatoes, sugar beets, tobacco, and flax are north of the Corn Belt, in regions of cooler summers and shorter growing seasons. Oats are grown extensively in the Corn Belt for stock food, and as a spring-sown crop in the system of rotation, but their culture extends to the northern border of the United States. Soybeans are another important crop of the Corn Belt. Enormous quantities of eggs and poultry meat are produced in the North Central Region, much of it coming from grain and stock farms rather than from specialized poultry farms. Sheep raising came into the region during its early settlement and has been retained as part of the farming system especially in southern Michigan and in Ohio where sheep are better adapted to the hilly pasture lands in the southeastern quarter than are cattle. With the exception of limited areas, sheep are now produced primarily for mutton.

PROBLEMS

1. Can the North Central Section maintain a population as dense as that of Germany?

2. Can the North Central Section maintain its position as the leading agricultural region of the United States?

3. Does prosperity in the Corn Belt depend upon the corn crop?

4. What change in the center of production of each of the leading crops of the North Central Section is likely to occur within the next century?

5. To what extent are geographic factors responsible for agricultural prosperity in the North Central Section?

6. To what extent are the farmer, manufacturer, banker, transporter, and city dweller interdependent?

7. To what extent does the prosperity of the United States farmer depend upon the prosperity of people in other parts of the world?

8. What states may equal or excel Wisconsin in dairying?

CHAPTER 9

North Central Section—
The Industrial Lower Lake Region

A Region of Manifold Industries.   The Industrial Lower Lake Region includes southern Michigan and Wisconsin, Ohio, Indiana, and Illinois, to which St. Louis is closely allied. It is a region of agriculture, mining, manufacturing, commerce, trains, trucks, buses, airplanes, boats, and many large cities. Among its people engaged in gainful occupations, approximately 32 per cent are in manufacturing industries; 15 per cent in transportation, communication and other public utilities; and 13 per cent in agriculture, indicating clearly the dominance of industry in the region.

Here are produced and collected great quantities of raw materials— iron ore from the north, coal from Illinois, Indiana, and the East, salt, forest products, rubber, petroleum and other minerals, wheat, oats, cattle, hogs, and many other farm and orchard products. These materials are fabricated into a multitude of finished articles—products of slaughtering and meat packing, of iron and steel plants, and of foundry and machine shops, automobiles, agricultural implements, rubber tires, engines, clothing, boots and shoes, *ad infinitum*—to meet the wants of the people in all parts of the world. It possesses a remarkable combination of vital resources that integrate so as to make it approximately an economic unit. These resources probably provide better for an all-round development than do the natural resources of any other section of the United States, and probably are unequaled in that respect outside the north central plains of Europe. In addition to the resources within the bounds of the Industrial Lower Lake Region, the coal power of Pennsylvania, West Virginia, Kentucky, and Tennessee may be drawn upon. However, the inland location places upon this region a freight-cost handicap in competition with the East which partially negates the advantages accruing from its superior wealth of natural resources. Since the upper waters of America's two great waterways—the Great Lakes-St. Lawrence, and the Mississippi—are but a short distance apart, a more effective commercial connection is likely to come ultimately. Such a connection will lessen but not remove entirely the disadvantage of location, as there are many economic factors unfavorable to long inland canal and river navigation compared with all-year transportation on the modern railroad or by highway. Today the Lower Lake Region is covered with a close network of excellent railways, airways, and highways and is traversed by the main transcontinental lines of the country.

FUEL AND POWER

Coal.   Coal is still the chief source of fuel and power and, probably, is the most important factor in modern manufacturing development. Two of America's most important coal fields are located partially within the region, and one of the minor fields is confined to Michigan. Nearly all the Eastern Interior province lies in Illinois and Indiana, and part of the Appalachian province is in Ohio. Illinois, Ohio, and Indiana pro-

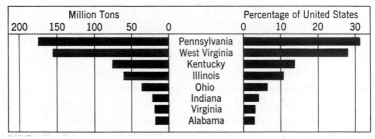

Fig. 99. Coal production by leading states. Three-year average. These eight states produce nine-tenths of the bituminous, lignite, and anthracite coal.

duce a fifth of the annual output of the country, and rank fourth, fifth, and sixth, respectively, among the states in the amount mined annually. Michigan produces a small amount, which is used locally, as better coal can be obtained easily. The reserves of bituminous coal are enormous. Those of the Interior province and part of the Appalachian province in Ohio, which lie wholly or largely in the Lower Lake Region, are approximately 530,000 million tons, and constitute more than two-fifths of the total bituminous reserves of the United States. The presence of these coals as a power source, in the midst of a rich agricultural region, has been a large factor in the rapid manufacturing development, in the growth of transportation facilities by rail and boat, and in the growth of such centers as St. Louis, Kansas City, Chicago, Cleveland, and many other Lake Cities where the coal meets the iron ore and where the products of the factory may secure cheap transportation. Coal as raw material has likewise given rise to coke and gas plants and to the production of many by-products.

Petroleum and Natural Gas. As petroleum and natural gas production spread westward from Pennsylvania, Ohio, Indiana, and Illinois became leading states. But oil and natural gas are ephemeral bases of industry, as a large output continues for only a relatively few years in any field. Many villages were born, grew rapidly with the rise of the oil and gas industry, and sank into insignificance with its decline. For many years, petroleum and natural gas wielded a large influence in the indus-

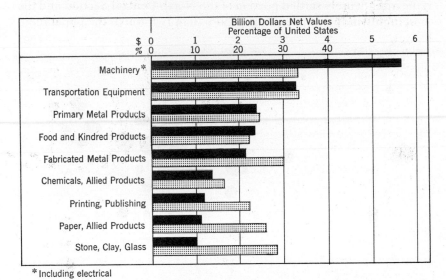

* Including electrical

Fig. 100. Typical industrial groups of the Lower Lake Region (1951). The manufacturing industries of the Lower Lake Region are large and varied whether measured by net value or by percentage of the country's total production.

trial developmet of the region, and they are still of considerable importance, although most of the oil for refining comes into the region from more productive fields. The production is now small compared with that of other fields. The refining of petroleum remains a large industry, as oil is brought through pipe lines from the southwestern fields.

MAJOR INDUSTRIES

A Highly Developed Manufacturing Region. The Lower Lake Region possesses the essentials for successful manufacturing development: (1) abundant power, (2) abundant raw materials of great variety, (3) abundant labor and capital, (4) excellent transportation facilities, and (5) excellent, accessible market both within and without the region. Cities and manufacturing centers at focal points along the Lake shores profit by the great advantage of location. Veritably, they are creations of the Great Lakes; born but yesterday, their growth within a few generations has been phenomenal.

The industries of the region are almost as varied as human wants. For many years food products ranked first among its larger industrial groups, but is now surpassed by machinery, primary metal products, and transportation equipment, especially motor vehicles. The Lower Lake Region is the most densely settled portion of the North Central Section and the most highly industrialized. It has more than two-thirds the population,

Fig. 101. The meat-packing industry is localized in the Corn Belt or near its margin. The industry in New York and New Jersey is centralized chiefly in the urban area about New York City where it meets the requirements of the large population for fresh meat.

produces more than four-fifths of the net-value of manufactures, and has the same ratio of the manufacturing employees. The value of its manufactures constitutes one-third of the total for the United States.

Meat Packing.   Among the food products, meat packing ranks high in value of products though its net value is relatively small. The industry is by no means confined to the Lower Lake Region. However, the high cost of shipping live animals, the loss sustained by injuries and in weight in shipping them, and the fact that only about half the live weight is meat have tended to centralize slaughtering and meat packing in the Corn Belt and on its margin. The principal centers are Chicago, St. Louis-East St. Louis, Omaha, Kansas City, St. Paul, St. Joseph, Denver, and Sioux City.

At the beginning of the nineteenth century livestock of the Central West had no market except a local one; but early in that century cattle were driven across the mountains from the Ohio Valley to the markets of Baltimore, Philadelphia, and New York. This method of marketing later extended to Indiana, Illinois, and Kentucky, and ended with the establishment of railroad connections with the East. As the railways were

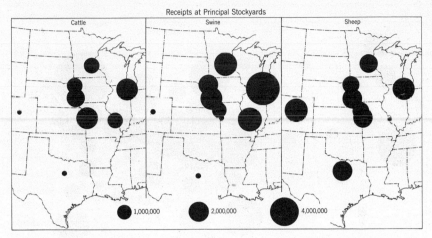

Fig. 102. Receipts at principal stockyards. These nine stockyards handle slightly more than half of all cattle, sheep, and swine received at the 68 public stockyards reporting.

built still farther west, "cattle drives" from Texas and the high plains to "cow towns," located at the end of the rails, were organized. As the rails were pushed on still farther and farther west new "cow towns" arose at their termini. As the development of transportation was a controlling factor in the westward expansion of cattle raising, making it possible to ship animals to distant markets, the development of refrigeration (1875–1885) and other methods of preserving meat transformed the slaughtering industry from a local one to one of large-scale production at great railroad foci in the food- and animal-producing section, and made the world a market for meat products. Before the perfection of refrigeration, slaughtering was largely a winter industry and ceased almost entirely during the warm summer months except in very large consuming centers. With rapid transportation, refrigeration, a population able to buy such high-quality food as meat, and the concentration of the industry at great centers, have arisen giant corporations able to effect economies to a high degree and to utilize every part of the animal. Chicago was one of the first important centers and is still the leading one. Its stockyards receive approximately 6,100,000 animals annually, and the output of its meat-packing establishments is valued in the billions of dollars, exclusive of the numerous by-products.

Flour Milling. Flour milling (Fig. 103) is as typical of the North Central Region as are slaughtering and meat packing and the manufacture of agricultural implements. The modern large merchant flour mill tends to locate at transportation centers in or near the wheat-producing regions

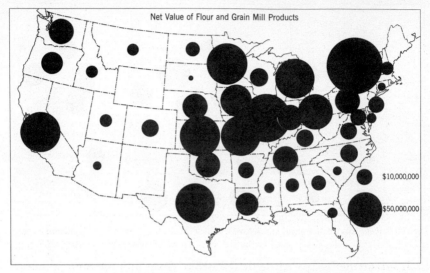

Fig. 103. Distribution of the flour and gristmill industry.

or in large consuming centers having low-cost transportation for wheat. Minneapolis illustrates the first type of location and is one of the largest wheat markets and flour-milling centers in the world. Coincident with the decline of the lumber industry and the invention of the processes that make possible the production of high-grade flour from spring wheat, the industry grew up about the power supplied by the Falls of St. Anthony. Kansas City, St. Louis, and Wichita are other centers of this type; and Chicago and Buffalo belong to the second class, where wheat may be brought by lake at low cost and where a dense population within a small radius provides a large market. The flour-milling industry in Buffalo— the concentration point at the east end of Lake Erie and on the principal route to the markets of the East and Europe—has grown rapidly, and that city now excels Minneapolis as a flour-producing center. Its location at the eastern end of Lake Erie and the water route for wheat, excellent power resources from Niagara Falls and from Pennsylvania coal, and nearness to a large market give it decided advantages over Minneapolis.

Iron and Steel Industry. Large-scale production of iron and steel has attained commanding significance since about 1920. The use of iron

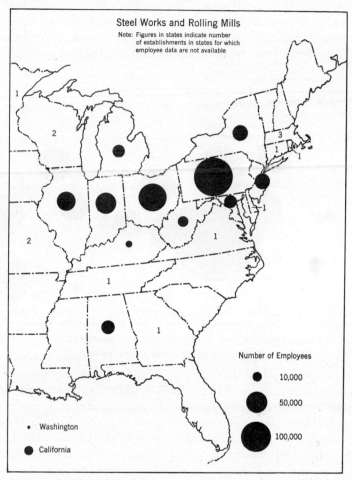

Fig. 104. More than two-fifths of the net-value of the output of blast furnaces, and iron and steel mills is contributed by the Lower Lake Region, and more than four-fifths of the iron ore produced by the United States annually comes from the Upper Lake Region.

and steel today is very largely a measure of the industrial importance of a nation. Modern industry demands power, especially coal, and millions of tons of steel. The evolution of the iron and steel industry in America may be divided into three quite distinct periods on the basis of the fuel

used, viz., charcoal, anthracite, and coke. The coke period brought the
Lake Superior region into prominence. Previous to 1855, charcoal was
dominant and furnaces were scattered widely to meet local needs, as in
the case of the old sawmills and gristmills. Between 1855 and 1875 anthracite led. Since a small area in northeastern Pennsylvania had all the
fuel, was able to make large quantities of iron, and was near the New
York and Philadelphia markets, the first opportunity for leadership in
the United States iron industry was offered and the first great producing

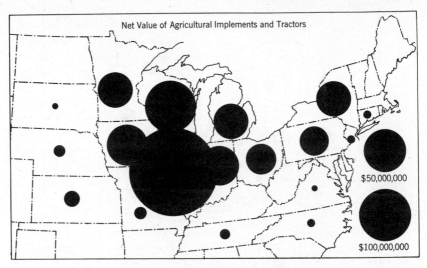

Fig. 105. Measured by net value, seven-tenths of the agricultural implement industry is
situated in the Great Lakes States.

center was established there. In 1870 half of all the pig iron was made
with anthracite, but by 1910 this ratio had declined to 2.4 per cent.

By 1875 the greater efficiency of bituminous coal and coke in this industry had been demonstrated. The most important supply of coal and
coke lay west of the Appalachians, as did the iron ore and limestone;
hence before 1880 the industry had shifted to western Pensylvania. The
introduction of the Bessemer process led to rapid development, and by
1880 the best local ores had been used. Nearness to Lake Erie and cheap
lake transportation made it impossible for the lean ores of western Pennsylvania to compete with the high-grade ores from Lake Superior; hence
by 1883 western Pennsylvania produced more pig iron than any other
district in the United States. Pittsburgh could not avoid becoming an
iron and steel center. It commanded Lake ores and the best of coke from
nearby centers, and had good transportation facilities by water and rail,
natural gas, an established eastern market, a rapidly growing interior

market, and a local market produced by the growth of allied industries. For more than half a century these advantages have made Pennsylvania the leading iron- and steel-making state.

Since enormous quantities of heavy raw materials such as iron ore, coke, and limestone must be brought together in the iron and steel industry of the country, it is evident that efficient low-cost transportation is a very imporant factor in plant location. With development of an efficient railroad system and the conversion of coal to coke at the steel mill where the by-product gas may be used for power, the Lake shores have become focal points at which the greatest economies could be effected, and the industry has shifted in that direction. Here are such centers as Duluth, Milwaukee, Chicago, Gary, Toledo, Cleveland, Lorain, and Buffalo (Lackawanna). Other large producing mills are in the Youngstown, Ohio, district, which has about the same advantages as Pittsburgh. Today the Lower Lake Region has more than one-third of the steel works and rolling mills of the country and produces more than two-fifths of the pig iron and the net value of steel works and rolling mills. As long as the Lake Superior district continues to be the major source of iron ore it appears likely that this region will continue to be a leading producer of iron and steel, as it provides for the assembling of abundant low-cost fuel, power, ore, and limestone, and an efficient railroad system makes accessible the markets of the Middle West and East. Abundant capital and both skilled and unskilled labor are available also.

The iron and steel industry itself has many branches and produces a multitude of products—blast furnaces, pipe mills, and rolling mills with their plates, sheets, structural steel, railroad rails, rods, etc. To hundreds of other plants the product of the steel mill is raw material. The products of these are legion, including cars, engines, automobiles, agricultural implements, ships, and the output of the foundry and machine shop. The production of agricultural implements is confined largely to the Lower Lake Region. Seven-tenths (net value) of the agricultural implements of the United States is produced here, and nearly two-fifths in Illinois alone (Fig. 105).

The Automobile Industry. The Lower Lake Region was formerly noted for its horse-drawn vehicles and for furniture. These industries arose and prospered in the midst of an abundant supply of hardwoods. Then came the invention and development of the automobile, and many of the carriage and wagon plants were converted into automobile factories. The production of horse-drawn carriages in the United States declined from about 2,000,000 in 1910 to about 10,000 a dozen years later. The rapid rise of the automobile industry is without parallel in industrial history. In the short period 1915–1930 it rose from eighth place among the industries of the country to first place. Today more than half (net value) the motor vehicles and equipment made in the United States is produced in the lower Lake region, and the industry has more than 700,000 employees. More than two-fifths of the output comes from Michigan (Fig. 106).

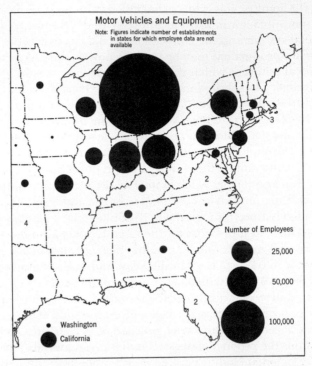

Motor Vehicles and Equipment

Note: Figures indicate number of establishments in states for which employee data are not available

Number of Employees

25,000

50,000

100,000

• Washington

● California

Fig. 106. Motor vehicles, bodies, and parts. The motor-vehicle industry is centralized in the Great Lakes states, where more than half of the net value for the United States is produced. The dominant position of Michigan is a striking feature of the industry.

The growth of the industry in Michigan, and especially in the Detroit area, has been extraordinary, and its influence in turn no less so. In 1900, 39 per cent of Michigan's population was urban. By 1930 the urban population had increased to 68 per cent and the farm population had declined to 16 per cent. The population shift in these decades was due primarily to the rapid development of the automobile and allied industries. The populations of the leading automobile cities of Detroit, Flint, Pontiac, and Lansing increased at a rapid rate. The Detroit metropolitan area now ranks third in the United States in net value of products and in number of employees. The industry soon spread beyond the city bounds into the suburbs. Towns that were small rustic hamlets a few years before were converted into large modern cities, all of which depended, directly or indirectly, upon the motor-vehicle industry. Thousands of other people, not counted in the population of these cities, drove many miles daily to work in the factories. They came from the surrounding farms and villages over the paved highways that crisscross the area in a close network. Many of the farms for miles about these industrial centers produced foodstuffs for the rapidly growing urban population, and truck farming increased rapidly. Thus the whole cultural landscape of the motor-vehicle-manufacturing region has undergone a revolutionary change in a very brief period. However, large producing centers are not confined to Michigan. Cleveland, Toledo, South Bend, and Akron—the great tire center—are rivals.

The location of the industry in Detroit rather than in some other city is probably an accident. The city happened to be where it was first established on a mass-production scale. However, besides being the natural successor to the carriage and wagon industry and having the advantage of an early start, automobile manufacutring finds other favorable factors in the Lower Lake Region. This section affords cheap lake transportation for raw materials and for some completed automobiles and trucks; has some hardwood and an abundance of steel and other metals; has excellent railway transportation, as the main lines from East to West pass through it; and is near the center of population, which minimizes the cost of marketing a bulky product.

INDUSTRIAL CENTERS

Cities are the Epitome of Human Endeavor. Modern cities are the compendium of a mechanistic civilization. In prerailroad days, town sites were determined largely by the need of transshipment at foci of natural routes. Towns grew at natural junctions of land, river, and lake routes, at the head of navigation, at breaks in navigation, at fords, at the junction of navigable tributaries, and at points where there was a salient change in river direction. Such centers became the marts for all kinds of tributary products, and later the focal points for canals, highways, and railways. The larger environmental factors, such as climate, soil, power, minerals, and regional location, continue to function, but in most cases the factor that determined the immediate location has ceased to be of great significance. Chicago would probably continue to be a great city if the Great Lakes should cease to exist. The modern city is a complex unit of closely crowded humanity, a great railroad center, a great market, a center of skilled and unskilled labor, a great collecting, distributing, and manufacturing center with large-scale business organizations having great capital investments in established plants. Many of the large railroad, truck, and airline cities of today were the water-route cities of the prerailroad period. Three-fifths of the section's major cities are situated on navigable rivers or on the Great Lakes. All these cities are important railroad centers. River traffic has ceased to be of great importance, but the Lake traffic wields a large influence.

The Chicago District.   Someone has aptly described Chicago as "the epitome and climax of the prairie and Lake region." Its immediate site was determined by the Chicago River, which served as a harbor and led by a low portage through the old outlet channel of glacial Lake Chicago, to the navigable Des Plaines and Illinois Rivers and thence to the Mississippi. At times of high water canoes passed from the lake to the Des Plaines without portaging. This route was followed by the Indians long before the advent of the white man. Far more important in the growth of Chicago has been its location near the southern end of Lake Michigan where the lake projects into a vast plains area whose continuity of fertility and productiveness is unequaled anywhere else in the world. Today nearly every important railway east of the Appalachian Mountains enters Chicago. All the main trunklines from East to West pass around the southern end of the lake and have their terminals in Chicago. All railroads from the Northwest make their connections there. No railroad passes through Chicago. It is also the focal point of the continental interior for air service. It has become a huge collecting, distributing, and manufacturing center. To it may be gathered all the manifold products of the Middle West: wheat from the Dakotas and Kansas; livestock from the Corn Belt and western grazing lands; iron ore and timber from the Upper Lake Region; and coal from Illinois, Ohio, and Pennsylvania. From it may be distributed with equal facility the products of its factories. The total number of people engaged in manufacturing enterprises within the city limits is greater than the total population of any one of nine states. From a city of 4400 people in 1840, it has risen to second place among the cities of the country in population and in the value of its manufactures. It has become the world's greatest grain, meat-packing, and railroad center, and one of the largest airports of the country. Its industries are large and varied and based chiefly on the raw materials of the region which it serves and supplying the demands of a dense population. Chicago is a product of the machine age, like most other American cities, and its accomplishments are measured largely by materialistic standards.

The Chicago metropolitan area, as defined by the census, extends from the north boundary of Illinois southward along the lake shore, including five counties in Illinois and one in Indiana, and has a population of

4,825,000. The population of this intensively industrial area is approximately the same as that of the state of Massachusetts, but the net value of its products is two-fifths larger. Into it has poured a rapidly increasing flow of humanity. Only seven states in the Union, other than Illinois, have as many people as are concentrated in this beehive of industry at the southern end of Lake Michigan. Chicago overshadows all other cities, but numerous other urban centers are located in the area, such as Gary, Hammond, Elgin, Joliet, Aurora, Evanston, and Waukegan. It is the focal point for the richest agricultural region of the size in the world, a region which is also equipped with an abundance of basic minerals such as coal, iron, copper, lead, and zinc, and the vast reaches of the level prairie land offer few obstacles to the development of transportation. The present producing and consuming population of its tributary area is scarcely a fifth that of a similar area in western Europe, but the potentials for an increased production of crops, domestic animals, dairy products, minerals, and forest products are very great. Today the metropolitan area is traversed by a close network of wide, paved highways over which thousands of trucks, buses, and passenger cars travel daily to serve the industrial and pleasure demands of the area and its extensive hinterland.

Industries of nearly every kind, designed to meet all human wants, are found among its 12,280 manufacturing establishments. Among the industries, turning out products having a net value of more than $100,-000,000, may be mentioned meat packing, iron and steel and its allied industries, machinery, printing and publishing, petroleum refining, and food products. The net value of its manifold industrial products equals nearly half that of all New England, a fourth that of the Middle Atlantic States, and about a third that of the whole Lower Lake Region outside the metropolitan area. This value is exceeded by only one other industrial area, viz., the New York metropolitan area.

Within the Illinois portion of the metropolitan area are located nearly three-fifths of the population of the state, three-fourths of the manufactures measured by net value, and a similar concentration of manufacturing employees. This great amassment of population has led to the development of jealousy and fear throughout the rest of the state—a fear of political domination by the large city. As a result, the democratic theories that representation in state government should be in proportion to population and that people should not be taxed without proportionate representation have been abandoned completely. Chicago has long been denied such representation in the State Legislature. All efforts to enforce the provisions of the state constitution so as to equalize representation have failed. That portion of the state outside Chicago is in power and it intends to stay in power. Even the State Supreme Court has ruled that the legislature cannot be compelled to carry out the law of the land and give Chicago its proportionate representation.

Closely associated with the Chicago metropolitan area are such urban centers as Milwaukee, Racine, and Kenosha, Wisconsin, with their extensive iron and steel, motor-vehicle, beverage, machinery, meat-packing, leather, and leather goods establishments, The industries of the whole district utilize the raw materials of the Middle West—agriculture, mine, and forest—and many products find their chief market there, e.g., farm machinery. All the principal centers put out a great variety of metal products. All have profited in the past by their location on Lake Michigan, and Gary, Milwaukee, and South Chicago depend upon it now for the delivery of Upper Lake ore. Though the lake commerce of Chicago and Milwaukee is of considerable industrial significance to them, it is relatively less so than formerly and is very small compared with the huge movement of commodities by rail and truck.

The Lake Erie District.   From Detroit to Buffalo, at foci of lake and land transportation, have grown up a number of important industrial centers. These include the automobile city of Detroit, which is discussed elsewhere, Cleveland and Toledo with their iron and steel mills and automobile plants, and several lesser ones. The manufacturing industries of the Ohio counties bordering Lake Erie are confined largely to Cleveland and Toledo where iron ore of the north meets coal from the south. The net value of the manufacturing enterprises in these lake-border counties constitutes more than a third of that of the state of Ohio. From the lake shore centers, iron ore is distributed to many other Ohio iron- and steel-working cities, particularly in the Youngstown area.

River Industrial Centers.   Though river traffic is no longer of paramount importance, many river cities have continued their growth with the development of railroad service. The largest of these is St. Louis, Missouri, with East St. Louis just across the Mississippi in Illinois. St. Louis is the fourth largest city in the North Central Section in population, and correspondingly large industrially. Situated near the confluence of the Mississippi and three other navigable rivers—the Missouri, Ohio, and Illinois—it occupied a commanding position when rivers were the principal means of transport. Its strategic commercial position naturally made it a focal point for railroads as they were extended westward. It was, therefore, enabled to maintain its commanding position in the Southwest. It occupies a central position in the producing areas of corn, wheat, cattle, and swine, and has become a marketing center for these products and a distributing point for the many commodities required by an agricultural population. Its industries are highly varied, and no one holds such a commanding position as do automobiles in Detroit or flour milling in Minneapolis. Meat packing is its leading industry, and it is the greatest boot- and shoe-manufacturing center outside of New England. Meat packing is the dominant industry of the Kansas City center and of Omaha, which, like St. Louis, are near the junction of the stock-food producing prairies and the western grazing lands. Other important meat-packing centers are South St. Paul, Minnesota, St. Joseph, Missouri, and Sioux City, Iowa.

Cincinnati, situated at a salient change in river direction and near the confluence of the historically important Miami and Ohio, is south of the steel-working cities of Ohio. It is tributary to the Bluegrass Region of Kentucky and productive agricultural lands at the north. In its early stage it was an important concentration point for settlers moving down the Ohio, and became a leading river port and later a railroad center. It was the leading livestock and meat-packing center until surpassed by Chicago in 1860, and that industry continues to be a leading one. Its other leading industries include machinery, men's and women's clothing, beverages, and chemicals.

Minneapolis-St. Paul, the "Twin Cities," at the head of Mississippi navigation, are independent political rivals but essentially one continuous urban center. Minneapolis arose as a lumber city at the Falls of St. Anthony. With the decline of lumbering, the advance of settlers into the fertile lands of the Northwest and the production of wheat, the power of the falls was utilized to operate great flour mills. Flour milling continues to be one of the major industries, measured by net value of product. But flour milling is largely an automatic process; the value of the raw material—wheat—is relatively high, and few men are needed to turn out a finished product of high value. The net value of the city's flour mills constitutes only a small part of that of its many industries, and the mills employ a correspondingly small number of all persons engaged in manufactures. St. Paul arose when the Mississippi was the great highway to the Northwest. It was then the end of the boat journey. Today boat traffic on the great river is small. St. Paul is largely a wholesale distributing center—a huge warehouse—for the Northwest. It has no outstanding industry but ranks high in many, among which are meat packing (South St. Paul), machinery, paints, paper, and printing and publishing.

The industries of both cities have far outgrown the available water-power resources, and coal must be brought by lake and rail.

THE ST. LAWRENCE-GREAT LAKES SEAWAY PROJECT

The St. Lawrence project is intended to eliminate barriers to deep draft vessels that now exist between the Great Lakes and the Atlantic.

The major barrier is the rapids of the St. Lawrence around which there is now a narrow, 14-foot canal. The proposed Seaway will have a minimum depth of 27 feet throughout 2347 miles, from Duluth to deep water of the Gulf of St. Lawrence. Estimates indicate that the route is now approximately 90 per cent complete. The Welland Canal now overcomes the 324-foot difference in level between Lakes Erie and Ontario.

The growth of agriculture, manufacturing, transportation—in fact, the whole cultural landscape of the Great Lakes Region—has been profoundly influenced, directly or indirectly, by the availability of Lake Superior iron ores and the movement of goods on the Great Lakes. Near exhaustion of the high-grade ores of Minnesota and Michigan has stimulated interest in the Seaway. Such exhaustion necessitates a low-cost method of utilizing the low-grade taconite ores, a new source of high-grade ore, or possible shifting of the steel industry to tidewater where foreign ores may be obtained.[1] Foreign sources would probably include Labrador, Newfoundland, Brazil, Cuba, and Venezuela. The Adirondack region could supply a few million tons, but the production capacity is inadequate to meet the needs of the steel industry. It is probable that Labrador will be the major source of high grade ore for midwestern steel mills. However, that depends upon completion of a Seaway sufficiently large to handle the traffic. It is estimated that the Seaway will carry approximately "30 to 37½ million tons of iron ore, 6½ to 11½ million tons of grain, and about 4 million tons of bituminous coal." With the development of the oil fields in western Canada there is likely to be a considerable traffic in oil. These estimates do not include a possible expansion of foreign trade and of local traffic. The bottleneck is likely to be created by the limited number of vessels that can be passed through the Welland Canal in a 24-hour period.

A RURAL-URBAN UNIT IN OHIO

From among the many areas that might be selected as typifying the eastern portion of the North Central States, Marion County, Ohio, has been chosen as representative (Fig. 107). The county lies near the eastern margin of the Corn Belt, just northwest of the center of Ohio and about 45 miles from Columbus. Its surface features are strikingly uniform— with an elevation range of only 200 feet—as it occupies a part of the

[1] This trend is indicated by the proposed steel mill at New London, Connecticut, and the new mill at Morrisville, Pennsylvania, both of which will depend primarily upon imported ore. The large, fully integrated mill at Morrisville has an annual capacity of 1.8 million tons of ingots. Its ore will come chiefly from the Cerro Bolivar deposit in Venezuela.

broad, smooth-to-gently undulating glacial plain that forms the divide between the Ohio and Great Lakes drainage basins. The local elevation differences are due to stream erosion, but the slopes are sufficiently gentle to be used for agricultural purposes, and very few are steep enough to erode seriously. Nearly nine-tenths of the entire area is mantled with fertile, silty clay loam derived from the glacial drift.

The climate is healthful, invigorating, and favorable to crop production. The mean summer temperature is 72°, and the growing season averages 152 days in length. Nearly three-fifths of the annual rainfall of 38.5 inches comes during the spring and summer months, and a winter snowfall of 26.5 inches usually provides ample protection to winter wheat.

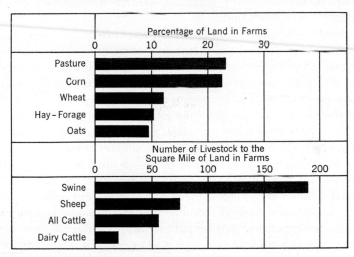

Fig. 107. Utilization of the land in Marion County, Ohio.

The first immigrants came from Virginia, Pennsylvania, New York, Kentucky, and New England, and were largely English, with some of Dutch, Irish, and German ancestry. These first settlers made their homes in the southern part of the area in 1806–1815, and by 1821 the population had grown sufficiently to organize the county. In 1950 the area had a population of 49,900, nearly seven-tenths of which lived in the city of Marion. The city of Marion, located near the center of the county, occupies a commanding position, and has nearly nine-tenths of the urban population. The present farm population averages 17 to the square mile of land in farms, even though it has decreased since 1930. Today the area has the appearance of a mature and thriving community with its farm homes and other buildings well built and well cared for and its economic, social, and political life centered on one large urban community. More than nine-tenths of the farm homes have electric service and radios, more than half have telephones, and two-fifths have running water. There are many more tractors and automobiles than farm operators. This is an area in which so-called advantages of urban living are widespread. More than nine-tenths of the land area of the county is in farms, and only about 6 per cent of the land area is woodland. The average value of land, buildings, machinery, and livestock is $17,450 a farm, and four-fifths of the farms are operated by owners and part owners. Highly developed means of transportation are available, as railroads traverse all parts of the area, most of the highways maintained by the county are hard-surfaced, and all the state highways in the county are paved. Educational facilities are excellent. Rural townships maintain centralized schools which are housed in modern brick buildings.

Agriculture.   The higher lands, which were originally covered by virgin hardwood forests, were the first to be cleared and cultivated. Not until later years were the lower treeless and swampy lands reclaimed and farmed. The early farm products were much the same as are produced today, except that the area devoted to each has changed relatively. Shipments from Marion (city) in the 1850's included wheat, corn, oats, clover seed, wool, cattle, swine, sheep, horses, and hay. Since then the relative acreage of corn has increased, and the wheat acreage has decreased proportionally. Nearly seven-tenths of the cultivated land now produces corn, hay and forage, oats and wheat, and nearly a quarter of all land in farms is devoted to pasture. Present-day agriculture consists of general farming combined with stock feeding. Wheat, soybeans, cream, butter, chickens, and eggs are the principal products yielding a cash income. Though numerous other crops are grown they occupy a very minor position. Potatoes, small fruits, and orchard fruits are raised chiefly for home consumption but with a small surplus for local markets.

The feed crops are converted into cash through the medium of stock feeding on the farms. There are 64,700 hogs, 18,800 cattle, and 25,700 sheep in the county, or an average of more than 280 animals to the square mile of farm land, exclusive of horses and poultry. More than three-fourths of the farm income is derived from the sale of livestock and livestock products. Many of the beef cattle and sheep are feeders shipped from western parts of the country to be fattened for the market. They are usually imported early in the season, and kept on the pastures through the summers. In the fall the cattle are turned into the corn fields or are fed shelled corn, silage, and other fattening foods; the sheep are placed in the stubble fields from which the wheat has been harvested, or in the corn fields. Both animals are later put in prime condition by more intensive feeding. The swine are raised in the area, pastured during the summer, and fattened chiefly on corn in the fall and winter. The fattened stock is shipped to market in Marion, Columbus, Pittsburgh, Cleveland, Buffalo, and Chicago.

The agricultural industries of Marion County are conducted on what is commonly called the "extensive-pasture scale," with a minimum of soiling to supply additional feed. Most of the feeding is done in the open, and there are comparatively few covered feeding grounds or sheds. Dairying is of local importance, especially around the city of Marion and about some of the villages where creameries have been established.

Urban Centers and Manufacturing.   Marion, located near the center of the area, is the leading city, and its population of 33,800 comprises nearly seven-tenths of the county's total population. Each of the seven other municipalities had a population of less than 1000 in 1950. Marion has superior transportation facilities, as many railroads and many hard-surfaced and paved highways radiate from it in all directions, giving access to all the principal markets of the country. It is a prosperous manufacturing city whose major industrial plants produce steam shovels, road rollers, engines, threshing machinery, conveyors, alloy steel, brass and malleable castings, steel bodies for automobile trucks, and iron and steel beams. Among other important products and industries are rubber tires, lime, meat packing, flour mills, and woodworking. Its factories give employment to more than 95 per cent of all the manufacturing employees in the county. The net value of its products exceeds $35,800,000, which is approximately five times the gross value of all farm products produced in the county. The city affords a good market for a large, easily accessible territory, and adjacent farm land has considerably higher value than the average for the county, which was $143 an acre in 1950.

PROBLEMS

1. Does the Great Lakes-to-Gulf project or the Great Lakes-St. Lawrence project offer greater permanent value to the North Central States?

2. Will completion of either project named in Problem 1 materially increase the commerce of the Great Lakes?

3. Will Duluth, Chicago, or Buffalo profit most by completion of the Great Lakes-St. Lawrence project?

4. Will completion of either or both of the two Great Lakes-to-sea projects enable the North Central States to attain a higher material development than any other section of the country?

5. Will the North Central States become the leading manufacturing section of the United States?

6. Resolved: That the Lower Lake Region possesses greater advantages as a home for man than does any other equal area of North America.

7. Will the Lower Lake Region become the leading iron- and steel-manufacturing section of the United States?

8. Will agriculture or manufacturing be the leading industry in the Lower Lake Region?

9. Will Chicago maintain its position as the leading city of the North Central Section?

10. Will the lower Lake Region ultimately have a populaiton as dense as that of the Middle Atlantic States?

CHAPTER 10

North Central Section— The Upper Lake Region

A Region of Extractive Industries. The Upper Lake Region includes northeastern Minnesota and northern Wiscosin and Michigan. Its southern boundary is a broad transition zone of cut-over forest land. Human occupancy on the south has led to an advanced stage of land utilization, as previously described. On the north the land and living conditions are largely primitive or frontier in character, except in local areas. All its industries are extractive in character; it is a land of exploitation. Its long, cold winters, with heavy snowfall; short, cool growing season; abundant rain; and thin sandy loam soils have been conducive to coniferous and to mixed forest growth but unfavorable to agriculture. The ancient sedimentary and crystalline rocks have provided exceptionally rich deposits of iron and copper, and the Great Lakes have provided cheap transportation to eastern and southern markets for the products of mine and forest. As the great continental glaciers moved over the region, the less resistant rocks were gouged out and the glacial drift was distributed unequally over the land surface, forming thousands of deep lake basins; the shallower basins thus formed became swamps and muskegs. The region probably has at least 10,000 lakes in the virgin forest and cut-over lands, many of which are being developed as summer resorts—the most recent phase of man's utilization of the natural resources.

IRON MINING

Significance of the Iron Deposits. Iron-ore deposits situated like those of the Lake Superior district, of such high grade, in such a limited area, and so easily mined on a large scale, could not fail to affect the whole nation. Their extraction has been the chief industry of the Upper Lake Region for many years, having far exceeded forest exploitation in importance. The average yearly output of the mines varies from three-fourths to more than four-fifths of the entire ore production of the United States and nearly half that of the world. Only three mines in the

251

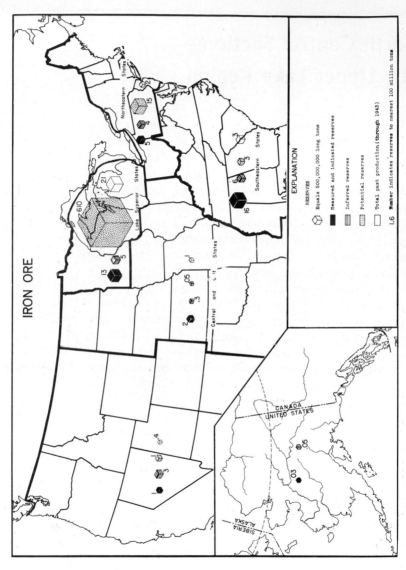

Fig. 108. Iron in comparatively small quantities is produced in numerous localities, but three-fourths to four-fifths of the annual production comes from the mines of Minnesota, Wisconsin, and Michigan in the Lake Superior district. *Courtesy, U. S. Geological Survey and Bureau of Mines.*

United States outside the region produce more than 1,000,000 tons each annually, and the usable ore output of one mine in this region is twice that of any other iron-mining district. The use of these ores also accounts for the growth of population in the region, the growth of numerous Lake cities, and the rapid growth of the steel industry and its many allied industries. They have, therefore, had a profound influence upon the whole country.

The Iron-Ore Fields. The Lake Superior ore district consists of five principal ranges: the Marquette and Menominee in Michigan; the Gogebic in Michigan and Wisconsin; and the Mesabi, Vermilion, and Cuyuna in northeastern Minnesota. The annual production of ore is now

Fig. 109. A part of the Hull-Rust open-pit mine on the Mesabi Range in Minnesota.
Courtesy, Oliver Mining Co.

80 to 85 million tons. The Mesabi and Vermilion are 60-90 miles northwest, and the Cuyuna about the same distance west and south, of Duluth-Superior and Two Harbors, from which the ore is shipped to lower Lake ports. The Marquette Range is near the city of Marquette, the Menominee Range near Escanaba, and the Gogebic Range 25–50 miles from Ashland. Thus each range has an adequate outlet by water, a factor of great significance in its development.

Iron ore was discovered on the Marquette Range in 1844, and the first ore was taken from the region the following year. During the succeeding 8 years, efforts were made to smelt the ore with charcoal fuel, but the iron could not be marketed in competition with that of the steel mills of the East. In 1853 the first shipment of consequence was made to Sharon, Pennsylvania, where the first real test of the ore was made. The ore proved to be of such high grade that a demand for more was created.

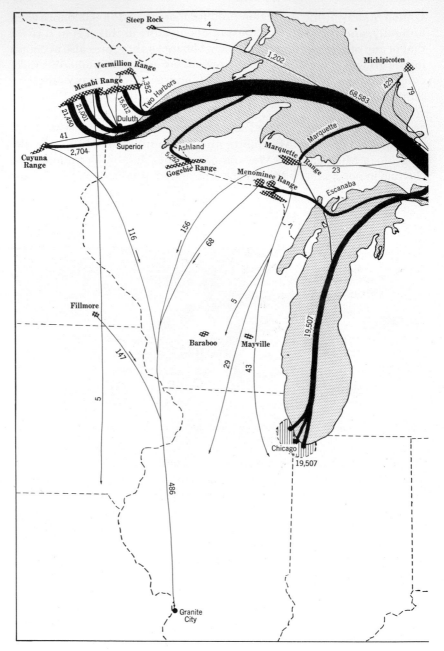

Fig. 110. Flow of iron ore with mining districts, major iron and steel

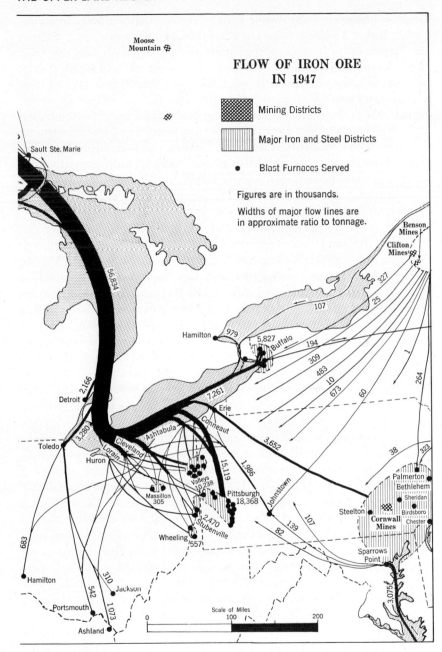

Moose
Mountain ⊕

FLOW OF IRON ORE
IN 1947

Mining Districts

Major Iron and Steel Districts

● Blast Furnaces Served

Figures are in thousands.

Widths of major flow lines are
in approximate ratio to tonnage.

Sault Ste. Marie

Benson
Mines

Clifton
Mines

56,834

107

327

25

Hamilton   979   5,827 Buffalo   194

2,166

309

483

10

673

60

1

264

Detroit

Erie

7,261

Conneaut

3,652

38

323

Ashtabula

3,280

Cleveland

Toledo

Lorain

Palmerton

Huron

Bethlehem

15,119

1,986

Sheridan

Valleys
10,238

Johnstown

Steelton

Birdsboro

Massillon
305

Pittsburgh
18,368

107

Cornwall
Mines

Chester

139

2,470
Stubenville

82

Wheeling

557

683

Sparrows
Point

310 Jackson

Hamilton

542

3,075

Portsmouth

1,073

Scale of Miles
0   100   200

Ashland

districts, and blast furnaces served. *Data from Lake Superior Iron Ore Association.*

Progress, however, was slow for a time. The ore deposits were in an un-broken forest, 14 miles from the shore of Lake Superior, and without suitable means of transport; they had to be portaged around the Saint Marys Rapids and reloaded; the lake vessels were few and small; the ore had to be introduced into the market; and many of the iron workers were reluctant to experiment, as some had declared the ore useless. However, the opening of the Sault Canal and the demand for iron created by the Civil War resulted in a rapid increase in production. The Marquette Range had no competition until 1877, when the first shipment of im-portance was made from the Menominee Range. Though the presence of other ore was known in the early 1850's, production of importance awaited transportation facilities. The Gogebic and Vermilion Ranges then rose rapidly into the million-ton class.

The first ore pit in the Mesabi Range was made in 1890. Other dis-coveries of rich ore followed rapidly. In 1892, 29,000 tons were produced, the next year 2,000,000 tons. Since then the production of the Mesabi Range has been phenomenal. From it has come nearly two-thirds of all the ore ever mined in the Upper Lake Region. In a single year the output has exceeded 70,000,000 tons, and its yearly average is about four times that of any foreign country. It continues to produce more than half of the annual output of the United States; two-thirds of that of the Lake Superior district; and one-third of the world' annual production.

The Mesabi iron deposits are covered thickly with glacial drift, but when this has been removed great ore bodies of large horizontal extent, compared with their thickness, are exposed. This ore is a soft, porous, brown, red or blue hematite of high grade, and varies from a finely pow-dered to a compact mass. These conditions make possible low-cost, open-pit mining with power shovels, as the ore is loaded directly onto the rail-road car in the mine. Estimates of merchantable ore indicate reserves of nearly a billion tons, and many times that amount for ores not available under present market conditions. The Mesabi has become of paramount importance in the country's iron and steel industry and the world's greatest iron producer, for a number of reasons: (1) The ore is of high quality. For many years, most steel was made by the Bessemer process, which demanded high-grade, non-phosphorous ores. Much Lake Super-ior ore met these conditions and, once on the market, the demand for this ore grew rapidly. (2) Cheap mining methods are possible in most places. The character of the deposits made possible open-pit, power-shovel mining on the Mesabi and comparatively cheap mining on some of the other ranges. The low cost of mining on the Mesabi is probably not equaled anywhere else in the world. (3) Transportation methods by water and rail and mechanical devices for handling the cargoes have been so improved that the handicap of distance between the coke and ore has been nearly overcome. (4) The commercial and industrial development of the country has created an unprecedented market for iron and steel products. (5) The concentration of industries under the management of large corporations has made possible the expenditure of great sums in perfecting methods of mining, transportation, manufacture, and in the elimination of waste.

The iron-ore reserves of the Upper Lake Region are large, though about 2,500,000,000 tons have been removed. The reserves of high-grade ore available under present market conditions are estimated to be more

Fig. 111. A small part of the Duluth-Superior harbor showing a few of the docks.
Courtesy, U. S. Marketing and Administration Service.

than 1,800,000,000 tons, an amount sufficient for about 15 or 20 years if the present rate of production could be maintained. The low-grade reserves—similar to many ores used in Europe—are approximately thirty-five times the high-grade reserves, and if they can compete with the low-grade ores of the East the industry can survive for many generations. Otherwise much of the mining region will probably revert to forest and the now thriving cities will become ghost towns. Competition promises to be difficult, as the agriculturally controlled legislature of Minnesota tends to place an increasing tax burden upon iron ore, in addition to other local taxes.

Iron Ore and Great Lakes Commerce.   As late as 1845, Lake Superior commerce was largely in furs, and one horse hauled all the freight that passed around St. Marys Rapids. The ground scarcely had been broken for copper and iron mining. When the Sault Canal was opened ten years later the traffic amounted to 14,500 tons a year. The growth of commerce was rapid, and the canal was enlarged several times in succeeding years. More than 110,000,000 tons of freight now pass through the canal annually, more than seven-tenths of which is iron ore, and nearly one-sixth is coal carried in returning ore boats to supply the Northwest. The eastbound ore and the westbound coal constitute nearly nine-tenths of the traffic. Since these two commodities form a very large part of the Great

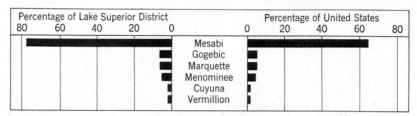

Fig. 112. Relative production of iron ranges in Lake Superior district, 5-year average. From 1950 to 1953 annual *shipments* averaged 84,150,000 tons.

Lakes commerce, it is evident that the commercial prestige of the Great Lakes depends upon the northern iron mines. The water route, steel vessels of great capacity, cheap fuel, coal as a return cargo, the Sault Canal, river and harbor improvements, the growing demand for ore, consolidation of management, and the extensive use of modern machinery, all have contributed toward producing the lowest freight rates in the world for similar service.

Development of City Centers.   Iron mining has wielded a strong influence in the growth of three classes of city centers, viz., the mining, shipping, and receiving centers. A cluster of houses and stores soon followed the opening of mines, and upon the latter the prosperity of the village depended. To this group belong such places as Hibbing, Virginia, Eveleth, Ironwood, Iron Mountain, and Ishpeming. To the ore-shipping group belong Duluth-Superior, Two Harbors, Ashland, Marquette, and Escanaba; and to the receiving class, such centers as Chicago-Gary, Detroit, Cleveland, Toledo, Lorain, and Buffalo. Since nearly all the ore mined leaves the Upper Lake Region, the influence of iron and steel manufacturing is felt only indirectly in the region.

The growth of the shipping and receiving cities is in striking contrast. The shipping cities are distinctly the *transfer* type, and the goods pass on to some other center for fabrication or distribution. The receiving cities are distinctly *distributing* and *manufacturing* centers and have far surpassed the others in size. Duluth-Superior would have considerable importance without the iron mines. They lead all the other Upper Lake cities in growth, diversified interests, and possibilities, because of (1) strategic position at the head of Lake Superior, (2) commodious, landlocked harbor of 360 acres, (3) water power from Saint Louis Falls, (4) cheap coal by returning ore boats, (5) abundance of iron ore, (6) rich though distant agricultural hinterland, (7) and an increasing market to the south, west, and northwest. Duluth now has the only steel mill of importance north of the Lower Lake Region, but nearly all other industries are based on things other than iron and steel. Although the lumber, grain, and flour-milling industries have been of much importance, the influence of the iron mines has been even greater. The development of allied iron and steel industries is yet to come, with further development of the northwestern hinterland.

COPPER

Pure metalic copper occurs in the Keweenaw Peninsula of Michigan and was worked by the Indians before the advent of the white man. Mining by the white man began in the 1840's, and for many years Michigan was the leading copper-producing state. Though huge quantities of copper have been taken from the mines and though it is now more than a mile from the entrance of some of the mines to the farthest workings, and the costs are high compared with other copper mining districts, Michigan ranks sixth as a copper producer. The ore is reduced, and the copper made ready for commercial use, near the mines. Local reduction of the ores is favored by the low-cost coal brought to the mills by returning iron-ore vessels. However, the production of 20,000 tons is insignificant compared to that of Arizona and Utah, and very small compared to Montana, Nevada, and New Mexico. Like iron, copper is converted into its many industrial uses in other parts of the country and hence contributes little to the development of this region, except in the mining and local concentration processes.

FORESTS

This region was originally forest covered, with such valuable trees as the white pine, hemlock, spruce, fir, beech, and maple. Abundant rainfall and cool summers produced a splendid growth. The heavy winter snows and the ice-covered rivers and lakes favored exploitation when the lumberman had exhausted the easily accessible forests of New

England and moved westward. The Michigan forests were the first to be attacked, and Michigan led in production for a number of years, followed in turn by Wisconsin and Minnesota. The lumberman then moved on to the forest of the South and is now attacking those of the Pacific Coast. Michigan, once a leading lumber-producing state, can no longer supply its own needs, and thousands of acres once covered with splendid forests now present a scene of desolation. Today only a small fraction of the magnificent stand of original forest remains in the Upper Lake Region. A few mills are still operating, and lumbering and pulp making are still leading industries, but the quality of many of the logs being sawed is far below that of former years. Traveling across the district, one is confronted by mile upon mile of cut-over and burned-over forest lands, with here and there a clearing where some hardy pioneer is endeavoring to make a living by agriculture. One must now penetrate areas remote from transportation routes to find an undisturbed virgin stand of any considerable size.

AGRICULTURE

Some of the cut-over land is suited to agriculture, and probably 40,-000,000 acres in the Lake States as a whole is best adapted to forest growth. Properly planted and protected from fire, this acreage can be made to produce an annual tree crop of great value. It seems probable that, with the exhaustion of the iron and copper, a forest growth with agriculture interspersed on the more fertile areas, supplemented by work in the lumber camps during the winter months and the expansion of the summer-resort business on its many lakes, will be the future of the Upper Lake Region. With such agriculture can go livestock and the dairy industry. At present agriculture depends chiefly upon the mining and resort centers for a market. These will continue to be the market for some years, but ultimately the agricultural products must be in a form to stand the cost of transportation to more distant consuming centers.

A LAKE REGION TRANSITION UNIT

In the broad transition zone between the undeveloped northern part and the highly developed southern part of the Great Lakes Region are numerous unit areas that typify the evolution of the Lake country as the home of man. From among these areas, Outagamie County, Wisconsin, which lies south and west of Green Bay and north of Lake Winnebago, has been selected. Historically, it is one of the oldest traversed sections of Wisconsin, as its principal river, the Fox, was followed by Indians and early explorers in passing from Lake Michigan to the Wisconsin and Mississippi Rivers. Only 51 years after the Pilgrim Fathers landed at Plymouth, Pére Allouez founded a mission at De Pere where the first rapids of the Fox are encountered in the ascent from Green Bay. The first white settler in Outagamie County located near the present city of Kaukauna about 1790, the year after Washington became the first president. In 1843 a colony of Dutch immigrants settled at Little Chute, and the first homes were built in Appleton the same year. Fur trading was the chief occupation until about 1840, but soon thereafter began the rapid removal of the pine and hardwood forests and the expansion of agriculture and other industries. The Fox, improved by canals and locks, continued to be the principal means of transportation until the arrival of the railroads about 1860. Today the splendid forests of pine, maple, beech, oak, hemlock, and ash are gone; more than nine-tenths of the land is in farms; the farm population averages 26 to the square mile of farm land; fine, modern farm homes dot the landscape; more than 150 manufacturing establishments are in operation; and many miles of railroads, and hard-surfaced and paved highways give adequate avenues of transport. As imagination takes one back to the wilderness days of the hardy fur trader, explorer, and intrepid missionary, the change seems remarkable, yet the evolutionary process has required more than 2½ centuries since that first Mission was established on the Fox. At first a land of exploitation, this area has become a land of permanent homes and has attained a substantial basis of human economy in comparatively recent years. It may be described aptly as old, yet new, as its substantial development represents a comparatively recent stage in man's northward migration.

Surface and Soils.   The area is typical of a glaciated region, as it lies within that part of Wisconsin covered by the Green Bay Lobe of the continental ice sheet. About two-thirds of the county, comprising the central, southern, and eastern parts, is covered by glacial drift. Its rolling surface consists of low hills and shallow basins distributed without definite relation to drainage lines. Many of the low, marshy basins have been drained artificially. Numerous nearly level areas that lie somewhat below the general level of the surrounding land have soils of lacustrine or outwash origin. Along the Wolf, Shioc, and Embarrass Rivers in the northwest is an extensive belt of gently undulating to nearly level alluvial soils and large areas of poorly drained peat marshes. These sluggish, meandering streams overflow large areas bordering their channels.

More than four-fifths of the county is covered by loam soils which vary from fine sandy loam to clay loam. Considerable areas in the Fox River Valley have red clay soils which were deposited in the quiet waters of Lake Michigan when it stood at a higher level. The extensive belt of glacial and lacustrine soils, which extends across the central portion of the county from northeast to southwest and embraces the greater part of it, has a red clay subsoil which acts as retainer of soil moisture. This belt produces all the common crops and supports many fine farms.

All the numerous streams find their way directly or indirectly into Lake Michigan. The historic Fox crosses the southeastern corner of the county in its course from Lake Winnebago to Green Bay. It flows in a gorge 50–60 feet deep between banks of red clay and can be dammed without flooding adjacent farm lands. Lake Winnebago acts as a natural reservoir regulating the flow of the river so that it is affected but slightly by drought or by heavy rains. Within a distance of 9 miles the Fox has a fall of 134 feet and 5 rapids, each of which has determined the location of an urban manufacturing center, the leading ones being Appleton and Kaukauna. These rapids, together with three others in the Lower Fox, constitute one of the best water-power units in the state. The water power is now well developed and it has been a very important factor in making the Fox River Valley a large pulp and paper producer and one of the leading manufacturing centers of Wisconsin.

Climate.   The climate is representative of east-central Wisconsin. It is healthful, invigorating, and favorable to a mixed farming-livestock type of agricultural economy. The winters are long and severe. Temperatures of $-20°$ are frequent, but temperatures below $0°$ rarely continue for more than a week at a time. The snow cover commonly remains from December to March and protects the winter crops of wheat, clover, and alfalfa. The summers are short and mild. Maximum temperatures of $100°$ occur, but such extremes are rare and hot periods seldom extend through more than a few days. The annual precipitation of 32.6 inches is ample for all needs, as about two-thirds comes during the growing season of 140–150 days.

Agriculture.   Agricultural development began first along the Fox, as that was where the first settlements were made and where the forests were first cleared away. Following closely the lumberman as he advanced farther and farther into the wilderness, the pioneer farmer cleared away the stumps and established his small farmstead near the margin of the great expanse of cut-over land. These early settlers grew wheat, corn, potatoes, hay, and root crops for local use. Essentially all the merchantable timber has been removed, and most of the region is now under cultivation. Though 90 per cent of the county is in farms only 64 per cent is in cultivated crops which represents a marked increase since about 1930. More than 38,000 acres are not included in farms and are undeveloped. These are in part cut-over land, and low, wet lands, chiefly in the northwest.

During the long history of the region there has been no marked change in the kinds of general farm crops grown, but the relative importance of some has changed greatly in the last half century. During the period from 1880 to 1950—for which cansus data are available—the proportion of improved farm land devoted to corn and barley fluctuated slightly, and the proportion devoted to oats made a substantial gain, thus indicating a strong tendency toward their permanent retention in the agricultural system. At present 3 crops dominate the agricultural econ-

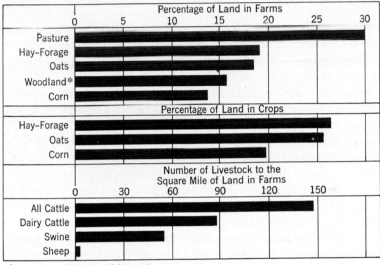

*About four–fifth is used for pasture

Fig. 113. The use of land in Outagamie County, Wisconsin.

omy. More than seven-tenths of the cropland is devoted to hay, oats, and corn. In addition more than 111,000 acres are used for pasture. An average of 206 domestic animals, exclusive of horses and poultry, is now maintained to the square mile of farm land.

Present-day agriculture consists of intensive production of stock feed, and dairying. More than a quarter of the cropped land produces hay and forage, more than two-thirds of which consists of cultivated grasses such as clover and alfalfa. A quarter of the crop acreage is devoted to oats, and about a fifth to corn and other feed crops. Practically all crops yield an income. Some are sold directly from the farm, but most of the hay, forage, oats, and corn are fed to livestock and reach the market as dairy products, pork, and beef.

The raising of livestock is a very important industry and an integral part of the agricultural system, with dairying (Fig. 114) as the dominant branch. Nearly three-fifths of the cattle are maintained for dairy purposes. Ninety per cent of the total farm income is now derived from livestock and livestock products, more than half of which is from dairy products. This indicates clearly the high stage of development attained in the feed crop-livestock-dairying type of land use. Much of this development has come in comparatively recent years. Recent data show that the county has 46 cheese factories, 2 creameries, and 7 receiving stations, and produces nearly 45,000,000 pounds of dairy products for market. These figures depict the evolution of a dairy section and appear large when standing alone. However, in its output of dairy products, Outagamie County is exceeded by a dozen or more other Wisconsin counties where the industry has reached a higher stage of development.

Though it is more than 280 years since the first mission was established in the Fox River Valley and more than a century and a half since the first crops were grown in Outagamie County, a substantial type of agricultural economy has developed. Opportunities in other parts of the state and nation that were more favorable to the gaining of a livelihood by agriculture have delayed the extensive occupation of these more northerly forested and cut-over lands. The stability of the type of agricultural economy practiced, the increased use of improved farm equipment, improved living conditions on the farm, and the growth of urban markets may be related to the small increase in rural population since about 1930. When will the whole upper Lake region reach a stage of agricultural development comparable to that of Outagamie County?

Urban Centers and Manufacturing. Measured by number of employees Outagamie County has become one of the 7 leading counties of the state. There are 12 urban centers, ranging in population from 475 to 34,000, but only 2 centers exceed 8000. These 12 centers contain more than two-thirds of the total population of the county. All the leading centers are along the Fox River where abundant water power and good transportation facilities are available. Appleton is the largest center and is a thoroughly modern and thriving industrial city. More than two-fifths of the population of the county is concentrated here, and Appleton gives employment to more than half the manufacturing employees of the county. Kaukauna ranks second, though it is only a quarter as large as Appleton. Factories for the production of dairy products are scattered throughout the county. While the forests were near at hand the valley was one of the principal lumber, pulp, and paper-making regions of the state; but, as the forest frontier retreated farther and farther, these industries declined relatively. However, paper manufacture and various allied industries still lead. Appleton now has several large paper mills and paper-converting plants. Its 72 manufacturing establishments give employment to more than 5000 people and turn out products having a net value of approximately $26,000,000.

The dairy industry now concentrates on three major products, viz., cheese, condensed milk, and powdered milk products. Its 46 cheese factories produce more than 15,300,000 pounds of American cheese (Cheddar and Colby). Other plants produce nearly 29,000,000 pounds of condensed and powdered milk products. Its butter production is small in comparison, although the annual output is about 750,000 pounds. Although most of the milk produced is processed in the county, nearly 15,-000,000 pounds of milk and butterfat are shipped to other states.

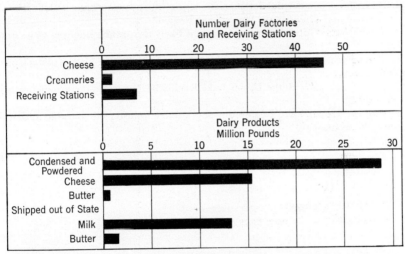

Fig. 114. Dairy establishments and products, Outagamie County, Wisconsin.

Summary. Because of its location on the Fox River route between Lake Michigan and the Mississippi River, Outagamie County was traversed by the white man very early in the history of the United States. Glaciation gave it a great variety of soils on a gently undulating surface, and many large marshland areas. Over all its upland the humid climate with long, cold winters and short, mild summers fostered a luxuriant forest growth. This combination of water route, surface, climate, and forest made it the natural home of many fur-bearing animals and the Mecca of fur trader, explorer, and missionary to the Indian. Later came the lumberman to harvest the native forest. Then followed the farmer, who found the varied soils and cool summer climate conducive to mixed farming and dairying. The water power of the county's principal streams and the advent of modern transportation facilities likewise fostered the development of manufacturing, especially the pulp and paper industries, which drew their raw material from the hinterland. Though agriculture and other industries are firmly established, the process of human utilization of nature's resources is still in progress as there are large areas yet undeveloped.

PROBLEMS

1. Resolved: That the Upper Lake Region offers greater opportunities as a home for man than do any two countries of northern Europe.

2. Can the Upper Lake Region maintain a population as large as either Norway or Sweden and on an equally high standard of living? •

3. Will exhaustion of the high-grade iron ore of the Lake Superior region result in a transfer of the iron-mining industry to the East and South?

4. Is expansion of industrial development dependent upon maintenance of the relative importance of iron mining in the Upper Lake Region?

5. Describe the Upper Lake Region as it is likely to appear a hundred years from now.

6. Will agriculture and forest industries become the leading industries of the Upper Lake Region?

7. Should esentially all the Upper Lake Region be devoted to the production of a forest crop?

8. Can the Upper Lake Region develop a dairy industry comparable to that of southern Wisconsin?

CHAPTER II

The Physiographic Regions
of the South

Southern Civilization and Its Physical Environment. There is no sharp line separating the South, or the Southern States, from the two sections to the north, although the Mason and Dixon line (the southern boundary of Pennsylvania), the Ohio River, and the southern boundaries of Missouri and Kansas form the Census Bureau's line of demarcation.

Politically, culturally, and historically the South is that portion of the United States in which slavery persisted longest. From this fact it is evident that the South overlaps the Census Bureau's line to include most of Missouri, which was a slave-holding state. The distribution of slavery as an economic institution was closely correlated with certain climatic conditions that favored the growing of certain staple crops in which culture slave labor could, the southern planter thought, be profitably employed. The northern boundary of the territory was not sharp, for climatic boundaries on plains are rarely definite in their localization. However, it is significant that this boundary is essentially a climatic one, separating a humid, warm, temperate climate in the south from a humid intermediate climate on the north (see Fig. 9).

The institution of slavery, the political doctrine of States' Rights, and the long and costly and destructive Civil War welded the people of the South into a political and cultural unit whose strength time has not weakened. The Solid South is something more than a political slogan. It is a reality. State boundaries there are within the South, but they are not so prominent in the sentiments of the people as in the North—the North as delimited by the Census Bureau.

We have stated in an earlier chapter that regional differentiation in economic activities in the American colonies began early. The northern colonists farmed some, fished much, manufactured more, and did a large part of the carrying trade of America. The southerners manufactured a little; they found on the land opportunities enough to absorb most of their energy. Agriculture has remained the dominant economic activity with the South ever since; although there has been rapid increase in manufacturing since about 1930, agriculture will long continue to occupy the attention of the majority of the people.

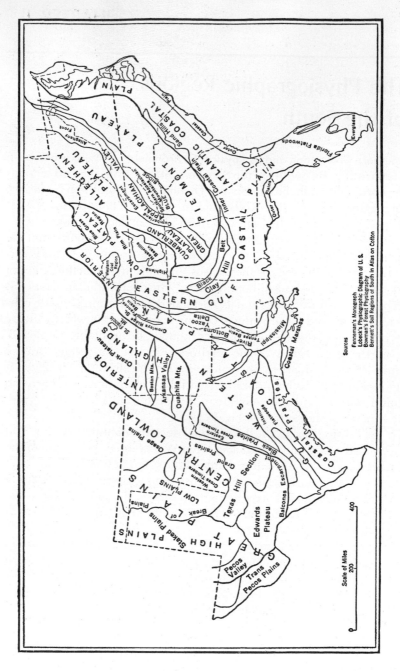

Fig. 115. The physiographic regions of the south.

Southern civilization, therefore, is preponderately an agrarian civilization. There is no such quantity and concentration of wealth as one finds in the industrial East. Rural communities are often poorer than urban ones. The taxable wealth of the entire South is much less than that of the three Middle Atlantic States. There is, therefore, less public money for schools, colleges, libraries, museums, and public improvements.

The tempo of life is the tempo of an agrarian community. It lacks the snap and vigor of industrial regions. There is more conservatism, for conservatism finds an optimum environment in slowly changing economic regions. A new day, a new economic order, a new vision of the relation of man to nature, however, is spreading over the South. Although only a beginning has been made, the new order is on a firm foundation. The old order utilized but little more than one resource—the soil. The new is making strides toward the exploitation of all the varied and abundant resources known to science. Manufacturing is slowly and surely advancing to demand a larger share of the attention of the enterprising southerners. The South is tending, therefore, toward a more balanced economic order.

We begin our study of the geography of the Southern States by a brief consideration of the physiographic features, i.e., of the lay of the land, the bedrock, the distribution of the minerals as the physical background of southern civilization and development.

The physiographic regions of the Southern States east of the Mississippi River are for the most part extensions of those of the Northeastern States, previously described. Although the surface, soils, and minerals are similar in the two sections, the southern regions differ enough from those to the north to demand further consideration (Fig. 115).

The Coastal Plain. The Coastal Plain, which has a slight development, as we have seen, in New England, New York, and New Jersey, is almost entirely a Southern physiographic province, for it borders the South Atlantic and Gulf Coasts from Delaware Bay to Veracruz, Mexico, and is much wider in the South than in the Northeastern States or in Mexico. In North Carolina it is 200 miles wide, and in eastern Texas more than 300. In the United States its total area is about 365,000 square miles, with about 255,000 square miles in the South.

The Coastal Plain and the Continental Shelf are the outer edges of the North American continental plateau, the Continental Shelf being the submerged portion of this plateau. The eastern shore line of the continent has not always held its present position. At the beginning of the formation of the Coastal Plain, several millions of years ago, the shore line was somewhere near the present inner border of the plain, and during these millions of years it has been gradually receding. The older deposits of the

Coastal Plain are, therefore, at the inner border, and at the outer, the advance of the land on the sea is still in progress. The rock of the Coastal Plain consists of marine deposits, the material being derived from the old land to the west and northwest. Since the Coastal Plain is young geologically, the rock material is largely unconsolidated.

From Chesapeake Bay to the Rio Grande, with the exception of southern Florida, the coastal features are much the same—sandy barrier beaches thrown up by the waves, smoothed in outline on the outer margin by alongshore currents, and separated from the mainland, except here and there, by tidal lagoons or salt-water marshes.

The barrier beaches that form a cordon along the shore are broken by numerous tidal inlets or by broad estuaries. Chesapeake Bay, Albemarle, and Pamlico Sounds, Mobile Bay, and Galveston Bay are the larger submerged bays and estuaries. Submergence has been greatest in the northern part of the Coastal Plain. In the Chesapeake Bay region it has been so great that tidal waters extend across the Coastal Plain, and Baltimore, Washington, and Richmond, like Philadelphia and New York, although on the inner edge of the Coastal Plain, are reached by ocean vessels.

The rivers of the Coastal Plain in their lower course are aggrading streams, building alluvial flood plains and attempting to fill the estuaries by bars or deltas. This tendency toward the filling of the bays and estuaries, which are naturally shallow, as is characteristic of sandy coast lands, puts a great financial burden on our National Government in keeping these channels open for navigation in order that ocean vessels may reach the ports on the borders and upper reaches of the estuaries. This work has given deep, navigable channels for ocean vessels to Baltimore, Norfolk, Wilmington, Charleston, Savannah, Brunswick, Jacksonville, Tampa, Pensacola, Mobile, New Orleans, Galveston, and Houston.

Interesting coastal features of the Atlantic Coastal Plain are the scallops, cusps, and offshore shoals that occur on the coast of the Carolinas and affect coastwise navigation. These are attributed to the action of eddies that have a counterclockwise movement and lie between the shore and the Gulf Stream. The material of the cusps and shoals comes from the outer edge of the Coastal Plain, from the shallow parts of the ocean bottom, or from stream deposits. That of the Cape Fear cusp and Frying Pan Shoal is derived largely from silt and sand brought down by the Cape Fear River. The more prominent of the shoals are those that lie offshore from Cape Fear, Cape Lookout, and Cape Hatteras, Cape Hatteras being so dangerous to navigation that it is sometimes called the "graveyard" of the Atlantic Coast.

Although submergence along the outer edge of the Coastal Plain has been of some advantage to water transportation, river, coastwise, and overseas, the estuaries hinder land traffic. Roads and railroads, paralleling the coast, generally lie inland beyond the heads of the estuaries. To reach the cities at the outer edge of the Coastal Plain, the more important roads and railroads are forced to follow the longer axes of the peninsulas that lie between the estuaries.

The Inner Border. At only a few places on the inner border of the Atlantic Coastal Plain is the contact with the old land to the west a sharp one, either in surface expression or in mantle rock. In some places there are prominent sand hills; but, farther north, sands and gravels that show wave and river action, characteristic of the Coastal Plain, mantle the eastern edge of the crystalline rock region. In this zone of contact, most of the Atlantic Coast rivers have formed a series of rapids, in the larger rivers these are 15–25 miles long, as they flow over the crystalline rock at the edge of the old land into the valleys and channels which they have carved in the Coastal Plain. Not only is this zone evident in the rivers of the Atlantic Coastal Plain from the James River in Virginia to the Altamaha in Georgia, but it is also marked on the border of the Gulf Coastal Plain by the rapids in the Tennessee River near Muscle Shoals and in the hard rock in the Arkansas Valley near Little Rock, Arkansas. The line connecting the series of rapids has long been known as the Fall Line. At Baltimore the outer edge of the Fall Line zone is at sea level; at Augusta, Georgia, it is 98 feet above tide; at Macon, 280 feet; and near Muscle Shoals even higher.

The Peninsula of Florida. The peninsula of Florida is a portion of the coastal platform or plateau that has been warped upward sufficiently to bring a large area of land above sea level. A small portion of Florida stands 300 feet above tide, but the larger part of the area of the state is less than 100 feet above sea level, and all the southern third lies between 0 and 50 feet. Limestone is the basal rock of most of Florida and is the surface rock of a large part of the interior (Fig. 116).

The Belts of the Coastal Plain. The rock materials of the Coastal Plain are arranged roughly into longitudinal belts that are more or less parallel to the borders of the plain. It is this belted arrangement that has given origin to the term "Belted Coastal Plain." Detailed study and mapping have revealed numerous belts many of which are continuous across one or more states, but in our study we shall recognize but two: an outer, low, flat belt known as the Flatwoods and Coastal Prairies; and an inner and higher belt, called the Inner Coastal Plain.

The Flatwoods, extending southward from Delaware Bay in a more or less continuous belt, with only a few interruptions, to the alluvial valley of the Mississippi, is about 20–40 miles wide. Its surface is almost a dead level with only a few sandy hillocks or broad, swamp-covered shallow

valleys to break the monotony. Some areas are so flat as to be covered
with water much of the year. Locally, such swamps are known as "bays,"
"pocosins," and, in some sections, "swamps." They support a hydrophytic
type of vegetation. These marshy patches on the uplands are distinctly
different in origin from the marshes bordering the sluggish streams that
meander through the Flatwoods belt. The marsh patches on uplands are

Fig. 116. A palm-bordered drainage channel in the Everglades of Florida, on the
Seminole Indian Reservation. *Courtesy, Florida News Bureau.*

merely inheritances from the elevated Continental Shelf; the marshes
along the lower courses of streams are the result of submergence of shallow valleys carved in the outer edge of the Coastal Plain when it stood at
a higher level in very recent times.

The Flatwoods belt is interrupted in southern Georgia and southeastern Alabama by the Florida anticlinorium, but from Mobile Bay westward it is well defined. In the west Gulf region, this low, flat area, inland
from the coastal lagoons and barrier beaches, is known as the Coastal
Prairies, and in some parts of Louisiana and Texas is 50 or even 100 miles
wide.

The inner belt of the Coastal Plain is much wider than the Flatwoods
and Coastal Prairie belt, and is higher and rougher. North of North Caro-

lina, most of the western belt lies less than 200–300 feet above the sea, with only the westernmost edge reaching 400 feet; but farther south it is higher. In Alabama, Tennessee, Arkansas, and Texas, the inner border in general reaches 500–600 feet, and a few areas are 1000 feet above sea level. The higher altitudes of this inner belt and the looseness and unconsolidated condition of the material have given the rivers free scope in their work of dissection. The gradient of the Coastal Plain streams is less than the oceanward slope of the land; hence the valleys are deepest near the inner border of the Inner Coastal Plain. From central North Carolina to western Alabama, and even westward, there is a strip, 5 to 25 miles wide, of thoroughly dissected land known as the Sand Hill section, so hilly and sandy as to be of little use except for the growing of forests and orchards.

In the early period of the formation of the Gulf Coastal Plain, a great bay extended as far north as the site of the present mouth of the Ohio. Western Kentucky and Tennessee, even portions of Missouri and eastern Arkansas, therefore, form a part of the Coastal Plain, although 300–500 miles from the Gulf.

The only exception to the belted arrangement of the Coastal Plains is the alluvial valley of the Mississippi River which cuts across the belts and divides the Gulf Coastal Plain into two parts, the East Gulf Coastal Plain and the West Gulf Coastal Plain. These are discussed as the Mississippi Valley Plains.

The Black Belts. In western Georgia, across Alabama, and in Mississippi, the hill region stands prominently above an inner lowland of calcareous materials, known as the Black Belt because of its dark soil, which is admirably suited to the growing of cotton. Because of its early adaptability to cotton growing, it has a dense Negro population. Texas also has a Black Belt, known as the Black Prairies, which is separated from another area of calcareous soil to the west, also with dark soil, called the Grand Prairies, by an outcropping belt of limestone called the Cross Timbers.

Minerals of the Coastal Plains. Since the rock materials of the Coastal Plain are marine in origin and, probably, in no section have been disturbed by igneous intrusions or extrusions, the minerals must be such as are deposited in marine water accumulated in marine marshes and lagoons, or formed by chemical action subsequent to deposition. The more important minerals are salt, gypsum, sulfur, oil, gas, lignite, coal, marl, clay, and limestone.

The Mississippi Valley Plains. The alluvial valley of the Mississippi is an aggraded plain 20–75 miles wide and 600 miles long. It is bordered on the east by an almost continuous line of bluffs interrupted by only a few small streams. Its western border, although there are here and there low bluffs, is broken by several broad alluvial plains like those of the Arkansas, Red, Ouachita, and other rivers. The profile of the Mississippi River is concave, and the slope very gentle—4.8 inches per mile from Cairo to Vicksburg, 2.9 inches from Vicksburg to the mouth of the Red River, and about 2 inches from the Red to the head of the passes. As a result of these conditions, the stream is continually aggrading, and in flood stage its surface stands several feet above the level of the alluvial plain on either side. There are about 30,000 square miles of rich alluvial land between Cairo and the Gulf, and the larger part of this is subject to overflow during the flood period unless protected by levees.

The Piedmont.   The Piedmont Plateau lies just to the west and northwest of the Coastal Plain. Its length is about 900 miles and its width is from 20 miles in Maryland and 50 miles in central Virginia, to 150 or more in North Carolina. Farther south, it decreases in width. Its entire area is about 74,000 square miles. As one views its surface from the top of a high building in any of the Piedmont cities, one sees an almost perfectly dead-level plain with here and there a few low, rounded hills rising above the general level. These elevations are monadnocks, residuals, due to superior hardness and to location on the divide between river systems. Being in a region of heavy rains, the surface of the Piedmont is creased by many rivers and valleys, shallow and broad as a rule in the central portion of the Piedmont, but narrower on the eastern border. The larger streams pursue a course over the gently sloping surface toward the sea, irrespective, in general, of the hardness of rock; but some of the tributaries show rock adjustment. The channels of the larger streams, therefore, have numerous rapids and pools. Since the inner border of the Piedmont stands 700–1500 feet above the sea, and the outer from sea level to about 800 feet, the Piedmont streams have much water power. The slopes of the land are, as a rule, except near the inner border, gentle, and the relief is slight. Railroads, therefore, find easy grades; topography has little influence on the road; and cultivation is little interfered with by rough lands. A large proportion of the land is tillable.

The rocks of the Piedmont are largely crystallines, so deeply weathered that in places the residual disintegrated rock is 50 or more feet thick. Igneous intrusions and extrusions are common. Most of the monadnocks, like Stone Mountain, near Atlanta, are intrusions. It is largely the intruded rock that is worked in the granite quarries of North Carolina and Georgia.

The inner edge of the Piedmont is marked by numerous outliers of the Blue Ridge. The Piedmont Plateau and the Blue Ridge belt of mountains form in the South what is commonly known as Older Appalachians, an expansion of the physiographic province of that name in the Northeastern States (Fig. 117).

The Blue Ridge Province.   The Blue Ridge from North Carolina northward is a fairly distinct ridge of resistant rock flanked by numerous hills of sandstone and other hard rocks, which separate deep coves or valleys. In North Carolina and southward, the Blue Ridge is the eastern escarpment, some slopes of which rise 2000 feet in 3 or 4 miles, of the mountain area, the Southern Appalachian Mountains. This mountainous area, 75 or more miles wide in North Carolina, consists of several short, rather distinct, chains that lack uniformity in trend. There are numerous cross ranges, but some of the more prominent ranges, like the Unakas and Great Smoky, have a trend parallel to the general trend of the Blue Ridge belt. The crests of most of these mountains fall into a rather uniform plain when seen from a height of 2000–2600 feet, and are thought to

Fig. 117. A generalized cross section from the Atlantic westward across the Appalachian Highlands at about the latitude of Washington, D. C. It shows the positions of the Older and Newer Appalachians, and the relation of Coastal Plain to Piedmont, Blue Ridge, Great Valley, and Allegheny Plateau. *After A. K. Lobeck.*

be remnants of a former extensive plateau now so deeply dissected and destroyed by erosion that valley bottoms and mountain slopes take up most of the area. The peaks are rounded, and the slopes covered with a deep layer of mantle rock and humus, except where the removal of the forest has given the erosive forces full play. The most prominent of the mountain peaks is Mount Mitchell, 6684 feet above the sea, the highest mountain east of the Rockies. Other prominent peaks are Mount Guyot, Clingman's Dome, Mount Le Conte, Grandfather Mountain, Mount Pisgah, and Black Mountain.

The rocks of the Southern Appalachian Mountains are largely metamorphosed igneous, but on the western border there are quartzites and slates. The summit of the Unakas on the western border is capped with resistant quartzites. The mountains yield a great variety of economic minerals, largely igneous in origin, such as rare earths, mica, feldspar, and metallic minerals, but nowhere in quantities great enough to attract much capital. This can hardly be classed as an important mineral region.

The Blue Ridge in Virginia is cut by three prominent streams, the Potomac, the James, and the Roanoke; and in addition to these there are a large number of wind gaps. All these gaps permit considerable freedom of movement of goods and people; but the Southern Appalachian Mountains are a distinct barrier to transportation and communication except along a few valleys. Asheville, in the Asheville basin, carved in less resistant rock by the French Broad and two of its tributaries that here join the main stream, is a railroad center and the center of radiating highways. Agriculture is possible only in the valley bottoms and on the lower and less steep slopes of the Southern Appalachian Mountains. Most of the slopes of the mountains are too steep for permanent cultivation and should be kept covered with forests.

The Great Valley.   The Great Appalachian Valley in the Southern and Northeastern States is similar in origin and general characteristics. In the South the larger divisions of the Great Valley are the Cumberland Valley in Maryland, the Shenandoah in Virginia, the Valley of East Tennessee, and the Coosa in Alabama. From the Potomac southwestward to southwestern Virginia, the Great Valley narrows to 8–15 miles in places; but in Tennessee it is from 40 to 60 miles wide. The highest part of the Great Valley in the south is in southwestern Virginia. From this higher land in southwestern Virginia and the nearby portion of North Carolina, several streams take their rise: the James, Roanoke, New, Sandy, Clinch, and Holston. From Staunton, Virginia, northward, the valley slopes toward the Potomac and is drained by the Shenandoah. The Tennessee River and its tributaries drain southwest Virginia and east Tennessee, and the Coosa and its tributaries carry off much of the water of the Great Valley in Georgia and Alabama. From southwest Virginia to central Alabama, the valley slopes from about 2700 feet above sea level to above 500 feet.

There are no canoe-shaped valleys in the Southern States in the Great Valley, but evidences of intensive folding and faulting are common, and one finds the same repetition of rock-cored ridges as in the North. Many of the limestone beds have been metamorphosed into marble, which is being quarried in Tennessee and Georgia. Some of the marble outcrop ridges may be traced for scores of miles, but it is only here and there, where transportation facilities are adequate, that the marble is quarried. Most of the ridges of the Great Valley are of resistant sandstone or quartzite or of cherty dolomitic limestone. Some of the chert ridges stand up 100 feet or more above the nearby valley floor and, being too steep and sterile for profitable cultivation, are used as pasture lands or left in forest.

In Pennsylvania the dominant movement of men and goods in the Great Appalachian Valley is across the general trend of the topography, even though the ridges are distinct barriers; but in the South the movement has been largely along the valley, thus utilizing the low grades of the plains between the ridges.

From the early part of the eighteenth century, man has used this valley as a thoroughfare; first came the pioneer on his way to find a home in the valley, and later in the Bluegrass region of Kentucky and the Nashville basin. In the Civil War it was the scene of bloody battles. The level surface, short ridges, numerous gaps in the Blue Ridge in Virginia, the mountainlike borders in Tennessee, and the continuity of elevation with the Piedmont in Georgia and Alabama all influenced the movemet of armies. Railroads and roads running along the trend of the valley find that the low grades and the ease of communication north and south, coupled with valuable resources of coal, iron ore, and other metallic minerals, timber, agricultural products, and water power favor the growth of industrial cities. Although most of these urban groups are small and unimportant at present, the future has much in store for them. The Shenandoah Valley has long been famous as an agricultural section, and during the last half century or more has come to be an important fruit region. The valley of east Tennessee and southward, though not so fertile as the Shenandoah basin, is one of the better agricultural areas of the south.

The Appalachian Plateaus.   Along the whole western border of the Great Valley, like a thousand-foot wall, stretch the Allegheny Front and the Cumberland Escarpment. They are the eastern edge of the Appalachian Plateaus. The Appalachian Plateaus region and the Great Valley are known as Newer Appalachia.

The New River and the Tennessee are the only rivers that have cut gorges across the plateaus, and only a few small streams have notched the eastern front. These Appalachian Plateaus and their east-facing escarpments are the most formidable barriers to transportation in the eastern United States. This barrier, with its southwestward trend, deflected the westward-moving frontiersmen from Pennsylvania, Maryland, and Virginia southwestward to Cumberland Gap.

There is little uniformity in the surface features of the Appalachian Plateaus in the Southern States. In Tennessee, erosion has been less active, and here exists the largest area, some 5000 square miles, of truly plateau land. There are a few elevations above and a few valleys, like the Sequatchie Valley in Tennessee, and numerous smaller valleys in Alabama, below the general level; yet, as seen from an eminence, its surface lies as flat as the surface of the Outer Coastal Plain. Erosion has been more active in Alabama than in Tennessee. In eastern Kentucky and West Virginia, however, the rivers have carried on their work of dissection most actively and the former plateau level is indicated only by the accordance of the tops of the numerous ridges and knobs, which are the divides of that huge labyrinth of 800-1000 foot valleys and coves that dissect the plateau. The plateau in Kentucky and West Virginia is truly mountainous, for only in geologic history does it have real existence; but there is little excuse for the term Cumberland Mountains as applied to the Cumberland Plateau in Tennessee.

The plateaus will not in our generation become important agricultural districts, but they have rich stores of coal and building stones and are natural forest lands. They should not be denuded of their timber cover.

The Bluegrass Basins.   The basins of Kentucky (Bluegrass region) and Tennessee (Nashville or Middle Tennessee basin) and the surrounding highland plains form a distinct physiographic province, a part of the great Interior Plain. The basins were once domes, parts of the Cincinnati Anticline, the main axis of which lies parallel to the trend of the topography of Newer Appalachia. Erosion removed the more resistant cherty limestone of the domes and exposed the more easily eroded shales and limestones beneath, and the domes were etched into basins. The basins are rimmed about, with the exception of the north border of the Bluegrass region, by escarpments 300–400 feet high, which force highway and railroad to employ many of the well-known engineering devices used in mountainous areas in providing traffic routes to and from the basins. The surface of the basins is gently rolling, interrupted here and there, particularly on stream divides, by hills or knobs of gentle slopes, yet the percentage of tillable land, some of the richest in America, is large. The minerals of the basins are few, limestone for building purposes, road ballast, plaster, and cement being the chief ones. But to the south of Nashville are large deposits of phosphates which are mined in open pits, concentrated, and shipped to fertilizer factories, mainly in the South.

The Ozark Plateau.   Physiographers see, in origin and general surface features, a great similarity in the Ozark Plateau and the Boston and Ouchita Mountains west of the Mississippi River, and the two provinces of the Newer Appalachian region just described. The Ozark Plateau corresponds to the Cumberland Plateau; the Boston Mountains to the Escarpments; and the Arkansas Valley and the Ouachita ridges to the Great Appalachian Valley. These areas west of the Mississippi may, therefore, be considered as outliers of the Newer Appalachians, separated from the province to the east by a down-warping of the land, the original surface features being covered with deposits of the Coastal Plain and the alluvial valley of the Mississippi.

Western Texas and the most of Oklahoma lie in two physiographic provinces: the Prairies, a phase of the Interior Lowland province; and the Great Plains, which are divided into the Low Plains and the High Plains. These two provinces have their greatest development in the North Central States. The Prairie province is represented in Texas by the Black and Grand Prairies, separated by a cuesta of resistant sandstone known as the Cross Timbers, as previously described.

The western part of Texas in the Great Plains belt is classed in this book as a part of the West, and is discussed with the Western States.

QUESTIONS, EXERCISES, AND PROBLEMS

1. In a journey from Louisville, Kentucky, eastward to Norfolk, what physiographic regions would one cross? Describe each region.

2. What regions would one cross in traveling from Louisville to Florida by way of Nashville and Chattanooga, Tennessee?

3. What are the effects of the drowning of the coasts of the South on agriculture, navigation, and commerce?

4. Why has the National Government not reclaimed the swampy lands of the South as it has the arid lands of the West?

5. Make a careful study of the most disastrous floods that have occurred in the Mississippi Valley. What physical conditions make for floods? Is flood-protection work a duty of the National Government or of the individual states? What engineering projects may be worked out to reduce the disastrous effects of the floods on the Mississippi?

6. What geographic conditions make western North Carolina a "playground" for both North and South? What contributions has man made to this phase of land utilization?

7. Look up "Tennessee Valley Project" and "Tennessee Valley Authority." From the standpoint of size of area drained, rainfall of the region, gradient of the river, and its location, show the suitability of this valley for such a project.

CHAPTER 12

Agriculture
in the South

Perhaps in no other section of the United States has there been such a phenomenal change in agriculture (since 1910) as in the South. The effects of the Tennessee Valley development, the cotton boll weevil, industrial development, the application of machines to agriculture, and other factors have brought about shifts in cotton farming away from the Piedmont and the old South to the river flood plains of the Mississippi, to Texas, and to the less humid lands of Oklahoma. Rapid progress is being made in diversification of crops. Livestock has become increasingly important, tenancy is decreasing, rural electrification is advancing rapidly, and more attention is being given to soil erosion and tree crops, as well as to forestry. An attempt is made in the following paragraphs to analyze agriculture in the South from the standpoint of all environmental conditions involved.

THE DEVELOPMENT OF AGRICULTURE IN THE SOUTH

Agriculture in the Virginia Colony.   Agriculture in English America had its beginning in Virginia. Here was done much of the early colonial experimenting in southern agriculture. The contrasts in summer temperature between old England and the lower Chesapeake country led the people who directed the economic policies of the mother colony to believe that many subtropical products could be grown here. Subtropical and tropical products were much preferred, for in the growing of these the Virginia farmers would not compete with the farmers of the mother country. The fig, the orange, and the French grape were all tried out in the Jamestown settlement. The presence of the wild mulberry led the colonists to try the raising of silkworms. The cultivation of these was soon abandoned because of the great amount of careful and skilled labor involved, and farming activities were fixed upon two of the several cultivated plants the Indians had long been raising as staples—corn and tobacco. It is recorded that, under the direction of Captain John Smith, a crop of corn was raised in 1609, probably the first corn raised in English

America by Englishmen. Wheat, oats, and barley were sown later, with some success; but tobacco, the first crop of which was raised in 1612, soon became the leading money crop. It is reported that the people of Virginia were wont to say "God in the creation did first make a woman, then a man, thirdly great maize or Indian corn, and fourthly tobacco." Cattle were introduced as early as 1609, and, by 1611, 160 had been brought across the Atlantic. By 1631 there were about 5000, of English and Irish breeds chiefly, although some had been brought from the Spanish West Indies. Horses were the first livestock to reach Virginia. Goats and hogs multiplied with great rapidity, but it was not until the close of the seventeenth century that sheep were at all numerous, for they easily fell a prey to wild animals in a newly settled country.

Agricultural practices were chiefly those of old England, with some slight modification due to Indian influence. For tobacco and corn, hand labor was used. Little could be done in the growing of cereals until plows became common. In 1618 there was only one wooden plow in the colony; and 30 years later, when the population numbered 15,000 whites and 300 slaves, the majority of whom were tillers of the soil, only 150 plows were in existence in Virginia.

The settlement on the James River was the nucleus for agricultural expansion northward, southward, and westward; but always, for more than half a century, the new settlements were planted on or near tidewater, that contact might be maintained with the mother country.

The rapid depletion of the soil by tobacco culture, the resultant migratory agriculture (a field was rarely cultivated more than 3 to 6 or 7 years before being abandoned), and the increasing number of colonists, particularly near the middle of the seventeenth century during the civil wars in England, brought about an active expansion of the agricultural area. By 1620 the Jamestown settlement had expanded up the James River 70 miles, and extended back from the river on either side a distance of 20 miles or more. About 40 years later, there were almost continuous settlements from Maryland to the Albemarle country.

Expansion of the Agricultural Area.   By 1700 a few farmers had gone far inland on the Piedmont, but most of the settlements were to the east of the Fall Line. The Great Appalachian Valley was entered by farmers by 1750, and in this great thoroughfare Virginians mingled with land seekers from Pennsylvania, Maryland, and New York. Thirty years later, hundreds of hardy farmers, following daring hunters and traders, were crossing the Appalachian Highlands and staking out farms in the Monongahela and Ohio Valleys, the fertile Bluegrass region of Kentucky, and the Nashville basin; and by 1790 there were in southwest Pennsylvania and nearby portions of Ohio and West Virginia and Kentucky nearly

74,000, and in Tennessee nearly 36,000 pioneers. From these centers people spread out into other parts of these and nearby states, being guided in their movements largely by the rivers, and planting their new settlements for the most part on the more fertile lands, for always the great majority of migrants were farmers. Kentucky and Tennessee contributed large quotas to the early settlers in Indiana, Illinois, Missouri, Arkansas, Alabama, Louisiana, and Texas.

In all this back country, the crops and agricultural practices were somewhat changed from those early used in Virginia; general farming was the rule, for each community was by necessity largely self-supporting and the crops raised were supply crops.

Agriculture in the Carolinas.   The settlements in northeastern North Carolina were an expansion of those of southern Virginia. About 100 farmers had settled at Chowan on the shores of the broad Albemarle Sound by 1653. Nine years later, large accessions, mostly to Quakers, were made to the Chowan settlement. By 1665 there were 300-400 families on the borders of the sound. In time the Albemarle settlements expanded westward over the Piedmont, and 100 years or more later the Carolinas sent land-hungry pioneers into the eastern Tennessee and trans-Allegheny regions.

In 1664 a few English colonists from Barbados cleared the bottom lands along the Cape Fear River, well back from the coast, and began the cultivation of cotton. The Charleston settlement dates from 1670. Cotton was from the first much cultivated. Settlements in this area grew rapidly, and it is claimed that by 1732 there was not a thousand-acre tract within 100 miles of Charleston or within 20 miles of a navigable stream that was not claimed as farm land by English, New England, Scotch-Irish, Dutch, French Hugenot, Acadian, or English Quaker colonists. The introduction of rice culture, and, a half-century later, of indigo, added greatly to the wealth of the communities.

The Georgia Colony.   In the Georgia colony, the first settlement was at Savannah in 1733. Rice, indigo, and upland cotton received attention; but sea-island cotton from the first proved a profitable money crop, and its cultivation spread rapidly on the coast islands.

Rice, indigo, and sea-island cotton were coast products; hence they played little or no part in the expansion of agriculture in the Lower South. As long as the colonists of the Lower South hugged the coast line, these products dominated in agriculture; but upland cotton, with which the upland farmers had long been experimenting, brought about the great westward movement in agriculture in the Lower South.

Early Practices in Agriculture.   In an era of agricultural expansion, with large areas of virgin soil that were purchased in large blocks at only a

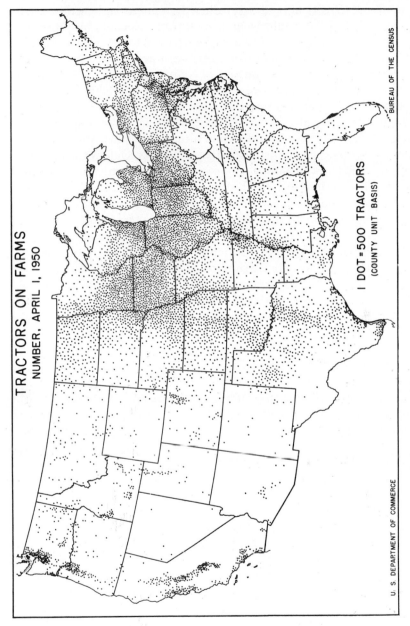

Fig 118. The distribution of tractors used on farms in the United States.

nominal sum, little attention was paid to improvement in agricultural practices. Extensive agriculture, rather than intensive, was the rule, for, as long as new lands could be had, greater profits could be obtained by soil robbing than by careful tillage. Economical tobacco raising by slave labor was thought to demand 50 acres of arable land to a Negro, and as an overseer was dear unless he had 20 Negroes under him; 1000 acres of arable land, it was thought, was necessary for the profitable use of capital. The same condition held true for cotton.

Here and there attempts were made at improvement in methods of cultivation, in livestock, and in machinery. Virginia and Maryland, grown poor by the exhaustive cultivation of tobacco, were among the leaders in agricultural improvement. A state agricultural society was founded in Virginia in 1790. Baltimore had a *Farmer's Weekly* in 1835, and a chair in agriculture was established at the University of Georgia in 1834. Yet it is claimed that until 1856 a plow was almost unknown in many counties in South Carolina.

Modernizing Agriculture.   Machinery, until about 1910, has never been much used in the southern states. There has long been a prevalent notion among southern farmers that the Negro, whose chief implement for a century or more in America was the grub hoe, could not handle machinery. This idea, however, is fast being changed. The South has begun to multiply its manpower by the use of power machinery. It should be remembered, however, that for many of the southern crops the invention of satisfactory machinery was slow in coming. A cotton-picking machine, of which there are several types, has only come since about 1930. It is expensive and applicable only on the large level areas found in Mississippi and Texas. Tobacco still requires much hand labor, particularly in harvesting and curing. The longer tillage and growing season partly compensates for the inadequacy and the scarcity of farm machinery. A farmer has many more days in the Southern States to fit his ground for planting or sowing, and a longer harvest season, than the farmer of the Northern States, and thus has less need for machinery (Fig. 118).

Today no section of the country is changing its age-long agricultural practices and traditions so rapidly as the South, chiefly because there is a great chance for improvement. The boll weevil, although destroying hundreds of thousands of bales of cotton each year, is, after all, proving a blessing. The one-crop system is doomed. Farmers are learning that more money is to be made from semi-luxuries, like citrus fruits, peaches, apples, early vegetables and small fruits, dairy products, and beef cattle, than from the staple foods and fibers. There is a limit, of course, to which these intensive types of land utilization may be carried, but that limit is not yet reached.

FACTORS AFFECTING AGRICULTURAL PRODUCTIVITY

Agriculture is predominantly the occupation of the people of the Southern States. Although the South has but 30 per cent of the total population of the country, it has 46 per cent of the rural population, and only 20 per cent of the urban. Although agriculture dominates the activities of the people, the South is not today so great an agricultural region, from the standpoint of production, as the Northern (Northeastern and North Central) States. The total land area of the two sections differs but little: the North has 30.9 per cent of the land area of the United States, and the South 29.8 per cent; yet the South had only about 95 per cent as many acres of farm land as the North in 1950; and the area of cropland was only 53 per cent of that of the North; the value of farm property (land and buildings) 60 per cent; and the gross income from all agricultural products, about 55 per cent.

This lower ranking is not wholly, if at all, the result of natural geographic conditions adverse to the farmer. It is probable, as later discussion tries to show, that the physical environment of the Southern States is quite as favorable for agriculture as that of the North.

The Population Factor.   The rural population in each section numbers about the same, but the North has nearly twice the total population. Although the two sections are similar in age of settlement, the North is older in its economic development. There are, therefore, fewer acres per person of total population in the North than in the South. The value of the agricultural land is greater, more extensive improvements have been made, the land is tilled better, and consequently the returns are greater. Agriculture has reached a more advanced stage of development, and man is utilizing nature's resources to a fuller extent than he does in the South.

In the South are large areas of forests yet to be cleared, much cut-over land not included in farms adapted to special types of farming, and many millions of acres of wet land capable of intensive cultivation when once drained. In fact, the South Atlantic and Gulf Coastal Plain, extending a considerable distance southwestward on the Texas coast, contains the major portion of the wet reclaimable lands of the United States. These lands will be used more and more as population increases.

Tenancy and Size of Farm.   Tenancy is more prevalent in the South in general than in the other major sections of our country. The percentage of farms operated by tenants and croppers in the North ranges from 40 for Illinois, 42 for Iowa, 36 for Kansas, down to 8 for New York, 4 for Vermont, 3 for Massachusetts, and 3 for Maine. In the west 8 per cent of the farms of Nevada are so operated, 17 per cent in Montana, 12 per cent in California, and 12 per cent in Washington. In the South the fig-

ures are 15 per cent for West Virginia, 28 for Virginia, 64 for North Carolina, 50 for Tennessee, 80 for South Carolina, 80 for Georgia, 96 for
Mississippi, 40 for Texas and 63 for Arkansas. The Wheat Belt, Corn
Belt, and Cotton Belt have the largest percentage of tenants. The evil
effects of tenancy need no comment. In the North and West the tenant
farmer is normally working toward buying a farm, and his tenancy thus
represents merely a stage on the way to ownership. In the South, on the
other hand, there are large numbers of tenants who do not look forward
to ownership and for whom tenancy is the normal economic situation.

Since the Civil War there has been much splitting up of large plantations, yet not enough for the best agricultural interests of the South.
The census figures are very misleading as to the size of land holdings.
They show that in 1950 over 50 per cent of the farms of the South had
less than 50 acres; 72 per cent had less than 100; and only 10 per cent
of the total number had more than 1000 acres; and that in the South
Atlantic States the average size of the farms had decreased from 376.3
acres in 1850 to 157.4 acres in 1880, and 100 in 1950. In two other divisions of the South there had been similar decreases. But a farm in the
census reports "is all the land which is directly farmed by one person
managing and conducting agricultural operations either by his own labor
alone or with the assistance of members of his household or hired employees . . . . When a land owner has one or more tenants, renters, croppers, or managers, the land operated by each is considered a farm." A
large percentage of the plantations of the South are divided into plots
and rented out to tenants, mostly Negroes, each "one-horse" or "two-
horse" farm being considered a farm by the census, although the owner,
in many if not most cases, exercises almost complete control over the
tillage. Tenants of this sort are at best only poor agriculturists, and undoubtedly the plantation as a whole would yield much more than the
present output if it were divided and tilled by owners.

At present, there are indications that tenancy—long a symbol of
Southern poverty—has passed its peak. The Southern Regional Council
in Atlanta, Georgia, notes a decided rise in farm ownership and a drop
in farm tenancy, along with better pay for farm workers still on the land.
New industries are locating in the South more rapidly than in any other
large section of the country. This means jobs for many who were formerly
"share-croppers," and that type of farmer is fast disappearing from many
sections. Also, many persons from the farms have migrated to industrial
jobs in both North and South since 1940. The use of agricultural machinery is rapidly increasing, and the livestock industry is increasing, all
of which requires less manpower.

The Long Distance to Market.   The long haul to the greater markets of the country is a factor that has retarded agriculutral development. Of the crops that are raised in both North and South, only the early crops of the South can compete successfully in the northern markets. The development of industries in the South and an increase in the consuming population accompanying each development will prove a great advantage to the farmers. The larger population will increase land values, increase taxes, and force the farmers to get more out of their land.

The Soil Factor.   The South has a great variety of soils, owing to the wide variety of rocks from which the parent material was derived (see Chapter 2 for full discussion of soils; this should be reviewed by the student) and the varied climatic topographic conditions under which the mature soils have evolved. The South, east of the 100th meridian or the 25-inch isohyet, has humid-region soils, the pedalfers. In order from north to south are the Gray-Brown Podzolic, and the Red and Yellow Podzolic Soils. The Yellow Soils are wide-spread over the Coastal Plain from eastern Virginia to central Texas. North and west of these are the Red Soils. They dominate in the inner, hilly portion of the Coastal Plain, on the Piedmont, in the Great Valley south of the Virginia-Tennessee boundary, in northern Alabama and Mississippi, and in most of Arkansas. Figure 12 shows the states and parts of states in which the Gray-Brown Soils are found, and these are far superior in productive power to the Red or the Yellow groups to the south. The dark soils of the Black Belts of Alabama and Texas are known as Prairie Soils.

Soils of the Coastal Plains.   Quartz forms a large part of the soil material of the Coastal Plain. Chapter 2 discusses the origin of the parent soil material. In its journey to the sea the weathered rock was subjected to solution and abrasion, and after deposition in the ocean there was further solution and comminution by waves and currents. The material from which the present-day topsoils have been derived was therefore poor in soluble mineral matter. In texture both the parent material and the mature soil are largely gravel, sand, silt, and a little clay. Leaching, due to the heavy rainfall and the high porosity of the soil, has been active during the evolution of the parent material into what the farmer is tilling today. Coastal Plain soils need heavy application of fertilizers for profitable crops. In the Black Earth Belts in Alabama and Texas Prairie Soils predominate.

Soils of the Piedmont.   In the Piedmont province the parent materials from which the Red Soils are derived are residual, old, and therefore well decomposed chemically. They are deep, except on slopes. Sandy loam, clay loams, and clay predominate and are reddish in color owing to the oxidation of the iron oxides. The subsoil is much more compact than the surface soil. In many parts of the Piedmont the lighter soil on an impervious base offers the best of conditions for soil wash and gullying. The control of the soil erosion is a problem on most farms, particularly in the southern portion where the winter is not cold enough to freeze the ground. In the northern sections of the Piedmont the snow and ice cover checks winter erosion; and the freezing of the soil water produces an open structure in the soil which favors sink-in during the summer.

The heavier soil of the Piedmont provinces requires heavier agricultural implements than are used in the Coastal Plain. As the soil is fairly uniform in quality and lithological compositon, the varety is not great. Differences in temperature, due to a wide range in latitude and altitude, are an important factor in crop distribution. Cotton grows southeastward of a line from Petersburg, Virginia, to the southern end of the mountains in northern Georgia. Corn and other cereals, legumes, tobacco, and fodder may be produced over the entire area. Tobacco, however, is confined chiefly to southern Virginia and northern and eastern North Carolina. It is also grown on the Coastal Plain in both South Carolina and Georgia.

Soils of the Southern Appalachian Mountains. Though most of the parent soil material of this physiographic region has been derived from igneous and metamorphic rocks, like the rocks of the Piedmont, the mature soils are classed in the Gray-Brown Podzol group. The temperatures in the mountains are lower than on the Piedmont, the rainfall is heavier, and deciduous trees dominate in the forests.. The mature soils, therefore, have evolved in an environment quite unlike that of the Piedmont. Except along the major valleys that are traversed by railroads and hard-surface roads, farming is confined chiefly to the production of home supply crops. Mountains in most parts of the world are the natural habitat for the livestock industry. A beginning has been made in the Southern Appalachians in the production of butter and cheese, scattered patches of mountain pasturage being utilized; but the mountain slopes are too densely wooded in their natural state to permit the growth of an abundance of fodder, nor do they rise sufficiently high for the development of "alps" as in Europe. Truck gardening and fruit raising are increasing in importance in the valleys well supplied with roads.

The Great Valley Soils in Tennessee and Alabama. The soils of the Great Valley in Tennessee belong to the Red Soil group. The parent soil material in much of the Valley has been derived from dolomite. It is gravelly and stony, leaches actively, and if in ridges washes badly. Mature soils are scarce. Sandstone, shale, and marble have also contributed soil material. Flat lands are, as has been stated, formed where shale and marble are the bedrock. The most potentially productive soils are on the flat, moderately drained lands. Most of these soils are a dark red, almost as dark as hematite ore.

Limestone Soils.   The valley soils of Virginia, developed from limestone, are residual, like those of the Bluegrass region and the Nashville basin, are gray brown in color on the gentle slopes. They have the other characteristics of Gray-Brown Soils. These are among the most productive in the South. In both Kentucky and Tennessee the soils are rich in phosphate.

Plateau and Highland Rim Soils.   The Cumberland Plateau soils are light in color and texture. The parent material was derived largely from sandstone but some was derived from siliceous shale. In Alabama the color is a light gray, in Tennessee a darker gray. The farmers in the Allegheny Plateau in Kentucky and West Virginia are largely tilling valley soils, some of which are developed from material washed from the hill slopes and mixed with residual limestone silt. So varied are the topography and the source of soil-making material that generalizations do not give a true picture of the soil conditions.

Some portions of the Highland Rim Plain, like the broad plains about Bowling Green, Kentucky, have highly productive soils, the parent soil material having been derived from limestone; but a large part of the Highland Rim region is in slope so steep that erosion and leaching are rapid. Taken as a whole the soils of the Highland Rim are to be classed as indifferent to poor in quality.

Some parts of the Ozarks resemble the Appalachian Plateau region in topography and soils. There are, however, here and there very excellent limestone valleys that are highly productive.

The Loessal Area.   A large area of loessal soil some 15-40 miles wide extends along the eastern edge of the alluvial valley of the Mississippi from the Ohio to within a few miles of Lake Pontchartrain. Loess is found here and there on the west side of the Mississippi Valley, but it is only in patches. It is believed that the material of these relatively fertile, fine-textured, buff-colored, silty deposits, so well seen in the bluffs and borders of ravines at Memphis, Vicksburg, and elsewhere, was brought southward from the glaciated area by the river, deposited in bars, and carried by winds to the bluffs bordering the valley. Loessal soils are adapted to intensive cultivation, truck gardening, and the raising of small fruit. The loessal province is an area of well-tilled soil with little unused land.

Soils of the Arid Lands.   All the western part of Texas and Oklahoma lies in the Great Plains region, the parent soil materials of which are de-

rived from the weathering of sedimentary rocks, chiefly by mechanical
processes. Since chemical decomposition and solution have not been active, the soils have almost the same mineral constituents as the bedrock.
These soils are classed by soil students as pedocals. They have a calcium
layer near the surface in the black and chocolate-colored soils. In the
gray soils of southwestern Texas the calcium layer comes to the surface.
Both the black (Chernozem) and the Dark Brown Soils are in themselves
productive. The dominating factor in agriculture, however, in this portion of the South, is not soil but climate. The chief problem of the agriculturist is moisture control. (The problem of the agriculturist in the dry
lands of the United States is discussed in Chapter 16).

Alluvial Soils.   The largest alluvial area, along the Mississippi River
from Cairo to the Gulf, 550 miles or more long, 75–100 miles wide, has
soil as productive as the famous plains of Mesopotamia and possibly the
Nile Valley. The Colorado, the Brazos, Red, Arkansas, and many shorter
rivers to the east have in the aggregate many thousands of square miles
of alluvial lands. The soils vary from clays and silt loams to sand and
gravel. There is little gravel, however, in the flood plains of the larger
rivers. The mineral composition of the alluvial soils varies greatly in the
different valleys. In general, the soil material is well mixed lithologically,
for the material deposited in the flood plains of the larger rivers comes
from diverse physiographic regions. Soil students class most alluvial soils
as immature and potentially not as productive as soils on the uplands of
gentle slopes. The high yields of alluvial soils are probably due to the
abundance and availability of soil water.

Factors Affecting Soil Fertility.   Although a statement as to the relative
fertility of the soils of North and South, considering the areas as a whole,
is difficult to prove and needs many qualifications, we know that the
North is more productive than the South, and most soil students would
attribute this to the higher fertility of the soils.

The soils of the South are almost entirely the result of chemical weathering. Reds, browns, and yellows predominate in color, showing active
oxidation. Most of the area of the South is in slope and is subject to surface wash and rapid drainage and leaching. The mild winters permit soil
wash and leaching to continue, over most of the South, 12 months in the
year. In most parts of the Northern States the soil is a sheet of frozen solid
rock, as impervious as a slab of slate, for 4 or more months each year.
There is, in general, less humus in the soils of the South than in those of
the North, for the high temperature dries out the ground and "burns
out" the humus. Southern soils, in general, are lighter in color than those
of the North. As an evidence of low fertility of the soils of the southern
states, one may point to the fact that farmers, to secure profitable fields

of crops, are forced, in many areas, to use large quantities of fertilizer. In 1951 the farmers of the North used 4,634,000 tons of fertilizer, and those of the South 10,900,000 tons.

The Climatic Factor.   But there are conditions, other than mineral composition and physical conditions of soils, that influence the productivity of a region. One of the more important factors is climate. Soil students of today have come to realize that climate has a strong influence on the character of the soil (as indicated above), besides being a factor operating on the plant itself, influencing the activity of the protoplasm, the rate of photosynthesis, the rate of transpiration, and the water content of the cells.

The South is a favored section of the country when the climatic elements that affect plant growth are considered. Of all the climatic factors, rainfall and temperature are the two most important.

The Abundant Rainfall.   More than three-fourths of the area of the South receives 40 or more inches of rain each year, and three-eighths of the area gets 50 or more inches. About 8 per cent has less than 20 inches, and 16 per cent less than 30. Of the 902,000 square miles in the South, about 120,000 square miles must be classed as semiarid, where agriculture is profitable only by employing moisture-conservation methods and where cattle and sheep raising is the dominant phase of land utilization. Eastward from the 30-inch isohyet, humid agriculture is everywhere possible.

The rainfall is well distributed throughout the year (Fig. 6). Western Texas, most of the Gulf region east of Texas, and the South Atlantic States, including West Virginia, receives 30–40 per cent of their rainfall in June, July, and August. In Central Texas and most of Oklahoma and Arkansas, spring rains are the rule, about 30 per cent of the annual rainfall coming in March, April, and May. Over most of the remainder of the southern states a late summer minimum is the tendency, yet the driest month, on the average, differs from the wettest by only 2 or 3 inches. Texas and Oklahoma, bordering the arid lands of the West, are subject to long spells of dry weather; 2, 3, and even 4 months of drought are common experiences. Droughts do occur in other sections, and there is rarely a year that crops are not retarded in their growth by dry weather. Widespread crop failures east of the semiarid region are of rare occurrence.

The Temperature Regions.   With a latitude extent of 15° or 1000 miles, and altitudes varying from sea level to 5000 or 6000 (Mount Mitchell, 6684) feet, there is scope for a wide range of temperature conditions in the South. (Review the temperature-region map of North America, Fig. 4). The most important temperature condition affecting agriculture is the long growing season and the early advent of spring. How man has adjusted his agriculture to these factors is discussed in the following sections.

In a large part of southern Florida and southern Texas, crops are grown the year round. In a strip of country bordering the Gulf, 50-75 miles wide, there are, as a rule, no frosts between March 1 and December 1. All of the Lower South has at least 7 months of growing season and, except for the mountain-plateau areas, all of the South has at least 6 months.

Effect of Passing Highs and Lows.   Although the Southern States lie to the south of their major paths, the passing Highs and Lows have general effects as far south as the Gulf. The low relief of the Great Central Plain, extending northward from the Gulf, permits the free passage of air, warm from the south, cool or cold from the north. The presence of a well-developed, slowly moving High in the central United States in the winter often brings freezing weather to the Gulf Coast and far into Florida. At such times great harm is done to vegetation and crops, and consequently cold spells have been closely studied and recorded. The earliest recorded freeze occurred in January, 1766, when fruit trees were killed in St. Augustine. Probably the coldest weather that has ever been felt in Florida occurred February 7, 1835, when the temperature at Jacksonville fell to 7° below zero, the St. John's River had ice on its borders, and all fruit trees were killed. Only since 1871 have official records been kept. Since then freezing weather has occurred in central Florida many times. Since the citrus fruit industry has reached the commercial stage disastrous frosts occurred in 1886 and in 1894, and quite serious damage has occurred in more recent years. Western Texas also suffers greatly from "cold spells." A "norther" in western Texas is a phenomenon always dreaded in the winter. People suffer greatly, and even cattle on the open plains are frozen by the hundreds.

Optimum Conditions for Plants.   In most parts of the South, east of the 100th meridian, the conditions for plant growth, insofar as climate affects them, are particularly favorable. In fact, in neither of the other major divisions of the United States—North or West—is there such a large area in which the climatic elements—rainfall, temperature, evaporation, humidity, and length of season, considered as a whole—approach the optimum that they do in the Southern States.

THE LEADING CROPS

Classification of the Crops.   A great variety of crops are grown in the South. For purposes of discussion we may divide the products associated with southern agriculture into four large groups:

1. Crops grown for the early markets of the North. In this group are included garden truck, strawberries, bush fruits, and peaches.

2. Crops that are better adapted climatically to the Northern States but are grown in the South largely as supply crops and rarely on a commercial scale. In this group may be placed corn, wheat, oats, barley, hay and forage, apples, and also a large part of the products of the livestock industry.

3. A crop such as tobacco, which has a wide range of distribution, that grows in a belt or zone that overlaps both North and South but has its greatest areal extent in the Southern States.

4. Crops distinctly southern in their distribution, such as cotton, sugar cane, rice, peanuts, pecans, and citrus fruits. California, because of its southern location and its mountain-rimmed valleys, produces all of these, but in none except citrus fruit does it approach the South in quantity.

The First Group of Crops

Early Vegetables. The early advent of spring, the rapid warming of the light, well-drained soil of the Coastal Plain, the short season needed for the development of vegetables and small fruits, rapid transportation, and refrigeration enable the southern producers to monopolize northern markets before Northern competition begins, and this is for about 6 months of the year.[1] Early in January, even before New York and other northern cities have experienced their coldest weather, southern Florida and the Texas Coastal Plain near the Mexican border begin their shipment of quick-maturing, cool-weather vegetables. For 10 to 30 days they enjoy the monopoly, and the New York City housewives pay fancy prices for a handful of radishes, onions, lettuce, or peas that have made a 1000- or 1200-mile journey in a refrigerator car or airplane (Fig. 119). The monopoly is not complete, however, for the high prices that vegetables command at this time of year in northern markets has stimulated many northern gardeners to produce hothouse lettuce, spinach, and a few other vegetables that call for only a small space to grow successfully.

By late January and early February, northern Florida and perhaps southern Georgia, if a January or February "cold spell" has not delayed growth or killed the plants outright, usurps control, supplanting the regions to the south, for freight charges to markets are less. As the season advances farther northward, the Savannah-Charleston regions, next the Wilmington, the lower Chesapeake, and finally the upper Chesapeake and Delaware Bay areas, each in turn has the monopoly, for a brief period, until northern New Jersey and Long Island assume control.

[1] Vegetables "grown for home use" are not considered in this discussion.

The centers of production of early vegetables in the South are southern and north central Florida, south central Mississippi, southern Louisiana, Savannah, Charleston, the coastal plain of Virginia, Maryland, and Delaware. Railroad and fast steamship lines to large northern cities have an important influence in the localization of trucking areas for early vegetables. The Illinois Central, the Southern Railroad, and the Atlantic Coast Line carry the bulk of fruit and vegetables to the North.

Fig. 119. Picking string beans for northern markets near Ruskin, Florida. *Courtesy, Tampa Chamber of Commerce*. The growing season here is nearly 12 months, and sometimes 4 crops of vegetables a year are possible.

The Effect of Soil on Time of Maturing.   All the early vegetables are raised on the well-drained, light, warm, dry sands. These soils are not fertile and, unless fertilized heavily, produce a poor quality of vegetable that is likely to deteriorate in shipment; yet the rapidity of growth on these soils offsets these adverse factors. The relation of latitude and quality and character of soil to market period is shown in Table XI. Each

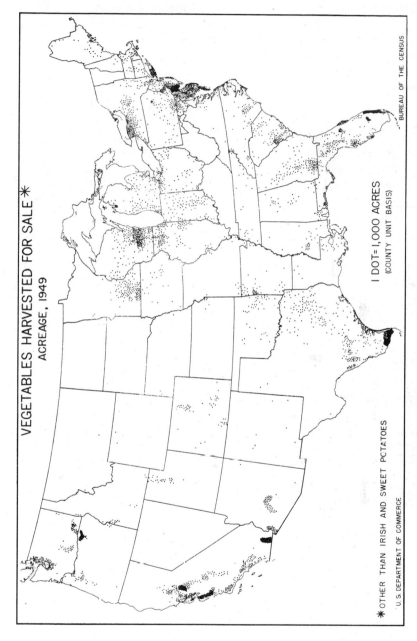

Fig. 120. The distribution of acreage of vegetables harvested for sale in the United States.

of the regions named in the table enjoys a monopoly of northern markets for 10 to 15 days, for vegetables grown on the same types of soil.

TABLE XI.   Market Periods for Fresh Vegetables*

	Jan. 15–31	Feb. 1–15	Feb. 15–28	Mar. 1–15	Mar. 15–31	Apr. 1–15
Fla. and Ga.	Sand	Fine sand	Sandy loam	Fine loamy sand	Loam	Silt loam
S.C.		Sand	Fine sand	Sandy loam	Fine sandy loam	Loam
N.C.			Sand	Fine sand	Sandy loam	Fine sandy loam
Va.				Sand	Fine sand	Sandy loam
Md. and Del.					Sand	Fine sand
L.I.						Sand

*Bulletin 96, U.S. Bureau of Soils.

Texas, Louisiana, Mississippi, and Arkansas hold the monopoly of the city markets of the North Central States longer than do truck-garden regions on the Atlantic Coastal Plain, because little competition is offered by the states between the North Central markets and the Gulf Coastal Plains.

The raising of truck products for early markets is a precarious venture for the Coastal Plain gardener, for the period of market control on which success depends is brief, and local cold spells or heavy rains may so delay the period of maturing that regions to the north, if not so affected, may capture the markets. Markets are frequently glutted. The cost of production is high, and the yield of the earliest vegetables, which must be grown on the light, warm, sandy soils, is low unless large quantities of fertilizer are used. The money returns vary greatly; some years large sums are made, other years many face seeming failure; but, as in treasure hunting, no one knows when success may come, hence the gardeners stick to the hoe. The cities of the South offer a market for both early and late vegetables, but their aggregate population is not large.

The Rank of the South in Vegetable Growing.   In number of acres used in the growing of vegetables offered for sale, exclusive of potatoes, the South Atlantic States led all other sections, chiefly because of the large area of the Coastal Plain included in this division and the long time each year during which the truck gardeners dominate northern markets. The census data do not distinguish early vegetables from late. We know, however, that, in spite of the high prices paid for early vegetables, the total production of late vegetables, measured in dollars, is far greater than that of the early, for summer is the chief vegetable-eating season. In the value of vegetables raised for sale the South Atlantic Section stood second in 1950, with California leading (Fig. 120).

In comparing individual states, only Texas, Florida, Maryland, and Georgia, in the Southern States, stand out as leaders in vegetable production. No other state of the South exceeds any one of the Middle Atlantic or the East North Central States. California leads the nation in acreage devoted to vegetables, followed by Texas, Wisconsin, New York, and Florida. Both Texas and Florida have made very rapid advances since 1930.

There were few vegetables raised for early markets in the South prior to 1865, and few small fruits and nursery products, because the population was scarce. There were no large southern cities to serve as markets, and labor was needed for cotton, rice, and corn. Furthermore, Negro labor was considered not intelligent enough to till and care for vegetables, and transportation was so poor that markets in large cities could not be reached. The value of vegetables and fruits as foods was not appreciated, and refrigeration was unknown until 1875. Since 1940 there has been great development in truck gardening and in the number of varieties of vegetables. In the areas producing commercial vegetables, commercial varieties, which will stand shipping and look well at the end of the journey, dominate. In many sections a variety of truck is raised, for there is less chance for failure; yet certain of the areas have found it profitable to specialize.

Climate and soil are favorable factors in truck gardening, but the great distance to the northern markets for early vegetables, the small urban population in the South, and the low per capita consumption in the South limit the industry.

Strawberry Growing.   Strawberry growers in the South who seek early northern markets have many of the difficulties of the truck gardeners. The annual production varies greatly. In the South the average crop is 100,000,000 quarts, but in 1944, a short crop year, the South produced only 38,000,000 quarts, and the entire northeastern area and the northern states were also low in strawberry production in 1944. The leading states in strawberry production in 1950 were California, Arkansas, and Louisiana, in the order named. The South produced more than 50 per cent of the nation's crop.

Peach Growing in the South.   In Georgia, northeastern Texas, Arkansas, central Oklahoma, North Carolina, and Virginia most of the peaches of the South are raised. These and several minor regions have about 50 per cent of the peach trees of the country, and produce about 30 per cent of the crop. California alone, however, produces about 39 per cent of the total for the United States (Fig. 121).

Even when the Spaniards held Florida, there were large peach orchards in that state and elsewhere in the South. From these orchards stock was secured for the peach orchards found on a large number of southern plantations until after the Civil War. Careful selection and

favorable soil and climate have preserved or even enhanced the color and
flavor of the Spanish variety. It is still a favorite.

About 1870–1875, the first attempts were made to place Georgia
peaches on northern markets; but this was before the days of special
fruit trains, refrigerator cars, and scientific methods of packing. Many
experiments were tried, but almost always the reports to the shipper
were the same, "spoiled in transit." Finally the refrigerator car solved
the problem, and in 1889 the first large peach crop was successfully marketed. The planting of peach orchards soon became active in many parts

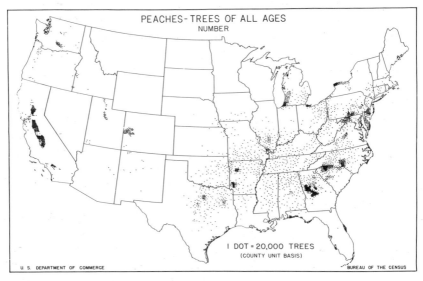

Fig. 121. Number of peach trees of all ages in the United States. *Courtesy, U. S. Department of Agriculture.* Peaches are widely distributed in the United States. Since about 1910
Michigan has entered into commercial production of this fruit. Georgia had three-fourths
as many trees as California, yet California produced more than five times as many
bushels.

of Georgia. Many failures resulted through lack of knowledge of air
drainage, adaptation to soil, and adaptation of variety to conditions.
Experience has taught that the hill slopes in northwestern Georgia in the
Great Appalachian Valley are suitable, and here is found a large acreage; but the leading peach region has come to be central Georgia, to the
southwest of Macon, centering about Fort Valley and Marshallville.
These towns are on broad interstream uplands with plenty of slope. The
peach region of Georgia is shifting northward to the hill lands on the
outer edge of the Piedmont, and into the old cotton-growing section of
the Piedmont in South Carolina.

Peach growing in the South is not without its losses. On the average, 1 crop out of 3 or 4 is lost by late frosts. The warm days of late February and early March may start spring growth in the trees in central Georgia and Texas—slightly later farther north—and killing frosts may come as late as April 1. Because of the long budding and blossoming season, many blossoms or buds usually escape the 1 or 2 days of cold weather, and enough peaches will mature to make a paying crop. In comparison with California, the yield per tree is low. Georgia has nearly as many bearing trees as California, yet the yield is less than one-third as many bushels. The yield per tree, however, in Georgia is higher than in most of the northern states. There are, of course, factors other than geographic ones that influence the output of orchards. The Georgia Fruit Exchange, with agents in many cities, and the active cooperation of the railroads assist the producers in getting their product on the market at opportune times. About 85 per cent of the peach growers belong to the exchange.

The Second Group of Crops

Little need be said about the second group of products, for a discussion of these belongs properly in the sections devoted to the Northern States. Any of the cereals will grow over a large part of the South. Barley and oats are sown for winter cover crops and pasturage and for plowing under. Wheat, confined chiefly to the Upper South, is ground in local mills, mainly for local consumption. Corn is widely distributed, cornfields being found in every part except in the lower Mississippi delta, east Gulf regions, and most of Florida. Yet Illinois and Iowa together in 1950 produced considerably more than the crop of the entire South. Much corn is consumed as human food, the per capita being much greater than in the North; but because of the relatively slight importance of livestock in southern agriculture there is not the demand for corn that there is in the Corn Belt. The South has a large area in which the climate is nearly, if not quite, as good as in the North. Some of the largest "corn club" yields have been produced in the South, which leads one to venture the opinion that with better tillage and attention to seed selection the returns might be greatly increased. The heavy rainfall and high temperatures tend to develop more stalk and leaf than in the North, and often this growth is at the expense of the kernels.

Apples have long been grown in the South, but only since about 1860 have commercial orchards been planted. Planting is still in progress. The chief producing orchards are on the ridges of the Appalachian Valley and on the Blue Ridge in Virginia, in the Southern Appalachian Mountains in North Carolina, and in northwestern Arkansas in the Ozark Plateau. The apple-growing regions of the United States do not extend southward much beyond the middle South. About one-third of the bearing apple trees in the country are in the South, but the total production is generally less than one-fourth.

Southern Livestock Industry.   Even today the South ranks well among the other sections of the United States in the livestock industry, the value of southern livestock being about 25 per cent of the total for the country. Little attention has been paid to the raising of blooded or special-purpose

Fig. 122. A typical landscape in the Bluegrass region of Kentucky, on residual soils developed from limestone. *Courtesy, Lexington Herald-Leader.* Here the paddocks are enclosed with board fences instead of wire, as a protection against possible injury to horses. This region has long been noted for the breeding of the American thoroughbred trotting, pacing, and race horses.

stock until about 1930, although a few planters have all along raised pedigreed horses and cattle. Kentucky and Tennessee have long bred race horses, an industry well adapted to the Bluegrass soils. It is claimed by many that bluegrass is the ideal pasture for the horse (Fig. 122). In the early part of the nineteenth century, Devon and Shorthorn cattle were brought from England, but in most parts they were crossed with other breeds. Strains of these may still be seen among the "scrubs" in some sections.

The raising of cattle has been easy, and little attention was formerly given to the maintenance of quality. Since earliest colonial times it has been the general practice to turn cattle, and hogs, also, free to range the forests for a living. In colonial times they were not herded, as in New England, by public herders, but were "branded" and allowed free range, and once a year "round-ups" were held and tl ncrease allocated. The loss of cattle was considerable. Flint writes that in pre-Revolutionary War days the planters expected that such "multitudes" would die each winter as to "supply hides enough for shoeing the negroes on every farm." This was a matter "generally and constantly anticipated."

Nature developed two distinct varieties of cattle in the South, the Texas "longhorns" and the "piney woods" cattle. With them may be classed the "razor back" hog. They do not conform to man's ideas of spe-

Fig. 123. Herd of Brahman cattle on the Texas Coastal Prairies. *Courtesy of Hudgins Ranch, Hungerford, Texas.* The introduction and crossbreeding of Brahman cattle with native stock produces animals more nearly immune to tick fever—a promising aspect of the beef cattle industry in the South.

cial-purpose animals, but are not to be classed as degenerates. They are the product of nature's breeding. All "purebred stock" needs the watchful care of man. These so-called "scrubs" will thrive better in their environment than the pampered product of man's careful selection.

The days of the so-called "scrubs" in the South are numbered. Nearly all the "longhorns," some with a spread of horns of 8 feet or more, disappeared by 1885. There are still large herds of "piney woods" cattle and a few "razor back" hogs. "Round-ups" are still held in the cut-over regions of the Coastal Plain, but commercial clubs, chambers of commerce, banks, railroads, state agricultural colleges, county agents, and farm journals have in many places educated the southern farmer to the value of blooded stock. Only a beginning has been made, however. The first public sale of pure-bred cattle in the South was held in Oklahoma City in 1903, and the second sale in 1904 at Auburn, Alabama. Elsewhere many more have been held each year. The South lacks packing houses, but some have been established at Fort Worth, Nashville, Macon, and elsewhere. Creameries, condenseries, and cheese factories are becoming more numerous. The long grazing season, large area for cattle ranges on the cut-over lands of Coastal Plains and mountain slopes, and the abundance of the more concentrated foods, as cottonseed and peanut meal, ensilage, and leguminous plants are conditions that will not long be overlooked. The tick, the most important barrier to livestock raising in the past, is now being controlled.

On the Texas Gulf Coastal Plain introductions of Brahman cattle for crossbreeding has produced a variety more nearly immune to tick fever than uncrossed breeds. Today some large herds are to be found in the longleaf pine forests of northern Florida, in the thornbush section of the southeast coast of Texas, on the coastal prairies of Louisiana, as well as on the grassy coastal prairies and forest lands of east Texas.

The Gulf Coastal Plain with large areas of range land and grasses, a mild winter, with plentiful rainfall, and high prices for beef, is undoubtedly due to expand its cattle industry (Fig. 123).

The Third Group of Crops

Tobacco in the South.   Tobacco, a product common to both the Northern and Southern States, is, after all, a southern crop. About 90 per cent of the product of the country comes from the South, and Kentucky alone produces more than twice as much and North Carolina nearly five times as much as all the Northern States combined. The yield to the acre in pounds is on the average only about 50–70 per cent of that in the Northern States.

Like corn, tobacco is a gift of the first Americans to our European ancestors who colonized the continent. At one time, tobacco raising at Jamestown was so profitable that the borders of the streets were planted and the production of food crops was neglected. From the Chesapeake Bay region tobacco culture was carried southward and westward. It was finally found that the best environment for the plant is in central Kentucky, southern Virginia on the Piedmont, northern and eastern North Carolina, and eastern South Carolina, chiefly on the Coastal Plain. These are the more important tobacco-growing centers of the United States (Figs. 124 and 125).

At present, tobacco is a product chiefly of the small farm, and only a few acres on a farm are devoted to it. Its culture on many farms is a family affair, and one family of average size is able to raise 5–10 acres. In North Carolina and Kentucky, the average size of the patches is less than 5 acres. On some of the large farms where labor is employed for general agriculture, the tobacco fields often have 20–30 acres per farm.

The Fourth Group of Crops

Cotton, the Most Important Crop.   Cotton was found by the early Spanish explorers in many parts of America—in the West Indies, Mexico, Central America, and Peru—and in all these sections it was being used by the Indians in the manufacture of cloth. The West Indies is probably the chief source of the cotton introduced into southeastern North America. The history of cotton is intermingled with that of the South from the earliest colonial period. It was experimented with in Virginia about 1608, and was early spoken of as a promising crop. By 1621 it was listed as one of the export crops of the colony, but we have no data to

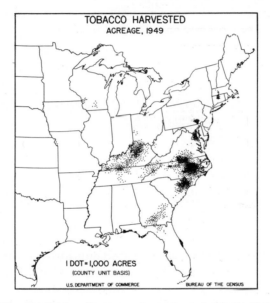

Fig. 124. The distribution of acreage tobacco harvested in the United States.

tell how much was shipped. In the colonies to the south of Virginia, cotton was always among the first crops attempted. When the Revolutionary War cut off the supply of English cotton goods, efforts were made in America to increase production and to manufacture cloth. By this time the revolutionary inventions in the textile industry had already been made, and England at the close of the war was able to supply cheaper cotton goods than ever before. The expansion of the textile industry in England and of cotton raising in America was retarded by the great amount of labor needed to separate seed and fiber.

Sea-island cotton had already been introduced into Georgia, and a crude roller gin had been devised—exactly like the churka used in India for many centuries—which worked very well with this long staple. But long-staple sea-island cotton was very limited in amount. The Whitney gin invented in 1793, and the improvement added by Holmes—saws instead of spikes on rollers—solved the problem. In 1791 the production of the United States was more than 4000 bales; in 1801, it was 100,000; and 10 years later, 167,000. During 1801–1810 cotton culture expanded westward into the Gulf States, but was somewhat retarded by the presence of Indian tribes. South Carolina and Georgia continued to be the chief producing states, to the extent of more than one-half the production. The Louisiana Purchase (1803) added much territory to the country, but only a part was suitable for producing cotton. Only 4000 bales were produced in 1811 in Louisiana. Texas was admitted to the Union in 1845, its annexation being strongly urged by cotton planters, and a vast cotton territory was added.

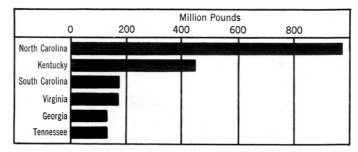

Fig. 125. Tobacco production in the United States by leading states in 1951.

For more than a century the United States held first place in cotton production. In 1792 this country exported only about 275 bales (adjusted for 500-pound bales), but by 1800, 36,000. Most of these went to England. By 1860 about 85 per cent of the raw cotton consumed by the cotton factories of England came from the United States. The dangers of depending solely on one country for a product that supplied work for hundreds of thousands of people became evident in England shortly after the beginning of the Civil War; and when danger was realized a conference was called and stock taken of the possible cotton lands in the world outside the United States. The results were most gratifying; more than 30 countries could produce cotton. There were prospects, therefore, that never again would England have to depend exclusively on the United States; but when the Civil War was over the South again got into production. Its environmental superiority in the growing of cheap, high-grade cotton insures it a leading place. In no other section of the world is there such a large area suitable for the growing of cotton; favorable climate, excellent transportation facilities, good labor and intelligent supervision,

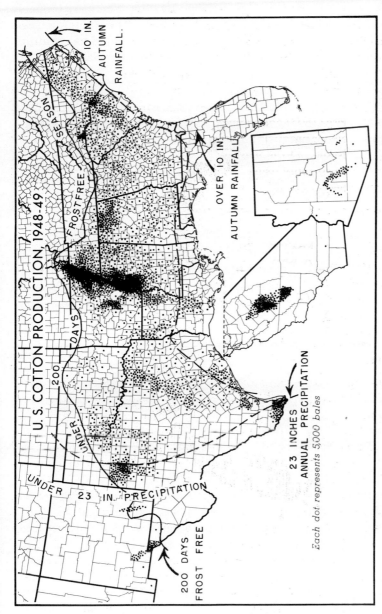

Fig. 126. The relation of climate to cotton production. *Courtesy, U. S. Department of Agriculture.* What conclusions do you draw as to length of growing season and amount and distribution of precipitation best for cotton? There has been a slight shift westward in cotton production since 1920. Why? In the older cotton states, particularly the Carolinas, Georgia and Alabama, there has been a decline. Why?

large invested capital, and well-established traditions and practices (Fig. 126). The United States could produce many times as much as it does now if there were markets to absorb the production. There are probably more than 300,000,000 acres in the Cotton Belt, but in most late years about 20,000,000 to 40,000,000 acres have been devoted to its culture. Other sections of the world may cut in on the southern leadership, but

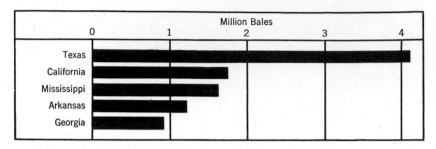

Fig. 127. Cotton production in the United States by leading states in 1951.

the South is likely to remain dominant in this great textile staple (Figs. 127 and 128). Should some of the European textile countries become independent of United States raw cotton, they would meet in the markets of the world the competition of the United States mills using home-grown cotton.

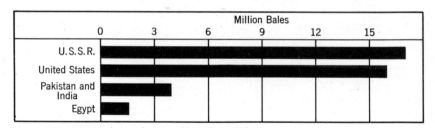

Fig. 128. Cotton production by leading countries of the world in 1951.

Since 1920, due to wars and economic conditions resulting therefrom, the foreign market has been curtailed. There has been a large "carry-over" crop and low prices. In addition, rayon and other synthetic fibers are increasing in competition for the market. The government has attempted to solve the problem by limiting the acreage devoted to cotton. Times have been hard for the cotton grower, but in general this loss of cotton market, and limiting of acreage may result in good for southern agriculture. It encourages diversification, mechanization, and cattle raising, as well as the application of science to seed selection and improving the varieties of cotton to give greater yields per acre. It is not a question of how much cotton the South can produce, but how much the market will take.

The Rice Crop.   The native home of rice for thousands of years has been eastern and southeastern Asia, where the summer temperatures are high and the rainfall is heavy. Asia continues to produce a large part of the rice crop of the world. In 1947 it was estimated that Asia had 191 million acres in rice, whereas the acreage in the United States was less than 2 million. Nevertheless, rice is an important crop in parts of the South. In the United States, a similar environment to that in parts of Asia, except that the season is not quite so long, is found along the Gulf and Souh Atlantic coasts and in the alluvial valley of the Arkansas and Mississippi.

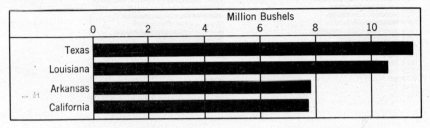

Fig. 129. Rice production in the United States by leading states in 1950.

In 1950, the leading states in the Union in rice production were Texas, producing 27,600,000 bushels; Louisiana 26,500,000 bushels; Arkansas and California each over 19,000,000 bushels; Mississippi, South Carolina, Georgia, and a few other states of the South produce small quantities. The rice crop of the United States in 1950 was over 90,000,000 bushels, about 85 per cent coming from the South. California is the only state of importance outside of the South; it ranked fourth in production in 1950 (Fig. 129). There are possibly 20,000,000 acres in the United States that may be devoted to rice culture. The low per capita consumption in the United States is the chief reason for low production.

The culture of rice in the South reached a peak in 1850, when nearly 6,500,000 bushels were grown; 3,300,000 in South Carolina, 3,100,000 in Georgia. Carolina rice had a good reputation in Europe. One author in London wrote, "By far the best imported rice is from South Carolina. It is larger and better tasting than that from India, which is smaller, meager, and often broken." The cultivation of rice raised by the help of slave labor brought great prosperity. Men grew rich, built fine homes, and educated their children in northern and European schools, from the fields of rice. Rice growers were the leading agriculturists of the South in the use of scientific methods—rotation of crops and the use of fertilizer.

During the Civil War the industry was almost destroyed. The canals became filled with swampy vegetation, the fields were neglected, and the planters emigrated to the interior. In 1890 the growing of rice was reestablished in South Carolina and Georgia, but by that time it had begun to be grown in the west Gulf lands by irrigation methods. In 1879 South Carolina Produced 1,873,000 bushels; Georgia, 900,000; and Louisiana, 800,000. By 1889 Louisiana took the lead, the crop being

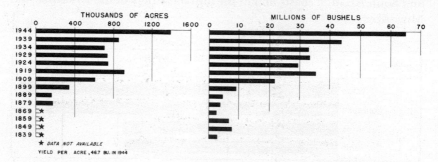

RICE (ROUGH OR PADDY) THRESHED—ACREAGE, 1879 TO 1944; AND PRODUCTION, 1839 TO 1944; FOR THE UNITED STATES

Fig. 130. The trend of rice production in the United States.

2,700,000 and that of South Carolina but 1,000,000 bushels. By 1909 rice growing in the South Atlantic States was of little importance. Since 1940 rice growing has extended along the Gulf Coast of Texas and into the Arkansas Valley. Probably the most recent extension of rice culture is into the St. Francis Basin of northeastern Arkansas, where level land permits the use of machinery and water is pumped from deep wells, with relatively little expense[2] (Fig. 130).

Rice culture in Louisiana, Texas, and Arkansas is much like wheat culture in the grain states of the North. The application of grain machinery to rice culture by farmers from the Middle West since the 1880's make the growing of this oriental cereal on a large scale possible. Here one finds irrigation practiced in a region where the rainfall is sufficient for other humid-land crops. The water is pumped from the bayous or wells, or furnished by flowing wells, and distributed over the land, much as it is in the arid sections of the West. The flatness of the Coastal Prairies, the great depth of soil, and its looseness make the construction of distributing channels easy. Low levees are, as a rule, thrown up about the

[2]A well near Paragould, Arkansas, 1000 feet deep, pumped by the power of a gasoline tractor, furnishes a 10-inch stream of water, nearly 2,000 gallons per day, to irrigate 80 acres of rice.

borders of the patches of ground, sufficiently high to hold the waters yet low enough to permit the free movement of farm machinery over them.

The land is plowed and harrowed and the seed is drilled in by the ordinary grain drills used in grain fields. After the small plants reach the height of an inch or two, the fields are flooded and kept flooded throughout the greater part of the growing season. When the heads of rice are nearly formed, the fields are drained and allowed to dry out. This decrease in moisture hastens the maturing of the seed and gives a firm bed

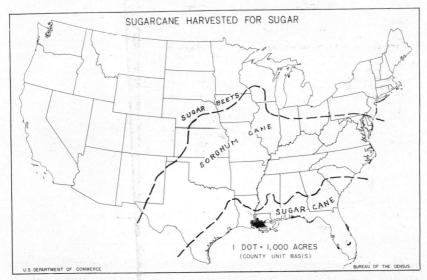

Fig. 131. Sugar cane harvested for sugar, and other sugar areas in the United States. Louisiana grows most of the cane from which sugar is produced in the United States; however much cane is grown for syrup in the Lower South. Sorghum cane is grown mainly for syrup and little, if any, for sugar. The approximate limits of beets, sorghum, and cane are shown on this map. The canes, particularly sugar cane, require the longer seasons. Louisiana truly contains the "sugar bowl."

for the heavy binders that harvest the crop. In September and October when the harvesting and threshing season is on, the rice farms remind one of the wheat lands of the North Central States, with binders, rice stack, and threshing machines, except that Negro labor is doing most of the work.

Sugar in Louisiana.   Although sugar cane is grown for sugar in 8 of the Southern States, Louisiana produces nearly the total commercial crop. Even here, but for the tariff barrier to foreign sugar, the industry could not exist. Sugar is a crop that does best only in the tropics and must be produced on a large scale, for the mills used in its manufacture, if they

are to produce sugar low enough in cost to meet the competition elsewhere, are necessarily large and costly. All through the Lower South,
however, sugar cane is grown on tens of thousands of farms in each
state—over 200,000 farms in all—merely for the making of sugar and
syrup for home consumption (Fig. 131).

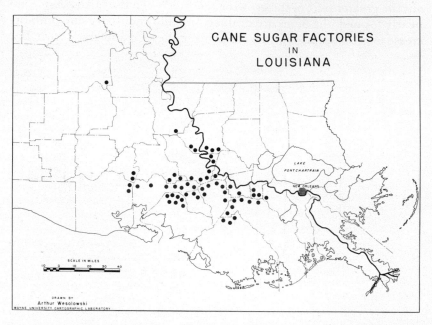

Fig. 132. Cane sugar factories in Louisiana. *Arthur Wesolowski.* In the early history of
cane sugar making there were many mills scattered throughout the cane-growing area.
As improvements were made the refining process became more complex, small mills
were not economical, and fewer but larger mills developed. Each mill is now centrally
located in a cane-producing area, and all are on the newer delta lands and prairies.

Little can be promised as to the growth of the sugar industry in the
South because of the many unfavorable conditions to be overcome by
Southern cane growers, such as adverse climate, labor scarcity, competition with beet sugar, and the changing tariff. Throughout most of United
States history there has been a tariff on sugar imports, as a protection for
the mainland industry. Today there is perhaps more to justify such a
tariff because of the useful by-products which come from the sugar mills,
particularly in the case of cane sugar. These are molasses and fiber board.
Molasses is one of the basic sources of industrial alcohol, as well as a feed-
stuff for fattening cattle. Fiber board is a building board made from
"bagasse," the waste of sugar cane stalks after the juice has been extracted. It is a highly satisfactory building material and an insulator used

in refrigerators, as well as a sound absorber used in many ways. The fiber board industry in Louisiana yields about as much profit as the sugar. (Fig. 132).

The United States produces less than one-third of its total sugar consumption (both beet and cane). The remainder comes from the West Indies, Hawaii, and the Philippines (Fig. 133). The Everglades region of Florida has begun sugar production from cane. This area has an advantage over Louisiana in that it is relatively free from frost, and the cane does not have to be replanted each year as is the case in Louisiana. The Everglades could become a large sugar producer, but congressional legislation limits the amount to be produced.

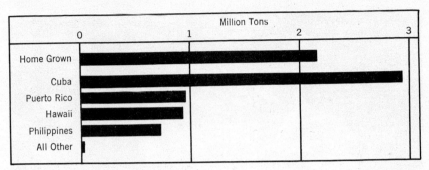

Fig. 133. Sources of sugar used in the United States in 1951. (Three-fourths of all home-grown sugar was from beets; practically all imported sugar was from cane.)

There is so much good, free land in the tropics and the yield is so much better there, that the industry in the South will probably last only as long as it is encouraged by favorable tariff laws.

Citrus Fruits. There is a large area along the Gulf Coast stretching from the Rio Grande to Pensacola that is adapted to the growing of oranges, but only a small part of this region is utilized. Most of the orange groves are in Florida and Texas, south of 29° N. (Fig. 134). It is believed that the Spaniards brought the bitter Seville orange from Europe when they occupied the eastern Gulf Coast regions. Some of these trees have been used as stock for grafting. The modern orange-growing industry dates from about 1875, when the East Coast Railway was completed. At one time Florida dominated northern and eastern orange markets, but severe freezes in 1886, 1894, and 1899 destroyed three-fourths of the plantings and thus gave California an opportunity to win markets. Replanting followed in Florida but not in the northern part of the state. The orange region was shifted southward. In 1929 the Mediterranean fruit fly forced an embargo on the shipment of citrus fruit from more than 8,000,-000 acres which grew about 70 per cent of the bearing trees of Florida.

This embargo gave the fruit growers of the lower Rio Grande Valley, which was just producing its initial large crop, a comparatively free market. The production, average for 1940–1949, for the three states (in boxes) is as follows:

	Oranges	Grapefruit	Lemons
Florida	46,070,000	27,280,000	—
California	48,196,000	2,892,000	12,993,000
Texas	3,616,000	17,387,000	—

The yield per tree and the relative value of the crop is generally lower in Florida than in California, owing undoubtedly to poor methods of pro-

Fig. 134. Workers in orange grove in central Florida. *Courtesy, Florida News Bureau.*

duction and marketing. Only since about 1935 has a Florida fruit exchange done much advertising. In some markets in the eastern United States, Florida and Texas oranges compete successfully with the California product because they can be put on the market at a much lower price. They are sent 1000 miles or more by carload or truckload without boxing.

Grapefruit, or pomelo, grows in much the same region as the orange. In the production and delivery to northern markets, Florida made the beginning and has since retained its leadership. The lower Rio Grande region is now arising as a strong competitor of Florida in pomelos. About 80 per cent of the pomelo trees of the country are in the South; and, if

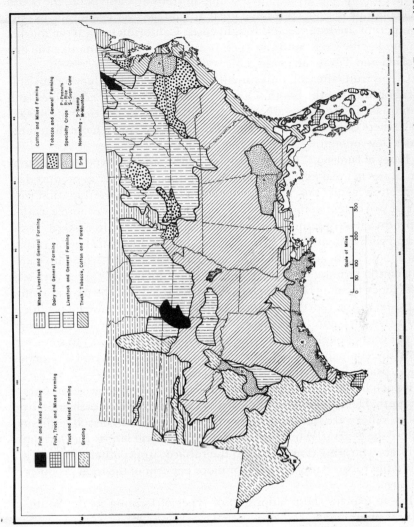

Fig. 135. Types of farming in the South. *Adapted from "Types of Farming," Bureau of Agricultural Economics, 1950.*

proper attention is given to marketing and careful cultivation, the South will continue to lead, for it has a great advantage over California, its only competitor, in distance and freight costs. Califorina has a large market on the Pacific Coast and the West in general, but nothing like the one Florida and Texas can command.

Citrus fruit, after all, bulks small when compared with other agricultural products of the South. Oranges, grapefruit, limes, tangerines, and kumquats, in the aggregate, were in 1950 valued at less than $500,000,-000, whereas the cotton crop, including seed, was worth more than three times that amount.

Types of Farming. Cotton farming is the dominant type in the Southern States in areal extent; but rarely is cotton the only crop produced on the cotton farms (Fig. 135). Most cotton is grown in combination with one or two or more other products. In western Texas, for example, cotton is produced with some grain sorghum and livestock; in eastern Texas cotton with fruit and truck. In the Black Belt of Alabama cotton raising is combined with general farming and dairying; in southern South Carolina cotton farming with part-time farming and in some areas with self-sufficiency farming; but always in the area shown on the map as cotton farming, cotton represents 40 per cent at least of the value of products. In the cotton combination types, cotton dominates, but forms less than 40 per cent of total value of crops. The combinations vary. In some sections the companion product is livestock, in others peanuts, potatoes, truck, peaches, citrus fruit, pecans, tobacco, etc.

Ranch livestock farming is the dominant type in the western part of the south. Here also is most of the cash grain farming and cash grain livestock. Where are the mixed-farming areas? Where the self-sufficing? Where the general? Where are the non-agricultural lands? In what states is tobacco farming dominant? In the tobacco areas other products are raised but tobacco represents 40 or more per cent of the total products of the farm.

Try to explain the relationship of types of farming in the South to natural environmental conditions and markets.

QUESTIONS, EXERCISES, AND PROBLEMS

1. Some writers claim that the South offers excellent advantages to the home seeker in search of farm lands. Can you justify such claims? Make use of all the needed climatic, physical, and agricultural maps in the text.

2. Make a statistical comparison of agriculture in Mississippi and Iowa. Data may be secured from the Census Report, volumes on agriculture, the *Yearbooks* of the Department of Agriculture, and the *Statistical Abstract*. Compare land areas, population, farm lands, improved farm lands, crops, livestock, automobiles on farms, water in houses, tele-

phones, value of farm property and of machinery, and other items on which you secure data. What are your conclusions? What explanations can you offer for the differences?

3. Select a county on the Coastal Plain of North Carolina (Green County), one on the Piedmont (Guilford County), one in western North Carolina (Harwood County), and compare the agricultural conditions. Secure data from the Census Reports.

4. Make a statistical comparison of agriculture in a county in the Black Belt of Texas (Ellis or Dallas County) with a county in the black-earth section of Nebraska (Adams or Clay County). Write your conclusions.

5. Compare yields to the acre of several crops grown in both North Central and Southern States. What explanations do you offer? Secure data from the *Yearbook* of the Department of Agriculture.

6. To what extent is the South improving its cattle, sheep, and swine by the introduction of pure-bred animals? Compare with some of the states of the North. Does the presence of a large number of Negro tenants have any influence on agricultural improvement?

7. Make a study of share-cropping in the South. How do you account for this practice? What changes are in progress?

8. How do you explain the tendency toward intensification in agriculture in some sections of the South with a population density as low as it is?

9. Classify the several Southern States as to location in the agricultural regions shown in Fig. 135, also as to the dominant type of farming in each.

10. What improvements in the methods and practices of agriculture would you suggest to make the South a greater agricultural section?

CHAPTER 13

Manufacturing
in the South

INDUSTRIAL OPPORTUNITIES

Some Comparisons. The value of the manufactured products of the South (16 southern states as listed in the census reports) in 1950 was greater than the output of the factories of the entire United States in 1889, and nearly twice the output of the country in 1879. The aggregate cotton spindles active in Southern cotton mills in 1950 numbered nearly as many as those of the United States in 1900. The South produced more pig iron in 1950 than the entire country in 1880, cut nearly as much lumber, mined five times as much coal, and produced fifty times as much petroleum. Since about 1935 there has been a greater increase in manufacturing in the southern states than in any other section of the country.

This is indeed remarkable progress in industrial development; yet other sections have grown likewise in the last half century. However, it is true that the South is not producing its share of the manufactured goods of the country, when relative areas and populations are considered. Although the South has nearly 30 per cent of the area of the country, and more than 30 per cent of the people, it produces only 18 per cent of the manufactured goods of the country, and the net value is but 17.5 per cent of that for the country as a whole. The Northeastern Region produced about two and one-half times as much, and the north Central States also about two and one-half times as much. New York, the leading manufacturing state, produced three-fourths as much as all of the South (based on net value) (Fig. 136). These comparisons bespeak a retarded development, past and present; yet the progress made since World War I offers great hope for the future of Southern manufacture. *What are the causes for this retarded condition? Should the people of the South be optimistic for the future?*

CAUSES FOR RETARDED INDUSTRIAL DEVELOPMENT

The Dominance of Agriculture. The South traditionally is an agricultural section. In 1950 more than 30 per cent of the farm population of the country resided in the South; and 55 per cent of the people were classed as rural. In colonial days there were here and there in the South, as in the Northern States, small industrial plants of various sorts built to cater to local needs only. As settlements spread westward along the small, non-navigable streams, and especially beyond the mountains, there was a call for local industries, and these supplied all community needs until the coming of the railroad. Such was the condition over all parts of the South beyond the tidewater areas. Except for the invention of textile machinery in England and the cotton gin in America, it seems probable that there would have developed in time an industrial and commercial population along with an agricultural, in such relative numbers as to make each community, or natural trade region, self-sustaining insofar as local resources would permit.

Cotton Becomes King.   It was discovered, however, two or three decades after 1793, that great profits were to be made in the growing of

Fig. 136. Net value of manufacturing in the United States by geographic divisions in 1950.

cotton. Accordingly, most of the available capital of the South went into land, farm buildings, tools, and slaves. Most industries, unless associated with cotton culture, languished. Before the middle of the nineteenth century cotton production came to exceed the demand. Cotton prices reached such a low level that cotton culture lost some of its glamour. Some capitalists, for a few years at least, sought channels other than agriculture. Some thoughtful men came to realize the ill effects of the industrial dependence on New England and old England; they saw it was bad economy to ship the raw products hundreds of miles to be fabricated, and to have the articles returned and purchased at several times the cost of the raw material, while capital and labor got such low returns in agricultural pursuits. Political antagonism toward the North made this commercial and economic vassaldom all the more galling. But what could be done? The basic economic activity of a country is not to be changed in a day, and agriculture was the dominant activity. The South in 1850 was producing only about 10 per cent of the manufactured goods of the country.

Effects of the Civil War. During the Civil War, cut off from the factories of the North and Europe, every available plant in the South was at work producing clothing, food, munitions, railroad equipment, and other articles needed for war. The small factories scattered all over the South were expanded, and other plants built to take care of the emergency demand. By the close of the war, all these factories were idle or had been destroyed. But the South had its land, its abundant rain, genial temperatures, and life-giving sunshine, and these largely came to save it, if saved it was. Its economic life was to be intimately associated with these enduring factors. It again became the producer of raw materials for northern and eastern factories. Its economic affiliations, as well as its political, were again merged with those of the country at large.

Coal and Railroads Gave North Advantage. In the two decades preceding 1870, coal for steam power had come to be an important factor in the industries in the Northeastern States. In 1850 the country at large used 6,250,000 tons of coal; by 1860 the consumption had reached more than 13,000,000 tons; and by 1870 nearly 30,000,000. Nearly all of this was consumed in the North, and a large part in northern factories, which gave this section a decided advantage in the production of manufactured articles. Moreover, railroad consolidation had progressed to such an extent by 1870 that northern manufactured goods had access to southern markets. With the absence of tariff barriers to check the influx of northern-made goods and to protect the young and feeble industries in the South, little progress in manufacturing was made. The trans-Rocky movement of population and capital, initiated by the discovery of gold in 1848 and wonderfully aided by the construction of the transcontinental railroad, was going on apace. In national development and industrial expansion, the South was forgotten by the North and Northeast, the sections best equipped to furnish capital. A few Northern men, however, who had participated in the campaigns in the South, saw great possibilities here and returned at the close of the Civil War with some capital.

In 1870 the factories of the South produced only 6.6 per cent of the manufactured goods of the country; in 1880, only 6.3 per cent; in 1890, 7.5 per cent; in 1900, 9.1 per cent; in 1909, 12.2 per cent, and in 1950, 18 per cent. Thus at no period in its history has the South produced the portion of the manufactured goods that its area and population call for. Its past has been fundamentally associated with agriculture.

Effects of Low Population Density. Another cause for the retarded development is the low population density. It is a well-known principle that the occupations dominant in a country bear a fairly definite relation to the density of population. The countries or sections of countries dominantly manufacturing have high population densities. Belgium as a whole has a population density of more than 711 to the square mile; England and Wales, about 685; Massachusetts, 546; New York State, with fully 90 per cent of its factories concentrated in a narrow strip along the Hudson and Mohawk Rivers and the Lake Plains south of Lake Ontario, and with large areas of agricultural and forest land, has an average density of 281. The average for all of New England is 133, for the middle Atlantic states, 274.

In the South, the states east of the Mississippi have an average density of about 77; those to the west, 40. The most densely populated state in the South is Maryland, with a density of 184; and the lowest is Texas, with 24. The average for the South is only about 59.

In the past the densities of the South have been even lower. Georgia, which may be taken as representing the medium density in 1950, had in 1800 a population density of 1.5. Massachusetts in the same year had a density of 52.6; and Rhode Island, 64.8. At no time in the history of the South have densities approached those of the states of the North and East nor of European countries in which manufacturing has long been active.

Some Reasons for the Low Density. There are several possible reasons for the low population density in the South. Immigration has never been active from the North or from Europe. By the time that the yearly arrival of immigrants from Europe had reached 100,000 or more, just before the middle of the nineteenth century, all the great passenger liners docked at northern ports; and into New York, Boston, and Philadelphia poured by far the larger part of the European arrivals, to collect in the northern manufacturing cities or to move westward to the cities and farms of the Middle West and West. In 1950 about 2.5 per cent of the white population of the South was foreign born. For New England, the percentage was 16; and for the Middle Atlantic States, 17. Former census reports have shown even greater percentages of foreign born in the New England and Middle Atlantic States.

Most students of population phenomena contend that the population of the United States would have been what it now is without immigration, that the presence of the foreign element has hindered the normal population increase of native-born whites. These contentions may be correct, but the sections using foreign labor certainly are benefited by immigration, for a large proportion of the immigrants are beyond the "age of infancy" when they arrive and are thus ready to begin economic production. The South has had to rear all its labor, and thus has been handicapped to some extent as compared to the North and East. Moreover, in the earlier days when the bulk of the immigrants came from northwestern Europe, there were many skilled workmen among them who contributed much to the growth of industry in the sections in which they settled.

In the new movement of population within the country, the South has been passed by, the migrants moving westward. The West had, all along, new and cheap lands. It had mineral prizes to offer, and has great commercial opportunities. It has long been advertised freely. When such a movement of population has once been started, it changes its direction but slowly. The feeling of sectionalism probably has little or nothing to do with the seeming neglect of the South. Economic motives are usually more dominant than political or traditional ones.

The Negro, before and since the Civil War, undoubtedly kept out many immigrants from both Europe and the North. Free labor felt it could not adjust itself to a slavery regime, and after the emancipation of the Negro white labor did not wish to compete with colored labor with low living standards. In fact, the wage scale was adjusted to Negro labor and was too low for whites to make a respectable living. There were few opportunities for whites to secure work in the factories of the South; besides, all labor with the hands was generally held in disrepute. Many whites undoubtedly were deterred from coming to the South because of false notions about high summer temperatures and poor health conditions. The South has never, until about 1935, striven to bring in foreigners and people from the North. It prides itself on being the purest Anglo-Saxon section of the United States and wishes to remain so. Moreover, during the many decades that these factors were checking or preventing migration to the South, there has been a stream leaving the southern states. Fully 960,000 native-born Southerners in 1860 were living beyond southern boundaries, and every decade since has shown increasing numbers.

It is difficult to say to what extent each of the above factors has influenced the population growth. The fact is, the South has not increased in population in the last 100 years as rapidly as the country at large nor, of course, as rapidly as other sections. The century's increase for the South has been six-fold; for the country at large, about eight-fold.

Conclusions as to Effect of Low Density.   Throughout its entire history, therefore, the population density for the South has been that of a grazing, lumbering, and agricultural region. Normal development would have carried the South through these stages with an accompanying increase in population, as has occurred in other sections of the United States of equal area, and into the industrial; but accidents have occurred here and there in its economic development to check the growth of manufactures. Its potentialities lie dormant. Anyone acquainted with the scope and variety

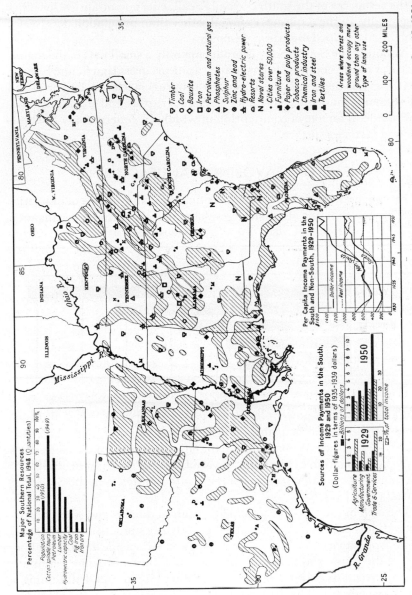

Fig. 137. Mineral, forest, and industrial resources in the South. *Courtesy of Focus (American Geographical Society), Oct. 15, 1951.*

of the resources of the south certainly realize its potentialities, for it has practically all the requisites essential, other than population density, for a highly developed industrial economy.

Although the South today is producing only a small part of the manufactures of the country, it has made rapid progress (particularly since 1940), as has been indicated, and the progress made is substantial and permanent, made in accordance with geographic and economic laws, and made in an age of competition in which, in general, only the best-located factories survive.

FACTORS FAVORING MANUFACTURING

The Abundance of Coal. It is considered by all students of industrial phenomena that one of the strongest factors in the ultimate localization

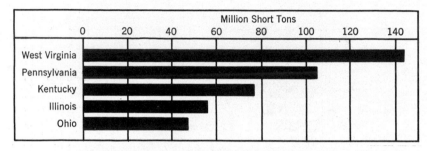

Fig. 138. United States bituminous coal production by leading states in 1950.

of manufactures is power—coal, oil, gas, water power, tides, and sunshine. Of the most practicable of these sources of power, coal, the South has an abundance. Probably more than 60 per cent of the coal reserves of the Appalachian field, the most valuable and the most accessible to the densely populated sections of the United States, is in the Southern States[1] (Fig. 137).

The coal of the Appalachian field is high in quality and wide in variety, and it is particularly accessible because it lies practically horizontal in the Appalachian Plateaus and outcrops on either side and on the borders of the numerous valleys that dissect the plateaus. Some seams are pierced by shafts driven from the top of the plateau, but drift mining is the more common. The field lies for the most part on the divide between the Gulf and Atlantic rivers. Along some of the deeper rivers, coal may be carried in barges; but most of the coal reaches the markets of the nearby

[1] "Investigation of National Resources," hearings before a subcommittee of the Committee on Public Lands, U. S. Senate, May 1947. Government Printing Office. Washington, D. C.

cities and tidewater by rail, gravity assisting greatly the heavily laden cars as they move down grade along the valleys.

West Kentucky has 6400 square miles of bituminous coal lands, and 10,000 square miles of land in Oklahoma are largely underlaid with bituminous and semi-anthracite coal. The coal of the central Texas field, being of low grade, finds its market chiefly in the nearby cities and on the railroads. Besides the higher-grade coal, there are many thousands of square miles of lignite on the Coastal Plain.

The wide distribution of coal is of particular advantage to the cities of the South in which, or near which, the factories of the future will be located. Baltimore is within 150 miles of the Maryland field; Louisville, about 150 miles from the east Kentucky and 100 miles from the west Kentucky field; Nashville, 100–120 from either the Appalachian or the west Kentucky field; Atlanta is about 100 miles from, and Chattanooga and Birmingham are near or within, the southern Appalachian

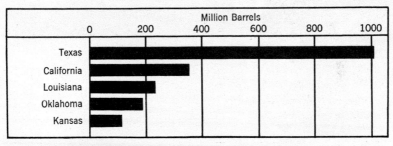

Fig. 139. Petroleum production in the United States by leading states in 1951.

field. Memphis is reached by rail or water from the west Kentucky field; and New Orleans, Mobile, and Pensacola may be supplied by river barges from the Birmingham field. Dallas, Fort Worth, and San Antonio lie near the central Texas field. Galveston and Houston get some coal from central Texas and are readily reached from Birmingham or the Chesapeake coal ports by barge and boat. Tampa and the south Atlantic ports are best reached by coasting vessels from the lower Chesapeake ports. With such an abundance of coal and such a wide distribution of high-quality coal, southern industries are sure to be plentifully supplied at a minimum cost, as long as coal dominates industrial development (Fig. 138).

Petroleum and Natural Gas.   Petroleum and natural gas, the two other sources of power, are also abundant. Reserves in the ground are difficult to determine. However, it has been estimated that the proved petroleum resource of the United States, at the present, is about 20,-100,000,000 barrels, a large part of which is recoverable by modern methods. The fields of the South were believed to contain possibly 61 per cent of the total.[2] Of the five leading states in oil production, three were Southern—Texas, Louisiana and Oklahoma. Oil is being obtained from all of the Southern States west of the Mississippi, as well as from Kentucky and West Virginia, and a small amount from Tennessee. The yield of the South in 1950 was 1,350,000,000 barrels, or more than two-thirds of the total of the country (Fig. 139).

The Water Power of the South.   The power that will never become exhausted, and that, once harnessed, continues to do man's bidding at only a small overhead cost, including repairs, is water power. Of this the South

Fig. 140. The Saluda dam and power project, located 15 miles from Columbia, South Carolina, looking over the dam and downstream. The heavy rainfall of this region supplies rivers with water gathered from the Southern Appalachians. *Courtesy, Columbia Chamber of Commerce.*

has a fair share. The potential power of any stream is determined largely by the volume of water, the degree of constancy of flow, and the fall. Most of the usable water power of the South is in the numerous rivers that flow out of the southern Appalachian highlands (Fig. 140).

All the important rivers of the South east of the Mississippi have their sources in these highlands. They include the Roanoke, Santee, Peedee, Cape Fear, Savannah, Altamaha, and Coosa with their numerous tributaries leading towards the Atlantic and Gulf, as well as the Tennessee River which outlets to the Mississippi system. The channels of the streams are not completely graded, owing to the varying hardness of rock or to accidents, and in the channels there are many pools and rapids, furnish-

[2] "Investigation of National Resources," U. S. Senate, May 1947.

ing numerous sites for dams. The heavy rainfall in the highlands gives the rivers a copious flow, and the fairly even seasonal distribution of rain and forest cover at the headwaters tend toward a constant flow. The streams are particularly free from ice, except in the northern section, and the general absence of snows in the watersheds minimizes the danger from floods. The potential minimum water power of the South is estimated to be 6,320,000 hp available 90 per cent of the time. This is about 15 per cent of the potential for the United States. In 1950 the installed capacity of water power in the United States was estimated to be 18,-500,000 kilowatts, and that for the South 5,962,000 kilowatts, or slightly less than one-third that for the country as a whole. In the South, particularly, there is a growing tendency towards harnessing of rivers for flood control and navigation, as well as for power. It is estimated that the hydroelectric power plants of the South today could furnish, if all of the power were used in the industries, nearly half that needed to turn all the wheels of southern factories.

In the earlier history of the United States, the building of power dams was most active on many small sites in the Northeastern States, as is shown in our study of that section. However, since the development of hydroelectric power there has been a shift to the larger streams of the country, such as the Colorado and Columbia Rivers of the West. The numerous rivers from the Southern Appalachians and Piedmont have been fairly well developed, and into this area the cotton manufacturing industry has moved since 1900. The Tennessee Valley development is more recent, and holds forth the greatest promise of all water power developments in the South.

The Tennessee Valley Authority has attracted world-wide attention, because it is a great experiment in socioeconomic planning and development. It aims not only to develop power but also to control floods, regulate run-off from large areas heretofore much eroded or subject to erosion, provide navigation, and encourage manufacturing. Today there are many dams with a total installed capacity of about 2,000,000 kilowatts (1950) and many more to come in the future (Fig. 141).

The Tennessee Valley proper includes an area of over 40,000 square miles, but the Tennessee Valley Authority operates in an area about twice that size. This organization has much that is necessary for this type of project: coal, petroleum, hydroelectric power, lumber, farm lands, metals, chemicals, fertilizer materials, abrasives, stone. Unquestionably it is proving a great aid to the upbuilding of the economy of the entire South.

Most of the great power companies now operating in the South—steam and water alike—have interconnected their power systems. Many

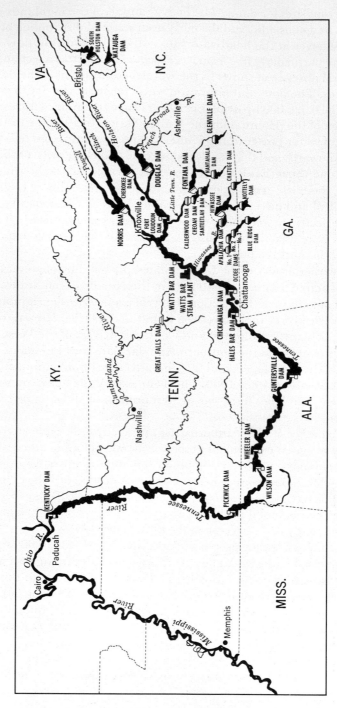

Fig. 141. The Tennessee River. Note the numerous tributaries and the locations of dams.

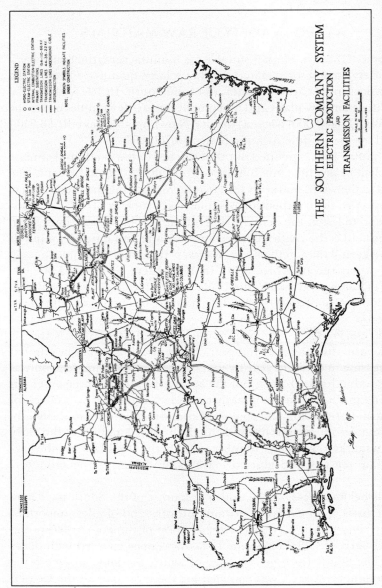

Fig. 142. Electric production and transmission lines of the Southern Company. *Courtesy, Southern Company.* Steam and water plants are frequently interconnected so that in emergencies plants may receive assistance. Water and steam power plants are likewise interconnected in the Carolinas and Virginia.

large steam-electric systems are located in or near coal fields, which may be called upon in emergencies. Thus, the power source of the South is fairly constant (Fig. 142).

A LARGE VARIETY OF RAW MATERIALS

Cotton. Of raw materials suitable for manufacture, the South has a wide variety, and of some materials it has a large quantity. Cotton is the most important of the raw materials of the South. In 1947, alone, the expenditure for new plant and equipment for textile manufacure in the South was $11,280,000, whereas that for New England was only $8,540,-000 and for the Middle Atlantic States $8,700,000.

In Chapter 12 it is pointed out that the South has lands and climate to enable it to produce much more cotton than it does at present. The demand in the world market is the great factor limiting the production of this crop. Also the competition of other fibers such as rayon (discussed later) tend to lessen the demand for cotton. The latter is serious, for in no other field is the rivalry between man-made and natural materials felt more keenly than in the fibers. Rayon is the major contender among several others recently produced. In 1951 there were 1,294,000,000 pounds of rayon produced in the United States, which was estimated to be the equivalent of 2,800,000 bales of cotton, or about one-fifth of the cotton crop.

Other Farm Products. Among the other agricultural products are cottonseed, corn, the tung nut, and peanuts, all yielding vegetable oils that are increasing in demand year by year. Cottonseed will increase only as cotton production increases; but the areas given to the three other oil-producing products may be greatly extended. Fruit and vegetables for canning and preserving find congenial climatic conditions in the South. At present, production is limited chiefly by the demands of the early northern markets. A greater number of canneries would reduce the hazard of late seasons and glutted markets, and benefit the producers greatly.

The Timber Resources. The timber resources of the South have long been the basis of an extensive sawmill industry and of a less important woodworking industry. Nearly every portion of the South, except the semiarid parts of Oklahoma and Texas, was once covered with dense forests. The Southern or yellow pine, of which the longleaf pine is the most prominent variety, was confined for the most part to the Coastal Plain. Over the remainder of the forest area there were hardwoods. Most of the hardwoods and some of the pines on the lower lands have been removed to make way for agriculture. The pines for two centuries have dominated the lumber industry, the hardwoods becoming of importance only since about 1900.

Although the slaughter of the forests has been great—the southern states furnishing 42 per cent of the lumber cut in the United States—there are still great stretches of hardwood in the Appalachian Highlands and of pines in Mississippi, Florida, Alabama, Louisiana, and Texas. These will be rapidly removed if the present rate of cutting continues. The adoption of and adherence to a sane forestry policy, utilizing all the essential areas at the headwaters of streams along which there are water-power plants, and growing trees on the rough, hilly, stony areas and areas that are unprofitable as agricultural land, would enable the South to grow sufficient timber to meet its needs for a long time, if not for all time to come. There are tens of thousands of square miles of cut-over land on the Coastal Plain, now idle or supporting a few cattle to

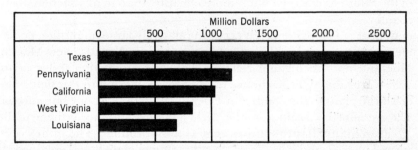

Fig. 143. The value of mineral production in the five leading states in the United States in 1950.

the square mile, that should be growing timber. All that need be done to put much of this land to the production of forests is to modify the tax laws in favor of forest lands. Nowhere in the United States do forest trees grow so rapidly. Reliable authority states that commercial pine timber may be grown in 30 years, and pulpwood in considerably less than that time. The timber crop, which is the basis of many industries, can be made as constant a product as corn or cotton. Had good forestry practices been followed since timber cutting began in the South, a dozen or more crops could have been produced.

The Mineral Resources. The rocks of every geologic period are represented in the southern states. There are old igneous, metamorphic, young igneous, old sedimentary, and recent sedimentary. It is not surprising, therefore, that the variety of minerals of economic importance is great. Of a few—and happily they are among the more useful—the South has great stores, in fact, holds front rank (Fig. 143).

Iron Ores. Iron ore is widely distributed and, in general, excellent in quality. A recent estimate gives the South about 46 per cent of the 3,726,-000,000 long tons that are "measured and indicated" to be the reserves of iron ore in the United States.[3] In 1950 there were mined 7,507,000 long tons of iron ore in the South. This means that, even with great increases in mining, there will be iron ores in the South for a long time to come. During the period of high prices and active demand ten or more of the Southern States mined and shipped iron ore. The chief deposits are located in the Great Appalachian Valley, occurring here and there from western Virginia to central Alabama.

At only a few places in the Great Appalachian Valley are the ore deposits being mined. There is thus great opportunity for further expansion in the number of blast furnaces and the iron industry in general, for good coking coal and limestone exist within a few miles of nearly every deposit. Thus geographic conditions favor the production of iron in the South as cheaply, if not more cheaply, than in any section of the country.

Copper. Copper does not occur in relatively large quantities, nor do the deposits compare with those of Utah, Arizona, Nevada, New Mexico, Montana, and Michigan in richness of ore and production and reserves. There is probably little chance for greater expansion in this field. The one large plant in the South is at Ducktown, to the east of Chattanooga. The ore mined is a sulfide, and in 1898 a large addition was made to the plant to manufacture sulfuric acid as a by-product. The mines were opened in 1842, and it was from them the Confederate States obtained all their copper during the Civil War.

Bauxite. Of bauxite, the ore from which aluminum or aluminum salts and artificial corundum are obtained, the South has a monopoly. However, the production in the United States is only about half the total amount consumed. Imports come largely from Surinam and British Guiana. Arkansas bauxite dominates the aluminum industry to the extent of furnishing more than 90 per cent of all the bauxite produced in the United States. Tennessee, Alabama, and Georgia also have deposits. The South, therefore, is intimately interested in any expansion that may take place in this industry in the future.

Sulfur. Since 1906 the South has come to hold a leading position in sulfur production in the United States, and even in the world, for about 80 per cent of the sulfur consumed in the United States and 75 per cent of that of the world comes from Texas. In these states the sulfur occurs

[3] "Investigation of National Resources," hearings before a committee. U. S. Senate, May 1947.

in huge domes 100 feet or more thick, and 3 or more miles across. The Fresch process, which employs superheated water to melt the sulfur in the ground and air pressure to force the melted sulfur to the surface, greatly reduces the production cost of this useful mineral. Sulfur is produced at so low a cost in the Gulf area that only by agreement between Italy and the American companies are prices maintained sufficiently high to permit the mines of Sicily to operate. In 1920 Louisiana and Texas produced more than 1,500,000 tons; and Texas alone, in 1950, about 4,000,000 tons. The sulfur deposits of Louisiana have been worked since 1940, producing approximately 1,000,000 tons in 1950. Before 1906, Sicily furnished the world with sulfur. The demand for sulfur is increasing year by year in many industries because of the great use of sulfuric acid in many chemical processes. The immense quantities and the low cost of production make it certain that the South will maintain its dominance in this mineral for many decades to come.

Phosphate Rock and Clays. The State of Florida alone produces about 75 per cent of the phosphate rock in the United States, and about 47 per cent of the total of the world. The importance of this resource in agriculture can hardly be estimated, because it is an element of soil fertility, readily depleted by repeated cropping. Idaho, Montana, Utah, and Wyoming have tremendous reserves of this rock, but they are far from the markets. The demand will certainly increase as our soils become more depleted of their phosphorus content and intensified farming increases.

Raw materials for the clay industry, in all its phases from common brick to porcelain, are widely distributed, and so also are the ingredients for cement.

Other Minerals. Among the other minerals which are produced in large quantities in the southern states, for which there is a call in the industries, are zinc, asbestos, mica, graphite, feldspar, limestone, gypsum, lead, and salt.

OTHER FACTORS AFFECTING THE GROWTH OF INDUSTRY

Other factors influencing the localization of factories are capital, labor, and markets. Capital is mobile. It tends to flow to the region that promises the largest return and the greatest security. For a century or more, the greatest movement in the United States has been westward. Some capital has come south; but for the most part the South has been overlooked. There are many reasons for this condition; slavery, the Civil War, and others. The South has never advertised like the West. With active and honest advertising of the advantages to be found in the South by manufacturers, the inflow of capital from the great financial centers should be far greater than it has been in the past.

The low population density and the consequent scarcity of manufacturing population in the South have previously been discussed. Whether or not the South will be checked in its industrial development by the low population density will depend upon the rate at which new factories are introduced. Even without immigration, the rate at which industries are now being introduced will need to be increased materially to utilize the labor that the normal population increase will provide. Inasmuch as the rural population of the South exceeds the urban, most of the laborers demanded for the new factories will come from the farms, and the increasing use of farm machinery tends to release labor for the factories.

The South does not possess the proportion of skilled labor that the older manufacturing sections of the country do. This condition, though of some importance, is not so serious as formerly when hand labor was more prevalent in industry. Automatic machinery, moreover, is greatly reducing the number of skilled laborers needed in any factory. The initiative and proverbial inherent ingenuity of the people of the United States— and most of the laborers of the South are native-born—enables any plant to develop skilled workmen within a short while. The experience of superintendents in cotton mills, furniture factories, and machine shops, in dealing with raw industrial help, shows what may be done even by unskilled workmen. Operators and foremen who are acquainted with labor and labor conditions, in both northern and southern factories, point out many favorable characteristics in southern laborers. In most trades and in most parts of the South, labor is cheaper than in other sections of the country. Some wage scales are dominated by the presence of Negro labor, but this is not the basic cause of low wages. Many of the laborers are fresh from the farms and unaccustomed to large labor returns. Living expenses of laborers are generally low in the South, for coal bills, housing costs, and clothing bills are influenced by the genial climate of the southern latitudes. Laborers accustomed to farm life are more economical in their living than those accustomed to urban life. They are unionized only with difficulty and are not easily led by labor leaders. How long the manufacturers will be able to take advantage of these favorable conditions, and how long these characteristics will persist as factors in enticing manufacturers to the South, is problematic.

The problem of markets, their accessibility and absorbing power, is also of prime importance in the localization of industries. Inasmuch as the South is now producing, and will in the future produce, commodities similar for the most part to those of the factories of the North, it can hardly hope to send much of its goods northward. Its hope lies, first of all, in developing its own local markets and thus replacing northern-made goods. This it should do since it can in most industries manufacture products more cheaply than northern factories, and has the advantage of short haul. Its own markets are of no mean proportion, for here are more than 30 per cent of the people of the United States, and the purchasing power of these people is great. In the contest with the North or Europe for foreign markets, the South again has the natural advantage in position when markets are sought on the American mediterranean and nearly all countries bordering the Pacific. The Panama Canal gives the

Fig. 144. Grain elevator and warehouses at the Port of New Orleans. *Courtesy, New Orleans Chamber of Commerce.* Warehouses cover many acres of this port, some of which have been set aside as a "Free Port" area, not subject to customs duties and regulations. Much cotton is stored and shipped, as well as cane sugar, wheat, lumber, and farm machinery.

South a decided advantage in obtaining the trade of the west coast countries of South America and the Pacific possessions of the United States. New Orleans is 450 miles nearer Valpariso, Chile, than New York is, and more than 1000 miles nearer than Liverpool is. New Orleans is 500 miles nearer Puget Sound by way of the Panama Canal than New York is. If proper port facilities and ocean traffic lines are provided, the geographic position of the South will be of particular advantage to its manufacturers seeking markets in these regions. Every important port in the South today, on the Gulf and the Atlantic, is active in providing wharves, railroad terminal facilities, and warehouses, and is enlarging its shipping. New Orleans has developed and enlarged its port facilities, including a "free trade" zone with large docks and warehouses in which many millions of dollars are invested (Fig. 144).

In Southern port development there is much rivalry in organizing traffic routes, securing particularly favorable railroad rates with interior points, and providing the best port facilities. At Memphis, Tennessee, a river port, the city is justly proud of the two railway bridges and a new highway bridge over the Mississippi River (Fig. 145). Houston, Texas has perhaps led all other cities in its efforts to improve its position. After many years of work and great expense, a 50-mile-long ship channel has

Fig. 145. The Mississippi River at Memphis, Tennessee. *Photo by Paul A. Moore, Tennesee Conservation Department.* The picture shows barges on the river and bridges across the river. This port has large municipal river and rail terminals, and thus has all-water connections with the ports of the world. In the foreground is the new Memphis and Arkansas Bridge, a four-lane, toll-free highway bridge. The other two bridges (one indistinct in this picture) are for the use of railroads exclusively.

been dug, connecting Houston with the Gulf and making of it a Gulf port. It has a well-arranged turning basin for ships, and many industries have been attracted to the place, for it taps an area of great production in petroleum, cotton, and wheat. In 1950 Houston's population reached 594,000, and it thus replaces New Orleans as the largest city of the South (Fig. 146).

Of considerable importance to the South is the Intracoastal Waterway, which was originally planned to connect New York with Brownsville, Texas, as a continuous waterway, making use of lagoons behind sand bars, and sometimes cutting through the Coastal Plain. It is complete

Fig. 146. The turning basin and ship channel at Houston, Texas. This 34-foot-deep channel, 50 miles long, is an example of how man has made a port out of an inland city. Houston boasts of being the second port of the nation in tonnage handled annually. Along this channel are located 38 chemical plants, producing 100 different industrial organic and inorganic chemicals. It is predicted that Houston will some day be the world's leading chemical port.

except across northern Florida, but an extension reaches Key West. On the Gulf Coast it is complete from Florida to Corpus Christi. Its importance along the South Atlantic Coast is that it offers a relatively safe route for pleasure craft reaching the Florida resorts. From Mobile and westward along the coast it links with the Mississippi system. Considerable heavy barge traffic reaches Galveston, and some as far beyond as

Fig. 147. Scene along the Intracoastal Waterway near Jacksonville, Florida. *Florida State News Bureau.*

the sulfur mines at Freeport, and even to Corpus Christi. As industries develop along the Gulf and South Atlantic Coasts, this waterway should be of greater importance (Fig. 147).

THE MAJOR INDUSTRIES

Iron and Steel

The Beginning of the Industry.   One of the earliest industries established in the Jamestown settlement was the manufacture of iron. During the first half of the eighteenth century several furnaces and forges were built in Virginia near the Potomac River and the Chesapeake Bay, where "hollow ware" was cast and sold throughout the colonies to the south.

Some of the pig iron was sent to England, and even to Massachusetts and Rhode Island, for further manufacture.

At many of the settlements later established beyond the Blue Ridge, there were small forges and furnaces, making iron implements and utensils that could be brought from the Eastern foundries only with great difficulty and at considerable cost.

In 1810 the South was producing about 18 per cent of the pig iron of the country. Virginia stood second among the states of the Union, and Maryland fourth. By 1840, 26 per cent of the country's iron was made in the South; but about this time there began a rapid concentration of the iron industry nearer the anthracite coal fields in the Scranton and Wilkes-Barre region and anthracite replaced charcoal as a fuel in Pennsylvania. Then began the rapid rise of the iron industry in the North.

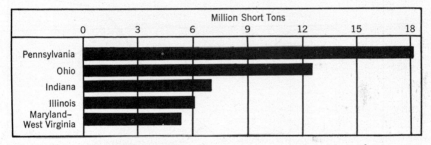

Fig. 148. The production of pig iron in the five leading states of the United States in 1950.

During the Civil War the iron industry necessarily increased greatly in the South, because it had no competition and was called upon for emergency production. Furnaces were built in most of the iron ore districts. The west central Tennessee furnaces, after the Union invasion of Tennessee, were closed; but those of central and northern Alabama, northwest Georgia, and southeast Virginia continued in operation until near the close of the war. However, many of these ceased operation or curtailed their output during Reconstruction times. It is estimated that not over 5 per cent of the output of pig iron of the United States was made in the South at the close of the war. Since 1880 the production of the Southern States has ranged from approximately 8 to 20 per cent of that of the country. In 1950 the output was about one-sixth that of the country, and almost one-half that of Pennsylvania (Fig. 148).

The Rise of Birmingham.   In the decade between 1880 and 1890 the Birmingham region began its rise, but this decade also saw the opening of the rich iron ore deposits west of Lake Superior and their cheap transportation to the Pittsburgh region; so it is not surprising that the growth of the industry in the country as a whole was greater than that in the South.

The modern iron industry of the South really began in 1867 with the building of the Rockwood furnaces at Rockwood, Tennessee, by ex-Union army officials who were attracted to the area by the admirable natural conditions offered for the production of pig iron. The modern industry in Alabama dates from 1876 when a coke oven was opened at Oxmoor. Three years later the first coke oven at Birmingham was com-

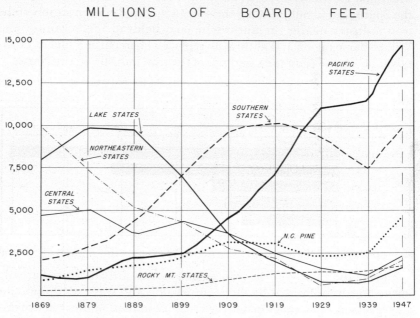

Fig. 149. The rise and decline of lumbering in the various forest regions of the United States. Interpret these curves. Write the history of lumbering in each of the regions. Lumbermen have often migrated from one region to another. How do these curves show the direction of migration?

pleted, the rich hematite displaced the limonite which had been the ore mostly used in the forges and small furnaces, and coke displaced charcoal.

Distribution of Furnaces.   By far the largest number of active furnaces in the South today are located in the Great Appalachian Valley. Alabama and Tennessee contain most of them. The outlook for the industry in the South is bright so far as environmental conditions are concerned, for ore, fuel, and limestone are in proximity. Man is largely the determining factor of the industry. He may take advantage of these favorable environmental conditions and avail himself of the opportunities offered. The increasing use of agricultural implements on southern farms, the active construction of large business and public buildings requiring steel structures, the improvement of railroads, the extension of the underground pipe lines of various sorts, and the expansion of the foreign trade all call for a great amount of iron and steel. During World War II the development of a large steel industry at Sparrows Point, Maryland, shows the importance of cheap water transport. Birmingham steel rails and other iron commodities are finding their way into the great Asiatic markets as well as to the Pacific Coast of the United States and Latin America. But the industry will concentrate at Birmingham as it is now doing. Undoubtedly, the Tennessee Valley Authority is a great influence in bringing an industrial development to this part of the South.

The Forest and Woodworking Industries

Forest Industry One of Long Standing.   The history of the lumber industry in the South does not stir one who is interested in the welfare of

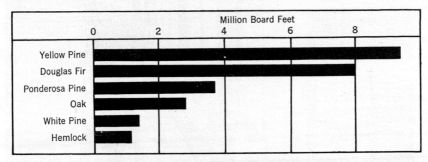

Fig. 150. Lumber production in the United States by species. Average 1940–1949 inclusive.

these states with the spirit of exultation, like the story of cotton. The story of the lumber industry is a recital of three centuries of wanton waste and destruction, with no attempt until about 1930 to reduce the waste and to compensate, by reforesting, for the destruction and devastation. For 300 years the forests have been a revenue-producing resource, a resource whose value has ever been increasing. For 250 years the forests were largely believed to be an obstruction to agriculture. It is only since about 1900 that they have become one of the leading sources of commercial timber for the country. It is estimated that four-fifths of the original yellow pine stand has been cut since 1870. For some 10 or 12 years before the Civil War, the southern states were producing about 15 per cent of the lumber cut of the United States. During and following the Civil War, the cut in the South declined and did not reach its prewar importance until about 1885. Most of the lumber consumed in the country until

about 1850 came from the Northeastern States. By that date the Great
Lakes Region was just at the beginning of its spectacular rise; it reached
its highest point of production in 1885, and by 1890 was on the decline.
The Northeastern States had been declining for half a century. From
1899 to 1930 the South was the leading lumber-producing region in the
country (Fig. 149). It now holds second rank, the Pacific lumber region
being first. Since about 1930 the Southern yellow pine has been the chief

Fig. 151. Sawmill and lumber yard near Greenville, South Carolina. *Courtesy, South
Carolina State Forestry.* The Southern Appalachians are productive of lumber and several
sorts of wood for the paper mills. In this photograph, notice carefully how the lumber is
stacked. Relate what you see to the fact that this portion of South Carolina has an average
annual precipitation of about 50 inches.

lumber-producing tree in the United States (Fig. 150). Most lumber
yards in the United States east of the Mississippi River carry southern-
grown and -sawed lumber. Southern hardwoods, which are shipped
chiefly from Nashville and Memphis, are used in furniture factories, implement and wagon works, planing mills, etc., as far west as the Rocky
Mountains (Fig. 151).

Southern forests including cut-over areas now take on an increased
importance because of technical advances which permit the making of

pulp, and the rayon and plastics industries which use considerable wood. For many years the high resinous content of southern pine prohibited its use as pulp, but it was discovered that only the older trees, more than 25 years old, have resin. The southern forests have been cut so thoroughly that now most of the forests contain growths that are less than 25 years of age, and regrowth is rapid. The South promises to become the great future source of pulp for various uses.

Since about 1930 the waste in the lumber industry has been greatly reduced. Some of the larger lumber plants of the South have paper mills and turpentine and chemical distilling plants in proximity to the sawmills and planing mills, so that limbs, stumps, and low-grade timber are no longer burned or left to rot but are manufactured into valuable by-products.

Naval-Stores Industry. Naval stores, paper and pulp, and articles of wood are largely products of secondary forest industries. The naval-stores industry has existed since colonial days. About 1700 the British Government offered a bounty for the production of naval stores. The center of the industry has migrated southward. It is largely centered at present in western Florida and southern Georgia. Savannah is still the chief export port for naval stores. The general use of the cup, introduced in some parts about 1904, has greatly reduced the damage to trees and prolonged the life of the industry. Today there is much turpentining in connection with the lumber industry. The trees are tapped and bled for 2 or 3 years before being cut for lumber. The refuse of many mills is used for paper (Fig. 152).

Paper and Pulp Industry. The paper and pulp industry is new to the South. In 1909 Virginia produced only 1.4 per cent, in value, of the paper and pulp of the United States, and West Virginia 1 per cent. From 1909 to 1947 the output of the industry in Virginia increased from 48,600 tons to 630,000 tons, and there were also mills in Louisiana, Maryland, West Virginia, Tennessee, North Carolina, Delaware, and Texas. The forests of the Appalachian Highlands are the chief source of the woods used in the sulfite process. A process has been perfected for producing high-grade kraft paper from Southern pine at a cost about as low as from other woods; and Dr. Herty has demonstrated that a white newspaper may be produced from the sap wood of slash pine, which is stronger and lighter in weight than newspaper stock from Canadian spruce. This is greatly stimulating the pulp industry of the South and it is assuming greater importance every year. The decline of imported pulp from Scandinavia due to the war, and the increased use of paper cartons for packing has stimulated the industry in the South. The increase in paper pulp from southern mills from 1930 to 1940 was 187 per cent, showing a greater advance in the industry than in any other section of the country.

There is a great future for the industry in the Southern States, for the northern forests are about depleted and pulpwood may be grown rapidly in the South. The present high price of paper has made possible the use of cotton lint as a raw product for the manufacture of a beautiful, pure,

Fig. 152. "Dipping." *Courtesy of North Carolina Department of Conservation and Development.* Gathering crude gum on a naval stores experimental plot on the North Carolina Department of Conservation and Development's Division of Forestry, Bladen Lakes State Forest.

high-grade paper. Today there are several score of kraft paper and pulp mills in the deep South, and much newsprint is coming from that section. Large mills are located at Orange and Lufkin, Texas, and at Savannah, Tennessee, and Rome, Georgia, as well as numerous other places. Considering the natural advantages for production, the South is destined to dominate the paper and pulp industry in the future.

Tanning.   In many parts of the South, particularly those near or within the Appalachian Highlands, there has been in the past a considerable industry in tanneries, and tannin extract plants, using oak bark, chestnut bark, and wood. The ravages of the chestnut blight which kills the trees, the depletion of oak forests, together with improved chemical processes applied to the tanning of leather, has caused a decline in these industries.

The Furniture Industry.   In the furniture industry, the South is making a beginning in the complete manufacture of its forest products. In 1950 more than one-third of the net value of the manufacture of wooden furniture, not upholstered, in the United States, came from the South. The South Atlantic States, alone, produced more than $250,000,000 worth.

The presence of hardwood in the Central Western States first localized the furniture industry in Grand Rapids, Evansville, and other cities; and the momentum of establishment has carried it on to its high rank in these states. The South has every advantage that these states originally had. It now has the greater bulk of the hardwood of the country and is nearer

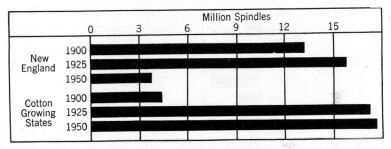

Fig. 153. Change in location of cotton spindles in the United States since 1900. (New York State has quite recently increased its number of cotton spindles in place, but elsewhere there are few cotton spindles.)

the cabinet-wood supply of tropical America than the northern furniture centers. Time will give the southern workmen skill and artistry, and their goods will win markets. Already much of the southern-made furniture is sold in northern salesrooms, and it should soon dominate all southern furniture markets. The central Piedmont leads in the furniture industry of the South. High Point, North Carolina, is to the South what Grand Rapids is to the North. Martinsville and Bassett, Virginia, are other leading centers. Bedroom and dining-room furniture is quite a specialty, but in general the southern industries turn out a medium-grade furniture to meet the large market of the middle classes.

Textile Manufactures

Cotton Manufacturing Migrates Southward.   The most rapidly growing industry in the South today is textile manufacturing. From 561,000 active spindles in 1880 to 18,545,000 spindles in 1951 is the growth that has taken place. This growth has been most rapid in Virginia, North Carolina, South Carolina, Georgia and Alabama—the southern Piedmont. New England was for a long while the leading section of the country in textile manufacturing, but the South had about equaled New England in numbers of spindles by 1920, and in 1951 it had over 90 per cent of the active cotton spindles in the country and about one-tenth of the number in the world. The industry has been dominated by cotton (Figs. 153 and 154).

There has been little expansion in New England industries since 1930. Most of the water-power sites in southern New England have been utilized. Many mills were equipped with machinery which was antiquated

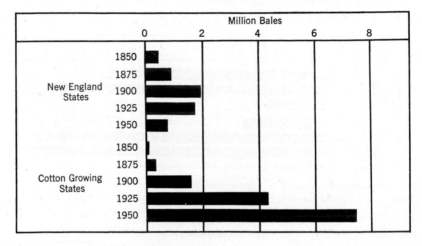

Fig. 154. Domestic cotton consumption by New England and southern mills since 1850.

yet too good to be scrapped. Labor unions, adverse legislation, and other factors are restraining the textile industry from further expansion in New England. It is more economical to operate in the Southern States where there is plenty of clear water in streams, cheap hydroelectric power, cheap land, low taxes, raw products close at hand, and an adequate supply of English-speaking labor, intelligent and quick to learn. All these conditions are found in the Piedmont extending from Virginia through the Carolinas into Georgia. In general, cotton manufacturing centers about Charlotte, North Carolina.

Some Comparisons.   Southern mill towns, in the main, have a wholesome environment. Lower wages and longer hours have prevailed in the South, but this latter condition is rapidly passing, for the influence of labor unions has increased. The belief that the output of labor could not equal that of the North, and that the southern mills could not turn out as fine a grade of cloth as in the North, has been dispelled.

The growing seasons are longer in the South, and winters are not so severe as in the North. Population is sparse, and factory workers may have open spaces for living, where vegetables may be grown, and costs of keeping a household kept relatively low. This lower cost of living in the South has tended to offset the higher wages in the North.

Rayon. The development of the textile industry in the South has been on the basis of cotton as the fiber, but any discussion of the shift of textile manufacturing must account for the important rise of the rayon industry, particularly since World War I. Rayon is a product of the chemical laboratory, in which plant cellulose is obtained, treated, and by a complicated technical process turned out as fiber resembling natural fibers. It may seem strange that this fiber has entered competition with cotton, when the South has tremendous possibilities of cotton production. World-wide unstable economic conditions, the boll weevil, competition with other cotton-producing countries, and the advance in technology in industry all enter as factors in explaining the rise of rayon. Also remarkable is the fact that cellulose is obtained largely from wood and from cotton linters;[4] both of which the South supplies, and the same factors that enter the localizing of cotton manufacturing applies to rayon, for sometimes the fibers are mixed. Much of the rayon manufacturing is controlled by large corporations. Of the 26 large rayon plants in the United States in 1949 the state of Virginia had 7; Tennessee had 5; Pennsylvania 3; West Virginia, Georgia, and Ohio had 2 each; North Carolina, Alabama, Maryland, South Carolina and New York each had 1. The South contains the major portion of the rayon industry. Rayon can be made inexpensively, and it promises to continue in strong competition with cotton.

Nylon. A second fiber that has come to play an important part in the textile industry is nylon. This fiber is one among many that have been developed by the du Pont and other research chemists, and it is truly a synthetic fiber, first made up into a raw material which the chemists call "amide salt." It is prepared either from coal, as in the du Pont ammonia plant at Belle, West Virginia, or from gaseous hydrocarbons as by-products in petroleum refining, for which there is a large plant at Orange, Texas. In the vicinity of this city is produced more "nylon salt" than any other place on earth. Other plants are located in Virginia and Tennessee. There is a tendency for this industry to locate in the South in proximity to coal, petroleum, and natural gas.

[4] Linters consist of the remaining cotton fibers which cling to the seed in the ginning process.

After the production of amide salt, there remains still the technical process of producing the filament. It can be fine, resembling silk, or coarse for such use as brush fibers; transparent sheets may be prepared for various purposes, and it may be used as a plastic. This material first entered commercial production in 1939; by 1951 the output was more than 60,000,000 pounds, and hosiery mills were using it extensively. Coming at a time when the Japanese silk industry was practically destroyed, in order to turn industries to war materials, nylon production in the United States thrived. It can be made so inexpensively that there is little likelihood that the silk industry will revive, for nylon may be used for nearly all the purposes for which silk was used.

Beyond rayon and nylon there is also great promise held for the future fiber manufacture from synthetic resins, proteins, and glass. Some of the basic materials that enter are the soybean, peanut, cottonseed, and chemicals, which the South could produce in great quantities.

Industries Related to Petroleum and Natural Gas

Petroleum. Petroleum of the Oklahoma, Texas, and Gulf Coast fields was formerly transported by boat, tank car, and pipe line to the north central and northeastern states where it was refined. Considerable of this continues, but with the stimulus of World War II there has been a rapid growth of petroleum refining in the oil fields, particularly along the Gulf Coast and in cities not far inland. Large refineries are located at Dallas, Fort Worth, Waco, Beaumont, Port Arthur, Corpus Christi, Baton Rouge, and other places. East Texas leads the world in petroleum refining. The war-created demand for aviation gasoline has brought great changes in the refining industry because it has resulted in several new product industries that are associated therewith. These are found all along the Gulf Coast. Among such are toluene plants for the manufacture of a basic material for trinitrotoluene (TNT), butadiene plants for the manufacture of synthetic rubber, and many others.

Natural Gas. Much attention is now being given to natural gas. Since gas is closely associated with petroleum, often issuing from petroleum wells, much was wasted in the early days of the industry. Often it was fired and let burn so as to have it out of the way. Now such gas is controlled in its flow, and put to use. Gas pipe lines, like oil lines, are now extended long distances to the north and northeast, and gas is put to use, largely for fuel in household and industry. This has become a large business. Also in the oil fields and along the Gulf Coast there are now recycling plants that "strip" natural gas of gasoline, butane, and other minerals. Carbon black is made from natural gas; Texas and the Gulf

Coast produces more than three-fourths of the United States supply. This product is an indispensable ingredient in the manufacture of rubber tires, without which our economy could not function in either peace or war. All these products are basic materials in industry, which when coupled with salt, sulfur, bauxite, and other raw materials serve to attract many industries to locations in the South. The Dow Chemical Company is located at Freeport, Texas, making metallic magnesium from Gulf waters; alumina is made from bauxite at Mobile, Alabama; Houston has a steel industry using natural gas and iron and steel scrap metals; Corpus Christi has a zinc smelter and an alkali plant; Texas City has tin smelting; basic materials for rayon manufacture are turned out at Orange, Texas; paper and pulp mills are located throughout the South; many others could be named.

During and since World War II much of the heavy chemical industry and shipbuilding has been attracted to the Gulf Coast. The entire south Atlantic and Gulf Coasts of the South are gradually growing in importance as trade with Latin America increases, but the development on the Gulf Coast industries has been phenomenal since 1940, and it holds great promise for the future.

Tobacco Manufacturing

Wherever tobacco is grown the industry that turns out the finished product is likely to be carried on, in a large way. The Kentucky "burley" tobacco is made into cigars mainly at Louisville, and into cigarettes only in that town. The industry is found in many towns in Tennessee, Georgia, South Carolina, and Florida, but the industry is largely centered in the "bright tobacco" region of Virginia and North Carolina. Since World War I cigarette smoking has increased tremendously, so that today a much greater proportion of the tobacco crop goes into cigarettes and consequently less into plug tobacco, cigars, snuff, and other uses, than was formerly so. The thin soils of Virginia and North Carolina are well adapted to "bright tobacco" culture, and here many people have studied and solved the intricate problems of growing and manufacturing the product. Durham, North Carolina, was built around a tobacco factory. Greensboro is a leading cigar manufacturing center, and Winston-Salem alone produces about two-thirds of the nation's cigarettes. Tampa, Florida, ranks high in the manufacture of "Havana" hand-wrapped cigars.

OUTLOOK

Undoubtedly the saying "Cotton is King" in the South is being seriously disputed. The Civil War, boll weevil, diversification of crops, wars, machinery, and technology have brought about great changes. The physical fact of facing the South Atlantic and Gulf is of increasing importance. Some sections will remain retarded for a long time in the future, but as a whole the South seems assured of playing a much greater part in industry, and in the future overall economy of the nation than it has up to the middle of the twentieth century.

QUESTIONS, EXERCISES, AND PROBLEMS

1. There is every indication that the industrial frontier is moving into the South. Some people ascribe this movement to the cheap labor of the South, some to the tyranny of labor unions in the Northeastern States, others to the excellence of the geographic conditions favoring localization of industries. What do you think is the cause or are the causes? You must be able to present data for your decision.

2. Is the Negro a factor, directly or indirectly, in the development of manufactures in the South?

3. Where in the South, in the future, do you think will be located the larger industrial centers? You must decide what locations in the South are similar to the industrial centers of the Northeastern States in water power, coal resources, iron-ore deposits, petroleum and natural gas, land and water transportation facilities, and contact with markets.

4. The coniferous forests of the South have supplied products to commerce and industry for more than three centuries. Make a thorough study of the forest-products industries and write a paper on the importance of southern forests in the economic life of the people, considering all forest products. For what reasons will the South become an important producer of paper?

5. Make a study of the dock and warehouse facilities provided by the Louisiana state commission at New Orleans. How do they compare with those at St. Louis? At Houston? At Memphis?

6. It is claimed by some people of South Carolina that, had the National Government spent as much money in harbor improvements at Charleston as at New York, Charleston today would be as large as New York. Construct curves of the population growth of both cities. Data may be secured from the *Statistical Abstract* or the *Census Reports*. What geographic and historical factors can you find to explain the differences in the growth of these two cities? What competitors does Charleston have in the South?

7. Look up recent improvements and plans for Charleston harbor, particularly relating to harbor improvements, water supply, and hydroelectric power. Will this make a difference as to Charleston's future growth? How?

CHAPTER 14

The Physiographic Regions
of the West

A Preview. "Out where the West begins" is far from being a well-recognized, well-established physical line of demarcation. The Census Bureau, which supplies official statistical data for the sections and political divisions of the United States, fixes the eastern boundaries of the Rocky Mountain States as the beginning of the West. Popular opinion, however, has always thought of the semiarid, grass-covered Great Plains, the home of ranching and cowboys, as one of the most important regional divisions of this most romatic section of the country. But since about 1890, the farming frontier has ever pushed westward, encroaching on the cattle country. Today it is in the western half, approximately, of the Great Plains that the cattle country begins.

The West is a land of contrasts. One finds lands of wonderful fertility on which there is cultivation of the highest intensity, and vast areas of land of almost utter worthlessness where a "cow" requires 70 acres or more for sustenance, or of absolute worthlessness where life is almost nonexistent. There are densely populated cities, and there are immense areas where there is no more evidence of man than when the earliest Spanish explorers traversed the American Southwest. There are areas having subtropical climates and vegetation, and there are areas of ice and snow. There are areas of heavy rainfall, the heaviest on the North American continent, and areas of extreme desert.

The West is the last of the major sections of the United States to be occupied by English-speaking people. It is the youngest, therefore, of these sections, yet one finds man and his industries and institutions, the cultural landscapes, as well established as in the older settled communities of the eastern half of the United States. Since before 1848, the West has dangled wonderful economic attractions before the imagination of men, and hordes of immigrants have kept the trails and traffic lines crowded on their westward trek of one, two, or even three thousand miles to the land of their dreams. Near the beginning of the nineteenth century fur traders and fishermen from New England rounded the Horn or trekked westward to the Columbia River section to win a fortune from stream and mountain forest. In the late 1830's, missionaries from the East established centers of civilization on the Willamette and the Columbia. The first groups of pioneers from the Middle West frontier reached the Willamette Valley in 1839, the vanguard of many thousands that firmly established American civilization in the Oregon country. By 1840, Oregon had a population of some 8000. More than 4000 traversed the Oregon Trail in 1847. In 1848, the discovery of gold started a trek over forest and mountain and grassy and bush-covered plateaus that gave California nearly 93,000 people by 1850. In nearly every section of the entire West during the next 10 years, prospectors were driving shafts into mountain slopes in the fond expectation of becoming rich overnight. By 1860, the Mountain States had 174,000 people, and the Pacific Coast States, 444,000. This was some years before the first transcontinental railway was completed. Most of these 600,000 and more, went westward on foot, horseback, or in ox-drawn or horse-drawn covered wagons. America had never seen such a movement of land and wealth seekers. And gold, silver, copper, zinc, lead, coal, iron ore, forests, grazing lands, irrigated lands, and dry farming have continued to attract thousands of people yearly in search of wealth. For nearly a century the West has been the most rapidly growing major section of the United States. Between 1910 and 1950 the Pacific States trebled in population, and the Mountain States increased by 80 percent. The New England advance was nearly 50 per cent, the East South Central 40, and the West North Central less than 18.

The scenic attractions—massive, lofty, glacial-topped, forest-covered mountains, profound canyons, cloudless skies, many-hued deserts, ancient forests in stone,hot springs, spouting geysers, falls and rivers, giant engineering works, well-kept cities, and even more interesting villages, ancient and modern, of primitive Americans—draw several millions of tourists each year.

Most easterners are astounded at what man has accomplished in the West in the face of seemingly insurmountable obstacles. To the westerner nothing, seemingly, had proved impossible in the past; hence, everything seems possible. Here you find United States optimism, enterprise, and individual accomplishment at the maximum.

The chapters that follow present the natural environmental background of western civilization, and man at work, and his accomplishments. We begin our study with the most fundamental environmental element in the West, the physiography.

General Features and Divisions.   Mountains and plateaus dominate the topography of the West. Very little of the area may be considered as plains; even the Great Plains area is considered by many a plateau. Since the plateaus are highlands between mountains or border the mountains, the trend of the major mountain systems determines the trend of the topography. The trend, or the grain, so to speak, of the topography is roughly north and south. An east-west cross section approximately through Denver and San Francisco illustrates well this general feature.

Fig. 155. The physiographic regions of the West. The major divisions are largely based on the monograph of the physiographic divisions of the United States by Fenneman and others.

Four major physiographic regions are recognied: the Rocky Mountain System, the Intermontane Plateaus, the Pacific Slope, and the Great Plains (Figs. 155 and 156).

The Pacific Mountain System.   The Pacific Mountain system consists of two rows of mountains, the Coast Ranges on the west, and the Sierra Nevada-Cascade Mountains on the east, with a long valley trough between. The valley trough, however, is interrupted by a mountain mass,

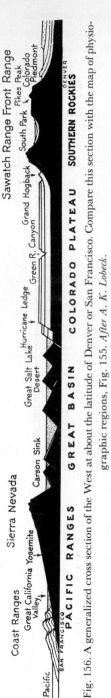

Fig. 156. A generalized cross section of the West at about the latitude of Denver or San Francisco. Compare this section with the map of physiographic regions, Fig. 155. *After A. K. Lobeck.*

the Klamath Mountains, in southern Oregon and northern California, and thus two troughs result, the Puget Sound Trough in the north and the Valley of California, or the California Trough, in the south. South of 34° N. is a third trough, the Salton Sink Trough, the landward continuation of the Gulf of California Depression. Although from a physiographic standpoint the Gulf of California Depression forms a part of the great Pacific Slope Depression which extends from Lynn Canal in Alaska to the tip of Lower California, Salton Sink is generally classed as a basin of the Basin and Range province, and will be so considered in this discussion.

The Coast Range of Oregon and Washington.   The Coast Range of Oregon and Washington is low, and is largely a dissected, warped plateau, broken by many rivers. It is a region of rough topography, ill suited for agriculture, except in its valleys, but well adapted to the growing of forests, the oceanic climate being particularly favorable to plant life.

The Klamath Mountain group, which may be considered a part of the Coast Range, for it touches the coast, is a plateau, so thoroughly dissected by the several short, swift rivers that enter the Pacific between 41° and 43° N. that nearly the whole area is in slope. Ridges and peaks are the rule, but erosion has progressed sufficiently to have formed many valleys broad enough to encourage agriculture. The group is a distinct barrier to traffic and communication between the Puget Sound and California troughs (Fig. 157).

The Coast Ranges of California.   Southward from the Klamath Mountains to the latitude of Los Angeles, the coastal mountains consist of a series of parallel ranges, some short, some long. Each of the numerous headlands that characterize the California coast is one of these ranges projecting obliquely into the Pacific. The broad, open bays between headlands are, as a rule, the seaward ends of valleys that lie between the ridges. None of the bays, except San Francisco Bay, furnishes shelter to ships; and the high, bold cliffs and strong onshore winds at times make the entire Pacific Coast foreboding to the mariner.

San Francisco Bay, one of the finest harbors of the world, occupies the drowned portion of a structural depression between two ranges, and the entrance to the bay, Golden Gate, is a drowned valley in the outer range. There is also a break through the inner range, so that ocean-going vessels tie up at wharves on the very

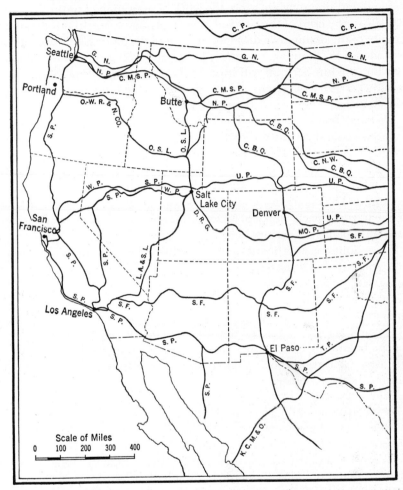

Fig. 157. The important railroads of the West. Railroad building in the West began with the Union and Central Pacific in 1869. The union of these two lines was made near Salt Lake City. Much of the freight carried is "through-traffic" from the humid Pacific slope to the humid East. East and west lines dominate. The Pacific Trough and Rocky Mountains have lines north and south.

edge of the Valley of California. The long shore line of the bay gives ample room for the expansion of the numerous cities.

Southward from Los Angeles, the coastal mountain region consists of a number of short, low ranges, the most prominent being the Santa Ana and San Jacinto. The valleys between the ridges are partly waste filled. The harbors at San Pedro (Los Angeles harbor) and San Diego are on the outer edge of the Coastal Plain bordering the Coast Range. In their present condition they are more the work of man than of nature.

Little of the land of the Coastal Range province is cultivated, largely because of the dominance of slope. In most of northern California and in Oregon and Washington, the dairy farmer and fruit growers have made a start but the lumberman still holds sway over a large area. Southward from 39°, aridity in general limits the cultivable lands to the irrigated valleys.

The Puget Sound Trough.   The Puget Sound Trough extends from the Canadian border southward to about 43° 30' N. The northern part of the trough is occupied by Puget Sound, which is bordered by sandy, gravelly plains, and hills largely glacial and fluvio-glacial in origin. The southern limit of the glaciated area is about 15 miles south of the southern end of the sound. The enterprising cities of the trough give a profitable market for the garden truck, dairy products, and deciduous fruits produced on the humid plains bordering them.

Puget Sound is another of the fine harbors of the world; in fact, it is a group of harbors all connected by deep water. The linear distribution of the water surface, mainly transverse to the prevailing winds, and the numerous bordering hills give shipping excellent protection from the wind and waves. Moreover, the harbor is open the year round. The sound is the result of drowning of the northern end of the Puget Trough; in fact, it is the beginning of the long "Inside Passage" that extends northward to Alaska. Glaciation, too, has had its part in widening and deepening the channels of the sound.

The Willamette River, which drains the trough in Oregon for most of its course, is an aggrading stream. It flows through a broad, alluvial plain, 10–15 miles wide in places. Here are to be found the most highly productive portions of Oregon, in fact, some of the best humid farming land in the West. Most of the agricultural land of the trough in Oregon lies on the flood plains of the Willamette, for much of the bordering rolling land and the tributary valleys have been cleared. The chief trading center of the Willamette Valley is Portland, which, though 120 miles inland, is nevertheless an ocean port.

The Valley of California.   The Valley of California, 400 miles long and 30–60 miles wide, is drained by two large rivers, the Sacramento and the San Joaquin, and their tributaries. Even in the northern portion the rainfall is not sufficient for humid agriculture, and the southern portion is a bunchgrass-covered semidesert except where irrigation is practiced.

The valley trough is structural, its formation being associated with the tilting that formed the Sierra Nevada and the warping that gave rise to the Coastal Ranges. A long, narrow sea probably once occupied the trough, but alluvial deposits in the form of fans and flood plains have displaced the sea. Deposition is most active along the eastern border of the valley where the swift, copious streams on the western slope of the Sierra Nevada bring down large quantities of detritus and form compound alluvial fans. Much of the surface of the valley to the west of the fans is a dead-level plain on which drainage of even the slight rain is slow and difficult. Marshes are common, the largest being at the junction of the Sacramento and San Joaquin rivers, about Tulare Lake, and near the Marysville Buttes. The deep soil and flat surface of the valley offer excellent conditions for agriculture where the rainfall is sufficient for dry farming, or where water is available for irrigation; and for irrigation the many copious streams from the Sierras are utilized. The tilled land of the northern half of the valley is largely dry farmed; that of the southern half is mostly "under ditch."

The Sierra Nevada-Cascade System.   The Sierra Nevada and Cascade Mountains do not form a continuous system. There is a gap in the system in the vicinity of the Feather and Pitt rivers, and here are Mt. Shasta and Lassen Peak, both volcanic in origin, Lassen Peak still being active at times.

The Cascade Mountain region is an elevated upland (probably an elevated peneplain) of sedimentary and granitic rocks above which rise numerous volcanic peaks, the more prominent being Baker, Rainier, St. Helens, Adams, Hood, Jefferson, Pitt, Shasta, and Lassen Peak. Not all the eminences, however, are volcanic in origin; some are monadnocks on the old peneplain surface. In places the Cascades are 60–80 miles wide. Although there are large flat areas on the crest of the main axis, erosion has formed deep valleys on the borders. In the northern section, glaciation has deepened a few of these valleys, the Lake Chelan Valley being the most conspicuous example of this type. Some of the valleys on the eastern slope and bordering lowlands, more easily reclaimed than those on the west because of the scantier forest growth, have become famous as fruit-growing sections. Such are the Wenatchie, the Yakima, and the Hood River Valleys.

The Cascade Range is much more broken in Washington than in Oregon. Not only do the railroads find fairly easy grades to tunnel through the breaks in the range, as at Snoqualmie Pass, Stevens Pass (Cascade Tunnel), and Stampede Pass, but also the westerly winds carry moisture over the range to the Columbia Plateau in Washington, Idaho, and Oregon in quantities sufficient to make the raising of wheat by dry-farming operations possible. The large area of farm lands of southeastern

Washington contrasts strikingly with the nearly worthless desert areas of southeastern Oregon, and this contrast is partly the result of differences in mountain heights and the resulting differences in rainfall.

The Sierra Nevada Range is a huge tilted block, the uplift occuring along the eastern portion of the block. The eastern face is steep; the western slope is gentle but roughened by many deep gorges produced by glaciers and rivers. Some gorges are rift valleys. Southward from the latitude of Sacramento nearly to 36° N., the Sierra block rises to 10,000 feet or more. This is the High Sierras, a region of great beauty and ruggedness with many lofty peaks ranging from 12,000 to more than 14,000 feet.

The Sierras are a barrier to the movements of man, for the passes are few and the entrances to them are far up on the flanks of the mountains, 7000–9000 feet above sea level. It was only after long and diligent search that the pioneers in the 1840's found feasible routes across the mountains.

The Sierras are also a climate barrier. Greater contrasts on the east and west sides of the range in rainfall and temperatures are probably not found in any other part of the world except in the Himalayas. In crossing the Sierras along the Southern Pacific from Reno, one passes from the bleak sagebrush desert, where the annual rainfall is but 8.65 inches, up into fine forests which are a response to abundant rains. Blue Canyon station on the western slope of the mountains, at an elevation of 4701 feet, has a rainfall of 74 inches. The temperature regions traversed also indicate great contrasts. (Study Fig. 4.) The plateau to the east of Reno is in the *Hot Summer and Cold Winter* temperature region. In going up over the mountain range one passes through the *Cold Winter and Mild Summer* belt on the summit and upper slopes into the *Cool Winter and Mild Summer* region on the western slope, and then down into the *Hot Summer and Cool Winter* region of the valley.

The Intermontane Plateaus.   The Intermontane Plateaus region, covering the vast area between the Sierra Nevada-Cascade system and the Rocky Mountains, is naturally divided into three subdivisions: the Columbia Plateau, the Basin and Range province, and the Colorado Plateau. Each has its distinct type of topography.

The Columbia River Plateau.   The Columbia Plateau, with an area of about 250,000 square miles, has for its bedrock horizontal layers of lavas, which evidently came out of numerous vents at various times, and spread over large areas, burying in most parts the old land surfaces. In some deep canyons in the plateau, 100 distinct layers, representing 100 outflows, may be seen. A few areas, like the Blue Mountains, are higher than the surface of the lava beds and stand like islands surrounded by a lava sea. Weathering, in which physical processes predominate, combined with active wind transportation, has covered the area with a deep soil, dark in color, and highly productive, where moisture is sufficient. The Palouse region in Washington, western Idaho, and Oregon has a dark soil, porous and fine enough to retain a large part of the scanty supply of rain water and give it up to the wheat crop, the dominant agricultural product of the region. The soil of the Palouse country is in color and physical characteristics like that of the eastern edge of the Great Plains.

The Columbia and its tributary, the Snake, are the largest rivers of the Plateau. Although serving as rather important highways of travel and transportation in the past, their chief value today is to furnish water for irrigation and hydroelectric power. The Columbia is one of the greatest salmon streams in the world.

The Basin and Range Province. The Basin and Range province is the largest of the Intermontane Plateaus, extending from about 42° N. to the southern boundaries of the United States, and eastward from the Cascades and the Sierra Nevada ranges to the Rockies, and from the Coast Range in southern California through Arizona and New Mexico to the Great Plains beyond the Rio Grande. The surface features throughout the entire area are very similar, consisting of numerous short ranges and vast stretches of waste plains, the material of which has been deposited by water and winds. Throughout its extent the Basin and Range province is a region of scanty precipitation; the occasional rain that comes falls in a heavy downpour. It is the most arid of the provinces in the West. Its scant rainfall and rapid evaporation and its topographic features are typical of desert lands. All of this Basin and Range province, west and north of the Colordo River, lies in the Great Basin, an area of interior drainage. The Great Basin is really a region of basins, the more prominent being the Great Salt Lake basin, the Carson Sink area, Death Valley, Salton Sink basin, and the Lower Colorado basin.

Great Salt Lake is the shrunken remnant of a large lake, Lake Bonneville, whose surface during the glacial period stood 1000 or more feet above the present level, and which was comparable in area (19,750 square miles) to Lake Michigan. Lake Bonneville was a fresh-water lake, the drainage going northward into Snake River. The terraces of the ancient lake are to be seen as huge benches high on the slopes of the Wasatch Range and the mountains on the western border of the lake basin. The present level of the lake varies from time to time, depending on the relative amount of rain.

With the constant shrinkage that has been going on for thousands of years there has been a concentration of the mineral compounds, until now the water is so salty that animal life is almost precluded, the only permanent life being a small "brine shrimp." Another form seen at some seasons is the larva of a small fly. The density of the water is so great that bathers can float on the surface nearly as easily as a cork floats on fresh water. The Carson Sink basin was also once partly occupied by a large lake in the glacial period, Lake Lahontan, the waters coming from the glaciers in the High Sierras.

Salton Sink basin is the remnant of an arm of the Gulf of California which has been isolated by the formation of the Colorado River delta. In late years the basin has come to be called the Imperial Valley and is one

Fig. 158. Scene in the Sonoran Desert in southern Arizona. Here the rainfall is less than 10 inches each year, the vegetation is sparse, and salt or alkalai flats occupy the low areas.

of the most productive irrigated areas in the West. The surface level of the lake is 241 feet below sea level. It is easy, therefore, to secure from the Colorado River water for irrigating the land about the Salton Sea. In 1891 and again in 1905, during periods of high water, the Colorado, to the extent of about 85 per cent of its volume, became diverted toward Salton Sink along a diversion canal which was not provided with gates, and only after much effort and at great expense were the flood waters again directed toward the Gulf and protective dams constructed. Because of its southern location, and the fact that it is in a normal high-pressure area with bright sunlight, the basin raises all the subtropical crops of both the New World and the Old.

Besides these large basins there are scores of minor basins within the Great Basin that receive the water from the nearby low ridges or surrounding plateau surfaces, and which, during moist periods, are occupied by water that evaporates in dry periods and leaves salt or alkaline incrustations or mud flats. Such lakes are known as salinas, alkali lakes, and playas, respectively (Fig. 158).

Most of the ranges of the Basin and Range province, particularly the shore of the Great Basin, are the fault-block type of mountain, the height and form of which have been greatly modified by erosion. The axes of the ranges are more or less parallel, and all have a north-south trend. About each range are large flat areas of loose mantle rock, spread out in sheets over the volcanic bedrock by wind and water. In California, Arizona, and New Mexico, plains occupy more of the surface by far than mountains. In the Lower Colorado Basin, nearly 90 per cent of the area is flat or nearly flat land, and thus large areas are topographically suitable for irrigation.

Except in the Humbolt River basin, in the Carson Sink area, and the Imperial Valley, there is little irrigation in the Great Basin, for water is very scarce.

The Colorado Plateau.   The Colorado Plateau, the third division of the Intermontane Plateaus, is higher than the Basin and Range province. Although there has been some faulting and movement of blocks, little tilting and practically no folding has occurred. The plateau is characterized by deep gorges. The highest portion of the plateau is a broad zone along the western and southwestern edge from central Utah into New Mexico. The rainfall over much of the plateau is sufficient to grow a fair supply of grasses and edible weeds for summer grazing. The higher portions of the plateau have enough moisture for a good stand of pine, and are largely held as national forests and lumbered under the direction of the Forest Service.

The canyons of the Colorado, the Grand Canyon being the most impressive, are probably the most conspicuous topographic features of the Colorado Plateau and are distinct barriers to communication and transportation.

As a whole, the Colorado Plateau province is thinly settled. There are a few rather progressive little towns, whose economic life depends on mining, repair work at railroad shops, lumbering, and grazing. Agriculture, necessarily based on irrigation, is little practiced except in western Colorado and central Utah near the headwaters of some of the tributaries of the upper Colorado River. Grazing is the leading industry, the stations along the Santa Fe, the only railroad of the plateau except the Denver and Rio Grande in the far north, receiving cattle from ranches scores of miles distant. The Indians on their reservations are among the most active of the pastoralists.

The Rocky Mountain Province.   The Rocky Mountain province is a broad, elevated tract 1200 miles long and 200 miles wide, on the average. It is made up of a large number of more or less parallel ranges, few of them more than 200 or 300 miles long, separated by numerous valleys and basins. Like the Sierra Nevada-Cascade system, the Rocky Mountain system is divided into a Northern Rocky Mountain Province and a Southern Rocky Mountain province, separated by a stretch of lower land in Wyoming, known as the Wyoming or Great Divide basin. The Wyoming basin is topographically a continuation of the Great Plains to the east and the Colorado Plateau to the south. Because of the easy approach from the east and the low passes across the Rocky Mountains, the routes of the earliest overland trails and the first trans-Rocky Mountain railroad were located in Wyoming. (Location also a factor.)

The Northern Rockies.   The Northern Rockies are widest in Montana, and here are the largest number of ranges—the Big Belt, Little Belt, Gallatin, Lewis, Mission, Kootenai, Cabinet, and others. In the vicinity of Yellowstone Park the system is narrow, but southward several ranges spread out like a fan from the lofty Yellowstone Park Plateau. The courses of the rivers are determined only in part by the mountain ranges and the trenches. Some streams flow across the trenches and cut through mountain ranges with little regard to the trend of the major topographic features. This condition makes the Northern Rockies in Montana so easily, comparatively speaking, traversed by the trans-Rocky Mountain railroads. Civilization is concerned chiefly with the valleys, basins, and trenches; here are the agricultural lands, cities, and railroads. The mountains, owing to the moderate rainfall and low evaporation, are well forested and are little visited except by hunter, trapper, lumberman, or forester. The National Forests, particularly where transportation is provided, are great attractions for tourists. In general the forested mountains are of inestimable value to the irrigation farmers of Montana.

In central Idaho, to the west of the Bitter Root Range, is a large mountain pass, produced by the intensive erosion of a high plateau. There is little or no system to the ridges except that their direction bears a fairly definite relation to the drainage lines, the result of erosion. Those in the Clearwater River basin are called Clearwater Mountains, and the Salmon River group lies in the Salmon River basin. The many canyonlike valleys give little opportunity, even though the rainfall is sufficient, for agriculture. Through railroads have shunned the region. The whole area, more than twice the size of Massachusetts, has only about 20,000 people.

The principal ranges in northern and western Wyoming are the Absaroka, the Shoshone, the Big Horn, the Wind River, and the Teton. Between the Absaroka Range and the Big Horn Mountains is the Big Horn basin. Although the rainfall is less than 10 inches a year, the basin is irrigated by numerous streams that come from the bordering mountains, and the 308,000 acres of irrigated lands are highly productive. South of Yellowstone Park and at the east base of the Teton Range is Jackson Hole, an intermontane basin that contains Jackson Lake and several smaller lakes which drain into the Snake River. Forests, marshes, and lakes serve as regulators and natural storage areas along the main course of the Snake in Idaho, Oregon, and Washington. The Big Horn Mountain group is similar in general character and origin to the Black Hills and the Uinta Mountains, all three being domes more or less dissected.

Another important range of the Northern Rockies is the Wasatch in northern Utah. The great longitudinal extent of the Wasatch Range and its height of 4000-6000 feet above the Great Salt Lake Plains on the west, and the steep slopes, give many difficulties to the railroad and road builders. Fortunately, a few antecedent streams have cut gorges across the range, and these offer feasible routes. The Oregon Trail avoided the range, making a sharp turn to the north at its eastern base, but the Mormon Road crossed the Wasatch in the latitude of Salt Lake City, through Emigrant Pass. The Denver, Rio Grande and Western Railroad reaches the Great Salt Lake Plains by way of the Spanish Fork, and the Union Pacific through Weber Canyon. The chief value of the range to man, besides its mineral resources, is the water that falls on its western slopes and that has been directed with great skill upon the thirsty, sagebrush Piedmont Plains. In 1929 there were 1,350,000 acres of irrigated land at the base of the Wasatch, carefully tilled and highly productive, a vast oasis in still vaster stretches of sagebrush and greasewood desert plains. The area under irrigation here has not been extended much because the limit of possibility has been reached.

The Southern Rockies.   The Southern Rocky Mountain province is, throughout its length, a double row of ridges with basins between. The two ridges are remnants of two more or less continuous parallel folds with a synclinal depression between. Erosion has removed most of the sedimentary rock from the ridges, exposing the igneous cores; but sedimentary material is to be found in the hogbacks on either side of the ranges and in the intermontane basins.

In southern Wyoming, the Laramie Range, the eastern front range, is a low, folded mountain. The summit is a gently rolling peneplain. The approach from either side of the crest at Sherman (8009 feet) is very gentle. The Union Pacific Railroad crosses the Laramie Range with low grades. To the west of the Laramie Range, in southern Wyoming, is the Medicine Bow Range, and between the two is the broad Laramie basin or Plains.

The Front Range in Colorado is the easternmost range, as the name implies. Its serrated crest and towering peaks, which rise 13,000–14,000 or more feet above sea level, may be seen from points on the High Plains scores of miles distant. Pikes Peak has an elevation of 14,110 feet, and Longs Peak is 14,225 feet. Much of the summit of the Front Range, as seen from an elevated position like Pikes Peak, is an upland cut by many deep canyons, yet also with a large acreage of relatively flat land and capable of supporting large flocks and herds during the warm season. Glaciation has been active in the past. Cirques, lakes, and moraines are common features in the upland areas and add much to their picturesqueness. The Front Range extends only to the Arkansas River, beyond which the Wet Mountains become the front range. Farther south, the Sangre de Cristo, which extends into New Mexico even beyond Santa Fe, is the easternmost range.

The western series of mountain ridges of the Southern Rocky system is formed by the Park Range, the Sawatch, and the San Juan Mountains. There are a few other ranges in west central Colorado, which belong to the Southern Rocky Mountain system, but they are of minor importance.

The small intermontane basins of the Rockies, called "parks," are from north to south, North Park, Middle Park, South Park, and San Luis Park. On the eastern slope of the Front Range is Estes Park, much visited by tourists. The parks, although they lie between prominent ranges with their north and south rims much lower than the east and west mountain borders, are isolated from each other, and their drainage waters take devious routes. North Park drains into the Platte by way of the North Platte River. The waters of South Park pass eastward through Royal Gorge, carved in the front range by the South Platte; and San Luis Park is drained by the Rio Grande.

The basin floor of the parks is fairly level, the basins being waste filled; but Middle Park has a hilly surface. San Luis Park, the largest, offers exceedingly attractive opportunities for agriculture. Its surface is as level as the bed of a lake, and the land is easily irrigated and easily drained.

Colorado has by far a larger number of lofty peaks and a larger area of land above 10,000 feet than any other state. There are 180 peaks that exceed 12,000 feet in height, more than 110 above 13,000, and over 50 that rise to heights of more than 14,000 feet. The large area of high land athwart the eastward drift of the air in the *Westerlies* is the explanation for the relatively heavy rainfall, which makes possible the large area of valuable commercial timber and supplies water to the 3,390,000 acres of land that have been irrigated in the state, as well as to many thousands of acres beyond the borders. Colorado, although an interior state 700 or more miles from the Pacific, ranks second among the states of the West in number of acres of land irrigated. The mountains and ridges, however valuable they may be to the timber industry and agriculture, indirectly, are a barrier to east and west traffic; and the railroads that do cross the Rockies in Colorado have spent huge sums in bridging canyons and tunneling mountains. They make frequent use of "horseshoe" curves in order to reduce grades, yet their traction costs are heavy.

The Great Divide Basin. The Wyoming or Great Divide basin, surrounded on almost all sides by ridges of mountains, receives less than 10 inches of rain. (This is approximately the rainfall of the Green River basin, the Big Horn basin, and the Wind River basin in Wyoming also.) It has all the characteristics of a true desert. The streams that flow from the surrounding ridges lose themselves in the sands, or their waters spread out into flats that become playas or salinas. Near the western edge of this basin and in the lowest portion is the Red Desert, an area of drifting sand of various colors—vermilion, brick red, and russet, even green, purple, gray, and yellow. The bunchgrass is so scant and so scattered that the color of the landscape is determined largely by the colors of the sands that nearly everywhere mantle the surface. Barren and desolate as the landscape is, there are periods of the year, particularly in the winter, when large herds of cattle and sheep find pasturage here.

The Great Plains.[1] The Great Plains province is undoubtedly, next to the Coastal Plain, one of the most unified in surface features of the physiographic provinces of the United States. Its north and south extent is about 1400 miles and its width approximately 400. Could its original surface be restored, it would be a gently sloping plain, not unlike the Atlantic Coastal Plain, in many of its features. The rock material forming its strata has been derived largely from the Rocky Mountain area to the west. The lower strata of sandstone, shales, and limestones dip gently eastward, but are synclinal in structure, and at the western edge are sharply upturned, particularly in Colorado (in the Garden of the Gods they stand almost vertical) as if they once extended over the exposed core of the Rocky Mountains. On the top of these older consolidated deposits

[1] Only the western edge of the Great Plains province is within the Western States as delimited by the Census Bureau, but considered from the standpoint of climate and land utilization the whole province may be included in the West. In the minds of the general public it is western. In this book the province is discussed along with the other natural regions of the Western States, but census data, unless otherwise stated, are for the 11 states that the Census Bureau calls the West.

are younger sands, gravels, and mud, only partly indurated. These, too, slope eastward. Erosion in some parts has been very active, probably amounting to several thousands of feet. The western border at present has an elevation of about 6000 feet above sea level in the central or Wyoming-Colorado region, and 4000 feet to the north and south.

North of the northern boundary of Nebraska, more exactly the Pine Ridge Escarpment, the Great Plains slope all the way from the mountains, with little or no interruption except for a few isolated hills whose flat tops indicate the level of the former surface of the plain, to the Mis-

Fig. 159. High Plains landforms in Scott County, Kansas. *Courtesy, Kansas State Chamber of Commerce.* The High Plains are broken much by valleys where floods may be damaging after heavy rains in the mountains to the west. Such valleys afford good grazing for parts of the year. The bison was originally at home on these plains, but those shown in the picture are in a park.

souri River. This portion of the province is the Missouri Plateau. The eastern edge of the plateau is the Missouri Coteau, an escarpment 200–600 feet high in places. North and east of the Missouri River the plateau has been under the ice of the Keewatin ice sheet and has typical morainic topography. Although the Missouri Plateau has no more rain than the Great Plains farther south, the cooler summer temperature does not make for excessive evaporation in much of the area, and dry farming is fairly successful. The rivers from the Northern Rockies supply much water for the irrigation of lands in the Missouri Plateau.

South of the Pine Ridge Escarpment, three distinct types of topography are recognized in the surface features of the Great Plains. These are arranged in north and south belts. The central belt, in which much of the original strata of sand and gravel are preserved and which stands higher in general than the belts east and west, is the High Plains. In most of Nebraska the High Plains extend across the Great Plains province, but farther south the belt is only about 200 miles wide. In western Texas the High Plains are known as the Llano Estacado, and farther south as the Edwards Plateau. To the east of the High Plains are the Low Plains, the line of separation being in general a low escarpment called the Break of the Plains. Erosion is more rapid along the western edge of the Low Plains than in the most of the High Plains, because the rainfall is greater. The streams are constantly shifting the western boundary as they erode into the steeper lands at the Break of the Plains (Fig. 159).

Along the western edge of the Great Plains between the High Plains and the Rockies is a long, narrow strip, more or less continuous, in which erosion has been active and which has formed a series of troughs or holes, or basins, not unlike an "inner lowland." In western Nebraska is the Goshen Hole, carved by the many tributaries of the North Platte. In Colorado is the Colorado Piedmont, eroded by the South Platte and the Arkansas and their tributaries; and in New Mexico and western Texas is the Pecos Valley. All the major streams and some of the tributaries in the inner lowland belt are supplied with water from the mountains and are therefore able to erode actively. The bedrock in this area, in the early part of the present cycle of erosion, was higher than that to the east, and, as in all "inner lowland areas," was subject to rapid erosion. The upturned edges of some of the strata present points of attack for weathering agencies. Moreover, the plant life is scanty and thus does not form a protective cover against erosion, as it does farther east. These are probably the reasons for the formation of the "inner lowland" areas.

The Great Plains province has the largest area of continuous agricultural and grazing land in the West. The province is a transition zone between the humid East and the arid West, a transition zone in topography, soil, climate, plant life, and land utilization. For this reason the boundaries delimiting it as a whole, or delimiting its divisions, are open to dispute. Its western boundaries and the boundaries of its three divisions are fixed readily by natural features, but the eastern limits are located more or less arbitrarily. The soil student recognizes the western boundary as decided on by the physiographer, and for the eastern boundary uses color of soil as a criterion to delimit the divisions. Three belts or divisions are recognized: an eastern Chernozem belt; a middle Dark Brown soil belt; and a western Brown Soil belt. The amount of humus in the soil, which affects the color, decreases westward. Soil profiles show, on the other hand, an increasing amount of calcareous material in the soil, increasing in percentage and thickness but decreasing in depth toward the west. The calcareous layer measures the depth of root penetration. Both color of soil and depth and thickness of calcareous layers are responses to the amount of rain and the depth to which the rain penetrates. The Chernozem belt lies in general to the east of the 20-inch isohyet.

The ecologist recognizes three belts of plant formation, and the agriculturist three belts based on man's utilization of the land. In the Chernozem soil belt, grain growing dominates the agricultural activities, with livestock-raising subordinate. In the Dark Brown belt, farming is less certain than in the belt to the east, and livestock often tides the farmer over lean years. This is therefore, a farming-grazing belt. In the westernmost belt, grazing predominates.

QUESTIONS, EXERCISES, AND PROBLEMS

1. Do you think the railroads of the West are justified in advising Americans to "See America first"? List the "natural wonders" of the West visited by tourists. Of what economic value to the West are these recreation grounds? To what extent has the National Government contributed to the recreation business of the West? Make a list of the National Parks and Monuments. What are the natural features in each that attract people? Write to the Department of the Interior, Washington, D. C., for booklets on National Parks and Monuments. What types of business in the West are benefited by the tourist trade?

2. Plan three journeys across the Western States, one in the North, one along the overland route to California, and one in the South. Write descriptions of or reports on the more important natural geographic features and human activities that one would see along each route.

3. What physiographic features located the first railroad to the Pacific Coast along the central route?

4. Make a study of the natural features of Puget Sound, the lower Columbia River, and San Francisco Bay as harbors. Make detailed sketches. How did Los Angeles provide for a commercial contact with the Pacific? What adverse conditions did it overcome?

CHAPTER 15

The Climate
of the West

The dominating factor in the geography of the West is aridity. Its influence is seen in many ways: in the topographic forms, in the chemical composition and physical characteristics of the soil, in the character and distribution of plant life, in man's utilization of the land, in the architecture of the homes, the density and distribution of population, the wealth of the people, and the distribution and mileage of roads and railroads. In this chapter are discussed the distribution of rainfall and temperatures, climatic plant geography, land utilization, and density and distribution of population.[1]

RAINFALL

Areas of Rainfall Regions. The West, as delimited by the Census Bureau, has an area of 1,189,000 square miles; but if aridity be taken as the criterion the eastern boundary is the 20-inch isohyet, or approximately the 100th meridian. This larger West has an approximate area of 1,300,000 square miles, more than two-fifths of the area of the continental United States, exclusive of Alaska.

Of this vast area, only about 135,000 square miles, mainly the Pacific Slope north of 37° and north central of Idaho, have a rainfall of 30 inches or more, the amount generally considered essential in intermediate latitudes, if well distributed seasonally, for the more productive phases of humid agriculture. Much of this area is too rugged to be utilized for large-scale agriculture as now practiced in the United States. Even within the region commonly considered as the humid portion of the Pacific Slope, some of the valleys, particularly in southern Oregon and northern California, in the rainshadow of the Coast Range, are semihumid and re-

[1] In no section of the United States is human adjustment to climatic conditions quite so evident as in the Western States. In northern Canada and the West, climatic influences are so all-powerful that they approach controls. For these reasons a chapter is being devoted to the climate of the West instead of making climate incidental to the other phases of the geography as is done in most other sectional treatments.

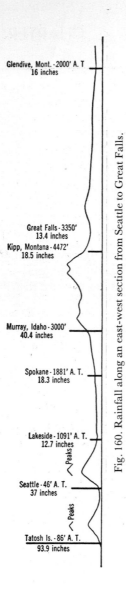

Glendive, Mont. - 2000' A. T
16 inches

Great Falls - 3350'
13.4 inches
Kipp, Montana - 4472'
18.5 inches

Murray, Idaho - 3000'
40.4 inches

Spokane - 1881' A. T.
18.3 inches

Lakeside - 1091' A. T.
12.7 inches
Peaks

Seattle - 46' A. T.
37 inches
Peaks

Tatosh Is. - 86' A. T.
93.9 inches

Fig. 160. Rainfall along an east-west section from Seattle to Great Falls.

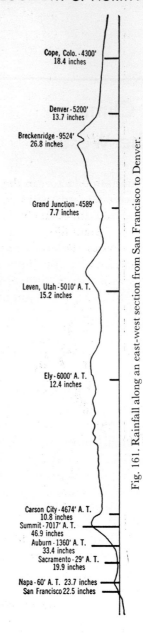

Cope, Colo. - 4300'
18.4 inches

Denver - 5200'
13.7 inches

Breckenridge - 9524'
26.8 inches

Grand Junction - 4589'
7.7 inches

Leven, Utah - 5010' A. T.
15.2 inches

Ely - 6000' A. T.
12.4 inches

Carson City - 4674' A. T.
10.8 inches
Summit - 7017' A. T.
46.9 inches
Auburn - 1360' A. T.
33.4 inches
Sacramento - 29' A. T.
19.9 inches
Napa - 60' A. T. 23.7 inches
San Francisco 22.5 inches

Fig. 161. Rainfall along an east-west section from San Francisco to Denver.

quire irrigation for profitable agriculture. About 900,000 square miles (some 70 per cent) have 10-20 inches of rain a year; and 240,000 square miles (about 18 per cent), less than 10 inches. More than 60,000 square miles are absolute desert.

Generalizations as to Rainfall Regions. The distribution of rainfall and its causes are discussed in Chapter 1. Only a few generalizations need to be made here. In general, in much of the West, the quantity of rainfall is a function of the altitude and location with respect to the ocean and winds. The regions of heavy and of very heavy rainfall, 40 inches or more, are on the westward-facing slopes of the Coast Ranges and the Sierra Nevada-Cascade Mountains, north of 37°, approximately. North of 39°, most of the higher slopes of the mountains receive 60 inches or more, and a few small areas 100 inches or more. Areas having 30-40 inches are to be found in Idaho north of 44°, and on a few of the higher mountain masses in Colorado. Most of the 20–30-inch areas are on mountains and plateaus of moderate elevation, as in California south of 37°, in Arizona, Colorado, Wyoming, Montana, and Idaho. In general, the basins or lowlands in the lee of the higher mountains, and plateaus have less than 20 inches of rain (Figs. 160 and 161). The large area that lies between the Pacific mountains and the Rockies, with the exception of a plateau area near central Arizona and a mountain area in northeastern Oregon, is very arid. The climatic deserts are in portions of the less-than-10-inch rainfall areas.

The seasonal distribution of rainfall, as discussed earlier, is a factor of large importance in plant growth, both native and cultivated. On the whole Pacific Slope, west of the Sierra Nevada-Cascade Mountains, and on a part of the Intermontane Plateau to the east, 30–50 or more per cent of the rainfall comes in the fall and winter months. In this large area the growing season is relatively dry. This is particularly the condition over the largest part of California, most of which has 50 per cent of the rain in the winter months. The summer droughts affect not only the plant life but also the constancy of the water supply for domestic use, for irrigation, and for water power. In most of the remaining area of the West the rain comes in summer or early spring or is more or less evenly distributed throughout the year.

TEMPERATURE

The great range in altitude and latitude and the wide longitudinal extent from the shores of the Pacific to the interior of the continent are the reasons for the great variety of temperature types. (See Figs. 4 and 9 and the discussion in Chapter 1.) One of the striking characteristics of the geography of the West, no doubt, is the strong contrast in temperature conditions between the mountain section of the interior and the Pacific Slope.

Temperature Regions.　　As a result of the dominance of plateaus and mountains, surface temperature regions extend into much lower latitudes than in the eastern United States. The *Cold Winter and Mild Summer* type of temperature has its greatest areal development in Canada and in the West, even as far south as northern New Mexico in the Rocky Mountain highlands. It also occurs in the Sierra Nevada and in eastern Colorado. A 90-day (or less) frostless season—generally considered the growing season—covers a large area. Only a small part of this mountain plateau section has more than 150 days free from frost each year. Mountains and plateaus, therefore, bring Canadian lowland temperatures far south into the United States.

The West, from the highest mountains to the lowest basins, has all the temperature regions recognized, except the truly tropical, i.e., the *always hot*. All types except this one occur in California, the only state that is so distinguished.

PLANT GEOGRAPHY

Factors Affecting Plant Life.　　Many elements of the physical environment affect the distribution and characteristics of plant life. Among the more important are mineral composition and physical condition (depth, porosity, size of particles, humus content, topographic position) of the soil, the amount of rainfall and its seasonal distribution, the length of droughts, the humidity of the air, winds, temperature of air and ground, length of growing day, length of growing season, and amount of sunlight. With so many factors involved, the correlation of plant life and physical conditions is a difficult task and one in which errors are likely to arise, particularly where attempts are made at simplification seems essential. When large areas and slight differences in plant life are thought of, soil, temperature, and rainfall may be taken as the chief elements of the climatic environment. In fact, nearly all the factors stated above are variants or resultants of these three. In the brief discussion that follows, in which an attempt is made to indicate possible correlations between plant types and physical conditions, these three are the elements considered in the physical environment (Fig. 162).

A study of the characteristics and distribution of the native plant life of the West is primarily a question of available soil moisture and water demands. The physical conditions of the soil greatly affect the available supply of soil water. The rainfall is never great enough to saturate the

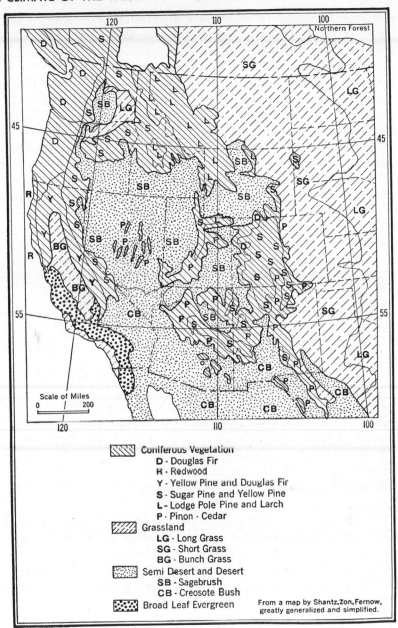

Fig. 162. Plant regions of the West.

soils to great depths; the subsoil in most of the arid region is permanently dry. After a rain, water penetrates the ground, in heavy soils, not more than 6 or 8 inches, in light soils, 1 or 2 feet. The depth of penetration is also affected by the amount of rain and other factors. From this upper layer, the roots take up the water and the plant gives it to the air by transpiration. Some water is lost by evaporation from the soil. In heavier soils the growth of vegetation may be rapid, but the supply of moisture is quickly used up, and the plants early begin to show the effects of drought. On the light soils, since penetration is deeper and there is little movement of water upward or laterally, the plants must send their roots to the soil water. The plant life on light soils is not so luxuriant as in fine or heavy soils, but the growing season is longer because there is a greater supply of water. Fortunately for plant life, light soils predominate in the West. The sink-in is relatively greater than in humid lands, for the soil is porous. The heavy downpours that characterize the rainfall of the arid areas, unfortunately, tend to reduce sink-in, the surface water running off into mud or alkali flats or into streams, with the result that it is largely lost to plant life.

The water demands of the plants vary greatly, being correlated more closely with evaporation rate than with other climatic elements. As a general rule, plants in the southern part of the arid lands require about twice as much water as in the north. It has been found that 518 tons of water are needed to produce 1 ton of dry alfalfa at Williston, North Dakota, but 1005 tons are required at Dalhart, Texas.[2] This difference is due primarily to the greater amount of transpiration into the hot, dry air of the south. In many parts of the Great Basin, where rainfall is 10 inches or less, the annual evaporation from a free surface is roughly 100 inches. In most of the Basin and Range provinces, precipitation is only about 20 per cent of the evaporation from a free surface, measured in inches.

Types of the Conifers.   In the humid and subhumid parts of the West, coniferous forests predominate. Broad-leaved hardwood forests, like those in humid eastern United States or humid northeastern Europe, where climatic conditions are essentially like those of the Pacific Northwest, are wanting. Some plant geographers have suggested that the absence of broad-leaved deciduous trees is a question of dispersal, mountain barriers and aridity preventing migration from the East, the nearest center from which dispersal could take place. The question, however, is unsettled. Climatic conditions may not account for the absence of deciduous trees, but there seems to be a definite correlation, in a rough way at least, of size of tree and density of stand to amount of rainfall, and of species to

[2] Briggs and Shantz, Second Pan-American Scientific Congress, Washington, 1915–1916.

climate, soil, and moisture. Six types of coniferous forests are recognized in the West. Figure 162 shows the distribution of the several types. The pinion-juniper plant formation, also coniferous, is a woodland. It grows on the desert edge of the coniferous forests (Fig. 163).

Sclerophyll Vegetation. The broad-leaved evergreen, or broad-leaved sclerophyll, chiefly of California south of San Francisco Bay, is a plant type that develops in areas that are semihumid, with winter rain and summer drought, and that have moderate winter temperatures. The drought comes in the growing season when the temperatures are high

Fig. 163. Pines in the high and cool Gallatin National Forest of Montana, showing Ha-Nana Lake. *Courtesy, Forest Service.* This resort and camp is noted for scenery. Here the precipitation is uniform throughout the year, but the land is too rocky and mountainous for agriculture. Sheep are sometimes driven in for summer pasture.

and the air dry. To survive under natural conditions, the plants must therefore possess drought-resisting devices. The local name for this formation is chaparral, but the formation is readily correlated with the well-known mediterranean type, being characterized by trees with leathery, strongly cutinized, evergreen leaves, thick bark, short, knotty trunks, gnarly branches, and a large root development. Bulbous or tuberous biennials are numerous, and there are some succulent plants like the cactus.

Desert Vegetation Types. There are three main types of desert and semidesert vegetation in the Western States: a northern or semidesert

sagebrush type, mainly on the Intermontane Plateau between 37° and
44° N. latitude; a southern or creosote-brush type in desert areas south
of 37°, and mainly in the area that has 10 inches or less of rain a year;
and a third type where the mantle rock is composed of shifting sands or is
highly alkaline, which is not a climatic but largely an edaphic desert, the
result probably of geologic or topographic conditions. Succulent plants
are more characteristic of this edaphic desert than of the climatic. Salinas
or salt plains have a fourth type known as greasewood. This type occupies but a small area in the West. The annuals, or rather wet-season
plants, of the desert have few of the above characteristics. They are
mesophytic in structure and physiology. They germinate after a rain, if
temperature conditions are favorable, and grow as long as there is a supply of moisture; as the supply decreases, they blossom, produce seeds, and
die as the supply is exhausted. The seeds lie dormant in the desert sands
until the next wet spell, which may occur in a few days, months, or even
years. The annuals change the barren desert landscape into flowery
meadows, ephemeral at best.

LAND UTILIZATION

The humid coniferous forest regions, those of the Pacific Northwest and
the Northern Rockies, where topographic conditions permit, are suitable
for humid agriculture. Dry farming is possible in most of the Great Plains
grasslands and the grasslands of California, the yellow sugar pine areas,
and the chaparral. Some of the sagebrush lands are dry-farmed, although
agricultural operations are often precarious. Failure is certain in the creosote-brush rea. Irrigation is possible in any of the areas if water is available; but in the creosote-brush area the soil, if strongly alkaline, needs to
be freed of alkali by repeated washings. Most of the edaphic, salt, and
alkali deserts are probably impossible of reclamation. Grazing is possible
on all the non-agricultural lands, but the carrying power of the ranges
varies greatly. Their capacity is influenced largely by the relative amount
of rainfall and evaporation. (See discussion on grazing, Chapter 17.)

DISTRIBUTION OF POPULATION

The Population of the Future.   The type of ultimate land utilization (see
also Chapter 2) is an index of the future population that may be supported. Close settlement is possible in the humid areas, where topographic conditions permit, and on irrigated lands; both dry-land farming and grazing make for scattered and few people. The humid area of
the West is roughly only about 7 per cent of the total area, and only a
small part of this has slopes low enough for cultivation. Careful calcula-

tions show that not more than 5 per cent of the arid land west of the 20-inch isohyet may be irrigated, even when all available water is utilized, unless economies in the use of water not now practiced are discovered. Probably, therefore, not more than 10 per cent of the entire area of the western states can ultimately have well-peopled settlements. There is no way of determining or estimating the future density of population that may exist on this 10 per cent of area, for commerce, manufacturing, and mining set no limits to population density; but 90 per cent of the total area is destined to remain a region (or regions) of scattered houses with densities but little greater than at present.

Factors in Population Distribution.   Today the West, although 20 per cent larger in area than the North and 34 per cent larger than the South, has only about one-third of the population of the South and one-sixth that of the North. Aridity is not the sole factor that limits the number of people, for the West is younger than the East, but it is certainly the chief factor. The people, in general, may be found largely on the humid lowlands of the Pacific Northwest, on the irrigated lands, and in the mining sections.

QUESTIONS, EXERCISES, AND PROBLEMS

1. Construct a structure section similar to Fig. 161 along a line through San Diego, Tucson, and El Paso. Secure data from Weather Bureau bulletins or from the Statistical Abstract.

2. Draw a structure section across the Pacific Slope and indicate thereon the temperature regions. Explain the location of each region.

3. Make a detailed study of the rainfall and temperature types of California in relation to surface features. Write your findings, giving explanations.

4. What correlation do you make between vegetation and climate in California?

5. Make a careful study of the relation of distribution of population and water supply for agriculture in the West.

6. What are the climatic and physiographic reasons for the general lack of navigable rivers and the dominance of railroads in transportation?

7. Why was it that the National Government had to encourage western railroad building by grants of land?

8. Why is it that reds, browns, and yellows are the dominant colors in the landscapes of the West?

9. What climatic conditions make the resort and recreational business of Colorado, New Mexico, Arizona, and southern California profitable? Write to the chambers of commerce of cities in these regions for literature.

10. The securing of an adequate supply of pure water is a difficult problem for every city that attains any great size. In the humid portions of the United States, the large cities have spent tens of millions of dollars each to provide suitable supplies of water. In the arid and semiarid portions of the United States the problem is still more difficult of solution. Make a careful study of the ways in which San Francisco, Portland, and Los Angeles have solved the problem. Emphasize, first of all, the adverse physical conditions they had to overcome, the opportunities nature offers, and how these opportunities were utilized.

CHAPTER 16

Agriculture
in the West

In any discussion of agriculture in the West it must be noted immediately that this section does not rank highly when compared with other parts of the country. In 1950 there were 1,158,000,000 acres listed as "land in farms" in the United States, and the West accounted for 324,-500,000 acres, or only about 28 per cent regardless of the fact that more than one-third the area of the country is in this section. Steep mountainous slopes, bare rocks, and aridity are the limiting factors. Well over two-thirds of the West is classed as arid and semiarid. However, since the West contains only about 12.8 per cent of the population of the country, agriculture becomes relatively an important business of the people. Considering land in farms, the United States has about 700 acres in farms per 100 of its population; the West has about 1620 acres per 100.

There are three types of agriculture practiced in the West, each adapted to particular conditions. They are (1) irrigation farming, widely distributed and found in all states; (2) dry-land farming, most successful in the Great Plains and in the northern half of the Rocky Mountain area and the Intermontane Plateau area, but also found in all other states; and (3) humid agriculture, almost entirely limited to the Pacific Northwest.

In humid farming and dry-land farming, man uses the moisture as nature distributes it. In humid farming the water is generally so plentiful that man gives little heed to its conservation. In dry-land farming precipitation is so slight that he is forced to use every device that experience and science have taught him to conserve it in order that he may have enough to supply the crops. In irrigation farming man is not satisfied with nature's distribution. He collects the water from a large area, or utilizes nature's devices for collecting it, and distributes it over a small area. All three types require rain; hence the amount and distribution of the rainfall of the West, discussed previously, are as much determining factors in the amount of crops as they are in humid America; and even more so, for the total amount of water is nearer the minimum requirement in the West than in the North and South.

376

IRRIGATION AGRICULTURE

In all states west of the Mississippi River irrigation is practiced to a considerable extent except perhaps in Minnesota, Iowa, and Missouri where no projects are of sufficient importance to be considered. In Arkansas, Louisiana, and along the Gulf Coast in Texas, in lands of approximately 40 inches of precipitation, irrigation is applied mainly in rice growing, which requires level land, terracing, flooding of fields, and therefore more water than nature provides. In all of the remaining western states aridity results in the need for irrigation, at least in some parts, if man is to produce abundantly from the lands.

Of the 11 Western States, generally considered to be the West, only about 2.75 per cent of the area is irrigated, and this amount represents almost one-half the total acreage capable of irrigation. This fact is all the more remarkable when, as has been stated, the entire West is considered to be over two-thirds arid and semiarid. Some areas are bare rock and steep slopes, some have alkaline soils, and many are far from available water so as to make irrigation not economically feasible. It has been estimated that projects could be developed to irrigate 22,120,000 acres in states west of the 100th meridian, in addition to the 20,395,000 acres already under irrigation.

In general, through the past century, the irrigable lands have been overestimated. There has been a constant revision downward of the amount. Furthermore, a large portion of lands now irrigated need more water on them to bring them to higher possible production. At the same time, it is also true in some areas that there is a great need for a more effective use of water now available.

The Beginning of Irrigation. The methods and practices used in the irrigated lands of the West are largely United States' own. In a crude way, irrigation has been practiced for centuries in all the ancient countries: Egypt, Assyria, Babylon, Persia, India, China, Greece, and Italy. In the arid southwest, the Spaniards in the sixteenth century found the more progressive Indians with canals and ditches for distributing the water over their patches of corn. People of the United States received little knowledge of irrigation practices from any of these sources.

At first the devices used in the West to get water on the land were very simple. The Mormons, near Great Salt Lake, were the first whites in English-America to attempt irrigation. In 1847 or 1848 they diverted the water from small streams of the alluvial fans on the western slopes of the Wasatch Mountains. Only simple dams were needed. Nearly all the irrigation in the West was as simple as this. Experience gave confidence, and larger projects were undertaken and completed successfully. The large, costly projects undertaken by the Reclamation Service of the United States find their equal from an engineering standpoint in the work of the British engineers in Egypt and India.

Sources of Irrigation Water.   In general, there are two sources of water for irrigation—streams or lakes, and wells. Only about 13 per cent comes from wells, thus leaving streams and lakes the major sources by far. In the 17 Western States, plus Arkansas and Louisiana, there were approximately 70,000 pumped wells used in irrigation in 1950. Out of this number California accounted for about 50,000, the greater part of which

Fig. 164. Natural irrigation at the base of the Sierra Madre Mountains in southern California. For this orange grove considerable water is supplied by seepage from the mountains in the background. *Courtesy, California Fruit Growers Exchange.*

were in the Great Central Valley. In a few places "natural irrigation" is effective on piedmonts and lower slopes by seepage from uplands (Fig. 164).

Man has adapted gravity flow for perhaps nearly 70 per cent of all projects, though this figure is only approximate. In many projects, water is lifted from streams to reservoirs, and gravity flow is used thereafter. The most common engineering device is the diversion dam on streams with canals leading away from the pond or lake thus made above the dam. The small project has been most common, but with increases in engineering skills there is a growing tendency towards the large project, involving a great dam or dams, canals that are long and sometimes con-

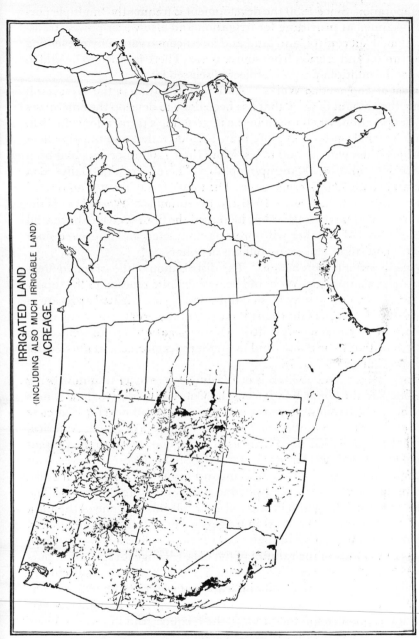

IRRIGATED LAND
(INCLUDING ALSO MUCH IRRIGABLE LAND)
ACREAGE,

Fig. 165. The irrigated lands east of the 20-inch isohyet are used to grow rice. Discuss the distribution of the irrigated lands in their relation to mountain areas and rivers.

crete lined to prevent seepage, or covered tunnels or tubes to prevent loss by evaporation. Since 1930 the development is frequently "multiple purpose"—aimed at providing for irrigation and also water power, transportation, flood control, and land and forest conservation by preventing rapid run-off and erosion from source areas. There is much to be said in favor of the multiple-purpose project, discussed later.

Extent of Engineering Works. Although irrigation in the West is still young, the amount of work that has been done to develop the enterprises now in operation, when taken in the aggregate, is tremendous. In 1940 the main canals measured more than 127,000 miles, and the pipe lines connected therewith 28,500 miles. More than 7700 reservoirs had been provided, besides 78,000 pumping plants. There were 34,000 diversion dams and nearly 4600 storage dams. The total capital invested amounted to over a billion dollars. Since 1940 and the stimulus of World War II the development of large projects has increased the figures given above, and when considered together with projects completed and approved since 1940 the costs represent many billions of dollars.

Water a Factor in Distribution. The distribution of the irrigated areas is very irregular over the West and bears a definite relation to the supply of water. In general, it may be said that most of the irrigated areas are in the valleys of the rivers that take their rise in the great mountain areas. This pattern is broken only a little where irrigation is from wells, as in west Texas, the Great Plains, and in southern California and the Central Valley of California (Fig. 165).

Nearly all the irrigated lands of Washington (except that now being developed on the Great Bend, from the Columbia), derive their waters from the rivers that flow down the east slope (rainshadow) of the Cascade Mountains. The Columbia, one of the great rivers of North America, with its large flow, has been little used for irrigation up to the present time, if one excludes its large tributary, the Snake River. However, with the completion of Grand Coulee Dam and Franklin D. Roosevelt Lake, irrigation is beginning to be applied to parts of the Big Bend area. The Snake River, the largest tributary of the Columbia, is one of the most important streams of the West in irrigation. Both the Sacramento and the San Joaquin get most of their water from the Sierra Nevada. Little use has been made of the rainfall of the Coast Range for irrigation purposes, for in Washington, Oregon, and northern California agriculture is possible without the artificial application of water. South of San Francisco Bay, all the way to Mexico, the rain is torrential in its fall. However, irrigation is practiced in the Salinas, the Sisquoc, and in several others of the small valleys that outlet to the Pacific.

The Rocky Mountain region is by far the chief source of the water used in irrigation in the West. The Snake, the Green, the Bear, the many short streams of the Wasatch, the Grand, and the Gunnison, and other rivers tributary to the Colorado all have their sources on the western slope of the Rockies. On the eastern slope of the Rockies are many important rivers. In Montana, the main stream of the Missouri, and a score or more of smaller tributaries, besides the large Yellowstone and the Big Horn, supply water to large areas. Most of the land irrigated is in the river valleys and, therefore, does not occur in large blocks but has a linear distribution along the stream courses. The North Platte in Wyoming and the South Platte in Colorado, with all the tributaries of the Platte, furnish water to more than 2,300,000 acres. The Arkansas, farther south, gets its water from the highest parts of the Southern Rockies and irrigates 750,000 acres, mainly in Colorado. The Rio Grande is another Rocky Mountain river that irrigates land all along its course, even on its flood plain near the Gulf of Mexico. The only streams of importance, supplying irrigated lands, that do not rise in the Coast Range, Sierra Nevada-Cascade Mountains, or the Rockies are the Gila River in Arizona and the Humboldt in Nevada. The four most important rivers in the West are the Snake River irrigating 3,819,000 acres, the Colorado, 2,638,000 acres, the Platte, 2,315,000 acres and the San Joaquin, 2,405,000 acres. California, with an irrigated area of 5,069,000 acres, Colorado, with 3,220,-000, and Idaho, with 2,277,000, are the leading states, chiefly because of the proximity of great mountain areas that have a heavy rainfall.

Organization of Irrigation Enterprises. The greatest number of irrigation enterprises in the West are organized on an Individual or Partnership basis, consisting of individual farmers and neighbors who use small works employing gravity diversion from rivers, or sometimes water from wells, without a formal organization. In 1950, approximately 34 per cent of the irrigated lands of the West were under this type of sponsorship.

A second type of organization is the Cooperative or Mutual Enterprise, accounting for 31.5 per cent of the irrigated area. In this type, water is distributed according to the ownership of stock in the corporation. Still another type of organization is the Irrigation District, a public corporation established under state laws, which give the inhabitants of the district the power to obtain funds, build irrigation works, and perform other corporate duties. It applies to 16.5 per cent of the irrigated lands.

The commercial enterprise supplies water to farmers who have no financial interest in the works. It is a business which sells water privileges at a profit, and applies to about 7 per cent of irrigated lands. It is declining in importance. The Bureau of Indian Affairs projects are gov-

ernment built and operated solely for Indian reservations. They constitute 2.5 per cent of the irrigated lands.

The last type is the United States Bureau of Reclamation project,
which resulted from laws passed in 1902. The type applies to large developments, most frequently multiple purpose, as stated before, and is supported by public funds as well as by taxing the beneficiaries. It is a long-
range plan, and, as a type, it is increasing in importance, accounting for
about 8.5 per cent of all irrigated lands in 1950 (Fig. 166).

Crops on Irrigated Lands.   In nearly all irrigated lands of the West,
alfalfa and perhaps some small grains are grown, largely for local use.
Wherever dairying or cattle fattening is practiced in irrigated areas, or
on lands closely associated with irrigation, as in Utah and Central California, alfalfa is an important stock food. This hay crop serves also as a

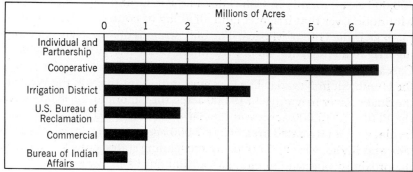

Fig. 166. Irrigation by types of enterprise. The acreage of the irrigated lands in the
Federal Reclamation projects, contrary to general opinion, is but a small part of the
total irrigated acreage of the West.

soil-building crop because of its high nitrogen value. The West produced
more than one-third of the alfalfa hay crop of the country in 1950, and
more than one-half of the alfalfa seed. Utah and Arizona led all states in
alfalfa seed production, nearly all of which came from irrigated lands.

In general throughout the West, alfalfa, sugar beets, and cotton play
an important part as combination crops in irrigated farm economy because of the feed value for livestock—mainly cattle, discussed in the
following chapter. All of them are crops applicable for intensive agriculture on irrigated lands where water is costly. Cotton is confined to the
southern parts of the West where seasons are long, sugar beets are confined to the central, western, and northern portions where the seasons are
shorter and temperatures are not so high, but alfalfa is widely grown
throughout most irrigated areas.

Truck crops play an important part in the production of most irrigated
lands, because they demand intensive cultivation. They supply the home

market for most areas, but frequently a specialty is made of one or more crops, where by canning, refrigeration, advertising, scientific packing, and good transportation a crop may reach the wider markets of the coun-

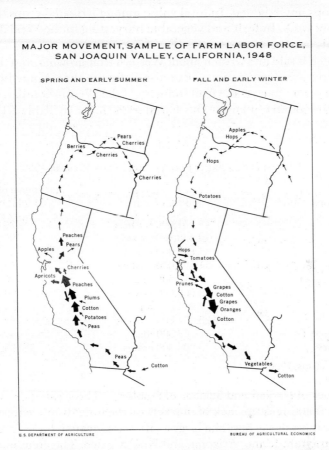

MAJOR MOVEMENT, SAMPLE OF FARM LABOR FORCE,
SAN JOAQUIN VALLEY, CALIFORNIA, 1948

SPRING AND EARLY SUMMER   FALL AND EARLY WINTER

U.S. DEPARTMENT OF AGRICULTURE   BUREAU OF AGRICULTURAL ECONOMICS

Fig. 167. Farm-labor movement by seasons on the West Coast, San Joachin Valley, California, 1948. The labor supply becomes an important factor in harvesting fruit and other crops in the West Coast states. The differences in seasonal requirements for various crops result in a northward movement of labor in spring and early summer, and a return movement in fall and early winter. The demand for labor is particularly heavy in the San Joaquin Valley. Mexicans and many others from the South make up the large part of this transient labor force. *Courtesy, U. S. Bureau of Agricultural Economics.*

try. Thus, potatoes from the Pocatello Idaho region and canned peas from the Blue Mountains irrigated areas in Washington and Oregon reach the larger market outside the West. Other important crops that reach the larger markets are tomatoes, beans, cauliflower, asparagus, carrots, lettuce, celery, and artichokes. California is by far the leading state in the crops named, and it supplies the bulk of the early truck crop of the United States.

In all agriculture of the West irrigated crops are far more important than crops not irrigated. In total value among irrigated crops the fruits take front rank. In fruit and vegetable harvesting in the West the labor problems become acute at times (Fig. 167).

So much is said and written about Western fruit growing, and the Western cooperative associations advertise so freely, that it may be well to consider a summary of the fruit industry of the West in comparison with that of the country at large. This summary is shown in Table XII.

TABLE XII

A Summary of Fruit Production in the West in 1950

Fruit Crops	Production	Percentage of Product of United States
Apple	48,061,000 bushels	26
Grape	2,458,800 tons	90
Orange	44,800,000 boxes	39
Peach	31,557,000 bushels	59
Plum and prune	412,500 tons	98
Lemon	13,000,000 boxes	99+
Apricot	215,000 tons	99+
Pear	25,864,000 bushels	82
Sweet cherry	68,000 tons	83
Strawberry	3,900,000 crates	35

U. S. Census, 1950.

The Lack of Markets and Solution of Problem.　　The greatest drawback to western farming is the lack of markets or the long distance to markets. The coastal states, where the largest cities are located, have better markets than Utah, Idaho, Arizona, and New Mexico. The great market for any of the money crops is the densely settled portion of the United States.[1]

Since about 1920, cooperative associations and exchanges in the West have striven to develop the markets of the eastern states for some of their products. They have succeeded in giving the public a reliable product of uniform grade, tastefully and carefully packed. The work of these agencies is diverse. They secure capital and credit, adapt production to market demands, establish grades and standards for the products, provide

[1] In railroad rates the coastal district has an advantage over interior sections on some commodities, the rate for goods between New York and San Francisco being lower than between Salt Lake City and New York.

cold-storage facilities, select brands and trade marks, advertise, develop old and extend new markets, secure favorable freight rates, utilize by-products, eliminate waste, and purchase supplies. The perishable nature of the products they handle, the great distance to market, the strong competition offered by areas nearer the great markets of the country, and the small land units controlled by the individual producer have brought the associations into existence. The marvelous success of western fruit in capturing and holding eastern markets is due largely to the admirable work of these cooperative associations. Perhaps in no place in the world have cooperatives been as well developed and more influential than those associated with fruit growing in the West. The large returns and the stability of the market have brought prosperity and satisfaction to the producers.

Relative Success of Irrigation. How successful is irrigation agriculture in comparison with agriculture in the humid sections of our country? Official statistics are not available that will enable one to draw definite conclusions. Many enterprises have been highly successful as measured in dollars and cents, and still more so in terms of social and individual betterment. Others have been miserable failures. Some irrigation developments were, and are, poorly located; the supply of water is inadequate or the low temperatures and the short growing season restrict the variety of crops. On some projects extensive crops are grown, but the high cost of water makes only intensive agriculture profitable. Contacts with markets are inadequate. Marketing associations are not well developed or do not function adequately. The irrigation farmers lack the techniques essential to success. Lands have been reduced in yield or damaged beyond recovery by excessive flooding or improper drainage. The cost of water on some projects is very high, and much is lost by seepage. On only a few projects has all the land that the irrigation works are capable of irrigating been taken up. In 1950 the works were capable of irrigating considerably more than 31,000,000 acres, but less than 25,000,000 were actively irrigated.

Since the cost of the irrigation works is supposed to be spread over the whole acreage, either the water consumers or the "enterprise" that built the irrigation works must absorb the sums apportioned to the 5,000,000 or more acres. This adds to the already heavy cost of water to the farmer and reduces the returns to the enterprise that provided the irrigation works. On the whole, the yield to the acre of irrigated land is but little more than on non-irrigated, humid lands, and, as a rule, the investment, maintenance, and cost of operation to the acre are greater.

When the irrigation movement was young, real estate dealers in irrigated lands and irrigation enthusiasts led people to believe that the ownership of a parcel of irrigated land in the West was a surcease of all earthly cares and ceaseless toil. Soil with an abundance of soluble matter, bright cloudless skies which favored photosynthesis, and a supply of water responsive to man's will—what more could one desire! But people have long since realized that on most projects in the West success has not been so great as was anticipated. Success requires even greater intelligence and enterprise and harder work on irrigated farms in the West than it does in the humid sections of our country.

The Bureau of Reclamation projects insofar as irrigation is concerned have been costly, but it must be kept in mind that only about 9 per cent of irrigated land in the West is under this type of organization. About two-thirds of all irrigated lands are Individual, Partnership, or Cooperatively organized, and in these irrigation is generally considered to be successful. They are the oldest in irrigation and they occupy generally the best sites. Also they are not multiple-purpose to the extent that is true of the Bureau of Reclamation projects. In many cases, farmers using irrigation on Bureau projects have not and could not pay the costs allocated for water use.

It is claimed by many that such heavy subsidizing of agriculture on government projects is wholly unfair to the irrigation farmers who by their own enterprise and funds have had to provide their own lands and irrigation works.

Whatever the injustices may be resulting from the management of some irrigation projects, or whatever may be the failures of some projects, and without any attempt to say what should have been done, one must evaluate the entire process of irrigation from the standpoint of the benefits to the people as a whole. This will involve a consideration of other possible benefits frequently associated with irrigation projects, such as water power, harbor and navigation improvements, flood control and domestic water supplies.

IMPORTANT IRRIGATED AREAS

In a treatise of this nature it will be impossible to describe all the hundreds of irrigation projects, large and small, in the West, but an attempt is made in the following paragraphs to discuss briefly a few of the important ones. They are (1) the Salt River Valley, (2) the Colorado Delta, (3) the Rio Grande, (4) the Colorado-Big Thompson project, (5) the Uncompahgre project, (6) the Salt Lake Oasis, (7) the Snake River projects, (8) The Apple Valleys of the Columbia Basin, (9) the Nevada projects, (10) the Los Angeles Area, and (11) The Great Valley of California (Fig. 168).

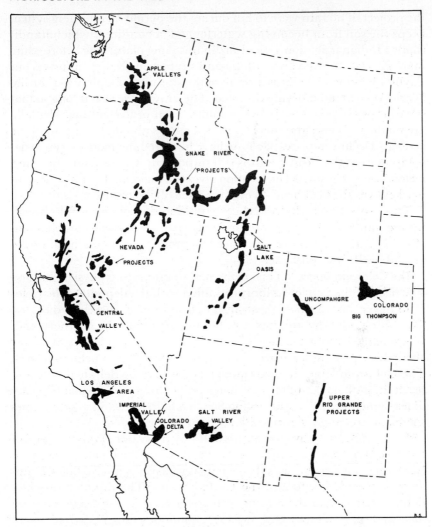

Fig. 168. Irrigation projects and areas in the West. This map is intended to show locations of representative irrigation areas discussed in the text. There are numerous other very important projects on the upper Missouri, the Platte, the Arkansas and elsewhere in the West.

The Salt River Valley. This project is located to the north of Phoenix, Arizona, on the Salt River, a tributary of the Gila. Here about 225,000 acres receive water from Roosevelt Lake impounded behind the large Roosevelt Dam. This is one of the first of the Bureau of Reclamation projects, and it was completed in 1911 at a cost of $3,890,000. So large is Roosevelt Lake that it is said to contain a 2-year supply of water for the project, if no rain were to fall during the period. A pumping system keeps the soil from becoming waterlogged, a condition which handicapped Indian irrigation agriculture in this same place, long before white man. At first the area grew alfalfa and supported a dairy industry, but Egyptian cotton came in as a result of the stimulus of high prices during World War I, and dairying declined. The growing season is long so that some crops are produced in every month. Four or five cuttings of alfalfa are made in a year, and this crop still occupies about 50 per cent of the acreage. Decline in prices of cotton have hindered the more extensive development of this crop, but it is still important. Citrus fruits, figs, and melons are also grown. The location gives the region a slight handicap in market over the California-grown produce of like nature.

This project as a whole has been considered very successful, though the amount of silt brought into the lake at present is sufficient to fill it in about 2 centuries. There is great need for erosion control in the drainage area above Roosevelt Lake.

The Colorado Delta.   This region has an interesting physical history. The head of the Gulf of California is filled with the deposits of the Colorado River, one of the highest silt-laden streams in the United States. The filling in of the gulf has resulted in cutting off the northern end, where high evaporation and low rainfall have created Salton Sea, now about 270 square miles in area, with a surface of 248 feet below sea level. The Colorado River has extended itself across the deltaic deposits to reach the gulf, no doubt having changed the position of its channel many times, sometimes filling the Salton Sea to a high level and at other times leaving it to evaporate to a low level.

To complicate man's use of this delta by irrigation, for it is a land of less than 10 inches of precipitation, is the fact that the boundary between California and Arizona cuts through it, as well as the international boundary between Mexico and the United States. The question of water rights has arisen, for the volume of the river varies greatly between flood stage and times of low water, and the amount of sediment carried is very great. The building of dikes to control the water has been a problem.

The Bureau of Reclamation created the Yuma project on the Arizona side of the delta and the Imperial Valley on the California side. These contain about 50,000 and 800,000 acres, respectively. The natural and most economical route for a canal to lead Colorado River waters to Imperial Valley was through Mexican territory, but this raised some international problems; therefore a rather expensive "All American" canal was constructed, paralleling the national boundary but entirely on United States territory. This canal feeds the Imperial Valley to the southeast of Salton Sea, and the Coachella branch leads to the east and north of this sea. Some lifting of the water is necessary, but great use is made of gravity flow.

These projects have over 300 frost-free days per year and hence are suited for tropical-subtropical crops. The citrus fruits, figs, dates, vegetables, melons, long-fiber cotton, and alfalfa are all important. Iceberg lettuce is a specialty in the Imperial Valley, and this product reaches the market throughout the United States. Range cattle and some sheep are brought to be fattened on alfalfa and then marketed mainly in the Los Angeles area. The rich, deep alluvial soils have caused the Colorado delta to be referred to as "The American Egypt."

The Rio Grande Project.   Although the Rio Grande supplies water for numerous irrigation projects along its course, serious difficulties have arisen in the development and operation of them. This stream has its main source in the Rocky Mountains of southern Colorado and northern New Mexico, flowing southward across New Mexico; then it turns generally southeastward at El Paso and reaches to the Gulf of Mexico. For the long stretch below El Paso it forms the Texas-Mexican boundary. The stream is long, it flows through semiarid country, it carries much sediment, and it is subject to floods and low-water stages.

Indians had used the upper Rio Grande waters for irrigation in pre-Columbian times, and Mexicans developed some projects even before 1800, mainly opposite El Paso and downstream a short distance. Early diversion of Rio Grande waters in New Mexico before 1910 resulted in insufficient supply for the Mexican projects below, and that country threatened to bring suit for damages. The outcome was that the Reclamation Bureau of the United States built Elephant Butte Dam at Hot Spring, New Mexico, about 120 miles above El Paso, in 1916. It impounds a great amount of water in Elephant Butte Reservoir, capable of regulating the flow, supplying nearly 200,000 acres in New Mexico with irrigation water, and guaranteeing 60,000 acre-feet of water a year for Mexican irrigation just below El Paso.

Today the irrigated area along the Rio Grande in New Mexico between Elephant Butte and El Paso is one of the garden spots of the Southwest. It contains many villages and numerous diversion canals. The growing season here is long, and, though some alfalfa and fruit are grown, the major crop is long-staple cotton. Mexican labor is used to a considerable extent.

Space does not permit a description of many other irrigated areas along the Rio Grande, but the Elephant Butte project is one of the most important of them. It was built to settle a question of floods and water rights with a neighboring country, but this difficulty may arise again for it is reported that the Elephant Butte Reservoir is filling with sediment very rapidly. When this occurs floods again will harass El Paso and the Mexican border adjacent, and at low stages there will not be enough water for the Mexican irrigation. This project is an excellent example of the necessity for regional planning, whereby methods of erosion control could have been practiced in the source areas above the reservoir. The long-distance future of the Elephant Butte Project does not appear bright.

The Colorado-Big Thompson Project.   The largest irrigated area on the Great Plains is the Colorado-Big Thompson project. It lies on the Rocky Mountain Piedmont, generally in the source area of the South Platte River, north of Denver. It includes the lands of the Greeley Colony which was founded there in 1870. There was a great shortage of water in the area in the 1930's, which led the Bureau of Reclamation to construct the project. Construction began in 1938, the first power was developed in 1943 ,and water for irrigation was provided soon after.

This project is somewhat unique, though several smaller ones of like nature had preceded it. It lies entirely to the east of the Rocky Mountains, yet it takes water from the Grand Reservoir and other reservoirs to the west of the divide, through a 13.1-mile tunnel 9.5 feet in diameter and capable of carrying 550 second-feet of water. A considerable amount of water power is developed. The original plan of the Bureau was that one-half the cost was to be repaid from hydroelectric power, and the other half, not to exceed $25,000,000, was to come from the users of water, organized as the Northern Colorado Water Conservancy District. Numerous reservoirs in the mountains, but mainly Grand Lake, provide for storage and thus conserve and regulate the flow of the upper Colorado River from which this water is taken.

This project has not worked out to the complete satisfaction of the water users of the area. It provides only water supplemental to what was available before, and it has been found that very little if any, new lands have been added. The cost of the project has reached over twice the original estimate, and it was not yet completed in 1952. It is claimed that the water users cannot and will not pay. Advocates who favor the work of the Bureau, however, point to the great advantages derived from hydroelectric power, as well as the indirect benefits of the project to public welfare in regulation of stream flow, soil conservation, flood control, forestry, wild life, etc. It should be noted that this supplemental supply of water would be sufficient to prevent a severe water shortage in the region, such as that experienced in the 1930's when losses were estimated to have reached $5,000,000 annually for each of several years in the decade.

The elevation of the irrigated area is between 3500 and 5400 feet, it has about 15 inches of rainfall (great annual variability), from 4 to 5 months only for growing season, and an average mean temperature of 48°. Obviously this is not a subtropical land. The chief crops are sugar beets, potatoes, beans, corn, small grain, fruits, alfalfa, vegetables, dairy products, poultry, and eggs. Hogs, cattle, and lambs are fattened on alfalfa and the by-products of sugar beets. Denver is the chief market.

This project is largely responsible for Colorado's high rank among the states in the production of sugar beets, potatoes, and beans. In 1951, Colorado ranked second in sugar beets, eighth in potatoes, and fourth in dry edible beans.

The Uncompahgre Project. In earlier days, many small irrigation projects were developed within the Rocky Mountain region to supply produce largely for mining towns. These were mostly private or state-developed projects, but since the first decade of the twentieth century the United States Bureau of Reclamation has developed several areas within the Rocky Mountains, one of the important ones being the Uncompahgre project in southwestern Colorado. In this area, the Gunnison and Uncompahgre Rivers flow westward and northward from the mountains of central and southern Colorado to join the Colorado River. The Gunnison is the larger of the two tributaries, and carries a considerable volume of water, but there are no lands adjacent suitable for irrigation. The smaller Uncompahgre, at one place only a few miles away, has a low volume of water, but it does have about 200,000 acres of broad flat lands bordering it, suitable for irrigation. This project involved the diverting of waters from the Gunnison River to the Uncompahgre by a tunnel 6 miles long, and the building of Taylor Park Reservoir in the source waters of the Gunnison Valley, as a regulator of flow. The Bureau completed the project in the first decade of the twentieth century, at which time the Uncompahgre Valley Water Users Association agreed to repay construction costs in forty annual installments.

The Uncompahgre Valley is considered a successful irrigation project, and it is a garden spot of southwestern Colorado. It is served by United States Highway 50, and by the Denver Rio Grande Railway. It has an annual rainfall of only 9.5 inches, an average growing season of 175 days, and a mean temperature of about 50° F. The season is not long enough for cotton or subtropical fruits, but it specializes in onions, sugar beets, and potatoes, along with the seemingly indispensable alfalfa, beans, and the small grains.

The Salt Lake Oasis. Lying to the east and south of Great Salt Lake, Utah, are a number of non-contiguous irrigated areas referred to collectively as the Valley of Great Salt Lake or the Salt Lake Oasis. They contain more than 1,000,000 acres, and constitute the heart of the state of Utah, with two-thirds of the population of the state.

The particular physical conditions here are the high Wasatch Mountains trending north-south, the heavy rainfall and snow-capped western slopes, the broad Piedmont on the west side of the mountains, and the numerous westward-flowing streams from the mountains across the Piedmont, which lose themselves in the arid basin beyond. The conditions were ideal for numerous small projects where stream diversion was easily accomplished on the Piedmont, either as private or commercial projects. These were the first irrigated lands of the West, and the general nature of the place fit in well with the communal living of the followers of the Mormon Church. It was to this region that Brigham Young led the Mormons, well before the California Gold Rush and the coming of numerous other whites into the West.

The Mormon population grew rapidly in this oasis, and the irrigable land was settled rapidly. There has been no great extension of irrigation since before the Civil War, but methods of diverting and using water have been much improved. The people live mostly in villages and travel out to the croplands, which are generally small holdings farmed intensively. Invariably villages are located on streams where water may be made available: they may be but a few miles apart along a stream, but in traveling north-south one often crosses desert stretches between villages. Sugar beets, grains, alfalfa, and fruits and vegetables are grown. Near Utah Lake and Great Salt Lake the soil is often waterlogged and too alkaline for cropping, but much is used as grazing land. On adjoining lands, not irrigated, considerable wheat is grown by dry-farming methods (discussed later), but this is only to supplement irrigation farms. One seldom sees farmsteads on the adjacent arid wheat lands.

The Snake River Projects. The Snake River, a tributary of the Columbia, rises in the high Rockies of western Montana and flows generally westward and northward, making a long southward bend through Idaho, and, after forming the boundary between Oregon and Idaho, it joins the Columbia in southeastern Washington. Through southern Idaho the Snake has numerous tributaries and wide areas of land suitable for irrigation. Projects are developed all along the Snake River so that it is sometimes said that the Snake is the most thoroughly used for irrigation of any of the large streams of the West. The state of Idaho has over 2,-000,000 acres under irrigation, and a large part of these are in the Snake River Valley. As the Salt Lake Valley is the heart of Utah, the Snake River Valley is the heart of Idaho. Here live more than one-half the

AGRICULTURE IN THE (left page)

Irrigation is practi
very numerous, and i
terspersed with ranchi
central and southern
largest region of irriga
acres out of the state'
Artesian wells have pla
in the valley, but there
cating the lowering of

Throughout most of
rights to land owners.
lowed owners of land a
streams in undiminish
where irrigation must
of water on some wort
canals from leading w
vntage. In a large part
has been applied to wa
ously a strict applicatio
use of water when appl
litigation over water rig

Among the field cro
Rice is grown entirely i
and where the heavy cla
tivation. California pro
mainder coming from t
Texas and Louisiana, a

Alfalfa is grown thro
many as six cuttings are
dry beans, and cotton. S
and Salinas Valleys. Be
and long-fiber cotton is

Considerable attenti
Joaquin Valley, but for t
to the Los Angeles basin
main fruit crop of the C
About 90 per cent of the
marketed largely as raisi
but the large part of this
Napa Coastal Valleys. T
plums and prunes produ

AGRICULTURE IN TH (middle page)

a natural reservoir. V
now some diversion
Ranges. Maximum
rado River water rea

The Great Valley o
of California and ext
miles wide and 400 m
It is bordered on the e
the west by the lower C
type; their gentle slope

Fig. 170. Picking oranges in Orai
representing thousands of years

east. The Coast Ranges, in
above the sea, whereas the Sie
the sea. Moisture-bearing wi
on the west slopes of these ra
gentle west slope of the high S
of erosion have resulted in a
several hundreds of feet in dept
have cut deep canyons and forr

The Coast Ranges are brok
Francisco Bay, and thus the d
Sacramento River drains the tro

AGRICULTURE IN THE WEST

people of the state, here are grown most of the crops, and here lies a large part of the wealth of the state.

Fruit is important in the west end of this valley, but throughout the main crops are alfalfa, beans, potatoes, and wheat. Dairying is important, and sheep are grazed on nearby National Forests in summer and fattened on irrigation farms in winter. The Idaho potato famed as being a "baking potato" comes largely from the Pocatello area of the Snake Valley.

The Apple Valleys of the Columbia Basin. A series of small rivers on the eastern rainshadow slope of the Cascade Mountains drain to the Columbia River. They flow through a land where the rainfall is too low for agriculture, but they have considerable volume because they rise in the high Cascades to the west. Not a great amount of level land is available for irrigation except narrow strips along the rivers, but these valleys constitute a world-famous apple-growing area—the Yakima, Wenatchee, Chelan, Okanogan, Hood River, and Deschutes Valleys.

Irrigation works are arranged to impound waters and distribute them largely by gravity flow (Fig. 169). The frost-free season is nearly 200 days, and rarely do freezes occur to injure orchards. However, positions on slopes are selected for orchards in order to take advantage of air drainage. The high percentage of sunshine is said to give the fruit an attractive color.

In 1951 the state of Washington produced 35,500,000 bushels of apples, and thus accounted for more than one-fourth of the total crop of the United States.

The Nevada Projects. In Nevada, a Great Basin state, aridity prevails throughout. A large portion of the state has an average annual precipitation of less than 10 inches, yet there are several small streams which rise in the Sierras and other mountains generally draining into the state to lose themselves in the salt and alkali flats of the interior. Small irrigation projects are developed along these streams to total perhaps less than 1 per cent of the area of the state. Otherwise Nevada is desert or sparse grazing land.

The important streams that furnish irrigation waters are the Truckee, Walker, Carson, and Humboldt. Some of these become important because they lie on the main route of travel across the state, and thus have a market at home for alfalfa, dairy products, wheat, and vegetables, which are the main crops.

The Los Angeles Area. To the east and southeast of the city of Los Angeles for a distance of 40 or 50 miles is an irrigated area of more than 300,000 acres, which has become one of the best known in the West. The Santa Ana and San Gabriel Rivers rise respectively in the San Bernar-

dino and Sa
southwestwa
brought grea
area at the fo
spread their s
Pacific Ocean
mountains, an
son is approxi
thus the rate o

Fig. 169. Method of ir
A wooden flume is us
pli

Irrigation began
to Riverside and Sa
grapes were grown
oranges and lemons
was suitable for then
comes from this area
crop of the United S
Japanese persimmon
production of Englis
bulk of this crop com
somewhat recent ne
market under the trad
Nearly three-fourth
some flowing but most

from the sout
of the Great
separation fr
the arid clim

The medi
the Great Va
of the rainfal
frosts are exp
inches annua
inally a grea
cause of the
west slope.

Because o
land. The gra
part, but the

There are
occupance" (
Beginning wi
to occupy mo
the northern
great growth
ing, for which
lation becam
and cattle ra
farming. Rai
more rocky s
California wa
areas of the c

In the earl
began to take
growing. It w
tain streams a
had with rela
farming to a
tables. Today
vegetable gro
crops produce
duction of mi
Valley, but it
tensively culti
of the Great V

world crop. Peach production is centered about Merced and Fresno and has since 1930 spread into the lower Sacramento Valley, where the cling-stone variety seems to be at its best. Canning of peaches is increasing over drying. Fresno has long been the peach-drying center. Apricots, cherries, figs, and olives are important fruit crops in the central and southern San Joaquin Valley. Pears and apples require the cooler temperatures and are grown in the Bay area and the Sacramento Valley.

The Central Valley of California produces large quantities of vegetables. Many are used locally, but large quantities of potatoes, celery, artichokes, asparagus, beans, peas, and tomatoes are produced in the Delta District about San Francisco Bay, where canning is important, and thus they reach the wider markets to the east.

DRY-LAND FARMING

Dry-land farming, as defined by one of the great authorities, is "the profitable production of useful crops, without irrigation, on lands that receive annually a rainfall of 20 inches or less." Dry-land farming is really farming under drier conditions than exist in humid sections, and it is probably best not to introduce the question of amount of rainfall. Even where the rainfall is 30 inches or more, some farmers increase their yield by careful tillage, and it seems possible that the soil response to careful tillage here is similar to that in semiarid areas. It is impossible to state the area of the West that is dry farmed, for no census data have been collected on this type of farming.

Problems of the Dry-Land Farmer. In humid lands the farmer endeavors to maintain soil fertility by keeping the soil in good physical condition, by maintaining the required amount of essential chemical elements in the soil, and by providing a suitable amount of humus. Only in a minor way does he think of water conservation, and, although the adaptation of varieties of crops to soil moisture is essential for the most profitable farming, the fact that little attention has been given to this adjustment shows that it is not essential to success. In the arid lands the problems confronting the farmer are far greater, for besides the maintenance of soil fertility he has the problem of water conservation, the most critical of all, and also the selection of crops that will grow best with the limited amount of water available. Successful dry-land farming calls for careful, painstaking, intelligent husbandry.

Experiments at the various agricultural experiment stations in the dry-land farming area have demonstrated that a rainfall of 10 inches, if all is saved, will furnish enough water to give yields of wheat and other crops, far above the average of the country.[2] Fortunately for the farmer, nature has provided a natural storage reservoir in the soils of the semiarid land. These soils contain a little clay, as a rule, are porous, granular and, therefore, permeable and deep. Soil and subsoil are practically alike. The water table (if there is one) is so far from the surface that the rain water rarely percolates far enough to reach it. The water that falls as rain forms a sheet of gravitational water in the upper interstices of soil and subsoil and gradually works its way down, becoming capillary water. By becoming capillary water, its downward journey is checked, and if the soil is properly worked a large amount of this capillary water remains within reach of the roots of the plant. This is soon used up if the soil is heavily cropped; frequently a sufficient amount of water may be stored to give fairly good yields of "drought-resisting" plants.

The problem of the farmer is so to work his land that all or nearly all the water that falls will soak into the ground and be retained there for the production of crops only. Formerly the practice was to plow deeply, and keep the upper surface well pulverized, forming a dry mulch to prevent evaporation. With the experiences of disastrous "wind-blows" and soil erosion of the 1930's many farmers are turning to contour plowing and terracing, strip cropping, and stubble listing, and avoid the dry mulch surface where soil blowing might begin. The new methods are advocated widely, but many farmers still cling to the older methods. Fallowing is always necessary where the rainfall is much below 20 inches. In many sections crops are grown only every other year, or the fallowing may extend over 2 years. It has been found that 20 inches or more of rain may easily be stored in the upper horizons of soil and thus be reached by the roots of the plants. Weeds should not be permitted to grow, for they absorb as much moisture as crop plants.

The Problem of Plant Selection. Plant selection is another problem. As a result of many trials and failures in the breeding of new varieties, and by the importation of plants from the semiarid regions of Europe, Asia, and Africa, this problem is being solved. Barley, rye, and some varieties of wheat have long been recognized as adapted to dry, porous soils. Corn, although the cool nights check its growth, does fairly well, particularly in the southern portions of the West. Many of the grain sorghums are widely used, as Kafir corn, durra, and milo. Alfalfa is raised for its seed.

[2] At a Utah experiment station, experiments have shown that it takes 45 tons of water to produce 1 bushel of wheat. A rainfall of 10 inches a year is equivalent to 1130 tons of water an acre. If all this could be directed into the wheat plants without loss in run-off, evaporation, or seepage, it would supply the water required for 25 bushels of wheat. If half the rain water were lost, 10 inches of rain would grow 12½ bushels, and 20 inches would grow 25 bushels.

Many of the crops now grown in the arid lands are centuries old. Civilization developed in irrigated river valleys and the semiarid deserts of Asia and Africa, and many of the crops we raise today were cultivated by man even in the primitive stages of his development. From the Old World semiarid areas we have introduced, mostly since 1910, plants admirably suited to the arid land of the West. Many agricultural practices in these Old World lands, although primitive and traditional to a high degree, are nevertheless successful and must be considered as dry-land farming methods. The Indians of northern Mexico and southwestern United States, long before the coming of the Spaniards, raised corn and must perforce have used some of the methods now employed by the white man. Certain phases of dry-land farming have long been practiced on the chalk downs of England and France, in many parts of the Mediterranean area, and in southern Russia.

Important Dry-Land Farming Areas.   Dry-land farming in English-America dates from about 1850, when some Mormons, through sheer desperation, because of failure to get water for irrigation, cleared a small area of sagebrush land and secured fair returns from the wheat sown. There are no definite records of these early experiments or of the methods used, but it is believed that many Mormons tilled the dry lands on the Wasatch Piedmont by methods they had worked out and found successful as early as 1854 or 1855. Moisture-conserving methods were used in the Sacramento Valley as early as 1861; in the Bear River Valley, Utah, by 1863; on Sand Ridge between Salt Lake City and Ogden, about 1865; and in eastern Washington in the Palouse region and in the Cache Valley, Utah, by 1870.

Considerable dry-land farming is still practiced in these areas today. Generally the nearness to irrigated lands with their crop varieties and cattle feed is an important factor in successful dry-land farming. Undoubtedly wheat is the leading crop, with the sorghums and other small grains also important.

The Palouse region and the southern part of the Great Bend of the Columbia Plateau has for more than three-quarters of a century been the most noted dry-land farming region of the country, and a major world wheat-producing land. It averages from 5 to 22 inches of precipitation annually, and the year-to-year variability is not quite as great as in most low-rainfall lands. The soils are basically lava and wind-blown loessal materials, and the original vegetation was sagebrush and bunchgrass. The land is sufficiently level for the use of large machinery to be applied to the culture of wheat. At first the machinery was drawn by horses and mules, but now the tractor-drawn gang plows, disks, and combines are used nearly everywhere. The major part of the wheat is the winter variety which is well suited to this land of maximum precipitation in the winter months, with a considerable portion of it in the form of snow. In 1951 the state of Washington ranked fourth as a wheat producer among the states. Its crop was over 75,000,000 bushels, a large part of which was grown by dry-land farming methods on the Columbia Plateau.

Because of the one-crop practice of growing wheat the soils of the Columbia Plateau have become worn, some erosion by wind and water has taken place, ground water has been partially depleted, and the wheat acreage has had a tendency to decline. Thus one of the aims of the Columbia River Basin Reclamation Project is to irrigate a large portion of the Great Bend area with water drawn from the Franklin D. Roosevelt Lake above Grand Coulee Dam. The dam and Grand Coulee Reservoir are complete, canals to lead the waters over the plateau, and some irrigation has begun.

In the early 1880's many farmers were attracted to the Great Plains of Kansas and Nebraska by cheap land and immense yields of wheat. They used humid-land seed and methods in a region that had long been considered as a part of the "Great American Desert." The idea was advanced that rain—in increasing amount—followed the plow. All that was needed, therefore, to make the Great American Desert a productive farming region was to turn over the sod. The great profits made for the first few years attracted farmers from all over the northern states and some from the South. These ventures happened to have been made during a period of rainfall heavier than the normal, and when the annual precipitation went back to the normal there were failures on every hand. Farms, villages, and towns were abandoned, although a few farmers remained. Some of the farmers went into stock raising; others modified their methods of tillage and were able to live on, yet with greatly reduced standards of living. They were the first of the dry-land farmers of the Great Plains.

Again following World War I there was a demand for wheat to feed Europe's millions where wheat lands had been devastated by armies and production was curtailed by the disturbed economic conditions. The United States Government supported high prices, and with the aid of tractors and improved machinery dry-land wheat farming encroached again upon the more arid grass and range lands. In the 1920's, years of above normal rainfall further encouraged wheat growing, but in 1930, 1934, and 1936 the rainfall was below normal. Many thousands of wheat farmers went bankrupt because of having no crops. Dust storms prevailed on the Great Plains from Texas to the Dakotas and were the most severe in the history of the Great Plains. The most vigorously blown area was the winter wheat and grazing land of southwestern Kansas and portions of the adjoining states, referred to as the "Dust Bowl," though this term is also generally applied to all of the Great Plains that was wind blown.

It has been estimated that about 16,000,000 acres were damaged by having the topsoil blown away, thus leaving the land unsuited for dry farming, or even for grazing thereafter. Since the 1930's the rainfall has

Fig. 171. A shelter belt in the dry-land farming section of northern Texas. The planting of trees was government supported, and much advocated following the dust storms of the 1930's, in all the eastern Great Plains region from Canada to Mexico. It is claimed trees serve as protection against hot winds in summer, and cold winds in winter; they preserve moisture; they aid in preventing soil being blown away; and they furnish wood.

been mostly normal or above, and natural grasses are slowly returning. Man has aided by regrassing large areas, and has used new farming techniques and soil-erosion preventive measures of the federal and state agencies (Fig. 171). The Dust Bowl is gradually being reclaimed, but the loss has been great.

The Great Plains is naturally a grazing and dry-land farming region, but throughout its history it has been a major land-use problem area.

Undoubtedly it is, in the main, capable of great production but somehow man must use such methods that when drought years come losses may be curtailed and the soil saved from being blown away.

HUMID-LAND FARMING

The area devoted to humid-land farming in the West, as earlier stated, is very limited, being confined almost entirely to the Puget Sound Trough in Washington and Oregon.

The Physical Environment in the Trough.   The term "trough" no doubt implies in the minds of some readers an area of level lowland between parallel mountain areas. But the surface is anything but level. The central portion of the trough is chiefly rolling uplands interrupted by hills and broad valleys; and the borders of the trough are thoroughly dissected foothills or lower slopes of the mountain areas. The area is remarkably well drained, marshes or ponds being found only on the valley flats.

The trough is structural in origin. The northern portion is glaciated. There are deposits, therefore, from the glacier and from the fluvio-glacial waters. Stream action, both before and since the glacial period, has produced minor erosion features both in the trough and on the bordering slopes; and the water from the mountain areas has deposited some rock debris. Four types of soils, based on origin, are recognized: residual soil on the uplands, hills, and mountains; soils from deposits by glacial ice and by fluvio-glacial waters, occurring in morainic deposits, kames, outwash plains, and terraces or dissected valley trains; soils of (recent) flood plains; and a few small areas of lacustrine or marsh soils.

The moist climate over the whole area favors the growth of forests; and, since the portions first lumbered were along the larger streams, it is in the bottoms and on the terraces that the older settlements and the denser populaion are found. The great difficulty of clearing the land is no doubt one cause of the slow economic development. The dense stand of timber and the large size of the trees make burning about the only method that may be used to rid the land of stumps and unmerchantable logs after the lumberman has taken his toll, and this makes the cost of clearing much greater than in other forested sections of the country. Burning also destroys much of the humus of the soil.

The Youth of the Region.   One of the earliest settlements in the Pacific Northwest, a trading post, was made on the Columbia by the Hudson Bay Fur Company in 1828. In many respects the area under consideration is young. Its agricultural youthfulness is shown in the small amount of land in farms, the small amount of farm land improved, the general lack of attention given crop rotation and its relation to soil fertility, the neglect of most of the orchards, and the general lack of specialization and adaptation of crops to climate and soil. It has been discovered, however, that a few products and types of agriculture give better returns than others.

Land Utilization.   The cool, wet winters (about 50 per cent of the rain comes between November and February) and mild, moderately dry summers, with the ground most of the year well supplied with water, offer admirable conditions for the growing of cool-weather crops. Oats,

Fig. 172. Fertile farm land in the Willamette Valley of western Oregon.

flax, and hemp are grown on the alluvial bottom lands. The yield of oats is high. Hops growing was once important but has greatly declined, owing chiefly to the uncertainty of securing paying prices for the crop. Potatoes seldom fail to produce abundantly. Nearly all garden vegetables are grown in all sections. Cabbage, kale, and mustard do exceptionally well, but are grown largely for the home market. The leading cabbage-seed-producing area in the United States, however, is centered in King and Skagit counties, Washington. Canned peas from Puget Sound now also reach the markets east of the Mississippi River. The abundant fodder, the long grazing season, the mild winters, and the pure water of the streams favor livestock raising. Dairying is one of the leading types of agriculture in the region. A large plant for the manufacture of condensed milk is located in Washington, and numerous small creameries are scattered over all these counties, supplying cream and butter to the larger cities of the trough. The breeding of improved livestock is receiving considerable attention. Most of the dairying and raising of livestock is found on the upland areas.

Fig. 173. The Puyallup Valley in western Washington. *Courtesy, Tacoma Chamber of Commerce.* Although lofty Mount Rainier in the background (14,408 feet) is snow covered the year round, the climate in the valley and Puget Sound region is mild both summer and winter. Daffodils shown in the foreground bloom in March and April. This valley is near Tacoma and is noted for bulbs and berries.

Because of the great expense of clearing more land throughout most of the Puget Sound—Williamette Valleys—there is a tendency towards a more intensive use of land (Fig. 172). Butter and cheese is of increasing importance. The poultry industry is particularly profitable in the Puget Sound area where cooperative egg marketing follows the model of Petaluma, California.

Among the deciduous fruits, prunes receive most attention. The center of production is in Oregon where orchards are numerous and much attention is given to their care. Apples, pears, cherries, and quinces are beginning to be grown on a commercial basis. Since 1940 the filbert has become an important nut-tree crop in the trough. Most of this comes from Oregon, but considered together with the Washington crop it constitutes about 99 per cent of the total for the United States, and frequently has an annual value of over $3,000,000.

Since World War I the growing of daffodil bulbs has become important in the Puyallup Valley, where the climate has a striking resemblance to that of Holland. Dutchmen migrating to Washington brought the business with them and the prominent growers today are Dutch. The bulbs reach the eastern market for winter use, and they represent about 50 per cent of the daffodil bulb crop of the United States (Fig. 173).

There is an apparent tendency to select rolling land and slopes for orchard crops. Every year shows an increasing attempt to adjust the products of the area to improved market conditions. The production of bush fruits is profitable, the climate being particularly adapted to the growing of raspberries, blackberries, loganberries, and strawberries. An evergreen blackberry grows wild and furnishes a valuable crop in the newer sections. The present production of any of these crops is no indication of the potentialities of the region. Although this humid area has been settled for about a century, the rate of agricultural development has been slow and is much slower than in the irrigated areas. Economic development here is the result of individual initiative with only a minimum of cooperation of state or national paternalism.

The Markets for the Region.　The trough offers fairly easy grades for railroad building, although numerous cuts and fills are necessary, and since it contains all the large urban centers of the Pacific Northwest the farmers everywhere have good railroad transportation facilities to the trough cities, and from these cities to the other parts of the United States. The bulk of the surplus agricultural products finds a market in the cities of the trough. Condensed milk and dried prunes have long been the chief products that reached distant markets, but since about 1935, as has been stated, the filbert has been added to the list, and there are increases of distant marketing for berries, and a few other crops. A beginning has been made at cooperative production and marketing in the trough, and this promises to increase.

CHAPTER 17

The Livestock Industry in the West

SOME GENERAL CONSIDERATIONS

Because of the large area of mountains, and aridity and remoteness, the West has been and continues to be a grazing land in preference to one for field crops. In the area between the Rocky Mountains and the Sierra Nevada-Cascade Mountains only about 3.5 per cent of the land is in field crops, and this cannot be appreciably extended even by irrigation. Obviously for a long time before the coming of white man, the bison, deer, and antelope ranged the Great Plains as well as the other semiarid grasslands throughout the West, including southern California and the Great Valley. Animals were hunted by the Indians, but probably never to the extent that their numbers were cut down materially, nor is it likely that these animals overgrazed the lands, for they were free to shift about as grasses became short in given places. There was an adjustment of animal life to vegetation in such a way that no great "dust bowls" developed, and there was no forced overgrazing of the lands for profits, since Indians had not domesticated the grazing animals.

Horses, cattle, hogs, and sheep as we know these animals of common and widespread use in North America did not exist here before the discovery of America. It is true that fossil remains of the horse and camel are found in the rocks of North America, but these animals had been extinct for many centuries before Columbus.

Animals of the European varieties were brought by the Spaniards; at first the horse was used as a means of travel, and the others perhaps as an assurance of a supply of meat in a new and unfamiliar land. Many animals escaped or were turned loose as they became no longer useful on the exploring expeditions. Hogs became wild and thrived in their natural habitats of oak, hickory, and beech forests of the Appalachians, the Ozarks, and elsewhere. Horses and cattle found the grasslands a natural habitat, where they thrived and reproduced in numbers so greatly as to compete for the range with the bison and other native grazing animals. It must be noted that Spaniards first brought the European grazing animals shortly after 1500. It was not till after 1800 that Americans began to move into the great area west of the Mississippi River. Three centuries of time had been sufficient for great droves of cattle and horses to have been produced and spread, particularly in the grasslands of Mexico, southwestern United States, and on the Great Plains. Then too, in these areas, all of which were claimed and thinly occupied by the Spaniards, the grazing industry began. Though many Spaniards came because of the lure of precious metals, the Catholic missions were established and grazing industries grew around them because of their stationary nature. Spaniards who failed to find metals turned to ranching. This was true for many places in what is now known as Texas, New Mexico, Arizona, and California.

As early as 1769 the Spanish began their missions in southern California, and the cattle barons soon followed, selecting suitable coastal valleys and even some parts of the Great Valley. Even in the 1700's, long before the California Gold Rush the Spanish had extended ranching into southern Arizona and into the upper Rio Grande Valley, where large lands were held as grants from the Spanish crown. In fact, the Spanish had a marked influence on the entire Southwest. Their cattle, sheep, and horses formed the basis for the Southwest's grazing industry. Their horses gave mobility to the Indians, and in their missions and scattered settlements, such as those at Santa Fe, Los Angeles, and San Diego, they left the stamp of their architecture, which is still a model.

The chief products of the Spanish cattle industry were hides and tallow. San Diego became a port where Yankee ships traded and left their New England wares, and this trade reached as far inland as Santa Fe. The Spanish cattle and horses from Texas found an early market at New Orleans and Baton Rouge during the first two decades of the nineteenth century.

THE AMERICAN CATTLE INDUSTRY IN THE WEST

The American cattle industry was greatly stimulated after the Mexican War and the California Gold Rush. In California and the far Southwest the large Spanish ranchos were gradually taken over by Americans who found an increasing meat market in that state, for the population had passed 100,000 by 1851. Soon thereafter the cattle-ranching business was extended throughout the lower Great Valley and into parts of the northern Great Valley.

It was in the High Plains region, however, that the cattle industry took on large proportions in the decades following the Gold Rush. England was growing industrially; the population of the entire United States was also growing rapidly; and the demand for meat products rose. As roads and railways were extended westward from the Mississippi the bison was much hunted and was rapidly exterminated. It was estimated that in 1889 there were not more than 1000 head on the Great Plains, and the cattle era had been ushered in during the 1870's and 1880's. The decrease in numbers of bison made more range for cattle; and in addition to the great cattle drives from Texas to the railroad ends such as at Abilene and Dodge City, many drives were made for the purpose of stocking the ranges northward in the Great Plains.

The cattle business became one of the "open range" throughout the West, but mainly on the Great Plains. No one owned the land. Watering

Fig. 174. Beef cattle—the white-faced Hereford on the High Plains in the Panhandle region of Texas. *Courtesy, U. S. Department of Agriculture.* This photograph shows a field that has been turned back to grama grass after cultivation. It covers the soil completely, thus preventing "blow-outs" common in the region.

places were commanded, and cattle were grazed far and wide from these as centers. There began to be great competition among cattlemen for rights at watering places, also a competition with settlers who were homesteading and initiating wheat growing. Barbed wire was invented in 1873 and was soon to be had on the market. With it the cattlemen and wheat farmers alike could fence their holdings readily with the scant supply of posts provided by such growths of trees as could be found along streams and other places in this semiarid land. Gradually cattle ranching was crowded onto the more arid lands, which ceased to be "open range." Cattlemen have come to the practice of owning or leasing lands and to having them fenced.

Since about 1910, although cattle have increased in numbers in the West as a whole, they have not increased in many parts of the Great Plains. World wars and the economic conditions resulting therefrom stimulated prices for wheat, and farmers with improved agricultural machinery encroached farther into the more arid High Plains for the profits to be made in extensive wheat culture. The low rainfall and a drop in wheat prices later brought disaster to wheat farmers and to the lands of the region in the 1930's. Wind erosion on millions of acres created the United States "Dust Bowl." Although ranching is gradually returning to much of the area, it will require a long time and good management to bring back the growth of grasses suitable for profitable grazing. For some areas it may never be accomplished.

Regardless of the encroachment of wheat culture, the dominant industry on the Great Plains is ranching. The size of a ranch may be large—2000 to 100,000 acres—for the carrying capacity of the range in some places is so low that from 15 to 40 acres or more are required for one cow. Throughout this entire region the variability of the precipitation from year to year remains an important factor. Even after the experiences of the past, the range is still overstocked in many places. However, the most hopeful aspect is that there is an increasing number of conservative cattlemen who will not stock their ranches with more cattle than can be carried in dry years (Fig. 174).

Originally the natural springs and streams of water were relied on for watering cattle. With improvements in well drilling to secure deep-rock water or larger wells of surface water, the windmill and gasoline pump have been put to use to supply tanks for watering. This makes it possible to graze much land where water was not available before.

In numerous areas throughout the Rocky Mountains and Intermontane basins and Plateaus of the West cattle ranching continues to be an important business. The large ranch dominates here also because it is best suited to the semiarid and mountainous lands which have a low carrying capacity (Fig. 175). It is estimated that fully 50 per cent of the grazing land of the West is still public land, not privately owned, and cattlemen have long practiced driving their stock to the public lands for short grazing periods (Fig. 176). This is particularly true in mountainous areas where it is too cold and the snows are too deep for cattle in winter, but there is good grazing in the summer. This transhumance—herding animals to mountain pastures in summer, and back to home ranches in winter—is a widespread practice throughout the West (Figs. 177 and 178).

The evils of the practice lie in the fact that it was made a "free-for-all" in a contest for the pastures, and resulted in overgrazing to such an extent that laws have been passed regarding it. The Taylor Grazing Act of 1933

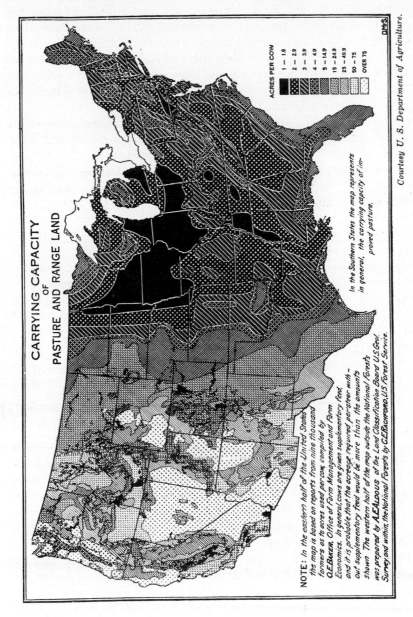

Fig. 175. Carrying capacity of pasture and range land in the United States.

Courtesy U. S. Department of Agriculture.

closed much public land for further homesteading, providing for grazing fees, and limited and regulated the amount of grazing on the Public Domain. At first this law incensed many cattlemen because it interfered with what had for a long time been their privilege, and it probably resulted in financial hardships for some. However, since the law went into effect the carrying capacity of the public lands has increased to the benefit of cattlemen in general.

Perhaps the most important change in the cattle industry of the entire West since about 1935 is the decline in shipping "feeder" cattle eastward to the Corn Belt for fattening, though considerable of this is still done, and the increase in the fattening of cattle at home. Advances in irrigation for crops has brought about a combination of ranching and cropping where cattle are fattened on the ranch. In Texas, southern California, the

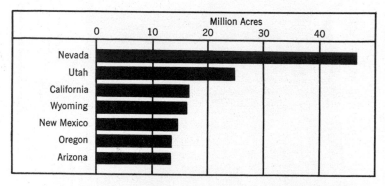

Fig. 176. Vacant public land in the United States, by leading states in 1950.

Yuma district in Arizona, and other locations in the South, the feed is cottonseed cake and alfalfa. In the middle and northern parts of the West, the fattening of cattle is associated with the sugar beet crop, where pulp is used as a feed along with alfalfa and other hay crops. Also, since the great dust storms of the 1930's, there has been an improvement in dry-farming methods, and other soil conservation measures, so that agriculture is encroaching westward again on the Great Plains where the cattle business is associated with mixed farming on ranches that are not large, and the breeds of cattle are much improved over those used in former times.

Although the cattle industry still is important in the West, it should be noted that, for the area included, it is not so impressive. The West contains more than one-third the surface of continental United States, but it had only about one-sixth of all cattle in 1950. However, in comparison with the total population of the West, the record is better. When these

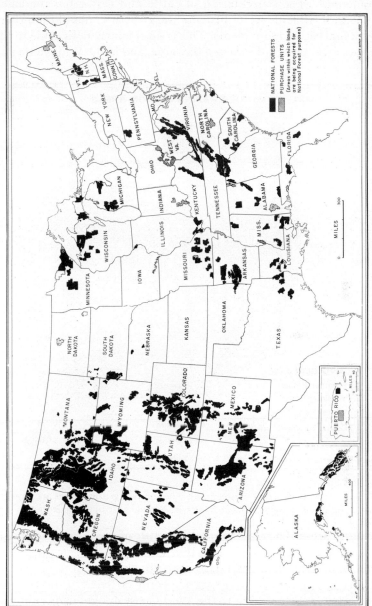

Fig. 177. National Forests of the United States. *Courtesy, U. S. Forest Service.* The dominance in the West is due to the large area of unappropriated public lands that was turned over to the Forest Service merely by an Act of Congress. Most of the forest reserves in the eastern half of the country have been secured only by purchase.

numbers are reduced to the basis of cattle per 100 people (1950) the West had 70 and the country as a whole 55.

Slaughtering. The slaughtering of cattle and calves has increased since 1940 in the Pacific states because the growth in population there provides a market for more meats. This is particularly noticeable in the Los Angeles area, the San Francisco Bay area, and in the Willamette and

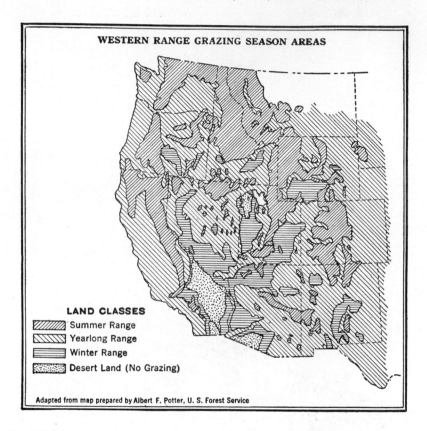

WESTERN RANGE GRAZING SEASON AREAS

LAND CLASSES
Summer Range
Yearlong Range
Winter Range
Desert Land (No Grazing)

Adapted from map prepared by Albert F. Potter, U. S. Forest Service

Fig. 178. Western range grazing season areas. The summer grazing lands are largely in the mountains and higher plateaus: the winter ranges are in the lower lands.

Puget Sound areas. The chief market for cattle of the West continues to be the supplying of "feeder" cattle to the agricultural interior where they are fattened on grain and good pastures before being sent to market for beef. However, increasing numbers are being fattened in the West on irrigated areas, and shipment to the West Coast slaughtering centers is increasing. Some cattle from the Great Plains now reach the West Coast market.

Denver has long been the leading livestock and packing center in the West because of its central location in the Great Plains. However, the entire West, with the exception of California and Washington, is still the large surplus-cattle-producing section of the United States (Fig. 179).

Dairying. Dairying in the West, as in other sections, is associated with large population centers. In the Los Angeles area there is much dairying

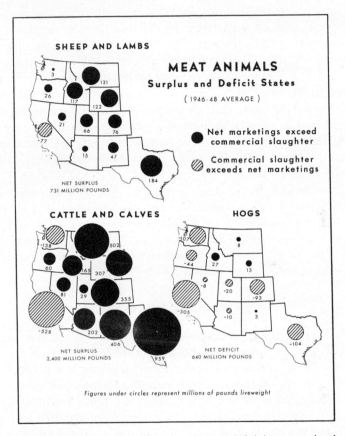

Fig. 179. Western states showing surplus and deficit in meat animals.

in irrigated lands where alfalfa and other hay crops along with some root crops are produced for feed. Alfalfa is a highly nutritious food for animals, and several crops may be produced each year if irrigated lands are managed well in this subtropical climate. In the San Francisco Bay area dairying is carried on extensively in the marsh lands, particularly to the south of the bay and in the lower San Joaquin Valley. Here also much alfalfa and other feed crops are grown, and considerable use is made of the native grasses where the soil is too compact and too high in alkaline materials to be used for truck crops. In the Puget Sound region and the Willamette Valley great dairying interests are found, which supply fluid milk for the urban centers. The moist, mild climate is particularly suited to dairying. The Denver area is supplied with dairy products largely from the irrigated lands to the northeast of the city, where alfalfa, sugar beets, and other root crops are important dairy-cattle feeds.

At many places throughout the West both dairying and beef-cattle raising are associated with irrigation. The cattle industry has brought success to many irrigated tracts. The feeds are easily grown. The labor of the farm or ranch is used to a better advantage than would otherwise be possible. The "off-season" is reduced to the minimum, for here is continuity of production. The returns are certain. Cattle also furnish the best of fertilizers for the land, which is called upon to produce its maximum. The number of dairy cattle in the beef-producing areas, away from population centers, however, is small. The families on many beef-cattle ranches purchase condensed milk for family use and buy out-of-state butter or butter substitutes.

It should be kept in mind, however, that slaughtering and dairying are small in the West, indeed, when compared with that in the North Central States, or even with some other sections of the country. With approximately one-third the area and one-seventh the population of the United States in 1950 the West produced for sale only one-twelfth of the milk of the country and one-fifteenth of the butter.

HORSES IN THE WEST

The horse played a great part in the development of the West, as it did in other sections of the country. Because of the long distances to be covered in the West, and the use of the horse for riding and cattle driving, and earlier, in drawing covered wagons and stage coaches, the use of this animal was spectacular. As has been noted, the horse was introduced by the Spanish in the early sixteenth century, and it multiplied and spread widely in the West, till, when the American westward movement reached the area in the 1800's, the numbers were great, particularly on the Great Plains, in California, and the Southwest. The adoption of the horse made many Indians more mobile than they would have been otherwise, and affected the course of history particularly throughout the entire West.

The horse became wild in the West. The early ranchers, to be sure, caught and tamed sufficient numbers for their use, but great droves of horses ranged the grasslands, taking the feed from the more profitable cattle, so that the cattlemen considered the horse a nuisance and in many instances destroyed large droves. In the wild state the horse in the West managed to maintain life even until the present time in the isolated, mountainous lands of Colorado and elsewhere. During the early decades of the twentieth century, the great interior grain belt was using many horses for draft purposes and prices were high. The tractor and automobile had not yet come. Some ranchers introduced draft breeds, thus building up on the ranges a type of western horse that could be shipped to the interior agricultural areas for sale to farmers. The farmers bought western horses (broncos) at low cost and tamed them to work, sometimes with much difficulty, for these animals were still semi-wild, to say the least. Frequently they made good, inexpensive work animals.

By the 1920's the tractor, the automobile, and hard-surface roads had come. The result was that fewer draft animals were needed, and the number of horses in the United States as a whole decreased from a peak of about 29,000,000 at the close of World War I to 5,500,000 in 1950. The decline was greatest in the agricultural interior, but it also affected all of the states of the West. Not one of the Western States has as many horses today as it had at some peak period earlier. On the basis of population the United States had 5.25 horses and mules per 100 of population, whereas the West had less than 5 per 100 in 1950.

In the cattle business, the horse is still a necessity in herding, roundups, and driving of cattle, but the total number of horses required is small. Horses are important still, in sections where roads are poor or nonexistent. The Navajo Indians have become great users of the horse, because their roads are poor, distances are great; they use them in herding their flocks of cattle, sheep, and goats, and also perhaps because they are too poor and too unschooled in the necessary mechanics to own and operate automobiles. A Navajo's importance is still determined by the number of horses he possesses. However, the horse requires grasses of the range that might be a support for other animals, and the Navajo Reservation has for a long time been an overgrazed land and is becoming less and less capable of supporting the people. The United States Government has made some attempts to encourage a decrease in the number of horses on the reservation.

"Dude ranches" are now numerous in the West, and they make use of a considerable number of horses. Some people in some areas will continue to use the horse, but the day for large numbers of them has passed.

OTHER ANIMALS

Sheep. The Spanish sheep introduced into California and the upper Rio Grande were a hardy variety. Since their introduction they have not

been as important on the whole as cattle, but in some sections they have
been herded throughout the history of the region. The Navajo Indians
took to sheep herding in the Spanish colonial period, and there was a
period of sheep herding in the San Joaquin Valley before fruit growing
began.

Due to the fact that sheep can browse on leaves, weeds, and woody
plants and can nibble the grasses closer to the ground than cattle, sheep
can make a living on much of the land of the West where cattle cannot
get along. Regardless of this fact cattle became the dominant range ani-

Fig. 180. Sheep on summer pasture in the Gallatin National Forest in Montana. *Courtesy,
U. S. Forest Service.*

mal in the West. They are larger than sheep and capable of traveling
greater distances for grasses. They can run to escape forest and grassland
fires; they can defend themselves against predatory animals where sheep
become an easy prey. Nevertheless, the large area of arid and mountainous lands in the West makes it a natural region for sheep, and there has
been much improvement in breeds since World War I. If western Texas
is included with the 11 Western States, these states contained about two-
thirds of the sheep and lambs in the country in 1950. The leading states
were Texas with 6,628,000; Wyoming with 2,170,000; and Montana with
2,139,000. Sheep in the past were raised in the Western States mainly for

their wool, but now the sale of lambs brings in more than 50 per cent of the revenue.

Some Adjustments.   Sheep raising in the West, as in all regions of scanty rainfall, is a pasture-chasing occupation. In the densely populated, humid portion of the United States the animals are kept in enclosed pasture lands in summer, and in barns or sheds, where they are fed, during the winter. These sheep produce the highest quality of mutton and wool. In the West, sheep raising is on the extensive plan; the flocks are large; the losses great; and the risks so many that the industry is often spoken of

Fig. 181. A flock of sheep on mountain pasture in Wyoming. *Photo by Miller.*

as a "game." The large size of the herds and the scanty pasturage force the industry to be, for the most part, migratory. In Texas and New Mexico enclosed pastures are common, but in many parts of the West it is only in the winter that the sheep are "at home" on their own lowland pasture lands. Here they graze on nature-cured hay or on green bunchgrass that comes up after the fall rains. In inclement weather and when food on the pasture lands is scarce or the surface is covered with snow, they are fed in corrals or housed in sheds. In the spring after shearing, the sheep are driven, or transported, to leased pasture lands or open ranges on higher, cooler, and moister plateaus and mountains (Fig. 180). In the Rockies, the Cascades, and Sierra Nevada, their summer grazing lands may be above the tree line and even bordering the summer snow line. A large part of the revenue derived from the National Forests is from cattle (previously discussed) and sheep leases. Since about 1940, grazing permits for 3,200,000 sheep and goats, and 1,200,000 cattle, have returned to the National Government about $2,800,000 annually.

Summer grazing requires the services of herders, who keep the flocks in fresh pastures, care for the sick, and protect their charges from predatory animals. One man, with a saddle horse and a dog, can care for 2000 to 5000 sheep. With an "outfit" consisting of a covered wagon, bedding, cooking utensils, and other accoutrements, the herder follows the flock for months at a time. The herder is visited frequently by a tender from the home ranch who brings supplies (Fig. 181).

It is expected, if the year is good, that the wool clip will meet all expenses and perhaps return some profits. During such years the money derived from the sale of lambs is pure profit, but often, even with this, there is a deficit. The dry-land farmer has now so encroached upon the open ranges in the northern and cooler parts of the semiarid West that summer pasture lands are about limited to the National Forest reservations and the mountains. The free-range lands, as earlier stated, are so much in demand and so much depleted that most of the operators are forced to purchase tracts or lease from others. With leasing fees to pay or land to purchase, and increased wages since World War II, sheep raising is not so profitable as formerly. Careful management is a prime requisite for success, and more and more expensive equipment is being found necessary. In 1950 there were only 12,700,000 sheep and lambs in the 11 western states, in comparison to 33,000,000 in 1900. Many large operators have gone out of business, but since 1940 the number of small flocks in irrigated areas has increased.

Goats.   Since goats are not used much as meat animals their numbers in the West have never been large. In 1849 the Angora goat was introduced into the United States. It was discovered that they did well in semiarid areas and that their long fleeces of fine mohair made a valuable product that could be used in upholstering furniture and automobiles. However, not till 1920 did the Southwest turn to goat raising on a commercial basis. By far the largest number of goats in the country are to be found on the Edwards Plateau in southwest Texas, where 90 per cent of the mohair of the United States is produced. New Mexico, Arizona, and Oregon produce a small amount each. This animal is exceedingly well adapted to the Edwards Plateau because, like the sheep, it browses on leaves of plants and coarse vegetation, as well as on grass. This part of Texas is chaparral country of cedar bushes, scrub oak, yucca, cactus, and prickly pear. The goat can manage to browse here even better than the sheep, and, too, the goat will put up a defense against dogs and predatory animals where sheep are helpless. Frequently goat ranching is combined with cattle and sheep ranching.

In 1950 Texas produced 12,643,000 pounds of mohair; New Mexico, the second leading state, produced only 155,000 pounds.

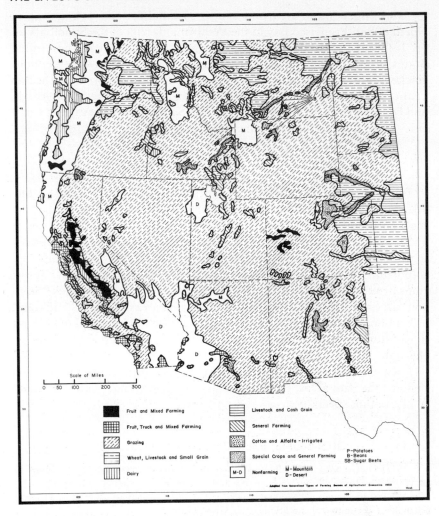

Fig. 182. Types of farming in the West. *Adapted from Types of Farming, Bureau of Agricultural Economics, 1950.*

Swine. Although the raising of hogs fits well into the economy of an agricultural region that produces cattle, alfalfa, and sugar beets, the western states have few hogs in comparison with other sections of the country. There were in 1952 only 1,978,000 in the 11 Western States, to 46,000,-000 for the North, and 14,200,000 for the South. California had nearly one third of the total for the western states.

The Poultry Industry. In all of the West there is no important poultry industry except in the coastal valleys of California, the Willamette Valley, and Puget Sound area, and some associated with the urban centers. North of San Francisco Bay in the Petaluma district of the Sonoma Valley is found the most important egg-producing center in the United States, if not in the world. A specialty is made of the white Leghorn chickens, and eggs are produced in quantity to supply more than the San Francisco area market. Great attention is given to marketing methods, and considerable quantities are exported. Some reach the Atlantic Coast cities in fresh condition and bring high prices.

A REVIEW OF AGRICULTURE IN THE WEST

Types of Farming in the West. The following map exercises on Fig. 182, an adaptation of a part of the Bureau of Agricultural Economics map entitled "Generalized Types of Farming in the United States in 1949," will serve as a review of the chapters on agriculture and livestock in the West. Study Fig. 182. In what portions of the West are grain crops important? What is the amount of rainfall in these areas? In what sections are the fruit crops? In what temperature regions are they? See if you can establish any direct relation of grazing areas to rainfall and relief.

What explanations can you give for the West having so large an acreage of non-agricultural land? Be specific. Discuss each area shown on the map.

Locate topographically and climatically (temperature and rainfall regions) the fruit areas; the dairy areas; cotton farming; poultry specialty areas; potato specialty areas.

QUESTIONS, EXERCISES, AND PROBLEMS

1. What contributions have plant explorers and plant breeders made to agriculture in the West? This task will require much research into literature dealing with crops.

2. What is the Campbell Method of dry-land farming? What adjustments did Campbell make to the semiarid conditions of the Great Plains?

3. What effect has increasing density of population in the Great Plains had on land utilization there?

4. What has been the relationship of the West and Middle West in the beef- and mutton-producing industries?

5. Make a study of Hoover (Boulder) Dam on the Colorado River. Note carefully the location of the area affected. To what extent is this project devoted to water-power development? To what extent to irrigation for cropping and livestock industries? Give arguments for and against the expending of public money for such a development.

6. Make a study of the cattle industry of the West. The bibliography in this book supplies some references. Seek others. Write a paper on this industry as carried on in the West, emphasizing the adjustments man has had to make to climate, vegetation, density of population, diseases and pests, markets, and competition with other sections.

7. Make a statistical comparison of agriculture in Nevada and Ohio. What explanation can be made for the vast differences?

8. Seek library references of Reclamation Service, Census Reports, or other sources to make a study of one or more of the following: The Imperial Valley Irrigation project, the Central Valley project of California, the Grand Coulee Dam and Columbia Basin Reclamation project. Emphasize source and amount of water, power development, crops, seasons, markets, etc.

CHAPTER 18

Manufacturing, Mining, and Other Industries in the West

MANUFACTURING

Comparison with Other Sections of the United States.　The West is new. Its greatest growth in population has been made since 1870, in which year the territories of these 11 states had only about 1,000,000 people. In 1950 the population was 19,435,000, and, although it increased over nineteen times in 80 years, there is still much room for expansion. As was stated previously, not half the potential irrigable land has been settled on, and certainly large areas of dry land are yet to be developed, and many hundreds of square miles of virgin forest that will some day be removed to give place to agriculture remain on the lowlands and slopes of the humid Pacific Northwest. History demonstrates that, as long as a people have large open spaces and new lands that may be developed, they will not be inclined to turn to the confinement of factory work with its exacting hours. To this extent the West has been handicapped in the development of manufacturing.

In manufacturing, the West is behind the country as a whole, yet there has been surprising development in spite of the youth of the region, and the extent of its undeveloped lands. The per capita net value of manufactures in the West in 1950 was 71 per cent of the average of the country at large—$565 per capita for the United States, and $405 for the West. These states produced 9 per cent of the net value of manufactures for the country in 1950, while the population was almost 13 per cent of that for the country.

Some Reasons for Growth of Manufacturing.　One should think of the West as a section in which manufacturing is getting a good start and assuming greater importance every year, particularly in a limited number of types of industries: those producing articles largely for local consumption, and those involved in the preparation of raw materials for the distant markets where secondary manufacturing takes place. There are

424

several reasons for the relative importance that manufacturing assumes in the economic life of the western states.

The Advantage of Distance from the East.   First of all, it is less expensive for the West to produce many of the manufactured goods that it consumes than to import them, because of the long distance from the industrial centers of eastern United States and the consequently high freight rates. The long distance from eastern factories is an advantage to the western manufacturer, enabling him to pay higher wages than the eastern manufacturer and yet sell cheaper in western markets. The bulkier the article, the greater the advantage the western manufacturer has.

However, it must be noted that the West is demonstrating that in a few lines of manufacturing, the long distances from eastern markets and the great open spaces are not sufficient handicaps to prevent the develop-

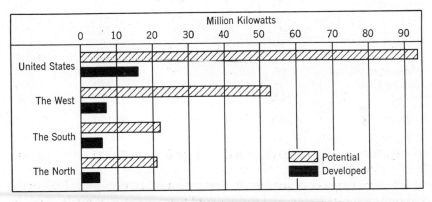

Fig. 183. Potential and developed water power of the United States and major sections. Federal Power Commission estimates, *Statistical Abstract*, 1949, p. 520.

ment of manufacturing beyond the needs of the market of the western states alone. This is true of the airplane industry of Los Angeles and Seattle. It is also true of the production of aluminum and magnesium at or near the great hydroelectric power sites, and of the research, experimentation, and production of nuclear materials in the great arid and sparsely populated sections.

Water-Power Resources of the West.   A second reason for the growth of manufactures is the great supply of water power in the two sections where manufacturing is most important—the Pacific Slope and the Rocky Mountains. There is more power in the streams of the Pacific Coast states than in any other section of equal area in the United States (Figs. 24 and 183).

The potential water power of the West is estimated to be 52,803,000 kilowatts, or 52 per cent of the total for the United States. In 1947 the

installed capacity of waterwheels in the West was 6,413,000 kilowatts, or
40 per cent of that of the country. The installed capacity represents only
12 per cent of the potential of the West (Table XIII).

TABLE XIII

DEVELOPED AND UNDEVELOPED WATER POWER OF THE WEST IN 1947
(thousands of kilowatts)

| | Developed | | | | Total |
	Utilities	Industrial	Total	Undeveloped	Potential
Washington	1,642	27	1,670	14,182	15,852
California	1,986	2	1,988	7,925	9,913
Oregon	713	17	730	6,528	7,258
Montana	358	1	359	3,711	4,070
Idaho	282	2	284	7,746	8,030
Arizona	541	—	541	2,731	3,272
Utah	92	—	92	1,081	1,173
Colorado	87	1	88	1,115	1,203
Wyoming	50	—	50	928	978
New Mexico	25	—	25	183	208
Nevada	586	1	587	259	846
Total	6,362	51	6,413	46,390	52,803
Total for United States	14,971	985	15,956	77,130	93,086

The water-power plant, like the irrigation enterprise, must look to the
mountains for its water, and the water of many streams is made to do the
double duty of furnishing power and irrigating land; and in addition may
be used, on its downward journey to the sea, if it ever reaches the sea, for
domestic purposes.

The great fall of the mountain streams is the chief reason for the large
amount of potential water power. In Washington, the richest state in the
Union in water power, with more than a 15,000,000-kilowatt power potential, an additional factor is the heavy rainfall. Some of the mountain
areas have the heaviest rainfall of the country. The same conditions prevail in most of western Oregon, northern California, and the northern
part of the Sierra Nevada slope. In many parts of the Cascades and the
Sierra Nevada, copious supplies of water are furnished by the melting
glaciers on the high mountains.

All the states of the West richly endowed in water power, are, except
California, in northern latitudes. Steep slopes, vast forests, numerous
lakes, and a fairly low evaporation rate are all favorable conditions. Flathead Lake, Lake Pend Oreille, Lake Coeur d'Alene, and Lake Chelan

are the larger lakes of value in equalizing stream flow. The Flathead River, the Snake, the Columbia, and many other streams have large water-power potentials.

The Great Basin, except about its borders where streams come down from the mountains, has little available water power. The rivers that rise in the Southern Rocky Mountain area, though not possessing so much power as those of the Northern Rockies, have enough to supply the increasing needs of the people in this part of the West for many decades.

Since about 1935 there has been a great increase in the development of water power in the West, particularly in the form of the large multiple-purpose project, largely by the United States Bureau of Reclamation. To a considerable extent these projects have been stimulated by the effort of the country in military production, but at the same time they have filled an urgent need for waters for irrigation, flood control, metropolitan uses, etc. Projects that are completed, nearing completion, and those in the initial stages will provide abundant power for the West, beyond the present needs of industry. In 1948 the West ranked high among the states in the percentage of farms receiving electric service, most of which was hydroelectric. Idaho and the coastal states now advertise abundance of electric power at reasonable rates to attract industry. Space does not permit of treatment of the numerous power projects of the West, but a brief descripion will be given of the three most important multiple-purpose projects, which have been brought to the attention of people everywhere. They are (1) The Columbia River Basin projects, (2) The Colorado River projects, and (3) the Central Valley project of California.

The Columbia River Basin Projects. The ultimate aim of the planners is to develop all the resources of the Columbia River that lie within United States territory (Fig. 184). The river rises in the snow-capped Rockies of British Columbia, and enters the United States in northeastern Washington. Together with its tributaries, the Snake, Spokane, and numerous others, the Columbia River basin within the United States includes much of the states of Washington, Oregon, and Idaho, as well as portions of Montana, Wyoming, Utah, and Nevada. The area is about 220,000 square miles, or one-seventh of the total area of the United States. The discharge of the Columbia River into the Pacific Ocean is estimated to be 160,000,000 acre-feet annually, thus being, next to the Mississippi, the largest in the country. On the way from the Canadian border to where it empties into the Pacific Ocean, a distance of 750 miles, the Columbia falls 1300 feet in elevation, a fact which, combined with the heavy precipitation in the mountain sources, gives the Columbia River, by far, a greater water-power potential than any river in the United States.

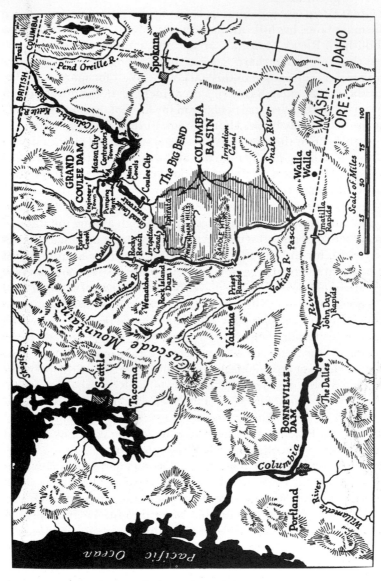

Fig. 184. The Columbia River basin showing main features of this multiple-purpose project—Grand Coulee Dam and Reservoir, Bonneville Dam, irrigation canals in the Great Bend, and the apple valleys, *Courtesy, Fortune*, July 1937, p. 84.

Numerous power sites are associated with the irrigation works on the Snake, the Spokane, and the many smaller tributaries, but the largest are at Grand Coulee and Bonneville. In 1950 there were over 200 hydroelectric power plants in the basin, with a generating capacity of 2,100,-000 kilowatts. This was only about one-fifth of the potential water power of the basin, yet it represented 14.5 per cent of the water power of the nation. At present more than one-half of all hydroelectric power in the basin is developed at Grand Coulee and Bonneville, the most recent large developments in the region.

Grand Coulee Dam is located on the Columbia River in the state of Washington, about 100 miles south of the British Columbia boundary. It is the largest concrete dam in the world, and creates, in Franklin D. Roosevelt Lake, a reservoir of 5,000,000 acre-feet storage capacity. It is the master unit in the development of the entire basin, being strategically located at the beginning of the Great Bend where water is lifted into the Grand Coulee reservoir for irrigation on the Columbia Plateau, mentioned in Chapter 16.

Bonneville Dam is located on the Columbia about 50 miles above Portland, Oregon, where the river breaks through the Cascades. Its ultimate power capacity is 430,000 kilowatts. Although the Grand Coulee and Bonneville projects are the largest units in the basin and most important for power, they are only a part of the eventual total development where the purpose is supplying water for irrigation, flood control, and regulation of the waters, as well as power. During World War II the Northwest became the great center for electrometallurgical plants, especially aluminum, as well as the atom-smashing plants of the Hanford Engineering Works. All power systems, public and private, were interconnected to form the Northwestern Power Pool; the load factor was thus raised, and this in turn raised the total power available—an excellent illustration of regional planning and cooperation.

Power lines now deliver hydroelectric power throughout the Northwest, including all the cities of Puget Sound, and Portland, Spokane, and numerous others.

Colorado River Projects. The development of projects on the Colorado River represents one of the most ambitious attempts of man to put the waters of a nation to use (Fig. 185). This river has its sources in the Rocky Mountains of Wyoming, Colorado, Utah, Arizona, and a part of New Mexico. Here rainfall is plentiful, but the river flows southwestward and south through parts of Utah, Arizona, and southern California, as well as a part of Mexico, which is the driest region on the North American continent. The stream has been called America's most dangerous, because of its flash floods, its low water periods, its canyons, its heavy load

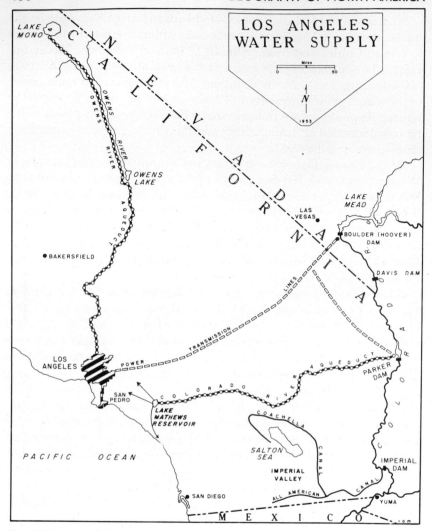

Fig. 185. Map of Colorado River multiple-purpose project. Note the location of Lake
Mead, the dams, power lines, canals, and aqueducts, which carry water to Los Angeles,
the Imperial Valley and southern California.

of silt, and its tendency to shift its channels in the Delta area at the
entrance into the Gulf of California.

Today the Colorado River is fairly well under control. The key project
is the Hoover Dam on the Arizona-Nevada border, which impounds
Lake Mead. This dam is 726.4 feet high, and is said to be the highest in
the world. The lake has a capacity of 30,500,000 acre-feet, and is the

world's largest reservoir. The power plant has a capacity of 1,317,500 kilowatts. About 75 miles downstream is the Davis Dam, built largely as a reservoir to control the flow of the river and also for power generation. Still farther downstream, about 50 miles, is the Parker Dam, which develops power, regulates stream flow, and furnishes water for irrigation; but, perhaps most important of all, Havasu Lake above the dam furnishes water for the Colorado River aqueduct which in turn supplies the Metropolitan Water District of Southern California, mentioned in Chapter 16. Farther below in the Delta area above Yuma, Arizona, are the Imperial and Laguna Dams, which have multiple purposes, but which mainly impound water for irrigation projects—the Imperial Valley, Coachella Valley, Yuma, and Gila—and control the silt load of the river.

The main power development on the Colorado River is at Hoover Dam. From here a transmission line of high voltage carries power to Los Angeles, a distance of 300 miles. It is said to be the longest transmission line and the highest voltage (285,000 volts) used in the United States. Power from the Colorado River now reaches all of southern California and parts of Arziona and Nevada. The Colorado River development is truly a multiple-purpose project.

The Central Valley Project.   The Central Valley of California is an area of about 25,000 square miles drained from the north by the Sacramento River and from the south by the San Joaquin, which join in a marshy delta near Stockton and then outlet into San Francisco Bay and the Pacific Ocean (Fig. 186). The valley is flanked on the east by the Sierras and on the west by the coast ranges. As has been stated previously, irrigation is practiced widely in the valley, with the major portion in the San Joaquin basin.

There are numerous water-power developments within the valley, but in the past there was no regional plan for coordinating the development of the water resources throughout. In 1930 a "State Water Plan" was suggested, which eventually became the "Central Valley Project" under the United States Bureau of Reclamation.

The stated purpose of the project is to provide storage and distribution of water for irrigation in the Sacramento and San Joaquin Valleys, to repel salt water from the Delta lands around San Francisco Bay, to produce power, to supply fresh water for municipal and industrial purposes, and to provide improvements for navigation and flood control. Construction began in 1937.

The entire project is unique in that the area is 400 miles long, and the Sacramento Valley has about two-thirds of the water supply whereas the San Joaquin Valley has about two-thirds of the land suitable for use. The

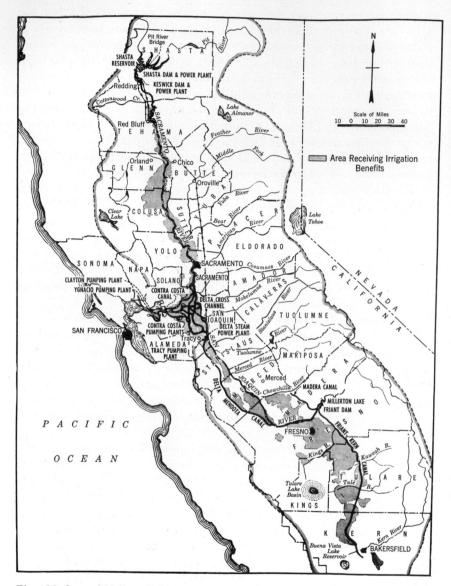

Fig. 186. Central Valley, California. One of the large multiple projects in the West, showing dams, canals, and irrigation areas in relation to Sacramento and San Joaquin Rivers. *From Reclamation Project data, 1948.*

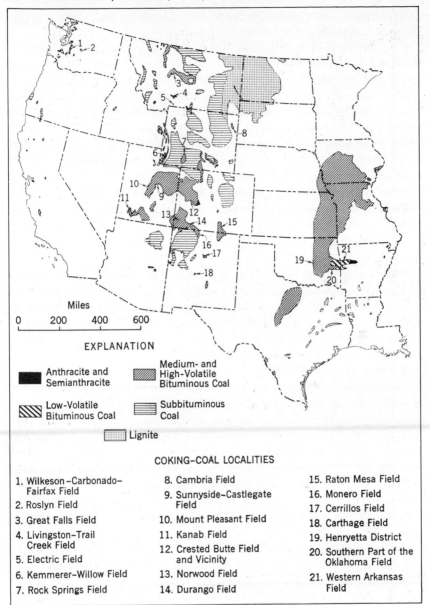

Miles

0   200   400   600

EXPLANATION

Anthracite and
Semianthracite

Medium- and
High-Volatile
Bituminous Coal

Low-Volatile
Bituminous Coal

Subbituminous
Coal

Lignite

COKING-COAL LOCALITIES

1. Wilkeson–Carbonado–
   Fairfax Field
2. Roslyn Field
3. Great Falls Field
4. Livingston–Trail
   Creek Field
5. Electric Field
6. Kemmerer–Willow Field
7. Rock Springs Field

8. Cambria Field
9. Sunnyside–Castlegate
   Field
10. Mount Pleasant Field
11. Kanab Field
12. Crested Butte Field
    and Vicinity
13. Norwood Field
14. Durango Field

15. Raton Mesa Field
16. Monero Field
17. Cerrillos Field
18. Carthage Field
19. Henryetta District
20. Southern Part of the
    Oklahoma Field
21. Western Arkansas
    Field

Fig. 187. Coking coal localities in the West. Note the concentration in the Northern
Great Plains and in the Rocky Mountains; there is little in the Pacific States.

project thus involves a plan for taking water from the Sacramento to supplement the small supply of the San Joaquin.

The key unit in the Central Valley project is the Shasta Dam and Reservoir in the northern part of the valley. Here the winter flood waters are stored, and delivered through a system of canals to the San Joaquin Valley. Keswick Dam is located 9 miles down stream from Shasta Dam to provide regulation and storage of waters released from the Shasta power plant and spillways. At the south the Friant Dam forms a reservoir for the waters of the upper San Joaquin and supplies the Madera and Friant-Kern canals for irrigating the upper San Joaquin Valley. In the bay area the waters of the Sacramento are led farther southward by the Delta Cross Channel, from which they are lifted 197 feet by electrically driven pumps into the Delta Mendota Canal. The latter canal flows southward, on the west side of the San Joaquin River for a distance of about 100 miles, thus supplying the San Joaquin Valley with Sacramento River water.

Power is developed mainly at the Shasta Dam, which has a capacity of 375,000 kilowatts. The project will irrigate over 2,000,000 acres of land, besides accomplishing the other purposes stated above. The Central Valley project is indeed a multiple-purpose project. Its financial support will come mainly from the sale of water for irrigation, the sale of electric power, and government funds.

Coal Reserves. The total reserve of coal in the West is estimated to be nearly one-half that of the entire United States. It is true that much of it lies at great depth, and a large amount is lignite or subbituminous, pariculary in Wyoming, Montana, and Colorado (Figs. 21 and 187). Yet, expressed in terms of bituminous coal equivalent, it is further estimated that Wyoming leads all states with a reserve of 439.4 billion tons. The second-ranking state is North Dakota in the Great Plains with 293.4 billion tons, followed by Colorado and Montana with 284.9 and 200.5 billion tons, respectively. Washington and Utah have considerable reserves. Oregon's reserve is small, and California is practically without coal.

The coal of Colorado, Utah, and Wyoming supplements greatly the meager water-power resources in the middle Rocky Mountain area. Montana is the richest of the Rocky Mountain States in power resources, for, in addition to its large reserve of coal, it has a great water-power potential.[1]

In the future, when the coal reserves of other sections of the United States become depleted, these great reserves of the West will undoubtedly be worked and become important.

[1] United States Department of Interior, Bureau of Mines, "Mineral Position of the United States in 1947."

Petroleum and Oil-Shale Resources.   The great stock of oil in the Bakersfield and Los Angeles regions is called upon to supply fuel and power for the growing population, industries, and shipping of the West Coast, and to railroads extending into the interior. These reserves are fortunately located too, because of the lack of coal in California. Since about 1925 California has exceeded Oklahoma, and ranked second to Texas, as the country's greatest oil producer (Figs. 25 and 27).

There have been significant developments of oil fields in Montana, Wyoming, Colorado, and New Mexico. In 1950, Montana produced 60,467,000 barrels of oil, placing it seventh in rank among the states in petroleum.

It is impossible to state what the national reserve of petroleum is, much less that of the oil shales of the West. Of the latter the West has the largest reserves in the country. One estimate gives 75,000,000,000 barrels as the possible reserve in the oil shales of the Rocky Mountains, a large part of which lies in northwestern Colorado and northeastern Utah. Up to the

Fig. 188. Forest reserves of the United States and the West compared.

present this reserve has not been levied on, because of the high cost of extraction. In the future, when the petroleum supply becomes more nearly exhausted, these oil-shale reserves may be tapped.

The West has power, therefore, far in excess of its needs for a long time to come. It has been shown that water-power development has now exceeded the local demand, and the West invites industries to come to the supply. The coal production in the West in 1950 was 21,400,000 tons, out of a total of 560,388,000 tons for the United States. Much of the Western coal is used on the railroads.

Raw Products for Manufacturing.   The Western States have great quantities of a few raw products that must undergo some manufacture in preparation for the market, which is largely in the Eastern States. Foremost among these primary manufactures are those turning out forest products, canned fruit and vegetables, fish, flour, and sugar, and the precious, semiprecious and more useful metals.

The Commercial Forests of the West.   The distribution of the forests of the West has been noted. In the Pacific Northwest occur the heaviest forest stands in North America, and the three coastal states now contain about 62 per cent of the remaining saw timber of the United States (Fig. 188, also Figs. 28–32). In 1950, the 11 Western States furnished almost one-half of the lumber cut of the country (Fig. 189). The lumber cut was 35,404,000,000 board feet for the United States, and 16,278,000,000 board feet for the West. Oregon was far in the lead as the nation's greatest lumbering state; and Washington, Oregon, and California produced nearly 90 per cent of the lumber cut of the West.

Because of the economic youth of the West and the great distance from the large timber markets, the slaughter of the forests has been much less than in the eastern part of the country, thus accouning for the high percentage of remaining saw timber in the West.

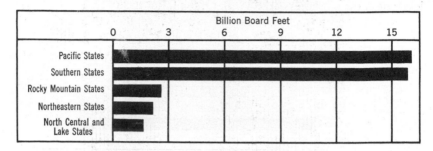

Fig. 189. Lumber production by regions in the United States in 1950.

The Lumber Industry in the Northwest.   Although the first commercial sawmill in Oregon was constructed in 1844, and the first on Puget Sound in 1845, the lumber industry in the Pacific Northwest was of little importance until after the discovery of gold in California. Fifty or more years before this date, timber had been cut at various places along the coast for the construction of ships engaged in the Pacific trade, but it was not until the "Gold Rush" brought thousands of people to the semiarid regions in the lower Sacramento and to San Francisco that there was a demand for the timber of the coast lands of Washington, Oregon, and northern California. A market was also developed in the Hawaiian Islands. Many New Englanders, some from the lumber regions of Maine, came in ships around the Horn with complete logging and sawmill equipment and began the slaughter of the forests, the lumber being sent by vessel to the San Francisco Bay ports.

For thirty or forty years after this, the development of settlements in the Northwest was slow and the demands for lumber were limited. Besides, home builders of the Prairie States and the Great Plains looked to the sawmills of the Great Lakes and upper Mississippi for lumber; but, with the decline of lumbering in the Middle West and the building of

Fig. 190. Scene in the redwood forest of western California. This is a unique tree in that it has a very restricted range. It is rarely found above 3500 feet altitude, and generally grows in valleys and sheltered places on coastal plains within 25 miles of the ocean where there is a constant moisture-laden air. It produces a great amount of lumber per tree. *Photo by Miller.*

railroads eastward from Portland and the Puget Sound cities, a greatly expanded market was opened up, and the Pacific Northwest began its rise as a lumber region, the most rapid rise being since the early 1880's. By 1885 there were 228 mills in operation in these two states. By 1910 this region had surpassed the Great Lakes states and the Northeastern States in amount of output, and by 1929 it had surpassed the Southern States.

The largest and best-equipped mills in the world today are to be found in the Pacific Coast lumber towns. This is due primarily to past experiences in the lumber industry and abundant capital from the East. When the industry started, Oregon was most active because it was first settled, but accessibility to the forests bordering the long shore line of Puget Sound soon gave Washington the lead. By 1939 the forests close to the Sound were being depleted, and timber farther from its shore were difficult to get because of the large sizes of trees, and the rough terrain. In that year Oregon took the lead again over Washington as the leading lumber producer, perhaps because of the use of the Columbia River for both logging and navigation.

The principal timber species of the Pacific Coast are the Douglas fir, cedar, spruce, red fir, yellow fir, and Oregon pine. About 25 per cent of the lumber cut in the United States in board feet is Douglas fir. It is claimed that the existing stand of this species is about 27 per cent of the standing timber of the United States, including both hardwood and softwood, and that there are 400,000 million board feet of Douglas fir west of the Cascades. It is the dominant forest tree in the Pacific Northwest, making up in some tracts which have been examined carefully 92 per cent of the stand. It is difficult for one to visualize the tremendous amount of timber on an acre unless one has traveled through these forests.

Another much-advertised species of the Northwest is the redwood, confined to a small area in northwestern California, mainly north of San Francisco Bay, and in southwestern Oregon (Fig. 190).

The large size of the timber, the great density of the stand, the lack of snow and ice, the relatively small volume of water in the mountain streams, and the roughness of the topography of much of the forested areas all offered new problems for the lumberman to solve. New methods of logging, transportation, and manufacture, vastly different from those in the East, had to be devised.

The sawmills of the Rockies and the Colorado Plateau are not so large or efficient as those of the Pacific Northwest. Logging is easier, but the timber is small and scattered, and the waste in lumbering and manufacturing relatively greater than with the "big" trees.

In northern Arizona considerable lumber comes from the National Forests. The chief species are Douglas fir, western yellow pine, and spruce. The most important logging operations are concentrated around Flagstaff and Williams. In Montana the lumbering centers are Missoula, Polson, and Kalispell. In Oregon the chief mill town and shipping center for lumber is Portland; in Washington, Longview on the Columbia and Seattle and Tacoma on the Sound are great centers (Fig. 191). At Tacoma are mills that not only produce lumber but also plywood, pulp, paper, and various other wood products. Seattle is one of the leading

Fig. 191. Tacoma harbor showing lumber stacked for shipment. *Courtesy, Tacoma Chamber of Commerce.*

lumber-producing and export points of the world. In northern California, McCloud and Susanville are important centers. At Susanville, wood products used in packing fruits and vegetables are turned out in great quantity (Fig. 192).

The West has always had a large home market for its timber products, in building material, props used in mines, and for firewood. But the market has developed broadly. It now covers the entire United States, except perhaps parts of Maine and some of the Southern States, also Australia, China, Japan, Hawaii, and the west coast of South America, Mexico, and Central America. The railroads extending eastward from the Pacific

Northwest have aided the industry greatly by granting low freight rates. Even today a large bulk of the east-bound freight consists of lumber and wood products. Lath and shingles from Portland, northern California, and Puget Sound sawmills are large exports. The West Coast States produce more than two-thirds of the laths turned out in the United States

Fig. 192. Mill facilities of fruit growers' supply at Susanville, California. This supply organization owns forests and operates mills for making boxes and crates used in marketing fruits and vegetables. *Courtesy, Eastman Studios, Susanville, California, and Fruit Growers' Association.*

and nearly all the wooden shingles, which come mostly from red cedar. There is an increasing development of the woodpulp industry in the Puget Sound region, where numerous mills are located. A considerable amount is exported, but there is a growth in the paper-making industry. There is an unlimited supply of clear water and power for the paper-making business, but the limited market in the West handicaps this industry. Tacoma is the leading center for pulp and paper manufacture. Seattle has a furniture-manufacturing industry of considerable importance.

The conservationist is well aware of the watershed function of western forests, but too frequently lumbering is practiced in such a way as to result in erosion, rapid run-off, floods, and sedimentation that do great and irreparable harm to western lands in general. Perhaps in no section of the country is the necessity to control lumbering on watersheds so great as in the West. The numerous National Parks and Forests of the West are located usually in areas that are sources of drainage and hence serve as controls of run-off.

CANNING, PRESERVING, AND DRYING INDUSTRY

The long distance from the great markets of the country and the "off-season" demand for fruits and vegetables are the chief reasons for the prominence of the western states in the canning and drying of fruits and vegetables. The net value of this industry in 1950 was over $225,000,000. Only five Western States are active in this industry—Washington, Oregon, California, Idaho, and Utah—yet they produced about 33 per cent of the canned fruits and vegetables of the country in 1950. The canneries of California are not only the most numerous but they are the most active of any state. They produced nearly three times as much, by value, as the canneries of New Jersey, the second state in rank. Apricots, peaches, and pears are the chief fruits canned in California, and berries in Washington and Oregon.

Since about 1930 the Pacific Coast States have been preparing juices for eastern markets. An increasing amount of the product of both oranges and lemons is going into juices frozen for the market. This industry serves as an economical market outlet for large crops (Fig. 193).

One fruit little known in the East until its introduction as a fruit juice is the loganberry, a hybrid of a raspberry and a blackberry, discovered by Judge James H. Logan in his garden in Oakland in 1882. The berry was given to the University of California for distribution to fruit growers of California. The center of production of loganberry juice is in Oregon and Washington. The boysenberry and other hybrids are canned. Refrigerated berries for distant markets are also shipped. Formerly the berries were packed in barrels and frozen for use in eastern markets. Now, along with other fruits and vegetables, they are wrapped for retail trade in small packages, then frozen for shipment. The general use of "quick-freeze" equipment has widened this market. There is also much canning of loganberries and other berries in Washington and Oregon. Since about 1930, tomato canning has increased, particularly in California. This state, together with Maryland, produced about one-half of the canned tomatoes of the country in 1950.

The products of western canneries are to be found in most groceries of the country.

Rainless summers and late autumns with bright sunlight and low humidity make California a natural region for the drying of fruits. Nearly all the dried raisins, peaches, and apricots consumed in the United States come from California, and this state produces practically all the dried prunes, and more than a third of the dried apples. The major part of the

Fig. 193. Plant of the Exchange Orange Products Company, Ontario, California. This wholly owned subsidiary of the California Fruit Growers' Exchange manufactures various products from oranges. A similar plant is located at Corona, California, for handling lemon products—juice, lemon oil, citric acid, pectin, and dried citrous peel for stock feed.
Courtesy, California Fruit Growers' Exchange.

canning and preserving of fruits and vegetables in the West is carried on in the smaller towns, and near the berry patches, orchards, and gardens. Nearly everywhere in irrigated areas of the West, where fruits and vegetables are grown, the small canning and preserving plant is a feature of the landscape. Most of the plants are cooperatively owned and operated. The products are manufactured under the best of sanitary conditions, and the raw materials used are carefully selected. The output is of the highest grade, for only a high-grade product can compete in eastern markets with eastern-manufactured goods.

Raisin drying is done in the vineyards, and only in a loose way may it be considered a type of manufacture. Fresno is the great center of this industry. Raisin-grape growing in California was first attempted in the southern part of the state where grape culture had been practiced since the early Spanish days. Raisins are still produced in large quantities in the San Bernardino Valley and nearby irrigated areas, but after the spread of the raisin-grape culture to the San Joaquin Valley it was discovered that the Fresno district—including parts of the five counties—offered better geographic conditions than southern California, and in time Fresno assumed leadership. It was not until the early 1880's that the raisin industry began to attract much attention, even in California. In 1879, a little more than 1,000,000 pounds of raisins were produced, but by 1886 the output reached 14,000,000 pounds and California raisins began to compete with the Spanish product in eastern markets of the United States. By 1892, the California crop equaled that of Spain, and the raisin imports of the United States from Spain were reduced fully 20 per cent. Since about 1940 the United States crop has been over 300,-000,000 pounds. The California Associated Raisin Company, which handles about 85 per cent of the California crop, is a cooperative organization that attempts to adjust production to market demands. Besides carrying on an active advertising campaign in the United States to educate the American public to a greater appreciation of the food value of raisins, with the hope of increasing the per capita consumption, it is developing foreign markets. California raisins now go to Canada, many countries of South America, and the Orient.

In still another field in canning the West is active. In 1950 the output of canned and preserved fish from the plants of the Pacific Coast states was valued at more than $175,000,000 (product shipped). The three Pacific Coast States produced 70 per cent of the canned and preserved fish, crab, shrimp, oysters, and clams, of the United States in 1950. A wide variety of fish is processed in the canneries of California, but salmon is the most important fish used in the canneries of Washington and Oregon. The canneries of necessity are located near the fisheries.

OTHER INDUSTRIES

In many of the irrigated regions condensed or evaporated milk is a product, and one of the largest milk-condensing plants of the West is in the Puget Sound Trough.

Much of the wheat of Oregon, California, Washington, and other Western States goes to the flour mills of Seattle, Tacoma, and San Francisco Bay cities. Some of the export flour of these mills finds a market in China and Japan. Portland is the leading flour-mill city, since it has easy access to the wheat fields of eastern Washington and Oregon. The Columbia River Valley ôffers lower railroad grades than are found across the Cascades. Spokane is a great wheat-milling center in eastern Washington, and wheat flour from Ogden, Utah, has long been known in the West.

Beet sugar factories are numerous in the northern and central parts of the West. In 1951 Colorado had 17, Utah 6, California 12, Montana 6, and Washington 2. The value of beet sugar in the United States in 1951 was approximately $270,000,000, and that for the 11 Western States represented $210,000,000, or about 75 per cent. California and Colorado were the leading states in beet-sugar production. California also ranks high in cane-sugar production, Hawaii furnishing the raw sugar. Refineries are located in the San Francisco Bay area.

The northwest has become nationally known in furniture manufacturing. The Douglas fir and some hardwoods furnish the lumber, though, strange to say, some importing of walnut, Philippine mahogany, and others hardwoods is done, for veneer and panel manufacturing. Portland and Tacoma are the chief centers, but furniture is also made in Los Angeles, San Francisco, and in a few other places. The market is largely local.

Rapid strides have been made since about 1930 in the manufacture of textiles and clothing. Wool has been important in the Willamette Valley since early days. Now this product reaches Portland from the Rocky Mountains and other interior locations, making this port the largest wool market in the country. Clothing manufacture centered at Portland and Seattle was for a long time, devoted mainly to lumbermen's wear, overalls, jackets, sweaters, and women's dresses. The coming of tourists has caused the industry to expand to sportswear. Although the manufacture of clothing in the Northwest has a national reputation, the major market is at home.

San Francisco and the Bay cities have considerable clothing manufacture, but Los Angeles now is recognized as one of the leading centers of the country, particularly for style in clothing. Cotton of southern California and the Southwest supply some of the raw product, but much is imported. The influence of Hollywood and motion-picture stars has resulted in much attention to style, so that Los Angeles is now thought of as a clothing style center along with Paris and New York. Also sportswear and all kinds of outdoor wear are emphasized in the Los Angeles clothing industries, and more attention is given to women's and children's wear than to that of men.

MINING AND METAL MANUFACTURING

Mining has long been one of the leading industries of the West, and the products of the mine are the basis of an active smelting and refining business.

The Iron and Steel Industry.   The iron ore reserves of the West are in Utah, Wyoming, California, and some in Colorado. Those of Utah and Wyoming have been worked for some time, and the amount of the reserve may be considerable, though it is not known. The reserves in the San Bernardino Mountains are small, and in no other localities of the West are iron ores known to exist in any great quantities. For a considerable time Pueblo, Colorado, was the only iron and steel city of the West. It has imported much iron ore, but has drawn some from more local ores in Utah and Wyoming, and uses coal mined near Trinidad, Colorado. Its market has been largely steel for railways and mining machinery. The market for iron and steel, in general, improves in the West as population increases, but World War II brought such an increase in demand that refining and smelting made much progress at Provo and Geneva, Utah, using ore and coal from nearby. Also the great demand for steel in the fast-growing industrial areas of Los Angeles, the Bay cities, and in the Puget Sound, which are far removed from the eastern sources of steel, resulted in a beginning of iron ore refining and steel making at Fontana and Pittsburg in Southern California, using ores from the San Bernardino mountains. Particularly during the war emergency, all western iron and steel industries made much use of scrap iron, and gave attention to beneficiation of iron ores produced locally. The production of vanadium and uranium was stimulated in Nevada, particularly from the Colorado and Utah ores. These metals have an important significance because of their uses—vanadium in the processing of steel and uranium in the development of atomic energy. Taken as a whole, the steel industry in the West is small indeed compared with that of the Pittsburgh, Pennsylvania, area.

Petroleum Refining.   California, as we have seen, is active in the production of petroleum, ranking second among the states. The output of the refineries is approximately 15 per cent of the output of the country. New Jersey refines 8 per cent of the product of the United States, and Texas nearly 27 per cent. These are the three leading states, Texas having gained much since about 1930.

The industry in the West is largely of recent development, following the great advance made in the production of petroleum, and the stimulus of the war years. The entire West and many countries bordering the Pacific are the markets for the output of the refineries. Oil-burning locomotives, stationary steam engines, internal-combustion engines, oil-burning ships, and airplanes consume large quantities of fuel oil. The refineries at Bakersfield, California, produce high-octane gasoline, so important in airplane service. However, most of the petroleum is refined in the coastal refineries of southern California, mainly in the Los Angeles region, not far from the producing wells.

The Importance of Non-Ferrous Minerals.   The metallic, and particularly the non-ferrous metallic, minerals make the Western States one of the greatest mineral regions of the world. Most of the ores are manufactured into metals before shipment for secondary manufacture. The East with its immense markets is the destination of most of the more useful metals, such as copper, lead, and zinc. Here they are used in making hundreds of manufactured articles that command a high price.

The ores of the more important metals occurring in paying quantities for mining in Western States are copper, zinc, lead, gold, silver, platinum, mercury, nickel, bismuth, chrome iron, antimony, and tungsten. Of these copper, zinc, lead, gold, and silver are the most widely distributed, being found in most of the states. Some of these deposits occur as native metal, but most of the ores are chemical compounds that generally occur in a rock matrix called gangue from which they are separated with difficulty. Placer gold is the most common of the minerals that occur as native metals. The first process in the treatment of ores is to separate them from the gangue. Because most of the ores are heavier than the gangue, stamp mills, or concentrators, using crushing machinery, water, and gravity, are common. There is a tendency for the concentration plants to be near the mines to save the expense of hauling worthless rock, yet a large supply of water is a prime requisite. After concentration comes the smelting process, which turns out the metal in a crude form. It often happens that the metal from the smelter is not pure, but may have considerable amounts of other metals combined. For instance, the so-called copper from the smelter may have gold and silver in it. In order to recover the gold and silver, as well as to have a refined copper, a third process—refining—is necessary. Refining is a highly technical business, generally done by the electrolysis method, which breaks down the chemical elements in a substance and requires a great amount of inexpensive electricity if it is to be done economically. For this reason, refineries are frequently located on water-power sites and use hydro-electric power. It thus works out that there are fewer refineries in the West than smelters, and fewer smelters than concentration plants. The important copper refineries in the West are at El Paso, Texas, Great Falls, Montana, Tacoma, Washington, Inspiration, Arizona, and Garfield, Utah. Thus the manufacture of metals, if such it may be called, in the West consists of mining and conditioning the raw product so that it may be transported economically to other manufacturing centers that have abundance of labor, management, and accessible markets.

Mining and Metallurgical Districts. Complete data that would give one the quantitative distribution of smelting and refining in the West are

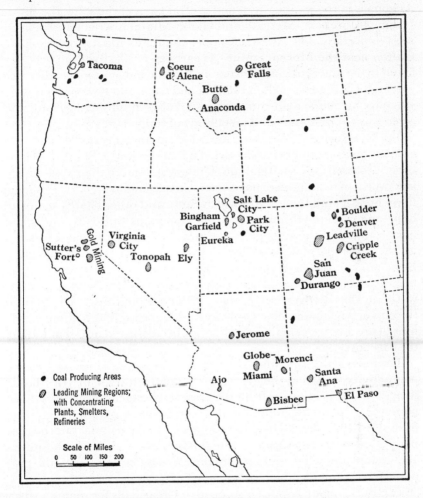

Fig. 194. The leading mineral regions of the West.

lacking, for many companies deem it necessary to keep the extent of their operations a secret (Fig. 194). We know that Arizona, Nevada, Montana, and Utah are the leading western states in smelting and refining. California continues to lead in the production of gold but is not active in its primary manufacture.

The Arizona District. Arizona probably has the largest smelter output of copper among the Western States, the production, measured in pounds of fine copper, being several times that of Montana, its strongest western competitor. New Jersey has been and still is, however, the leading state in the Union in copper manufacture. The leading copper-mining region of Arizona is in the southeastern and central parts of the state, the Bisbee, Jerome, Morencia, Metcalf, and Globe-Miami districts. Bisbee is the most important. The Arizona Copper Company has a large smelter at Clifton near the Morenci mine. As early as 1738, silver nuggets were found in the gravel of some streams in Arizona and, as stated earlier, gold was found in the channels of the Gila and Colorado Rivers. Tombstone was once an active gold-mining camp, but gold mining has long since given way to the mining and metallurgy of copper.

The Butte Region. The Butte area of Montana is considered one of the greatest mining centers in America if not in the world. Since 1940 it has been surpassed only by Bingham, Utah. Much more than a billion dollars' worth of metallic ores have been taken from the ground. The mines fairly honeycomb the hills on which Butte and other nearby towns are built, and scattered through the urban centers are tall smokestacks, steel hoist frames, machine shops, dingy mine buildings, railway yards, and all the accompaniments of deep mining. The first smelter erected in Butte was completed in 1800. In 1883 the Anaconda Copper Company began the construction of what is probably the largest smelter in the world, in Deer Lodge Valley, about 27 miles from Butte. Here grew up the city of Anaconda. The capacity of this great plant is about 12,000 tons of ore a day. A smaller smelter has been erected at Great Falls on the Missouri.

The once-active smelting industry at Butte has declined, but the former activity is read in the great number of dead trees and shrubs, destroyed by the acid fumes from the great smokestacks; even the soil was poisoned for plant life and it is only recently that vegetation is getting a fresh start. A similar destruction was begun at Anaconda, but the company a few years ago was forced to put in a by-product plant. Sulfuric acid is now produced, and reaches the eastern markets, when the price is high enough to pay the heavy freight charges.

The Butte region copper is shipped to Great Falls for refining where cheap hydroelectric power is available.

The Utah District. Mineral prospecting in Utah was delayed for many years by the adverse attitude of the Mormon Church, but in 1863 soldiers of the United States Army, stationed at Fort Douglas, discovered valuable ores in Bingham Canyon. Copper was first shipped in 1868, the first lot going to Baltimore, Maryland, since there were no smelters in the

West. Bingham today has the largest single mine in the world (Fig. 195). The ore outcrops on the side of a gulch, the face of which is 1600 feet high, and is mined at a very low cost by electric shovels working on many levels. Over 50,000,000 tons of ore have already been removed, and exploratory drilling indicates a reserve of nearly 400,000,000 tons.

There are two large concentrating plants at Garfield, the larger covering 20 acres. From the concentrating plants the "enriched" ore is taken to the smelter just to the west of Garfield. There are smelters also at Murray and Midvale, suburbs of Salt Lake City, and at Milford and Ogden.

Park City, on the east slope of the Wasatch, is another great mining district, the rock here carrying silver, lead, zinc, gold, and copper. It is

Fig. 195. Bingham Mines in Utah. This open-pin mine is one of the most spectacular views of the mining world. Electric shovels and trains operate on some fifteen or twenty levels. By numerous switchbacks and horseshoe curves, the ore cars carry ore from all levels to the village of Bingham below in the canyon, and out to Garfield for concentration and smelting. *Photo by Miller.*

one of the leading silver producers of the nation. The Tintic Mountains, to the southwest of Utah Lake, have deposits of silver and lead.

The Idaho District.   The Coeur d' Alene district lies in northern Idaho and has become one of the richest mining areas of the Northern Rocky Mountains. It produces silver and zinc, and about one-fourth of the nation's lead. The ores are complex and difficult to recover, but new processes and industrial expansion in the Northwest have operated to improve this industry in its isolated location.

The Leadville District.   The Leadville mining and smelting district is remarkable in its variety of minerals. Gold, discovered by prospectors in the boulders and sand deposits of California Gulch, attracted hundreds of miners in 1860 and resulted in the founding of Ore City, which in less than a year had 10,000 people.

The history of this city shows how short-lived is a community built up entirely because of mineral deposits, particularly on precious and semi-precious minerals. Ore City began as a gold camp in 1860, became a silver-lead-producing area in 1879, and, after the decline of these industries, became a lead- and zinc-producing region. Ore City continues to produce gold, silver, and lead, but zinc leads. Copper began to be mined about 1889 but only in small amounts. Local copper smelters work up much of the copper ore of the area. Iron, manganese, and bismuth are

Fig. 196. Pueblo, Colorado—"Steel City of the West." Nearness to the coal at Trinidad, Colorado, and iron ores in Utah and northern Colorado has been the chief advantage of this location for steel making. Railroads have been the chief market for steel rails made here. *Courtesy, Pueblo Chamber of Commerce.*

also found. There are several smelters at Leadville, but not all the primary manufacture is done here, some ore being sent to Pueblo and Denver (Fig. 196).

The adoption of a bimetal standard of money would greatly stimulate the mining industry of the West. Gold, silver, copper, zinc, and lead are frequently found mixed in the veins. This intimate mixing makes the cost of extracting any one metal expensive.

Leadville is still an important producer of lead and zinc, but since the 1930's it has become most important for molybdenum mined at Fremont Pass, 13 miles to the north. Here is located the world's most valuable deposit of molybdenum. It is said to contstitute 95 per cent of the world's known reserve, and from it the United States produces 66 per cent of the world's supply. This metal gives toughness and fatigue strength in alloys with iron and steel used in machine tools and motors for automobiles and airplanes. The United States makes great use of this mine.

Historic Mining Towns in Colorado. But few of the mining towns that date from the "gold fever days" have been as successful as Leadville in holding a place in the mining world. Many a "Queen of the Rockies" of the 1850's, 1860's, and 1870's is now wholly deserted. The number of public buildings, schools, stores, churches, and the inevitable saloons and dance halls with weathered exteriors, sagging roofs, broken windows, and gaping doors are indicative of the number of people, gathered from every quarter of the globe, that called these towns home. Among the larger historic towns are Carbondale, in western Colorado, Bachelor, Teller, Robinson, American City, Pearl, Nevadaville, Lulea, Tincup, Gothic, and Montezuma.

Other Districts in Colorado. Cripple Creek has a smelter and cyanide extracting plants for treating copper, silver, and gold ore, but most of the ore is sent elsewhere. The San Juan district in southwestern Colorado, about the cities of Telluride, Silverton, and Ouray, produces gold and silver. Ore-reducing plants are located at Durango and Salida, and smelting is done at Leadville. Pueblo is an iron-smelting and steel center. The numerous railroads that pass through the city bring ores from the mountain valleys and carry the smelter products eastward to the Atlantic seaboard states for further manufacture.

The Nevada District. Mining and the primary manufacture of ores are the chief activities of the people of Nevada. At present, about 90 per cent of the ore mined is refined in the state, but the metal obtained is sent elsewhere for further manufacture. The Comstock Lode, near Virginia City, as earlier stated, furnished the first silver and gold ore for refining.

Mining here has been a great gamble, for the veins vary greatly in richness; in some places the rock yields several thousands of dollars a ton; in others, very little. Since before 1880, the miners near Virginia City, and consequently the output of the concentrating and refining works, have been declining. The great importace of this mineral region in the economic life of the state is indicated in the decline of population. In 1880 the population of Nevada was more than 62,000; in 1900, a little more than 42,000. Subsequent discoveries of gold, silver, and copper deposits in the Goldfield-Tonapah district and in other districts both to the north and south, a slight increase in the output of the Comstock mines, and continued activity in the eastern part of the state brought prosperity for a time, and the population increased to nearly 82,000 in 1910, but fell to

77,000 in 1920. In 1927 gold was found at Weepah, and a "rush," bearing many of the characteristics of former days, was on. In 1950 the population of Nevada was 160,000. The population growth was given a great impetus again by increased mining and the metallurgical and other war industries at Las Vegas. The most active section of the state today in the metal industry is in the Ely district in eastern Nevada. Here is produced about 98 per cent of the copper of the state, besides lead and zinc. Concentrators and smelters prepare the metals, chiefly copper, for shipment. Lead ore is sent to Salt Lake City, and zinc ore to Iola, Kansas. A very large cyanide mill was erected near Virginia City for treating the low-grade ore of the Comstock Lode; thus this great deposit, which is credited with having yielded more than $400,000,000 worth of gold, is further to enrich its owners.

The Black Hills Mining Region.   The major metallic mining region of the Great Plains is in the Black Hills of South Dakota. Small quantities of various minerals have been produced here, such as silver, lead, copper, and tin, but gold is the most important. The famous Homestake mine with its associated refineries is located at Lead, South Dakota, and constitutes the largest single gold producer in the United States, if not in all the world. It stimulated the "gold rush" to the Black Hills in the 1870's, and has operated continuously since.

AUTOMOBILE ASSEMBLY AND AIRCRAFT INDUSTRIES

The practice of assemblying automobiles in regions far from the area of manufacture in the Lower Lakes Region has grown much since about 1930. In general it is less expensive to transport the parts of the automobile than to transport the finished product; consequently assembly plants have been located in many large cities throughout the country. In the West, the large centers for this business are the San Francisco Bay area and Los Angeles, Los Angeles being the largest in the West. Although the assembly industry is not truly manufacture, it employs great numbers of men, and brings about manufacturing of small parts, and in related fields. The great increase in population in the West, and hence increase in the market for automobiles, has stimulated the assembly industry. California now has a greater number of registered automobiles than any state in the Union. In the manufacture of rubber tires for the automobile, the plane, and other uses, Los Angeles is becoming a rival of Akron, Ohio, as the "Rubber Capital."

In the manufacture of aircraft Los Angeles has for a long time been the leading center in the country. The mildness of the climate, clear skies, and available space for the enormous assembly hangars have been cited as factors attracting this industry. Seattle is another center in the West important in this industry though the climatic conditions have not been so favorable. The advantage of an early start has seemed to fix the industry in Seattle (Fig. 197). During the World War II years, the shortage of labor in the West, and the urge to shift the aircraft industry inland to places less vulnerable to attack by an enemy has resulted in a dispersal of the aircraft manufacturing to the East and East Central States. Wichita, Kansas, and Fort Worth, Texas, developed and maintain large aircraft industries; however, the Los Angeles area continues to hold a prominent position as a leader in the industry.

Fig. 197. The Boeing Airplane Company at Seattle, Washington. This plant is the company's chief facility. It includes an assembly building, the plant proper, engineering laboratories, and administration quarters. This was the home of the World War II B-17's and the major assembly facilities for B-29's. *Courtesy, Seattle Chamber of Commerce.*

Los Angeles, the Bay cities, and Puget Sound cities all have important airplane landing fields, and these cities serve as termini for airliners from the East. San Francisco is the chief take-off point for Hawaii and cross-Pacific flying. The landing field at Alameda, on San Francisco Bay, is said to be one of the largest in the world.

THE FISHING INDUSTRY

The Pacific Coast as a section has led all others of the nation in fisheries since about 1940. In the period 1940-1949 the average annual number of fishermen employed was 30,000, the catch was 1,300,000,000 pounds, valued at almost $80,000,000. In the same period the corresponding annual averages for the historic New England section, long noted for its fisheries, were 25,000 fishermen, with a catch of 850,000,000 pounds, valued at $51,000,000.

In the Pacific Northwest salmon is the chief fish caught. The Columbia River, the Puget Sound, and the coastal waters to Alaska constitute the main fishing grounds. Since about 1930 the catch of salmon has decreased, but that of halibut, herring, tuna, oysters, and others has increased. Unlike the New England fisheries, most of the fish are taken in coastal waters and at the exits of streams, and most of the fish are canned. Canning is done in the ports near the catch, and consequently many of the towns in Puget Sound and on the coasts of Washington and Oregon have canneries. Important ones are Astoria, Aberdeen, Port Angeles, and Bellingham. Because of the habits of salmon in running upstream to spawn, the pollution of waters by man, building of dams, and overfishing during the "runs" have resulted in such a decrease of salmon as to threaten the future of this fish. Conservation measures are being applied in many ways to protect the salmon.

Both halibut and tuna fishing have increased since 1930 on the north Pacific Coast. Much of the halibut is marketed in the East as frozen fresh fish. Also, a million-dollar-a-year oyster-fishing industry is located in Willapa Bay on the Washington coast. Aberdeen is the oyster canning center.

Seattle profits greatly from the fishing industry because it is the chief home port of the fishing fleet for North Pacific waters, including also much of the Canadian coast and Alaska. Vessels are outfitted here, and many vessels leave with a supply of tin for cans, to be put into proper form for canning of fish in the ports near where the fish are caught in northern coastal waters. The fleet returns laden with fish, a large part of it canned; so Seattle becomes the distributing point for fish to markets. This port is one of the world's greatest distributing points for fish.

Since about 1935 southern California has become an important fishing region. Tuna and sardines are the chief fish caught. Tuna fishing grounds are alongshore south to Mexico, Central America, and as far as the equator, and westward as far as Hawaii. Large vessels are necessary because the tuna must be frozen on board soon after being caught, thus preserving them for the canneries on shore when the vessels return. San Diego and Los Angeles are the canning centers and homes of fishing fleets (Fig. 198). A portion of Los Angeles harbor is set aside for this industry, and is known as "Fish Harbor." Here are located the docks, canneries, homes of fishermen, oil stations, and all other services for outfitting the fleet.

Sardines are fished largely off Monterey Bay in the cool waters of the California current where they feed on plankton. Monterey is called "the Sardine Capital of the World" because of its successful competition with European suppliers since World War II. Sardines are canned in Monterey, which becomes a very busy place when the laden fishing vessels come in. Considerable sardine canning is also done in Los Angeles.

Tuna, sardines, mackerel, and an increasing amount of other fish are taken in different periods of the year. Tuna are caught from June to Sep-

Fig. 198. Fishing fleet in Los Angeles harbor. Here the fleet is at rest between trips. The great variety of fish available in waters off southern California makes fishing an important industry in Los Angeles County. Many canneries are located in the harbor area.
Courtesy, Los Angeles Chamber of Commerce.

tember, sardines from November to March, and mackerel largely in winter. This seasonal distribution gives employment for fishermen throughout the year. The newness of the fishing industry, the planned harbor and facilities, the large boats, and year-round employment of fishermen have resulted in making Los Angeles the best organized fishing port in the world.

San Francisco has its "Fisherman's Wharf" and is noted for crab fishing and abalone caught in the waters off Golden Gate, but it is not as important a fishing center as either Seattle or Los Angeles. Aside from the centers that have been named, there are numerous other fishing ports on the West Coast. The wide range for tuna fishing off the southern coast of California is an important factor in making California the leading state in the Union in value of fish and fish products.

THE RESORT AND TOURIST INDUSTRY

The improvement in means of transportation has brought to the West a resort and tourist business that affects people everywhere except in the most remote places. Its awe-inspiring mountains, canyons, caverns, big trees, petrified forests, geysers, lakes, deserts, subtropical beaches, and wide spaces are truly attractions that justify the advertising, "See America First." And though the West is not old, it offers many so-called "historic spots," recounting the spectacular early settlement and development days.

Early in the twentieth century the first resorts were sponsored by the railroads. Hotels and lodges were built in scenic places and much advertised. Resorters could come and stay for a period of time with all accommodations provided, or they could travel and see the West from the Pullman window. The United States Government took an interest in the preservation of scenic spots and created numerous National Parks, Monuments, and Forests, and to a considerable extent state and local governments did likewise. The automobile and modern highways have brought the West within reach of many who have small means, as well as those with wealth. Many miles of highways have been improved mainly to accommodate the tourist. Hotels, resorts, tourist cabins, and overnight lodgings are available wherever there are highways. Ski runs, dude ranches, fishing grounds, winter resorts, or summer resorts, any or all, may be had by selecting the place, and all the Western States advertise for tourists and receive them by the hundreds of thousands. Employment and income in the West resulting from catering to travelers, runs into millions of dollars annually, and in many instances is the sole support of entire towns and villages. El Paso, Santa Fe, and Tucson, just to name a few, are towns that make this a main business. Many others could be named. Railroads have fast trains to reach certain parts of the West, and airlines run to all large centers on the West Coast, thus providing swift transportation. Tourists truly bring a "big business" to the West.

THE MOTION PICTURE INDUSTRY

In 1900 there was not one movie theatre in the United States. In 1950 there were about 17,000 with a seating capacity of over 11,000,000. The making of motion pictures is a product of science and research, beginning with still pictures, then progressing to the film and motion pictures. The West was selected for picture making at first because it afforded the locale for popular "Wild West" stories. Since early picture making was mostly an outdoor business, it was necessary to have sunshine, cloudless skies, and mildness the year round. The first studios were located in Los Angeles in 1909, and others followed rapidly. The suburban section where most studios were segregated was Hollywood, which soon grew to be a distinct city. Hollywood still has most of the studios, but some are located within Los Angeles and the other suburbs. There is at present a growing tendency for studios to be located in the outlying areas about Hollywood.

In addition to mild climate and clear skies, the Los Angeles area has a great variety of outdoor scenery which can be used as a setting for almost any picture. Strange to say, however, the very factors that tended to locate this industry are no longer operative, for today most pictures are made in large enclosed studios with the aid of artificial lighting and painted scenery. Nevertheless the advantage of an early start seems to have fixed the Los Angeles area as the center of production. The newest threat to this business is television, which could make the numerous theatres throughout the country unnecessary because pictures could be seen at home, or it could result in change of location of picture making to a more central location to take advantage of transmission. No one knows what the outcome may be, but it has been demonstrated in the past that an early start that serves to entrench an industry in a certain location is a very strong factor in holding that industry to that place.

In 1950 the picture-making business was still dominately a United States industry, for 75 per cent of all moving pictures are made in this country, and 90 per cent of the United States product is from the Los Angeles area, mainly Hollywood. The payroll for the picture-making industry amounts to millions of dollars annually, and the number of actors, producers, writers, artists, craftsmen, cast, and common labor, with their families, make a sizable population. The motion-picture industry is an important factor contributing to the remarkable growth of population in the West.

THE OUTLOOK FOR INDUSTRIES IN THE WEST

The future for industries in the West seems to be rather bright, and particularly so in view of the remarkable increase in population. Increase in numbers of people means an increase in home market. Throughout the preceding discussion it has been pointed out repeatedly that, though the

West has great resources, it has a small local market, and the populous eastern market is far away, thus limiting the West, in a large measure, to the production and conditioning of raw materials to be manufactured elsewhere.

The West has made the most remarkable increase in population of any section of the country since 1930. In 1950 California and Arizona led all states in percentage of population gained over the preceding census. Both of these states showed more than 50 per cent increases in the decade. Nevada had a 44 per cent increase, and all other Western States except Idaho and Montana showed increases well above the national average. The "Westward Movement" has not ended. Population analysts are predicting further increases for 1960.

No doubt the reasons for great gains in population in the West are due to the abundance of resources previously discussed, to improvements in transportation, new techniques, and building of power projects, and to the stimulus of war and the armament program. Chemical and metallurgical industries are attracted to the great hydroelectric power sites, or within a 300-mile radius of them, for use of cheap power.

With the evident increase in importance of the Pacific and Far East in world affairs, the West Coast states will take on more of the nature of a front door than has been so in the past, and all of the West will be benefited therefrom.

QUESTIONS, EXERCISES, AND PROBLEMS

1. Will the West ever have a city as dominant among western cities as New York is among the cities of the East? Give reasons for your answers. Consider all factors, particularly those affecting the growth of manufactures.

2. Classify the larger urban groups of the West as to location and geographic conditions affecting their growth. Which are likely to be great industrial centers in the future?

3. Is it possible for California to develop an important iron and steel industry? Where is the best location for iron and steel plants in the West?

4. Make a study of the influence gold has had on the settlement and economic growth of the West. Has it affected the social conditions? There is enough material here for an excellent paper in historical geography.

5. Make a study of the geographic reasons for the location of the motion-picture industry in southern California. Do you think the West still has advantages over the East for carrying on this industry? How has the motion-picture industry influenced economic development of the West? How will television affect the location of the motion-picture industry?

6. Make a careful and detailed study of such mining centers as Leadville, Butte, and Virginia City. Do metallic mineral deposits lead to such permanence of settlement as coal beds? Give examples of your conclusions.

7. Analyze the airplane industry of the Los Angeles region from the standpoint of location, labor, raw resources, markets, and the possibilities of a shift of the industry to other places.

8. Seek statistics from recent census reports and study population increases in Western States. Contrast with other sections of the country. What of the future?

9. The "smog," resulting from gases, dust, humidity, smoke, and other causes in the Los Angeles area has been of much concern and interest lately. Seek information on this topic and learn of its causes, its handicaps, possible abatement, and future effects on the area.

CHAPTER 19

Alaska

Is Alaska suitable for a permanent home for white men in any considerable numbers? Do Alaskan resources warrant the conclusion that a population equal to that of Finland or of Sweden can be supported? Can Alaska ever become of importance as a home for man?

A Land of Retarded Development.   Alaska was first visited by the Russians in 1741, and Russian traders and trappers soon entered the country to obtain fur. They established the first settlement in 1784 on Kodiak Island, and in 1804 founded Sitka, which became the seat of government the following year. During the 83 years that Russia occupied Alaska it obtained $45,000,000 worth of furs but did little to develop the colony. The 500 colonists were even provided with food from Siberia. Russian rule ended in 1867 when the United States purchased Alaska for $7,200,-000. It was then popularly known as an arctic waste suitable only for primitive natives, trappers, and hunters. Fine furs were thought to be its only asset, and little attention was given to the territory for many years. It was in charge of the War Department with no government at all except near the army posts, and for 7 years more it was under the Treasury Department. Nearly 50 years elapsed before Alaska had any form of local government. During that time it was administered from Washington, 5000 miles distant. It was given a homestead law in 1903, the right to export timber in 1909, a Territorial Legislature in 1912, a coal-land leasing law in 1914, and an oil-land leasing law in 1920.

The negligent and dilatory attitude of Congress toward Alaska has been an important factor in retarding development. It is still a frontier land, a vast undeveloped territory of 586,400 square miles, a land containing resources of great potential wealth but few people (Fig. 199). The population has risen and fallen with the rise and fall of gold production. Hopes of a fortune quickly obtained brought a rush of prospectors, and failure to realize those hopes caused them to leave. The population is estimated to be approximately 100,000—about the same as that of Duluth, Minnesota—and most of the people live in the southern and south-eastern districts. Slightly more than half the total population are whites. The other half are primarily Eskimo, Indian, and Aleut, as less than 1000 people belong to other ethnic groups. There are 25 incorporated towns with more than 1000 people, Anchorage being the largest with about 15,000. More than 99 per cent of Alaska is still owned by the Federal Government, and both Federal and territorial income is collected as taxes or licenses, chiefly from the fisheries and business enterprises. Some people hold that development of a frontier country like Alaska cannot progress far under present leasing laws; others believe that these laws are adequate for present needs and will prevent acquisition of Alaska s wealth of resources by a few individuals or corporations. Whatever may be the correct viewpoint, it is certain that progress of a substantial nature can come only with the establishment of permanent industries. It is also clear that man will not risk large invesments in a frontier country like Alaska unless large profits are reasonably certain.

Past and Future Production. White men tend to go where great potential wealth exists, whether or not the laws of a stable government exist. This has been more or less true in Alaska. Notwithstanding the mining and leasing laws that have been in force, the total production from mines, fisheries, forests, agricultural, and pastoral lands has been very large. Though accurate statistics are not available, estimates indicate that Alaskan products, for the period 1867–1950, were valued at approximately $2,500,000,000. The major portion by far of this huge sum was derived from gold, copper, fisheries, and furs.

It appears that only a small fraction of the mineral and other resources has been taken. Minerals of excellent quality, in great variety and in large amounts, remain. The coal deposits exceed 50,000,000,000 tons; usable water power is abundant in southern Alaska; and prospects for producing petroleum on a commercial scale are considered good. The fisheries may be expanded and continued indefinitely under proper conservation regulations. The splendid forests are awaiting more extensive utilization. The large acreage of agricultural and grazing lands is almost wholly unexploited, though a start has been made. Greater production of raw materials and finished products for export, development of adequate interior transportation facilities, extension of manufacturing industries based upon utilization of local raw materials and power, and establishment of permanent local markets for the products of agriculture and grazing are all in the future. With their growth will come greater commerce and population. Alaska is still a land for the pioneer.

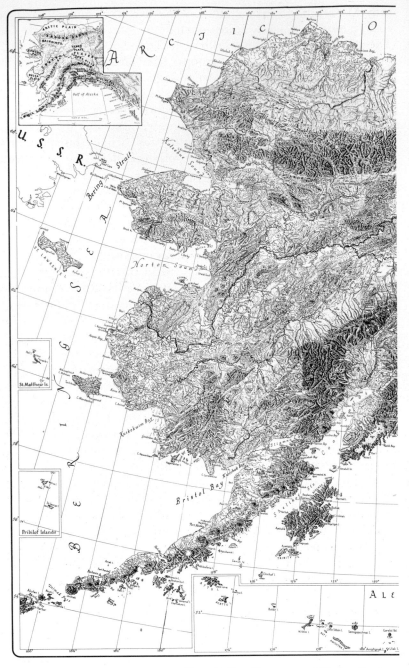

Fig. 199. Landform map of Alaska. *Courtesy,*

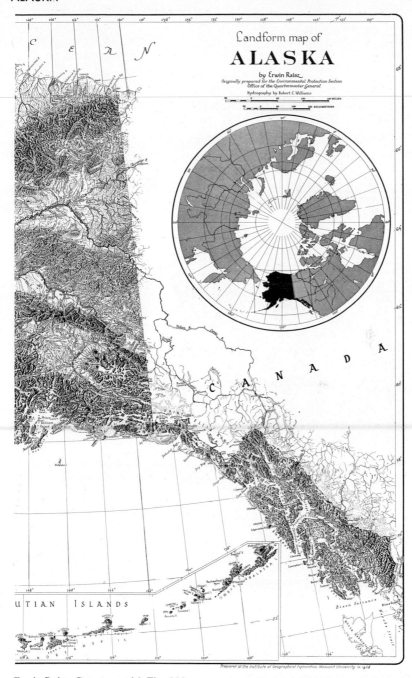

Erwin Raisz. Compare with Fig. 200.

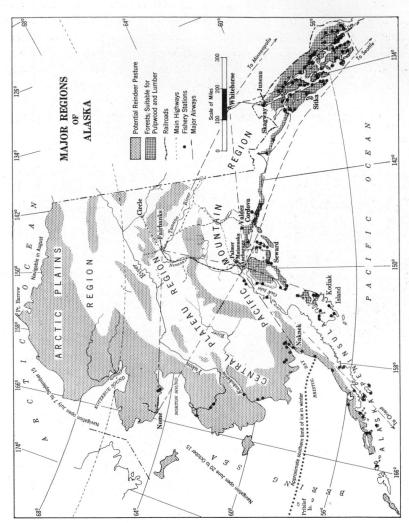

Fig. 200. Major regions of Alaska, its potential reindeer pastures, and its fisheries.

GEOGRAPHIC REGIONS

Alaska may be divided into three broad geographic provinces that present striking contrasts in surface, climate, vegetation, mineral resources, agricultural possibilities, and consequently in the opportunities for human use (Fig. 200). These provinces may be designated as (1) the Pacific Mountain region, (2) the Central Plateau region, and (3) the Arctic Plains region. The Territory has a very wide range of climate, with a corresponding range in native vegetation, varying from dense forests through the semiarid type to arctic tundra. These large variations are due to (1)

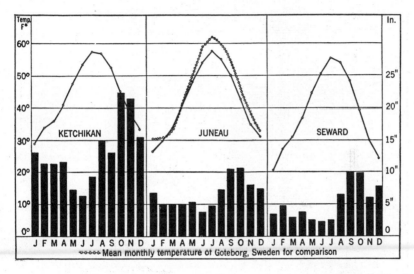

Fig. 201. Mean monthly precipitation and temperature at three stations along the Pacific Coast of Alaska.

great latitudinal extent, (2) the temperature of bordering waters: the warm Pacific, the cold Bering Sea and Arctic Ocean, (3) the direction of prevailing winds, and (4) the distribution and high altitude of the mountain ranges. The mean annual temperature varies from 40° in the south to 10° in the north, a greater range than prevails in continental United States (Fig. 202).

The Pacific Mountain Region. The Pacific Mountain region is a continuation of the rugged mountainous district of the United States and British Columbia. It is a region of high relief and of great valleys, and extends some 1200 miles along the coast and about 200 miles inland. Numerous snowcapped peaks, such as Mount McKinley (20,300 feet) in the Alaska Range, rise to high altitudes, and scores of large glaciers descend to the coast from the extensive snow fields. It is a region of cold winters, mild summers, and very heavy precipitation, ranging from 50 to 120 inches annually. Snowfall on the higher slopes is heavy (Fig. 201). Contrary to popular belief, the mean winter temperatures of Sitka, Juneau, and of St. Louis, Missouri, are nearly the same, but the extreme minimum of St. Louis is much lower. Seventeen of the twenty-five Weather Bureau stations on the Pacific Coast of Alaska have never recorded temperatures lower than the St. Louis minimum of −22°. The summers, how-

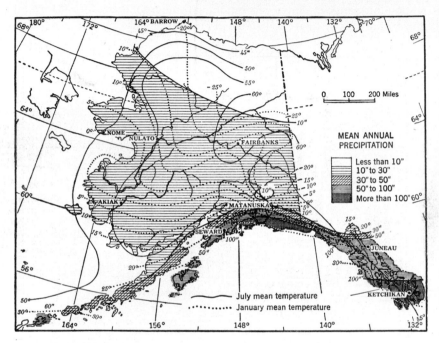

Fig. 202. Mean annual precipitation and mean temperatures for January and July. Compare with Figs. 203 and 204. *(After U. S. Weather Bureau maps.)*

ever, are damp and chilly. The lower mountain slopes are heavily forested with such valuable trees as hemlock, spruce, and cedar. Nearly all the best timber is included in the Federal reserves. The extensive forests comprise more than 26,700,000 acres and contain about 77,000,000,000 board feet of timber suitable for pulp and lumber. Much of the timber is now fully ripe and should be utilized at an early date. However, it probably cannot now compete in outside markets with the lumber of higher quality and greater variety available in Oregon, Washington, and British Columbia. The annual cut is now about 80,500,000 board feet, a large port of which is used for salmon cases. Fish, forests, and minerals are the

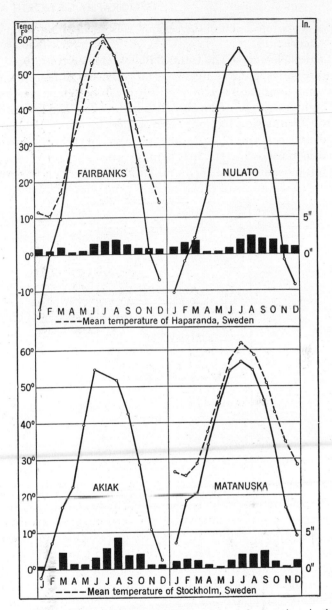

Fig. 203. Mean monthly precipitation and temperature at four stations in the Central
Plateau region of Alaska.

principal economic assets of the region. Agriculture in favored localities, is fairly successful.

The Central Plateau.   The Central Plateau region contains about 200,-000 square miles, an area nearly as large as that of Nebraska and the two Dakotas combined. It is of relatively low relief, characterized by flat-topped highlands separated by broad stream valleys and lowlands, except along the Bering Sea section where broad lowlands broken by low, rounded hills dominate the landscape. Within it lie the basins of the Yukon and Kuskowim, the first being Alaska's great highway in summer, as it is navigable for 2200 miles. This is a country of short, mild summers with 18–20 hours of sunshine daily; the winters are long and cold

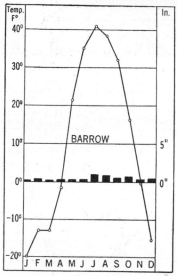

Fig. 204. Mean monthly precipitation and temperature on the Arctic Coast of Alaska.

(Fig. 203); and precipitation is scant (9–19 inches) with very little snowfall. The region contains much of the agricultural and grazing lands of Alaska and is rich in minerals; these are its two chief resources. A vast wealth of gold has already been obtained from alluvial gravels. About two-thirds of the area is forest of the woodland or small, open-growth type. However, not more than half the forested area carries timber suitable for commercial purposes and that cannot be utilized for more than local uses until transportation is provided. The principal species are white and black spruce, white birch, balsam poplar, black cottonwood, aspen, and tamarack. The forests of the Central Plateau are mere "scrubs" compared with those of the Pacific region, varying from almost nothing in the stunted black spruce areas to 20–30 cords an acre in the birch and aspen sections, and several thousand board feet an acre in the best white spruce areas. Highly valuable pastures occur over much of the area and offer opportunity for the grazing of reindeer.

Arctic Plains Region. The northern region, separated from the Central Region by the Brooks Range, contains about a sixth of the Territory and may be truly called Arctic Alaska. It is a region of more or less rolling low relief, a slightly elevated plateau dissected by northward-flowing streams. Its climate is of the true arctic type, with only about 6-8 inches of precipitation, long, cold winters, and cool summers. Summer extremes of 66° and winter extremes of −54° have been recorded (Fig. 204). The long period of continuous sunshine, extending through days and weeks except when the sky may be obscured by clouds, produces a luxuriant growth of mosses, flowers, lichens, and grasses over much of the area even though the soil cover thaws to a depth of only a foot or two before winter sets in again. So far as is known the mineral resources of the region are small, though coal and petroleum are present. Production of reindeer or muskox upon its extensive pastures is probably the greatest opportunity that it offers to man.

MINERALS

Alaska is rich in minerals. There are reserves of gold, copper, mercury, coal, silver, platinum, tungsten, lead, marble, gypsum, and numerous other minerals, all of which are likely to be of significance in the future development of Alaska. The known occurances of petroleum are being explored, but there is no commercial production at present. The mineral resources are widely distributed throughout the Central and Pacific regions (Figs. 205, 206).

Gold first attracted large numbers of people to the Territory, and it has also held many of them there, since they have a permanent interest in Alaska in contrast with employees of the fish canneries. When a man can wash a fortune from the gravels in a short time with no more equipment than pick, shovel, and pan, he can pay costly transportation and endure hardship. Under these conditions alluvial gold mining developed rapidly for a time along the Yukon and other interior streams. As the bonanzas became exhausted and the yield per cubic yard of gravel became small, production declined. Large, power-driven equipment is necessary to work such deposits profitably. Its use requires transportation facilities, far more of which must be provided before the mineral reserves can be exploited fully. With the use of modern dredging and lode-mining equipment the Yukon River basin produces four-fifths of the entire Alaska output. The reserves of alluvial gold probably exceed in value all that has been produced to date. Fifty years ago three-fifths of the mineral

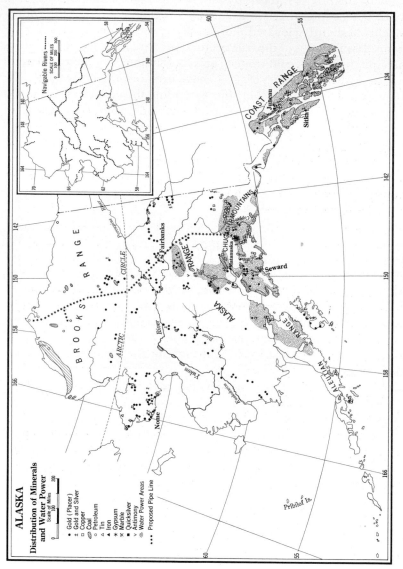

Fig. 205. Distribution of Alaska's minerals and navigable rivers.

output came from remote districts without good transportation, and now only one-twentieth. Hard-rock or lode mining can be conducted only where steamers, railroads, or good highways are available and freight rates relatively low. Fairbanks is the leading district. More remote deposits must await cheaper means of transportation than now exist. The total value of gold produced in Alaska is nearly ninety times larger than the price paid to Russia for the entire territory. Furthermore, the gold value alone is many times the net cost to the Federal Government for current expenses since the purchase in 1867.

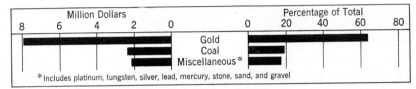

Fig. 206. Principal minerals produced in Alaska. Three-year average.

Silver, copper, and lead are derived almost exclusively as by-products from ores mined mainly for some other metal, chiefly from gold ores. The once highly productive Kennicott copper mines ceased operation in 1938, with the exhaustion of the economically workable ores.

Coal deposits are also widely distributed, and the reserves are estimated to be about 50,000,000,000 tons, at least half of which can be made available easily. Most of the reserves are of subbituminous coal and lignite, but the fuel value of the Matanuska coals is as high as that of any

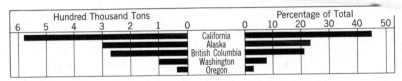

Fig. 207. Pacific Coast fisheries. Three-year average.

other coal on the Pacific Coast. Most of the present production of about 400,000 tons comes from the lower Matanuska Valley and Nenana fields, served by the Alaska Railroad. The Matanuska Valley is located about 45 miles northeast of Anchorage and the Nenana fields about 75 miles southwest of Fairbanks. The Matanuska coal is a good grade bituminous, and the Alaska Railroad provides the major market. However, the coal also has a good market throughout the southern coastal sections of Alaska. The Nenana (or Healy River field) coal is a high-grade lignite. The chief market is in the Fairbanks area where the coal supplies power and fuel for the city, and for mining, smelting, and various government installations. Other deposits along this railroad are now being developed. The present coal production is not sufficient to meet local needs, and some coal is imported annually. It is probable that the annual production will soon be sufficient to meet Alaskan needs. Coal mining by private companies was not feasible until 1914 when the government enacted a coal-land leasing law. The demand for coal in Alaska and on the Pacific Coast of the United States is sufficiently large to absorb all that can be mined for several years to come. An adequate market appears to be assured.

FISH AND FUR

Fisheries.   The fisheries are the most important industry and were the first to be developed extensively. Fishing was carried on by the Russians long before the purchase of Alaska by the United States, and many American fishermen visited its shores regularly while Alaska was still a Russian colony. The first salmon canneries were not built until 1878. There are now more than 100 in Alaska, but the number operating varies yearly. Exclusive of aquatic furs, the annual value of the fishery products approximates $40,000,000, more than three-fifths of which is derived from salmon. The average value of the fisheries is more than three times that of all minerals mined. It has been estimated that the food supplied by salmon annually is equal to that furnished by 3,500,000 cattle, the maintenance of which would require millions of acres of pasture and cropland.

Fish are taken throughout Alaskan waters, but the investment in the fisheries of southeastern Alaska is nearly equal to that of the western and central districts combined. Salmon, halibut, herring, cod, and whale are the principal fish utilized. Salmon streams are found along more than 2500 miles of coast, and in the Yukon salmon spawn 2000 miles inland. The young salmon finds its way to the sea, where it remains until it is from 2 to 5 years old, when it returns to fresh water to spawn. At that time immense shoals of salmon gather along the Alaskan shores, and it is then that huge numbers are caught. Since the largest runs occur periodically with corresponding years of smaller runs, the fishing industry fluctuates in harmony with the habits of the salmon. Employment is commonly provided for thousands of people. Nearly all these employees are transients who migrate to Alaska to gather the harvest of fish, when the "runs" are in full swing, and leave again at the close of the season. Investigations show sufficient salmon to maintain the commercial fisheries indefinitely under adequate conservation laws.

Fur Industry.   The search for fur first brought the Russians to Alaska, and fur remained the chief interest of the country for more than a century. Ruthless killing nearly exterminated the sea otter, and likewise the seal of the Pribilof Islands. Formerly, not less than 3,000,000 seal visited these islands annually, but the number had been reduced to only about 132,000 when the Federal Government took over the sealing industry in 1911 by authority of the North Atlantic Sealing Convention. By application of scientific methods of propagation and proper utilization of surplus animals the herd now exceeds 3,800,000, and, if the present methods of conservation are maintained, may increase its size. The annual kill of

Fig. 208. Salmon cannery in Excursion Inlet, Alaska. Note the forest that extends to the shore line, and the fog that enshrouds the forest. *Courtesy, U. S. Fish and Wildlife Service.*

excess males is now about 70,000. Alaska has many fur-bearing animals and produces several million dollars' worth of fur annually. Most of this amount is obtained from the seal, fox, muskrat, and mink. With the advancement of settlement, a fur industry based upon the capture of wild animals naturally declines. However, fur farming may be extended almost indefinitely and thus develop a profitable and permanent industry.

AGRICULTURE AND GRAZING

The feasibility of agriculture and grazing in Alaska has been demonstrated since crops and livestock have been produced by white men for more than a century. Though the agricultural resources are almost wholly undeveloped, crops of wheat, rye, oats, barley, hay, potatoes, and hardy vegetables are produced for local consumption. The most extensive development has taken place in the Matanuska and Fairbanks sections where the farm produce found a ready sale in the towns, mining camps, and military bases (Figs. 209, 210). Present crop production in Alaska is limited by transportation facilities and markets rather than by either climate or soil. Until time changes these conditions, large crops cannot be produced profitably, as Alaska's farmers cannot compete in exports with other countries. Present production, therefore, is merely indicative of what may be produced in the future. When the more desir-

Fig. 209. Agricultural pattern in Matanuska Valley. *Courtesy, U. S. Soil Conservation Service.*

able lands of the continent are taken up and the pressure of population is felt, as it has long since been felt in Europe and the Orient, Alaskan agricultural lands will be used.

Arable Land.   Estimates of Alaska's tillable and grazing lands vary from a realistic 7,100,000 acres to an unrealistic 60,000,000. The latter estimate disregards costly drainage, poor soils, and unfavorable climate. In addition there may be 150,000 to 200,000 square miles of reindeer pasture that varies greatly in quality. Figure 211 shows the basic land-resource areas as established by W. A. Rockie, of the Soil Conservation Service, after many years of field work throughout Alaska. Table XIV differentiates between that which can be cleared and cultivated and land suitable for grazing. It is probable that the best area is the Cook Inlet

Lowlands (15), of which Matanuska Valley is a part. The Fairbanks area
(9, 10, 11) will probably develop as a second major crop and livestock
center. Other regions offering large acreage for tillage and/or grazing are

Fig. 210 A farm home in a mountain setting southeast of Palmer. *Courtesy, U. S. Soil
Conservation Service.*

the Yukon-Tanana Uplands, the Aleutian Range, and the Alaska Ice
Cap, which is a large, rugged, mountainous land mass but with many
narrow valleys, with climate and soil favorable for agriculture. It is sig-

nificant to note that the minimum estimate of farming and grazing land is about half that of similar lands in Sweden and exceeds that of Finland by about 1,000,000 acres; these two countries now have large agricultural populations. Alaska also has large areas of land not considered of agricultural value, though poorer lands in parts of Europe are now producing crops. Much of the tillable and grazing land is in the Central Plateau

TABLE XIV

ESTIMATED ACREAGE OF AREA IN EACH LAND-CAPABILITY CLASS
(When land can be used by simply clearing and/or cultivating)
(000 Omitted)

	Tillable	Grazing
1. Arctic Lowlands	0	0
2. Brooks Range	0	0
3. Arctic Circle Uplands	2	3
4. Allakaket Lowlands	6	4
5. Upper Yukon Basin	110	105
6. Middle Yukon Basin	3	3
7. Lower Yukon Basin	90	210
8. Ophir-Iditarod Uplands	9	18
9. Yukon-Tanana Uplands	265	2395
10. Tanana Valley	180	120
11. Kuskokwim Valley	270	180
12. Bristol Bay Lowlands	75	50
13. Aleutian Range	525	350
14. Alaska Ice Cap	640	160
15. Cook Inlet Lowlands	500	500
16. Copper River Basin	105	70
17. Southeast Alaska Fiords	90	60
Total for Alaska	2870	4228

Courtesy U. S. Soil Conservation Service.

region, particularly areas 9, 10, and 11, which is climatically best suited to the growth of crops. Fully half the area has a growing season of 70-105 days and a maximum of 18-19 hours of daily sunshine during the summer period. The scant rainfall is a greater influencing factor than either temperature or growing season. The grazing season for cattle and sheep is only about 100 days, though there is some winter pasture in the drier parts. Eight to nine months of indoor feeding is a handicap to livestock production, hence it is carried on only incidental to mixed farming. The area of agricultural land in the Pacific Mountain region is also large, but is probably more valuable for forest growth. Notable exceptions are the Alaskan Peninsula, Kodiak, and adjacent islands that carry a luxuriant

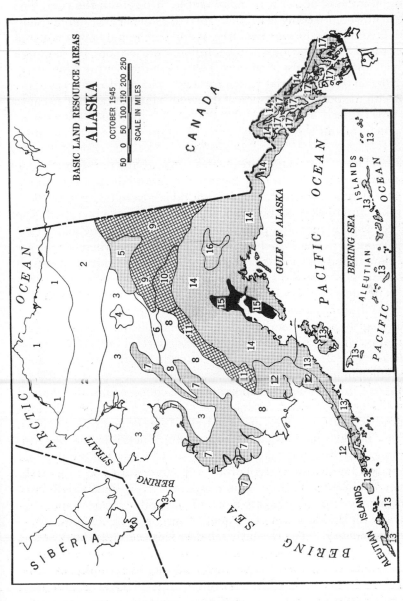

Fig. 211. Basic land-resource areas. *Courtesy, U. S. Soil Conservation Service.* The Cook Inlet Lowlands (15), which include Matanuska, probably rank first in agricultural potential, and the areas (9, 10, 11) centering on Fairbanks rank second. Each of the stippled areas has more than 100,000 potential acres. Other areas are insignificant for agricultural purposes. See Table XIV for names of numbered regions.

growth of grass. Cattle and sheep may be pastured for 6 to 8 months each year, and continuously in favored localities. These grazing lands are within 50 miles of ocean waters navigable throughout the year. The problem of winter feeding is yet to be solved, as the heavy summer rains are not favorable to the curing of hay. It appears probable that root and forage crops for ensilage may be the solution. Furthermore, the mosquito is a much less serious pest in this district than in the Central Plateau region. None of these potential agricultural areas have adequate transportation, with the possible exception of the small Matanuska and Fairbanks areas now utilized. However, 7,000,000 acres is an important agricultural potential and will provide homes for many people in some future period.

Soils. The soils of Alaska are of fair fertility. Only in the immediate vicinity of the streams can they be called rich and deep. Much of the agricultural area is wooded, and the ground is covered with moss. Both the timber and moss must be removed before crops can be raised. The heavy covering of moss is a poor conductor of heat, and beneath it the ground remains frozen. Much of the ground ice is a survival of a former colder climate and disappears or sinks to a level that permits crop growth when the moss is removed and the land cultivated. The ground ice that remains in cultivated lands during the dry summer is an advantage as it prevents drainage and supplies moisture to the crops. Where the soils are dominantly peat, from the accumulation of partially decayed vegetable matter, drainage is needed; in the driest parts of the interior irrigation may be necessary, though moisture supplied by the ground ice may prove sufficient.

So far as climate, soil, and topography are concerned, sufficient food can be produced to support a population of several million people. However, good accessible markets are essential to large crop production. The sparsity of markets for Alaskan agricultural products is in contrast with the abundance of such markets available to the farmer of Sweden and Finland. Further growth of agriculture, therefore, must await the establishment of other industries on a more extensive scale than exists at present, the more complete occupation of more favorably located lands elsewhere, and the development of adequate transportation facilities.

Reindeer Industry. The raising of reindeer for meat undoubtedly offers the greatest immediate opportunity for utilization of Alaska's pasture lands. Perhaps reindeer are to be the forerunner of agricultural settlement, as cattle were in the United States proper. However, vast areas suited only to the reindeer, or some similar animal, will remain after the agricultural land is taken up. The first small herd of 10 was introduced in 1891. From the natural increase and by subsequent importations, the number has grown to about 350,000. About two-thirds of these are owned by natives and are their chief source of food, clothing, and wealth. The practicability of the industry has been fully demonstrated. Estimates indicate that the natural grazing lands available are capable of maintaining 3–4,000,000 head. It is probable that the annual meat production from such a herd would exceed in value all the precious metals mined and would be second only to the fisheries as a permanent source of income. At least 1,000,000 reindeer could be maintained on lands that are now sufficiently accessible for profitable use.

TRANSPORTATION AND TRADE

Transportation. Modern man will not make his permanent home far from a modern system of transportation. Rivers serve fairly well in a new country, but if development is to take place more efficient means of moving men and goods are essential. Because of its great size, wide distribution of important resources, and long distance from American and foreign markets, adequate transportation is of vital significance to Alaska. Though the Yukon is navigable for river boats to Whitehorse in Canada, a distance of 2200 miles, it is open only 3 months. The Kuskokwim is navigable for 650 miles, and ocean vessels may reach its mouth during 4 months. These two rivers with their tributaries provide about 5000 miles of navigable waters which serve their basins in a very meager way. The snow cover and the ice on rivers, lakes, and bays favor overland travel in winter, but transportation by dog- or reindeer-drawn sledges is primitive at best and wholly inadequate for industrial progress. There are about 570 miles of main-line railroad completed, most of which is in the government railroad connecting Seward with Fairbanks along the Suisitna and Nenana valleys. A branch line extends into the agricultural and coal lands of the Matanuska Valley. There are also about 700 miles of gravel-surfaced highway, and airplane service has been established between the principal towns. The Alaska Highway now provides an overland route for automobiles, buses, and trucks (Fig. 212). A start, therefore, has been made to provide better transportation facilities, far more of which are needed.

Trade. The total trade of Alaska averages about $230,000,000 annually, with exports exceeding imports by a third. More than half the exports are fish products, and furs, gold, and platinum contribute a little more than 7 per cent. Imports are highly varied, with machinery, animal products, beverages, and petroleum products leading. Nearly all trade is with continental United States (Fig. 213).

Manufacturing. Processing of fish is the dominant manufacturing enterprise. The value of its products constitutes about 95 per cent of the value of all manufactures produced in Alaska. Other leading industries include smelters, lumber, printing and publishing, bakery, boat building, and machine shops.

Fig. 212. The Alaska Highway.

ALASKA, SWEDEN, FINLAND

Alaska, Sweden, and Finland are in approximately the same latitudes, and present some interesting comparisons (Fig. 214). Alaska has a more favorable oceanic location, but the other two have access to far better markets. Sweden and Finland, respectively, have populations sixty-six and thirty-eight times larger than Alaska. Their people are progressive, capable, sturdy, energetic, and cultured. Both countries have evolved high types of civilization. This has been accomplished in environments possessing unfavorable climate and poorly endowed with other natural resources. Sweden has the larger potential water power, and Finland the larger area of good timber, but Alaska surpasses both countries in all other resources except iron. The extent and quality of the Alaskan iron deposits have not been determined. Alaska's potential food resources, measured in agricultural lands, grazing lands, and fisheries, are greater. The same is equally true of its metallic mineral reserves and of its power resources measured by fuels and water power combined. Fully three-

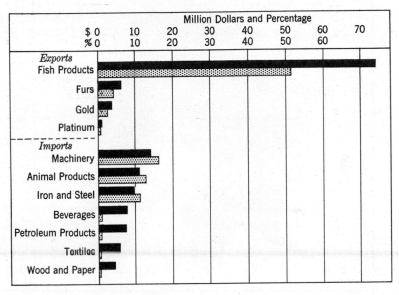

Fig. 213. Principal products in Alaskan trade. Three-year averages.

fourths of Alaska has a climate superior to that of Finland and to much of Sweden. Sweden and Finland far excel Alaska in the present utilization of resources. This is strikingly true of the agricultural and grazing lands. Finland, with only a tenth of the arable land of Alaska, is an exporter of dairy products. A large proportion of its farms are relatively small, and the small farmer finds work during the winter months in forest industries. Much of Alaska's agricultural and grazing lands are in the interior, and the better forest areas are on the coast. Hence, if the Alaska farmer is to find work in the lumber camps during the long winters, he must travel considerable distances. Both Finland and Sweden are favorably located in relation to the markets of Europe, in contrast with the remoteness of Alaska from any outside markets. If Finland can support

3,850,000, and Sweden 6,600,000, people, with natural resources inferior to those of Alaska, it seems reasonable to assume that Alaska may eventually maintain many more people than it now has. Nevertheless, the time when its population will compare favorably with either Sweden, Finland, or Norway is far in the future. People will not undertake the hardships of pioneer life in Alaska until better markets and transportation facilities are provided. This will come with the development of industries other

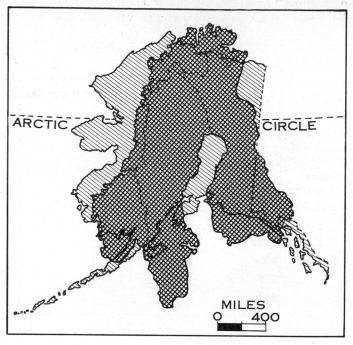

Fig. 214. Alaska is larger than Norway, Sweden, and Finland combined. They are located in the same latitude. Is Alaska potentially equal to those three countries as a home for man?

than agriculture. Alaska may therefore be looked upon as a reserve for the future, to be used when the better lands and other choice assets of the United States have been more fully taken.

PROBLEMS

1. Is Alaska as suitable as a home for man as the Rocky Mountain and Plateau States?

2. Can Alaskan meat production equal that of the Rocky Mountain and Plateau States?

3. Will the agricultural and livestock industries become the leading ones in Alaska?

4. Can Alaska maintain a population equal to that of California?

5. What three factors have been most important in retarding the development of Alaska?

6. What resource is likely to wield the greatest influence in the future development of Alaska?

7. When will Alaska be as densely settled as Norway?

8. How does Alaska compare with Scotland as a home for man?

9. Which geographic region of Alaska is likely to have the largest population in the future?

PART III

Canada

CHAPTER 20

The Dominion of Canada

In this chapter we wish to survey the Dominion as a whole and observe the efforts of a people to build a nation from the materials of a northerly land.[1] *What is the general character of that land? What handicaps and what advantages does the land present to these people? What are the outstanding uses that have been made of the natural resources? Can the Canadian people develop a unified nation in opposition to the natural forces that tend to foster separation? What efforts are being made to bridge the barriers that separate the more fertile areas? Do the natural forces tend toward political unity with the United States rather than toward an east-west unity? Do these forces tend toward friendly, reciprocal relations with the United States?* These are a few of the many problems that arise as we study the Dominion.

THE POLITICAL UNIT

Canada occupies nearly all of that portion of North America lying north of the United States. Its southern extremity reaches 41° 41′ N. in southern Ontario, which corresponds with southern Italy. If we were to transfer the British Isles to central Canada, Lands End would rest at Winnipeg and the northern shores of Scotland would reach the mouth of the Churchill River.

Unlike most countries, Canada has three oceanic boundaries, but two are wholly or partly closed during a portion of the year. All its provinces except two border on salt walter. The Pacific and the Atlantic are its great natural outlets. On the east is has the estuary of the St. Lawrence; on the west the Prince Rupert and Vancouver entrances; and in Hudson Bay, Churchill and Moosonee. Considerable freight, especially grain, is now being handled at Churchill, but development is yet to come, if it ever does, at Moosonee. Canada is a northern or high-latitude country with all the climatic limitations that such a location implies. Only a small part of its area lies south of latitude 50°—probably less than 800,000

---

[1] Only a general view of Canada as a whole is presented here. This procedure is followed so the student may picture the country as a national unit rather than as isolated sections. Detail applicable to human-use regions is presented in the discussion of those regions even though apparent repetition occurs. See Chapters 21–24 for more detail.

square miles. Canada is across the narrower part of the Atlantic from the great markets of Europe, especially from the British markets with which it maintains preferential trade relations. It has a most favorable location in relation to the great markets of the United States, in which it can dispose of much of its surplus raw and manufactured materials and from which it can purchase manufactured products and attract American investments. It is the shortest route from the Orient to Europe, by which route small packages of high value may be shipped.

Canada is a vast country with many variations in climate and other resources. The area is 3,843,000 square miles, and the water area is 228,-307 square miles exclusive of Hudson, Ungava, and Fundy Bays, the Gulf of St. Lawrence, and other tidal waters (Table XV). In area, therefore,

TABLE XV

LAND AND WATER AREA OF CANADA BY PROVINCES AND TERRITORIES

Provinces	Land, Square Miles	Fresh Water, Square Miles	Total Land and Water, Square Miles
Prince Edward Island	2,184	——	2,184
Nova Scotia	20,743	325	21,068
New Brunswick	27,473	512	27,985
Quebec	523,860	71,000	594,860
Ontario	363,282	49,300	412,582
Manitoba	219,723	26,789	246,512
Saskatchewan	237,975	13,725	251,700
Alberta	248,800	6,485	255,285
British Columbia	359,979	6,976	366,255
Yukon	205,346	1,730	207,076
Northwest Territories			
Franklin	541,753	7,500	554,253
Keewatin	218,460	9,700	228,160
Mackenzie	493,225	34,265	527,490
Newfoundland	——	——	42,734
Labrador	——	——	110,000
Total	3,462,103	228,307	3,843,144

it is larger than the United States and Alaska or the European mainland. At present its developed portion is only an attenuated area along the southern border, an hourglass-shaped region which is restricted at Winnipeg, through which all east and west traffic must pass. Its eastern and western settled areas are separated by hundreds of miles of forested and little-used land—essentially a primitive wilderness with very limited potentialities. Economically and socially, it is essentially a northern extension of the United States. The interchange of commercial products is not unlike that between the South and West and the industrial northeastern section of the United States. Under modern conditions the settled or developed portions of a country do not extend far from transportation lines; hence vast areas of Canada are very sparsely settled, and much has not been explored except along the streams. The future development of the Dominion depends to a large extent upon the expansion of its transportation system, especially its railroads.

Canada was formerly chiefly a producer of raw materials—the products of the fertile lands, forests, mines, and fisheries. Agriculture held a dominant position in the production of wealth and in the employment of its people. Now secondary production, especially manufacturing, has taken the leading position. In spite of this relative decline agriculture ranks second. Yet the change is indicative of the tendency of a country, as it matures, to convert its raw materials into finished products within its own bounds.

THE PEOPLE OF CANADA

Distribution and Growth of Population. Examination of the population map of Canada (Fig. 215) reveals a land of large area and few people. Vast stretches of country are almost uninhabited. The concentration of its 13,200,000 people along the southern border emphasizes the attenuated character of the country. If the southern boundary were moved 150 miles north, Canada would lose nearly all its people. The reason for this is understood when one considers the climate, soil, and surface. Three-fifths of the total population is in Quebec and Ontario, nearly all being in the Great Lakes-St. Lawrence Lowlands. Here are located all, except two, of Canada's cities of more than 100,000 population; three-fifths of all cities of 30,000 or more; and the only cities—Montreal and Toronto that exceed 500,000. This is also the dominant manufacturing, commercial, and financial section of Canada.

The urban population of Canada now exceeds the rural, as 54 per cent of the people live in cities, towns, and incorporated villages. During the last census decade, urban communities absorbed approximately three-fifths of the total population increase of Canada. These figures, however, are not comparable to those of the United States, where towns of less than 2500 are counted as rural. Quebec, Ontario, British Columbia, and Newfoundland are the only provinces in which the urban population exceeds the rural. In Newfoundland and Labrador nearly all the population is concentrated in urban communities along the coast.

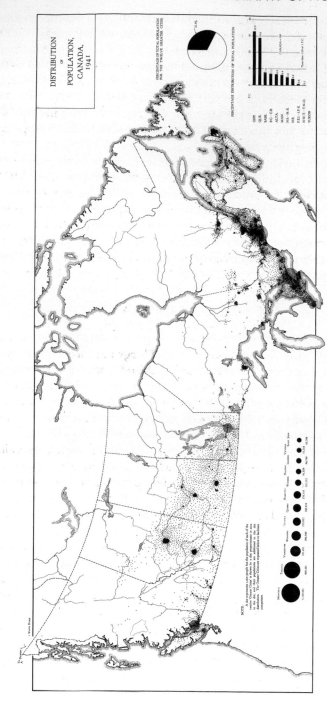

Fig. 215. Distribution of population, 1941. *Courtesy, Dominion Bureau of Statistics.* Note: One dot represents 1000 people, but the population of each of the 12 "Greater Cities" is shown by a disc proportionate in area to the dot, and their populations are additional to the dot distribution. The Greater Cities are repeated at the lower left to facilitate comparison.

The growth of Canada's population has been slow compared with that of the United States. Only during recent census periods has the increase reached or exceeded 1,000,000. The tendency for the population to shift from the east to the west, as in the development of the United States, appears to have ceased. Net gain in the Prairie Provinces has been small, whereas British Columbia has increased nearly a third. However, the absolute increase in the Great Lakes-St. Lawrence Lowland was very much greater, reflecting the extensive industrial advancement.

Composition.   The population of Canada presents a striking homogeneity in contrast with the heterogeneity of ethnic stocks in the United States. British stock makes up half of the present population, about a fourth being English. About 30 per cent of the total is French. It will be seen, therefore, that four-fifths of the people belong to two human stocks. The remaining one-fifth is divided among thirty or more ethnic groups. More than three-fourths of the French are in Quebec, where they constitute four-fifths of the total population. The British are much more widely scattered throughout Canada, yet nearly half are in Ontario, where they comprise three-fourths of the total population.

PHYSIOGRAPHIC REGIONS AND CLIMATE

The surface features of Canada are primarily a northward extension of similar features in the United States, particularly the lofty mountain mass in the west, the mountainous section in the east, and the Central Plains. On the basis of surface and structure, Canadians have divided their country into six major physiographic regions (Fig. 216): the Maritime Region, the Canadian Shield, the St. Lawrence Region, the Interior Plains Region, the Pacific Coast Region, and the Arctic Archipelago and Hudson Bay Lowland. These regions should not be confused with present regions of human-use discussed in subsequent chapters. Human use regions are not coexistent with physiographic or climatic regions.

Maritime Region.   The Maritime Region has an area of approximately 80,000 square miles. It includes the Maritime Provinces, that part of Quebec on the southeast side of the St. Lawrence River, and Newfoundland. Its surface is mountainlike, but when compared with the Cordillera on the west it would be described as hilly. The rocks are made up chiefly of sedimentary and igneous strata which were laid down from preCambrian times onward, then folded, faulted, and invaded by igneous rocks. Though settled at an early date, much of this area has not been thoroughly examined for mineral resources. Of the minerals, coal is of first importance, occurring in Nova Scotia and New Brunswick. It is estimated that Nova Scotia has a probable bituminous coal reserve of 1,967,-

000,000 tons, and New Brunswick 89,800,000. The iron reserves of New-foundland are estimated to be in excess of 2,500,000,000 tons. Asbestos is the next mineral in importance and occurs in the vicinity of Thetford and Black Lake in southeastern Quebec, where, from a few square miles, is obtained most of the world's supply.

The region is well drained by numerous small streams, the rapids and waterfalls of which offer power possibilities. Owing to the character of its

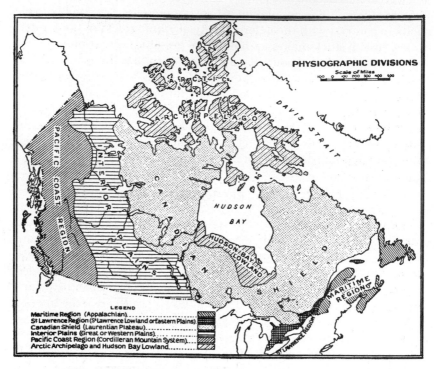

Fig. 216. The major physiographic regions of Canada. *Courtesy, Dominion Bureau of Statistics.*

surface, its soil areas suitable for agricultural purposes are limited, although many sections are today producing crops and still other areas are capable of agricultural utilization. The climate has many of the char-acteristics of the continental interior since the air mass moves eastward as a part of the prevailing westerly winds. Springs are later near the sea, and summers are a little cooler. Summer temperatures of 85° and even 95°, and subzero winter temperatures are not uncommon. October is a month of severe frosts. In Nova Scotia the winters are slightly warmer than in southern Ontario, but in New Brunswick they are colder and are comparable to those of western Quebec. Precipitation is abundant, being slightly greater in the fall and winter half of the year, and exceeds 50 inches on the south shore of Nova Scotia, though 40–45 inches is more general. The snowfall in northern New Brunswick is very heavy, exceeding 100 inches.

Canadian Shield. The Canadian Shield, or Laurentian Plateau, occupies approximately 1,800,000 square miles about Hudson Bay. It is roughly triangular in outline with the apex south of Lake Superior in the United States, and the base on the Arctic Ocean and Davis Strait. The western boundary extends southward from the Arctic Ocean along the line of lakes from Great Bear, Great Slave, Athabaska, and Winnipeg, to Lake of the Woods, where it crosses into United States territory. The southern boundary extends from the southeastern part of Georgian Bay to the vicinity of Quebec, and includes the Labrador Peninsula.

This vast region is known only partially even along its southern boundary. Much of its interior has not been explored except along the streams. It is made up largely of granite, gneiss, limestones, and slates. Geologically, its rocks arc among the oldest forming the land surface of North America. Portions of its area are barren rock surfaces, but in most places there is sufficient soil in the various depressions or crevices to sustain forest cover. South of James Bay is a large area known as the Clay Belt, covering part of the bed of an old glacial lake, which is thought to have agricultural possibilities. The Shield as a whole was largely stripped of its soil by the glacier and other erosive agents. Here and there are local areas suitable for farm land. The region, in general, is of moderate relief broken by river valleys, by lake basins, or by occasional rocky hills that rise above the general level. Nowhere, except in northern Labrador, does it exceed 2000 feet in elevation, and in most places it is less than 1000 feet above sea level. In general it resembles a plainlike country depressed toward the north and in the center, and elevated slightly along the southern and eastern borders. Portions are true plains, and other parts arc somewhat rugged but not comparable to a mountainous country. Most of its streams flow into Hudson Bay; others flow to the Great Lakes, Arctic, and Atlantic outlets. Thousands of lakes dot its surface. From the standpoint of human occupancy the Shield constitutes a wedgelike barrier between the Great Lakes-St. Lawrence Lowlands and the Interior Plains and is bridged by non-productive railroads, and partly by transportation on the Great Lakes.

Over such a large extent of territory, variation in climate, minerals, plant life, and other resources is to be expected. The southern portion is known to be rich in minerals, and it is highly probable that mineral deposits of economic value may be discovered throughout the area.

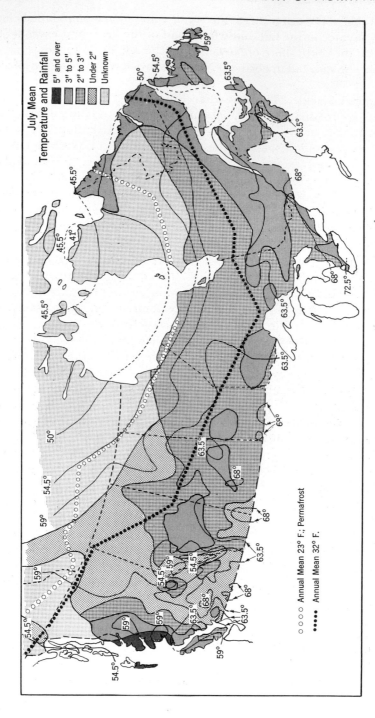

Fig. 217. Distribution of July precipitation and temperature. *After Canadian Meteorological Service.* Compare with Figs. 218 and 219.

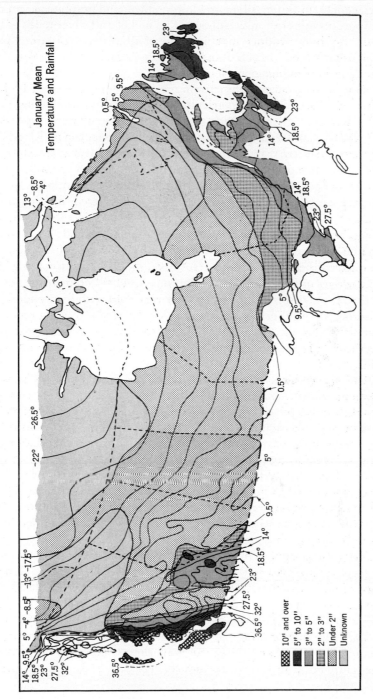

January Mean
Temperature and Rainfall

10" and over
5" to 10"
3" to 5"
2" to 3"
Under 2"
Unknown

Fig. 218. Distribution of January precipitation and temperature. Compare with Figs. 217 and 219. *After Canadian Meteorological Service.*

Nickel, copper, uranium, silver, gold, iron, mica, and graphite are among the important minerals now utilized. The nickel and silver fields of Cobalt and Sudbury produce most in value of all minerals obtained from the Canadian Shield. Much of the area is forested, and the forests of the southern part are of high commercial value.

Few meteorological stations exist in most of the area lying north of the St. Lawrence Region and the agricultural area of the Prairie Plains. Over the vast area of northern Canada, the climate is the subarctic type (Figs. 9, 217, 218) except for local variations; e.g., in the Mackenzie River Valley the summers are warm, and wheat has been matured north of the Arctic Circle. It is probable that similar mild conditions prevail over the region lying between the Mackenzie and the Rocky Mountains. On the whole, the winters are cold, and it is May before there is much growth. Frosts begin in September, and the winter begins in October. Summer rain is scant, and snowfall is light over the entire area. The climate of the north and east shores of Lakes Superior and Huron and of Hudson Bay is modified by these water bodies. However, the region is swept in winter by cold waves of great severity which pass unchecked over the region from the far northwest. The winters are very cold with heavy snowfall; the summers are generally warm, temperatures of 90° being recorded during the heat spells. Over much of the region, however, the margin of temperature safety is small, and frosts may occur during the summer months.

St. Lawrence Region.   The St. Lawrence Region or Eastern Plains lies between the Maritime Region on the east and the Canadian Shield. It is the smallest of the physiographic regions, having an area of about 35,000 square miles. This region is a series of plains areas in Quebec and Ontario, extending west from the city of Quebec along the St. Lawrence Valley, and including the triangular portion of Ontario lying between Georgian Bay and Lakes Erie and Ontario. It may be subdivided into three sections: (1) the Ontario peninsula with a steep escarpment of limestone on its eastern border, (2) the Eastern Ontario basin, separated from the (3) St. Lawrence River Plain by a narrow southward projection of crystalline rocks. It has a great variety of fertile soil, which offers excellent agricultural opportunities, and is the region in which most of the people of Canada live. So far as is known, it has no metals or coal, but it has gypsum, petroleum, natural gas, salt, and clay suitable for the manufacture of structural materials.

In the peninsular portion of Ontario, April is a true spring month. Frosts are rare in May, and the trees are usually in full leaf by the end of that month. The mean temperatures are slightly above 70° in July, and only slightly lower in June and August (Figs. 217, 218). The tempering effects of the Great Lakes are evident in this section. Abundant sunshine and rainfall coming in showers prevail during the summer, and the winter monthly precipitation is about the same as that of the summer months. The autumn may begin in the latter part of September, but it is generally October before severe frosts prevail. Northward into the Ottawa Valley spring comes later than in the south, and autumn comes earlier. However, the summer temperatures are much lower. Here the ground is covered with snow earlier than in the south, which is an important factor in lumbering operations.

At Montreal, farther east along the St. Lawrence in southern Quebec, March is a winter month, although April and May are as warm as in Toronto, and in midwinter Montreal is slightly warmer. The autumn is similar to that of southwestern Ontario, and is followed by a rapid fall of temperature in winter and a normal temperature 10° lower than Toronto. There is usually 1 to 3 inches of snow cover during a period of 4 months. Farther eastward in the St. Lawrence Valley, the summers are cooler, and the winters colder, with late springs. May is the spring month, and mid-September the beginning of fall. Throughout this area the precipitation is nearly uniform during the year.

Interior Plains Region.   The Interior Plains extend from the Canadian Shield westward to the mountains and northward from the United States boundary to the Arctic, including an area of approximately 500,000 square miles. They embrace parts of Manitoba, Saskatchewan, British Columbia, the Northwest Territories, and nearly all of Alberta. The region as a whole has a nearly continuous soil cover of glacial, fluviatile, and lacustrine deposits which vary in thickness from a few to several hundred feet. Only on steep slopes or in the large stream beds is the underlying bedrock exposed. The country is relatively flat, increasing in altitude westward by a series of escarpments which divide the plains into three prairie levels. The first prairie level has an elevation of about 800 feet, and includes the almost flat Red River Valley, once the bed of Lake Agassiz. Its western border is a series of hills rising from 500 to 1000 feet and known as the Manitoba Escarpment. These hills extend northwestward about 300 miles from the middle of the southern boundary of Manitoba and parallel with Lakes Manitoba and Winnipegosis. The second prairie level has an average elevation of 1600 feet and a gently undulating surface, and extends westward some 250 miles to the Coteau or second escarpment. This escarpment, or series of hills, rises 200–500 feet, is nearly parallel with the first, and extends diagonally across Saskatchewan from near its southeast corner into Alberta. The third prairie level, with an elevation of 2500 feet in the east, rises to more than 4000 feet along its western border at the base of the Rockies. Its surface,

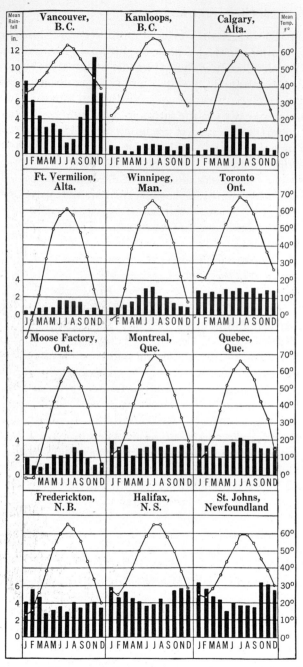

Fig. 219. Mean monthly precipitation and temperature at 12 stations. Describe the precipitation and temperature characteristics in each section of the Dominion. Compare with Figs. 217 and 218.

as a whole, is more irregular than that of the second level, as it is broken
by deep valleys and tablelands like Cypress Hills and Wood Mountain,
rising 1000–2000 feet above the surrounding level plain. The valleys,
however, are scarcely discernible as one looks across the vast expanse of
plains, as they are entrenched in a very flat country.

Like the St. Lawrence Lowland, or Eastern Plains, this region lacks
metals, but has vast deposits of coal, chiefly lignite. The probable bituminous coal reserves of Alberta are estimated to be 35 billion tons, and the
lignite reserves of Manitoba and Saskatchewan 13 billion. The petroleum
reserves are not yet known, but exploration to date indicates reserves to
be measured in terms of 2 to 5 billion barrels. There are also enormous
reserves of natural gas and oil-bearing bituminous sands. The Interior
Plains region also has gypsum and clay suitable for the manufacture of
brick, tile, cement, etc. Most of this region is drained either to the Arctic
Ocean or to Hudson Bay. Many of the streams are navigable in their
plains portions, and others are utilized for irrigation purposes, particularly in southern Alberta.

The climatic variations over the Prairie Plains are considerable, and
correspond very roughly to the first, second, and third prairie levels (Fig.
219). Manitoba, which corresponds roughly to the first prairie level, lies
almost in the center of the continent and hence has the characteristics of
the continental type of climate (Fig. 9). The mean annual range of temperature at Winnipeg is 71°, compared with 21° at Victoria, British
Columbia. There is also a wide variation from the normal temperatures
of winter. The January means for different years have ranged from 8°
below normal to 13° above, and the February means from 25° above to
13° below. Frosts and light snows may occur in May, but are not usually
severe. April is a spring month, with temperature rising rapidly during
the summer. Winnipeg has an average daily maximum of 75° in June
and 78° in July. Severe heat spells characterize the summers, when temperatures rise from 90° to 103°. The mean annual precipitation is 19
inches, being heaviest in the east and decreasing westward. Fifty per cent
of it comes between May and August, largely from local convection
storms. Snowfall in the east is about 52 inches, decreasing to 44 inches in
the west. The ground is usually well covered with snow from December
to March.

Saskatchewan, which corresponds roughly with the second prairie
level, is similar climatically to Manitoba except that the spring is earlier
in the southwest than in the north and east, and the midwinter Chinook
extends at times eastward to Regina. The spring temperature is also a
little higher, up to May, but the summer temperature is a little lower.
Temperature extremes are greater than in Manitoba, being −56° and

107° at Regina. The daily range of summer temperatures is large, as in all the other Prairie Provinces. Frosts may occur during early June and the latter half of August. The average annual rainfall is 14–18 inches, 60 per cent of which comes during the growing season from May to August. There are 30–36 inches of snow in the west and south, and 40–50 inches in the east and north.

In southern Alberta, which corresponds roughly with the third prairie level, the winter climate is highly variable. The normal winter is cold. The extreme cold prevails from November to March in some years; in other years the winter is warm and sunshiny, on account of the constancy of the Chinook. This variation is shown strikingly by a series of temperature changes at Calgary: the mean in November for one year was 39°, and for another year it was 2°; in January the mean one year was –6° and the following year it was 26°. April is a true spring month, and by that time seeding is well along or may be completed. The temperature increases rapidly during May and June, reaching the maximum in July and August, which are hot months. The heaviest rainfall occurs from the middle of May to the end of July, and is about the same as that of southern Ontario and Quebec during the same period. The margin of safety, however, is small, hence a slight decrease below normal may seriously decrease crop yield.

The climate of this region has two striking features: (1) The summer isotherms run nearly north and south with a mean temperature nearly as high in the extreme north as in the south, and the long summer days of the north result in a very rapid growth of plant life. (2) The Chinook winds, which usually occur with strong west and southwest winds, are most frequent in the south, but occur frequently in the Peace River country in the north. The arrival of this wind may bring a temperature change from –20° to 40° in a few hours. The Chinook tends to shorten the winter season and reduce the severity of winter temperatures. Under its influence the grasslands are usually free from snow during the winter months, making grazing possible on the open range.

Pacific Coast Region. The Pacific Coast or Cordilleran Region extends from the Interior Plains to the Pacific Ocean, and includes nearly all of British Columbia and Yukon Territory and part of Alberta and the Northwest Territories. It has an average width of about 400 miles and extends nearly 1500 miles north and south, containing approximately 650,000 square miles. It is a region of lofty, rugged mountain systems with limited agricultural lands in the valleys. On the east are the Rocky Mountains, and on the west the Coast Range with a small central plateau which is broken by numerous smaller ranges. Just west of the Rockies is a valley known as the Rocky Mountain Trench, extending in a northwest-southeast direction for about 700 miles and containing parts of the courses of the Columbia, Frazier, and Kootenay Rivers, and two trib- utaries of the Liard and two of the Peace Rivers. West of the Coast Range is a paritally submerged mountain mass, appearing in Vancouver and Queen Charlotte Islands, which is probably a continuation of the Coast Range of the United States. Owing to the rugged character and few passes, the mountains form a barrier between the coast and the interior, which barrier has now been only partially overcome by the construction of railroads and highways. The Pacific Coast region differs from the west- ern highland section of the United States in a number of striking ways. It is only about one-half as wide, with less interior plateau, with no en- closed drainage basin, and with no truly arid area. It forms about one- sixth of Canada, compared with one-third of the United States; and is mainly forested. Many streams drain the area to the Pacific, Arctic, and Hudson basins. In the south, these streams follow the parallel valleys be- tween the mountain masses but make sharp turns, cutting through the mountains in deep canyons with many rapids and falls, making water power available in large amounts. Many long, narrow lakes, the product of glacial erosion and deposition, occur in the valleys and along the water courses. The coast is of the fiord type and is estimated to be 7000 miles long.

The region is rich in mineral resources. Coal deposits occur throughout its length, and gold, silver, copper, lead, and zinc are abundant. The great placer gold fields of the Klondike are well known.

The prevailing Westerlies bring to the coast of this region the modify- ing influence of the ocean. The climate varies strikingly with altitude and distance from the sea (Figs. 217 and 218). Along the coast the rainfall exceeds 100 inches, but is less than half that amount only a comparatively short distance east. The dry period occurs from May to September, and the period of heavy rain from September to March when the warm oceanic winds are blowing on cool lands of high altitude. Severe frosts rarely occur at the lower levels. These levels, west of the Selkirks, have a mild climate, where spring arrives early, and frost rarely occurs later than April, and March is distinctly a spring month. The summers are warm and the winters usually mild and rainy, especially near the coast. About 70 miles inland at Agassiz, the average January temperature is 35°, and the July average 64°, while − 13° and 103° are recorded ex- tremes. The average annual rainfall is 67 inches, two-thirds of which falls from October to March inclusive (Fig. 219).

East of the Coast Range, marked climatic changes occur. The Wester- lies leave most of their moisture on the west side of the mountains, and, in descending, become warm and evaporating winds; hence the plateau between the Coast and the Selkirk ranges is dry. The summers are warm and the winters colder than on the coastal lowlands. The colder winter, however, is not severe, and the heat of summer is not unpleasant as the air is dry and the nights are cool.

In the more southerly sections of British Columbia, April temperatures resemble those of England, which bears a similar relation to water bodies, and the summers are similar to those of southern Ontario except that there is less rainfall and the air is drier.

Arctic Archipelago and Hudson Bay Lowland.   This region is a continuation of the Canadian Shield and consists chiefly of the islands north of the mainland. Its basic rock structure is made up of ancient crystalline rocks, overlain by Paleozoic formations. In the west coal deposits occur in Pennsylvanian Strata. The region has a polar climate (Fig. 9), and the vegetation is the tundra type.

General Climatic Features.   The climate of Canada as a whole is characterized by considerable variations due to its large land mass, diversified topography, large latitude extent, and proximity of portions of the area to water bodies.[2] The lofty mountain mass of the west is probably the most important topographic feature, as it confines the tempering influence of the ocean to the West Coast, which has the only true maritime type of climate. The interior is characterized by zero and subzero temperatures in winter and high temperatures in summer. The Pacific Coast is mild throughout the year, whereas the Atlantic Coast is mild in winter and hot in summer, the average July temperatures being similar to those of the interior. Winter rainfall is heavy on the Pacific, abundant over most of the Atlantic and St. Lawrence sections, and scant in the interior. Summer rainfall is more evenly distributed over the southern half of Canada. It is more abundant in the east and far west than in the interior, where semiarid conditions prevail in southern Alberta, Saskatchewan, and parts of the Pacific Coast Region.

NATIVE PLANT LIFE

Canada's native plant life is one of its greatest assets. Its distribution illustrates an interesting adjustment to geographic environment, particularly to varying precipitation, temperature, and soil. Since nearly all of Canada was covered by ice during the Glacial Epoch, the plant life that flourished before that time migrated southward, or northward into the unglaciated portions of Alaska, though some species were probably destroyed. As the ice receded northward, vegetation followed the ice front; hence the present native plant life is composed almost entirely of

[2] For more detailed description, see *Canada Yearbook*, 1949, p. 41.

postglacial immigrants, which established themselves in provinces or zones in which the climate and soil met their special requirements. Few plants not of particular significance to man are considered here. The forests may be divided roughly into three areas: (1) the fir forest of the Pacific Coast and Rocky Mountains; (2) the northern coniferous forest extending in a wide curve from Labrador north of the Great Lakes to the Yukon; and (3) the deciduous hardwood and mixed hard- and softwood forest stretching from the Atlantic Coast through southern Quebec and Ontario to Lake Huron. It is estimated that 1,306,000 square miles are forest covered, nearly seven-tenths of which is accessible and productive forest area, and one-third carries merchantable timber (Table XVI). Some of this land is suitable for agricultural purposes, but it is probable that at least 1,100,000 square miles is best adapted to forest growth. Nearly a third of the saw timber is inaccessible under present economic conditions. For geographical purposes we may divide Canada into six plant provinces, or zones. These provinces are the Arctic; Subarctic and Northern Softwood Forest; Hardwood and Mixed Hardwood and Softwood Forest; Prairie; Rocky Mountain and Plateau; and Coast Mountains (Fig. 220).

TABLE XVI

ESTIMATED STAND OF TIMBER IN CANADA *

	Conifers		Broad-Leaved		Totals	
	Saw Timber (Million feet board measure)	Small Timber (000 Cords)	Saw Timber (Million feet board measure)	Small Timber (000 Cords)	Saw Timber (Million feet board measure)	Small Timber (000 Cords)
Prince Edward Island	65	560	40	240	105	800
Nova Scotia	4,850	23,165	1,600	5,940	6,450	29,105
New Brunswick	6,000	50,000	3,000	30,000	9,000	80,000
Quebec	41,110	453,330	14,390	176,120	55,500	629,450
Ontario	42,560	273,790	11,390	286,140	53,950	559,930
Manitoba	855	9,645	1,620	19,110	2,475	28,755
Saskatchewan	1,850	8,920	2,100	51,060	3,950	59,980
Alberta	7,000	74,400	2,080	36,000	9,080	110,400
British Columbia	109,740	186,290	No data	No data	109,740	186,290
Accessible	214,030	1,080,100	36,220	604,610	250,250	1,684,710
Inaccessible	176,345	873,385	3,700	136,260	180,045	1,009,645
Total	390,375	1,953,485	39,920	740,870	430,295	2,694,355

* Exclusive of Newfoundland.

Arctic Province. That portion of Canada lying north of the tree line may be considered the Arctic Province. It is, therefore, a treeless region,

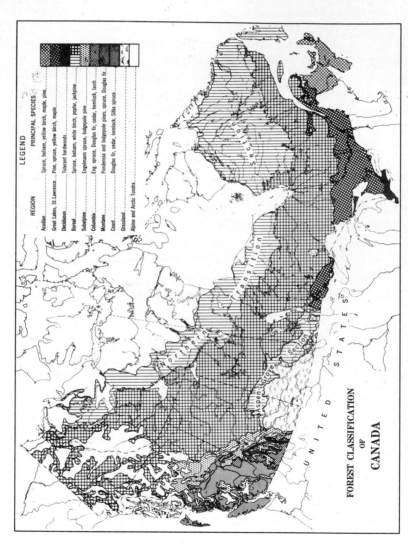

Fig. 220 The forests of Canada. *After and by Courtesy of the Dominion Bureau of Statistics.*

the southern boundary of which extends far south of the Arctic Circle, along a line extending roughly from the mouth of the Mackenzie River around the south shore of Hudson Bay to the eastern shore of Ungava Bay, and southeasterly to Hamilton Inlet in Labrador. The vegetation is low-growing or dwarfed, with the woody types often prostrate or trailing on the ground. Willows and dwarf birches are among the most prominent woody forms in the north, and members of the blueberry family in the south. Grasses, mosses, and flowers in profusion cover large areas during the short growing season, constituting a true arctic prairie. In some portions the vegetation grows in bunches similar in many respects to that of the arid regions farther south. Nearly all the plants are perennials; some go through the long winter with leaf, bud, and flower well advanced, and bloom with great rapidity the following spring. The future economic value of this region probably lies in its utilization for the production of reindeer, caribou, or muskox, though the fur industries will continue to be of importance.

Subarctic and Northern Softwood Forest Province. The southern boundary of this region extends southward and eastward from where the Arctic Circle crosses the Alaskan boundary, along the foothills of the Rocky Mountains, the northern border of the prairies to the southern end of Lake Winnipeg, and across the Gaspé Peninsula to southern Labrador, including Newfoundland. This boundary is also practically the northern limit of white and red pine. The province is dominantly a coniferous forest area with a striking uniformity in species and general character. The trees are relatively small in size, and there are comparatively few species. Black and white spruce predominate. Among other trees are the Banksian pine, which supplies lumber to the prairie section, aspen, balsam poplar, white birch, larch, and balsam fir. The province is largely unsettled at the present time, but the pulp and paper industry is now entering the area.

Hardwood and Mixed Hardwood and Softwood Forest Province. This province includes that portion of Canada south of the Northern Softwood Forest which lies east of the southern end of Lake Winnipeg. It is characterized by deciduous trees, the principal ones being yellow birch, basswood, sugar maple, red maple, black ash, white elm, red oak, burr oak, hickory, and beech. A few coniferous trees, such as white and red pine, hemlock, and white cedar, are scattered through the forest and increase in relative numbers northward. The abundant moisture and fairly long growing season provide for a luxuriant growth of plant life. Extensive lumber and pulp industries are now carried on in this province.

Prairie Province. The Prairie Province extends from the foothills of the Rocky Mountains on the west and the Subarctic province on the north to the Hardwood Forest province on the east. It includes the grass-land areas of Alberta, Saskatchewan, and Manitoba. The vegetation cover varies with the rain and snow supply, being more luxuriant in the east and varying to the semiarid and arid types in the west, where in the foothills it mingles with the Alpine types of the Rockies. The quantity of vegetation in any given season bears very close relation to the abundance of rainfall, and the snow supply of the preceding winter. If these supplies are small, vegetation will be sparse, but if the moisture supply is abundant, vegetation will likewise be abundant. Along the streams of the first prairie level there are a few trees, such as ash, elm, poplar, and Manitoba maple; but the area is treeless away from the streams. Poplar and oaks occur along the escarpments, but the major part of the second prairie level is a grass-covered steppe, though shrubs occur in thickets. The third prairie level is treeless, except on Wood Mountain and Cypress Hills, and the vegetation is scant and desertlike in appearance and character, many of the plants being of the drought-resisting type. This province is dominantly an agricultural and grazing country.

Rocky Mountain and Plateau Province.   This includes the Rocky Mountains on the east and extends to the Coast Mountains on the west. There is considerable variation in the native plant life of this region; in fact, the region might be divided into the Interior Wet Belt province and the Interior Dry Belt province. The Rocky Mountain province is mainly covered with coniferous forest except on the higher slopes, the principal trees being the lodgepole and white bark pine, white spruce, balsam fir, and larch. Above the tree line there are many species of herbaceous vegetation, including many brightly colored flowers characteristic of Alpine regions. Many of these species are also found in the Arctic province. The Interior Wet Belt has more moisture than the Rocky Mountains, and the alpine meadows extend to the snow line. The dominant trees are cedar, Douglas fir, hemlock, and Engelmann spruce. The Dry Belts include the Okanagon and Kamloops districts, within which there is considerable variation. One section has bunchgrass of "wild rye" and no forest; the second section has limited forests of yellow pine. In general, the Dry Belts have a parklike character with desert ground vegetation.

Coast Mountain Province.   This province contains many species not found elsewhere in Canada, although it also has a large number of species common to the Selkirk region. Because of the high average temperature, heavy rainfall, and long growing season, the vegetation of the coast and lowland valleys approaches a sutbropical appearance in its luxuriance and growth. In many undisturbed sections, fallen trees, shrubs, ferns, and other herbaceous plants form almost a jungle. Even where the forest stand is dense, the undergrowth is abundant; and, along the coast, grass grows luxuriantly. Douglas fir, Sitka spruce, red cedar, western hemlock, red alder, and broad-leaved maple are the principal trees. The Douglas fir, cedar, and spruce reach a size that may be truly described as gigantic. The Douglas fir attains a height of 300 feet and a circumference of 50 feet, and is distributed over most of southern British Columbia, but disappears about 50° north latitude. The largest trees occur on Vancouver Island and along the mainland coast. The lumber resources of this particular province are very large.

FOREST INDUSTRIES

Forest Products. The forest resources are among the greatest held by any country in the world. Forest products rank next to those of agriculture in value. Sawmill and pulpmill products are the most important and

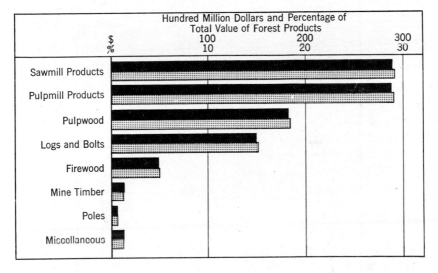

Fig. 221. Principal forest products of Canada. Three-year average.

are nearly alike in value. Other leading products are pulpwood, logs and bolts, firewood, mine timbers, poles, and squared timber for export. British Columbia leads in sawmill products, followed by Quebec and Ontario, the three producing more than four-fifths of the total. New Brunswick and Nova Scotia rank next in order.

The rise of woodpulp and paper manufacture to the rank of a major industry is relatively recent. The first pulp mill is said to have been erected in 1866. Fourteen years later, 5 pulp mills were in operation, and 24 in 1891. Since then the industry has experienced a rapid growth. At

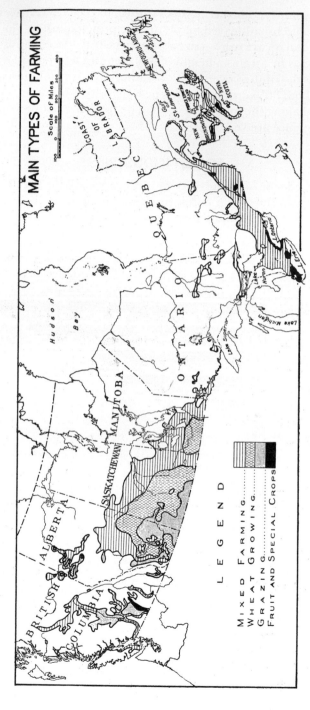

Fig. 222. Main types of farming in Canada. The East is predominantly a land of mixed farming and dairying, and the West a land of grain growing, especially wheat, and of ranching. *Courtesy, Dominion Bureau of Statistics.*

present, 113 mills are engaged in the production of pulp and paper. This development is due primarily to the coexistence of abundant water power and great resources of the species of trees best adapted to present processes of pulp manufacture. Probably only slightly less important is the proximity of excellent markets in the United States. Pulpwood, which is now second in rank among the primary forest products, is produced from spruce, balsam fir, hemlock, poplar, and Jack pine, most of it being derived from spruce. Quebec and Ontario lead in woodpulp production, yielding four-fifths of the total output. The paper-making industry grew rapidly during the 1940's and early 1950's, and Canada has become the world's leading producer of newsprint—nearly three-fifths of the world output. All but a small fraction is produced in Quebec and Ontario. The pulp and paper industry has now become one of the leading manufacturing industries of the Dominion.

Surplus Produced.   With the vast forest resources, one would expect the people to produce more than was needed for home consumption. The exports of forest products rank next to the exports of agricultural products. The United States and the United Kingdom are the principal markets, nearly seven-tenths of the exports going to the United States. The United States receives annually all of Canada's exports of pulpwood and more than four-fifths of its woodpulp and newsprint. More than half of the newsprint paper consumed in the United States yearly is either manufactured in Canada or is made from imported Canadian pulpwood and pulp. Owing to the depleted condition of its forests, the United States may be considered as not only the greatest present market, but also a permanent one, for Canada. As the vast forest resources of Canada have scarcely been touched at present, they may be expected to make a large contribution to the economic welfare of the Canadian people. It has been said that in no other country do "forests play a more vital part in sustaining the industries of the country."

FOOD PRODUCTION

Agriculture

Agriculture is second among the leading industries, measured by value, but it gives employment to many more people than any other industry. More than a quarter of the people in gainful occupations depend upon it. It is limited almost entirely to the southern border, where there are large areas of virgin, fertile soil, with favorable climatic conditions for hardy grains and fruits, hay and forage, and root crops. The crop acreage of Saskatchewan is larger than that of any other province, and is followed by Alberta, Ontario, Manitoba, and Quebec. Measured by value of field crops produced, Saskatchewan, Ontario, and Alberta, in order, are the leading agricultural provinces, and their combined revenue forms more than two-thirds the total of Canada. The crop map (Fig. 222) emphasizes the fact that agriculture is confined to two major regions, the Great Lakes-St. Lawrence Lowland and the Prairie Plains. Two minor agricultural sections are the Maritime Provinces and the Pacific Mountain Region. The leading crops of Canada, shown in Fig. 223, clearly indicate present land use. Nearly all (98.7 per cent) of the cropland is used to produce nine crops. However, three-fifths is devoted to wheat and oats alone, and another fifth to hay crops. Hay and forage (both cultivated and wild hay) are a very important Canadian crop, exceeding any other crop, except wheat, in value.

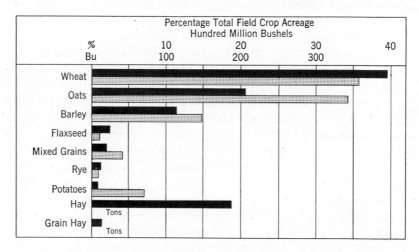

Fig: 223. Principal field crops of Canada. Three-year average. These nine crops occupy nearly all (98.7 per cent) of the cultivated land of Canada.

Livestock.   The principal livestock raised on Canadian farms are cattle, swine, sheep, and poultry. The total number is small in comparison with the number of livestock in the United States, but it compares favorably with leading single states. As cattle are raised on nearly every farm, their distribution corresponds fairly closely with the agricultural area. Nearly half the cattle, however, are confined to the Great Lakes-St. Lawrence Lowland and the adjoining margin of the Canadian Shield, where dairying has been making rapid progress. Butter and cheese are the leading products of the dairy factories. Dairying has also become a very important industry in the Prairie Plains.

Surplus Produced.   Canada now produces a surplus of a number of food products. This is especially true of grain and animal products.

Wheat and wheat flour constitute the largest items in the grain group. Dairy products stand first among the animal products, followed by meats. This indicates that the people of Canada are producing annually considerably more than is needed for their own consumption, and raises the question of present and future land utilization.

Agricultural Area.   Only a small portion of the land area of Canada is now used for crop production. The occupied farm land is one-half of the potential agricultural land, and the crop average is less than one-fourth though it has made a substantial gain.

TABLE XVII

Occupied and Potential Agricultural Land in Canada *

	Land Area (square miles)	Occupied		Total Potential Agricultural Land		
		Square Miles	Per Cent of Potential	Square Miles	Per Cent of Total Potential	Per Cent of Land Area
Prince Edward Island	2,184	1,826	92.6	1,970	0.3	90.2
Nova Scotia	20,743	5,963	47.1	12,640	2.4	60.9
New Brunswick	27,473	6,194	36.9	16,750	3.1	60.9
Quebec	523,860	28,222	42.3	66,615	12.5	12.7
Ontario	363,282	34,981	34.0	102,870	19.3	28.3
Manitoba	219,723	26,393	52.1	50,590	9.5	23.0
Saskatchewan	237,975	93,689	74.9	125,080	23.4	52.5
Alberta	248,800	67,621	49.4	136,640	25.6	54.9
British Columbia	359,279	6,302	30.4	20,700	3.9	5.7
Total	2,003,319	271,191	50.7	533,855	100.0	26.6
Yukon and Northwest Territories	1,458,784	4		14,069	2.5	0.9
Total	3,462,103	271,195	49.4	547,924		15.8

* Newfoundland and Labrador are not included because available data are inadequate.

It is not possible to state the potential agricultural area with any great degree of accuracy. Nevertheless, available figures are sufficiently accurate to show large agricultural possibilities, and to assure a food-producing capacity sufficient to maintain a much larger population. Canada has an estimated arable area of approximately 341,670,000 acres, or about a fourth of the total area, exclusive of the Northwest and Yukon Territories, which have little or no crop value, or which are not likely to be used for crop production until the more desirable land elsewhere is utilized. The arable land of Newfoundland might add 20,000 or 30,000 acres to the total. The potential acreage varies from 6 per cent of British

Columbia to 90 per cent of Prince Edward Island. The distribution by provinces is shown in Table XVII. Nearly half the potential agricultural land is in Saskatchewan and Alberta, and nearly a third in Quebec and Ontario.

FISHERIES

The First Industry.   Fishing was the first industry to be followed systematically by Europeans in what is now the Canadian domain. When Cabot first sighted the North American mainland in 1498, he named it "Bacalaos," the Basque word meaning codfish. It was the early French fishermen who contributed the familiar name Cape Breton. Many other names stand as memorials to the pioneers on Canadian fishing grounds. The French, Spanish, and Portuguese were there before 1502, plying their trade in the primitive manner of the time. Though the fishing industry got an early start, it remained small for more than three centuries. Its principal growth has occurred comparatively recently. In 1844 the value of the catch was only about $125,000; by 1860 it was somewhat in excess of $1,000,000; and 10 years later it amounted to $6,000,000. Today the industry is conducted on a large commercial scale on the Atlantic and Pacific Coasts and in inland waters. It yields products worth $121,125,-000 and gives full-time employment to 36,400 people, four times as many being engaged in the sea fisheries as in the inland fisheries.

Inland Fisheries.   The inland fisheries are small compared with the sea fisheries of either coast. Nearly two-thirds of the total catch is taken in Ontario. Whitefish, the most important inland commercial fish, is found in the Great Lakes, Lake Winnipeg, and its tributaries. Others are pickerel, trout, goldeyes, and pike.

Surplus.   The production of fish products greatly exceeds the home demand. The value of the exports is more than two-thirds of the total value produced annually. The United States and the United Kingdom are the principal markets, more than seven times as much going to the former as to the latter. The other important markets are the West Indies, France, Australia, and Brazil.

MINERALS

Distribution and Production.   Scattered over the large area of Canada, minerals occur in great variety. Those that may be considered critical in the development of modern nations, viz., coal, oil, and iron, are unfavorably distributed as they are on or near the Pacific and Atlantic margins of the country. So far as a survey of mineral resources is concerned, only the southern portion of Canada is known, and that only partially. Minerals are known to exist in isolated places over the vast stretch of northern Canada, but little more is known about them. Minerals were among the first of Canada's resources to be recognized as of importance. Iron, silver, copper, and amethyst were discovered as early as 1604, and coal was known by at least the last quarter of the same century. Development of minerals on more than a local basis did not occur until many years later. The growth of mineral production has been gradual, and to-day the mineral industries make a large annual contribution to the wealth of Canada and occupy the attention of many people. The production of minerals is widespread throughout Canada, operations being conducted from British Columbia to Newfoundland and northward into Arctic lands. However, more than half the value of minerals produced annually is contributed by Ontario and Quebec.

The average annual value of the mineral production of Canada is nearly $500,000,000. Measured by value gold leads, followed by copper, coal, and nickel. The nine minerals shown in Fig. 224 contribute more than four-fifths of the annual mineral production.

Coal.   The coal resources of Canada are very large if all kinds of coal are considered. Nearly half the total is in Alberta and is practically all

TABLE XVIII

ESTIMATED COAL RESERVES OF CANADA

	Probable (000 tons)	Percentage Bituminous and Anthracite	Possible (000 tons)	Percentage Bituminous and Anthracite	Percentage Total Probable and Possible of Canada	Percentage Total and Probable Possible Reserves of Bituminous and Anthracite
Alberta	34,437,710	100.0	13,436,560	99.9	48.4	66.7
Saskatchewan	13,126,880	nil	11,004,000	nil	24.4	nil
British Columbia	11,795,480	98.7	7,034,556	98.3	19.0	25.8
Nova Scotia	1,967,024	100.0	1,147,382	100.0	3.1	4.3
Yukon	434,500	25.7	1,449,840	14.5	1.9	0.45
Northwest Territories	140,000	21.6	2,489,760	68.1	2.6	2.4
Ontario	100,000	nil	50,000	nil	0.1	nil
New Brunswick	89,814	100.0	11,566	100.0	0.1	0.14
Manitoba	33,600	nil	67,200	nil	1.0	nil
Total	62,125,098	77.8	36,690,864	63.8	100.0	100.00

bituminous and anthracite. Other valuable deposits of anthracite and bituminous are in Nova Scotia, New Brunswick, and British Columbia. It is apparent that the great coal resources of Canada are very unfavor-bly locted, from the standpoint of human use, under present conditions. Their position in the far east and the far west, separated by the coalless

Canadian Shield, leaves the Great Lakes-St. Lawrence Lowland, where most of the people live, dependent upon the United States for most of its coal, as transportation costs prevent the use of Canadian coal. Nearly three-fifths of the production is in Alberta and British Columbia, and more than 30 per cent in the Maritime Provinces. This places the effective production on opposite sides of the country. To meet the needs of the more densely settled and industrial Lowlands, Canada imports two-thirds of the coal it consumes annually. Some British Columbia coal finds a market along the Pacific Coast of the United States, and some of the Nova Scotia coal goes to New England.

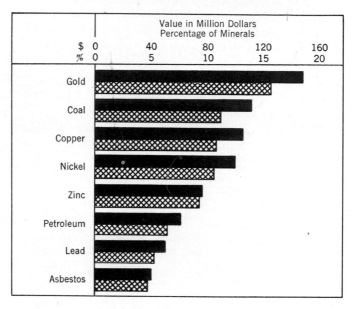

Fig. 224. Principal minerals produced in Canada. These eight account for more than three-fourths of the value of all minerals produced in Canada.

Surplus. The mining industry has reached a stage where a net surplus of some minerals is available for export. Precious metals (gold) lead the list, followed by asbestos and nickel. The production of asbestos and nickel constitutes most of the world's supply.

MANUFACTURES

Growth. The growth of manufacturing industries in Canada has been slow compared with that in the United States and in other countries having greater population. However, the growth has been steady during the last half century. In 1870, less than 200,000 people were employed in manufacturing, and the number now exceeds 1,150,000. During the first half of the nineteenth century, manufacturing was mostly of the household type. The so-called "Industrial Revolution," or development of the factory system of production for a national or international market, commenced shortly before Confederation (1867), and is still in progress. World War I accelerated production profoundly, and its influence continued to World War II, which stimulated manufacturing development still more. Many of the large industrial establishments are subsidiaries of

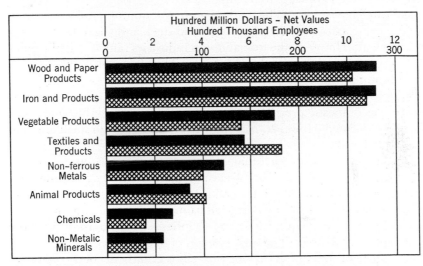

Fig. 225. Manufacturing by leading industrial groups. With the exception of textiles, Canadian manufactures are based primarily upon the utilization of domestic raw materials. Forest industries lead net value of products, but the iron industries give employment to more people.

United States corporations. These branch plants avoid Canadian import tariffs for the home market and gain preferential tariff rates to other parts of the British Empire. A large-scale organization of industries is not widespread at present, but has begun and will probably increase with an increase in population that gives a market to large amounts of standard products. Also, production for international markets is now well established. Canada's exports to British Empire countries are largely manufactured products, and the exports of manufactured and semimanufactured goods to the United States are larger than the exports of raw materials.

Canada's manufacturing industries (Fig. 225) are built chiefly upon the use of domestic raw materials and a home market for the finished products. There is a tendency to import raw materials to supply manufactures not only to home markets but also to world markets. This is shown by the imports of raw cotton from the United States, hides from Argentina, rubber from the Straits Settlements and Malay Peninsula, sugar from the West Indies, wool from Australia and New Zealand; and by the exports of manufactured articles. True measures of the importance of manufactures are the value added by the manufacturing process and the number of people employed, but, since fluctuation in prices greatly lessens the significance of value added by manufacturing, both measures are used in the following discussion.

Principal Industries.   The leading groups of manufactures measured by net value are wood and paper, iron and steel, and vegetable and textile products. However, the iron and steel industries rank first in the number of people employed, and textiles third. The high rank of the iron and steel group is indicative of the industrial evolution that is taking place, as much of the raw material is imported. Both iron ore and coal are imported, as domestic production is inadequate, and suitable coal is unfavorably located. However, Nova Scotia produces coal to smelt ore from Newfoundland.

The first six leading individual industries, measured by product value, are pulp and paper making, meat packing, smelting of non-ferrous metals, sawmilling, flour and feed milling, and butter and cheese making, and are based on local raw materials from forest, farm, and mine. The seventh—electrical equipment and supplies—is based upon the great water-power resources. The high position of this industry is suggestive of the absence of coal in the regions where it is greatly needed, and of the effort of the Canadian people to solve this problem by utilizing one of their resources.

Distribution.   Ontario and Quebec are the leading industrial provinces, as they produce four-fifths of the manufactures (net value) of Canada and have a like proportion of employees. Iron, and coal for manufacturing purposes, are imported very largely from the United States, since the coal of the Maritime provinces and the iron from Newfoundland are too distant to compete. The development of water power to supplant coal is progressing rapidly in this region. Four-fifths of Canada's industry is now operated by electricity. All other provinces are of comparatively small importance in manufacturing.

As the growth and prosperity of cities are intimately associated with the development of manufactures, the localization of manufacturing becomes of great interest. The 6 leading manufacturing metropolitan areas are Montreal, Toronto, Hamilton, Vancouver, Windsor, Winnipeg—4 of which are in the Great Lakes-St. Lawrence Lowland. Nearly one-half of the manufacturing industry of Canada is concentrated in these 6 areas, whether measured by net value or by number of employees (Fig. 226). However, there is a marked difference in their relative rank. Montreal and Toronto are the premier industrial cities and hold a commanding position over all others. Those two areas alone contribute nearly one-third of the net value of Canada's manufactures. All other cities are of relatively small importance although each is of considerable significance locally. *What factors have contributed to the growth of industry in these cities? Can Canada become one of the leading manufacturing countries of the world?*

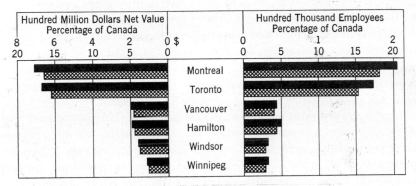

Fig. 226. The six leading manufacturing metropolitan areas of Canada.

TRANSPORTATION

Railroads and Highways. Canada's broad expanse of territory, the large extent of area with very small production, and the 13,200,000 people scattered along its southern border present a big problem of transportation and communication, a problem that must be solved before the resources of large portions of the country can be developed. The productive parts of Canada are separated from each other by areas of wilderness, e.g., the region between Quebec and New Brunswick; and the area north of Lakes Superior and Huron, separating the industrial region of the Great Lakes-St. Lawrence Lowland from the agricultural region of the Prairie Plains. In a country like Canada, with its sparse population, a western agricultural section that produces mainly for export, and an eastern manufacturing section that produces largely for consumption in distant parts, efficient transportation is a necessity. When Canada depended upon water routes for transportation, its economic life practically stood still during the season when its waterways were closed by ice.

Railways are the fundamental means of modern land transportation and must precede settlement in the present age. This necessity has led to the extension of government aid to private railroads in order that they might be built through sparsely settled districts with little available traffic, or in advance of settlement. The first railway was built in 1835, but the railway era began in 1851. At that time there were only 66 miles of railroad in Canada. Since then the main mileage has been expanded to 42,300, exclusive of 700 miles of narrow gauge in Newfoundland, which is a creditable growth when one considers the small population of the country. Much of this growth has been brought about through government aid or construction, 21,556 miles now being owned and operated by the Dominion Government. About one-fourth of Canada's railway mileage is in Ontario. The Dominion now has three transcontinental lines, one the Canadian Pacific, and two of the Canadian National Railways. It is probable that immediate future growth will consist of the construction of a network of feeders to these main lines in order better to serve and develop the country now open for settlement.

Highways probably rank next to railways in making occupancy and development of a country possible. To provide highways adequate to serve such a large area, having only a few people, is a very expensive undertaking. Relative to the area the 554,000 miles now in use appears very small; however, the southern portion, where most of the people live, may be considered well served. The trans-Canada highway makes it possible for motor vehicles to traverse the country from Halifax to Vancouver. The Alaska Highway gives access to the Northwest.

Canals. Before the railroad era, the St. Lawrence and Ottawa Rivers and Great Lakes were the principal avenues of transportation. However, portages were necessary along these routes; hence canal construction has been designed as a means to overcome these obstacles. The canals of Canada may be placed in four groups: (1) the St. Lawrence and Great Lakes groups, consisting of nine canals, including the Welland and Sault Ste. Marie, which are of first importance; (2) the Ottawa and Rideau Rivers group, consisting of four canals; (3) the Richelieu River group, having two canals; and (4) a miscellaneous group, consisting of Trent, St. Peter's and St. Andrew's Canals. Collectively they provide 509 miles of navigable waterways, though their relative importance is not to be measured by their length. Most of the canal traffic occurs during the summer and fall months, and consists chiefly of bulky or heavy mine products, such as coal, and farm products, especially wheat.

Airways. A network of government and privately owned airlines provides passenger and cargo service to southern Canada. The main lines extend across the country from east to west, and other lines serve the north country to Yukon, Labrador, and the Arctic. In addition, charter service is available to many sections of the country otherwise inaccessible. The mileage flown has reached the impressive figure of 26,000,000, the number of passengers carried more than 800,000, and the freight poundage 25,000,000.

Other Means of Communication. The telegraph, telephone, wireless, and mails are probably of only slightly less importance than railroads, highways, and airlines in tying together the widely scattered settlements of the country and making effective its economic life. The first telegraph line was built in 1846; telephone development dates from 1880; and scores of radio-telegraph stations have been installed since 1903. Government and private systems now extend throughout the settled areas and reach many remote points of the Dominion.

FOREIGN TRADE

Growth. Canada's foreign trade experienced a steady growth until the beginning of World War I, when the closing of old avenues of world trade and the opening of new ones brought about rapid development. Until the time of this rapid growth, imports had considerably exceeded exports; but with the stimulus of high prices and war production this situation was reversed, and so continued until about 1921. The decline in trade during the next year shows the influence of the contraction of industry and world trade following war conditions. World War II again stimulated production and trade, which have continued to grow to meet world demand for products. With only about 0.5 per cent of the world's population, Canada now ranks as one of the top trading nations. In a country like Canada with a small population, a high living standard, large resources, and production of basic commodities, foreign trade is vital to domestic economy. Approximately a third of the national income is derived from foreign trade. *What basal factors favor future growth in foreign trade?*

Character of Trade. The home produce that enters Canadian commerce is the product of its farms, forests, mines, and seas. For many years Canada was primarily a seller of raw and partly manufactured material and a buyer of manufactured articles. This is likely to be true of new countries in their earlier stages of economic development. However, with the United States market for forest products, and the growth of manufacturing plants, a change in the character of Canada's trade is now in progress. Manufactured forest products—newsprint paper, lumber, and woodpulp—now lead in the export trade, with wheat and wheat flour ranking second. Fully half the total exports are now fully manufactured products, and a quarter are semimanufactured. Major imports are still manufactures with machinery, of all kinds, in the lead. The outstanding raw material imported is coal, to meet a deficiency which Canada cannot supply. About seven-tenths of all imports are fully manufactured goods (Fig. 227).

Countries with Which Canada Trades.   Two countries buy from Canada considerably more than half of all it has to sell, and sell to it nearly all that it buys. More than a third of all its exports are purchased by the United States, and more than a quarter by the United Kingdom. More than three-fourths of its imports come from the United States; hence the

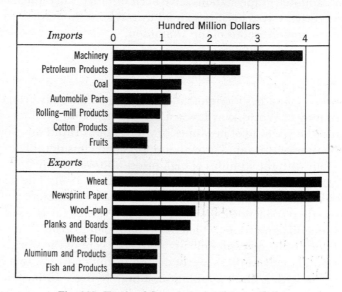

Fig. 227. Trade of Canada by leading products.

economic welfare of its people is linked closely with conditions prevailing in those two countries. Among the many factors that contribute to the dominance of the United States in Canadian trade are: a common language; proximity and free movement of people; minimum of exchange problems, growth of subsidiary or branch manufacturing plants of United States in Canada; influence of United States radio, magazines, and extensive advertising; and the great demand in the United States for Canadian forest products, especially woodpulp and newsprint paper. The balance of Canadian trade is widespread throughout the world, and includes British West Indies, South Africa, Australia, India, Argentina, Brazil, Venezuela, and many European countries. Foodstuffs, especially wheat

and flour, are the major products that go to the United Kingdom
(Fig. 228).

Foreign Trade by Regions.   The foreign trade of Canada may conveniently be divided into four principal trade regions. The Quebec and
Ontario region, which is essentially the Great Lakes-St. Lawrence Lowland, is by far the most important, having more than half the total foreign
trade. The principal ports are Montreal, Toronto, Cobourg, Fort William, Port Arthur, and Sault Ste. Marie. This is the region with most of
the population, large production, excellent inland transportation, good
harbors, and accessibility to the great markets of western Europe. The
Maritime Provinces rank second, British Columbia third, and the Prairie

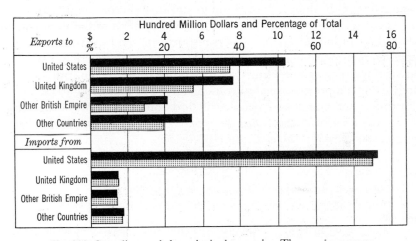

Fig. 228. Canadian trade by principal countries. Three-year average.

Plains and Arctic fourth. Halifax, Saint John, Sydney, and Saint John's
are the dominant ports for the Maritime Provinces; Emerson, Churchill,
and North Portal for the Prairie Provinces; Vancouver and Victoria for
British Columbia. The Maritime Provinces and British Columbia have
excellent water outlets, whereas the commerce of the Prairie Provinces
must depend upon extensive inland transportation, and transhipment to
the Great Lakes.

THE FUTURE

The northerly location of Canada, its climatic limitations, erroneous
conceptions of its resources, and the known opportunities offered by the
United States determined that its development should be delayed until

the more enticing opportunities offered the immigrant in the United States became fewer. That a region with such extensive forest, mineral, water, and sea resources should eventually attract a population and develop transportation, commerce, and manufactures, was inevitable, though such development has scarcely more than made a start. Today the cultivated land and food production per capita ranks among the highest in the world, whereas the potential agricultural land of Canada is capable of providing food and homes for several times the present population. Its vast forest resources have scarcely been touched, though they now engage the attention of many people. Great varieties of minerals are known to exist, and most of the country still remains to be examined. All these resources may supply raw materials to manufacturing industries, which are yet in their infancy, and its streams, petroleum, natural gas, and coal may supply the power. The development of these industries should result in the expansion of transportation and wider extension of commerce to world markets, and should advance settlement to habitable areas now unpeopled. Thus Canada stands today as a nation looking forward to a more intensive utilization of its geographic resources, and to the time when many more people will find homes within its borders. *Has it a sound foundation upon which to build? What have the people done in its geographic regions thus far, and what may they do?*

PROBLEMS

1. Will Canada become the most important unit in the British Empire?
2. Have the people of Canada attained more than half the industrial development possible?
3. Is it probable that Canada can produce four or five times its present agricultural output?
4. Can Canada become one of the three or four leading manufacturing and commercial nations of the world?
5. Are the natural assets of Canada more favorable to the evolution of a strong and prosperous nation than are those of either Brazil or Argentina?
6. Are the natural resources favorable to the maintenance of three or four times as many people as now live in Canada?
7. Do the natural resources of Canada make it as desirable a home for man as that part of Europe which lies within the same latitudinal limits?
8. Is Cnada at least half as favorable as a home for man as the United States?
9. Arrange the following items in order of their relative importance in the present and future development of Canada: (1) type of human human stock, (2) minerals, (3) climate, (4) rivers and lakes, (5) topography, (6) soil, (7) coast, (8) location, (9) forests.
10. Why have the Great Lakes been of less importance to Canada than to the United States?

CHAPTER 21

The Maritime Provinces

The Maritime Provinces have been aptly described as the "land that was passed by." Though the first settlement in Canada was established in Nova Scotia, and though the provinces are supplied with resources, they have remained essentially static. During the period of early settlement the flow of immigrants "passed by" to the more promising interior lands. Hundreds of miles of uninhabited forest separate the region from the more densely peopled St. Lawrence Lowland and Ontario Plains; and the St. Lawrence—the national highway—is closed by ice for half the year. Even the Intercolonial Railway, which passes north of Maine in order to remain in Canadian territory, is used but little and is operated at a loss. Only the coastal fringe of Nova Scotia, New Brunswick, Prince Edward Island, and Newfoundland are at all densely populated. People are more evenly distributed over Prince Edward Island than any other Province. Prince Edward's gently rolling surface, dotted with comfortable rural homes, presents a pleasing agricultural landscape. A large part of the interior of New Brunswick, Nova Scotia, and Newfoundland is very sparsely settled. Large areas are uninhabited.

In general the surface is mountainlike, with the highlands, lowlands, and large coastal indentations trending northeast-southwest in conformity with the Appalachian system. A large part of New Brunswick and Prince Edward Island has an average elevation of only a few hundred feet, but it is by no means flat. In northwestern New Brunswick is a broken, highly hilly district reaching an elevation of 2500 feet, and a similar plateaulike country borders the Bay of Fundy. The central ridge of Nova Scotia reaches an elevation of 1500 feet in Cape Breton Island. Aside from Prince Edward Island, which is mostly arable, the region contains many more or less isolated fertile areas, though it is essentially a rugged, hilly country. Among these productive areas are the Annapolis-Cornwallis Valley in Nova Scotia and the St. John Valley in New Brunswick. Much of the region is forest covered and is traversed by many streams. The coast line is long and, with its many good harbors and shallow offshore waters teeming with fish, has wielded a strong influence in the development of the region.

The region has abundant rainfall, and sufficiently long and warm summers to mature all temperate fruits and other crops and produce a luxuriant growth of native forest. Though it is located in the latitude of southern France, the winters are cold, owing chiefly to the cold continental northwest winds, and secondarily to the onshore winds from the Labrador Current.

Many minerals of economic value occur. Coal is abundant. Probably few places in the world possess conditions as favorable for the manufacture of iron and steel as are found on Cape Breton Island where coal is mined at tidewater. The steel mills are located on the harbor at Sydney, and the ore and limestone are obtained by a short voyage from Newfoundland where it is mined at tidewater. New Brunswick likewise has extensive coal deposits. Other minerals now in production include barites, gypsum, silica, sand and gravel, zinc, lead, copper, gold, salt. The salt mine near Malagash, Nova Scotia, is said to be the only one in Canada. However, salt is produced by pumping and evaporation near Amherst.

The present relative backwardness of the region is due only in part to geographical factors. Difficulties of transportation, except by way of the Atlantic, the "patchy" character of good soil areas, and rugged surface are serious handicaps, but it is likely that unfavorable United States tariffs are a greater disadvantage. The resources and location of the region bring its products into competition with those of New England. If reciprocity existed, it is probable that industrial development would take place. *What would have been the history of the Maritime Provinces had the international boundary been located along the St. Lawrence River?*

UTILIZATION OF FOUR PRINCIPAL RESOURCES

Agriculture. The agricultural areas and present development are related closely to the geological structure. Fully three-fourths of the agricultural land is on Carboniferous and Triassic formations near the coast, has fertile soils, and is low and sheltered. Prince Edward Island, the diked tidal marshes at the head of the Bay of Fundy, and the Annapolis-Cornwallis Valley typify the better agricultural lands. Other fertile areas occur on similar rock formations, in New Brunswick and Cape Breton Island, on the alluvial bottoms of numerous river valleys, and in patches on the higher lands. The total potential agricultural land is estimated to be 20,100,000 acres. However, much of the acreage is covered with forests and is remote from transportation, and other areas must be drained or diked. Agriculture is most developed on Prince Edward Island—a land of agriculture, fishing, and fur farming. Over nine-tenths of its area is arable, and nearly three-tenths of the arable land is now in crops. About 60 per cent of the land area of New Brunswick and a like proportion of Nova Scotia is arable, but only about 1 per cent of these lands is cultivated. The agricultural potential of Newfoundland is very small.

Except on Prince Edward Island, agricultural development is still in its infancy (Fig. 229). Sixty-five per cent of the acreage in field crops is devoted to hay, and nearly one-fifth to oats, which is indicative of livestock raising and the production of dairy products. Cattle are more widely distributed than any field crop unless it is hay, but few are raised on the relatively unsettled, hilly, crystalline uplands. Other important crops are potatoes, fruit, and mixed grains. The Annapolis-Cornwallis Valley, known as "The Garden of Nova Scotia," and celebrated for its apples, extends from the Bay of Minas to the head of Annapolis Basin. It is about 80 miles long and from 10 to 15 miles wide. North Mountain separates

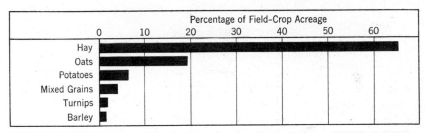

Fig. 229. Use of agricultural land for field crops in Maritime Provinces, exclusive of Newfoundland.

it from the Bay of Fundy and gives protection from the northwest winds and fogs, and South Mountain forms the other side of the valley. Only about one-tenth of the valley is under cultivation. The warm winter winds from the Bay of Fundy produce a pronounced moderating effect, the average winter temperature of Annapolis being 5°–6° higher than that of Halifax. The bay likewise affords protection from killing frosts in spring and fall, giving the valley a long growing season. Even on very still nights during the critical danger periods, the air movements created by the exceptionally high tidal range of the bay constitute an additional factor in protection from frost. Another important advantage possessed by the valley is its location near ports from which its annual crop of 1–2,000,000 barrels of apples may be exported.

Fur Farming. It is probable that 25 years ago no one in Prince Edward Island expected ever to amass a fortune. However, two enterprising farmers conceived the idea of breeding black silver fox, as the pelts commonly brought prices of $1000–$2000 each. The fur of the domesticated animal was more valuable than that of the wild as it was taken when prime and was uninjured. The industry proved so successful that the value of the animals for breeding purposes soon far exceeded the value of the pelts. High prices led to a rapid expansion of the industry and the production of breeding animals. Fur farming also met with success in Nova Scotia and New Brunswick, and for many years the Maritime Provinces held a leading position in the industry. However, the possibilities of fur farming having been demonstrated, the industry spread rapidly to all parts of Canada, and Ontario and Alberta now occupy the leading position. The fox has proved to be one of the best animals for domestic production, and there are now nearly 100,000 on Canadian fur farms. However, the value of mink is greater than the combined value of all other animals on fur farms of Canada. Other important animals include chinchilla, fisher, and marten. Such has been the rapid growth of a comparatively new industry, which is capable of great expansion. See Table XIX.

TABLE XIX

Fur Farming in the Maritime Provinces and Canada

	Fur Farms		Fur-Bearing Animals	
	Number	Value of Land and Buildings	Value	Percentage of Total Value
Prince Edward Island	503	614,030	574,222	3.5
Nova Scotia	350	249,293	421,333	2.5
New Brunswick	383	274,915	467,125	2.8
Quebec	1,768	1,751,435	2,595,564	15.8
Ontario	1,348	2,490,908	4,318,112	26.4
Manitoba	638	2,021,523	2,367,444	14.4
Saskatchewan	467	935,260	1,357,211	8.3
Alberta	1,027	2,383,295	3,049,500	18.6
British Columbia	313	831,831	1,184,776	7.2
Total	6,797	11,552,490	16,335,287	99.5

Fisheries. The Atlantic fisheries of Canada are a historic industry. Breton and Basque fishermen frequented the "banks," especially the Grand Banks, in small vessels, as early as 1502, catching fish by hook and line and marketing them in France. When it was discovered that fish were as plentiful inshore as on the outer banks, huts were built on the shore, and fish were salted and dried and taken to France at the end of the season. Later, permanent fishing villages were established, and these became the bases of operations. The natural conditions that have fostered these fisheries since they were first initiated by Europeans are exceptionally favorable. From southwestern New Brunswick to Labrador extends a fishing coast of some 5000 miles. Including the Bay of Fundy

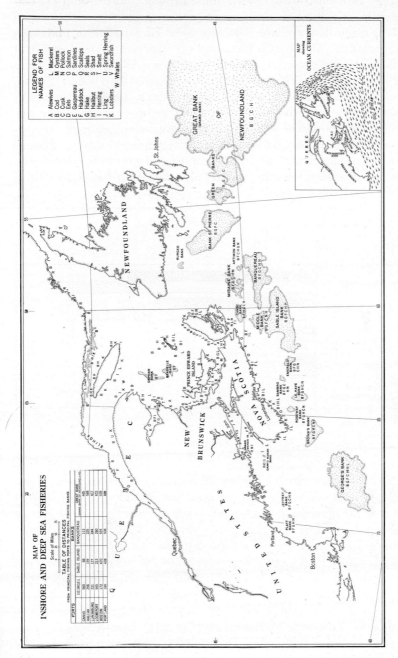

Fig. 230. The fishing banks in proximity to the Maritime Provinces are among the best in the world. Both deep-sea and inshore fisheries are carried on, but deep-sea is the more important. *After map by National Resources Intelligence Service.*

and the St. Lawrence Gulf, the Maritime Provinces have about 215,000 square miles of fishing grounds, or more than four-fifths of the area of the fishing grounds of the North Atlantic. The long shore line, numerous harbors, relatively shallow and cool offshore waters, and the presence of abundant fish food provide one of the world's best fishing grounds. Here are feeding and spawning grounds of such valuable food fish as the cod, herring, lobster, halibut, mackerel, and haddock. The first three rank next to salmon among the fish produced in Canada (Fig. 263). The lobster fisheries are said to be without a peer. Government assistance in conservation and protection, maintenance of hatcheries, awarding of bounties, and aid in marketing has been an important factor in developing the fisheries. For generations the scarcity of soil and the bleak climate of

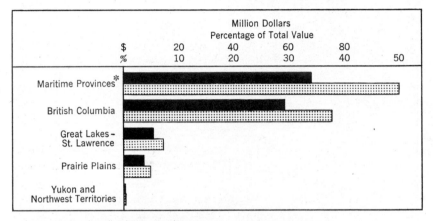

* Includes Newfoundland exports only

Fig. 231. Fisheries of Canada by regions.

much of the coastal lands discouraged agriculture and caused people to turn to the sea as a source of livelihood, as available resources of the sea were plentiful. However, with the introduction of the large steam trawler and motor, the movement has been checked and the number of persons engaged in the fisheries has remained essentially static while the investment in equipment has more than quadrupled.

The Maritime Provinces bear a relation to the world's supply of fish similar to the relation of the Prairie Plains region to the supply of wheat. More than half the total value of the Dominion's fisheries comes from these Provinces, Nova Scotia and Newfoundland leading with more than three-fourths of the total for the region (Fig. 231). The inshore fisheries, which are carried on within 10-12 miles of the coast, are more important than those of the deep sea. They are safer, entail less hardship, require less equipment, and are more profitable, as a large part of the catch is shipped fresh each day to Quebec, Ontario, and the New England States. The deep-sea fisherman requires larger and more expensive equipment and may be out for several weeks or even months, and must pack and salt the fish on board ship. Lunenburg is the chief center in Nova Scotia for the fishing fleets, although nearly every village along the coast has its

Fig. 232. Part of the harbor of the fishing village of Lunenberg. *Photo by Miller*. This is the leading fishing center of Nova Scotia. A large fish flake is shown in the center. The docks and warehouses are in the background. The fishing fleet was "out" when this picture was taken.

fishing vessels, drying sheds, and canneries (Figs. 232 and 233). Most of the cured fish goes to the West Indies, South America, and European countries, especially Spain.

Forests.   The forests have long been a heavy contributor to the wealth and revenue of the region, and with the application of modern methods of

TABLE XX *

PRODUCTION OF FOREST PRODUCTS OF MARITIME PROVINCES

	Sawmill Products		Pulp and Paper	
	Value	Percentage	Value	Percentage
New Brunswick	14,640,600	49.5	35,684,000	42.3
Nova Scotia	11,395,200	38.5	5,838,600	6.9
Newfoundland (estimated)	3,100,000	10.5	42,700,000	50.6
Prince Edward Island	407,800	1.3	—	—
Total	29,543,600	99.8	84,222,600	99.8

* Compiled from *Canada Yearbook*.

conservation may remain so indefinitely. They are similar to those of New England, red spruce being the characteristic tree. Others of commercial value include white spruce, balsam fir, white pine, hemlock, yellow birch, maple, beech, and cedar. Many billions of feet of timber are available for exploitation. Estimates give New Brunswick a forest resource of 9,000,000,000 board feet of saw timber and some 80,000,000 cords of pulpwood, and for Nova Scotia 6,450,000,000 and 29,105,000, respectively. It is estimated that Newfoundland, exclusive of Labrador, has approximately 38,550,000 cords suitable for pulp. Exploitation of forest resources is carried on most extensively in New Brunswick, where the annual income from forest products exceeds the gross agricultural revenue. Measured in value, this province alone produces about half the sawmill products of the region. However Newfoundland produces half the pulp and paper (Table XX).

Fig. 233. A small fishing village on the Atlantic coast of Cape Breton Island. *Photo by Miller.* The life of the community is tied closely to the sea.

Mining (Fig. 234).   Compared with New England, the Maritime Provinces are rich in mineral resources, but they appear poverty stricken in comparison with the resources and mineral production of the Middle Atlantic States. A few resources may be of great significance in a small area, and this may be so in the future of Nova Scotia and New Brunswick. Large deposits of coal of high quality occur accessible to tidewater, and are likely to be of increasing importance. Except for the small deposits of anthracite in Rhode Island, the coal deposits of the Maritime Provinces are the only ones on the Atlantic seaboard of North America. The rich Sydney fields now produce about three-fourths of the annual output of Nova Scotia. With more than 1,300,000 tons of hematite iron ore from Newfoundland annually brought only 400 miles by boat, with abundant coal suitable for blast-furnace coke, gas, and steam, with good harbors such as Sydney, Louisburg, and New Glasgow for shipment up the St.

Lawrence to the coalless and ironless sections of Quebec and Ontario, or
to other parts of the world, Cape Breton Island and Pictou County of
Nova Scotia should become very important coal-producing, and iron-
and steel-manufacturing centers. If more ore is needed in the future, the
Labrador[1] deposits may be drawn upon. The iron and steel industry of
Nova Scotia is now one of the most important in Canada. Coal is the only
non-metallic mineral of outstanding importance produced at the present
time. It constitutes over 85 per cent of the total value of Nova Scotia's
mineral production and 43 per cent of that of New Brunswick. Together,
these provinces produce two-fifths of the annual output of Canada. Gypsum ranks second in value. As with coal, the deposits are at or near tidewater and are capable of extensive development. Most of the gypsum

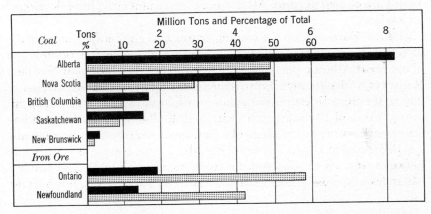

Fig. 234. Coal and iron-ore production of Canada by provinces. Three-year average.

produced is marketed in the United States. Much of it is resold to the
Canadians in the form of plaster. Among other minerals of present or of
potential economic significance should be mentioned gold, salt, manganese, limestone, and excellent clay.

Manufactures.   Manufacturing in the Maritime Provinces is based
directly upon the utilization of the local natural resources—agricultural,
forest, fishery, and mineral—and has become the chief source of income.
Manufacturing is more fully developed in Nova Scotia than in any other
province; New Brunswick is second. Shipbuilding, iron and steel, and
fishery products lead in Nova Scotia, whose two leading enterprises are
the outgrowth of the utilization of the local coal and the iron ore from
Newfoundland. In New Brunswick the forest industries—pulp and
paper, sawmill products—are nearly five times greater than the third in-

[1] Along the Quebec border. Further, Ungava deposits may become available.

dustry, which is the curing and packing of fish. Fishery products, butter and cheese, fruit and vegetable products lead on Prince Edward Island, and the pulp and paper industry is the only one of importance in Newfoundland.

CITIES

Urban population has been growing at the expense of rural. This tendency has become pronounced, especially in Nova Scotia, where the rural and urban populations are nearly alike. This movement is in keeping with the industrial development. However, nearly two-thirds of the population of New Brunswick and three-fourths of that of Prince Edward Island are classed as rural. All the more important cities have developed on harbors.

Halifax-Dartmouth is the leading center and gives employment to the largest number of people in its industries. Halifax expects to become one of the great Atlantic ports. It is the terminal of the Canadian National Railways, with extensive improvements to make it a great ocean port; it has an ice-free, siltless outer harbor 1 mile square and 70 feet deep, an inner harbor of 10 square miles with a 45-foot depth at the piers at low water, and average tidal range of 4 feet, free from troublesome currents; it is protected at the entrance by islands; it is on the main trade route between western Europe and the northeastern United States; and it is 616 miles nearer Liverpool than New York is (Table XXI). It is now the

TABLE XXI

COMPARATIVE TABLE OF DISTANCES FROM HALIFAX AND NEW YORK TO SIX TRADE CENTERS

To	Miles from Halifax	Miles from New York
Liverpool	2450	3100
Pernambuco	3451	3678
Rio de Janeiro	4611	4748
Montevideo	5586	5723
Buenos Aires	5701	5838
Cape Town	6423	6786

leading port of the Maritime Provinces, though Saint John is a close second, and its registered tonnage is larger than that of Quebec and nearly three-fifths that of Montreal. Like Saint John it is of special importance to Canada as a winter port when the St. Lawrence is closed by ice. Large quantities of grain, lumber, dairy products, woodpulp, fish, and fish products are exported; raw sugar, coffee, tea, crude oil, machinery, textiles and many other manufactures are imported. Halifax and Saint John now handle nearly a third of Canada's Atlantic shipping.

Saint John is the second city in size and in number of people engaged in manufacturing industries. It is the focal point of New Brunswick, and particularly of the fertile and productive valley of the Saint John River; it is the eastern terminal and winter port of the Canadian Pacific Railway and is nearer Montreal than Halifax is, though farther from Liverpool by 200 miles. It possesses a good harbor, kept ice-free by the large tidal range which gives a depth of 32 feet at low tide and 58 feet at high tide. The character of the commerce is very similar to that of Halifax.

At the north on Cape Breton Island is Sydney industrial district, located in the rich coal fields, and the center of the iron and steel industry. It has 15 square miles of harbor 40 feet deep, with 30 feet at the piers. Fogs are rare, but under unfavorable wind conditions ice blocks the entrance at times for 2 months. These three urban centers dominate the manufacturing and commercial life of the region.

NEWFOUNDLAND AND LABRADOR

Location and Surface. The development of transoceanic aviation and World War II have emphasized the locational significance of Newfoundland—it is only about 2360 airline miles from Gander airport to London. Blocking the entrance to the Gulf of St. Lawrence except for narrow passages 60 miles wide on the south and 10–15 on the north, its high, rocky, and deeply indented coast appears barren and forbidding when approached from the sea (Fig. 235A). Less than a mile inland it is still a primitive wilderness. In the unsettled interior are stretches of fertile soil, and along its streams and numerous lakes are excellent forests. Structurally and economically it is a part of the Maritime Provinces. Geologically it is a part of Greater Acadia, and is essentially a plateau having a gently rolling surface, rising from east to west from about 700 feet in Avalon Peninsula to about 2000 feet in the Long Range Mountains. Its surface is cut by a number of river valley lowlands that break the island structure into belts trending northeast-southwest. During glacial times the whole area was covered and uplands were scraped to bedrock. The loose soil and other rock materials were carried out to sea or deposited in the valleys. Labrador is a part of the Canadian Shield. The plateau character of the south and southeast gives way to mountain ranges in the north.

Climate. The marine climate of Newfoundland is affected greatly by the surrounding cold waters and eastward movement of air masses from the continent. The Labrador Current embraces the island with cold waters laden with pack ice in winter, and icebergs from Greenland in the summer. Fogs frequently enshroud its coast, as the warm waters of the Gulf Stream Drift mingle with the cold waters of the Labrador Current. The fog, however, does not extend far inland. Winters are cold and

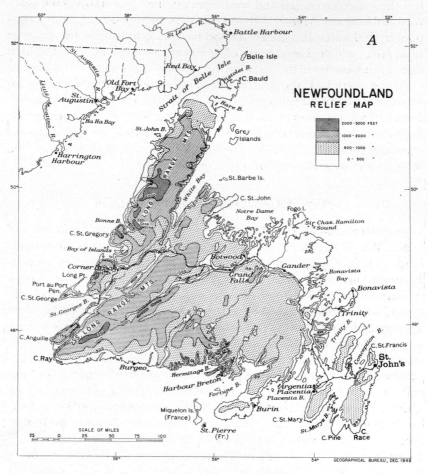

Fig. 235A. Newfoundland relief map. *Geographic Bureau,* 1948.

long and summers short and cool. Precipitation is abundant and well distributed over the island and throughout the year. Heavy snowfalls at the north decrease in amount toward the south. The climate of interior Labrador is arctic in character, with very low winter temperatures. Even though the coast is washed by cold waters the winters are much milder than those of the interior. Summers are cool to cold with moderate precipitation.

Soil and Vegetation. Much of the plateau area is covered by a thin layer of glacial gravels. Podzols prevail over nearly all Newfoundland and may be classed generally as unfertile. However, good agricultural

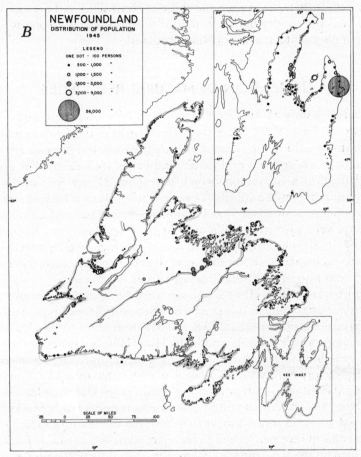

Fig. 235*B*. Distribution of population, Newfoundland, 1945. *Geographical Bureau,* 1948.

soils are found in restricted areas such as those of the west coast and in several river valleys. Neither climate nor soils encourage utilization of the land for crop production.

The long, cold winter and cool, humid summer favor the growth of coniferous rather than deciduous forests, though mixed forests occur. A little less than half (47 per cent) the land area of the island is forest covered. The better forest areas are located on the valley slopes of the principal rivers such as the Gander, Humber, Terra Nova, and Exploits. The more valuable trees consist of balsam fir, white spruce, black spruce, yellow birch, and white pine. The plateau areas are largely barren of trees but have extensive bogs, and also tundra at the higher elevations. The forests of southern Labrador and those of Newfoundland are essentially alike, and the tundra of the north and coastal area corresponds to that of the higher plateau areas of Newfoundland.

UTILIZATION OF NATURAL RESOURCES

There are only about 320,000 people in Newfoundland and 5500 in Labrador (Fig. 235B). More than nine-tenths of these are in scattered communities along the coast. The only towns in the interior are along the railway where forest and mining industries are located. The greatest concentration is in Avalon, which has about 45 per cent of the total population of Newfoundland. Greater Saint John's is located here and has a population of about 57,000. Both Newfoundland and Labrador are still in a very primitive stage of industrial development. Economy is based primarily on fishing, forestry, and mining. Fishing was the only industry of importance for 400 years. It is only comparatively recently that forests and minerals have been utilized.

Agriculture.   Both climate and soil are adverse to agriculture, and it is of minor importance. It is primarily of the subsistence type, with very few farmsteads of more than 50 acres. Major areas of commercial farming are in Avalon Peninsula and in the lower Humber valley of the southwest, near the larger consuming centers. More than half the acreage is devoted to hay and pasture. Agriculture is primarily a hay, dairy, and root-crop economy, with potatoes the main crop. Dairying leads on the west coast and in Avalon where milk products find a ready market.

Forestry.   Forests rank next to fisheries as the leading source of employment and income. Although there are some 900 sawmills employing 3000 men on the west and east coasts, the great bulk of the timber is used in the pulp and paper industry. This is the most important industry that has developed in Newfoundland in centuries, giving employment to nearly 7000 men. Newfoundland possesses excellent advantages for the development of this industry. The timber is cheap and excellent for pulp, is near good harbors free from ice on the south coast, and occurs in dense stands; the rivers are suitable for conveying logs to the mills and for hydroelectric power (Fig. 235C); Newfoundland is much nearer the markets of Europe than is the United States or other parts of Canada; and

there is an abundance of labor, especially during the off-season for fishing. Estimates indicate that, with reasonable fire protection, the forest
resources will last indefinitely since cut-over land reforests rapidly, and
the forests of Labrador are untouched.

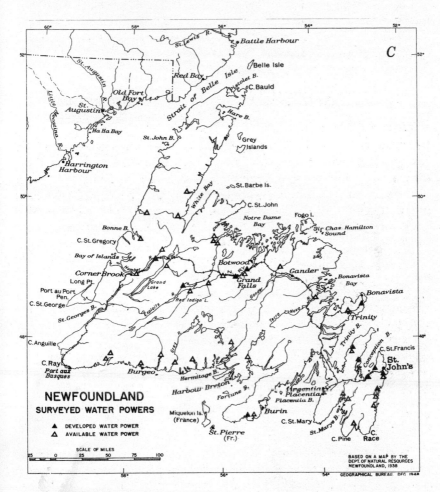

Fig. 235C. Surveyed water powers of Newfoundland. *Geographical Bureau*, 1948.

Minerals.   Minerals (Fig. 235*D*) are known to occur in considerable
variety, quantity, and quality, including iron, coal, lead, zinc, silver,
chromite, nickel-copper, and asbestos. Thus far the mining industry has
been wholly extractive for export. Coal mining has not been developed,
and there is no smelting industry. The Wabana iron ores of Bell Island
in Conception Bay are Newfoundland's largest mineral asset, and one of

the world's greatest deposits. Estimates of probable reserves vary from 2,500,000,000 to 10,000,000,000 tons of hematite ore. Mining is confined to the northwest side of the island, and operations extend 2¼ miles beneath Conception Bay. Production runs about 1,300,000 tons annu-

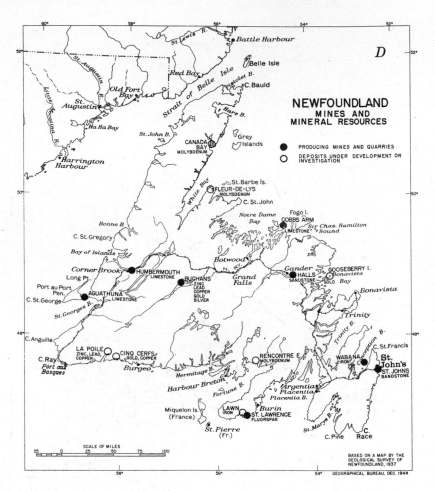

Fig. 235D. Mine and mineral resources, Newfoundland. *Geographical Bureau, 1948.*

ally, more than half of which goes to the steel mills at Sydney, Nova Scotia. Other exports are chiefly to Great Britain. Among the other leading metallic minerals are zinc, lead, and copper, about 120,000 tons of concentrates being produced annually.

Huge deposits of high-grade iron ore occur along the Labrador-Quebec boundary. No attempt has yet been made to estimate the probable reserves. However, sufficient deposits have been blocked out to warrant development. These ores will be brought by rail to the St. Lawrence for shipment. An abundance of water power of at least 1,200,000 hp is available for mining operations. With the decline of high-grade resources in the United States, and completion of the St. Lawrence Seaway, the United States may become the chief market for these ores.

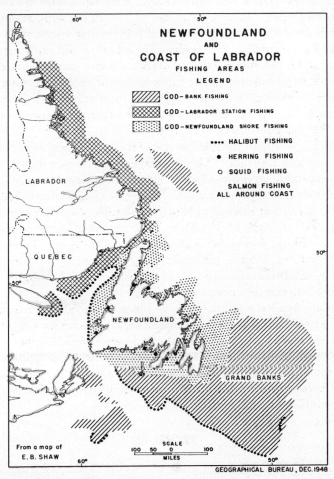

Fig. 236. Fishing areas, Newfoundland and coast of Labrador. *Geographical Bureau*, 1948. *From a map by E. B. Shaw.*

Fisheries, the Dominant Industry.   The cool and shallow waters of the Grand Banks, which lie 100 miles off the southeast shore, are one of the world's finest fishing grounds. Sunlight penetrates the cool, shallow waters, favoring the growth of plankton, upon which herring, caplin, and

squid feed. These fish constitute a large part of the food of cod, for which
the Banks are noted (Fig. 236). In addition to the cod fisheries of the
Banks, and those nearer shore, thousands of fishermen journey to the
fishing banks along the coast of Labrador during the summer. About the
middle of March each year, the sealing fleet sets out from Saint John's
to the sealing grounds along the north shores. Here on the ice floes, the
hair seal gives birth to its young. Only the bachelor seals are killed, but
the annual catch is declining. The hair seal is not the same as the fur seal.
Its skin is used for the manufacture of fine leather goods, such as belts,
bags, and cigar and cigarette cases. The oil extracted finds a market as
illuminant, for the manufacture of margarine and soap, and medicinally
as a cod-liver oil substitute. The cod is by far the most important product
of the sea. It accounts for four-fifths of the total value of all fishing products, nearly all of which are exported. The principal markets are Brazil,
Spain, Portugal, Italy, and West Indies.

Fishing is well-nigh the sole interest of the coastal people of both Newfoundland and Labrador. This is to be expected since the land is poor
and inhospitable, and the off-shore waters, countless bays, and open sea
teem with fish. The people have little interest in agriculture. Fishing has
been the dominant interest of Newfoundland's people for centuries. Its
economic life throughout its history has been based upon the fisheries of
the Grand Banks and along its shores. The people think in terms of cod,
herring, halibut, lobster, and seal. Fully 40 per cent of the people employed in gainful occupations are in the fisheries, and probably half the
total population is dependent on the industry.

For many years the annual value of the fisheries led all other products,
its relative position depending upon the export market for fish, especially
dried and salted cod. Now the pulp and paper industry ranks second,
supplying about 40 per cent of the value of exports. More than two-thirds
of Newfoundland's exports of all kinds of domestic produce find a market
in the United States and Great Britain, and it buys nine-tenths of its imports from Canada and United States.

PROBLEMS

1. Will the future growth of commerce, industry, wealth, and population in the Maritime Provinces give them a leadership in Canada comparable to the leadership now held
by the North Atlantic States in the United States?

2. The Maritime Provinces possess opportunities greater than those of New England
for commercial and industrial development.

3. Will Halifax and Saint John become the leading ports of eastern Canada?

4. It is more than three centuries since the first English settlement was made in Newfoundland. Has Newfoundland reached the highest stage of industrial development that
may be expected?

5. Would reciprocity with the United States produce a development of the Maritime Provinces comparable to that of New England?

6. Can the Maritime Provinces maintain a population greater than that of the Pacific Mountain Region?

7. What will be the two leading industries of the Maritime Provinces?

8. Will the proposed Great Lakes-St. Lawrence Seaway benefit or injure the Maritime Provinces?

CHAPTER 22

The Great Lakes-St. Lawrence Region

Politically this region includes the Provinces of Quebec and Ontario, but most of the vast area is primeval wilderness unprospected except along the major streams. From the standpoint of human occupancy the region is limited to the Great Lakes-St. Lawrence Lowland, including the triangular section of Ontario east of Lake Huron—Peninsular Ontario—a few shipping centers on Lake Superior, and a few mining or forest industry communities on the Canadian Shield. It is this comparatively small part of the region with which we are primarily concerned. Much of the economic development has been and still is associated closely with the St. Lawrence River and the Great Lakes, as the sparsely populated Shield occupies fully two-thirds of Ontario and nine-tenths of Quebec. The Lowland section, where most of the people live and where most of the development has taken place, is isolated from western Canada by hundreds of miles of rocky, lake- and swamp-studded, forested land of very low productivity. One of the large problems of Canada is to bridge this natural barrier.

Canadian Shield Section. The southern portion of the Canadian Shield is tributary to the Great Lakes-St. Lawrence Lowland. Its general characteristics are described earlier in the book. As a result of its geological history, it has a great variety of metallic minerals, most notable of which are nickel, copper, gold, uranium, and silver. Glaciation left much of its surface without soil, and hence sterile, though here and there are drift-filled valleys and small patches of glacial till. However, these soil areas are commonly located in poorly drained country and are difficult of access, hence of limited crop value. The most striking exception is the "Clay Belt" south of James Bay. It was expected that completion of a railroad across the Clay Belt to Moosonee would hasten its agricultural development. Glaciation also accounts for the vast number of lakes and muskegs that serve as reservoirs to regulate the stream flow, likewise for many of the falls and rapids that provide large water-power resources. Trees thrive in the soil areas or where the rocks are broken sufficiently for the roots to gain hold. In general the southern portion is densely for-

542

ested with valuable timber. Forests, minerals, and water power constitute the principal resources now utilized by man. Only a relatively small number of people actually live in the Canadian Shield portion of the region. Its water power, its minerals, its forests, its furs, and its other assets are tributary to the industrial centers of the Lowland. The labor of reclaiming its scattered and commonly isolated soil areas, and its large proportion of barren rock and boulder-strewn land make it less

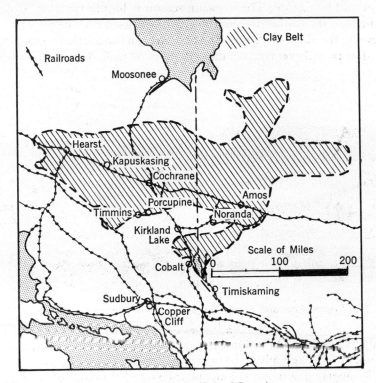

Fig. 237. The Clay Belt of Ontario.

desirable to the prospective home builder than the fertile western prairie where transportation facilities and markets are already available.

The Clay Belt. This region has gained prominence largely because of the efforts of both Quebec and Ontario to extend their agricultural area by promoting its development (Fig. 237). Though numerous small soil areas occur in the Shield, the major Clay Belt occupies some 40,000 square miles about 50 miles south of James Bay. It is roughly 450 miles long east and west and 50 to 150 miles wide north and south. Most of the area is the forest-covered bed of glacial Lake Ojibway, and the soils are peaty lacustrine clays, changing, in the northern section, to peaty glacial clays. The forest cover is chiefly black spruce and balsam suitable for pulpwood.

Its climate is the subarctic type, with an abundance of precipitation. Kapuskasing may be taken as typical of the central portion of the area, where the mean annual precipitation is 27 inches, and July and January mean temperatures are 62.4° and –1.7°, respectively. Late, cool rains in August and September are a serious handicap to ripening and drying grain and hay crops. The growing season is highly variable. Cold air drains into the lowlands, and the growing season may be only 35 to 45 days. On the shores of Lake Timiskaming, on the southern margin, the frost-free period averages 123 days. Perhaps 80 to 85 days is a fair average

Fig. 238. Typical long and narrow fields in the St. Lawrence Lowland of Quebec.
Photo by Miller.

for the region as a whole. However, frosts may occur during any summer month, making agriculture hazardous.

The poorly drained podzolic, peat-covered clay soils are difficult to put into good condition for cultivation and crop production. The peat cover ranges from 6 inches to 4 feet. The thicker layers must be removed by burning, and some are mixed with the clay for cultivation. The major crops are hay and oats for cattle feed. Vegetables and root crops are produced mainly in garden plots.

The most successful agricultural development is in the Timiskaming section, extending northward to Cochrane. As a whole the Clay Belt is still on the pioneer fringe. Fortunately the settler may clear his land and sell the timber as pulpwood at paper-mill centers such as Kapuskasing. The pulp and paper mills, and mining and smelting centers, such as Timmins, Noranda, Kirkland Lake, Cobalt, and Sudbury, also provide a market and part-time work for the pioneer farmer. Since the area is crossed by two railroads—Canadian National and Ontario Northland—transportation is available though the costs are high. It seems probable that occupancy of the area will proceed very slowly and success will depend upon maintenance of mining and forest industries, particularly pulp and paper.

The Lowland.   The Great Lakes-St. Lawrence Lowland extends from Lake Huron through Quebec and is divided into two major sections by an extension of the Shield which crosses the St. Lawrence between Kingston and Brockville. The surface is largely drift-covered sedimentaries and affords a great variety of fertile soils, in contrast with the hard granitic rocks of the Shield at the north. All parts have a climate suitable to

TABLE XXII

COMPARATIVE POSITION IN THE DOMINION OF THE
GREAT LAKES-ST. LAWRENCE REGION

1. 61.8 per cent of the population.
2. 71.1 per cent of the urban population.
3. 64.2 per cent of all cities of 5000 or more.
4. 31.8 per cent of potential agricultural land.
5. 23.8 per cent of the average acreage of field crops.
6. 33.4 per cent of the average gross agricultural revenue.
7. 65.2 per cent of the value of dairy products.
8. 75.3 per cent of the annual production of wood-pulp.
9. 81.4 per cent of the net value of manufactures.
10. 81.3 per cent of the manufacturing employees (average).
11. 55.2 per cent of the export trade, net weight.
12. 84.0 per cent of imports, net weight.
13. 54.1 per cent of the mineral production by value.
14. 82.2 per cent of installed water power.

the growth of cereals and temperate fruits. Since the Lowland extends some 600 miles from east to west and 300 miles north and south, and the western lake peninsula is nearly surrounded by water, there is also variety in climate. Crops such as wheat and corn will thrive best in the more southerly lake peninsula, and oats and barley at the north. This combination of fertile soils and favorable climate makes agriculture one of the greatest permanent industries of the region, if not the greatest. The agricultural opportunities and natural means of communication afforded by the Great Lakes and St. Lawrence led to the relatively early settling of these lowlands. The St. Lawrence and the Great Lakes are still among the region's greatest assets, and exercise a profound influence in the development of the region.

Its mineral resources are comparatively small, and it is without coal. However, the many streams that come tumbling from uplands of the Shield compensate for the absence of mineral fuels, as they provide a superabundance of power conveniently located. Fertile soils, favorable climate, good natural transportation facilities giving access to the open ocean, and vast tributary forest, mineral, and power resources have made this the most desirable region of Canada (Table XXII). Here is more than three-fifths of the population of the Dominion. Measured in terms of population, manufacturing, commerce, large cities, total wealth, educational institutions, or influence in national affairs, the Great Lakes-St. Lawrence Lowland is essentially Canada.

AGRICULTURE

Agricutural Area.   Agriculture is confined almost exclusively to the gently rolling glacial drift and alluvial soils of the lake peninsula and the lower St. Lawrence Valley. The peninsular section presents an agricultural landscape similar in many respects to that of northern Ohio and Indiana. However, as one approaches its northern border, along the Canadian Shield escarpment, conditions typical of a frontier settlement appear. Here the "bush" becomes dense, and scattered clearings of pioneer farmers dot the area. In the eastern, or Quebec, section the occupied area is almost wholly south of the St. Lawrence, the eastern townships constituting the most important section. This is a hilly agricultural and mining district. North of the river human occupancy is based on the forest industries—lumber, pulp, and paper. A striking feature in the agricultural landscape of the St. Lawrence Lowland is the long, narrow fields that stretch away from a line of transportation, such as the St. Lawrence or a highway (Fig. 238). Agricultural methods and rural living conditions are primitive compared to the central section of the United States or the southern portion of Peninsular Ontario. Outdoor bake ovens, and open wells with a long, weighted pole sweep to lift the water are common. However, change is now taking place, and it appears likely that at least some of the quaintness of old Quebec is passing.

The humid, continental type of climate favors the production of hay and forage, pasture, and oats. The opening of the cheap and fertile lands of the Prairie Plains and the migration of grain growing thereto made competition in the Lowland extremely difficult. These conditions, coupled with good home markets, led to the development of mixed farming and dairying, and especially the production of butter and cheese. Only in the more southerly section of the lake peninsula do corn and swine raising approximate the production to the square mile of Iowa.

Where lake and marine influences moderate the climate, fruits are grown for market. Noted apple regions are in the Montreal district south of Georgian Bay; and along the northern shores of Lakes Erie and Ontario; the Niagara peninsula also produces the less hardy strawberries, grapes, and peaches. Though the region has nearly one-third of the potential

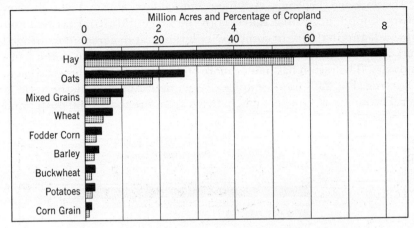

Fig. 239. Leading crops of the Great Lakes-St. Lawrence Region.

arable land of the Dominion only about one-sixth is now utilized for field crops, three-fifths of which is in the western or Ontario section. The region therefore has the potential agricultural resources which, combined with the denser population and accessibility to good domestic and foreign markets, should enable its people to maintain their relative agricultural position in competition with other regions.

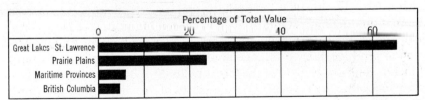

Fig. 240. The dairy industry by regions.

Leading Crops (Fig. 239).   The Lowland region is dominantly a hay and forage and oats country, as these crops are raised on more than three-fourths of the cultivated land. In the lower St. Lawrence section, nine-tenths of the crop acreage is devoted to these crops, and more than two-thirds to hay and forage alone; and in the Ontario section the proportion is nearly seven-tenths devoted to the two crops and more than half of this to hay and forage. Other crops include mixed grains, wheat, barley, buckwheat, potatoes, and corn. Over nine-tenths of the wheat is grown in the lake peninsula, where it provides a cash crop to this section. The Lowland has long been an important agricultural area, and, even though the open grasslands of the west have developed rapidly, it still produces a third of the total crop value of the Dominion.

Livestock and Dairying. A climate and soil favorable to the production of stock food, accessible markets in the large industrial centers and abroad, and inability to compete with the west in cereals encouraged mixed farming, the raising of livestock, and specialization in the dairy industry. The region has half or more of the cattle and swine of Canada. Dairying (Fig. 240) now occupies a very important place in the agricultural economy of Quebec, where there are more than 1000 butter and

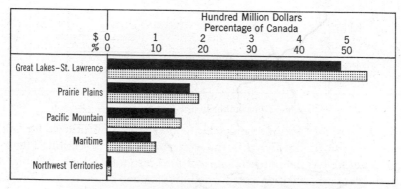

Fig. 241. Relative value of mineral production of Canada by regions. Three-year average.

cheese factories. Butter is its specialty, and it leads all other provinces in annual production, as Ontario does in cheese. However, the larger area, more favorable climate, soil, and markets have enabled the Ontario section to produce dairy products having a total value in excess of that of Quebec. The two sections of the Great Lakes-St. Lawrence Lowland produce more than half the butter, nine-tenths of the cheese, and two-thirds the value of all dairy products of Canada. In addition it is a very large producer of cattle and swine for slaughtering.

MINERALS

The Canadian Shield contributes the metallic mineral wealth and the Lowland contributes most of the non-metallics. Nearly all the metallic ore, except iron, is produced in the Sudbury-Kirkland-Lake Noranda-Porcupine Area of Ontario and Quebec (Fig. 237), the annual output of

Ontario being many times that of Quebec. The ores are mined primarily for gold, nickel, and copper but many others are obtained. About three-fourths of the world's supply of nickel comes from the Sudbury mines. Nearly all the nickel-copper ore is reduced in smelters at Copper Cliff and refined at Port Colborne. Metals of the platinum group, recovered in the refining process, are sent to Acton, England, for refining. Some of the matte from the nickel-copper smelters is sent to Kristiansand, Norway, for refining; however, this is probably less than a tenth of the nickel output. The Porcupine and Kirkland Lake areas are the major producers

Fig. 242. Part of open-pit asbestos mine in Quebec. The large fabricating plant is in the right background. *Photo by Miller*

of gold. The concentration of mining, smelting, and pulp and paper-mill communities in this section was one of the major factors in encouraging agricultural development of the Clay Belt. Except for Newfoundland the Shield also yields virtually all of Canada's iron ore. This ore comes from the newly developed mines at Steep Rock about 75 miles north of the Mesabi range of Minnesota and 125 miles west of Port Arthur. Here the ore is obtained from the bed of a drained lake. The ore is high grade, averaging about 60 per cent metal, and is low in phosphorous and silica. With depletion of high-grade ore in the United States, this ore will find a ready market there as well as in Canada. The Lowland produces building materials, asbestos, petroleum, and natural gas. The eastern town-

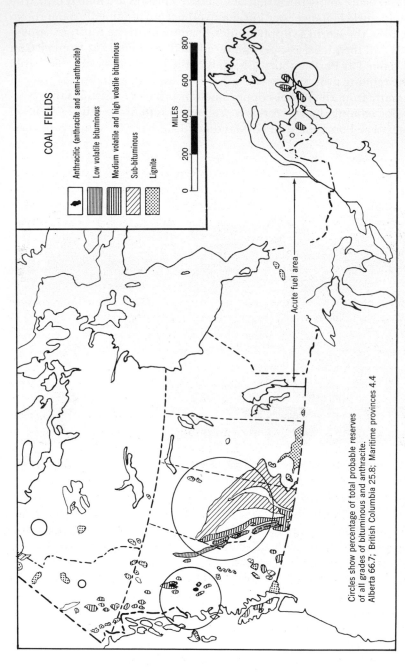

Fig. 243. Distribution of coal resources of Canada. The Great Lakes-St. Lawrence Region is seriously handicapped by a lack of coal. It depends very largely upon the coal from the United States.

ships in southern Quebec have the world's largest known deposits of asbestos and are the world's largest producer. Some asbestos is obtained by underground operations and some from open pits. The industry centers in the Asbestos-Thetford area northeast of Sherbrooke (Fig. 242). Peninsular Ontario produces some petroleum and natural gas, which is of considerable local significance.

Taken as a whole the Great Lakes-St. Lawrence Region is Canada's premier producer of minerals (Fig. 241). It mines annually more than four-fifths of Canada's output of gold, one-third of the silver, seven-tenths of the copper, three-fifths of the total mineral wealth, three-fourths of the world's nickel, and four-fifths of the world's asbestos. It is without coal and has little iron and oil. The new titanium-iron mines in the Lake Allard district of Quebec have a daily output of about 500 tons of iron and 700 tons of titanium concentrate. The present mineral-producing areas are widely scattered and give rise to isolated settlements whose future is dependent upon the mines.

WATER POWER

Here we have the most highly developed portion of the Dominion, yet without coal! Its factories and homes have been as dependent upon the United States for coal as has any section of that country, since Nova Scotia coal could not compete beyond Montreal (Fig. 243). Any country dependent on a foreign source of power is in a critical position. Even though its imported coal came from a friendly neighbor, Canada had no control over the closing of mines by strikes, or the price of coal. This situation became more acute with the increase in population and industrial growth and led to both private and public water power development. Today practically every important industrial center of the region utilizes hydroelectric power and has abundant potential resources accessible (Table XXIII). Quebec and Ontario not only have four-fifths of the water power developed, but have nearly half the potential at ordinary 6-months' flow of the rivers. Nature has endowed few other places in the world with such a large potential of water power—a fact of great significance in a coalless land. This is due to (1) the abundant and fairly uniform rainfall, (2) falls and rapids in the numerous streams that descend from the Canadian Shield bordering the Lowland on the north, and Niagara Falls, (3) the geological structure, and (4) the Great Lakes, and thousands of smaller lakes, muskegs, and forest cover on a comparatively level upland, which serve as storage reservoirs. These conditions give to the region a minimum potential of 13,860,000 hp, with 20,300,000 hp dependable for 6 months. Furthermore, a very large part of these reserves

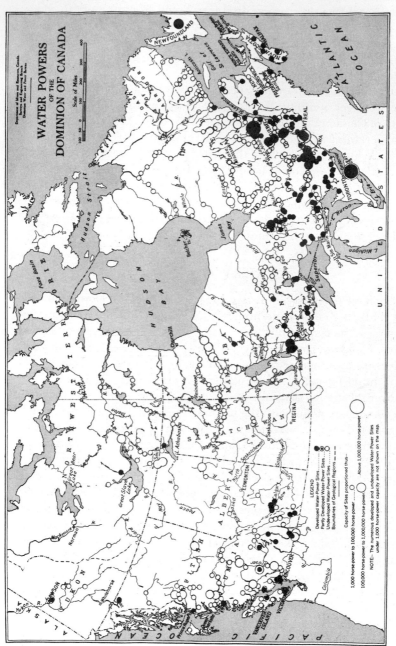

Fig. 244. Water power of Canada. *Department of Mines and Resources.* Most of the developed water power of Canada is in the Great Lakes-St. Lawrence region—The Acute Fuel Area. Compare with Fig. 243. Ontario and Quebec now have four-fifths of the developed water power of Canada, and about half the potential. The numerous developed and undeveloped water-power sites under 1000-hp capacity are not shown.

Fig. 245. Niagara Falls is an important source of power. Canadian plants are in the foreground. *Courtesy, Niagara Mohawk Power Corp.* Arrows indicate location of several power plants. Others are farther down the gorge.

is located near centers demanding power, and the reserves are well distributed throughout the region (Fig. 244). Ninety-eight per cent of the electricity now produced in Canada comes from central power stations.

TABLE XXIII

POTENTIAL AND DEVELOPED WATER POWER OF CANADA

	Potential Horsepower			Turbine Installation	
	At Minimum Flow (000)	At 6-Months' Flow (000)	Percentage 6-Months' Flow of Total	Horsepower, Jan. 1, 1950 (000)	Percentage of Total
Quebec	8,459	13,064	30.4	6,130	52.7
British Columbia	7,029	10,998	25.6	1,238	10.6
Ontario	5,407	7,261	16.9	2,896	24.9
Manitoba	3,309	5,344	12.4	557	4.8
Newfoundland	1,135	2,585	6.0	262	2.2
Saskatchewan	542	1,082	2.5	111	0.9
Alberta	507	1,258	2.9	107	0.9
Yukon and North-west Territories	382	814	1.8	28	0.2
New Brunswick	123	334	0.7	133	1.1
Nova Scotia	25	156	0.3	145	1.2
Prince Edward Island	—	3	—	2	—
Canada	26,914	42,899	99.5	11,613	99.5

A network of transmission lines extends throughout the Lowland and the southern portion of the Shield. The rapid development has been due largely to the need for power in a coalless land, and to the rapid growth

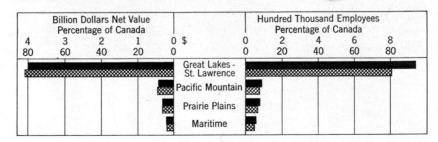

Fig. 246. Manufactures of Canada, by regions.

of the pulp and paper industry. Nearly 500,000 hp is developed by and used directly by that industry in addition to the power purchased from central stations. Fully 90 per cent of the machinery of the pulp and paper industry is driven by water power. The Province of Quebec is the largest user, industrial development being so closely associated with the utilization of its forests. The power reserve of the region is sufficient to meet the needs of a much larger population and a much greater industrial development.

MANUFACTURES

The Great Lakes-St. Lawrence Region is the premier manufacturing area of Canada, producing more than four-fifths of the net value and

Fig. 247. A large paper mill at Grand Mere, Quebec. *Courtesy, Royal Canadian Air Force.* Scores of such mills now utilize the abundant water power of the St. Lawrence region.

having a like proportion of the employees (Fig. 246). In spite of the rapid growth of manufacturing in other sections, such as British Columbia and the Prairie Provinces, it continues to maintain its relative position. Many factors have favored manufacturing development in this region, such as: the stimulus of two world wars; the Great Lakes-St. Lawrence waterway; variety of natural resources—forests, minerals, water power, agricultural lands; accessibility of iron ore from the Lake Superior district and Pennsylvania coking coal; large local population and accessibility of foreign markets in the United States and overseas; an able and industrious people; a tariff-protected home market and preferential rates in other parts of the British Empire. Many United States corporations have branch plants here, thus gaining tariff advantages, and accounting for much of the industrial development. Probably the greatest effect of producing for war purposes was the stimulus given to metal-working industries. This is especially noticeable in Ontario and is evident in Quebec. In both areas the abundant water-power resources have been utilized effectively.

TABLE XXIV

LEADING MANUFACTURING INDUSTRIES OF ONTARIO AND QUEBEC

	Net Value (000)	Percentage of All Industries	Number of Employees	Percentage of All Employees
Ontario				
Electrical products	146,043	6.8	35,518	6.6
Pulp and paper	115,462	5.4	16,927	3.1
Automobiles	109,754	5.1	23,281	4.3
Rubber goods	91,768	4.2	16,795	3.1
Machinery	81,711	3.8	17,417	3.2
Primary iron and steel	67,258	3.1	17,658	3.2
Automobile supplies	61,359	2.8	16,424	3.0
Non-ferrous metals	57,590	2.6	7,192	1.3
Quebec				
Pulp and paper	171,518	12.9	23,675	6.2
Clothing, women's	60,697	4.5	20,300	5.3
Electrical products	51,657	3.9	16,285	4.2
Clothing, men's	50,096	3.7	16,180	4.2
Non-ferrous metals	42,319	3.1	6,203	1.6
Railway rolling stock	40,527	3.0	13,339	3.5
Tobacco products	39,236	2.9	8,332	2.1
Cotton yarn and cloth	35,809	2.7	16,388	4.3

Manufacturing as a whole is based upon utilization of local raw materials, products of forests, mines, and agricultural lands, but much raw material is imported for processing. The outstanding industry of Quebec —pulp and paper (Fig. 247)—is based upon its forests and water power. Quebec produces about half the total output of Canada, and ships pulpwood and pulp for paper manufacture elsewhere. The textile and aluminum industries depend upon a foreign source for raw materials. Textiles are a very old, established industry and have maintained a leading position in the Dominion. Other industries include production of chemicals, railway equipment, non-ferrous metals, electrical, tobacco, and creamery products.

More than half the manufacturing industry of the Dominion is concentrated in the Ontario section. Its industries are highly diversified, but metal working industries occupy the leading position (Table XXIV). Many of these are subsidiaries of United States companies or became well-established war industries and have continued to thrive. Automobiles and electrical products are examples.

CITIES

With the development of manufacturing on a modern factory scale, people tend to concentrate in small areas; hence large urban centers arise. Three-fifths of Canada's people live in the Great Lakes-St. Lawrence Region, and nearly all are in the Lowland. Nearly two-thirds of the population of the region is urban, and this proportion is increasing yearly, a situation that indicates the increase in manufacturing that is taking place. All except two of the metropolitan centers of Canada having a population of more than 100,000 are located here. Because of the numerous natural assets previously named, this region has offered the greatest opportunities to man in the past and, for the same reasons, is likely to do so in the future. It appears unlikely that man will ever find any similar area of the Dominion so well adapted to his needs.

Montreal is the largest city. It is situated in the midst of the Lowland and in the most populous section of Canada, at the head of ocean navigation on the St. Lawrence, 300 miles nearer to Europe than New York is. It is at the foot of inland navigation on the Great Lakes, where railroads from the interior converge, and has an abundance of available water power. It leads in manufacturing and in foreign trade, even though its port is closed by ice for more than 4 months of the year. Its location makes it the most convenient and economical center for transshipment of exports and imports of both central and eastern Canada. It ranks among the world's grain ports, and handles a large share of Canada's total exports and imports. The leading exports include wheat and wheat flour, other grains, lumber, and woodpulp and paper; and the principal imports handled are raw and manufactured cotton, raw and manufactured wool, raw sugar, tea, and numerous manufactures. *What effect will the completion of the St. Lawrence Seaway project have on Montreal? Would you expect Montreal to support the project?*

Toronto is the second city of Canada in population and industrial development, and is the gateway to the southwestern lowlands, which are one of the most densely populated and wealthiest parts of the Dominion. It has a good lake harbor, is the railway focus of the section, and is the distributing center of a prosperous agricultural and manufacturing district. These advantages make it a close rival of Montreal. Other cities of 100,000 or more population are Windsor, Hamilton, Ottawa, and Quebec.

Quebec, the French-Canadian capital, with its ancient citadel, gray stone buildings, and "Lower Town" with its winding passages, narrow streets, and old houses, is one of the most picturesque cities in America. Located on the St. Lawrence where the Lowland begins, and over 100 miles northeast of Montreal, it is in a much less favorable position for commercial development. It has a large passenger traffic from ocean vessels that do not ascend to Montreal, and from passengers who desire to start the railway journey as soon as possible. It has large available water-power resources, and its railroads provide good connections with the Maritime Provinces and a more rapid access to the northwest than by way of Montreal. Its foreign trade is similar in many respects to that of Montreal. It typifies the lower St. Lawrence Lowland, of which it is the center. Along the great river highway that leads from the open ocean far inland, the explorer, voyageur, settler, traveler, as well as commerce and modern industry, have, in large part, passed by these lowlands to the head of navigation at Montreal, thus reminding one of "ships that pass in the night." The people of these lowlands have been left very much to themselves in a somewhat isolated relation to the rest of Canada. Here the French population, devoted to their religious faith, undisturbed by the passing tide of modern life, has developed a strong self-reliance and has retained many of the customs and much of the outlook on life of a century past. This evolution of a French Canada within the Dominion is in part the product of a natural environment which provided isolation yet permitted the progress made by several generations of other peoples to pass through it, wielding only a relatively small influence in the passage. Those at home now produce for, but are scarcely a part of the world outside. However, as a result of the high birth rate and pressure of population on local resources, the French Canadians are spreading into adjoining areas, and even migrating to distant parts of the Dominion. The strength of this ethnic group in Canada is evidenced by the recognition of both French and English as official languages.

PROBLEMS

1. Will the St. Lawrence Lowland continue to be the leading manufacturing and commercial section of Canada?

2. Do the water-power resources of the St. Lawrence Lowland compensate fully for its lack of coal?

3. Can Montreal maintain its position as the leading city and port of Canada?

4. Would free trade with the United States benefit the St. Lawrence Lowland?

5. The proposed Great Lakes-St. Lawrence Seaway would be of greater benefit to the St. Lawrence Lowland than to any other part of Canada.

6. Is the St. Lawrence Lowland dependent upon the Prairie Plains Region for a large part of its present industrial development?

7. Can the St. Lawrence Lowland maintain twice or three times its present population?

8. Will agriculture and the industries based thereon be of greater importance than the forest industries?

9. Can the industrial development of the Great Lakes-St. Lawrence Lowland Region equal that of the Great Lakes section of the United States?

10. Will the St. Lawrence Lowland continue to maintain its dominant position in the Dominion?

CHAPTER 23

The Prairie Plains
and Arctic Meadows

THE PRAIRIE PLAINS REGION

The Prairie Plains Region, for the purpose of this discussion, is the comparatively level, rolling country forming the southern portion of the great interior plain of Canada. Its northward limit in the west is an indefinite belt including the Peace River Valley, and in the east the Canadian Shield. From north to south it is divided into three natural belts. (1) The northern portion is a forested region, along the southern border of which are (2) numerous open grassland areas, whereas (3) the southern portion is true grass-covered prairie which merges into semiarid conditions at the southwest. The region is 800 miles wide along the international boundary and about half that width in latitude 56° north. From east to west in the southern part it is divided into the three prairie levels previously described. The first of these includes the approximately flat Red River Valley, famed for its fertile soils and immense wheat fields. The undulating surface of the second and the relatively level surface of the third are likewise noted for their vast expanse of potential agricultural land, which stretches out in all directions beyond the vision of the traveler.

Except for about 12,000 square miles in the southwest, the whole region drains eastward to Hudson Bay or northward to the Arctic Ocean, the largest drainage basins being the Saskatchewan, Peace, and Athabaska Rivers. The Saskatchewan River is considered navigable for shallow-draft vessels for 800 miles; the Athabaska, from Athabaska northward; and the Red, from United States territory to Lake Winnipeg, which is navigable throughout its length.

Because of tortuous courses, low water, rapids and other obstructions, unsuitable outlets, and the greater dependability of railroads through the year, and especially that part of the year when crops go to market, the rivers are of negligible commercial value. The streams of the southwest are used for irrigation purposes, a use which is likely to increase in importance. About one-sixth of the Dominion's minimum potential water power is in this region, with more than three-fourths of it in Manitoba (Table XXIII). This is an asset of great significance, owing to the sparsity and poor quality of the coal in Manitoba and Saskatchewan. The present water-power installation in the region, however, is less than a seventh of the minimum power available. This reserve will be available for manufacturing and irrigation as the region continues to develop. In contrast Alberta has very large power resources—water, coal, petroleum, and natural gas.

The distribution of people agrees very closely with the network of railways and the grain regions. The population of Saskatchewan is nearly

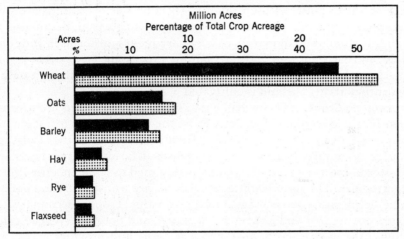

Fig. 248. Principal crops of the Prairie Plains region. The Prairie Plains region is a land of cereals among which wheat and oats occupy a dominant position. These six crops occupy 90.0 per cent of the crop acreage.

the same as that of Alberta, and the population of each exceeds that of Manitoba. However, the population of Alberta is increasing and that of Saskatchewan is decreasing. There has been a definite trend toward urban centers throughout the Prairie Plains, accompanying the growth of manufactures. The rivers have been of little significance in locating the people, as they are not commercially navigable nor do they lead to a satisfactory outlet. The total population has declined since about 1940. Since agriculture is the dominant industry, nearly three-fifths of the population is rural. Saskatchewan, which has few large towns or cities, has more than three-fifths of its population on farms. More than half the inhabitants of the region are of British origin, though it has a number of other population groups. Among other ethnic stocks are German,

Ukrainian, Scandinavian, French, Polish, and Russian, though each is small in number compared with the British. More than two-fifths of the people of Manitoba are in metropolitan Winnipeg.

Agriculture.   The Prairie Plains, in contrast with the Great Lakes-St. Lawrence Lowland, is a region with one dominant interest, viz., agriculture. All other activities are of relatively small importance, although marked changes are in progress. The great extent of level, fertile, arable land, ready for the plow without clearing; approximately 90 days' growing season with many hours of sunshine; high summer temperatures; a fair supply of rainfall in the growing season with dryness later in the summer; and snowfall in the eastern portion to supply early spring moisture have made it an especially suitable region for the growing of hardy grains of high quality. Its extensive grasslands are well adapted to grazing. However, the short growing season, fluctuation in rainfall, small rainfall margin of safety, frequent hailstorms in June and July, and early autumn frosts are limiting geographic factors. The region produces half the net agricultural revenue of Canada, though only a seventh of its arable land is cultivated.

Leading Crops.   The nearly flat to gently rolling plains are preeminently a land of grains (Fig. 248). From the vantage point of a slight hill elevation, or from the air, clusters of grain elevators dot the landscape and stand out like beacons on a treeless sea of farms and ranches. Each cluster marks the site of a town or city designed to serve an agricultural community. The three leading cereal crops are wheat, oats, and barley, whether measured in acreage, bushels, or value; crops of secondary importance are hay and forage, rye, flaxseed, and potatoes. Wheat is distinctly the pioneer crop, as it is easy to raise, and provides money for buildings and the purchase of livestock. This cash crop enables the settler to diversify his income later. Seven-tenths of the 43,160,000 acres devoted to field crops produce wheat and oats, the acreage of wheat being more than three times that of oats. However, the value of wheat represents nearly 60 per cent of the total crop value of the region, indicating the great importance of this crop in the agricultural economy of the Prairie Plains. In Saskatchewan wheat contributes nearly 70 per cent of the total value. It is chiefly upon this crop that the prosperity of the region depends, and the interior position and consequent great distance to foreign markets is a serious handicap. Low wheat prices bring economic distress.

The wheat belt is limited in the southwest by semiaridity, and on the north by relatively cool summers and a short growing season. The wheat district is a continuation of the spring-wheat section of the United States, and all the wheat produced is of the spring variety. Most of it is grown on the first and second prairie levels of Manitoba and Saskatchewan where

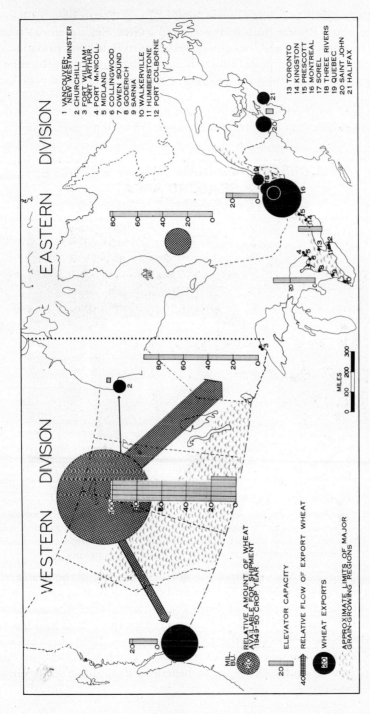

Fig. 249. Elevator capacity and leading export centers. *Data from Statistical Branch, Board of Grain Commissioners of Canada.*

the soils are similar to the chernozem or "Black Earth belt" of Russia and the black Prairie Soils of the United States. Spring wheat is also grown in south central Alberta where the warm Chinook prevails and the winters are shorter and milder than in other portions of the region. The dry climate is also an important factor in producing a very hard wheat.

The present distribution of the second crop—oats—is similar to that of wheat, except that it is commonly associated with mixed farming and

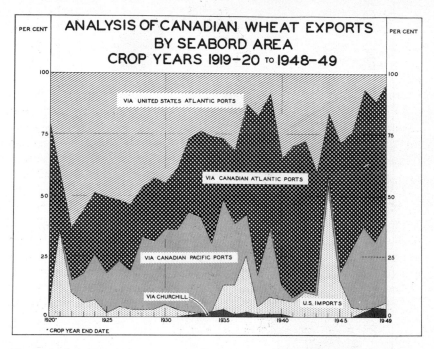

Fig. 250. Direction of export wheat. The great bulk of the wheat moves eastward to Atlantic ports. *Courtesy, Canadian Board of Grain Commissioners.* The interior location of the great wheat-producing region necessitates an extensive system of rail and water transportation, storage capacity, and export facilities. About three times as much wheat moves to eastern as to western mills and ports for export.

the maximum acreage lies along the northern margin of the wheat belt where the growing season is shorter and cooler than that required for wheat. The land devoted to oats is less than a third that of wheat, and the value only a fourth. Barley and flaxseed center in the first and second prairie levels, where most of these crops are grown. Both crops are well adapted to the climatic conditions imposed by high latitudes, and flaxseed will thrive under extremes of heat and drought. Flax is grown exclusively for seed, and usually on newly plowed prairie sod, as a "breaking" crop and because it is susceptible to disease when raised continuously on the same land. The distribution of cultivated hay and forage is similar to that of other crops. However, a large part, and probably most, of the annual crop comes from wild grass of the prairie; hence a considerable amount is produced beyond the cultivated districts.

Movement of the Wheat Crop. As in other new regions of small population and large production, most of the crop finds a market outside the region in which it is grown. Two-thirds or more of the wheat, but only a small proportion of the oats, is shipped out of the region, as the oats is used for stock feed locally. Thousands of elevators along the network of railroads that serve the region receive the grain from the farms. Practically all the wheat moving to the Atlantic seaboard utilizes the Great Lakes route, indicating the significance of those water bodies in marketing the crop. About two-thirds of the wheat shipments from the region go out through Fort William-Port Arthur (Fig. 251), which has very large elevator capacity. Figures 249 and 250 show the elevator capacity that has been built at major centers to serve storage and transit needs and relative importance of export ports. By far the largest share of the eastbound wheat follows the all-water route to ports on the St. Lawrence, Montreal being the principal one. Port Colborne and Buffalo are the leading ports on Lake Erie. An increasing amount is moving west by rail to Pacific ports. Vancouver-New Westminster now surpasses Montreal in elevator capacity, and its wheat exports are only a little smaller. Other minor routes are (1) by rail to Churchill on Hudson Bay (Fig. 252), (2) by rail and water to Georgian Bay and then by rail to eastern points.

Out of Canada's total overseas exports of wheat through Atlantic seaboard ports nearly a sixth passes out by way of United States ports, principally Baltimore and Philadelphia. This relatively small United States movement of Canadian grain is due to a number of geographic and non-geographic causes. The United States ports are open all year, whereas Montreal is open about 7 months; ocean insurance and freight rates are correspondingly lower than from Montreal; there is greater certainty of securing ship space when needed; both Canadian and United States lake vessels may carry the crop to United States ports, whereas only Canadian Lake vessels may carry the crop to Canadian ports and there are not enough such vessels to handle the crop.

The development of Vancouver as a wheat-exporting port is comparatively recent. In 1920 Vancouver handled 600,000 bushels, and in 1948–1949 more than 60,000,000. Adequate facilities for handling large quantities of grain have been provided, and it appears probable that annual wheat shipments by way of the Vancouver-Panama route to the markets of Europe will increase. Though Vancouver is twice as far from Liverpool by sea as Montreal is, the rail haul for wheat from Calgary to Vancouver is 640 miles less, and from Edmonton 460 miles less, than from those respective cities to Fort William-Port Arthur at the head of the Lakes. Vancouver also has the advantage of but one transfer—from rail to elevator and directly into an ocean-going vessel.

Livestock. The livestock industry has really just begun in the region, though the wild prairie grass provides excellent pasture, and cattle and horse ranches have existed for many years. With the advancement of settlement, many ranches suitable for crops were broken into farms, and

Fig. 251. A few of the grain elevators in the Fort William-Port Arthur harbor. *The Photographic Survey Corp., Ltd., Toronto, Ontario. Courtesy, Chamber of Commerce, Port Arthur.*

the rancher had to seek the rougher and less desirable parts of the region for grazing purposes. To raise stock intensively, however, requires considerable capital, and the severe climate necessitates warm buildings, the timber for which is not available on the treeless prairie. Moreover, several years are required to raise a herd of cattle, and the returns on the investment are small at first. Since land was abundant and cheap, and little capital was required to produce grain, the settler cultivated the soil in order to obtain quick returns. He has, therefore, just begun to develop mixed farming and livestock raising, and considerable progress has been made since about 1930.

Cattle are the most important livestock in both number and value.

They are produced throughout the region, but occur in greatest numbers on the first and second prairie levels where most of the crops are grown, and in south central Alberta on the third prairie level where the Chinook

Fig. 252. The harbor and grain elevator at Churchill. *Photo by Miller.*

produces a milder winter and melts the snow, making winter grazing possible, thus lessening the cost of shelter and feed. This district exceeds both Saskatchewan and Manitoba in the number of cattle, hogs, and sheep,

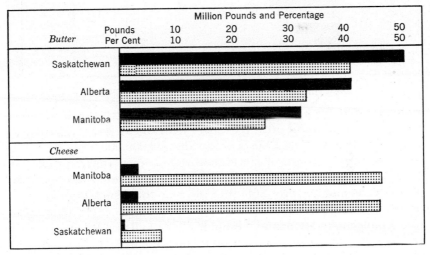

Fig. 253. Butter and cheese production in the Prairie Plains Region. Three-year average.

but is exceeded by Saskatchewan in the number of dairy cattle. Many of the milk cows at present are principally breeding stock for beef purposes. However, the dairy industry has made a substantial growth, with the value of raw milk alone nearly $125,000,000. Additional value is attained by production of nearly 125,000,000 pounds of butter and 7,000,000 pounds of cheese. These two products having high value per pound, compared with milk, can better absorb the cost of transportation to distant markets. The dairy industry has thus become an important source of cash income. Saskatchewan leads in butter production, and Manitoba and Alberta in cheese (Fig. 253). Swine are found in the more settled portions of the region where abundant food crops are grown, such as barley and oats, or where dairy by-products are available. The number, however, is small, and they are slaughtered primarily for local use.

The Future.   Measured from the standpoint of so-called "arable" land, a bright agricultural future for the region appears assured, as only about

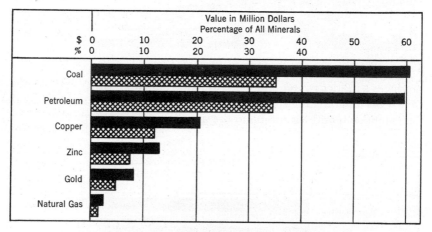

Fig. 254. Principal minerals produced in the Prairie Plains Region.

one-seventh of the area estimated as capable of cultivation is now used for field crops. With the present average yield and a 4-year crop rotation, the Prairie Plains are capable of producing 880,000,000 bushels of wheat or 6,900,000,000 bushels of oats annually, and other crops in proportion. However, "arable" land is not the only factor that enters into successful agriculture, and it is probable that the amount of such land has been overestimated. The climatic conditions limit the number of crops that are well adapted to rotation, and it is not likely that all arable land has equal productive value; hence such a production is not likely to be maintained if ever reached. Such figures merely indicate that potential agricultural resources are large and capable of sustaining a much larger population. Diversified farming, the use of fertilizers, the growth of domesticated hay and forage, and the raising of livestock for both meat and dairy purposes may lead to a substantial agricultural growth in the future. The extension of irrigation in the semiarid southwest, where more than 400,000 acres are now irrigated, will be an additional contributing factor. This district now has more than 2,460,000 acres of irrigable land in organized projects. When completed, other projects in Saskatchewan will provide water for 105,200 acres.

Minerals. This region of farming and grazing land is deficient in minerals compared with some other regions of Canada, though coal, petroluem, copper, zince, gold, natural gas, clay products, and silver are produced. The first four are the only ones that approach large production (Fig. 254). The metallic minerals are produced in the Shield portion of the region, north of the prairies, and nearly all come from the Flin Flon-Sherrit Gordon area on the Manitoba-Saskatchewan border. A considerable area in southern Saskatchewan and a large part of Alberta are underlaid with coal. The Saskatchewan coal is lignite, but near the base of the Rockies the coal improves in quality and increases in quantity, and essentially all coal in Alberta is bituminous and subbituminous. The probable reserves of Alberta are estimated to be about 35,000,000,-000 tons, and coal is now the leading mineral produced. The Crow's Nest field is one of the most important in production and quality; Lethbridge and Edmonton produce a lower-grade coal, chiefly for the local market.

More than 95 per cent of Canada's petroleum comes from the Prairie Plains Region. For many years Turner Valley was the chief source, and it is still an important contributor to Alberta's total output. The Leduc-Woodbend field, southwest of Edmonton, now leads. Other large producers are the Redwater area northeast of Edmonton, and Lloydminster on the Alberta-Saskatchewan border (Fig. 255). Lloydminster produces a heavy oil used extensively as railway locomotive fuel. The crude-oil production capacity is much greater than local refining facilities. The new pipe lines to Sarnia and Vancouver, carry crude oil to eastern and western refineries and provide an outlet for greater production. Usually, about 90 per cent of Canada's consumption of crude and refined oil products is imported. The potential reserve of these new fields indicate that imports will be reduced greatly, if not eliminated. The enormous deposits of tar sands and "liquid bitumen" in the McMurray region are practically untouched. The Alberta Government is now operating a small refinery at Bitumount. Alberta also produces more than four-fifths of Canada's natural gas. A projected pipe line, when completed, will provide a market in British Columbia, Washington, Oregon, and California.

The Peace River Region. The Peace River district is of special interest as a frontier, because of its high latitude (55° to 58°) in the lee of the Rockies, its many hours of daily sunshine in the summer months, its low but effective rainfall, its Chinook winds, and its agricultural productivity

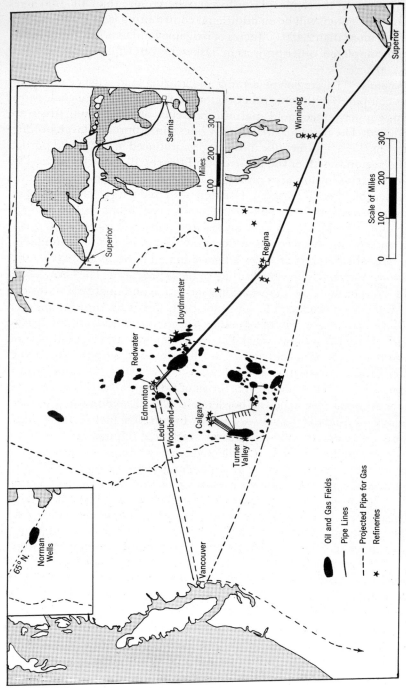

Fig. 255. The oil fields of the Prairie Plains Region.

and potentials. Its southern border is in the latitude of the south shore of Hudson Bay and its northern in that of Churchill, or nothern Labrador. However, the tundra landscape of Churchill and Labrador is in striking contrast with rolling, forested, morainic hills and farmlands of the Peace River country. The average annual rainfall is only about 15

Fig. 256. A farm home near Grimshaw. *Photo by Miller.*

inches, with a summer maximum, and winters are cold and summers warm. Chinook winds are a pronounced feature and bring balmy days to break the steady cold of the long winter. Spring arrives quickly and early, seeding is done from the middle of April through May, and the crop is harvested from the middle of August to the middle of September. Snows reach the region about the middle of November, and winter closes in.

Fig. 257. Typical agricultural community in the Peace River country. *Photo by Miller.*

Estimates indicate that the upper drainage basin of the Peace contains about 14 to 18 million acres of potential agricultural and grazing land. Only a small portion is now utilized by the present population of some 60,000. Agricultural development is localized in areas separated by bush and forest. Some of the wooded area has poor sandy soil, but much of it is good potential agricultural land. It is probable that the best Dark-Brown to Black Podzolic Soil areas with adequate transportation facilities have been occupied, and the new settler will have to accept the less desirable. The hills of the region are commonly warmer than the lowlands, the difference often being as much as 28°. The high lands are well suited to grain, and the region is noted for its high-grade wheat. The low areas are very good for grass and hay crops, and much hay and lawngrass seed are produced, especially bromegrass seed for hay and creeping red fescue seed for lawn grass. Other crops include oats, barley, buckwheat, vegetables, apples and small bush fruits. Cattle are the chief livestock. The farm lands and excellent farm homes about such centers as Grand Prairie, Sexsmith, Beaverlodge, Grimshaw (Fig. 256), Clairmont, and Rolla rival similar areas in Iowa. However, on the margin many log homesteads are still in the primitive frontier stage. The relative importance of agriculture, about the various village centers, may be judged by the number and size of the grain elevators, which are conspicuous features of the cultural landscape (Fig. 257). At present transportation costs to distant markets are too high to encourage agricultural expansion. The full productive capacity of the region will not be utilized until an adequate outlet has been provided westward to the Pacific. Even the development of its oil, natural gas, and coal resources can supply only a small additional local market.

Manufactures. Little manufacturing, compared with Ontario, has been done in the Prairie Plains country in the past. Since there is little water power except in the extreme western and eastern parts, and suitable coal in abundance only in the far west; since labor is scarce, opportunities for individual endeavor plentiful, and the market limited by sparse population, manufacturing on an extensive scale is not to be expected. However, industry has made substantial progress. Present manufacturing enterprises are related closely to the use of local raw materials, and include those types that serve the needs of a local community. Slaughtering and meat packing, and flour and feed mills account for one-third of the total value, followed by butter and cheese, and petroleum products (Fig. 258). The two leading industries rank first and second in each province. Manitoba with the concentration in metropolitan Winnipeg, ranks first in slaughtering and meat packing, and Alberta second. Saskatchewan leads in butter and cheese, Alberta in flour and feed mills and petroleum products, and Manitoba in railway rolling-stock.

Cities. Nearly all cities and towns of the Prairie Plains are based on an agricultural economy. They are centers for the collection, processing, and shipping of agricultural raw materials, distribution of manufactured products, and manufacturing, for the area served. Calgary and Edmonton might be considered partial exceptions because of petroleum refining, and, likewise, a few small centers based on mining. In the early days of settlement towns tended to locate at the intersection of railways, or along them, where agricultural conditions were good, and where their prosperity depended upon that of the tributary agricultural community. Winnipeg, Calgary, Edmonton, Regina, Saskatoon, Moosejaw, and Brandon owe their location and importance primarily to these causes. Calgary and Edmonton have grown to cities of more than 100,000 population.

Metropolitan Winnipeg is by far the most important, and with a population of about 300,000 it is the second-largest city west of the St. Lawrence Lowland. Its location in the narrow gap between Lake Winnipeg and Lake of the Woods directs all railways and all traffic from the eastern and western parts of Canada through it. Its hinterland is the

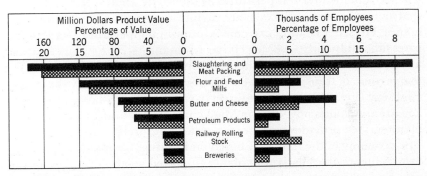

Fig. 258. Leading manufactures of the Prairie Plains region. These six account for more than half of the total value.

whole region, as most of the produce of the region passes through it on the way to the eastern markets of Canada, Europe, or the United States, and manufactures and other articles enter it for distribution to the region. It is, therefore, the commanding entrepôt of the Northwest. It has excellent water power available for industrial development. The growth of Winnipeg has corresponded with that of the Prairie Plains country which it serves, and its future progress will be determined by the development attained by the same area. Owing to its commanding position in a great agricultural area, it is frequently called "The Chicago of Canada."

THE ARCTIC LANDS

A Vast Area.   Far to the north, extending from the shores of the Arctic Ocean southward to the forests, lies an immense expanse of arctic meadow or tundra. More than 760 varieties of flowering plants, 330 varieties of mosses, and 28 of lichens are known to thrive natively upon its surface, and in many places the flowers, mosses, and lichens are completely obscured by the growth of grass, sedges, and the like. A still more northerly extension of the area includes many of the arctic islands and much of the shore of Greenland. Summer-season temperatures of 80°–100° are not uncommon near the Arctic Circle, though the average temperature is much less. During the many hours of continuous sunshine, vegetation grows with great rapidity. Latitude 70° N. may have sunshine for 73 days continuously except when the sun may be obscured by clouds; 66½° N. for 24 hours; and 60° N. for 18½ hours. At least several hundred thousand square miles has more than a month of continuous daylight. The winters are long, dark, and cold, but the snowfall is less than that of Chicago. Even the snowfall of Ellsmere Island is only about a tenth of that of St. Louis, Missouri. Most of the arctic land is covered with very little snow at any time of year, as the snow is swept away by the winds. The extreme winter temperatures of the arctic are not as low as those that occur in many places where white men now have comfortable homes. Herschel Island's extreme minimum temperature, −54°, compares faborably with −68° for Harve, Montana, −70° for Prince Albert, and −57° for Edmonton. The Mackenzie River system has been the major route of transportation for many years. More recently the Alaska Highway (Fig. 212) has given direct overland connections with the Yukon area. Airports now dot the Mackenzie Valley and Yukon, and airplane service provides transportation for both freight and passengers. The economy of the natives is based on hunting, trapping, and fishing. Sale of furs enables natives to obtain imported goods. Trapping by natives and white men yields approximately $2,000,000 worth of furs annually. With completion of an all-weather highway from Grimshaw, Alberta, to the Hay River settlement on the south shore of Great Slave Lake, trucks now carry goods north for distribution to Yellowknife, on the north shore of the lake, and throughout the Mackenzie District, and carry fresh fish to southern markets.

The presence of minerals has long been known, though only a relatively small portion of this vast area has been tested carefully. However, mining has become the major industry with an annual output of more than $8,500,000, two-thirds of which is gold. Yellowknife, on the north shore of Great Slave Lake, now surpasses the Dawson-Mayo district of Yukon. A hydroelectric plant about 90 miles north on the Snare River, with an installed capacity of 8350 hp, supplies power for the Yellowknife district. The Norman Wells petroleum field, with a production of about 400,000 barrels, provides fuel and other refined products for the Mackenzie area. Radium and uranium are produced near Port Radium on the east shore of Great Bear Lake. The mines are one of the world's major sources of these ores and the largest in North America.

A Land of the Future.   Native animal life is abundant both on the land and in the seas—seal, walrus, whale, fish, caribou, wolf, bear, fox, rabbit, ducks, geese, loon, etc. Caribou occur in millions and roam over the land, from the arctic islands far to the south, in herds containing thousands and hundreds of thousands. The caribou, or wild reindeer, is probably the principal animal of economic interest to man. The grass-eating muskox, or ovibo, is of only slightly less interest, as both animals are extremely well adapted to the region and their meat is excellent. The muskox also yields 10–15 pounds of wool, is a larger milk producer than the reindeer, and has the superior quality of moving about no more than is necessary to obtain food.

Most of the present scant Eskimo population lives along the shores, as fish, seal, and walrus are more dependable sources of food than the caribou, which travel long distances in herds. Today these people live in the hunting and fishing stage of human development. Such has been their history from an unknown date. What of tomorrow? An index to a possible future is the success of the reindeer industry in Alaska. If Alaska can support 3,000,000–4,000,000 (estimated) reindeer upon its grazing area, it seems probable that the Arctic Meadows of Canada can support at least twice as many. Even a much smaller number would provide a surplus of excellent meat and hides, to feed and clothe the people of warmer climes, and would assure a less precarious living to the native population. A beginning has been made by the importation of several thousand reindeer from Alaska to the excellent grazing grounds east of the delta of the Mackenzie River. Progress in building up this herd, and in the training of personnel, is being made at the Federal Government project near Aklavik. Other areas are being studied to determine their suitability for reindeer, and research is in progress to develop additional resources of the region, so as to widen the economy of the native population. Perhaps the muskox, or some hybrid obtained through it by breeding, may prove more profitable than the reindeer or better adapted to some sections. Such seems to be a possible future utilization of the resources of this region. When that time comes the population will increase, but will never be dense, and will be of the nomadic-herdsman type except in mining centers. Hunting and trapping for furs will continue to produce some wealth, and local areas of denser population may grow up about slaughtering centers or mines.

PROBLEMS

1. Can the Prairie Plains Region surpass the North Central Section of the United States in agricultural development?

2. What will be the permanent type of agricultural development in the Prairie Plains Region?

3. Will the proposed Great Lakes-St. Lawrence Seaway be of greater benefit to both the Prairie Plains and St. Lawrence Lowland Regions than to any other region of North America?

4. Can the Arctic Meadows of Canada maintain as many people as now live in British Columbia?

5. Will the Arctic Meadows ever produce as much meat as the Prairie Plains?

6. Can manufacturing become an important industry in the Prairie Plains Region?

7. Will the development of irrigation make Alberta as productive as California?

8. Can the Prairie Plains Region maintain a population as large as that of the St. Lawrence Lowland?

CHAPTER 24

The Pacific Mountain Region

The Pacific Mountain Region is a vast, mountainous mass whose snow-capped and glacier-clad peaks rise above a vast forest wilderness that extends downward into its deep valleys and plateaulike areas. It is the highest and most rugged part of Canada, many summits reaching a height of 10,000 feet and a few exceeding 16,000 feet, the highest being Mount Logan, 19,540 feet. The coast is characterized by long, deep, narrow, well-sheltered indentations or fiords, extending far inland, giving the region more harbors than can ever be utilized for the development of commercial centers. Some of these indentations are continued into the highland beyond, as ravines or glens. Others are too deep for good anchorage, have too narrow and winding entrances for safe and easy passage of ocean vessels, or are too difficult to reach from the interior, while a majority have too precipitous and rugged surroundings for the development of important commercial cities. In addition, Vancouver Island shuts off nearly half the coast from direct connection with the open sea. The coast is also fringed by islands separated by deep channels, forming an "inside passage" through which ships may sail for nearly 800 miles protected from the winds and storms of the Pacific.

In general the mountain masses trend north and south in three rather distinct ranges—Coast Mountains, Selkirk-Cariboo-Stikine Ranges and the Rocky Mountains. Between the first two lies a broad, dissected interior plateau, and the Rocky Mountain Trench lies between the second and third. This mountain and trench structure, as well as altitude and ruggedness, has had a profound influence upon the climate, distribution, and character of vegetation, and on man's occupancy of the region and utilization of its resources. Only a very small part of the region is suitable for agriculture. The north-south trend of isotherms (Fig. 259) and the east-west variation in rainfall, conforming closely with topography, are striking features. Climatic zones likewise trend north and south (Fig. 9). The prevailing Westerlies bring mild oceanic temperatures and heavy winter rainfall to the Pacific Coast, and the western slopes of the mountains are clothed with a dense forest in which the Douglas fir is the most valuable tree. In descending to the interior plateau the winds give only scant rainfall, and temperatures are higher in summer and lower in winter than on the coast. However, as these winds again rise over the mountains of the interior and the Rockies, rainfall occurs on their western slopes, and forests prevail. The mean rainfall at New Westminster on the Fraser Delta is 55.12 inches; at Penticton, in the Okanagon Valley of the interior, it is only 10.85 inches; and at Lethbridge, in the rainshadow of

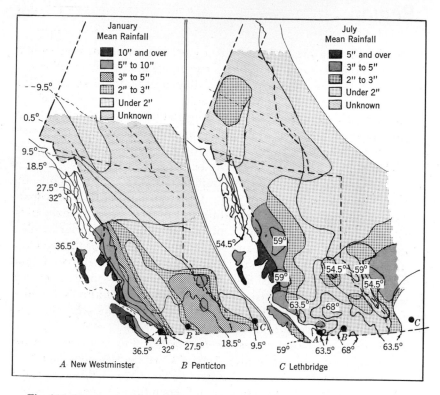

Fig. 259. Distribution of temperature and rainfall in the Pacific Mountain region.

the Rockies, 15 inches (Figs. 259 and 260). The interior plateau is semiarid and has a typical semiarid type of vegetation. Where ditch irrigation has been developed in the interior excellent fruit crops thrive. Large areas of hay and feed-crop lands are irrigated by flooding on many of the stock ranches.

The Fraser, Yukon, Skeena, and Stikine are the most important river systems. Though some of the rivers and the associated lakes are navigable for limited distances, most of the streams are characterized by numerous rapids and falls, which give the region a potential water power of nearly

11,000,000 hp, only 917,000 of which has been utilized thus far. The water-power reserve, plus the coal reserve, provides one essential for the development of manufactures which is likely to meet all probable future demands.

The population of about 1,100,000 is confined almost exclusively to the southern part and particularly to the southwestern coast, where fully three-fifths lives in the lower Fraser Valley and Delta. The two large cit-

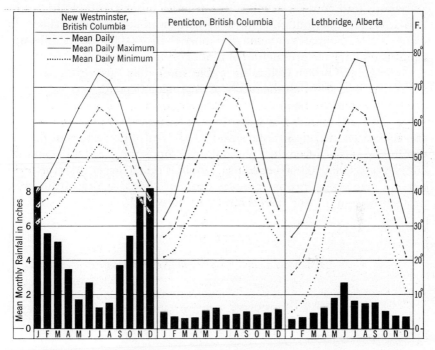

Fig. 260 Temperature and rainfall at stations across southern British Columbia. New Westminster is on the coast, Penticton is in the interior and Lethbridge in the rainshadow of the Rockies.

ies are Vancouver and New Westminster, but there are scores of small villages and towns. The southwest is also the most densely settled farming area. Some 8000 people in the Yukon mining district, 7000 in the port of Prince Rupert, and a few distributed along railway routes are the exceptions. More than half the people are in cities and villages; the remainder are scattered among the lumber and mining camps, or are engaged in agriculture and stock raising along the valleys or over the grasslands. Since 1940 the population has increased about 25,000 a year, a rate of growth larger than that of any other section of Canada. This growth has been chiefly in the southern district on the lowlands along the lower section of the Fraser River. Fully seven-tenths of the population are of British stock and most of the remainder of European origin. The demand for laborers, the opportunities offered in the fisheries, lumber camps, industrial and mining centers, intensive agriculture and horticulture, and accessibility by sea encourage immigration.

Forest Industries. The Pacific Mountain Region is a land of forests except on the far northern Arctic slope. These forests are almost entirely softwoods and contain much of the finest timber available in North America. The distribution of forest-, waste-, and arable land is shown in Table XXV. Estimates indicate that more than 200,000 square miles are suitable only for the production of timber. With only about 6 per cent of the land area of British Columbia arable, more than three-fifths of which is forested, it is clear that the future of the region depends very largely on the timber that can be produced. The climate and soil are excellent for forest growth. Measured by quantity it is estimated that nearly a fifth of the accessible, merchantable, standing timber of Canada is in British Columbia. It is believed that, without drain upon the growth, the annual cut can be 8,000,000,000 board feet, which is much larger than the present cut. However, proper conservation methods, reforestation, and protection from fire and insects must be enforced.

TABLE XXV

BRITISH COLUMBIA FOREST AND ARABLE LAND

	Merchantable (square miles)	Young Growth (square miles)	Total Productive (square miles)	Total Unproductive (square miles)	Waste and Arable	Percentage of Land Area Forested
Softwood	35,400	50,490	85,890	128,560		59.6
Waste land					137,163	38.1
Arable land						
Forested					13,034	3.6*
Non-forested					7,666	2.1

* Included in 59.6.
Data computed from *Canada Yearbook,* 1949, p. 29.

The Douglas Fir Coast District and the Interior Wet Belt are the leading lumber-producing districts. The Douglas Fir Coast District, with its heavy precipitation, high humidity, long growing season, and high average temperature with absence of extremes, produces a coniferous forest which is equaled for rapidity of growth, density, and acre yield only along the Washington and Oregon coasts. Much of the timber cut along or near the indented mainland coast and on Vancouver Island is brought to tidewater, where it is made into huge rafts and towed to sawmills located on some convenient harbor. Areas of mature trees yield 10,000–

100,000 board feet of lumber an acre, and average 20,000 feet. Douglas fir is the most important commercial type.

The climate of the Interior Wet Belt resembles that of both the coast and dry belts, with a comparatively humid atmosphere, a precipitation of 30–40 inches; a relatively long growing season, considering the high latitude and altitude; warm summers; cold winters, free from long periods of extreme low temperatures; and heavy snowfall, which assures an abundance of spring moisture. This region has a dense, rapidly growing forest cover, giving a large acre yield though not equal to that of the Douglas Fir Coast District. Cedar, hemlock, Douglas fir, spruce, and lodgepole pine thrive throughout most of the Interior Wet Belt, and western white pine occurs in the watersheds of the West Thompson and Columbia Rivers. Though second in commercial importance to the Coast

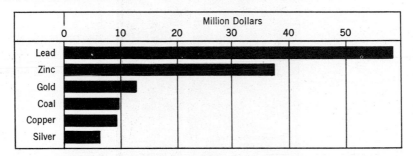

Fig. 261. Leading minerals of the Pacific Mountain region. More than four-fifths of the minerals produced are metals, with lead and zinc supplying more than three-fifths.

District, this district may even excel the lumber possibilities of the Coast District because of its large area of potential forest land, which is now covered with young trees.

The most important commercial trees of the Pacific Mountain Region are the Douglas fir, used for lumber and other structural purposes, mine timbers, ties, and paving blocks; red cedar, the most important Canadian wood, for shingles; Alaskan pine or western hemlock, used extensively for structural and pulp purposes; and Sitka spruce and Engelmann's spruce, which are especially valuable for airplanes and pulp manufacture.

Lumber, shingles, and lath are the leading forest products, and British Columbia produces more than 45 per cent of the sawmill products of the country. In addition this region produces about 7 per cent of the paper. The Prairie Plains Region was for many years the principal lumber market, but exports now go to Europe by way of the Panama Canal, to South Africa, and to many other wood-consuming countries.

Mining.   The mining district is a continuation of the Cordillera of South America, Mexico, and the United States. This mountain area con-

Fig. 262. The smelter at Trail on the Columbia River. *Photo by Miller.*

tains mineral wealth throughout its length. Coal was discovered in 1835, but the first mine, at Nanaimo, was not opened until 1851 and it has been worked ever since. Gold was discovered in the later 1850's, and the Fraser River rush began in 1858. In 1861 the Cariboo district was entered by prospectors, and the Williams and Lightning Creek districts were discovered. The Cassiar district was opened in 1873, and prospectors entered the Yukon before 1880. Klondike mining began in 1894, and the Yukon district reached its peak in 1900 with a gold production of $22,-000,000. The early crude methods of mining in the Yukon have given place to large dredges, and many of the early tailings are being reworked. The development of lode mining, which is now much more important than placer mining, followed railroad construction in southern British Columbia in the late 1890's. Lode mining is now carried on principally between the Thompson River and the United States boundary. The principal mining camps are near the southern boundary of British Columbia at Kimberley, Slocan, Nelson, Trail, Hedley, and Copper Mountain; in the Dawson-Mayo district in Yukon; along the coast at Brittania Beach; and at Zeballos on Vancouver Island. Other important metal-producing districts farther north in British Columbia include Bralorne, Bakerville, Fort St. James, Hazelton, and Premier.

The region is noted for its lead, zinc, coal, gold, silver, and copper. It produces 98 per cent of Canada's output of lead; 58 per cent of the zinc; and nearly half the silver. The six minerals listed in Fig. 261 make up nearly nine-tenths of the total mineral production of the region. The Sullivan lead-zinc-silver mine near Kimberly, with an ore body about 200 feet thick, yields 90 per cent of the total lead. The ore is crushed and concentrated in the vicinity of the mine and shipped to the smelter at Trail (Fig. 262), which is the largest in Canada. A chemical plant utilizes the sulfur in the production of sulfuric acid and fertilizers. Silver, as in other parts of the Dominion, is derived from ore mined chiefly for other metals, especially lead and zinc. Such districts as Cariboo, Kootenay, Hedley, and Zeballos are noted for gold, and Brittania Beach and Copper Mountain for copper. Tungsten comes from Yukon and southern British Columbia, and the Pinchi Lake district produces mercury. With vast areas yet to be examined carefully, and the probability of finding more rich mineral deposits, it seems likely that the people of the region will find the production of minerals one of the most profitable occupations for many years to come.

The major areas of bituminous coal mining are near Fernie, in southeastern British Columbia, and Nanaimo, Comax, and Suquash on Vancouver Island. Small amounts of coal are mined at several other locations. British Columbia coal is the best steam and coking variety on the Pacific

Coast of the Americas, with the possible exception of Alaska; hence it has great significance for domestic manufacturing and mining, and land- and ocean-transportation purposes. It has practically no competition in the market at the present time. The probable reserve of British Columbia is about 19 per cent of the total probable reserves of the Dominion. The coal is chiefly bituminous and anthracite, with a relatively small proportion of lignite. The Yukon coal is largely lignite, but there is more than a hundred million tons of bituminous.

In addition to fuel the region has excellent water power available. The estimated resource, at mean 6-month flow, is 11,000,000 hp, making it rank second to Quebec. The installed capacity is 917,000, leaving an

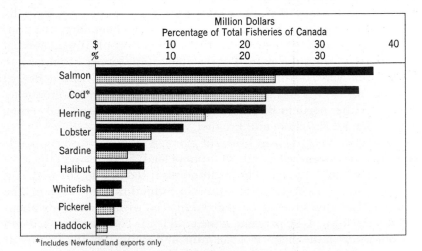

*Includes Newfoundland exports only

Fig. 263. Principal commercial fish of Canada.

enormous reserve for future use in the development of its forest, mining, manufacturing, and transportation industries. Yukon, at the north, also has several hundred thousand horsepower, only a small part of which has been utilized.

Fisheries.   The Pacific Coast, with its deep fiords and estuaries, and a sea ledge extending 50–100 miles from the coast, offers excellent feeding grounds for fish. Fishing was carried on in the region by the Hudson Bay Company before settlement began, but canning on a large scale started in 1873. Today the region ranks next to the Maritime Provinces (Fig. 231) in fisheries, the annual value being 38 per cent of that for the Dominion. The industry is built primarily upon the habits of the sockeye salmon, which spawns in British Columbia streams, particularly the Fraser River and its connecting lakes; the fingerling spends the first year of its life in these fresh waters. The following three years are spent in the ocean. It returns in the fourth year to spawn, entering the rivers from June to September, the run being at its height from the last of July to the middle of August. The catch is being made when the fish are entering these streams, as they die after spawning. Because of the life habits of the salmon, every fourth year usually produces a large catch. The sockeye salmon weighs 3–10 pounds and is noted for its fine quality and color. The quinnat is a much larger variety of salmon, weighing 18–30 and occasionally 100 pounds. It enters the Fraser in the spring, and the run continues through July. The cohoe is about the same size as the sockeye and runs in the Fraser in September and October after the sockeye salmon run is over. The salmon is the principal one fished in Canada, but probably would rank next to cod if comparable data for cod were available (Fig. 263).

In entering the Fraser River the salmon pass through many miles of United States waters were a large part of the salmon catch is taken by United States fishermen. This situation raises an international question and a grave problem of conservation. The catch during the 3 years of minimum run depletes the supply and, since the fish spawn in Canadian streams only, conservation can be accomplished only by cooperation between the Canadian and the United States governments. Fortunately, this cooperation has been successfully carried out. The principal salmon centers are the Fraser, Nass, and Skeena Rivers.

Attention has been directed to other fish, particularly the halibut. The principal halibut fisheries are on the banks of the Queen Charlotte Islands, from which the catch is taken to Prince Rupert and shipped frozen to the United States and eastern Canadian markets. The northern or Yukon fisheries are small compared with those in the southern part of the region. The chief foreign markets for Pacific fisheries are Great Britain and other European countries, where a large part of the catch is sold.

Agriculture.   Measured by gross annual value, agriculture ranks third as a producer of raw materials, with forests and minerals first and second, respectively. Development of agriculture, however, is greatly restricted, owing to the rugged topography, the problem of clearing the land for crop production, and the greater immediate opportunities presented by lumbering, mining, and fishing. The first farming took place in the Fraser Lake district in 1811. The fur-trading companies were the early agricultural pioneers. The Hudson Bay Company had a large farm near Fort Vancouver as early as 1837, producing grain, vegetables, and other crops, and raising livestock. This company also had large farms at Cowlitz and Nisqually, and smaller ones on Vancouver Island. The gold rush to the Cariboos in the 1850's and the establishment of mining camps supplied a market for agriculture produce, gave an impetus to farming, and accounted for the beginning of stock raising in the Nicola and Thompson valleys.

Though agriculture is confined chiefly to the south, the average value of field crops exceeds $33,000,000, and that of livestock on farms and ranches $37,000,000. Hay and forage, wheat, oats, rye, and potatoes are the leading field crops (Fig. 264). Cattle make up nearly three-fourths of the value of livestock and are produced for both meat and dairy purposes. The dairy industry has been growing, and the value of milk production alone now exceeds $17,800,000.

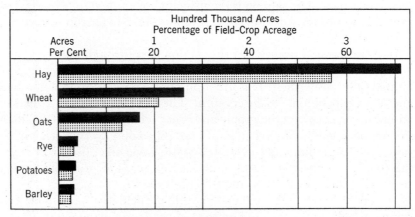

Fig. 264. Leading crops of British Columbia. These six crops occupy 98.8 per cent of the land in field crops. The region has less than 1000 square miles of land in field crops.

A considerable portion of British Columbia has both soil and climate suitable for growing fruits. Especially is this true in the long southern interior valleys, which have mild winters, and where fruit growing has made rapid progress. The tree fruits include apples, pears, peaches, plums, and apricots; and the small fruits include strawberries, currants, and raspberries. British Columbia now produces more than half the commercial fruit of the Dominion. Okanagan Valley, lower Fraser Valley, Kootenay-Arrow Lakes section, and Vancouver Island are the principal fruit regions. Okanagan Valley is indeed, a "land of fruit." More than 33,900 acres are irrigated out of an irrigable area of 36,140 acres in organized irrigation enterprises. The mountain highlands present a sun-dried, drab appearance in summer, but the deep-green orchards of the valley form a striking contrast where water from mountain streams has been carried to the alluvial areas by ditches. Kelowna and Penticton are important fruit centers. Penticton stands on a delta built across the valley, with Okanagan Lake on the north and Dog Lake on the south (Fig. 265). Here is a Canadian "Interlaken," but without the grandeur of mountain scenery that surrounds its Swiss counterpart. Its life centers around the growing, canning, packing, and shipping of fruit. A nearby mine also contributes to its activities. It is served by one east-west railroad, and by another which reaches it from the north by car ferries on Okanagan Lake.

Owing to the mountainous and plateau character at the south, the mountain and climatic limitations at the north, and limited markets, the land at present devoted to field crops is only about 627,000 acres, more

Fig. 265. Penticton in the Okanagan Valley and part of its irrigated orchards. *Photo by Miller.*

than half of which produce hay and forage crops. The cultivated land is confined almost exclusively to the warm southern valleys, terraces, deltas, and flood plains. The farms, unlike those of other parts of Canada, are small, usually not more than 25–30 acres, and are cultivated intensively. In addition to cropland, approximately 100,000 acres is used as range pasture. Estimates indicate that 4,225,000 acres are suitable for tillage, and a total of 14,528,000 for some form of agricultural use, and this is only about 6 per cent of the land area of British Columbia, but it is highly improbable that more than a small fraction of this potential acreage will be utilized for many generations to come.

Manufacturing. The Pacific Mountain Region was a frontier wilderness when the factory system of production was established in the East. Manufacturing in British Columbia never passed through the usual slow evolutionary stages from domestic handicrafts, into small work shops,

introduction of a small amount of machinery and tools of precision, and
thence into large factories with many employees, producing for universal
markets, as occurred in the older settled sections of the country. When

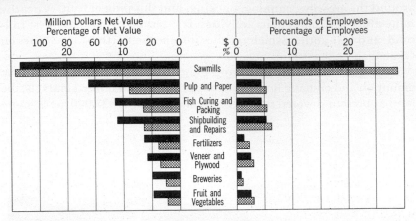

Fig. 266. Leading manufacturing industries of British Columbia. Forest industries
account for more than two-fifths of the manufacturing.

the time for manufacturing came British Columbia was ready to start
with the factory system. The coming of railroads was the first important
transforming event, as these gave connection with the interior. But the
real development of manufacturing began with the opening of the

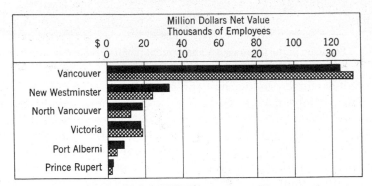

Fig. 267. Leading manufacturing cities of the Pacific Mountain region. More than half
the manufacturing of the region is on the delta of the Fraser.

Panama Canal in 1914 and the stimulus of World War I. As an alternative to the long trip around Cape Horn or the long and costly transcontinental route to European markets, the Canal was a great boon to
the region. In 1910 the product value of manufactures was $65,000,000
and there were 33,300 employees; in 1920 the figures were $237,000,000

and 35,100; in 1929, $276,000,000 and 51,300; and in 1948, $985,000,-000 and 86,600, respectively.

The industries that have thrived are those based upon the abundant natural resources of the region. The dominant ones utilize the splendid forest resources and make up more than two-fifths of the total net value of the manufactures of the region. Next in rank is fish curing and packing, followed by shipbuilding (Fig. 266). Shipbuilding gained first place during World War II, and, even though it has declined greatly since its peak year in 1943, it ranks second in the number of people employed. British Columbia has abundant resources of raw materials, coal, and water power, good railroad facilities to the Prairie Plains, and a water route, open all the year, to the markets of the world.

Cities. All the large cities are along the southwestern mainland coast and the southeastern coast of Vancouver Island (Fig. 267). Here are located Vancouver (Fig. 268), Victoria, Port Alberni, New Westminster, North Vancouver, Nanaimo, and numerous smaller cities. Prince Rupert, 500 miles north of this group, is the only other important coastal city. Near the southern border, along the railways, is a series of several minor cities among which may be mentioned Nelson, Kamloops, Vernon, Kelowna, and Cranbrook.

Vancouver is the most important; it is the third city in size in Canada and the largest city west of the St. Lawrence Lowland. In 1880 its site was a wilderness. When the Canadian Pacific Railway selected it for a terminus, growth was stimulated, and since about 1910 its population has increased from 29,000 to 275,000. This is a remarkable growth when one considers that Vancouver faces the Pacific, with its back to the rest of the Dominion, and is separated from it by many miles of forested mountain country. It has a fine, natural, ice-free harbor capable of accommodating all shipping that it is ever likely to have; oceanic connections with the United States, Alaska, the Orient, Australasia, and Europe, by way of the Panama Canal; a near hinterland that contains most of the population of the region and produces agricultural crops, livestock, and forest and mineral products. It is also economically accessible to the products and markets of the Prairie Plains; is near existing and probable future oceanic trade routes; is close to the populated centers of western United States and western Canada; is the entrepôt for British Columbia; is the center of the lumber industry; and the Vancouver metropolitan district produces more than half the manufactures of the province. As the markets for the products of agriculture, forest, and mines are Atlantic and southern Pacific points, its geographical advantages are greater than those of any more northerly Pacific port and seem to assure its prosperity as a commercial and industrial center. Its growth as a commercial port has been striking, and it now ranks with Montreal, Toronto, and Quebec as one of Canada's leading ports. With the exception of harbor superiority, the same factors affecting Vancouver may be said to apply to the neighboring towns in the district, including New Westminster and North Vancouver.

The capital city, Victoria, situated on the southern end of Vancouver Island, is primarily residential, and only a seventh the size of Vancouver. However, it ranks fourth in manufactures. It faces the state of Washington, whose mountains rise 7000 or 8000 feet from the sea, presenting a beautiful spectacle from the city. It was originally settled by British immigrants who came across the Isthmus of Central America and north along

Fig. 268. Part of Vancouver Harbor, Canada's principal Pacific port. Huge log rafts may be seen floating in the harbor. *Photo by Miller.*

the coast by ship, and Victoria has retained much of its English appearance and spirit. Victoria's harbor is too shallow for the larger vessels, and its island location, separated from the mainland, limits its commercial and industrial development and possibilities. Only the southern end of Vancouver Island about Victoria may be considered as cleared and populated, the balance being a rugged, timber-clad highland.

Prince Rupert was established as a Pacific terminus of the Grand Trunk Railway system. Though smaller than several other cities it is of special interest because it is spoken of as the future rival of Vancouver. It is the terminus and shortest route from eastern Canada to oriental ports north of Shanghai, and has an excellent harbor with a wide, direct, and short entrance to the open ocean, and ample suitable space for the growth of a city. It is also nearest the best agricultural section of the western prairie, but the present transportation routes by way of Yellowhead Pass make these sections nearer to Vancouver, and they have better grades. Its hinterland for 150 miles inland is a rugged, forest-covered area with small agricultural value, as it is near the northern limit of cultivable crops. The trees are smaller, of less commercial value, and fewer to the acre than farther south, and the region is not known to be rich in minerals. Probably its best opportunity for import trade is the development of the fresh-fish traffic from adjacent and Alaskan waters to the markets of the United States and Canada. However, such trade is not likely to produce a large city. Prince Rupert now ranks sixth among the manufacturing cities of British Columbia, and its principal industries include lumber mills, fish canneries, grain elevators, and cold-storage facilities.

PROBLEMS

1. The Pacific Mountain Region of Canada has possibilities for development as great as the Pacific states of the United States.

2. The Pacific Mountain Region offers more favorable and varied conditions as a permanent home for man than the Prairie Plains Region.

3. Will the Pacific Mountain and Prairie Plains Regions, taken as a unit, become the most productive and most important portion of Canada?

4. Will Vancouver become the leading commercial and manufacturing city on the Pacific Coast of North America?

5. What will be the two leading industries of the Pacific Mountain Region?

6. Can the Pacific Mountain Region maintain a population greater than the Rocky Mountain and Plateau states of the United States?

7. The highest development of the Pacific Mountain Region can come only by the unrestricted admission of oriental peoples.

8. Are the food-producing possibilities of the Pacific Mountain Region equal to those of Washington and Oregon?

PART IV

Mexico and Middle America

CHAPTER 25

Mexico

SOME MAJOR CONSIDERATIONS

The Effects of Physical Contrasts in Mexico. The nature of the physical environment is reflected well in the government of Mexico. If nations are to be governed effectively and economically, and if they are to have the currents of national life flow with serenity and force, they should consist of natural environmental units or groups of closely knit units. Canada lacks such unity in its natural environment, and Mexico exceeds Canada in this respect. Mexico consists of a broad tableland, two coastal plains, and two peninsulas. The tableland occupies the central portion and is sometimes called the Mexican or Anahuac Plateau, on which more than one-half of the country's people live. Bordering the plateau are mountain barriers, known as the Sierra Madre Occidental and Sierra Madre Oriental, which separate the plateau from the coastal slopes, where about one-third of the people live. Yucatan and Lower California are peninsulas, more closely associated with the United States commercially than with the remainder of Mexico, being separated by either tropical forest, desert, or large bodies of water. Further, the Highland of Chiapas lying to the east of the Isthmus of Tehuantepec is also isolated.

Contrasts of these physical divisions are further accentuated by differences in altitude and in climate. The low, flat plain of Yucatan is scarcely above sea level whereas the Mexican Plateau lies at 8000 feet, with numerous peaks 15,000–17,000 feet in elevation. One may stand amid tropical plants on the coastal plains at Veracruz and gaze on permanent fields of snow capping Mount Orizaba 75 miles away. The annual precipitation varies from more than 150 inches on the Gulf slope of the high land in southern Mexico to as little as 3 inches in the Colorado Delta. Mexico is, therefore, a land of contrasts and extremes, and lacking in geographic unity.

Climatically, four temperature zones are sometimes recognized in Mexico: *Tierra Caliente, Tierra Templada, Tierra Fria,* and *Tierra Heladas,* the hot, temperate, cold, and snow-capped, respectively. Their boundaries are rather indefinite because of differences in latitude, precipitation, and direction of extent of mountain ranges and coasts, and one may find *Caliente* enclaves at *Templada* altitudes, and vice versa. The *Tierra Caliente* region is low and hot, having a temperature range mainly between 68° and 110°, and lies generally below 3000 feet. *Tierra Templada* is the temperate region and lies approximately between 3000 and 6000 feet, being higher in the south than in the north. *Tierra Fria* lies above 6000 feet and thus includes much of the plateau and the surrounding highlands. *Tierra Heladas* is the permanently snow-capped and frozen land on the higher peaks and ridges. (Compare these regions with the temperature and climatic regions discussed in Chapter 1.)

In the seasonal distribution of rainfall there is some uniformity in the various regions. The northwestern part of Mexico lies for the most part south of the subtropical, high-pressure area of the Pacific, and, except in the extreme northwest, it is in the belt of the Northeast Trades, which in the American mediterranean region blow from almost due east. Eastward-facing slopes, i.e., windward slopes, receive a good supply of rain, and lee slopes are comparatively dry. Summer is the rainy season in Mexico. The northward shifting of the equatorial belt of calms with doldrum rains brings rain on slope, plain, and plateau. But since the Trades are also blowing, more rain falls on eastward-facing slopes than on the level or nearly level areas.

In the matter of rainfall, the west coast presents a strong contrast to the east. On the west coast, as far south as 22°–24° N., the prevailing winds for the year are from the northwest, from the Pacific High, and are therefore dry. This portion of Mexico is thus a continuation of the desert and semidesert of southern California and Arizona.

South of 22°–24° N., southwest winds in summer, similar to the southwest *Monsoons* in India, move into the low pressure over the plateau and give a light rainfall to the southwest-facing slopes of the Sierra del Sur and the Mexican Plateau. The surface of the great Plateau of Mexico, bordered on the east, south, and west by higher lands, thus has only a meager rain supply. At Mexico City, now known officially as Mexico, D.F. (Distrito Federal), the year's supply is only about 25 inches, falling mostly between May and October, inclusive; and at the northern border of the country the precipitation is only 8–10 inches, with the rainy season mainly in July, August, and September. The northern and northwestern parts of Mexico have not only the lowest rainfall but also the shortest rainy season. Most of Mexico north of 22°–24° N. has less than 20 inches of rainfall, and about a third of this area has less than 10 inches.

On the moist lowlands of the *Tierra Caliente,* conditions are suitable for tropical forest and the production of tropical crops. Humid temperate-zone forests and crops may be grown on the coastal slopes of the plateau, on the slopes of the mountain ranges, and on the plateau itself where water is available either from rain or through irrigation. Over a large part of Mexico, in the semiarid section, the pastoral industry will continue to dominate in man's use of the land.

The lack of unity in climate, natural vegetation, and crops would make for strength in some countries, inasmuch as some regions or groups are complementary to others (the arid are complements of the humid; the highlands of the lowlands; the temperate of the tropical), but the isolation of the various parts, the results of topography or location, prevents the country from reaping the advantages of these complementary conditions.

The Great Importance of Railways in Unifying Mexico.   In the physically disjointed lands that make up Canada many thousands of miles of railroads have been necessary to bind together into a fairly unified nation these contrasting geographic units. In Mexico the plateau and the east coast, together with the Isthmus of Tehuantepec, are fairly well connected by railroads. The northwest coast has rather poor railway connections with the plateau. The southern Pacific from Nogales, Arizona, runs southward along the desert coast by way of Guaymas, Mazatlan, and Guadalajara to Mexico, D.F. Short branch lines from this railroad serve the mining regions on the western slopes of the Sierra Madre Occidental, but no connections are made with the lines on the Mexican Plateau. Lower California and the Colorado Delta have practically no railroads. Yucatan has railroads serving its northwestern portion and much of its interior, but these lines make no connections with other railways of the country as a whole. Mexico has no large and navigable rivers that facilitate commerce. A few of its rivers are navigable in the lower courses, but contact with the sea is generally made difficult by sandbars, and great variations in depth and flow. The railroad is, therefore, all important in Mexico as in Canada in holding together the various geographic regions (Fig. 269).

Railroad construction meets with great engineering difficulties, particularly within and on the borders of the Volcanic Plateau on which Mexico, D.F., is located. In passing from one basin to another 4000–5000 feet above the sea, the railroads are in many cases forced to ascend to altitudes of 8000 feet or more. Mexico, D.F., had no rail connections with its chief port, Veracruz, until 1873 because of political conditions involved, and because of the engineering difficulty of reaching the 8200-foot elevation of the plateau.

Mexico, D.F., is the logical railroad center of the country and will, in time, when the railway network is extended, have close contacts with all sections. But at present Yucatan, Chiapas Plateau, Lower California,

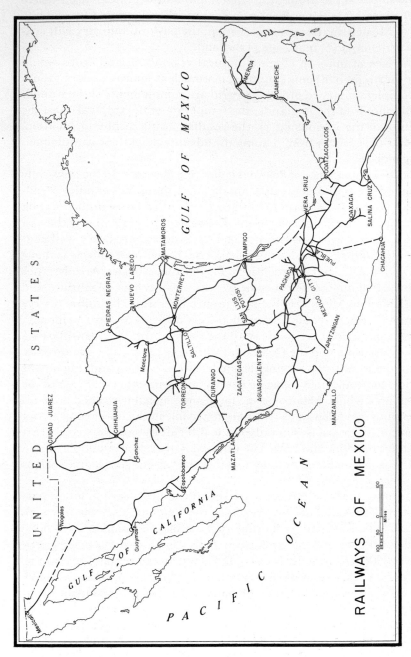

Fig. 269. Important railroads of Mexico. Note the congestion of lines in the vicinity of Mexico, D.F., the most important railroad center of the country.

the Colorado Delta, and much of the northwest coast are isolated from the capital city. A large part of northern Mexico is commercially tributary to the United States, for many railway lines cross the border, as at Brownsville, Laredo, Eagle Pass, El Paso, Nogales, and Presidio.

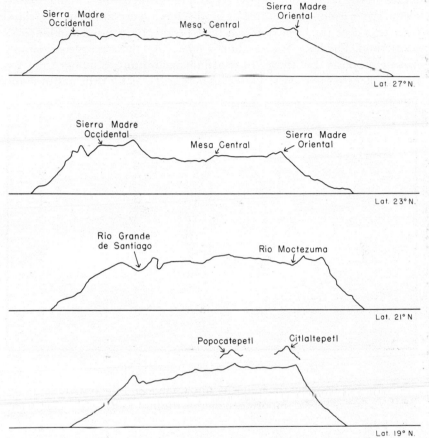

Fig. 270. Cross-sections at various latitudes, showing the Central Plateau and bordering Sierras of Mexico, narrowing and increasing in elevation towards the south.

Another feature of the railway net in Mexico is that there are few branch lines. This leaves many sections located far from the influence of the railway, and, since highways are often unimproved trails, and many people are poor, the donkey is the common beast of burden.

The Influence of the Spanish Ruling Class.   In Mexico there is a wide gulf between the ruling class and the common people. The ruling class is mainly of Spanish descent or nearly so, and number only about 1 in 13 of the total population of approximately 25,000,000. Full-blooded Indians number about 1 to 4, and the large group remaining are mestizos or mixed Spanish and Indian. During most of Mexican history the minority ruling class has owned most of the land, in great holdings known as haciendas, whereas the mestizo and Indian groups have been virtual slaves on the land, kept in poverty and ignorance, and having no part in the government. Attempts at land reform were made in 1915, and since that date the large holdings have been expropriated and lands redistributed. The large feudal estate is gone. Now there exists considerable private property, but there are also many community holdings known as the "ejido" (to be discussed later). There still exists a wide cultural and

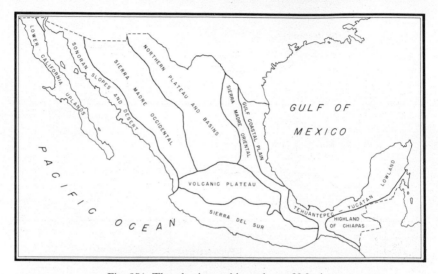

Fig. 271. The physiographic regions of Mexico.

economic gap between the minority upper class and the remainder of the people, a fact of major importance in any attempt to study the geography of a country.

PHYSIOGRAPHIC PROVINCES OF MEXICO

Because of the diverse nature of its physical environment, and the lack of a unified culture in its people, it is convenient to continue our study of Mexico by recognizing its major physiographic provinces and making an attempt thereby to localize and interpret the diverse human activities and cultural landscapes of the country.

Mexico consists of a peninsulalike southeastward extension of the Rocky Mountain Cordillera of Canada and the United States, curving and narrowing toward the Isthmus of Tehuantepec (Fig. 270). Its shape has been likened to that of a horn with the blunt apex located at the Isthmus. The form of the land is mainly that of a broad central plateau bordered by Sierras that increase in elevation and converge in a wild scramble of volcanic mountains toward the southeast. To the west and the east, the Sierras slope toward the Pacific and the Gulf of Mexico, respectively, forming narrow coastal plains. The isolated peninsulas of Lower California in the northwest and of Yucatan in the southeast complete the area of Mexico. Physiographically (Fig. 271), Mexico may be considered to be made up of the following provinces:[1]

1. Northern Plateau and Basins
2. Sierra Madre Occidental
3. Sonoran Slopes and Desert
4. Lower California Uplands
5. Sierra Madre Oriental
6. Gulf Coastal Plain
7. Volcanic Plateau
8. Sierra del Sur
9. Tehuantepec-Yucatan Lowland
10. Highlands of Chiapas

The Northern Plateau and Basins.   This province consists of a large, semiarid upland extending southeastward from the Colorado Plateau and the upper Rio Grande, bordered on either side by the Sierras, and ending at the south where the great knot of mountains forms the Volcanic Plateau. Sometimes this entire central upland is referred to as the Mexican Plateau, but in this study we distinguish the Northern Plateau and Basins from the Volcanic Plateau on the basis of structure. As we shall see later, the Volcanic Plateau consists of higher and much dissected volcanic land with a general east-west trend, whereas the Northern Plateau and Basins is a broad, semidesert area, trending largely north-south, with a drainage which loses itself in the bolsons[2] and playa lakes of the interior. Numerous mountains of uptilted rocks, forming ranges, feature the Plateau and Basins province, which has less of the lava formations in evidence, than are found in the Volcanic Plateau.

The surface of the Northern Plateau and Basins has an elevation of 3000 or 4000 feet on the United States border, but rises toward the south to 8000 feet. Though not a plain, the topography is subdued, with many filled basins and broad waste slopes. The bedrock is composed mostly of lava sheets laid down on old crystalline rocks. Sedimentary rocks occur

[1] Modified from W. N. Thayer, *Jour. of Geology*, XXIV, 1946.

[2] *Bolson*—a shallow, closed basin containing an ephemeral lake; a Spanish word means "purse."

in places and indicate a time when a part of the plateau lay beneath the level of the sea. Much of the bedrock of this province is mantled by aeolian, alluvial, and lacustrine deposits; the soils derived from these need only water to yield abundant crops. At the time of the rainy season, streams flow toward the interior, filling the numerous shallow basins to form lakes. During the dry seasons the lakes disappear, leaving broad

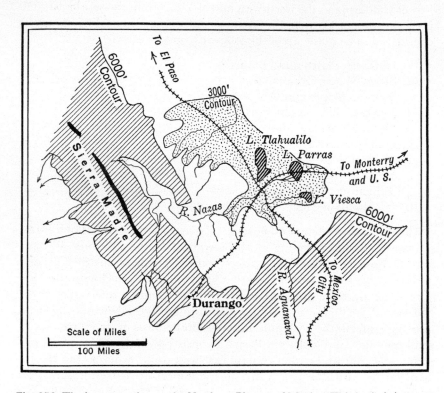

Fig. 272. The laguna region on the Northern Plateau of Mexico. This basin is in many respects like Carson Sink in western Nevada. The lakes vary greatly in height during the year. Irrigated lands bordering the streams produce a good quantity of cotton.

stretches of mud, salt, and alkali. These playas and salinas are numbered by the hundreds, but only a few are large enough to be represented on our small-scale maps. Three of the largest of these lakes lie in the vicinity of Torreon, and are fed by the rivers Nazas and Aguanaval, some of the water from which, in the rainy season, is diverted to vast fields of wheat and cotton. In this basin alone is produced about 60 per cent of Mexico's cotton crop. The Nazas, about 370 miles long, is called the Mexican Nile, and the lake district the Laguna (Fig. 272).

In the northern part of the Plateau and Basins province, one finds physical conditions similar to those that prevail in western Texas and southern New Mexico; yet what a contrast in the human occupants of the environment! In crossing the Rio Grande a person from the United States passes into a truly foreign country. The enterprise, progress, and aggressiveness that characterize the people of the United States are left behind. From the twentieth-century type of civilization of that country in which man has gone a long way toward conquering nature, one plunges into a land where man is only in the beginning of his cultural development. The difference lies not in the physical environment but chiefly in the difference in the human stock and government. There are untold treasures of mineral wealth beneath the surface in Mexico, and some of these deposits have been exploited for centuries; yet these riches have gone to benefit the few, while the vast majority of the people have remained in poverty and ignorance, unacquainted with the great progress that is being made in other parts of the Americas, in Europe, and the distant continents.

Aridity has found its response in a landscape that is characterized by scattered bits of vegetation and brightly colored soils and rocks; in adobe huts and pretentious, whitewashed dwellings of mud and clay; in frequent insurrections led by "generals," each with a few hundred half-starved, lawless, nomadic followers; in large estates; and in a sparse population. The chief wealth of the plateau, as previously stated, lies in the immense mineral resources that have for centuries been exploited and yet, relatively speaking have hardly been touched. Gold and silver are widely distributed and are mined in almost all the states of the Mexican Plateau. There are known deposits of copper, tin, cinnabar, and sulfur. The bituminous coal field of the state of Coahuila, an extension of the lignite field of Texas, is actively worked in Mexico, and from it comes nearly all the coal consumed in the country. The annual output in times of peace is about 800,000 to 1,000,000 tons. Near Durango is a famous hill of iron ore, Cerro de Mercado (640 feet high, 1100 feet wide, and 4800 feet long) which contains, it is estimated, 460,000,000 tons of high-grade ore. There are metallurgical works, smelters, and reduction plants for the preparation of metals for export in the several cities of the plateau. Monterey has a large iron and steel plant, and two iron and brass foundries. Although there are possibilities of much greater pastoral and agricultural development, one must not overestimate the soil resources, for aridity is greater here than in parts of the United States where the rainfall is the same, because evaporation is greater. Besides the cotton of the Laguna, wheat, corn, ixtle fiber, and maguey are the chief crops.

United States capital has invaded the Northern Plateau and Basins province, and has been invested in mines, forests, and lands. In this region the largest of the haciendas—the great landed estates—were found. Some included thousands of acres, numerous villages, and as many as 2000 people. The pattern of population distribution throughout most of the Northern Plateau and Basins province is one of many centers of density along drainage lines where moisture is available for cropping, at springs, or at irrigation centers, but with wide areas of sparse settlement between.

The Sierra Madre Occidental.   At the western edge of the Northern Plateau and Basins province lies the Sierra Madre Occidental, which forms a formidable barrier toward the Gulf of California. It includes a belt of elongated plateaus and mountain ranges varying from 50 to 100 miles in width and stretching from Arizona southeastward to the Volcanic Plateau in about latitude 21° N. The crests of this mountainous structure are mainly lava plateaus lying from 1000 to 2500 feet higher than the basins to the east. Numerous streams serrate the edges of these plateaus, and the result is very rough surfaces with deep canyons both to the east and to the west. These streams dwindle in volume after leaving the mountains, and most of them disappear to the east in the basins, and to the west on the desert slopes before reaching the Gulf of California.

The mineral wealth of the Sierra Madre Occidental is closely associated with the geologic history of this province. Ancient lava flows served to enrich the mountains with veins of gold, silver, copper, lead, and other metallic ores. These have been mined to a limited extent since the Spanish conquest. Erosion has laid bare much of this mineral wealth on the slopes of the Sierra Madre, and here, also, the rainfall is sufficient to support some forests of pine, oak, and cedar interspersed with grassland. Thus there is a timber supply for construction in the mines, and a water supply for mining camps, towns, and for irrigation in the lower valleys and arid plains on either side of the western Sierras.

Because of the roughness of the surface, the Sierra Madre Occidental is thinly populated, and is one of the least known parts of Mexico. No railroads cross from central Mexico to the Pacific. Indian tribes in the Sierra Madre escaped contacts with the conquering Spaniards, and to this day have few contacts with Mexican life.

The Sonoran Slopes and Desert.   Lying immediately to the west of the Sierra Madre Occidental province and occupying the slopes and the narrow coastal plain together with the Colorado Delta is the province which may be named the Sonoran Desert and Slopes. It faces the shallow Gulf of California and extends from California and Arizona southeastward to the Rio Grande de Santiago. Numerous streams rise in the high Sierra and cascade towards the Gulf, but many are lost in the sands of the narrow coastal plain, and thus never reach the Gulf. Particularly is this true towards the north, where, for a distance of 300 miles south of the Colorado, streams seldom reach the coast. Farther south the bordering Sierras are higher, and the rainfall is greater, thus providing some drainage which reaches the Gulf and the Pacific Ocean at all times.

The delta plains of the Colorado have very low rainfall, but irrigation is possible. United States capital is developing this section for the raising of long-staple cotton, alfalfa, and barley. Many enterprises are managed from the United States side of the boundary, and the products find their

Fig. 273. Wheat field in the Valle del Yaqui on the west coast of Sonora. There is considerable interest in the development of irrigation in Sonora. Here the climate is arid, but water exists in the ground of all the area immediately to the west of the Sierra Madre Occidental. A pump irrigation system supplies the water for the field of wheat shown in this photograph. Note the uncleared desert vegetation in the background. *Photograph from Rockefeller Foundation Agricultural Program for Mexico.*

chief market in the United States. The non-irrigated lands are owned by Mexican cattlemen, and, but for the enterprise of United States people in developing irrigation, all the lands would be devoted to grazing.

The section from Nogales to Guaymas is also arid, but irrigation is possible because of the large supply of water from streams coming from the higher Sierras, where the rainfall is 30 inches or more. Lack of capital and management, and a ready market has so far hindered any great development (Fig. 273).

Guaymas, although little more than a village, is the port for the state of Sonora. Far back in the 1860's, it had prospects of being of considerable commercial importance, being the Pacific terminus of one of the projected transcontinental lines of the United States. A railway was built from the Arizona border at Nogales southward along this coast, but Guaymas did not develop as a great port, though the railway reached it. This railway has been extended southeastward along the coastal plain, finally reaching Mexico, D.F., by way of Guadalajara. Several ports developed along this arid coast, such as Topolobampo and Mazatlan.

To the south of Guaymas, conditions similar to those of the state of Sonora prevail, although the rivers carry more water than those farther north, the result of higher mountains and heavier rainfall in the mountain areas and on the coastal plain. There are many prosperous irrigated areas on the several broad plains.

In the Fuerte Valley some companies have developed excellent sugar plantations with their own modern centrals or factories. There can be little hope for success, however, in the production of crops that must compete with those raised in the southern and southwestern United States as long as these crops must surmount a protective tariff barrier at the international boundary. Then, too, the home market in Mexico is not great. Yet, except for this, there are excellent opportunities for future expansion. The principal crops are chick peas, wheat, and rice. The culture of rice is being developed on a large scale. Chick peas, most of which are exported to Spain and Cuba, are an important crop.

Grazing is the dominant industry at present. In the past, fame of these states has rested on their mineral deposits, and the same will undoubtedly be true in the future. Indeed, it is claimed by some writers that this region is the richest in minerals in the world. Its gold helped fill the coffers of Spain even in the early colonial period. The traveler in regions distant from the railroad will find many old workings and tailings along the streams leading out of the canyons, some 1000 feet deep, that pierce the lofty western Sierra even to the old rocks that form the core of the Plateau of Mexico. These old rocks over most of the plateau, enriched by volcanic intrusions which brought deposits of gold, silver, copper, and lead, are buried deep by lava intrusions and riverine and lacustrine deposits, and are most easily reached at the edges of the plateau in these "shafts" carved by nature. This region is the Mexican Eldorado for United States capitalists interested in the exploitation of precious and semiprecious deposits; but the difficulty of transportation to the sea coast, or even to the railroad near the coast, has greatly reduced the profits and resulted in wasteful mining and smelting, the baser metals often being neglected. Gold, silver, and copper crushers and smelters are located near the workings, the "pigs" or bars being packed by mules or burros, 100 miles or more in many cases, to the railroad. Besides the metallic minerals, graphite of an excellent quality is mined near La Colorado, Sonora. Oil is known to be present in great quantities, and prospecting has hardly begun. The extensive beds of anthracite in Sonora, including some seams 12 or more feet thick, are pierced by only a few mines.

The Lower California Uplands.   This physiographic province known as Baja California territory is the most isolated in all of Mexico. It consists of a peninsula 50 to 150 miles wide and about 750 miles long, formed by a continuation of the Coast Range mountains of California. It is separated from the mainland of Mexico by the long and narrow Gulf of California. Much of the Lower California upland has an elevation of 4000 to 6000 feet, and the coastal plains are narrow and non-existent. In an overland journey from California to the southern tip of the peninsula, a journey replete with hardships and delays, for highways are poor, one views a series of landscapes of barren hills, desert plains, and rocky mountains, with here and there an irrigated valley. The upper slopes of the mountains are clad with thin forests of oak and pine. Wheat is grown in some of the northern valleys by Russian colonists; and in the far south Chinese gardeners and horticulturists, only a few hundred in number in all, raise vegetables and subtropical and tropical fruits. About 80 per cent of the people live in the southern portion of the peninsula, chiefly because of the greater rainfall in this section.

Yet Lower California is not without resources which, if developed, would support a population many times the present 95,000 people. There is some timber on the mountain slopes, economically inacessible at present, and valuable fisheries of pearl shells and edible fish. The interior, only partially explored geologically, is known to contain rich deposits of copper, silver, lead, zinc, and gold, and immense amounts of iron ore. The most productive copper mine, about the only mineral development in the peninsula, is owned by a French company at Santa Rosalie, which not only mines the ore but also smelts it. Development of these mineral and forest resources awaits better transportation facilities. The coastwise traffic is now mostly in the hands of United States people. United States merchants on the Pacific Coast furnish most of the imports of machinery, mine supplies, groceries, dry goods, gasoline, and kerosene; and a railroad, should one be built to penetrate far into the peninsula, must naturally come from the United States. Lower California is, therefore, bound to be absorbed by the great Republic on the north, perhaps not politically (several advances have been made toward its purchase), but commercially, and this has already been accomplished to some extent.

The Sierra Madre Oriental.   The Sierra Madre Oriental is a narrow belt of mountains bordering the Plateau and Basins province on the east, and extending from the Rio Grande southeastward to Oaxaca and the Sierra del Sur. Like the Plateau and Basins province, it increases in altitude towards the south. Only a small portion is higher than the inland plateau, and for this reason the Sierra Madre Oriental is sometimes considered as being only the eroded edge of that inland province, sloping eastward to the coastal plain. This eastern Sierra is not so high as its western counterpart, and it is composed mainly of folded limestones. Due to the abundance of rainfall the slopes are rounded, quite heavily forested, and form a less formidable barrier than the Sierra Madre Occidental.

The topography is mature, and the numerous valleys have a fertile soil produced from the limestones. Coupled with high temperatures and abundant rainfall, this province favors agriculture where the slopes are not too steep. The forested slopes furnish timber and charcoal, charcoal being the fuel in general use for the household, though oil is now replacing charcoal to some extent. Water power is abundant in the province, but it is not developed extensively except in the Orizaba region where it is utilized in the textile mills.

The Gulf Coastal Plain. The Gulf Coastal Plain is a continuation of the Coastal Plain of Texas, and, like that plain, is composed chiefly of sands, and is bordered on the east by lagoons and barrier beaches. It is crossed by numerous rivers that descend from the slopes of the Sierra Madre Oriental. In their lower courses, the rivers are, for the most part, aggrading streams. The Coastal Plain is approximately 150 miles wide along the Rio Grande at the north. Toward the south it narrows, and ends where the mountains nearly approach the Gulf, just north of Veracruz. The Sierra Madre Oriental is less a barrier at the north than at the south. In northeastern Mexico the mountainous border of the Northern Plateau and Basins province breaks down to the north of Saltillo, and railroads cross the lower courses of the Rio Grande to reach the plateau cities by easy grades. From Tampico, the great oil-exporting port, railways extend to Monterrey, San Luis Potosi, and other cities. The Coastal Plain is largely outside the belt of tropical rains, and, although the rainfall is ample, its distribution is irregular. Toward the southern end the rainfall is heavier, and tropical vegetation appears. Considerable cotton, sugar, bananas, rubber, and rice are grown on the coastal plain, and great possibilities for future development of agriculture exist, though, on the whole, little has yet been done. The chief commercial interest at present centers about the petroleum district of Tampico and Tuxpan.

The Volcanic Plateau. In central Mexico the great mountain ranges of the Sierra Madre Occidental and Oriental increase in elevation southward and converge in a wild scramble of volcanic mountains, basins, deep gorges, and ridges to form the Volcanic Plateau, commonly called the Mexican Plateau. It has an average elevation of about 8000 feet and differs from the Northern Plateau and Basins in that it has a general east-west extent instead of north-south, and it is chiefly volcanic in origin, although diastrophism has undoubtedly been active (Fig. 274). It stretches westward from the Sierra Madre Oriental near Veracruz practically to the Pacific where the deep gorge of the Rio Santiago brings it to an end. Evidences of vulcanism on a grand scale, even within the last 2–3000 years, were revealed by archeological studies near Mexico, D.F. There has been partially uncovered here a "Mexican Pompeii" buried

Fig. 274. Paricutin Volcano, Mexico, *Photo by R. T. Hatt, Cranbrook Institute of Science.* Though Popocatapetl Volcano is Mexico's most widely known, the most recent is Paricutin, in activity in 1944. Seen from the town (distance of 6 miles) of Angahuan one here looks into the crater. The fields about are covered with a heavy blanket of black ash. The hill slope at the left is the base of extinct volcano. The forest is mostly pine.
    Stone fences are largely made of volcanic bombs and lava from nearby volcanoes.

in volcanic mud and ashes. Gases are still exuding from some of the volcanic mountains, and bare scoriaceous lava fields exist in some parts.

    Veracruz is the port most commonly used by travelers to reach the Volcanic Plateau, the most densely populated part of Mexico. Here live about 50 per cent of the people of Mexico, although the area is about 10 per cent of the total of the country. Here are the most populous cities of the country and the most populous states. The states are smaller than in other parts of Mexico, and the land holdings smaller. This is the most attractive part of Mexico from the standpoint of temperature. Although the rainfall is not so great as farther south, it comes in the summer, and is sufficient for the development of large rivers, such as the Santiago and its tributaries. The Rio Santiago has in its middle course the largest lake of Mexico, Lake Chapala, 70 miles long and 20 miles wide in places. These rivers have cut deep gorges on the slopes of the Volcanic Plateau. They supply power to numerous factories, and some have hydroelectric plants supplying light and power to the cities. In nearly every valley, water is used for irrigation. Only a beginning has been made in the utili-

Fig. 275. A maguey crop on a hillside in the volcanic plateau region south of Mexico, D.F. This crop is used both for pulque and fiber production. *Courtesy, Rockefeller Foundation Agricultural Program.*

zation of the water resources of the Volcanic Plateau and the bordering slopes.

The Volcanic Plateau is one of great topographic diversity, and this results in a diversity of climatic conditions. Above the plateau which is in the *always mild* temperature region, rise the lofty volcanic mountains, Popocatepetl (17,881 feet), Orizaba (18,206 feet), and others, and below are many basins and gorgelike valleys. Oak and pine form forests on the lower and middle slopes of the mountains. On the plateau surface are great fields of beans, vegetables, maguey (Fig. 275), and cereals; and in the basins and valleys the irrigated lands are given over to corn, sugar cane, and tobacco. Coffee is grown on the well-drained slopes, and pasture lands are widespread.

Mexico, D.F., is the crowning glory of the cities of the country, and vies with, and in some respects even surpasses, the cities of Anglo America. Like other Hispanic capitals, it has numerous expensive government buildings and wonderful cathedrals, characterized by beautiful architectural lines, maze of detail, and solidarity of structure. The city lies in a beautiful basin some 40 miles long and 30 miles wide, which contains 6

Fig. 276. Mexico City about 1519. The city at this time, located on an island about 3 miles from the western shore of Lake Texcoco, also called Lake of Mexico, had a population of about 300,000. It was connected to the mainland by several well-built causeways.

withering lakes. In pre-Columbian days the city was on an island, connected to the mainland by a causeway, and all the lakes of the basin were larger (Figs. 276 and 277). In the conquest of the city in 1522, Cortez destroyed every block of buildings; but in the rebuilding the Aztec plan of the city was followed, the causeway became a roadway, the center of the ancient city became the plaza, and a huge cathedral was built on the site of the temple where human sacrifices had once been offered by the hundreds and thousands.

Mexico, D. F., has a population of 2,942,000 (1950) and is the center of Mexican civilization in all its aspects. To the other cities, villages, and communities in all parts of the country, it is a political and social center. Its shops contain goods from every manufacturing country in Europe, as well as from the United States. It is the most cosmopolitan of Mexican cities. Its numerous ecclesiastical buildings and temples and institutions of learning make it a great religious and educational center. If its influence fails to be felt in the most isolated part of the country, it is because

Fig. 277. Cultivation for crops on the old level lake bed of Texcoco, at Chapingo near Mexico, D.F. Industrial plants have been located elsewhere on this old lake bed to make use of the salts in the manufacture of potash and caustic soda. Also, the site of the airport is on this lake bed. *Courtesy, Rockefeller Foundation Agricultural Program.*

of the great physical barriers and the low economic and social status of many of the Mexican people.

The Sierra del Sur.   The slope from the Volcanic Plateau southward to the Pacific is the most dissected province of Mexico, and is referred to as the Sierra del Sur. It extends from the Rio Santiago eastward and ends in the State of Oaxaca in a steep escarpment overlooking the Isthmus of Tehuantepec. Much of the superficial volcanic material has been removed by the rivers that drain this slope. Remnants of erosion stand out as peaks whose summits are about equal to that of the Llanos of the Volcanic Plateau to the north.

In a cross section of the Sierra del Sur, from the Pacific to the Volcanic Plateau, one finds a variation in climatic conditions, natural vegetation, and crops similar to that of the eastern slope from Veracruz to the Volcanic Plateau. The coastal plain bordering the Pacific is narrow, yet in its 700 mile length there are valuable forests of cedar, mahogany, and other woods, for this section is well watered. Plantations growing sugar cane, cacao, coconuts, rubber, rice, fruits, and fiber, although widely scattered, indicate the possibilities of the section in tropical agriculture. At higher altitudes the vegetation and crops approach in character those of the Volcanic Plateau. The irrigated valleys are particularly productive. Agriculture is the chief reliance of the people, although there is much grazing, timber cutting, and mining. Immense deposits of minerals are known to exist, and scientific exploration has hardly begun. The inaccessibility of this section from the Volcanic Plateau and the dense vegetation are undoubtedly reasons that the world knows so little of the mineral resources here. The entire slope will have a great future when it becomes more densely settled and more railroads are provided. In the lowlands of Mexico, however, the Indian has never been disciplined in persistent labor. This region would have many of the possibilities of northern Italy, if it were properly worked.

The Tehuantepec-Yucatan Lowland. Beginning at the narrow Gulf Coastal Plain just north of Veracruz and extending southward and eastward the Coastal Lowland broadens and continues, to include all of Yucatan and a considerable strip across the Isthmus of Tehuantepec that widens along the Pacific Coast. This is the Tehuantepec-Yucatan Lowland, which differs in a number of respects from the Gulf Coastal Plain to the north. The Tehuantepec-Yucatan Lowland is bordered on the west by the Sierra del Sur and the volcanic slopes of the Sierra Madre Oriental, and toward the southeast by the Highland of Chiapas. In general this province consists of low-lying fertile plains sloping gently seaward. Its elevation is mostly under 2000 feet. Mangrove swamps and lagoons are characteristic of the Gulf margin, with the exception of northern Yucatan which is semiarid, due to lack of rivers in a land of porous limestones, and to less rainfall. Considerable development of plantation agriculture is found for some distance south of Veracruz, in the truly *Tierra Caliente* lowland. Sugar, rubber, bananas, and rice are the chief crops, and the natural vegetation is luxuriant because this entire province, with the exception of northern Yucatan, lies in the tropical rain zone.

Yucatan peninsula, also tropical in temperature, is even less populous than that portion of the lowland just discussed. About 3.5 per cent of the people of the country live in the peninsula. The density of population of the State of Yucatan, the most populous part of the peninsula, is only about nine to the square mile.

Yucatan peninsula is the "Florida" of Mexico in its geologic structure and origin. It is a low, flat, calcereous plain, practically without rivers, the excess water finding the sea through underground channels. As in parts of Florida, there are numerous sinks and caverns, some 100 feet or more in depth. These caverns are the source of water supply for the people over a large part of the peninsula, and for that reason the small settlements are often found near these caverns or open sinks.

The drying winds of the *Trades* (practically all the rain comes from the occasional tropical cyclone) restrict the vegetation to a scanty growth in the north, but this vegetation increases in size and density toward the south. Near the base of the peninsula where the rainfall is heavier, there are tropical forests of great density with the characteristic epiphytes, lianas, and the broad-leaved evergreens. Most of the peninsula outside the forest is given over to grazing, but in northern Yucatan henequen is the leading crop. This part of the peninsula is closely knit commercially with the United States, for henequen is in great demand as binder twine in the grain fields of America.

The economic life of most of the people of northern Yucatan is built upon the henequen industry: the growing of the plant, the extraction of the fiber, its transportation, and its shipment. The bulk of the freight carried by the numerous railroads is henequen, and the hundreds of miles of tramways transport the long, fleshy leaves from the fields where the plant is grown in rows that stretch for long distances across the low, rolling or hummocky plains, to the railway stations from which it is taken to the factories. Merida is the political and commercial center of the State of Yucatan, but Progreso is the only important port. There is no harbor at Progreso, for the whole coastline, like the eastern coast of Florida, is bordered by lagoons, barrier islands, and shallow water. Ships receive and discharge cargoes from lighters.

The Highland of Chiapas.   Eastward and southward from the Isthmus of Tehuantepec there rises a mountainous mass of folded sedimentary rocks and volcanic formations known as the Highland of Chiapas. It extends into Central America and increases in altitude towards the southeast. The Pacific slope rises to 9000 feet within 30 miles of the coast, and hence is very steep. The portion of this highland included in Mexico lies above tropical plains on either side and is very much isolated from the remainder of the country. It is, because of its altitude, about as well suited for higher cultural development as the Volcanic Plateau, and perhaps even better, because it has a more copious supply of rain. The density of population is about 13 to the square mile. Its greatest needs are people, roads, and railroads, and with these it has a grand future. The savannas are natural grazing grounds; the valleys may be irrigated; and the bordering tropical forests are as rich as any in the country.

CHAPTER 26

Mexico
as a National State

Area and Population. One of the first considerations in determining the importance of a nation is the number of its people and the size of the area they occupy. However, great powers of the world are not necessarily those with the largest population and the greatest area. Culture, amount, and development of resources, foreign trade, standard of living, government, and numerous other factors enter in the problem of ranking a nation among the powers of the world, a fact which is well illustrated in the case of Mexico.

The Spanish possessions in North America once bordered the Gulf and the Caribbean on their north and east and included much of North America westward from the Mississippi. The Pacific Coast from 42° N. to the Isthmus of Panama was Spanish, and Spain held a hazy claim even to parts of the Alaskan Pacific littoral. The Mexico that won its independence from Spain in the early part of the nineteenth century included only a part of this vast domain; yet, for about two decades, it was among the six or seven great countries of the world in area. The loss of the northern territories to the United States and the secession of Guatemala reduced the area to 763,944 square miles. Mexico is still among the nine leading nations in surface extent. It is seventy times as large as Belgium, seven times as large as Italy, about three times as large as France, and has more than six times the area of the United Kingdom, including Ireland.

As in most of the countries of the New World, Mexico's population is not as large as it can really support. The average density is only about 32 to the square mile, and the total population about 25,000,000. This, however, is about 35 per cent more than the population of Argentina, 45 per cent more than Canada, and more than three times that of Sweden or Australia. With the exception of Brazil, Mexico is the most populous of the Latin American countries of the New World. On the basis of area and population, therefore, Mexico ranks well among the nations of the world.

In spite of this high ranking in area and population, Mexico is classed among the minor nations along with most of the countries of South

America. However, since about 1930 Mexico has gained in international good-will and respect.

Antiquity of Mexico.   Some nations, like some individuals, claim recognition and homage because of the traditions and history that lie behind them. Surely Mexico should rank high in this respect. Archeological investigations in Mexico have convinced scientists that a people sufficiently advanced in their cultural development to construct great, rough, stone pyramids 100 feet high lived in the Valley of Mexico at least 3000 years ago. Their implements were very crude, consisting of flaked or chipped knives, bones, and scrapers, and roughly shaped pottery. These discoveries push American history back many centuries. Neither archeology nor history has yet been able to fix the date of man's coming to Mexico. As far as tradition goes, the country has always been inhabited. Certainly the southern part of the Mexican Plateau had been the center of an advanced civilization for many centuries before the Spanish came, and this civilization developed under conditions very similar to those of Egypt, Mesopotamia, and Central Asia, namely, isolation, limited area, healthfulness, high fertility of the soil, and irrigation. An equally old, and perhaps earlier, civilization thrived in the Yucatan peninsula, as archeological work has so clearly proved.

Legend and tradition fix the sixth century A.D. as the time when a group of Nahuas arrived in central Mexico. Toward the close of the seventh century a band of Toltecs, possibly descendants of this Nahua group, formed a settlement, the ruins of which are now known as Tula, about 50 miles north of Mexico, D.F. These early invaders were replaced by other tribes, yet Tula civilization dominated a large part of the plateau until the second half of the eleventh century. Some time after the year A.D. 1300, the Aztecs, also a branch of the Nahuas, appeared in the Valley of Mexico, looking for a "Promised Land" of which their deity had told them. They settled at many points in the valley, but about 1325 established themselves on an island amid the waters of Lake Texcoco. The insular position of the city gave its inhabitants protection.

The city grew rapidly; the Aztecs became powerful and expanded the frontiers of their country. Yet they were not the only people of advanced civilization that filled Mexico with palaces, temples, pyramids, and tombs, the ruins of which are a wonder of the modern world. Tradition fixes the third century A.D. as the time when the great Mayan tribe moved southward into Yucatan, a date even earlier than that of the genesis of the Toltecs and Aztecs. Archeology has much yet to decipher of the ancient civilization of Mexico. Evidences of its high development are numerous. The Toltecs worked in silver and gold, wove cotton, made pottery, cut stone, erected wonderful buildings, and on their walls left records in the form of picture writing. The splendor of the Aztec city of Mexico, which was the wonder of the conquering Spaniards, hardly surpassed the center of Toltec civilization.

The Aztecs left their records in hieroglyphics. In their primitive form of writing they drew maps of their country, left genealogies, and published their laws. They had a calendar of 18 months of 20 days each, with additional days each year. Leap years were allowed to accumulate, and every 52 years 12 to 14 days were added to the regular year. Among their artisans there were potters, paper makers, masons, and workers in metals. Placer deposits were worked, and silver was separated from the ore by chemical means. Gold was also separated by the amalgamation process. Cloth was made from cotton, palm, and cactus, and decorated with feathers. The Aztecs had aqueducts, reservoirs, suspension bridges, fortifications, and embankments. Other archeological exploration on the Mexican Plateaus has revealed pyramids and other public works antedating the Aztec remains. The glory of ancient Mexico is hardly less than that of ancient Egypt.

Mexico under Spain. As a Spanish colony, Mexico was one of the choicest of the New World possessions, and vied with Peru in yielding wealth to the Spanish Crown and court favorites.

The Spanish regime was fruitful in many respects. The first printing press in America was set up in Mexico about 1540. The second university founded in America was established in Mexico City about this time. The foundations of the Cathedral of Mexico, the beautiful structure still to be seen in the capital, were laid about 1575, and church architecture of this period has hardly been surpassed in America.

Attempts were made about this time to improve the health conditions of Mexico City by the excavation of a canal across the rim of the basin. Also, the church founded missions, and nobles and priests united in "uplifting the natives." Often their efforts were of little avail, for at times and in some sections slavery of the most brutal sort prevailed. Many of the Spanish Creoles of colonial days were wealthy and contributed much to the culture of the world.

Mexico under Diaz. For more than half a century after the War of Independence (proclaimed 1810, effected 1821), internal strife brought the fortunes of Mexico to a low ebb, to be rehabilitated under the masterful control of the dictator Diaz who ruled Mexico with an iron hand, and in some respects beneficently, from 1877 to 1911, with the exception of 4 years. No country ever made what seemed to be greater progress in the same period of time than Mexico during these 30 years. Diaz kept order throughout the whole land; foreigners could travel in safety anywhere. Mexican credit was good with any lending nation, for Diaz put the fin-

ances of his country on a firm basis. Harbor works were provided. He
also formulated a far-reaching scheme to cover the land with a modern
system of transportation and to that end increased the railway mileage
during his regime from 367 miles to 15,000. At the time of his resignation
there were nearly 40,000 miles of telegraph lines, 850 miles of federal telephone lines, 6 wireless offices, and 2974 post offices. Nearly 3000 vessels
entered, and about the same number cleared, the ports of Mexico each
year. Agriculture was prosperous, mines and factories busy, the banks
were solvent, and hundreds of millions of dollars of foreign capital were
invested in Mexican enterprises. Encouragement was given to schools
and colleges, the effect of which reached the aristocracy but not the
masses. The rule of Diaz showed the world what a dictator government
could do, but at what a cost to the great number of people living in
peonage!

THE RESOURCES OF MEXICO

The resources of the different divisions or regions of Mexico have been
pointed out. Let us here summarize these assets that we may better see
how they have served as the material basis of progress and well-being in
Mexico.

Forest Lands. The forest lands of Mexico cover some 44,000,000
acres, of which about 25,000,000 acres are timber lands that have a wide
variety of woods, as we have seen. The tropical forests bordering the
coasts, from which come rubber, gums, and lumber, can be the more
easily exploited because of nearness to the coast, but lumbering here as
in most tropical regions is difficult, for the timber trees do not grow in
close stands, and non-commercial trees and vines and undergrowth interfere with the operations of the lumberman. The ground is often soft,
making the use of wheeled vehicles difficult, and the logs have a high
specific gravity so that they are rafted only with difficulty. The exploitation of the wet tropical forests of Yucatan and elsewhere must await the
building of railroads; and the temperate zone forests of the slopes of the
interior mountains likewise will long be conserved because of their isolation, except those about mining properties which call for mine timbers.
In spite of the difficulty of lumbering, the forest resources of the country
are great and will be of great value in the timberless age that is fast coming in the United States and Europe. Importation into the United States
has already begun.

Agricultural Lands. The extent of potential agricultural lands is difficult to estimate, for man in Mexico is just at the beginning of his evolution
in land utilization. To what extent irrigation, dry farming, new crops,

and scientific practices will expand the agricultural frontiers is impossible to determine. Some authorities state that there are about 37,000,000 acres of tillable land; only 13,400,000 acres are cultivated, an area almost equivalent to one-third of the state of Indiana. This is less than 5 per cent of the total area of the country. The United States had in 1945 over 18 per cent of its total land area in harvested crops.

The lack of suitable agricultural lands in Mexico is well shown by the climatology of the country. It is estimated that land rated as deficient in moisture throughout the year is nearly 50 per cent; that having no deficiency in moisture, 12.8 per cent; that having moisture deficiency in summer, only 1.4 per cent; and that deficient in moisture in winter, 35.9 per cent. In a country with such a large percentage of arid land one would expect irrigation to be an important practice. It is important, but the projects are relatively small. The total irrigated area is estimated to be not much over 5,000,000 acres, and this in a country of nearly 25,000,000 people. Five large irrigation projects were completed by 1934, and several times that number were under construction or have been completed since. Numerous small irrigated areas are found in all the provinces except the tropical coasts on the east and south. Large irrigation and dry-farming areas are the Laguna, the Imperial Valley, and others, but the most notable ones are along the Rio Grande and its tributary, the Rio Conchos. Opposite El Paso on the Rio Grande and extending some 30 miles downstream is an important Mexican cotton-growing area. This section has not prospered, because of decreasing waters in the river resulting from a larger take of the water on the United States side and upstream. The Rio Conchos, which is a tributary of the Rio Grande coming out of Mexico, has a number of irrigated areas along its course; these are devoted to cotton. A large dam, far upstream, regulates the flow of the water. Irrigation along the Rio Salado in Nuevo Leon, opposite Laredo, Texas, has not been very successful because of the alkali in the soil. There has been considerable difficulty between Texas and Mexico along the Rio Grande over water rights of the river. The volume is low, and it becomes a question of who has the right to divert water for irrigation.

One factor of great promise in Mexico is the wide variety of agricultural products, many of which could and do find a market in the United States: henequen, ixtle fiber, tobacco, India rubber, coffee, and various fruits. Yucatan now produces about one-half the world's crop of henequen. Though much is used at home, the market for this fiber is dominantly foreign, but there is little foreign ownership in the plantations. It will be noted that considerable of the products mentioned above are of the hot, moist lowlands and valleys, the sections of the country that have been little developed. In the exploitation of the moist tropics, the work of the twentieth century, Mexico has an opportunity to reap great benefits, provided the capital and technical knowledge can be forthcoming.

It is evident, therefore, that there are great opportunities in Mexico in agriculture, yet few of these have been exploited, and Mexico as a producer of commercial agricultural products falls below some of the other Latin American countries.

The Pastoral Industry. One of the reasons for the lack of development of the agricultural resources is the prominence of the pastoral industry and of mining. In the United States, as we have seen, the pastoral industry has been pushed out of the natural grazing lands of the Great Plains by agriculture or a combination of agriculture and grazing, and forced to the regions of greater aridity. In parts of Yucatan a similar economic movement has occurred, but, for reasons stated previously, it seems unlikely that there will be much shifting of industries in the semi-arid sections of northern Mexico. According to some sources, there are 120,000,000 acres of grazing lands.

Stock raising in Mexico dates from the Spanish conquest and received much encouragement from the mother country. Mexican horses and cattle were the first to appropriate the grasslands of the Great Plains in the United States. Mexican horses were used by the Indians of the Great Plains, and white traders drove horses eastward from Texas to the United States frontier. Through neglect, poor pasturage, and scanty water supply, much of the stock in northern Mexico is poor in quality. Even though scrawny and small, the horses and cattle are tougher and longer lived than the livestock of the more humid lowlands in the south. Diseases spread by insect pests are more common in the humid regions. Yucatan is an exception, no doubt, because of the dry climate and the underground drainage.

Horses, mules, and donkeys are the transport animals in most parts of Mexico and, therefore, in demand. The general lack of good roads makes the ox-cart and the pack animal the means of transportation, away from the railways and major highways. Many mines maintain contact with the railroads by pack animals (Fig. 278).

Cheap lands and large-scale enterprise have made cattle raising profitable, even though the home market for beef is limited and the chief exports of the industry are hides and tallow. With more careful breeding of cattle, Mexico could find a large and profitable market for beef in the United States and Europe. This, however, calls for packing plants and control of disease. In the 1930's a good beginning was made in the beef-cattle and dairy industry in the plateau and southern basins, but the foot-and-mouth disease ended it. Exports to the United States have lately been resumed, but in general the great packing companies of the United States have overlooked the opportunities in Mexico or have decided that conditions are more favorable to their business in Argentina and Uruguay, 4000–5000 miles farther away.

Mining in Mexico.   Mexico, no doubt, is one of the greatest mineral regions of the world. The dominance of igneous rocks in the plateau, and the Sierras, as indicated previously, make these the great metal-producing sections. Coal and oil occur in the sedimentary rocks of the slopes and coastal lowlands. The history of the mining of precious metals is indissolubly associated with the post-Columbian history of the country. It was the hope of finding stores of gold and silver that led the Spanish *conquis-*

Fig. 278. The donkey continues to be an important beast of burden for many people in Mexico. *Courtesy, H. H. Jerudum.*

tadores over mountain, plain, and desert, hundreds of miles from the center of Spanish power. Within 2 or 3 years after the conquest of Mexico, the deposits of Zacatecas and San Luis Potosi were discovered by the Spanish. The silver vein of Guanajuato, one of the most famous silver-mining districts in the world, was discovered about 1525. The first silver mining of importance began about 1548, and for 300 years the mines of Guanajuato furnished one-fifth, and for 100 years about two-fifths, of the silver of the world. Today, even after 400 years of nearly continuous exploitation, the mines, until about 1940 dominated by United States capital that has caused the shafts to be deepened and huge metallurgical works to be erected are still paying dividends. Mexico still accounts for about 40 per cent of the world's output of silver. Up to date, the Guanajuato mineral region has produced upward of $1,500,000,000 worth of silver. Many of the great mining centers of today received their charters as cities from the Spanish Crown before the year 1550.

The stores of precious minerals helped to make many men of Spain gentlemen of leisure, adventurers, and cruel governors, disdainful of industry and trade. It is possible that some of these social ideals motivate the Spanish Creoles of Mexico today.

The War of Independence and the numerous revolutions that followed (1810–1821) interfered with the mining industry, for each revolutionary leader sought to control one or more mines as a source of revenue. Many mines were, therefore, abandoned by their owners. Also, the crude machinery used limited the depth to which shafts could be dug. Many mines became flooded because of inefficient pumps, and cave-ins occurred. Only the most productive ores were worked, and there has been much waste through lack of knowledge of scientific metallurgy.

Mining today is carried on in 24 of the 29 territories. Silver is by far the most common mineral mined, but since the 1920's copper has been produced in increasing quantities.

The list of minerals includes nearly all those known to man—mercury, lead, tin, antimony, zinc, graphite, salt, and asphalt, besides gold, silver, copper, and iron ore. Coal, as we have seen, exists in Coahuila and Sonora, and in the early 1920's Mexico was the second great oil-producing country in the world. In July, 1908, one of the greatest gushers known was struck in the Tampico region, producing 60,000–75,000 barrels of oil a day. The oil flowed in such quantities that the operators could not provide steel tanks, and dirt reservoirs were thrown up. In later developments several wells were bored that produced 100,000 barrels a day, and one well alone, up to 1920, produced more than 800,000,000 barrels. From 1921 to 1925 the average annual production was 156,000,000 barrels. But since 1925 there has been a decline. In 1939 only 43,000,000 barrels were pumped, and in 1950, 72,400,000 barrels. Producing wells now number about 800 and are not increasing. Most of the oil is exported in the crude state, but Mexico has two of the largest refineries in the world, and since 1945 a large oil refinery has been operative in the suburbs of Mexico City, turning out gasoline for the increasing home use. Both the production and consumption of petroleum are increasing in Mexico (Fig. 279).

Oil has long been known to exist, but, at first, efforts to secure it were not successful. In 1900 a United States firm, through encouragement from Diaz, purchased land from the Mexican Government and began drilling. Being pioneers, United States concerns were able to secure the larger part of the oil-bearing lands, and at one time, according to some reports, they controlled 80 per cent of the oil fields. The other holdings belonged to British and Mexican firms. Oil was the leading mineral product of the country. After 1921 there was a lull in production because of controversies over titles and export duties. The decision of the Supreme Court of Mexico late in 1927 gave much hope to companies that secured land titles before 1917, the date of the new constitution of Mexico. However, in 1938 the government expropriated the properties of all foreign oil companies and planned a compensation to be paid over a 10 year period. The new government-controlled company, known as Petroleos Mexicanos, or Pemex, has as its object the development of petroleum for the benefit of Mexico. The other oil region of Mexico of some promise is the Tehuantepec-Tabasco section.

Manufacturing. The natural conditions for manufacturing are excellent in many parts of Mexico. The raw materials are abundant and

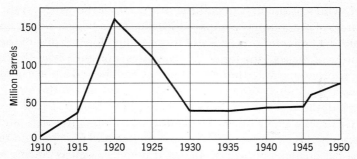

Fig. 279. The rise and decline of petroleum production in Mexico. *World Almanac, 1950.*

varied, and there is no lack of power resources. In the northern half of the country the low rainfall of the summer results in low water, and there are no lofty snow fields, but on the borders of the Central Plateau, as previously stated, the flow of streams is more constant and the total fall is immense. Most types of industries are represented in Mexico, but few by large-scale modern factories. These industries have grown up under the protection of a high tariff wall and also because of the high freight charges on imported goods. Because of the somewhat unsettled industrial conditions and the changing value of the peso in relation to foreign money, manufacturing did not thrive in the decade following 1930. An expansion began during World War II and has continued since that time. Mexico, D.F., produces more than one-fourth of all the manufactures, which are varied in nature, including clothing manufacture, oil refining, tobacco manufacturing, brewing, and food processing. The textile industry is centered at Puebla and Orizaba; Monterey is the "steel city." Since 1940 United States companies have established numerous branch manufacturing plants in Mexico, turning out machinery, photographic films, cellophane, pharmaceuticals, radios, and chemicals. To be sure, the manufacturing industry is very important to Mexico, but as yet it amounts to a very small figure compared with that of some of the states of the United States.

Manufactured products make up a large part of the imports, and, with the exception of metals, almost no manufactured goods are exported. Practically two-thirds of the export of Mexico is from the mines, and more than three-fourths of all exports go to the United States. Also, the United States supplies more than three-fourths of the imports. Mexico's proximity to the United States, now the greatest creditor nation of the world, with an abundance of capital ready to flow into foreign fields wherever safety is assured, should prove of great value in the development of manufactures in the future.

A Region of Undeveloped Resources. More than a century ago, Humboldt, who was the first to call the attention of the world to the great resources of the country, compared Mexico to "a beggar sitting on a bag of gold." That comparison is not inept today, for, in spite of the great resources of the soil, the forest, the pastures, and the rocks, the country is not prosperous; and, though at times it has risen to a place of promise among the nations of the world, for the larger part of the last century and a half the vast bulk of the people have been hungry and in rags, and the resources undeveloped. The country has long interested and often disappointed the capitalists of North America and Europe, and the civil unrest has created political problems at home, as well as placing a strain on foreign relations. *What are the reasons for this condition? Is there no hope for the future?*

The questions posed are difficult to answer. The greater diversity of lands and resources on the one hand, and the lack of success on the part of the Mexican people to bind themselves together as a firm national unit on the other hand are readily recited as cause and effect. It is undoubtedly true that the cause is closely related to the effect, but there is much more to a solution of the problem than this. The student realizes more than ever before that man himself—his history, traditions, culture, race—may play a great part in explaining human adjustments to the environment. To this end we should consider, in more detail, man in Mexico.

THE PEOPLE OF MEXICO

Mexico resembles most of the other Latin American countries in that it has been difficult for it to produce a firmly unified society. Here the original Spaniards met Indians who were somewhat advanced and already well established on the land, who worked the minerals, and who had a culture and a way of living that had been fixed by centuries. Their numbers, in all that is now Mexico, have been estimated at about 6,000,000, which some authorities believe is much too conservative. The Spaniards who came in the colonial period probably numbered not more than 300,000, but they had superior skills and techniques, and thus were able to make a political and economic conquest of the much larger body of native people.

In the homeland of old Spain there was never a very large population to bring about a pressure for emigration, and the people were solidly Roman Catholic. There were no great numbers to draw upon for colonization, and there was little likelihood that religious groups would arise to seek freedom in the new land; Mexico was far away and there were hardships and dangers there. The result was that many of the Spaniards who came to America did not bring women and children, but took Indian wives in Mexico. The population of the country soon became mixed, so that today Mexico's 25,000,000 people are about 90 per cent Indian and mestizo, 29 per cent being full-blooded Indians. Of unmixed European descent the numbers in the country are less than 9 per cent. The mestizos are gaining in numbers over the pure-blooded groups.

With this mixture of its people Mexico has struggled for more than 4 centuries to bring about a coherent society, and has only made a beginning, as is witnessed by the wide social and economic barriers that still exist between groups. Several millions of pure-blooded Indians live in isolated and mountain sections, having little if any connections with the national capitol, and do not even speak the Spanish language. A large part of the mestizo class has until the land reform of 1933 been landless and poverty-ridden, and a small minority of Spanish and a few mestizos have owned the property, been educated, lived well, and have governed the country.

Students of political history should interpret the lack of unification of the Mexican people with understanding. It does not necessarily follow that the Spaniards have proved themselves poor colonizers and ineffective builders of culture and unity in the people. The problems of establishing order among social groups with such differences have been much greater than was so in Anglo-America.

LAND TENURE AND THE REFORMS

The original Indians in Mexico knew serfdom, for it existed among them before the coming of the Spanish. Some Aztecs were large land

cienda, as is shown by the lower yields per acre of maize, cotton, and several other crops. In fact the average worker is not as well off from the standpoint of income as he was before the land reform of the 1930's. The redistribution of lands has resulted in expanding the agricultural areas into semiarid regions and into places with steeper slopes, to take care of the normal increase in population. These formerly landless people do not have experience; they lack knowledge and technical training, so necessary in dealing with water conservation, preservation of soil, and modern cropping practices; yet they are given federal aid and responsibility in developing new areas, and in carrying on in the older areas. It is reported there is a marked increase in gullying, soil erosion, silting of streams, loss of ground water, and other evidences, indicating the evil results of the land reform.

To all who oppose the land reforms it must be pointed out, as shown previously, that Mexico is a country with a large proportion of semi-arid and sloping lands, and the population is increasing. It is altogether possible that the evils attributed to the land reforms, cited above, might have taken place under a continuation of the hacienda system. Therefore, one should avoid attributing the evils to the ejido and private-ownership practices following the land reform. Furthermore, reports show that illiteracy is declining quite rapidly, having dropped from 70 per cent in 1910 to 51.5 per cent in 1940. Retail business has improved since 1940, for the country as a whole, which reflects the wider distribution of incomes. Undoubtedly the greater personal freedom given the people is a gain of great value, and will operate favorably toward bringing about a national unity. Time will be required for such intangible gains to be proved.

SUMMARY

Mexico is a country of great diversity in land and resources, as well as people. Poverty, revolutions, and lack of high national development cannot be attributed to the nature of its lands alone, but to the nature of its people as well. The impact of the Spaniards on Indians, involving great numbers of the Indians, created problems of tremendous proportions in bringing about a coherent society, which is so essential to national development. More than 4 centuries of history in Mexico records this lack of unity. Foreign capital invested in Mexico in mines, oil, railroads, and otherwise has been beneficial in some respects, but the benefits did not affect the masses.

The land reforms, nationalization of railroads, mines, and other resources all show that the nation is attempting to do something in this fundamental strife towards social unification in Mexico, without which there can be no firm national status.

QUESTIONS, EXERCISES, AND PROBLEMS

1. Throughout what physiographic provinces, temperature regions, and rainfall areas would one pass in a journey from Veracruz to Nogales by way of Mexico, D.F.? What type of vegetation and crops would one see?

2. Are there any reasons other than climate for so many people living in Mexico City? How do you account for its having so large a population?

3. To what extent has climate affected the distribution of population in Mexico?

4. Contrast the hacienda and the ejido as forms of land tenure in Mexico.

5. Make a study of the recent development of manufacturing in Mexico. Is there a firm basis in Mexico for increased manufacturing? How would an increase in manufacturing affect the general social order in Mexico?

6. Make a special study of Baja California. What are the prospects of its development?

CHAPTER 27

Middle America

GENERAL PHYSIOGRAPHIC CONSIDERATIONS

North America is joined to South America by a continuous land bridge through Mexico, Central America, and the Isthmus, with the exception of the narrow, man-made cut of the Panama Canal. The mountain belt is continuous from North America through Mexico, but it narrows and ends at the Isthmus of Tehuantepec. Central America is mountainous, but the nature of the mountains and the direction and extent of its ranges and peaks appear to exclude the idea that the Cordillera of North America is directly continuous with the Andes of the southern continent. After careful observation it will be noted that the highlands of Central America, together with the islands of the West Indies, form an orographical system quite distinct from that of North America or South America, the Isthmus of Tehuantepec being the northern boundary and the Atrato River in Colombia the southern. The chain of West Indian Islands extending from Cuba in the northwest to Trinidad in the southeast is really a partially submerged mountain range, also affording a link between the two continents. There is evidence that Central America owes its present form to the union of formerly separate islands which were joined by outpourings of volcanic material. Contrasts between the wild animals of South and North America indicate, likewise, that the continents were separate in early geologic time.

Central America and the West Indies are sufficiently different from the two large American continents, geologically, to warrant the name which we shall apply to them—Middle America. These two divisions of Middle America have many things in common, for, besides being similar in geologic origin and location, the shores of all are washed by the Caribbean Sea; they both lie in the path of the *Northeast Trades*; they have similar temperature conditions, similar indigenous plant life, and similar crops; and a large part of the main line of their histories is similar (Fig. 281).

CENTRAL AMERICA

The Central American Union. In Spanish colonial days the Central American states, exclusive of Panama, formed one province, Guatemala,

630

under a captain-general who had his seat of government at Guatemala City. Even Chiapas, now a state of Mexico, which is topographically, geologically, and climatically a part of Central America, was attached to Guatemala. The feeling of brotherhood that existed among the Latin American nations during and following the Wars of Independence no doubt was the reason for Guatemala's uniting, in 1821, with Mexico, with Iturbide as Emperor. But topographic conditions do not favor large political units anywhere in the highlands of tropical Latin America. To escape the discomforts of the hot, moist climate of the coastal lowlands

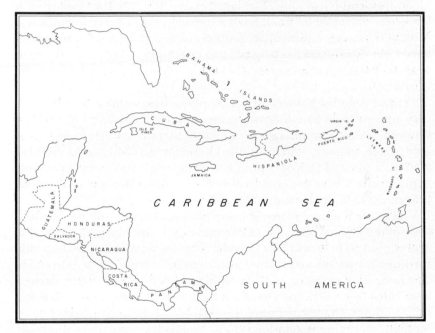

Fig. 281. Outline map of Middle America.

(Fig. 9), the white rulers in colonial days selected highlands for their homes, where the climate is more like that of Spain. There, centers of population grew up. These centers being separated from each other by scores or hundreds of miles, each became a seat of government. The size of the political unit formed depended for the most part on the distance between the centers. In 1823 Guatemala declared itself separate from Mexico (Chiapas remained), and the next year was reorganized as the Republic of Central America. But the tendency toward separation asserted itself again, one by one the natural political units separated from the Central American nation, and there came to be five small independent countries—Guatemala, Honduras, Salvador, Costa Rica, and Nicaragua.

There have been attempts to revive the Union, but until all the population nuclei that have grown up about each capital are closely united by railroads and highways there is little possibility of the formation of a strong federation.

Surface Features and Rocks.   The main topographic features of the countries of Central America are similar. There is a mountain and plateau highland extending longitudinally near the center. This highland area lies nearer the Pacific side of the area, and hence the steeper slope is on the west side. The eastern slope forms wide plains in Guatemala, Honduras, and Nicaragua. The larger rivers flow into the Caribbean, a few being navigable for small boats a considerable distance from the sea. Most of the rivers, however, are partially closed at their mouths by sand bars. Lake Nicaragua lies between two mountain ranges, and, although near the Pacific, it drains eastward through the San Juan River into the Caribbean.

Central America has a great variety of geologic formations. There are very ancient rocks like those of the Piedmont Plateau and Old Land of Canada, which contain a great variety of metallic minerals, including gold, silver, copper, lead, and tin. These deposits have been little exploited because of lack of capital and dense vegetation which prevents exploration. There are coal beds in rock of the same age as the coal-bearing rocks of the United States.

Vulcanism has been active in many parts of the highland area; in fact, some of the highest peaks are of volcanic origin, and the plateau to some degree owes its height to lava deposits. The region is young geologically, earthquakes are frequent, and violent volcanic eruptions are common. The rich soil of many parts of the highland is volcanic in origin, derived from volcanic cinders and ash which have buried large areas several feet deep at times. In other sections the high temperature, abundant moisture, and decaying vegetation rapidly disintegrate the rocks and make them into deep, rich soil. Although there is some surface wash from heavy rains and probably rapid leaching, the soil-making processes are rapid, and there is little depleted land.

Climate and Population Distribution.   Central America lies within the tropics. The lowlands are, therefore, in the *Tierra Caliente*. In the highland section the temperatures are mild and pleasant, making the plateau a delightful region in which to live, and the *Northeast Trades* bring great quantities of moisture from the Atlantic and the Caribbean Sea. On the eastern lowlands it is jokingly said that it rains 13 months in the year; yet there is here a wet season, the heaviest rain coming in the summer when the equatorial belt of rains shifts northward over all of Central America and much of Mexico. The western slopes and highland have their wet season from May to September. There is an overabundance of rain on the eastern lowlands, whereas on the western slopes there is need of irrigation in some places. At some points on the eastern lowlands the rainfall is 195 inches a year; on much of the highlands it is only 27 inches. The hot, moist climate on the eastern lowlands make that region unsuited to white population.

Most of the people of Central America, nearly all the important cities, and most of the railroads, roads, and cultivated lands are on the highlands. In some of the countries, 75 per cent or more of the people are on the plateau.

Climate and Plants. It is not difficult to find a correlation between vegetation density and amount of rainfall. The vegetation is more luxuri-and and varied on the lowlands, but still it is abundant in the higher and drier portions. There is a wide range of natural plant life and of culti-vated crops.

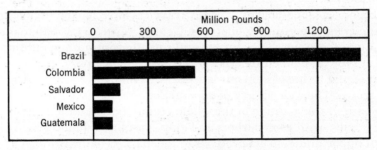

Fig. 282. Coffee imported into the United States by country of origin in 1951.

On the eastern lowlands the forests contain mahogany, ebony, rose-wood, and cedar, which are cut and shipped to the United States. In some sections a "chocolate" tree grows wild. There are also medicinal plants furnishing vegetable oils, and also rubber-producing trees. More than half a hundred varieties of banana trees are indigenous to the region. The drier parts of Central America are covered with savannas (tropical grasslands with scattered trees), excellent regions for the grazing of cattle and horses, and lands suitable for the cultivation of some crops. Some parts of Guatemala are too dry for cultivation except through irrigation. Pines and oaks are found in the higher parts of the uplands.

Temperature is a factor in the vertical distribution of economic plants in Central America. Up to 1500 feet the products are chiefly tropical. At a few places on the lowlands the forests have been removed, and great banana, rubber, cacao, and sugar plantations have been made, where native Indians and West Indian natives work under the supervision of white men from the Unted States or from the highlands of Central

America. For the most part, the chief occupation of the people on the lowlands, other than the work on the plantations, is timber cutting and the collecting of wild forest products that have commercial value. This region is producing only a small part of what it is capable of, because so few people live here. Coffee plantations are common in most of the republics between 2000 and 4500 feet above the sea (Fig. 282). Here, also, may be grown sugar cane and cotton. Some of these countries, particularly Costa Rica, produce a very excellent coffee which for a long time was sent mostly to European markets, but now the United States takes more than three-fourths of the export. In Guatemala, coffee plantations were chiefly in the hands of German settlers, till World War II, when the government confiscated much of the property and went into the plantation business for itself. Crops like those of central United States are grown on the highlands above 5000 feet—wheat, corn, beans, potatoes, and other vegetables. Corn and beans have a wide range of distribution.

Economic Opportunities.   Many travelers have spoken in high terms of the great opportunities offered in Central America for man to make a living and prosper. The climate and soil offer optimum conditions for plant growth. Bennett reports, "There is little soil erosion even on slopes that would be hopeless in our latitude." As many as 4 crops a year may be grown. The wide variety of mineral deposits has been commented on. The admirable position of the whole region, between the Atlantic and the Pacific, with good harbors and long coast lines, should give it abundant opportunities to get products to the markets of the world. The people in some of the countries have lived up to the opportunities nature offers and have made much progress.

Progress and Anarchy in Central American Countries.   Costa Rica and Salvador have made much advance in transportation, commerce, agriculture and education. Costa Rica is undoubtedly the most prosperous of the Central American republics. For the past century it has not had civil strife and revolutions to the extent found in other Central American republics. The Costa Ricans dislike wasting their resources in wars or on war material, preferring the arts of peace, and they welcome those bringing wealth from other countries. Foreign capital has been invested to help develop the resources. On the eastern coast, the United Fruit Company has large holdings of land. The forests have been removed from large areas, swamps drained, railroads built, and the land planted with banana trees. Limon is the chief port, and from this center 5,000,000 to 8,000,000 bunches (300 to 400 shiploads) of bananas are exported each year (Figs. 283 and 284).

In January, 1932, the independent banana growers of Costa Rica were informed that contracts with planters of old plantings would not be re-

Fig. 283. Workers transfer banana stems from the mechanical fruit washer to railroad cars for the trip to a Puerto Rican port, from where a United Fruit Company ship will carry them north. Bananas are cut when green, for, if they are allowed to ripen on the tree, they are injured in handling and become infested with insects. Mechanical equipment takes the place of much of the hand labor that was formerly employed in processing and shipping of bananas. *Courtesy, United Fruit Co.*

newed, the reason given being that the old, worn-out lands would not grow first-class fruit. The United Fruit Company has since brought prosperity to this hitherto undeveloped section. In 1948 Costa Rica had 38,500 acres devoted to banana plantations, ranking second only to Honduras among all Central American republics, which had 44,500 acres. A railway from Limon to San José gives a large area of productive land an outlet to United States and European markets. The company maintains a large fleet of fruit, freight, and passenger ships from Limon to United States ports. Much of the economic life of the plateau is based on coffee culture for export, and coffee growing has tended to keep the country free from revolutions. The planters early found that their orchards on which their prosperity depended and which required years to develop, could be destroyed within a few hours during a revolution. A start on production of rubber was begun in 1939 when more than 1000 acres were planted in the lowlands along the Caribbean littoral.

Costa Rica is a real democracy. There is freedom of the press and religion. The land for the most part is in small plots which, in general, are worked by the owners. There is no tax on land, a condition that encourages land ownership. The country has an excellent educational system with compulsory education, schools, and good teachers. The mineral de-

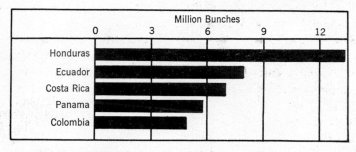

Fig. 284. Bananas imported into the United States, by country of origin in 1951.

posits are being worked actively, and the exports amount to about four times those of any other Central American country.

The character of the people is the chief reason for the fine progress that Costa Rica has made. Fully 60 per cent of the total population is white, and 80 per cent of the people of the *meseta* or central plateau are white. This part of Central America was settled by poor Spanish families, and, since the Indian population was small, slave labor or peonage has never been a factor in the economic life of the country. There are only 3500 pure-blooded aborigines in the country at present. The people, from the first, acquired habits of industry which today find their reward in the advancement the country has made. The name Costa Rica, it is said, was a joke in colonial days because the country was held by poor Spaniards who were forced to work for a living.

At the other extreme of economic and political development stands Honduras, with a public debt in 1909 of much over $135,000,000, most of which was interest which had not been paid since 1872. A part of this debt was contracted to construct railroads, most of which were never built, the funds being squandered by public officials. However, much progress has been made since, and by 1940 the country was operating on a balanced budget. There has been little development in the country except along the coast where foreign companies have banana and sugar plantations. However, the banana plantations on the Nicaraguan east coast were mostly destroyed by disease in 1940 and have not risen to great importance since. The laborers on these coast lands are mostly West Indian Negroes. Concessions have been granted for the exploitation of the forest and mineral resources, but little work has been done because of constant political disturbances. There are but few schools outside the towns. Roads are few, and all the half dozen short railroads are on the coastal lowlands and do not reach the section where most of the people are. The population density is about 12.5 to the square mile, and the population is largely made up of aboriginal Indians. About 20 per cent of the Indians are uncivilized. Similar in political and economic conditions to Honduras are Guatemala and Nicaragua.

Railroads and Ports. Transportation facilities, essential adjuncts to all economic development, are greatly lacking. Railroads are very few, and the lines are short. Railroad building is difficult because of the rough topography and the heavy forests in the tropical portions; and when once built, the railroads are subject to frequent and disastrous washouts from the heavy tropical rains. Some single rains cause more than a million dollars' damage on a single line and incapacitate the road for several months. The railroads in most cases are not paying ventures, because the population density is low, the flow of commerce is light, and there is no great system of routes that tends to bring about an exchange of commodities over a large area. Railroad building has been generally neglected in Central America, chiefly from lack of capital and the prevalence of graft, but also because the dictators have opposed it. "The dictator has seen in steel rails a drawbridge over the moat into his baronial castle." The area is really too small to develop any extensive system. Most of the roads in each country center at the capitals and extend to one of the important seaports. In Guatemala, Costa Rica, and Panama there are railroad connections between the east and west coasts. Port facilities are surprisingly good on the east coast. There are five natural harbors: Puerto Barrios in Guatemala; Trujillo and Puerto Cortez in Honduras; Limon in Costa Rica; and Bocas del Toro in Panama. These have been improved, but mostly by foreign companies. The handling of cargoes on the west coast is done with few exceptions by lighters. At some points the water is so shallow that even the lighters do not touch the shores, the longshoremen being obliged to wade to and from the lighter.

Before 1920, the most highly developed part of Central America was shut off from any contact with Europe and the United States by being located on the Pacific Slope, which necessitated a long land haul to get to the coast of the Caribbean or a long sea voyage around the Horn. The Panama Canal, however, has put the densely settled sections in easy contact with the Atlantic traffic lines and will aid greatly in their future growth and development. Unfortunately, the portions of these countries that produce the agricultural and forest products that Temperate Zone people are calling for, such as sugar, rubber, and bananas, have been shunned by the white man in the past and have been little developed. The highlands produce commodities that are comparable in many respects to those of temperate lands, and for which there is no great call in the markets of Europe and America. However, improved sanitation has reduced many of the "horrors" of the moist tropics, and the white man sees in these lands great possibilities. Some of the most prosperous and most peaceful sections of these countries today are on the east coast, where the great development companies have cleared off the forests, drained the land, built towns, wharves, railroads, hospitals, churches, and schools, given work to thousands, and maintained peace. The regeneration of these countries may yet come from the hitherto neglected wet tropical coast lands.

British Honduras is the only remaining colonial possession in Central America. It was acquired from Spain by the British in 1670. It is a tropical, rainy land poorly suited for permanent settlement except on the islands along the coast. The industries are extractive in nature and consist of the gathering of chicle and logs for lumber. The total population in 1950 was only 70,000, of which nearly 50 per cent were Negro and mulatto. About 25 per cent are Maya Indians, and only 4 per cent are white.

WEST INDIES

To the east of Central America and Yucatan and between North and South America is a great watery expanse, 1600 miles east and west, and 1200 miles north and south, strewn with islands varying in size from the area of a village lot to that of the average United States state. These islands number in the thousands; some are barren; some are in their native condition, covered with forests; some are unsettled; some have well tilled farms, plantations, and cities. Cuba, the largest of the West Indian islands, and one of the Greater Antilles, has an area of 44,000 square miles—about that of Tennessee. The second in area is the island of Hispaniola (Haiti), which has 30,000 square miles—nearly the size of South Carolina.

The Islands Classified as to Origin.   The West Indian islands are commonly divided into the Greater and the Lesser Antilles, the Anegada Passage to the east of the Virgin Islands forming the dividing line. The Bahama Islands, though somewhat isolated from the West Indies and forming a large group of some 700 islands and islets and more than 2000 rocks, may well be classed with that island world.

The physical features and bedrock vary greatly in the different islands of the West Indies. The Greater Antilles are continental in structure, character of rocks, and surface features. The Lesser Antilles are typical oceanic islands. The Bahamas are mostly low islands of calcareous materials.

Many of the islands of the Lesser Antilles are simply the tops of great mountain masses whose bases rest on the sea bottom several thousand feet below the surface of the ocean. One writer expresses this tersely by saying that in the Lesser Antilles one goes to the top of the mountain in a boat. In most of the islands, however, the mountain peaks stand far above the sea level.

In the West Indian section great earth movements have occurred in recent geologic periods. The whole of the region has been depressed, some portions more than others, those deeply depressed forming basins. Just to the north of Puerto Rico is a depressed ocean basin about 25,000 feet deep. The Bahamas are low hillocks on a broad submarine plain, similar in surface features to Florida, and might well be considered as an extension of the Florida peninsula.

The islands of the inner row of the Lesser Antilles are largely of volcanic material, or are remnants of huge heaps of old volcanic material carved by running water and waves. The outer row of the Lesser Antilles is truly coraline, coral forming massive layers of limestone that mantle the surface and form a fringe about the coast. It is possible that the core of many of these coraline islands is of igneous rock. Barbados has sandstone and sandy shale as its basal rock, much of which is impregnated with petroleum. Resting on this is deep-sea limestone and siliceous clay. Coral forming is active at present about the shores of most of the islands of the West Indies.

Climatic Conditions and Effects.   The climate is similar in all the islands of the West Indian region. The lowlands are in the *always hot* temperature region; the mountains are much cooler. In the highlands of the interior of Cuba the thermometer occasionally falls to freezing point, and thin ice will form in December and January when the winds are in the north. The whole region lies in the *Trades*, with steady winds from the northeast in the Greater Antilles, and from the east and southeast in the Lesser Antilles. Because there is so much water and so little land, the climate is oceanic in every respect. The range of temperature is slight, and the air has a high relative humidity. In the larger islands rain is heavy on the windward side of the mountain slopes. The outer parts of the lowlands and the offshore islands on the windward side of the larger islands have little rain.

On the leeward side there is also little rain, and irrigation is necessary for profitable agriculture on most of the islands. In Jamaica the annual rainfall in different sections varies from about 25 inches to nearly 200, and in Puerto Rico from 20 to 100 inches. Salt is made from sea water along the lagoons by natural evaporation, on the north shore of Cuba, because here the rain is slight and the *Trades* are drying winds. On the south slope of Cuba, the slight rainfall permits only a thin growth of trees. Here the Spaniards early settled to work the placer deposits of gold and silver. The distribution of crops is adjusted to these different amounts of rainfall. Sugar and bananas are the most important of the products raised on the hot, moist portions of the lowlands. In some islands, rubber, cacao, and rice are produced. Coffee is confined to well-drained hill and mountain slopes in the less humid sections, and some of the finest tobacco in the world comes from the southward-facing valleys of western Cuba where the rainfall is much less than on the northern slope. Cattle are raised in some of the isolated sections of the Greater Antilles, where the forests have been removed or where savannas are the natural vegetation. The Lesser Antilles in general have plenty of rainfall, heavy rains falling almost every day in summer. Occasionally there are cloudbursts that cause considerable damage. The most unfavorable features of the climate are the hurricanes, or tropical cyclones, which are common and very destructive.

The climate of the West Indies is remarkably healthful in spite of the fact that it is tropical. The *Trades* are the saving feature. On some of the islands, English and French people have lived for generations with little or no apparent ill effects. Alexander Hamilton, the father of Dumas *pére*, and the Empress Josephine were all born in the West Indies on colonial plantations. Some English family names have figured in the history of the West Indies for centuries. Sufficient time has not yet elapsed, however, to determine the fitness or unfitness of the islands for the white race. It is true that the Negro has multiplied with the luxuriance of tropical vegetation, and now far outnumbers the white on many of the islands, and has entirely displaced them on others; but the relative decrease in the number of whites is undoubtedly due, in some degree, to economic factors. The decline of the sugar industry has resulted in the emigration of many whites.

The Mingling of Races and Nations.

Probably in no other region of similar area on the earth would one find such a variety of history as in the West Indies. Some tiny islands have histories more voluminous than many an American commonwealth. Because of their position in the *Trade-Wind* belt, nearly opposite the Canary Islands, the point from which many of the early explorers departed, the West Indian islands were the first to be visited by Columbus. By 1514 the Spaniards had visited and taken possession of most of the West Indian islands. Other explorers from Europe came—Dutch, French, and English—and preyed on the Spanish settlements and on the commerce between Spain and the West Indies (a term which for a time included all the Spanish possessions in America). All the nations laid claim to lands in the great island world, sent colonists, and began to exploit the agricultural resources. As the climate was not found favorable for work for the white man, the Indians were enslaved and nearly exterminated by the Spaniards before the coming of other Europeans. Negroes from tropical Africa were imported. The first were brought by the Spaniards in 1502, and in the early part of the nineteenth century the British colonists alone imported 2000 slaves annually. The islands of the West Indies soon became the most valued possessions of the European nations. They were easily reached by sailing vessels following routes set by the North Atlantic winds and ocean currents. Their climate is salubrious, and their natural beauty makes them veritable fairylands. They became the chief source of the world's sugar supply. England, for a hundred years before beet sugar was developed in Europe, fought the Netherlands, Spain, and France for the West Indian sugar lands. In the sixteenth, seventeenth, and eighteenth centuries, the financial prosperity of western Europe was greatly increased by commerce with the West Indies, and the products of these islands were worth more "than all the gold and silver of the American continent." Muscovado,[1] which cost $100 a ton to produce with slave labor, sold for $300 a ton, and many a small West Indian plantation produced for its owner each year in sugar alone 50,000 to $100,000.

The West Indies, being such valuable possessions, naturally became pawns in the great game of empire building. Individual islands, being small and at the same time possessing value both because of their productivity and strategic position, repeatedly changed their political affiliations. In any of the many European wars, a victory for England meant that many of the more important islands became British; and, England being dominant on the sea, the choicest islands, particularly the more strategic, fell to its lot. Some of the less important islands have

[1] *Muscovado*—unrefined sugar.

been in the hands of one nation for centuries; others have frequently changed their flag. One finds French-speaking populations on the islands now owned by Britain, and Spanish-speaking populations on islands under United States control or protection. In Hispaniola the people in the western part speak French, and those in the eastern part, Spanish.

Location, and the various economic opportunities offered, have made the West Indies a region where races have comingled throughout all historic times. As these islands form a chain from the coast of South America to the tip of Florida and almost to Yucatan, it was easy for even primitive men, Caribs and Arawaks, to make a thousand-mile journey by sea in frail canoes on trips of conquest or commerce. The Caribs were canoe people. Columbus wrote of them that "they run through all the islands of India and plunder and take as much as they can." Civilized man in more seaworthy carrying agents has come from much longer distances. The Indian was supplanted by people from Europe and Africa, North America, and South America. Since 1900 thousands of Asiatic coolies have been brought to some of the islands to labor on the plantations, so that in these islands one finds representatives of five of the continents.

To add to the complexity of ethnic relations, there has been much intermarriage of races. Negroes have mixed with Indians, whites with Negroes and Indians, and Asiatics with Negroes and Indians. The pure whites of one nationality have mixed with those of another. The frequent raids of pirates and buccaneers in the early colonial periods added much to the complexity of the language, races, and moral standards. In the Lesser Antilles the Negro element dominates.

Isolation of Islands and Parts of Islands.   Seemingly at variance with the evidence of ethnic mixing is the fact that there is a general lack of intercommunication in the West Indies, a condition hardly to be expected when one considers the short sea distance that separates them. This condition is as true between the various parts of the larger islands as between the various islands. The lack of communication is probably the result of the hilly or mountainous topography of the interior of the islands, the primitive condition of many of the people, the general lack of ambition, the poorness of the roads, the density of the forests, the differences in speech, customs, and ideals, and the lack of development of maritime interests by the islanders themselves. As for maritime activity in colonial days, the whites were too busy with the affairs of their plantations to go to sea; there was no large middle class of whites dispossessed of lands; and the lower classes were held in bondage. Most of the carrying trade in colonial days was in the hands of seamen from New England and European countries. Most of the European colonizing nations had navigation laws prohibiting commerce between their colonies and the people of another nation. This checked intercolonial trade. The vessels in colonial days were so small that rarely was it necessary to visit several islands to discharge a cargo lot or secure a shipload. Similarity in products in the islands did not, and does not now, call for intertrade. Now, however, steamer lines make the circuit of many ports, and the water passages are used by many steamers.

The result of this lack of communication has been the development of distinct types of civilization, each of which "assumes the individuality and political importance of an independent empire." Nearby islands present great contrasts in customs, speech, institutions, and opportunities. Herne noted the lack of unity even between parts of the same island. He says, regarding Martinique, "People are born and buried in the same valley without ever having seen towns a few hours' journey beyond their native hills, and distinct racial types are formed within three leagues of each other."

Population Density.   Still another characteristic of the islands is the relatively high density of population. Cuba and Hispaniola are comparatively thinly populated, but most of the other islands are more densely peopled than the mainland of the Americas. The average density of the mulatto republic of Santo Domingo (the Dominican Republic) is about 70 (estimated), and for Cuba about 78.5, both of which are comparable to the average of the Southern States of the United States and much above those of the Central American republics. Jamaica has an average of about 211; Puerto Rico, 378; and Barbados, about 1020. The average for the Virgin Islands, a possession of the United States, is about 200. In Barbados the population density has about reached its saturation point, but in most of the other islands there is still much room for growth. So easy is life, so few are the demands nature makes on man, so abundantly does nature supply materials to meet these demands, and so low are the standards of living of the vast majority of the people, that the islands are capable of supporting a population many times as dense as the rural parts of the United States.

THE UNITED STATES SPHERE OF INFLUENCE

Cuba

United States Interests in Cuba.   The proximity of Cuba to the United States, 100 miles or so from the tip of Florida, and its strategic position at the Atlantic outlet of the Gulf of Mexico largely explain the interest the people of the United States have long had in that island.

During the nineteenth century it was much coveted by various elements in the United States, first by the leaders in the slave states to prevent the Latin American republics from making it a free territory, and later as a region for the extension of slave territory. From 1848 to 1861 there were repeated attempts to purchase it of Spain. John Quincy Adams, in the early part of the century, when it seemed as though Spain would be forced to relinquish its hold at the bidding of Britain, strongly urged the United States to take steps to acquire possession of the island because of its strategic position. The position of Cuba makes it imperative that its control should never go to a nation that could use it as a base of operations against the United States; and this might have happened as long as the island remained in the hands of a weak power like Spain. The widespread sympathy felt in the United States for the Cubans in their attempts to free themselves of Spanish misrule, and the fact that people of the United States had much capital invested in sugar lands, whose earning power was greatly reduced because of the unsettled conditions, were the chief causes that led the United States to make war against Spain in 1898. At the close of the war the United States assumed the role of protector and adviser of the Cubans whenever it was evident that peace was endangered. For a time the United States army held control in Cuba, but turned over the rule to the Cubans upon the establishment of a responsible government of their own. They seem to have demonstrated their ability for self-government, for in 1936 a treaty was signed with the United States abandoning the right which the United States formerly held of intervening in internal affairs.

United States capital has since the Spanish American war been going into Cuba in increasing amounts. Much of it is in sugar lands, centrals, and railroads and harbor works for the handling of sugar. About 60 per cent of the foreign investments of a billion dollars in sugar in the island is from the United States. Besides investments in the sugar industry, much United States money has gone into railroads, highways, public utilities, industries, mines, and banks.

The United States took about 75 per cent of the exports of Cuba and sold to Cuba over 80 per cent of its imports in 1950. The United States places a limit on importation of Cuban sugar as a protection for its sugar production at home. Nearness to the United States and the reciprocal trade agreements in effect account for the large percentages. United States physicians and sanitary experts in the past have performed inestimable services in Cuba in stamping out yellow fever and other tropical diseases. The 200,000 tourists that visit Cuba each year (in normal times) are largely from the United States, and their expenditures contribute much to the income of many Cubans. Another link that binds

Cuba and the United States is the leasing of Guantanamo Bay for a naval and coaling station, for which an annual rental is paid.

The Quality of the People. The prosperity of the islands (in normal times) and the high regard the great powers have for Cuba are due largely to the abundant resources of the island, the fine character of the Cubans in general, about 70 per cent of whom are white, and the fact that, up to 1936, peace and order were guaranteed, under the Platt Amendment, by the United States. Educational conditions are far superior to those in other American mediterranean countries. About 80 per cent of the people 10 years of age and over can read and write. In 1900 about 45 per cent of the population was illiterate. This change is indicative of the vigor with which the problem of raising the educational standards have been attacked. Free schools are now provided for all children, and attendance is compulsory between the ages of 7 and 14 years. High schools are to be found in most cities, and the University of Habana is one of the most efficient in Latin America.

Like most other Latins, the Cubans take politics seriously. Their temperament is political, and their history is one in which political misgovernment and misrule have played prominent roles. Election riots are common, but serious ones come infrequently.

Agriculture, the Basal Activity. Agriculture is the basal industry of the island, the surface features, soil, and climate being about as favorable as in any section of the world. The land is largely a rolling plain, except for the prominent Sierra Maestra Range (some peaks of which reach 3000–4000 feet and one about 8000) in the far eastern end of the island, the Organ Mountains in Pinar del Rio provinces in the west, and a few low groups of hills here and there in the intervening area. Even in the hills and mountains there are many fertile valleys.

The basal rock of the island is old crystalline, metamorphic, and igneous rock, which outcrops over a large area in the Sierra Maestra Range and here and there in other parts of the island where erosion has removed the sedimentary rock which apparently once covered most of the island. The dominant rock, however, is limestone, and it is from the limestone that most of the soils are derived, both the residual and the alluvial.

Lying on the equatorward side of the 68° isotherm for the coldest month, Cuba has a tropical climate (Fig. 9). Frosts are unknown except on the uplands. The monthly averages for Cienfuegos, which is fairly central and on the south shore, range between 76° for February, the coldest month, and 88° for September, the warmest. Temperatures below 50° and above 90° are rare. On the north coast the effect of a high summer sun is mitigated by the cool winds from the northeast. The rainfall is plentiful. The wet season, during which about two-thirds of the rainfall

occurs, is from April to November. The northern slopes of the island receive more rainfall than the southern, but the offshore islands on the
north coast are semiarid. Hurricanes, which visit the island once or twice
a decade, and severe droughts, which are not uncommon, are the discouraging features in agriculture.

Sugar.   Sugar, since even before 1800, has been the dominant export
crop of Cuba. Upon sugar, therefore, its price and production, depends
largely the degree of prosperity of the island. The value of Cuban foreign
commerce rises and falls with the changing price of sugar. There is always grave danger in so limited an economic base, and the history of
Cuba well bears this out. Improvements in ocean transportation, changing methods of production, invention of new machinery, new sources of
sugar, tariffs, subsidies, and rebates, not to speak of tropical hurricanes
and local rebellions, have worried Cuban sugar growers. Competition
with European beet sugar and Indian and Java cane has forced the

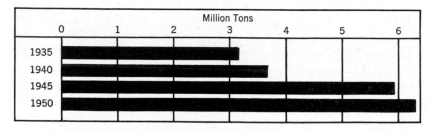

Fig. 285. Sugar production in Cuba, 1935 to 1950 inclusive.

island's industry to adopt modern, large-scale production. This gave an
opportunity for United States capital to enter. Large estates have been
created, large modern mills with bagasse furnaces, double-grinding and
powerful pressing machinery, and vacuum evaporators have been built.
Miles of temporary railways now connect each central with the cane
fields and larger railways, and give the centrals contact with the shipping
ports. The extensive type of cultivation still prevails, however. Migratory
cropping dominates on the larger estates, and from 3 to 6 cuttings are
taken from a single planting. The United States takes about 90 per cent
of the crop in normal times. Molasses, a by-product of sugar, also finds
a large market in the United States (Figs. 285, 286, and 287).

For many years Cuba, India, and Java have been the leading sugar-
producing regions of the world. Some years Cuba has been in the lead,
only to be surpassed in other years by Java or India. Since 1900 Germany, the United States, and France have increased their sugar production, this being largely from the sugar beet. These heavy producers,
along with the Hawaiian Islands, the Philippines, and several European

countries, can supply far more sugar than the world can consume. A reduction in the world's consumption leaves large stocks in the hands of the producers. Such has been the situation for many years since World War I. Conditions in the sugar regions of the world were desperate about 1925 and in following years.

Conferences of the world's sugar interests have worked out allotment plans. Under the Chadbourne Plan, the Sugar Stabilization Law, and other agreements and decrees, Cuba's normal crop of nearly 5,000,000

Fig. 286. A typical ox-cart for hauling sugar cane from the plantation to the mill. *Courtesy, Cuban Tourist Commission.* Modern power-driven machinery is fast replacing the oxen and much of the hand labor in the cane fields.

tons (1922–1926 average) had to be cut to but a little more than 3,000,000 for 1931. There was left over from previous years nearly 7,000,000 tons to be "segregated" and disposed of gradually.

The lower total production and the lower prices have brought great financial distress and much bitter feeling toward the United States sugar "barons." However, with the passing of time, adjustments have been made. In 1951 Cuba produced 6,800,000 tons (Fig. 288).

Tobacco. Cuban tobacco, and particularly Habana cigars and cigarettes, hold a high rank in the world's tobacco markets. The most famous tobacco district is on the southeastern slopes of the Organ Mountains in Pinar del Rio province. From here comes about three-fourths of the island's crop. Cuban soil and climate produce a tobacco distinct from all others in aroma. Mexican and United States tobacco, introduced after destructive wars had about destroyed the native variety, has been found, after being domesticated in Cuba for a few years, to take on many of the characteristics of the old Cuban variety. Santa Clara and Habana province are also heavy producers (Fig. 289).

The high quality demanded calls for intelligent, careful, white labor. Much tobacco is grown under cloth. Plants so grown produce high-grade

Fig. 287. Harvested sugar cane arrives at the mill of the American Sugar Refining Company's Central, Jaronu, Cuba. *Courtesy, United States Cuban Sugar Council.*

wrapper leaves, uniform in quality, low in gums and resins, and light in color and weight.

The United States is Cuba's best customer. Since Cuban tobacco has few rivals and is in the luxury class because of its high value, the industry suffers much less fluctuation in price and production than sugar.

Minor Products.   Fruits, nuts, and vegetables in great variety and quantity are produced, though the methods of cultivation are very primitive. Corn, oil seeds, sisal, honey, coffee, cacao, and yucca are other products. Rice finds Cuba a suitable habitat. The absence of an off season in plant growth enables Cuban farmers to produce grapefruit, pineapples, and garden truck for the winter markets of the United States.

Cuba also produces bananas for export and home consumption. The imports of corn, butter, eggs, vegetables, oils and lard, and canned milk are declining rapidly, and Cuba may soon be self-sufficing in these and other staples. The livestock industry is only in its beginning.

Transportation Facilities.   Transportation facilities, both within the island and on the seas, are fairly adequate. There are more than 3000 miles of railroad, not including the 2800 miles of private lines on the 200 large sugar estates. The island has a large number of very excellent harbors. Most are pouch-shaped with narrow entrances, thus offering large areas of well-protected waters for anchorage.

It is reported that automobilists have 1800 miles of good roads. A great Central Highway, 705 miles long, was formally opened in 1931 (Fig. 290). The long coast line and excellent harbors give abundant overseas contact.

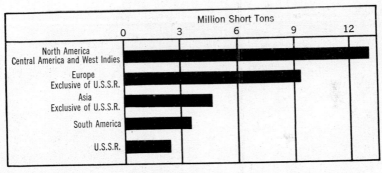

Fig. 288. The sugar crop of the world in 1950.

The Forests.   Large areas of Cuba are still in forest (some 8,600,000 acres) containing cabinet and dyewoods. Some of these forests are state owned, but many sugar companies have large areas on their estates, portions of which are cleared from time to time to supply virgin lands.

Manufactures.   Manufacturing is mainly the preparation of agricultural products for foreign markets. Raw sugar, cigars, and cigarettes are the most important products manufactured. Among the lesser manufactures are those producing leather, hats, clothing, alcoholic drinks, vegetable oils, furniture, textiles, paints, paper, glass, and cement. These have grown up under the protection of high tariffs to build up Cuban industries. Cuba is making steady progress toward self-sufficiency.

So far little has been done with the island's rich mineral resources. The Oriente province, where the old crystallines outcrop, is the great mineral region. Excellent Bessemer ore (60 per cent iron) is shipped, largely to the United States. High-grade manganese and copper are also mined. Iron ore and copper outcrop in various other sections of the island, wherever the old rocks are exposed. There are in several sections deposits of bitumens, varying from oils to asphalts and lignites. Coal of a high grade is lacking, a factor that serves to deter manufacturing. The building stone most used is limestone, soft when taken from the quarry; it may be shaped with an axe or sawed—it soon hardens when exposed to sun and wind. Some salt is produced.

Fig. 289. A tobacco plantation in the world-famous region of Vuelta Abajo, Pinar del Rio, Cuba. Here the soil is sandy and poor, but by the use of fertilizer some of the world's finest tobacco is grown. This tobacco seems to have a quality not obtained elsewhere.

Hispaniola

Hispaniola (Haiti), the second largest of the West Indian islands, lies approximately at latitude 18° north, between Cuba on the west and Puerto Rico on the east. Its area is 30,000 square miles, and it has a population of 5,714,000. Although its size is but one-third that of Cuba, the population is greater. (Cuba, 5,130,000). In a number of respects this island is remarkable. It was discovered and named by Columbus in 1492; gold, that great attraction for the Spanish in the New World, was first discovered here; it was made the center from which the Spanish operated in the Americas; and it was to this island that African slaves in great numbers were introduced to the New World. Yet, Hispaniola is less changed today by man than any of the West Indies.

Like Puerto Rico, it is a wet, tropical land especially on the *Trade-Wind* slopes on the north and east, but in the southwest and in the rainshadow of its mountains it is so arid that in places irrigation has been hampered by salinity of the soil. Lake Enriquillo in the southern part is so dried up that its surface is 100 feet below sea level. Though irregular in shape, Hispaniola is long in east-west direction, and its surface is mountainous. At least three distinct volcanic mountain ridges, 2000–10,000 feet, extend east-west across the island with valleys between, thus lying at right angles to the path of the *Northeast Trades,* and providing great variety for the physical landscape. In places one may travel but 20 or 30 miles and pass

Fig. 290. Typical scene along the Central Highway of Cuba. *Courtesy Cuban Tourist Commission.* When completed, this hard-surfaced road will extend from end to end of the island, a distance of over 700 miles, and will have branch highways connected with the various ports.

from wet, tropical banana land to thorn forest, or upslope to temperate-land crops and pine forests.

In geologic structure the island is complex. Igneous rocks of volcanic nature occupy the uplands, and there are many upturned sedimentary rocks on the slopes and dipping towards the sea. In the valleys coral limestones underlie the soil, which when weathered produce a soil of great fertility. Deposits of copper, silver, gold, platinum, iron, salt, coal, and petroleum are found, but the mining industry is undeveloped.

The political history of Hispaniola has been turbulent. Though the Spanish at first made it the center of their operations in the New World, established plantations, and enslaved Indians and the African Negro, the lure of precious metals on the American mainland resulted in the decline of settlements in the island. Slaves were abandoned or escaped to the interior, mixed with Indians and some whites, and increased in numbers. In 1677 the Spanish lost the island to the French, who rejuvenated plantation agriculture and imported more slaves from Africa. The suitability of the land for such tropical crops as sugar, cotton, tobacco, and coffee has always been an attraction. In the French Revolution of 1791 the slaves rebelled, and under their great black leader, Toussaint L'Ouverture, drove out the whites, and took over the rule of the island as Haitians. Civil wars and much bloodshed were the rule, till in 1844 the eastern two-thirds of the island rebelled from Haiti, and as the Dominican Republic set out on a period of revolutions of its own. Thus were born the Republic of Haiti and the Dominican Republic. Civil wars and revolutions, complicated by investment of foreign capital in plantation agriculture, continued till in 1915 and 1916 the public debts were so great that both republics went into receivership under the protection of the United States. These receiverships have since been withdrawn, and today each is a republic with a constitution and has a president elected by its own people.

Because of the nature of the past history of Hispaniola, as has been stated, the population is composed of a large percentage of Negroes. In Haiti the Negro element is dominant, but in the Dominican Republic the population is composed of whites and mulattos, and 19 per cent Negroes. Haiti has 50 per cent more people than the Dominican Republic, though it is but half as large. The less dense population thus accounts for the fact that the Dominican Republic opened some of its land to settlement by European refugees, the first contingent of which arrived in May, 1940. It is estimated that this republic could support eight times its present population. The United States has done much since about 1925 in encouraging road building, providing sanitation for cities, and establishing schools. However, much remains to be done along these lines. For the island as a whole, illiteracy was about 85 per cent in 1940. The ease of making an agricultural living in this warm land is not conducive to an industrial development.

The resource of lumber is great, for the island remains about 75 per cent forested. Lack of roads prevents its development. In 1950 over half the foreign trade of the island was with the United States. Sugar, coffee, cacao, tobacco, and sisal are the chief crops, and there are possibilities of greatly increased production in all of them.

Puerto Rico

Physical Setting.   Puerto Rico, over which the United States flag has waved since 1898, is, in the words of one writer, "one of the lovliest of all those regions of loveliness which are washed by the Caribbean Sea." It is a tropical island, wet on the slopes up which the *Trade Winds* blow, and so dry on the level lands and lee slopes that irrigation is necessary to get good returns from the land. Ocean winds, which are drying on most parts of the island, give low sensible temperatures and reduce the daily and annual maxima that would naturally occur on a land at this latitude. The monthly means rarely vary more than 6° during the year, and the extreme range is only about 40°. The high interior is cooler than the coasts. With the exception of the tropical hurricanes that may come between July and October, the island is a delightful home for its 2,150,000 inhabitants. The Spaniards who made the first settlement in 1509 found the moister parts of the island heavily wooded, many of the trees being of commercial value. Besides mahogany, cedar, ebony, logwood, and sandalwood, there are 28 medicinal plants, 8 plants that furnish resins, 12 that furnish condiments, and an equal number from which dyes and tannin may be obtained. During the 300 years that Puerto Rico was a penal colony for Spain, the forests remained almost intact. But about 1815, when colonists were allowed to take up land and with their slaves made preparations for sugar plantations, the forests were destroyed in the moist plains on the north side of the island. The exploitation and destruction of the forests have gone on apace, until little of the original stand is left.

In geologic structure the island is simple. There is a base of igneous rock that outcrops in the higher parts, and, resting on this on both north and south, are inclined beds of limestone that dip toward the sea. In harmony with the simplicity of the geology, there are few minerals, practically all coming from the igneous rocks. Gold was easily found in the stream beds by the Spaniards, but in small quantities; cinnabar occurs in some sections; and there are some deposits of iron ore. The building stones are few in variety.

Effects of United States Control.   During the long period that the island was under Spanish control, there was peace and prosperity but little progress. The better class of Spanish Creoles were satisfied with the rule of the Spanish Crown, and in the history of Puerto Rico there are few uprisings against the mother country. Possibly the futility of such disorder deterred the leaders, as the small size of the island reduces the chances for a successful revolution. The peasant class of Creoles was peaceable, indolent, unschooled, yet intelligent. They lived a quiet, simple life on their small patches of land. Their tools were primitive, and their methods were simple. The Negro first came as a slave, and after his emancipation remained to form a lower stratum of society. About 25 per cent of the population of the island is colored, consisting for the most part of mulattos. The great dominance of white blood among the people (75 per cent) is probably the chief reason for the rapid progress that has been made since the United States occupation.

With United States control came United States capital to be invested in sugar lands, coffee, tobacco, and banana plantations. Puerto Rican products now entered United States markets free of duty, and there was ushered in an era of prosperity. Only a small percentage of the people are engaged in the manufacturing industries, which includes the preparation of sugar, coffee, and tobacco for market and the making of soap, matches, furniture, vehicles, and machinery.

The greatest work of the United States has been done in the building of roads and railroads, in the improvement of sanitary conditions, and in the introduction of a practical modern educational system. Still, about 40 per cent of the people are illiterate. The percentage, when United States took over the islands in 1899, was about 80. There are now 1100 miles of roads and 335 miles of railroads. A railroad now encircles the island. There are common schools, high schools, manual training schools, agricultural schools, and a university.

Although there has been some agitation on the part of some of the Puerto Rican politicians for independence, the vast majority of the people are satisfied with United States control. Since the island forms a territory of the United States, its products enter United States markets free of tariff duties. This privilege probably would be withdrawn if independence were granted—a fact the advocates of independence frequently do not consider.

THE CANAL ZONE AND PANAMA CANAL

The Spanish-American War, begun in 1898, showed the people of the United States the great need of a canal across the isthmus connecting North and South America. They realized then, as never before, that a water route through this isthmus would enable them to protect their coasts with a much smaller navy, for vessels could be shifted readily from either coast to the other. Growing foreign commerce and repaid industrial development also called for a shorter water route to the Pacific.

Just after the settlement of the Oregon Question and the acquisition of California, the United States, seeing the need of bringing the Pacific Coast into closer touch with the eastern part of the country, made a treaty with Colombia, in 1846, obtaining the right to a transit route for a road, railroad, or canal across the isthmus. But the urge was not sufficient to lead to action, even though there was much traffic across the isthmus after the discovery of gold in California in 1848, and the right was allowed to lapse. When the urge to action came and investigations as to the most feasible route were completed, new treaties, this time with Panama, in 1904, had to be made for a lease on the Canal Zone and a right-of-way for a canal in this zone. In the meantime the French had attempted to excavate a canal but had failed through lack of funds and inability to cope with tropical diseases. By 1904 medical science had discovered many ways of controlling tropical fevers, a development of great importance to the United States in the Canal Zone.

Construction on the United States Panama Canal was begun in 1904, and the first boat passed from ocean to ocean on August 15, 1914. The great task of linking the Atlantic with the Pacific was completed in a little more than 10 years and 3 months, at a total cost of about $375,000,000.

The United States met and solved the same problems that had confronted the French. The floods of the Chagres River are regulated by a huge dam at Gatun, 7500 feet long, and 2100 feet wide at its greatest width, with a spillway 1.5 miles long, over which the flood waters flow after they have reached a sufficient height. A large "pool," Gatun Lake, is formed above the dam. Into this lake the water of the undrowned portions of the Chagres River flows, and across this lake, by means of embankments, the Panama Railroad is carried. The canal, for nearly a third of the distance across the isthmus, passes through this lake, excavations having been necessary at some places to give sufficient depth. Some of the water of the Chagres River is used for the operation of the canal. Gatun Lake, therefore, takes care of the excess water and at the same time furnishes water for the locks and eliminates the trouble arising from the crossing of the river channel and the canal.

The mountain ridge that forms the backbone of the isthmus is passed by a huge cut, called the Culebra (now Gaillard) Cut, nearly 500 feet deep and 7 miles long. The amount of excavation necessary to pass the mountain range was materially reduced by the use of locks. There are three double locks at Gatun, by which the largest ocean vessels are locked up from the Atlantic Ocean level to the level of Gatun Lake, 85 feet above the sea; and on the Pacific side of the isthmus there is one double lock at Pedro Miguel, and two double ones at Miraflores, by means of which vessels passing to the Pacific are lowered 85 feet to the Pacific level. The minimum depth of the canal is 41 feet; the width of the lock chambers is 110 feet, and the length 1000 feet, thus accommodating most of the largest ocean vessels.

On September 23, 1915, after the canal had been in operation a little more than a year, slides occurred on the sides of the Gaillard Cut after a heavy rain, and great masses of earth were pushed up from the bottom of the canal, nearly closing the channel. An examination showed that the angle of the slope of the cut was too steep for the earth to remain at rest under all conditions, and that the soft nature of the material in the hill and its great weight had resulted in the earth in the bottom of the cut being forced upward. Dredges were soon at work removing the obstruction. The canal remained closed to traffic until April of the following year. Since that time the slopes of the cut have been greatly reduced, and the hill lowered.

Another great problem that had to be solved was the most important of all and the one that really caused the failure of the French, as previously stated; this was the control of diseases. Forests were cut, undergrowth was removed, swamps were drained, a good source of domestic water was provided, buildings were thoroughly screened, and the garbage and sewage were properly disposed of. These measures made the Canal Zone cities and camps as sanitary and as healthful as most United States cities. It was even boasted that the death rate in Colon and Panama was lower than that in any United States city; but these low figures were due to the fact that many of the sick persons were removed from the zone before death occurred.

Many benefits accrued to the United States from the building of the Panama Canal. The journey across the isthmus by ship, if no delays are met with, takes from 7 to 8 hours, the record time being 4 hours and 10 minutes. The maximum capacity is about 17,000 ships a year. Without the canal, ships would have to sail southward the whole length of South America around the "Horn," or through the dangerous Strait of Magellan, and north along the west coast. Between New Orleans and San Francisco the Panama Canal saves vessels 8870 miles, or about 28 days of time. To Valparaiso from New Orleans, the saving is 4750 miles. San Francisco is nearer New York by 7870 miles; Yokohama, Japan, nearer by 3678 miles; and Hawaii, by 5280 miles. By the canal, Japan is 1800 miles nearer New York than Liverpool; Shanghai is nearer New York by 1600 miles; and Sydney, Australia, by 2400 miles. These shorter distances tend to reduce the importance of British entrepôts and greatly aid in the establishment of direct lines of steamers between New York and the Orient. Formerly, the west coast of South America was about as near to London as it was to New York by steamer. Now it can be reached from New York by sailing almost directly south.

New Orleans is more than 2600 miles nearer Callao than Liverpool is. The west coast of South America, like the Caribbean lands, is, distance considered, definitely within the commercial sphere of the United States. Vessels are now able to sail around the continent of South America and are not forced to retrace their route, as they formerly did. The western coast of the United States has cheaper freight rates than before, on goods to or from the eastern states.

But the Panama Canal is an expensive project. The original cost was approximately $375,000,000, and interest on the investment at 4 per cent has been about $15,000,000 annually. Much additional expense for upkeep and fortifications has been necessary. The total annual tonnage has been below 30,000,000 long tons most of the time, bringing an income of about $18,000,0000. However, the dollars and cents value of the canal is not a true measure of its worth. The influence of lower freight rates, particularly for our west coast lands, and the opening of such lands to markets, together with the military importance of the canal to the United States, must be considered. Many of the Rocky Mountain states are commrecially tributary to the western coast of the United States, whereas before the completion of the canal they had a tendency to look toward the East for most of their commercial dealings. The Gulf Coast of the United States has been benefited. Railroad lines extending north and south have increased their traffic greatly, and now draw much business from the Middle West that formerly went to New York. A saving of time means lower freight rates and cheaper products to the consumer.

The Canal Zone has an area of nearly 554 square miles, 5 miles wide on either side of the center of the canal, and some 40 miles long from deep water in the Caribbean to deep water on the Pacific Coast. In addition there are lands that are flooded by Gatun Lake, and lands for fortifications and for future dams that might be needed to maintain the water level of the lake in dry seasons.

The zone is virtually a government reservation in which private individuals are not permitted to own real estate, but the land may be leased for agriculture and also for building sites for enterprises engaged in businesses related to the chief functions of the canal, and interocean movement of ships engaged in commerce. The canal was conceived and constructed as a strategic venture, and most of the cost has been assumed by the War Department, but its function so far, at least has been largely commercial.

THE VIRGIN ISLANDS

The three small islands, St. Thomas, St. Croix, and St. John, of the Virgin Island group, were purchased by the United States from Denmark in 1917 for $25,000,000. The total area is 132 square miles (the cost, therefore, was nearly $300 an acre), only a part of which is of any agricultural value, because the islands are merely tops of mountains, and only a part of the upper slopes is level enough for cultivation. The strategic position of the islands, near the ocean route between North and South America, their location near the Anegada Passage—much used by ocean traffic—and the excellence of the harbor of St. Thomas on St.

Thomas Island were the chief considerations in their purchase. On two previous occasions the United States had begun negotiations with Denmark relative to the purchase of these islands, but the attempts had failed although both times the people of the islands had expressed their willingness to change flags. The possibility of Germany's securing them and thus getting a footing in the New World and challenging the Monroe Doctrine was the immediate cause of purchase. Already Germany had secured important harbor privileges at St. Thomas.

The islands had been a financial burden to the Danish government, having had, like the other colonies of European nations in the West Indies, economic reverses. The people welcomed the change in ownership, expecting that American control would bring prosperity to them as it had to Puerto Rico; but they have not received much attention beyond the opening of United States markets to their products, which consist of sugar, molasses, hides, and bay rum. The total population of 30,000 in 1947 was about 80 per cent Negro. Administrative officers for the islands are appointed by the United States Navy.

QUESTIONS, EXERCISES, AND PROBLEMS

1. What European nations possess colonies in Middle America? List the colonies belonging to each. Of what commercial value are they to these countries? Get the data on exports and imports and types of articles entering into commerce. To what extent do these colonies trade with the United States?

2. Rank the different political divisions of Middle America in area, population, illiteracy, miles of railroad, exports, imports, and any other data furnished in the *Statesman's Yearbook*. Has material progress been greater in independent countries or in the colonies? What is one of the reasons for the high rank Cuba holds among the independent countries? Rank the countries of Central America. Which one is lowest? How do you explain the difference? Is it environment or man?

3. At the present time the Cuban government is encouraging diversification of crops in Cuba. What are the reasons? How would diversification be a benefit?

4. Make a special study in comparing and contrasting Jamaica and Puerto Rico in size, population, products, industries, and general status of the people. How do you account for what you find?

5. What prompted the United States to construct the Panama Canal? In what ways have the United States benefited by its construction?

6. With what countries does Cuba have commercial relations? Does proximity to the United States have any bearing on the trade relations of Cuba? What other factors may affect the extent of our commerce with Cuba?

INDEX

PRESTON
46 KNIGHTSBRIDGE PARK
BELFAST, 9

TRILBY

"IT WAS TRILBY!"   [See page 305

TRILBY

𝔄 𝔑𝔬𝔳𝔢𝔩

BY

GEORGE DU MAURIER

AUTHOR OF 'PETER IBBETSON'

WITH 121 ILLUSTRATIONS BY THE AUTHOR

'*Aux nouvelles que j'apporte*
Vos beaux yeux vont pleurer'

LONDON
OSGOOD, McILVAINE & CO.
45 ALBEMARLE STREET, W.
MDCCCXCV

' Hélas !   Je sais un chant d'amour,
Triste et gai, tour à tour ! '

ILLUSTRATIONS

TRILBY

PART FIRST

'Mimi Pinson est une blonde,
Une blonde que l'on connaît ;
Elle n'a qu'une robe au monde,
Landérirette ! et qu'un bonnet !'

IT was a fine, sunny, showery day in April.

The big studio window was open at the top, and let
in a pleasant breeze from the north-west. Things were
beginning to look shipshape at last. The big piano, a
semi-grand by Broadwood, had arrived from England by
'the Little Quickness' (*la Petite Vitesse*, as the goods
trains are called in France), and lay, freshly tuned, along-
side the eastern wall ; on the wall opposite was a panoply
of foils, masks, and boxing-gloves.

A trapeze, a knotted rope, and two parallel cords,
supporting each a ring, depended from a huge beam in the
ceiling. The walls were of the usual dull red, relieved by
plaster casts of arms and legs and hands and feet ; and
Dante's mask, and Michael Angelo's alto-rilievo of Leda
and the swan, and a centaur and Lapith from the Elgin
Marbles—on none of these had the dust as yet had time
to settle.

B

There were also studies in oil from the nude ; copies of Titian, Rembrandt, Velasquez, Rubens, Tintoret, Leonardo da Vinci—none of the school of Botticelli, Mantegna, and Co.—a firm whose merits had not as yet been revealed to the many.

Along the walls, at a great height, ran a broad shelf, on which were other casts in plaster, terra-cotta, imitation bronze : a little Theseus, a little Venus of Milo, a little discobolus ; a little flayed man threatening high heaven (an act that seemed almost pardonable under the circumstances !) ; a lion and a boar by Barye ; an anatomical figure of a horse, with only one leg left and no ears ; a horse's head from the pediment of the Parthenon, earless also ; and the bust of Clytie, with her beautiful low brow, her sweet wan gaze, and the ineffable forward shrug of her dear shoulders that makes her bosom as a nest, a rest, a pillow, a refuge—the likeness of a thing to be loved and desired for ever, and sought for and wrought for and fought for by generation after generation of the sons of men.

Near the stove hung a gridiron, a frying-pan, a toasting-fork, and a pair of bellows. In an adjoining glazed corner cupboard were plates and glasses, black-handled knives, pewter spoons, and three-pronged steel forks ; a salad-bowl, vinegar cruets, an oil-flask, two mustard-pots (English and French), and such like things—all scrupulously clean. On the floor, which had been stained and waxed at considerable cost, lay two cheetah-skins and a large Persian praying-rug. One half of it, however (under the trapeze and at the end farthest from the window, beyond the model-throne), was covered with coarse matting, that one might fence or box without slipping down and splitting one's self in two, or fall without breaking any bones.

Two other windows of the usual French size and pattern, with shutters to them and heavy curtains of baize, opened east and west, to let in dawn or sunset, as the case might be, or haply keep them out. And there were alcoves, recesses, irregularities, odd little nooks and corners, to be filled up as time wore on with endless personal nick-nacks, bibelots, private properties and acquisitions—things that make a place genial, homelike, and good to remember, and sweet to muse upon (with fond regret) in after years.

And an immense divan spread itself in width and length and delightful thickness just beneath the big north window, the business window—a divan so immense that three well-fed, well-contented Englishmen could all lie lazily smoking their pipes on it at once without being in each other's way, and very often did!

At present one of these Englishmen—a Yorkshireman, by the way, called Taffy (and also the Man of Blood, because he was supposed to be distantly related to a baronet)—was more energetically engaged. Bare-armed, and in his shirt and trousers, he was twirling a pair of Indian clubs round his head. His face was flushed, and he was perspiring freely and looked fierce. He was a very big young man, fair, with kind but choleric blue eyes, and the muscles of his brawny arm were strong as iron bands.

For three years he had borne Her Majesty's commission, and had been through the Crimean campaign without a scratch. He would have been one of the famous six hundred in the famous charge at Balaklava but for a sprained ankle (caught playing leapfrog in the trenches), which kept him in hospital on that momentous day. So that he lost his chance of glory or the grave, and this humiliating misadventure had sickened him of soldiering for life, and he never quite got over it. Then, feeling within himself an irresistible vocation for art, he had sold out; and here he was in Paris, hard at work, as we see.

He was good-looking, with straight features; but I

regret to say that, besides his heavy plunger's moustache, he wore an immense pair of drooping auburn whiskers, of the kind that used to be called Piccadilly weepers, and were afterwards affected by Mr. Sothern in Lord Dundreary. It was a fashion to do so then for such of our gilded youth as could afford the time (and the hair); the bigger and fairer the whiskers, the more beautiful was thought the youth! It

TAFFY, ALIAS TALBOT WYNNE　seems incredible in these days, when even Her Majesty's Household Brigade go about with smooth cheeks and lips, like priests or play-actors.

> ' What's become of all the gold
> Used to hang and brush their bosoms . .　?'

Another inmate of this blissful abode—Sandy, the Laird of Cockpen, as he was called—sat in similarly simple attire at his easel, painting at a lifelike little picture of a Spanish toreador serenading a lady of high degree (in broad daylight).

He had never been to Spain, but he had a complete tore- ador's kit—a bargain which he had picked up for a mere song in the Boulevard du Temple—and he had hired the guitar. His pipe was in his mouth—reversed ; for it had gone out, and the ashes were spilled all over his trousers, where holes were often burned in this way.

Quite gratuitously, and with a pleasing Scotch accent, he began to declaim :

'THE LAIRD OF COCKPEN'

> ' A street there is in Paris famous
>   For which no rhyme our language yields ;
> Roo Nerve day Petty Shong its name is—
>   The New Street of the Little Fields. . . .'

And then, in his keen appreciation of the immortal stanza, he chuckled audibly, with a face so blithe and merry and well pleased that it did one good to look at him.

He also had entered life by another door. His parents (good, pious people in Dundee) had intended that he should be a solicitor, as his father and grandfather had been before him. And here he was in Paris famous, painting toreadors, and spouting the 'Ballad of the Bouillabaisse,' as he would often do out of sheer lightness of heart—much oftener, indeed, than he would say his prayers.

Kneeling on the divan, with his elbow on the window-sill, was a third and much younger youth. The third he was 'Little Billee.' He had pulled down the green baize blind, and was looking over the roofs and chimney-pots of Paris and all about with all his eyes, munching the while a roll and a savoury saveloy, in which there was evidence of much garlic. He ate with great relish, for he was very hungry ; he had been all the morning at Carrel's studio, drawing from the life.

Little Billee was small and slender, about twenty or twenty-one, and had a straight white forehead veined with blue, large dark blue eyes, delicate, regular features, and coal-black hair. He was also very graceful and well built, with very small hands and feet, and much better dressed than his friends, who went out of their way to outdo the denizens of the Quartier Latin in careless eccentricity of garb, and succeeded. And in his winning and handsome face there was just a faint suggestion of some possible very remote Jewish ancestor—just a tinge of that strong, sturdy, irrepressible, indomitable, indelible blood which is of such priceless value in diluted homœopathic doses, like the dry white Spanish wine called montijo, which is not meant to be taken pure ; but without a judicious admixture of which no sherry can go round the world and keep its flavour intact ; or like the

'THE THIRD HE WAS "LITTLE BILLEE"'

famous bulldog strain, which is not beautiful in itself, and yet just for lacking a little of the same no greyhound can ever hope to be a champion. So, at least, I have been told by wine merchants and dog-fanciers——the most veracious persons that can be. Fortunately for the world, and especially for ourselves, most of us have in our veins at least a minim of that precious fluid, whether we know it or show it or not. *Tant pis pour les autres !*

'IT DID ONE GOOD TO LOOK AT HIM'

As Little Billee munched he also gazed at the busy place below —the Place St. Anatole des Arts — at the old houses opposite, some of which were being pulled down, no doubt lest they should fall of their own sweet will. In the gaps between he would see discoloured, old, cracked, dingy walls, with mysterious windows and rusty iron balconies of great antiquity——sights that set him dreaming dreams of mediæval French love and wickedness and crime, bygone mysteries of Paris !

One gap went right through the block, and gave him

a glimpse of the river, the ' Cité,' and the ominous old Morgue ; a little to the right rose the gray towers of Notre Dame de Paris into the checkered April sky. Indeed, the top of nearly all Paris lay before him, with a little stretch of the imagination on his part ; and he gazed with a sense of novelty, an interest and a pleasure for which he could not have found any expression in mere language.

Paris ! Paris !! Paris !!!

The very name had always been one to conjure with, whether he thought of it as a mere sound on the lips and in the ear, or as a magical written or printed word for the eye. And here was the thing itself at last, and he, he himself, *ipsissimus*, in the very heart of it, to live there and learn there as long as he liked, and make himself the great artist he longed to be.

Then, his meal finished, he lit a pipe, and flung himself on the divan and sighed deeply, out of the over-full contentment of his heart.

He felt he had never known happiness like this, never even dreamed its possibility. And yet his life had been a happy one. He was young and tender, was Little Billee ; he had never been to any school, and was innocent of the world and its wicked ways ; innocent of French especially, and the ways of Paris and its Latin Quarter. He had been brought up and educated at home, had spent his boyhood in London with his mother and sister, who now lived in Devonshire on somewhat straitened means. His father, who was dead, had been a clerk in the Treasury.

He and his two friends, Taffy and the Laird, had taken this studio together. The Laird slept there, in a

small bedroom off the studio. Taffy had a bedroom at
the Hôtel de Seine, in the street of that name. Little
Billee lodged at the Hôtel Corneille, in the Place de
l'Odéon.

He looked at his two friends, and wondered if any
one, living or dead, had ever had such a glorious pair of
chums as these.

Whatever they did, whatever they said, was simply
perfect in his eyes ; they were his guides and philosophers
as well as his chums. On the other hand, Taffy and the
Laird were as fond of the boy as they could be.

His absolute belief in all they said and did touched
them none the less that they were conscious of its being
somewhat in excess of their deserts. His almost girlish
purity of mind amused and charmed them, and they did
all they could to preserve it, even in the Quartier Latin,
where purity is apt to go bad if it be kept too long.

They loved him for his affectionate disposition, his
lively and caressing ways ; and they admired him far
more than he ever knew, for they recognised in him a
quickness, a keenness, a delicacy of perception, in matters
of form and colour, a mysterious facility and felicity of
execution, a sense of all that was sweet and beautiful in
nature, and a ready power of expressing it, that had not
been vouchsafed to them in any such generous profusion,
and which, as they ungrudgingly admitted to themselves
and each other, amounted to true genius.

And when one within the immediate circle of our
intimates is gifted in this abnormal fashion, we either
hate or love him for it, in proportion to the greatness of
his gift ; according to the way we are built.

So Taffy and the Laird loved Little Billee——loved

him very much indeed. Not but what Little Billee had
his faults. For instance, he didn't interest himself very
warmly in other people's pictures. He didn't seem to
care for the Laird's guitar-playing toreador, nor for his
serenaded lady—at all events, he never said anything
about them, either in praise or blame. He looked at
Taffy's realisms (for Taffy was a realist) in silence, and
nothing tries true friendship so much as silence of this
kind.

But, then, to make up for it, when they all three went
to the Louvre, he didn't seem to trouble much about
Titian either, or Rembrandt, or Velasquez, Rubens,
Veronese, or Leonardo. He looked at the people who
looked at the pictures, instead of at the pictures themselves ; especially at the people who copied them, the
sometimes charming young lady painters—and these
seemed to him even more charming than they really were
—and he looked a great deal out of the Louvre windows,
where there was much to be seen : more Paris, for
instance—Paris, of which he could never have enough.

But when, surfeited with classical beauty, they all
three went and dined together, and Taffy and the Laird
said beautiful things about the old masters, and quarrelled
about them, he listened with deference and rapt attention
and reverentially agreed with all they said ; and afterwards made the most delightfully funny little pen-and-ink
sketches of them, saying all these beautiful things (which
he sent to his mother and sister at home) ; so lifelike, so
real, that you could almost hear the beautiful things they
said ; so beautifully drawn that you felt the old masters
couldn't have drawn them better themselves ; and so
irresistibly droll that you felt that the old masters could

AMONG THE OLD MASTERS

not have drawn them at all—any more than Milton
could have described the quarrel between Sairey Gamp
and Betsy Prig; no one, in short, but Little Billee.

Little Billee took up the 'Ballad of the Bouillabaisse'
where the Laird had left it off, and speculated on the
future of himself and his friends, when he should have got
to forty years—an almost impossibly remote future.

These speculations were interrupted by a loud knock
at the door, and two men came in.

First, a tall bony individual of any age between thirty
and forty-five, of Jewish aspect, well-featured but sinister.
He was very shabby and dirty, and wore a red *béret* and
a large velveteen cloak, with a big metal clasp at the
collar.   His thick, heavy, languid, lustreless black hair fell
down behind his ears on to his shoulders, in that musician-
like way that is so offensive to the normal Englishman.
He had bold, brilliant black eyes, with long heavy lids, a
thin, sallow face, and a beard of burnt-up black, which
grew almost from his under eyelids; and over it his
moustache, a shade lighter, fell in two long spiral twists.
He went by the name of Svengali, and spoke fluent
French with a German accent and humorous German
twists and idioms, and his voice was very thin and mean
and harsh, and often broke into a disagreeable falsetto.

His companion was a little swarthy young man—a
gypsy, possibly—much pitted with the smallpox, and also
very shabby.   He had large, soft, affectionate brown eyes,
like a King Charles spaniel.   He had small, nervous,
veiny hands, with nails bitten down to the quick, and
carried a fiddle and a fiddlestick under his arm, without a
case, as though he had been playing in the street.

'Ponchour, mes enfants,' said Svengali.   'Che vous

amène mon ami Checko, qui choue du fiolon gomme un anche !'

Little Billee, who adored all 'sweet musicianers,' jumped up and made Gecko as warmly welcome as he could in his early French.

' Ha ! le biâno !' exclaimed Svengali, flinging his red *béret* on it, and his cloak on the ground. ' Ch'espère qu'il est pon, et pien t'accord !'

And sitting down on the music-stool, he ran up and down the scales with that easy power, that smooth even crispness of touch, which reveal the master.

Then he fell to playing Chopin's impromptu in A flat, so beautifully that Little Billee's heart went nigh to bursting with suppressed emotion and delight. He had never heard any music of Chopin's before, nothing but British provincial home-made music—melodies with variations, 'Annie Laurie,' 'The Last Rose of Summer,' 'The Blue Bells of Scotland'; innocent little motherly and sisterly tinklings, invented to set the company at their ease on festive evenings, and make all-round conversation possible for shy people, who fear the unaccompanied sound of their own voices, and whose genial chatter always leaves off directly the music ceases.

He never forgot that impromptu, which he was destined to hear again one day in strange circumstances.

Then Svengali and Gecko made music together, divinely. Little fragmentary things, sometimes consisting of but a few bars, but these bars of *such* beauty and meaning ! Scraps, snatches, short melodies, meant to fetch, to charm immediately, or to melt or sadden or madden just for a moment, and that knew just when to leave off—czardas, gypsy dances, Hungarian love-plaints,

things little known out of eastern Europe in the fifties of
this century, till the Laird and Taffy were almost as wild
in their enthusiasm as Little Billee—a silent enthusiasm
too deep for speech. And when these two great artists
left off to smoke, the three Britishers were too much
moved even for that, and there was a stillness. . . .

Suddenly there came a loud knuckle-rapping at the
outer door, and a portentous voice of great volume, and
that might almost have belonged to any sex (even an
angel's), uttered the British milkman's yodel, ' Milk below ! '
and before any one could say ' Entrez,' a strange figure
appeared, framed by the gloom of the little antechamber.

It was the figure of a very tall and fully-developed
young female, clad in the gray overcoat of a French
infantry soldier, continued netherwards by a short striped
petticoat, beneath which were visible her bare white ankles
and insteps, and slim, straight, rosy heels, clean cut and
smooth as the back of a razor ; her toes lost themselves
in a huge pair of male slippers, which made her drag her
feet as she walked.

She bore herself with easy, unembarrassed grace, like
a person whose nerves and muscles are well in tune, whose
spirits are high, who has lived much in the atmosphere of
French studios, and feels at home in it.

This strange medley of garments was surmounted by
a small bare head with short, thick, wavy brown hair, and
a very healthy young face, which could scarcely be called
quite beautiful at first sight, since the eyes were too wide
apart, the mouth too large, the chin too massive, the complexion a mass of freckles. Besides, you can never tell
how beautiful (or how ugly) a face may be till you have
tried to draw it.

"WISTFUL AND SWEET"

But a small portion of her neck, down by the collar-bone, which just showed itself between the unbuttoned lapels of her military coat collar, was of a delicate privet-like whiteness that is never to be found on any French neck, and very few English ones. Also, she had a very fine brow, broad and low, with thick level eyebrows much darker than her hair, a broad, bony, high bridge to her short nose, and her full, broad cheeks were beautifully modelled. She would have made a singularly handsome boy.

As the creature looked round at the assembled company and flashed her big white teeth at them in an all-embracing smile of uncommon width and quite irresistible sweetness, simplicity, and friendly trust, one saw at a glance that she was out of the common clever, simple, humorous, honest, brave, and kind, and accustomed to be genially welcomed wherever she went. Then suddenly closing the door behind her, dropping her smile, and looking wistful and sweet, with her head on one side and her arms akimbo, 'Ye're all English, now, aren't ye?' she exclaimed. 'I heard the music, and thought I'd just come in for a bit, and pass the time of day: you don't mind? Trilby, that's my name—Trilby O'Ferrall.'

She said this in English, with an accent half Scotch and certain French intonations, and in a voice so rich and deep and full as almost to suggest an incipient *tenore robusto;* and one felt instinctively that it was a real pity she wasn't a boy, she would have made such a jolly one.

'We're delighted, on the contrary,' said Little Billee, and advanced a chair for her.

But she said, 'Oh, don't mind me; go on with the

music,' and sat herself down cross-legged on the model-throne near the piano.

As they still looked at her, curious and half embarrassed, she pulled a paper parcel containing food out of one of the coat-pockets, and exclaimed :

' I'll just take a bite, if you don't object ; I'm a model, you know, and it's just rung twelve—" the rest." I'm posing for Durien the sculptor, on the next floor. I pose to him for the altogether.'

' The altogether ? ' asked Little Billee.

' Yes—*l'ensemble*, you know—head, hands, and feet—everything—especially feet. That's my foot,' she said, kicking off her big slipper and stretching out the limb. ' It's the handsomest foot in all Paris. There's only one, in all Paris to match it, and here it is,' and she laughed heartily (like a merry peal of bells), and stuck out the other.

And in truth they were astonishingly beautiful feet, such as one only sees in pictures and statues—a true inspiration of shape and colour, all made up of delicate lengths and subtly-modulated curves and noble straightnesses and happy little dimpled arrangements in innocent young pink and white.

So that Little Billee, who had the quick, prehensile, æsthetic eye, and knew by the grace of Heaven what the shapes and sizes and colours of almost every bit of man, woman, or child should be (and so seldom are), was quite bewildered to find that a real, bare, live human foot could be such a charming object to look at, and felt that such a base or pedestal lent quite an antique and Olympian dignity to a figure that seemed just then rather grotesque in its mixed attire of military overcoat and female petticoat, and nothing else !

C

Poor Trilby !

The shape of those lovely slender feet (that were neither large nor small), facsimiled in dusty pale plaster of Paris, survives on the shelves and walls of many a studio throughout the world, and many a sculptor yet unborn has yet to marvel at their strange perfection, in studious despair.

For when Dame Nature takes it into her head to do her very best, and bestow her minutest attention on a mere detail, as happens now and then—once in a blue moon, perhaps—she makes it uphill work for poor human art to keep pace with her.

It is a wondrous thing, the human foot—like the human hand ; even more so, perhaps ; but, unlike the hand, with which we are so familiar, it is seldom a thing of beauty in civilised adults who go about in leather boots or shoes.

So that it is hidden away in disgrace, a thing to be thrust out of sight and forgotten. It can sometimes be very ugly indeed—the ugliest thing there is, even in the fairest and highest and most gifted of her sex ; and then it is of an ugliness to chill and kill romance, and scatter love's young dream, and almost break the heart.

And all for the sake of a high heel and a ridiculously-pointed toe—mean things, at the best !

Conversely, when Mother Nature has taken extra pains in the building of it, and proper care or happy chance has kept it free of lamentable deformations, indurations, and discolorations—all those grewsome boot-begotten abominations which have made it so generally unpopular —the sudden sight of it, uncovered, comes as a very rare and singularly pleasing surprise to the eye that has learned how to see !

Nothing else that Mother Nature has to show, not even the human face divine, has more subtle power to suggest high physical distinction, happy evolution, and supreme development; the lordship of man over beast, the lordship of man over man, the lordship of woman over all!

En voilà de l'éloquence—à propos de bottes!

Trilby had respected Mother Nature's special gift to herself—had never worn a leather boot or shoe, had always taken as much care of her feet as many a fine lady takes of her hands. It was her one coquetry, the only real vanity she had.

Gecko, his fiddle in one hand and his bow in the other, stared at her in open-mouthed admiration and delight, as she ate her sandwich of soldier's bread and *fromage à la crème* quite unconcerned.

When she had finished she licked the tips of her fingers clean of cheese, and produced a small tobacco-pouch from another military pocket, made herself a cigarette, and lit it and smoked it, inhaling the smoke in large whiffs, filling her lungs with it, and sending it back through her nostrils, with a look of great beatitude.

Svengali played Schubert's 'Rosemonde,' and flashed a pair of languishing black eyes at her with intent to kill.

But she didn't even look his way. She looked at Little Billee, at big Taffy, at the Laird, at the casts and studies, at the sky, the chimney-pots over the way, the towers of Notre Dame, just visible from where she sat.

Only when he finished she exclaimed: 'Maïe, aïe! c'est rudement bien tapé, c'te musique-là! Seulement, c'est pas gai, vous savez! Comment q'ça s'appelle?'

' It is called the " Rosemonde " of Schubert, matemoiselle,' replied Svengali.   (I will translate.)

' And what's that—Rosemonde ? ' said she.

' Rosemonde was a princess of Cyprus, matemoiselle,
and Cyprus is an island.'

' Ah, and Schubert, then—where's that ? '

' Schubert is not an island, matemoiselle.   Schubert
was a compatriot of mine, and made music, and played
the piano, just like me.'

' Ah, Schubert was a *monsieur*, then.   Don't know him ;
never heard his name.'

' That is a pity, matemoiselle.   He had some talent.
You like this better, perhaps,' and he strummed,

> ' Messieurs les étudiants,
> S'en vont à la chaumière
> Pour y danser le cancan,'

striking wrong notes, and banging out a bass in a different key—a hideously grotesque performance.

' Yes, I like that better.   It's gayer, you know.   Is that
also composed by a compatriot of yours ? ' asked the lady.

' Heaven forbid, matemoiselle.'

And the laugh was against Svengali.

But the real fun of it all (if there was any) lay in the
fact that she was perfectly sincere.

' Are you fond of music ? ' asked Little Billee.

' Oh, ain't I just ! ' she replied.   ' My father sang like
a bird.   He was a gentleman and a scholar, my father
was.   His name was Patrick Michael O'Ferrall, Fellow of
Trinity, Cambridge.   He used to sing " Ben Bolt."   Do
you know " Ben Bolt " ? '

' Oh yes, I know it well,' said Little Billee.   ' It's a
very pretty song.'

THE "ROSEMONDE" OF SCHUBERT

'I can sing it,' said Miss O'Ferrall.   'Shall I?'

'Oh, certainly, if you will be so kind.'

Miss O'Ferrall threw away the end of her cigarette, put her hands on her knees as she sat cross-legged on the model-throne, and sticking her elbows well out, she looked up to the ceiling with a tender, sentimental smile, and sang the touching song,

> 'Oh, don't you remember sweet Alice, Ben Bolt?
> Sweet Alice, with hair so brown?' etc. etc.

As some things are too sad and too deep for tears, so some things are too grotesque and too funny for laughter. Of such a kind was Miss O'Ferrall's performance of 'Ben Bolt.'

From that capacious mouth and through that high-bridged bony nose there rolled a volume of breathy sound, not loud, but so immense that it seemed to come from all round, to be reverberated from every surface in the studio. She followed more or less the shape of the tune, going up when it rose and down when it fell, but with such immense intervals between the notes as were never dreamed of in any mortal melody. It was as though she could never once have deviated into tune, never once have hit upon a true note, even by a fluke—in fact, as though she were absolutely tone-deaf, and without ear, although she stuck to the time correctly enough.

She finished her song amid an embarrassing silence. The audience didn't quite know whether it were meant for fun or seriously. One wondered if she were not paying out Svengali for his impertinent performance of 'Messieurs les étudiants.' If so, it was a capital piece of impromptu tit-for-tat admirably acted, and a very

ugly gleam yellowed the tawny black of Svengali's big
eyes. He was so fond of making fun of others that he
particularly resented being made fun of himself—
couldn't endure that any one should ever have the laugh
of *him.*

At length Little Billee said : ' Thank you so much.
It's a capital song.'

' Yes,' said Miss O'Ferrall. ' It's the only song I
know, unfortunately. My father used to sing it, just like
that, when he felt jolly after hot rum-and-water. It used
to make people cry ; he used to cry over it himself. *I*
never do. Some people think I can't sing a bit. All I
can say is that I've often had to sing it six or seven times
running in *lots* of studios. I vary it, you know—not the
words, but the tune. You must remember that I've only
taken to it lately. Do you know Litolff? Well, he's a
great composer, and he came to Durien's the other day,
and I sang " Ben Bolt," and what do you think he said ?
Why, he said Madame Alboni couldn't go nearly so high
or so low as I did, and that her voice wasn't half so big.
He gave me his word of honour. He said I breathed as
natural and straight as a baby, and all I want is to get
my voice a little more under control. That's what *he*
said.'

' Qu'est-ce qu'elle dit ? ' asked Svengali. And she
said it all over again to him in French—quite French
French—of the most colloquial kind. Her accent was
not that of the Comédie Française, nor yet that of the
Faubourg St. Germain, nor yet that of the shop, or the
pavement. It was quaint and expressive—' funny without being vulgar.'

' Barpleu ! he was right, Litolff,' said Svengali. ' I

assure you, matemoiselle, that I have never heard a voice that can equal yours ; you have a talent quite exceptional.'

She blushed with pleasure, and the others thought him a 'beastly cad' for poking fun at the poor girl in such a way. And they thought Monsieur Litolff another.

She then got up and shook the crumbs off her coat, and slipped her feet into Durien's slippers, saying, in English : 'Well, I've got to go back. Life ain't all beer and skittles, and more's the pity ; but what's the odds, so long as you're happy ? '

On her way out she stopped before Taffy's picture—a chiffonnier with his lantern, bending over a dust-heap. For Taffy was, or thought himself, a passionate realist in those days. He has changed, and now paints nothing but King Arthurs and Guineveres and Lancelots and Elaines, and floating Ladies of Shalott.

'That chiffonnier's basket isn't hitched high enough,' she remarked. 'How could he tap his pick against the rim and make the rag fall into it if it's hitched only half-way up his back? And he's got the wrong sabots, and the wrong lantern ; it's *all* wrong.'

'Dear me ! ' said Taffy, turning very red ; 'you seem to know a lot about it. It's a pity you don't paint, yourself.'

'Ah! now you're cross ! ' said Miss O'Ferrall. 'Oh, maïe aïe ! '

She went to the door and paused, looking round benignly. 'What nice teeth you've all three got ! That's because your Englishmen, I suppose, and clean them twice a day. I do too. Trilby O'Ferrall, that's my

name, 48 Rue des Pousse-Cailloux !—pose pour l'ensemble,
quand ça l'amuse ! va-t-en ville, et fait tout ce qui concerne
son état ! Don't forget. Thanks all, and good-bye.'

' En v'là une orichinale,' said Svengali.

' I think she's lovely,' said Little Billee, the young and
tender. ' Oh heavens, what angel's feet ! It makes me
sick to think she sits for the figure. I'm sure she's quite
a lady.'

And in five minutes or so, with the point of an old
compass, he scratched in white on the dark red wall a
three-quarter profile outline of Trilby's left foot, which
was perhaps the more perfect poem of the two.

Slight as it was, this little piece of impromptu etching,
in its sense of beauty, in its quick seizing of a peculiar
individuality, its subtle rendering of a strongly-received
impression, was already the work of a master. It was
Trilby's foot and nobody else's, nor could have been, and
nobody else but Little Billee could have drawn it in just
that inspired way.

' Qu'est-ce que c'est, " Ben Bolt " ? ' inquired Gecko.

Upon which Little Billee was made by Taffy to sit
down to the piano and sing it. He sang it very nicely
with his pleasant little throaty English barytone.

It was solely in order that Little Billee should have
opportunities of practising this graceful accomplishment
of his, for his own and his friends' delectation, that the
piano had been sent over from London, at great cost to
Taffy and the Laird. It had belonged to Taffy's mother,
who was dead.

Before he had finished the second verse, Svengali
exclaimed : ' Mais c'est tout-à-fait chentil ! Allons,
Gecko, chouez-nous ça ! '

TRILBY'S LEFT FOOT

And he put his big hands on the piano, over Little Billee's, pushed him off the music-stool with his great gaunt body, and, sitting on it himself, he played a masterly prelude. It was impressive to hear the complicated richness and volume of the sounds he evoked after Little Billee's gentle ' tink-a-tink.'

And Gecko, cuddling lovingly his violin and closing his upturned eyes, played that simple melody as it had probably never been played before—such passion, such pathos, such a tone!—and they turned it and twisted it, and went from one key to another, playing into each other's hands, Svengali taking the lead ; and fugued and canoned and counterpointed and battledored and shuttle-cocked it, high and low, soft and loud, in minor, in pizzicato, and in sordino—adagio, andante, allegretto, scherzo—and exhausted all its possibilities of beauty ; till their susceptible audience of three was all but crazed with delight and wonder ; and the masterful Ben Bolt, and his over-tender Alice, and his too submissive friend, and his old schoolmaster so kind and so true, and his long-dead schoolmates, and the rustic porch and the mill, and the slab of granite so gray,

> ' And the dear little nook
> By the clear running brook,'

were all magnified into a strange, almost holy poetic dignity and splendour quite undreamed of by whoever wrote the words and music of that unsophisticated little song, which has touched so many simple British hearts that don't know any better—and among them, once, that of the present scribe—long, long ago !

'Sacrepleu! il choue pien, le Checko, hein ? ' said Svengali, when they had brought this wonderful double improvisation to a climax and a close. 'C'est mon élèfe! che le fais chanter sur son fiolon, c'est comme si c'était *moi* qui chantais! ach! si ch'afais pour teux sous de voix, che serais le bremier chanteur du monte! I cannot sing!' he continued. (I will translate him into English, without attempting to translate his accent, which is a mere matter of judiciously transposing p's and b's, and t's and d's, and f's and v's, and g's and k's, and turning the soft French j into sch, and a pretty language into an ugly one.)

'I cannot sing myself, I cannot play the violin, but I can teach—hein, Gecko? And I have a pupil—hein, Gecko?—la betite Honorine;' and here he leered all round with a leer that was not engaging. 'The world shall hear of la betite Honorine some day—hein, Gecko? Listen all—this is how I teach la betite Honorine! Gecko, play me a little accompaniment in pizzicato.'

And he pulled out of his pocket a kind of little flexible flageolet (of his own invention, it seems), which he screwed together and put to his lips, and on this humble instrument he played 'Ben Bolt,' while Gecko accompanied him, using his fiddle as a guitar, his adoring eyes fixed in reverence on his master.

And it would be impossible to render in any words the deftness, the distinction, the grace, power, pathos, and passion with which this truly phenomenal artist executed the poor old twopenny tune on his elastic penny whistle —for it was little more—such thrilling, vibrating, piercing tenderness, now loud and full, a shrill scream of anguish, now soft as a whisper, a mere melodic breath, more human almost than the human voice itself, a perfection unattainable even by Gecko, a master, on an instrument which is the acknowledged king of all!

THE FLEXIBLE FLAGEOLET

So that the tear, which had been so close to the brink
of Little Billee's eye while Gecko was playing, now rose
and trembled under his eyelid and spilled itself down his
nose ; and he had to dissemble and surreptitiously mop
it up with his little finger as he leaned his chin on his
hand, and cough a little husky, unnatural cough—*pour se
donner une contenance !*

He had never heard such music as this, never dreamed
such music was possible. He was conscious, while it
lasted, that he saw deeper into the beauty, the sadness of
things, the very heart of them, and their pathetic evanescence, as with a new, inner eye—even into eternity
itself, beyond the veil—a vague cosmic vision that faded
when the music was over, but left an unfading reminiscence
of its having been, and a passionate desire to express the
like some day through the plastic medium of his own
beautiful art.

When Svengali ended, he leered again on his dumb-
struck audience, and said : 'That is how I teach la betite
Honorine to sing ; that is how I teach Gecko to play ;
that is how I teach " *il bel canto*" ! It was lost, the *bel
canto*—but I found it, in a dream—I, and nobody else—
I—Svengali—I—I—*I !* But that is enough of music ;
let us play at something else—let us play at this !' he
cried, jumping up and seizing a foil and bending it against
the wall. . . . 'Come along, Little Pillee, and I will show
you something more you don't know. . . .'

So Little Billee took off coat and waistcoat, donned
mask and glove and fencing-shoes, and they had an
'assault of arms,' as it is nobly called in French, and in
which poor Little Billee came off very badly. The
German Pole fenced wildly, but well.

Then it was the Laird's turn, and he came off badly too; so then Taffy took up the foil, and redeemed the honour of Great Britain, as became a British hussar and a Man of Blood. For Taffy, by long and assiduous practice in the best school in Paris (and also by virtue of his native aptitudes), was a match for any *maître d'armes* in the whole French army, and Svengali got 'what for.'

And when it was time to give up play and settle down to work, others dropped in—French, English, Swiss, German, American, Greek; curtains were drawn and shutters opened; the studio was flooded with light—and the afternoon was healthily spent in athletic and gymnastic exercises till dinner-time.

But Little Billee, who had had enough of fencing and gymnastics for the day, amused himself by filling up with black and white and red-chalk strokes the outline of Trilby's foot on the wall, lest he should forget his fresh vision of it, which was still to him as the thing itself—an absolute reality, born of a mere glance, a mere chance—a happy caprice!

Durien came in and looked over his shoulder, and exclaimed: 'Tiens! le pied de Trilby! vous avez fait ça d'après nature?'

'Nong!'

'De mémoire, alors?'

'Wee!'

'Je vous en fais mon compliment! Vous avez eu la main heureuse. Je voudrais bien avoir fait ça, moi! C'est un petit chef-d'œuvre que vous avez fait là—tout bonnement, mon cher! Mais vous élaborez trop. De grâce, n'y touchez plus!'

And Little Billee was pleased, and touched it no

more; for Durien was a great sculptor and sincerity itself.

And then—well, I happen to forget what sort of day this particular day turned into at about six of the clock.

If it was decently fine, the most of them went off to dine at the Restaurant de la Couronne, kept by the Père Trin (in the Rue de Monsieur), who gave you of his best to eat and drink for twenty sols Parisis, or one franc in the coin of the empire. Good distending soups, omelets that were only too savoury, lentils, red and white beans, meat so dressed and sauced and seasoned that you didn't know whether it was beef or mutton—flesh, fowl, or good red herring—or even bad, for that matter—nor very greatly cared.

And just the same lettuce, radishes, and cheese of Gruyère or Brie as you got at the Trois Frères Provençaux (but not the same butter!). And to wash it all down, generous wine in wooden *brocs*—that stained a lovely æsthetic blue everything it was spilled over.

And you hobnobbed with models, male and female, students of law and medicine, painters and sculptors, workmen and *blanchisseuses* and grisettes, and found them very good company, and most improving to your French, if your French was of the usual British kind, and even to some of your manners, if these were very British indeed. And the evening was innocently wound up with billiards, cards, or dominoes at the Café du Luxembourg opposite; or at the Théâtre du Luxembourg, in the Rue de Madame, to see funny farces with screamingly droll Englishmen in them; or, still better, at the Jardin Bullier (la Closerie des Lilas), to see the students dance the cancan, or try and dance it yourself, which is not so easy as it seems ; or, best of all, at the Théâtre de l'Odéon, to see some piece of the classical *répertoire.*

Or, if it were not only fine, but a Saturday afternoon into the bargain, the Laird would put on a necktie and a few other necessary things, and the three friends would walk arm-in-arm to Taffy's hotel in the Rue de Seine, and wait outside till he had made himself as presentable as the Laird, which did not take very long. And then

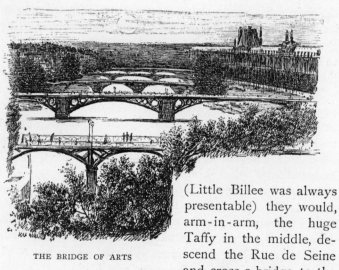

(Little Billee was always presentable) they would, arm-in-arm, the huge Taffy in the middle, descend the Rue de Seine and cross a bridge to the

THE BRIDGE OF ARTS

Cité, and have a look in at the Morgue. Then back again to the quays on the *rive gauche* by the Pont Neuf, to wend their way westward ; now on one side to look at the print and picture shops and the *magasins* of bric-à-brac, and haply sometimes buy thereof, now on the other

D

to finger and cheapen the second-hand books for sale on the parapet, and even pick up one or two utterly unwanted bargains, never to be read or opened again.

When they reached the Pont des Arts they would cross it, stopping in the middle to look up the river towards the old Cité and Notre Dame, eastward, and dream unutterable things, and try to utter them. Then, turning westward, they would gaze at the glowing sky and all it glowed upon—the corner of the Tuileries and the Louvre, the many bridges, the Chamber of Deputies, the golden river narrowing its perspective and broadening its bed as it went flowing and winding on its way between Passy and Grenelle to St. Cloud, to Rouen, to the Havre, to England perhaps—where *they* didn't want to be just then ; and they would try and express themselves to the effect that life was uncommonly well worth living in that particular city at that particular time of the day and year and century, at that particular epoch of their own mortal and uncertain lives.

Then, still arm-in-arm and chatting gaily, across the courtyard of the Louvre, through gilded gates well guarded by reckless imperial Zouaves, up the arcaded Rue de Rivoli as far as the Rue Castiglione, where they would stare with greedy eyes at the window of the great corner pastry-cook, and marvel at the beautiful assortment of bonbons, *pralines, dragées, marrons glacés*—saccharine, crystalline substances of all kinds and colours, as charming to look at as an illumination ; precious stones, delicately-frosted sweets, pearls and diamonds so arranged as to melt in the mouth ; especially, at this particular time of the year, the monstrous Easter-egg, of enchanting hue, enshrined like costly jewels in caskets of satin and gold; and the Laird, who was well read in his English classics and liked to show it, would opine that 'they managed these things better in France.'

Then across the street by a great gate into the Allée des Feuillants, and up to the Place de la Concorde—to gaze, but quite without base envy, at the smart people coming back from the Bois de Boulogne. For even in Paris 'carriage people' have a way of looking bored, of taking their pleasure sadly, of having nothing to say to each other, as though the vibration of so many wheels all rolling home the same way every afternoon had hypnotised them into silence, idiocy, and melancholia.

And our three musketeers of the brush would speculate on the vanity of wealth and rank and fashion; on the satiety that follows in the wake of self-indulgence and overtakes it; on the weariness of the pleasures that become a toil—as if they knew all about it, had found it all out for themselves, and nobody else had ever found it out before!

Then they found out something else—namely, that the sting of healthy appetite was becoming intolerable; so they would betake themselves to an English eating-house in the Rue de la Madeleine (on the left-hand side near the top), where they would renovate their strength and their patriotism on British beef and beer, and household bread, and bracing, biting, stinging yellow mustard, and heroic horseradish, and noble apple-pie, and Cheshire cheese; and get through as much of these in an hour or so as they could for talking, talking, talking; such happy talk! as full of sanguine hope and enthusiasm, of cock-sure commendation or condemnation of all painters, dead or alive, of modest but firm belief in themselves and each other, as a Paris Easter-egg is full of sweets and pleasantness (for the young).

And then a stroll on the crowded, well-lighted boulevards, and a bock at the café there, at a little three-legged marble table right out on the genial asphalt side pavement, still talking nineteen to the dozen.

Then home by dark, old, silent streets and some deserted bridge to their beloved Latin Quarter, the Morgue gleaming cold and still and fatal in the pale lamplight, and Notre Dame pricking up its watchful twin towers, which have looked down for so many centuries on so many happy, sanguine, expansive youths walking arm-in-arm by twos and threes, and for ever talking, talking, talking. . . .

The Laird and Little Billee would see Taffy safe to the door of his *hôtel garni* in the Rue de Seine, where they would find much to say to each other before they said good-night—so much that Taffy and Little Billee would see the Laird safe to *his* door, in the Place St. Anatole des Arts. And then a discussion would arise between Taffy and the Laird on the immortality of the soul, let us say, or the exact meaning of the word 'gentleman,' or the relative merits of Dickens and Thackeray, or some such recondite and quite unhackneyed theme, and Taffy and the Laird would escort Little Billee to *his* door, in the Place de l'Odéon, and he would re-escort them both back again, and so on till any hour you please.

Or again, if it rained, and Paris through the studio window loomed lead-coloured, with its shiny slate roofs under skies that were ashen and sober, and the wild west

"THREE MUSKETEERS OF THE BRUSH"

wind made woeful music among the chimney-pots, and little gray waves ran up the river the wrong way, and the Morgue looked chill and dark and wet, and almost uninviting (even to three healthy-minded young Britons), they would resolve to dine and spend a happy evening at home.

Little Billee, taking with him three francs (or even four), would dive into back streets and buy a yard or so of crusty new bread, well burned on the flat side, a fillet of beef, a litre of wine, potatoes and onions, butter, a little cylindrical cheese called 'bondon de Neufchâtel,' tender curly lettuce, with chervil, parsley, spring onions, and other fine herbs, and a pod of garlic, which would be rubbed on a crust of bread to flavour things with.

Taffy would lay the cloth English-wise, and also make the salad, for which, like everybody else I ever met, he had a special receipt of his own (putting in the oil first and the vinegar after); and indeed his salads were quite as good as everybody else's.

The Laird, bending over the stove, would cook the onions and beef into a savoury Scotch mess so cunningly that you could not taste the beef for the onions—nor always the onions for the garlic.

And they would dine far better than at le Père Trin's, far better than at the English Restaurant in the Rue de la Madeleine—better than anywhere else on earth !

And after dinner, what coffee, roasted and ground on the spot, what pipes and cigarettes of *caporal*, by the light of the three shaded lamps, while the rain beat against the big north window, and the wind went howling round the quaint old mediæval tower at the corner of the Rue

Vieille des Trois Mauvais Ladres (the old street of the three
bad lepers), and the damp logs hissed and crackled in the
stove!

What jolly talk into the small hours! Thackeray and
Dickens again, and Tenny-
son and Byron (who was
'not deed yet' in those
days); and Titian and
Velasquez, and young Millais
and Holman Hunt (just out);
and Monsieur Ingres and
Monsieur Delacroix, and
Balzac and Stendahl and
George Sand; and the good
Dumas! and Edgar Allan
Poe; and the glory that
was Greece and the grandeur
that was Rome. . . .

Good, honest, innocent,
artless prattle—not of the
wisest, perhaps, nor redolent
of the very highest culture
(which, by the way, can mar
as well as make), nor leading to any very practical
result; but quite pathetically
sweet from the sincerity and
fervour of its convictions, a
profound belief in their im-

TAFFY MAKES THE SALAD

portance, and a proud trust in their life-long immutability.

Oh, happy days and happy nights, sacred to art and
friendship! oh, happy times of careless impecuniosity, and

youth and hope and health and strength and freedom—
with all Paris for a playground, and its dear old un-
regenerate Latin Quarter for a workshop and a home !

And, up to then, no kill-joy complications of love !

No, decidedly no !   Little Billee had never known such
happiness as this—never even dreamed of its possibility.

A day or two after this, our opening day, but in the
afternoon, when the fencing and boxing had begun and
the trapeze was in full swing, Trilby's ' Milk below!' was
sounded at the door, and she appeared—clothed this time
and in her right mind, as it seemed : a tall, straight,
flat-backed, square-shouldered, deep-chested, full-bosomed
young grisette, in a snowy frilled cap, a neat black gown
and white apron, pretty faded, well-darned brown stockings, and well-worn, soft, gray, square-toed slippers of
list, without heels and originally shapeless ; but which her
feet, uncompromising and inexorable as boot-trees, had
ennobled into everlasting classic shapeliness, and stamped
with an unforgettable individuality, as does a beautiful
hand its well-worn glove—a fact Little Billee was not
slow to perceive, with a curious conscious thrill that was
only half æsthetic.

Then he looked into her freckled face, and met the
kind and tender mirthfulness of her gaze and the plucky
frankness of her fine wide smile with a thrill that was not
æsthetic at all (nor the reverse), but all of the heart.   And
in one of his quick flashes of intuitive insight he divined
far down beneath the shining surface of those eyes
(which seemed for a moment to reflect only a little image
of himself against the sky beyond the big north window)
a well of sweetness ; and floating somewhere in the

"THE GLORY THAT WAS GREECE"

midst of it the very heart of compassion, generosity, and
warm sisterly love ; and under that—alas ! at the bottom
of all—a thin slimy layer of sorrow and shame. And
just as long as it takes for a tear to rise and gather and
choke itself back again, this sudden revelation shook his
nervous little frame with a pang of pity and the knightly
wish to help. But he had no time to indulge in such soft
emotions. Trilby was met on her entrance by friendly
greetings on all sides.

'Tiens ! c'est la grande Trilby !' exclaimed Jules Guinot
through his fencing-mask. 'Comment ! t'es déjà debout
après hier soir ? Avons-nous assez rigolé chez Mathieu,
hein ? Crénom d'un nom, quelle noce ! V'là une
crémaillère qui peut se vanter d'être diantrement bien
pendue, j'espère ! Et la petite santé, c' matin ? '

'Hé, hé ! mon vieux,' answered Trilby. 'Ça boulotte,
apparemment ! Et toi ? et Victorine ? Comment qu'a s'
porte à c't'heure ? Elle avait un fier coup d'chasselas !
c'est-y jobard, hein ? de s' fich 'paf comme ça d'vant l'
monde ! Tiens, v'là, Gontran ! ça marche-t-y, Gontran,
Zouzou d' mon cœur ? '

'Comme sur des roulettes, ma biche !' said Gontran, *alias*
l'Zouzou—a corporal in the Zouaves. 'Mais tu t'es donc
mise chiffonnière, à présent ? T'as fait banque-route ? '

(For Trilby had a chiffonnier's basket strapped on her
back, and carried a pick and lantern.)

'Mais-z-oui, mon bon !' she said. 'Dame ! pas d'
veine hier soir ! t'as bien vu ! Dans la dêche jusqu'aux
omoplates, mon pauv' caporal-sous-off ! nom d'un canon
—faut bien vivre, s' pas ? '

Little Billee's heart-sluices had closed during this
interchange of courtesies. He felt it to be of a very

slangy kind, because he couldn't understand a word of it, and he hated slang. All he could make out was the free use of the *tu* and the *toi*, and he knew enough French to know that this implied a great familiarity, which he misunderstood.

So that Jules Guinot's polite inquiries whether Trilby were none the worse after Mathieu's house-warming (which was so jolly), Trilby's kind solicitude about the health of Victorine, who had very foolishly taken a drop too much on that occasion, Trilby's mock regrets that her own bad luck at cards had made it necessary that she should retrieve her fallen fortunes by rag-picking— all these innocent, playful little amenities (which I have tried to write down just as they were spoken) were couched in a language that was as Greek to him—and he felt out of it, jealous and indignant.

'Good-afternoon to you, Mr. Taffy,' said Trilby, in English. 'I've brought you these objects of art and virtu to make the peace with you. They're the real thing, you know. I borrowed 'em from le père Martin, chiffonnier en gros et en détail, grand officier de la Légion d'Honneur, membre de l'Institut et cetera, treize bis Rue du Puits d'Amour, rez-de-chaussée au fond de la cour à gauche, vis-à-vis le mont-de-piété! He's one of my intimate friends, and——'

'You don't mean to say you're the intimate friend of a *rag-picker?*' exclaimed the good Taffy.

'Oh yes! Pourquoi pas? I never brag; besides, there ain't any beastly pride about le père Martin,' said Trilby, with a wink. 'You'd soon find that out if *you* were an intimate friend of his. This is how it's put on. Do you see? If *you*'ll put it on I'll fasten it for you, and show

you how to hold the lantern and handle the pick. You
may come to it yourself some day, you know. Il ne faut
jurer de rien! Père Martin will pose for you in person,
if you like. He's generally disengaged in the afternoon.
He's poor but honest, you know, and very nice and clean ;
quite the gentleman. He likes artists, especially English
—they pay. His wife sells bric-à-brac and old masters :
Rembrandts from two francs fifty upwards. They've got
a little grandson—a love of a child. I'm his godmother.
You know French, I suppose ?'

'Oh yes,' said Taffy, much abashed. 'I'm very much
obliged to you—very much indeed—a—I—a——'

'Y a pas d' quoi!' said Trilby, divesting herself of
her basket and putting it, with the pick and lantern, in a
corner. 'Et maintenant, le temps d'absorber une fine de
fin sec [a cigarette] et je m' la brise [I'm off]. On
m'attend à l'Ambassade d'Autriche. Et puis zut!
Allez toujours, mes enfants. En avant la boxe !'

She sat herself down cross-legged on the model-
throne, and made herself a cigarette, and watched the
fencing and boxing. Little Billee brought her a chair,
which she refused ; so he sat down on it himself by her
side, and talked to her, just as he would have talked to
any young lady at home—about the weather, about
Verdi's new opera (which she had never heard), the
impressiveness of Notre Dame, and Victor Hugo's
beautiful romance (which she had never read), the
mysterious charm of Leonardo da Vinci's Lisa Gioconda's
smile (which she had never seen)—by all of which she
was no doubt rather tickled and a little embarrassed,
perhaps also a little touched.

Taffy brought her a cup of coffee, and conversed with

her in polite formal French very well and carefully pronounced ; and the Laird tried to do likewise. *His* French was of that honest English kind that breaks up the stiffness of even an English party ; and his jolly manners were such as to put an end to all shyness and constraint, and make self-consciousness impossible.

Others dropped in from neighbouring studios—the usual cosmopolite crew. It was a perpetual come-and-go in this particular studio between four and six in the afternoon.

There were ladies too, *en cheveux*, in caps and bonnets, some of whom knew Trilby, and thee'd and thou'd with familiar and friendly affection, while others mademoiselle'd her with distant politeness, and were mademoiselle'd and madame'd back again. 'Absolument comme à l'Ambassade d'Autriche,' as Trilby observed to the Laird, with a British wink that was by no means ambassadorial.

Then Svengali came and made some of his grandest music, which was as completely thrown away on Trilby as fireworks on a blind beggar, for all she held her tongue so piously.

Fencing and boxing and trapezing seemed to be more in her line ; and indeed, to a tone-deaf person, Taffy lunging his full spread with a foil, in all the splendour of his long, lithe, youthful strength, was a far gainlier sight than Svengali at the keyboard flashing his languid bold eyes with a sickly smile from one listener to another, as if to say : ' N'est-ce pas que che suis peau ? N'est-ce pas que ch'ai tu chénie ? N'est-ce pas que che suis suplime, enfin ? '

Then enter Durien the sculptor, who had been presented with a *baignoire* at the Porte St. Martin to see

La Dame aux Camélias, and he invited Trilby and another lady to dine with him *au cabaret* and share his box.

So Trilby didn't go to the Austrian embassy after all, as the Laird observed to Little Billee, with such a good imitation of her wink that Little Billee was bound to laugh.

But Little Billee was not inclined for fun ; a dulness, a sense of disenchantment, had come over him ; as he expressed it to himself, with pathetic self-pity :

> ' A feeling of sadness and longing
> That is not akin to pain,
> And resembles sorrow only
> As the mist resembles the rain.'

And the sadness, if he had known, was that all beautiful young women with kind sweet faces and noble figures and goddess-like extremities should not be good and pure as they were beautiful ; and the longing was a longing that Trilby could be turned into a young lady— say the vicar's daughter in a little Devonshire village— his sister's friend and co-teacher at the Sunday school, a simple, pure, and pious maiden of gentle birth.

For he adored piety in woman, although he was not pious by any means. His inarticulate, intuitive perceptions were not of form and colour secrets only, but strove to pierce the veil of deeper mysteries in impetuous and dogmatic boyish scorn of all received interpretations. For he flattered himself that he possessed the philosophical and scientific mind, and piqued himself on thinking clearly, and was intolerant of human inconsistency.

That small reserve portion of his ever-active brain which should have lain fallow while the rest of it was at work or play, perpetually plagued itself about the mysteries of life and death, and was for ever propounding unanswerable arguments against the Christian belief, through a kind of inverted sympathy with the believer. Fortunately for his friends, Little Billee was both shy and discreet, and very tender of other people's feelings ; so he kept all his immature juvenile agnosticism to himself.

To atone for such ungainly strong-mindedness in one so young and tender, he was the slave of many little traditional observances which have no very solid foundation in either science or philosophy. For instance, he wouldn't walk under a ladder for worlds, nor sit down thirteen to dinner, nor have his hair cut on a Friday, and was quite upset if he happened to see the new moon through glass. And he believed in lucky and unlucky numbers, and dearly loved the sights and scents and sounds of high mass in some dim old French cathedral, and found them secretly comforting.

Let us hope that he sometimes laughed at himself, if only in his sleeve !

And with all his keenness of insight into life he had a well-brought up, middle-class young Englishman's belief in the infallible efficacy of gentle birth—for gentle he considered his own and Taffy's and the Laird's, and that of most of the good people he had lived among in England—all people, in short, whose two parents and four grandparents had received a liberal education and belonged to the professional class. And with this belief he combined (or thought he did) a proper democratic scorn for bloated dukes and lords, and even poor inoffensive baronets, and all the landed gentry—everybody who was born an inch higher up than himself.

It is a fairly good middle-class social creed, if you can

only stick to it through life in despite of life's experience. It fosters independence and self-respect, and not a few stodgy practical virtues as well. At all events, it keeps you out of bad company, which is to be found both above and below. *In medio tutissimus ibis !*

And all this melancholy preoccupation, on Little Billee's part, from the momentary gleam and dazzle of a pair of over-perfect feet in an over-æsthetic eye, too much enamoured of mere form !

Reversing the usual process, he had idealised from the base upward !

Many of us, older and wiser than Little Billee, have seen in lovely female shapes the outer garment of a lovely female soul. The instinct which guides us to do this is, perhaps, a right one, more often than not. But more often than not, also, lovely female shapes are terrible complicators of the difficulties and dangers of this earthly life, especially for their owner, and more especially if she be a humble daughter of the people, poor and ignorant, of a yielding nature, too quick to love and trust. This is all so true as to be trite—so trite as to be a common platitude !

A modern teller of tales, most widely (and most justly) popular, tells us of Californian heroes and heroines who, like Lord Byron's Corsair, were linked with one virtue and a thousand crimes. And so dexterously does he weave his story that the Young Person may read it and learn nothing but good.

My poor heroine was the converse of these engaging criminals ; she had all the virtues but one ; but the virtue she lacked (the very one of all that plays the title-rôle, and gives its generic name to all the rest of that goodly company) was of such a kind that I have found it impossible so to tell her history as to make it quite fit and proper reading for the ubiquitous young person so dear to us all.

Most deeply to my regret. For I had fondly hoped it might one day be said of me that whatever my other literary shortcomings might be, I at least had never penned a line which a pure-minded young British mother might not read aloud to her little blue-eyed babe as it lies sucking its little bottle in its little bassinette.

Fate has willed it otherwise.

Would indeed that I could duly express poor Trilby's one shortcoming in some not too familiar medium—in Latin or Greek, let us say—lest the Young Person (in this ubiquitousness of hers, for which Heaven be praised) should happen to pry into these pages when her mother is looking another way.

Latin and Greek are languages the Young Person should not be taught to understand—seeing that they are highly improper languages, deservedly dead—in which pagan bards who should have known better have sung the filthy loves of their gods and goddesses.

But at least am I scholar enough to enter one little Latin plea on Trilby's behalf—the shortest, best, and most beautiful plea I can think of. It was once used in extenuation and condonation of the frailties of another poor weak woman, presumably beautiful, and a far worse offender than Trilby, but who, like Trilby, repented of her ways, and was most justly forgiven—

'Quia multum amavit!'

Whether it be an aggravation of her misdeeds or an

E

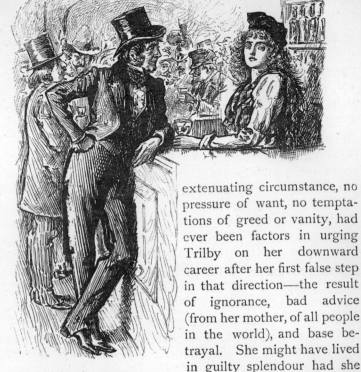

TRILBY'S FOREBEARS

extenuating circumstance, no pressure of want, no temptations of greed or vanity, had ever been factors in urging Trilby on her downward career after her first false step in that direction—the result of ignorance, bad advice (from her mother, of all people in the world), and base betrayal. She might have lived in guilty splendour had she chosen, but her wants were few. She had no vanity, and her tastes were of the simplest, and she earned enough to gratify them all, and to spare.

So she followed love for love's sake only, now and then, as she would have followed art if she had been a man—capriciously, desultorily, more in a frolicsome spirit of *camaraderie* than anything else. Like an amateur, in short—a distinguished amateur who is too proud to sell his pictures, but willingly gives one away now and then to some highly-valued and much-admiring friend.

Sheer gaiety of heart and genial good-fellowship, the difficulty of saying nay to earnest pleading. She was *bonne camarade et bonne fille* before everything. Though her heart was not large enough to harbour more than one light love at a time (even in that Latin Quarter of genially capacious hearts), it had room for many warm friendships; and she was the warmest, most helpful, and most compassionate of friends, far more serious and faithful in friendship than in love.

Indeed, she might almost be said to possess a virginal heart, so little did she know of love's heartaches and raptures and torments and clingings and jealousies.

With her it was lightly come and lightly go, and never come back again; as one or two, or perhaps three, picturesque Bohemians of the brush or chisel had found, at some cost to their vanity and self-esteem; perhaps even to a deeper feeling—who knows?

Trilby's father, as she had said, had been a gentleman, the son of a famous Dublin physician and friend of George the Fourth's. He had been a Fellow of his college, and had entered holy orders. He also had all the virtues but one; he was a drunkard, and began to drink quite early in life. He soon left the Church and became a classical tutor, and failed through this besetting sin of his, and fell into disgrace.

Then he went to Paris, and picked up a few English pupils there, and lost them, and earned a precarious livelihood from hand to mouth, anyhow, and sank from bad to worse.

And when his worst was about reached, he married the famous tartaned and tam-o'-shantered barmaid at the Montagnards Écossais, in the Rue du Paradis Poisson-

nière (a very fishy paradise indeed); she was a most
beautiful Highland lassie of low degree, and she
managed to support him, or helped him to support
himself, for ten or fifteen years. Trilby was born to
them, and was dragged up in some way—*à la grâce de
Dieu!*

Patrick O'Ferrall soon taught his wife to drown all
care and responsibility in his own simple way, and
opportunities for doing so were never lacking to her.

Then he died, and left a posthumous child—born ten
months after his death, alas! and whose birth cost its
mother her life.

Then Trilby became a *blanchisseuse de fin*, and in two
or three years came to grief through her trust in a friend
of her mother's. Then she became a model besides, and
was able to support her little brother, whom she dearly
loved.

At the time this story begins, this small waif and stray
was *en pension* with le père Martin, the rag-picker, and
his wife, the dealer in bric-à-brac and inexpensive old
masters. They were very good people, and had grown
fond of the child, who was beautiful to look at, and full
of pretty tricks and pluck and cleverness—a popular
favourite in the Rue du Puits d'Amour and its humble
neighbourhood.

Trilby, for some freak, always chose to speak of him
as her godson, and as the grandchild of le père et la mère
Martin, so that these good people had almost grown to
believe he really belonged to them.

And almost every one else believed that he was the
child of Trilby (in spite of her youth), and she was so
fond of him that she didn't mind in the least.

He might have had a worse home.

La mère Martin was pious, or pretended to be; le père Martin was the reverse. But they were equally good for their kind, and though coarse and ignorant and unscrupulous in many ways (as was natural enough), they were gifted in a very full measure with the saving graces of love and charity, especially he. And if people are to be judged by their works, this worthy pair are no doubt both equally well compensated by now for the trials and struggles of their sordid earthly life.

So much for Trilby's parentage.

And as she sat and wept at Madame Doche's impersonation of *La Dame aux Camélias* (with her hand in Durien's) she vaguely remembered, as in a waking dream, now the noble presence of Taffy as he towered cool and erect, foil in hand, gallantly waiting for his adversary to breathe, now the beautiful sensitive face of Little Billee and his deferential courtesy.

And during the *entr'actes* her heart went out in friendship to the jolly Scotch Laird of Cockpen, who came out now and then with such terrible French oaths and abominable expletives (and in the presence of ladies, too!), without the slightest notion of what they meant.

For the Laird had a quick ear, and a craving to be colloquial and idiomatic before everything else, and made many awkward and embarrassing mistakes.

It would be with him as though a polite Frenchman should say to a fair daughter of Albion, ' D——— my eyes, mees, your tea is getting ——— cold; let me tell that good old ——— of a Jules to bring you another cup.'

And so forth, till time and experience taught him better. It is perhaps well for him that his first experiments in conversational French were made in the unconventional circle of the Place St. Anatole des Arts.

PART SECOND

'Dieu ! qu'il fait bon la regarder,
    La gracieuse, bonne et belle !
    Pour les grands biens qui sont en elle
Chacun est prêt de la louer.'

NOBODY knew exactly how Svengali lived, and very few knew where (or why). He occupied a roomy dilapidated garret, *au sixième*, in the Rue Tire-Liard, with a truckle-bed and a pianoforte for furniture, and very little else.

He was poor, for in spite of his talent he had not yet made his mark in Paris. His manners may have been accountable for this. He would either fawn or bully, and could be grossly impertinent. He had a kind of cynical humour, which was more offensive than amusing, and always laughed at the wrong thing, at the wrong time, in the wrong place. And his laughter was always derisive and full of malice. And his egotism and conceit were not to be borne ; and then he was both tawdry and dirty in his person ; more greasily, mattedly unkempt than even a really successful pianist has any right to be even in the best society.

He was not a nice man, and there was no pathos in his poverty—a poverty that was not honourable, and need not have existed at all ; for he was constantly receiving supplies from his own people in Austria—his

old father and mother, his sisters, his cousins, and his
aunts, hard-working, frugal folk of whom he was the pride
and the darling.

He had but one virtue—his love of his art; or,
rather, his love of himself as a master of his art—*the*
master; for he despised, or affected to despise, all other
musicians, living or dead—even those whose work he
interpreted so divinely, and pitied them for not hearing
Svengali give utterance to their music, which of course
they could not utter themselves.

' Ils safent tous un peu toucher du biâno, mais pas
grand'chose ! '

He had been the best pianist of his time at the Con-
servatory in Leipsic; and, indeed, there was perhaps
some excuse for this overweening conceit, since he was
able to lend a quite peculiar individual charm of his own
to any music he played, except the highest and best of
all, in which he conspicuously failed.

He had to draw the line just above Chopin, where he
reached his highest level. It will not do to lend your
own quite peculiar individual charm to Handel and Bach
and Beethoven; and Chopin is not bad as a *pis-aller*.

He had ardently wished to sing, and had studied
hard to that end in Germany, in Italy, in France, with
the forlorn hope of evolving from some inner recess a
voice to sing with. But nature had been singularly
harsh to him in this one respect—inexorable. He was
absolutely without voice, beyond the harsh, hoarse, weak
raven's croak he used to speak with, and no method
availed to make one for him. But he grew to understand
the human voice as perhaps no one has understood it—
before or since.

So in his head he went for ever singing, singing, singing, as probably no human nightingale has ever yet been able to sing out loud for the glory and delight of his fellow-mortals; making unheard heavenly melody of the cheapest, trivialest tunes—tunes of the café concert, tunes of the nursery, the shop-parlour, the guard-room, the schoolroom, the pothouse, the slum. There was nothing so humble, so base even, but what his magic could transform it into the rarest beauty without altering a note. This seems impossible, I know. But if it didn't, where would the magic come in?

Whatever of heart or conscience—pity, love, tenderness, manliness, courage, reverence, charity—endowed him at his birth had been swallowed up by this one faculty, and nothing of them was left for the common uses of life. He poured them all into his little flexible flageolet.

Svengali playing Chopin on the pianoforte, even (or especially) Svengali playing 'Ben Bolt' on that penny whistle of his, was as one of the heavenly host.

Svengali walking up and down 'AS BAD AS THEY MAKE 'EM' the earth seeking whom he might cheat, betray, exploit, borrow money from, make brutal fun of, bully if he dared, cringe to if he must—man, woman, child, or dog—was about as bad as they make 'em.

To earn a few pence when he couldn't borrow them he played accompaniments at café concerts, and even then he gave offence; for in his contempt for the singer he would play too loud, and embroider his accompani-

ments with brilliant improvisations of his own, and lift
his hands on high and bring them down with a bang in
the sentimental parts, and shake his dirty mane and
shrug his shoulders, and smile and leer at the audience,
and do all he could to attract their attention to himself.
He also gave a few music lessons (not at ladies' schools,
let us hope), for which he was not well paid, presumably,
since he was always without a sou, always borrowing
money, that he never paid back, and exhausting the
pockets and the patience of one acquaintance after
another.

He had but two friends. There was Gecko, who
lived in a little garret close by in the Impasse des
Ramoneurs, and who was second violin in the orchestra
of the Gymnase, and shared his humble earnings with
his master, to whom, indeed, he owed his great talent,
not yet revealed to the world.

Svengali's other friend and pupil was (or rather had
been) the mysterious Honorine, of whose conquest he
was much given to boast, hinting that she was *une jeune
femme du monde.* This was not the case. Mademoiselle
Honorine Cahen (better known in the Quartier Latin as
Mimi la Salope) was a dirty, drabby little dolly-mop of a
Jewess, a model for the figure—a very humble person
indeed, socially.

She was, however, of a very lively disposition, and
had a charming voice, and a natural gift of singing so
sweetly that you forgot her accent, which was that of the
tout ce qu'il y a de plus canaille.

She used to sit at Carrel's, and during the pose she
would sing. When Little Billee first heard her he was
so fascinated that ' it made him sick to think she sat for

the figure'—an effect, by the way, that was always produced upon him by all specially attractive figure models of the gentler sex, for he had a reverence for woman. And before everything else, he had for the singing woman an absolute worship. He was especially thrall to the contralto—the deep low voice that breaks and changes in the middle and soars all at once into a magnified angelic boy treble. It pierced through his ears to his heart, and stirred his very vitals.

He had once heard Madame Alboni, and it had been an epoch in his life ; he would have been an easy prey to the sirens ! Even beauty paled before the lovely female voice singing in the middle of the note—the nightingale killed the bird of paradise.

I need hardly say that poor Mimi la Salope had not the voice of Madame Alboni, nor the art ; but it was a beautiful voice of its little kind, always in the very middle of the note, and her artless art had its quick seduction.

She sang little songs of Béranger's—' Grand'mère, parlez-nous de lui ! ' or ' T'en souviens-tu ? disait un capitaine—' or ' Enfants, c'est moi qui suis Lisette ! ' and such like pretty things, that almost brought the tears to Little Billee's easily-moistened eyes.

But soon she would sing little songs that were not by Béranger—little songs with slang words Little Billee hadn't French enough to understand ; but from the kind of laughter with which the points were received by the ' rapins ' in Carrel's studio he guessed these little songs were vile, though the touching little voice was as that of the seraphim still ; and he knew the pang of disenchantment and vicarious shame.

Svengali had heard her sing at the Brasserie des Porcherons in the Rue du Crapaud-volant, and had volunteered to teach her; and she went to see him in his garret, and he played to her, and leered and ogled, and flashed his bold, black, beady Jew's eyes into hers, and she straightway mentally prostrated herself in reverence and adoration before this dazzling specimen of her race.

So that her sordid, mercenary little gutter-draggled soul was filled with the sight and the sound of him, as of a lordly, godlike, shawm-playing, cymbal-banging hero and prophet of the Lord God of Israel—David and Saul in one!

And then he set himself to teach her—kindly and patiently at first, calling her sweet little pet names—his 'Rose of Sharon,' his 'pearl of Pabylon,' his 'cazelle-eyed liddle Cherusalem skylark'—and promised her that she should be the queen of the nightingales.

But before he could teach her anything he had to unteach her all she knew; her breathing, the production of her voice, its emission—everything was wrong. She worked indefatigably to please him, and soon succeeded in forgetting all the pretty little sympathetic tricks of voice and phrasing Mother Nature had taught her.

But though she had an exquisite ear she had no real musical intelligence—no intelligence of any kind except about sous and centimes; she was as stupid as a little downy owl, and her voice was just a light native warble, a throstle's pipe, all in the head and nose and throat (a voice he *didn't* understand, for once), a thing of mere youth and health and bloom and high spirits—like her beauty, such as it was—*beauté du diable, beauté damnée.*

"A VOICE HE DIDN'T UNDERSTAND"

She did her very best, and practised all she could in this new way, and sang herself hoarse : she scarcely ate or slept for practising. He grew harsh and impatient and coldly severe, and of course she loved him all the more ; and the more she loved him the more nervous she got and the worse she sang. Her voice cracked ; her ear became demoralised ; her attempts to vocalise grew almost as distressing as Trilby's. So that he lost his temper completely, and called her terrible names, and pinched and punched her with his big bony hands till she wept worse than Niobe, and borrowed money of her—five-franc pieces, even francs and demifrancs—which he never paid her back ; and browbeat and bullied and bully-ragged her till she went quite mad for love of him, and would have jumped out of his sixth-floor window to give him a moment's pleasure !

He did not ask her to do this—it never occurred to him, and would have given him no pleasure to speak of. But one fine Sabbath morning (a Saturday, of course) he took her by the shoulders and chucked her, neck and crop, out of his garret, with the threat that if she ever dared to show her face there again he would denounce her to the police—an awful threat to the likes of poor Mimi la Salope !

' For where did all those five-franc pieces come from— *hein ?*—with which she had tried to pay for all the singing lessons that had been thrown away upon her?   Not from merely sitting to painters—*hein ?* '

Thus the little gazelle-eyed Jerusalem skylark went back to her native streets again—a mere mud-lark of the Paris slums—her wings clipped, her spirit quenched and broken, and with no more singing left in her than a common or garden sparrow—not so much !

And so, no more of 'la betite Honorine!'

The morning after this adventure Svengali woke up in his garret with a tremendous longing to spend a happy day; for it was a Sunday, and a very fine one.

He made a long arm and reached his waistcoat and trousers off the floor, and emptied the contents of their pockets on to his tattered blanket; no silver, no gold, only a few sous and two-sou pieces, just enough to pay for a meagre *premier déjeuner !*

He had cleared out Gecko the day before, and spent the proceeds (ten francs, at least) in one night's riotous living— pleasures in which Gecko had had no share; and he could think of no one to borrow money from but Little Billee, Taffy, and the Laird, whom he had neglected and left untapped for days.

So he slipped into his clothes, and looked at himself in what remained of a little zinc mirror,

'AND SO, NO MORE'

and found that his forehead left little to be desired, but that his eyes and temples were decidedly grimy. Wherefore, he poured a little water out of a little jug into a little basin, and twisting the corner of his pocket-handkerchief round his dirty forefinger, he delicately dipped it, and removed the offending stains. His fingers, he thought, would do very well for another day or two as they were ; he ran them through his matted black mane, pushed it behind his ears, and gave it the twist he liked (and that was so much disliked by his English friends). Then he put on his *béret* and his velveteen cloak, and went forth into the sunny streets, with a sense of the fragrance and freedom and pleasantness of Sunday morning in Paris in the month of May.

He found Little Billee sitting in a zinc hip-bath, busy with soap and sponge ; and was so tickled and interested by the sight that he quite forgot for the moment what he had come for.

'Himmel ! Why the devil are you doing that ?' he asked, in his German-Hebrew-French.

'Doing *what ?*' asked Little Billee, in his French of Stratford-atte-Bowe.

'Sitting in water and playing with a cake of soap and a sponge !'

'Why, to try and get myself *clean*, I suppose !'

'Ach ! And how the devil did you get yourself *dirty*, then ?'

To this Little Billee found no immediate answer, and went on with his ablutions after the hissing, splashing, energetic fashion of Englishmen ; and Svengali laughed loud and long at the spectacle of a little Englishman trying to get himself clean—*tâchant de se nettoyer !*

When such cleanliness had been attained as was possible under the circumstances, Svengali begged for the loan of two hundred francs, and Little Billee gave him a five-franc piece.

Content with this, *faute de mieux*, the German asked

him when he would be trying to get himself clean again, as he would much like to come and see him do it.

'Demang mattang, à votre sairveece!' said Little Billee, with a courteous bow.

'*What!! Monday too!!* Gott in Himmel! you try to get yourself clean *every day?*'

And he laughed himself out of the room, out of the house, out of the Place de l'Odéon—all the way to the Rue de Seine, where dwelt the 'Man of Blood,' whom he meant to propitiate with the story of that original, Little Billee, trying to get himself clean—that he might borrow another five-franc piece, or perhaps two.

As the reader will no doubt anticipate, he found Taffy in his bath also, and fell to laughing with such convulsive laughter, such twistings, screwings, and doublings of himself up, such pointings of his dirty forefinger at the huge naked Briton, that Taffy was offended, and all but lost his temper.

'What the devil are you cackling at, sacred head of pig that you are? Do you want to be pitched out of that window into the Rue de Seine? You filthy black Hebrew sweep! Just you wait a bit; *I'll* wash your head for you!'

And Taffy jumped out of his bath, such a towering figure of righteous Herculean wrath that Svengali was appalled, and fled.

'Donnerwetter!' he exclaimed as he tumbled down the narrow staircase of the Hôtel de Seine; 'what for a thick head! what for a pigdog! what for a rotten, brutal, *verfluchter kerl* of an Englander!'

Then he paused for thought.

'Now will I go to that Scottish Englander, in the

F

'"TWO ENGLANDERS IN ONE DAY"'

Place St. Anatole des Arts, for that other five-franc piece. But first will I wait a little while till he has perhaps finished trying to get himself clean.'

So he breakfasted at the crémerie Souchet, in the Rue Clopin-Clopant, and, feeling quite safe again, he laughed and laughed till his very sides were sore.

Two Englanders in one day—as naked as your hand !— a big one and a little one, trying to get themselves clean !

He rather flattered himself he had scored off those two Englanders.

After all, he was right perhaps, from his point of view ; you can get as dirty in a week as in a lifetime, so what's the use of taking such a lot of trouble ? Besides, so long as you are clean enough to suit your kind, to be any cleaner would be priggish and pedantic, and get you disliked.

Just as Svengali was about to knock at the Laird's door, Trilby came downstairs from Durien's, very unlike herself. Her eyes were red with weeping, and there were great black rings round them ; she was pale under her freckles.

' Fous afcz du chacrin, matemoiselle ? ' asked he.

She told him that she had neuralgia in her eyes, a thing she was subject to ; that the pain was maddening, and generally lasted twenty-four hours.

' Perhaps I can cure you ; come in here with me.'

The Laird's ablutions (if he had indulged in any that morning) were evidently over for the day. He was breakfasting on a roll and butter, and coffee of his own brewing. He was deeply distressed at the sight of poor Trilby's sufferings, and offered whisky and coffee and gingernuts, which she would not touch.

Svengali told her to sit down on the divan, and sat opposite to her, and bade her look him well in the white of the eyes.

' Recartez-moi pien tans le planc tes yeux.'

Then he made little passes and counterpasses on her forehead and temples and down her cheek and neck. Soon her eyes closed and her face grew placid. After a while, a quarter of an hour perhaps, he asked her if she suffered still.

'Oh! presque plus du tout, monsieur—c'est le ciel.'

In a few minutes more he asked the Laird if he knew German.

'Just enough to understand,' said the Laird (who had spent a year in Düsseldorf), and Svengali said to him in German : 'See, she sleeps not, but she shall not open her eyes.   Ask her.'

'Are you asleep, Miss Trilby?' asked the Laird.

'No.'

'Then open your eyes and look at me.'

She strained to open her eyes, but could not, and said so.

Then Svengali said, again in German, 'She shall not open her mouth.   Ask her.'

'Why couldn't you open your eyes, Miss Trilby?'

She strained to open her mouth and speak, but in vain.

'She shall not rise from the divan.   Ask her.'

But Trilby was spellbound, and could not move.

'I will now set her free,' said Svengali.

And, lo! she got up and waved her arms, and cried, 'Vive la Prusse! me v'là guérie!' and in her gratitude she kissed Svengali's hand ; and he leered, and showed his big brown teeth and the yellow whites at the top of his big black eyes, and drew his breath with a hiss.

'Now I'll go to Durien's and sit.   How can I thank you, monsieur?   You have taken all my pain away.'

'Yes, matemoiselle.   I have got it myself; it is in my elbows.   But I love it, because it comes from you.   Every time you have pain you shall come to me, 12 Rue Tire-Liard, au sixième au-dessus de l'entresol, and I will cure you and take your pain myself——'

'Oh, you are too good!' and in her high spirits she

"'HIMMEL! THE ROOF OF YOUR MOUTH'"

turned round on her heel and uttered her portentous war-cry, 'Milk below!' The very rafters rang with it, and the piano gave out a solemn response.

'What is that you say, matemoiselle?'

'Oh, it's what the milkmen say in England.

'It is a wonderful cry, matemoiselle—*wunderschön!* It comes straight through the heart; it has its roots in the stomach, and blossoms into music on the lips like the voice of Madame Alboni—voce sulle labbre! It is good production—c'est un cri du cœur!'

Trilby blushed with pride and pleasure.

'Yes, matemoiselle! I only know one person in the whole world who can produce the voice so well as you! I give you my word of honour.'

'Who is it, monsieur—yourself?'

'Ach, no, matemoiselle; I have not that privilege. I have unfortunately no voice to produce. . . It is a waiter at the Café de la Rotonde, in the Palais Royal; when you call for coffee, he says "Boum!" in basso profondo. Tiefstimme—F moll below the line—it is phenomenal! It is like a cannon—a cannon also has very good production, matemoiselle. They pay him for it a thousand francs a year, because he brings many customers to the Café de la Rotonde, where the coffee isn't very good, although it costs three sous a cup dearer than at the Café Larsouille in the Rue Flamberge-au-Vent. When he dies they will search all France for another, and then all Germany, where the good big waiters come from—and the cannons—but they will not find him, and the Café de la Rotonde will be bankrupt —unless you will consent to take his place. Will you permit that I shall look into your mouth, matemoiselle?'

She opened her mouth wide, and he looked into it.

'Himmel! the roof of your mouth is like the dome of the Panthéon ; there is room in it for "toutes les gloires de la France," and a little to spare! The entrance to your throat is like the middle porch of St. Sulpice when the doors are open for the faithful on All Saints' Day ; and not one tooth is missing—thirty-two British teeth as white as milk and as big as knuckle-bones! and your little tongue is scooped out like the leaf of a pink peony, and the bridge of your nose is like the belly of a Stradivarius—what a sounding-board! and inside your beautiful big chest the lungs are made of leather! and your breath, it embalms—like the breath of a beautiful white heifer fed on the buttercups and daisies of the Vaterland! and you have a quick, soft, susceptible heart, a heart of gold, matemoiselle—all that sees itself in your face !

> ' " Votre cœur est un luth suspendu !
> Aussitôt qu'on le touche, il résonne. . . ."

What a pity you have not also the musical organisation !'

'Oh, but I *have*, monsieur ; you heard me sing "Ben Bolt," didn't you ? What makes you say that ?'

Svengali was confused for a moment. Then he said : 'When I play the "Rosemonde" of Schubert, matemoiselle, you look another way and smoke a cigarette. . . . You look at the big Taffy, at the Little Billee, at the pictures on the walls, or out of window, at the sky, the chimney-pots of Notre Dame de Paris ; you do not look at Svengali!—Svengali, who looks at you with all his eyes, and plays you the "Rosemonde" of Schubert !'

'Oh, maïe aïe !' exclaimed Trilby ; 'you *do* use lovely language !'

'But never mind, matemoisclle; when your pain arrives, then shall you come once more to Svengali, and he shall take it away from you, and keep it himself for a soufenir of you when you are gone. And when you have it no more, he shall play you the "Rosemonde" of Schubert, all alone for you; and then "Messieurs les étutiants, montez à la chaumière!" . . . because it is gayer! *And you shall see nothing, hear nothing, think of nothing but Svengali, Svengali, Svengali!*

Here he felt his peroration to be so happy and effective that he thought it well to go at once and make a good exit. So he bent over Trilby's shapely freckled hand and kissed it, and bowed himself out of the room, without even borrowing his five-franc piece.

'He's a rum 'un, ain't he?' said Trilby. 'He reminds me of a big hungry spider, and makes me feel like a fly! But he's cured my pain! he's cured my pain! Ah! you don't know what my pain is when it comes!'

'I wouldn't have much to do with him, all the same!' said the Laird. 'I'd sooner have any pain than have it cured in that unnatural way, and by such a man as that! He's a bad fellow, Svengali—I'm sure of it! He mesmerised you; that's what it is—mesmerism! I've often heard of it, but never seen it done before. They get you into their power, and just make you do any blessed thing they please—lie, murder, steal—anything! and kill yourself into the bargain when they've done with you! It's just too terrible to think of!'

So spake the Laird, earnestly, solemnly, surprised out of his usual self, and most painfully impressed—and his own impressiveness grew upon him and impressed him still more. He loomed quite prophetic.

Cold shivers went down Trilby's back as she listened. She had a singularly impressionable nature, as was shown by her quick and ready susceptibility to Svengali's hypnotic influence. And all that day, as she posed for Durien (to whom she did not mention her adventure), she was haunted by the memory of Svengali's big eyes and the touch of his soft, dirty finger-tips on her face; and her fear and her repulsion grew together.

And 'Svengali, Svengali, Svengali!' went ringing in her head and ears till it became an obsession, a dirge, a knell, an unendurable burden, almost as hard to bear as the pain in her eyes.

'*Svengali, Svengali, Svengali!*'

At last she asked Durien if he knew him.

'Parbleu! Si je connais Svengali!'

'Qu'est-ce que t'en penses?'

'Quand il sera mort, ça fera une fameuse crapule de moins!'

'CHEZ CARREL.'

Carrel's atelier (or painting school) was in the Rue Notre Dame des Potirons St. Michel, at the end of a large courtyard, where there were many large dirty windows facing north, and each window let the light of heaven into a large dirty studio.

The largest of these studios, and the dirtiest, was Carrel's, where some thirty or forty art students drew and painted from the nude model every day but Sunday from eight till twelve, and for two hours in the afternoon, except on Saturdays, when the afternoon was devoted to much-needed Augean sweepings and cleanings.

One week the model was male, the next female, and so on, alternating throughout the year.

A stove, a model-throne, stools, boxes, some fifty strongly-built low chairs with backs, a couple of score easels and many drawing-boards, completed the *mobilier*.

The bare walls were adorned with endless caricatures—*des charges*—in charcoal and white chalk ; and also the scrapings of many palettes—a polychromous decoration not unpleasing.

For the freedom of the studio and the use of the model each student paid ten francs a month to the *massier*, or senior student, the responsible bell-wether of the flock ; besides this, it was expected of you, on your entrance or initiation, that you should pay for your footing—your *bienvenue*—some thirty, forty, or fifty francs, to be spent on cakes and rum punch all round.

Every Friday Monsieur Carrel, a great artist, and also a stately, well-dressed, and most courteous gentleman (duly decorated with the red rosette of the Legion of Honour), came for two or three hours and went the round, spending a few minutes at each drawing-board or easel—ten or even twelve when the pupil was an industrious and promising one.

He did this for love, not money, and deserved all the reverence with which he inspired this somewhat irreverent and most unruly company, which was made up of all sorts.

Graybeards who had been drawing and painting there for thirty years and more, and remembered other masters than Carrel, and who could draw and paint a torso almost as well as Titian or Velasquez—almost, but not quite—and who could never do anything else, and were fixtures at Carrel's for life.

Younger men who in a year or two, or three or five, or ten or twenty, were bound to make their mark, and perhaps follow in the foot-

'"ÇA FERA UNE FAMEUSE CRAPULE DE MOINS"'

steps of the master; others as conspicuously singled out for failure and future mischance—for the hospital, the garret, the river, the Morgue, or, worse, the traveller's bag, the road, or even the paternal counter.

Irresponsible boys, mere *rapins*, all laugh and chaff and mischief—*blague et bagout Parisien;* little lords of misrule—wits, butts, bullies; the idle and industrious apprentice, the good and the bad, the clean and the dirty (especially the latter)—all more or less animated by a certain *esprit de corps,* and working very happily and genially together, on the whole, and always willing to help each other with sincere artistic counsel if it was

asked for seriously, though it was not always couched in
terms very flattering to one's self-love.

Before Little Billee became one of this band of
brothers he had been working for three or four years in a
London art school, drawing and painting from the life ;
he had also worked from the antique in the British
Museum—so that he was no novice.

As he made his début at Carrel's one Monday morning he felt somewhat shy and ill at ease.   He had studied
French most earnestly at home in England, and could
read it pretty well, and even write it and speak it after a
fashion ; but he spoke it with much difficulty, and found
studio French a different language altogether from the
formal and polite language he had been at such pains
to acquire.   Ollendorff does not cater for the Quartier
Latin.   Acting on Taffy's advice—for Taffy had
worked under Carrel—Little Billee handed sixty francs
to the *massier* for his *bienvenue*—a lordly sum—and
this liberality made a most favourable impression, and
went far to destroy any little prejudice that might have
been caused by the daintiness of his dress, the cleanliness of his person, and the politeness of his manners.
A place was assigned to him, and an easel and a
board ; for he elected to stand at his work and begin
with a chalk drawing.   The model (a male) was posed,
and work began in silence.   Monday morning is always
rather sulky everywhere (except perhaps in Judee).   During
the ten minutes' rest three or four students came and looked
at Little Billee's beginnings, and saw at a glance that he
thoroughly well knew what he was about, and respected
him for it.

Nature had given him a singularly light hand—or

rather two, for he was ambidextrous, and could use both
with equal skill ; and a few months' practice at a London
life school had quite cured him of that purposeless inde-
cision of touch which often characterises the prentice hand
for years of apprenticeship, and remains with the amateur
for life. The lightest and most careless of his pencil
strokes had a precision that was inimitable, and a charm
that specially belonged to him, and was easy to recognise
at a glance. His touch on either canvas or paper was like
Svengali's on the keyboard— unique.

As the morning ripened little attempts at conversation
were made—little breakings of the ice of silence. It was
Lambert, a youth with a singularly facetious face, who
first woke the stillness with the following uncalled-for
remarks in English very badly pronounced :

' Av you seen my fahzere's ole shoes ? '

' I av not seen your fahzere's ole shoes.'

Then, after a pause :

' Av you seen my fahzere's ole 'at ? '

' I av not seen your fahzere's ole 'at ! '

Presently another said, ' Je trouve qu'il a une jolie
tête, l'Anglais.'

But I will put it all into English :

' I find that he has a pretty head—the Englishman !
What say *you*, Barizel ? '

' Yes ; but why has he got eyes like brandy-balls, two
a penny ? '

' Because he's an Englishman ! '

' Yes; but why has he got a mouth like a guinea-pig, with
two big teeth in front like the double blank at dominoes ? '

' Because he's an Englishman ! '

' Yes ; but why has he got a back without any bend in

it, as if he'd swallowed the Colonne Vendôme as far up as
the battle of Austerlitz?'

'Because he's an Englishman!'

And so on, till all the supposed characteristics of Little
Billee's outer man were exhausted.   Then :

'Papelard!'

'What?'

'*I* should like to know if the Englishman says his
prayers before going to bed.'

'Ask him.'

'Ask him yourself!'

'*I* should like to know if the Englishman has sisters ;
and if so, how old and how many and what sex.'

'Ask him.'

'Ask him yourself!'

'*I* should like to know the detailed and circumstantial
history of the Englishman's first love, and how he lost his
innocence!'

'Ask him,' etc. etc. etc.

Little Billee, conscious that he was the subject of conversation, grew somewhat nervous.   Soon he was addressed
directly.

'Dites donc, l'Anglais?'

'Kwaw?' said Little Billee.

'Avez-vous une sœur?'

'Wee.'

'Est-ce qu'elle vous ressemble?'

'Nong.'

'C'est bien dommage!   Est-ce qu'elle dit ses prières,
le soir, en se couchant?'

A fierce look came into Little Billee's eyes and a
redness to his cheeks, and this particular form of overture
to friendship was abandoned.

"'AV YOU SEEN MY FAHZERE'S OLE SHOES?'"

Presently Lambert said, 'Si nous mettions l'Anglais à l'échelle?'

Little Billee, who had been warned, knew what this ordeal meant.

They tied you to a ladder, and carried you in procession up and down the courtyard, and if you were nasty about it they put you under the pump.

During the next rest it was explained to him that he must submit to this indignity, and the ladder (which was used for reaching the high shelves round the studio) was got ready.

Little Billee smiled a singularly winning smile, and suffered himself to be bound with such good-humour that they voted it wasn't amusing, and unbound him, and he escaped the ordeal by ladder.

Taffy had also escaped, but in another way. When they tried to seize him he took up the first *rapin* that came to hand, and using him as a kind of club, he swung him about so freely and knocked down so many students and easels and drawing-boards with him, and made such a terrific rumpus, that the whole studio had to cry for 'pax!' Then he performed feats of strength of such a surprising kind that the memory of him remained in Carrel's studio for years, and he became a legend, a tradition, a myth! It is now said (in what still remains of the Quartier Latin) that he was seven feet high, and used to juggle with the *massier* and model as with a pair of billiard balls, using only his left hand!

To return to Little Billee. When it struck twelve, the cakes and rum punch arrived—a very goodly sight that put every one in a good temper.

The cakes were of three kinds—Babas, Madeleines, and

TAFFY À L'ECHELLE!

G

Savarins—three sous apiece, fourpence-halfpenny the set of three. No nicer cakes are made in France, and they are as good in the Quartier Latin as anywhere else ; no nicer cakes are made in the whole world, that I know of. You must begin with the Madeleine, which is rich and rather heavy ; then the Baba ; and finish up with the Savarin, which is shaped like a ring, very light, and flavoured with rum. And then you must really leave off.

The rum punch was tepid, very sweet, and not a bit too strong.

They dragged the model-throne into the middle, and a chair was put on for Little Billee, who dispensed his hospitality in a very polite and attractive manner, helping the *massier* first, and then the other graybeards in the order of their grayness, and so on down to the model.

Presently, just as he was about to help himself, he was asked to sing them an English song. After a little pressing he sung them a song about a gay cavalier who went to serenade his mistress (and a ladder of ropes, and a pair of masculine gloves that didn't belong to the gay cavalier, but which he found in his lady's bower)—a poor sort of song, but it was the nearest approach to a comic song he knew. There are four verses to it, and each verse is rather long. It does not sound at all funny to a French audience, and even with an English one Little Billee was not good at comic songs.

He was, however, much applauded at the end of each verse. When he had finished, he was asked if he were *quite* sure there wasn't any more of it, and they expressed a deep regret ; and then each student, straddling on his little thick-set chair as on a horse, and clasping the back of it in both hands, galloped round Little Billee's throne quite seriously—the strangest procession he had ever seen. It made him laugh till he cried, so that he could not eat or drink.

Then he served more punch and cake all round ; and just as he was going to begin himself, Papelard said :

' Say, you others, I find that the Englishman has something of truly distinguished in the voice, something of sympathetic, of touching—something of *je ne sais quoi !* '

Bouchardy : ' Yes, yes—something of *je ne sais quoi !* That's the very phrase—n'est-ce pas, vous autres ?—that is a good phrase that Papelard has just invented to describe the voice of the Englishman. He is very intelligent—Papelard.'

Chorus : ' Perfect, perfect ; he has the genius of characterisation—Papelard. Dites donc, l'Anglais ! once more that beautiful song—*hein ?* Nous vous en prions tous.'

Little Billee willingly sang it again, with even greater applause, and again they galloped, but the other way round and faster, so that Little Billee became quite hysterical, and laughed till his sides ached.

Then Dubosc : ' I find there is something of very capitous and exciting in English music—of very stimulating. And you, Bouchardy ? '

Bouchardy : ' Oh, me ! It is above all the *words* that I admire ; they have something of passionate, of romantic—" ze-ese glâ-âves, zese glâ-âves, zey do not belong to me." I don't know what that means, but I love that sort of—of—of—of—*je ne sais quoi*, in short ! Just *once* more, l'Anglais ; only *once*, the *four* couplets.'

So he sang it a third time, all four verses, while they leisurely ate and drank and smoked and looked at each other, nodding solemn commendation of certain phrases in the song: 'Très bien!' 'Très bien!' 'Ah! voilà qui est bien réussi!' 'Épatant, ça!' 'Trés fin!' etc. etc. For, stimulated by success, and rising to the occasion, he did his very utmost to surpass himself in emphasis of gesture and accent and histrionic drollery— heedless of the fact that not one of his listeners had the slightest notion what his song was about.

It was a sorry performance.

And it was not till he had sung it four times that he discovered the whole thing was an elaborate impromptu farce, of which he was the butt, and that of all his royal spread not a crumb or a drop was left for himself.

It was the old fable of the fox and the crow! And to do him justice, he laughed as heartily as any one, as if he thoroughly enjoyed the joke—and when you take jokes in that way people soon leave off poking fun at you. It is almost as good as being very big, like Taffy, and having a choleric blue eye!

Such was Little Billee's first experience of Carrel's studio, where he spent many happy mornings and made many good friends.

No more popular student had ever worked there within the memory of the grayest graybeards; none more amiable, more genial, more cheerful, self-respecting, considerate, and polite, and certainly none with greater gifts for art.

Carrel would devote at least fifteen minutes to him, and invited him often to his own private studio. And often, on the fourth or fifth day of the week, a group of admiring students would be gathered by his easel watching him as he worked.

"THE FOX AND THE CROW"

'C'est un rude lapin, l'Anglais! au moins il sait son orthographe en peinture, ce coco-là!'

Such was the verdict on Little Billee at Carrel's studio; and I can conceive no much loftier praise.

.   .   .   .   .   .

Young as she was (seventeen or eighteen, or thereabouts), and also tender (like Little Billee), Trilby had singularly clear and quick perceptions in all matters that concerned her tastes, fancies, or affections, and thoroughly knew her own mind, and never lost much time in making it up.

On the occasion of her first visit to the studio in the Place St. Anatole des Arts, it took her just five minutes to decide that it was quite the nicest, homeliest, genialest, jolliest studio in the whole Quartier Latin, or out of it, and its three inhabitants, individually and collectively, were more to her taste than any one else she had ever met.

In the first place, they were English, and she loved to hear her mother-tongue and speak it. It awoke all manner of tender recollections, sweet reminiscences of her childhood, her parents, her old home—such a home as it was—or, rather, such homes; for there had been many flittings from one poor nest to another. The O'Ferralls had been as birds on the bough.

She had loved her parents very dearly; and, indeed, with all their faults, they had many endearing qualities—the qualities that so often go with those particular faults—charm, geniality, kindness, warmth of heart, the constant wish to please, the generosity that comes before justice, and lends its last sixpence and forgets to pay its debts!

She knew other English and American artists, and

had sat to them frequently for the head and hands ; but
none of these, for general agreeableness of aspect or
manner, could compare in her mind with the stalwart and
magnificent Taffy, the jolly fat Laird of Cockpen, the
refined, sympathetic, and elegant Little Billee ; and she
resolved that she would see as much of them as she
could, that she would make herself at home in that
particular studio, and necessary to its *locataires ;* and
without being the least bit vain or self-conscious, she had
no doubts whatever of her power to please—to make
herself both useful and ornamental if it suited her purpose
to do so.

Her first step in this direction was to borrow Père
Martin's basket and lantern and pick (he had more than
one set of these trade properties) for the use of Taffy,
whom she feared she might have offended by the freedom
of her comments on his picture.

Then, as often as she felt it to be discreet, she
sounded her war-cry at the studio door and went in and
made kind inquiries, and, sitting cross-legged on the
model-throne, ate her bread and cheese and smoked her
cigarette and 'passed the time of day,' as she chose to
call it ; telling them all such news of the Quartier as had
come within her own immediate ken. She was always
full of little stories of other studios, which, to do her
justice, were always good-natured, and probably true—
quite so, as far as she was concerned ; she was the most
literal person alive ; and she told all these *ragots, cancans,
et potins d'atelier* in a quaint and amusing manner. The
slightest look of gravity or boredom on one of those
three faces, and she made herself scarce at once.

She soon found opportunities for usefulness also. If

a costume were wanted, for instance, she knew where to borrow it, or hire it or buy it cheaper than any one anywhere else. She procured stuffs for them at cost price,

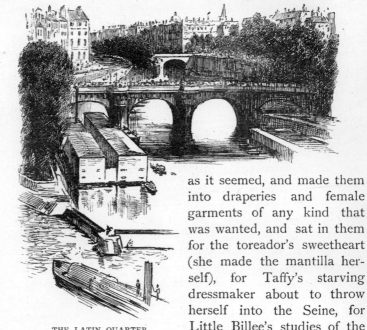

as it seemed, and made them into draperies and female garments of any kind that was wanted, and sat in them for the toreador's sweetheart (she made the mantilla herself), for Taffy's starving dressmaker about to throw herself into the Seine, for Little Billee's studies of the beautiful French peasant girl

THE LATIN QUARTER

in his picture, now so famous, called 'The Pitcher Goes to the Well.'

Then she darned their socks and mended their clothes, and got all their washing done properly and cheaply at her friend Madame Boisse's, in the Rue des Cloîtres Ste. Pétronille.

And then again, when they were hard up and wanted a good round sum of money for some little pleasure excursion, such as a trip to Fontainebleau or Barbizon for two or three days, it was she who took their watches and scarf-pins and things to the Mount of Piety in the Street of the Well of Love (where dwelt *ma tante*, which is French for 'my uncle' in this connection), in order to raise the necessary funds.

She was, of course, most liberally paid for all these little services, rendered with such pleasure and goodwill— far too liberally, she thought. She would have been really happier doing them for love.

Thus in a very short time she became a *persona gratissima*—a sunny and ever-welcome vision of health and grace and liveliness and unalterable good-humour, always ready to take any trouble to please her beloved 'Angliches,' as they were called by Madame Vinard, the handsome shrill-voiced *concierge*, who was almost jealous; for she was devoted to the Angliches too— and so was Monsieur Vinard—and so were the little Vinards.

She knew when to talk and when to laugh and when to hold her tongue; and the sight of her sitting cross-legged on the model-throne darning the Laird's socks or sewing buttons on his shirts or repairing the smoke-holes in his trousers was so pleasant that it was painted by all three. One of these sketches (in water-colour by Little Billee) sold the other day at Christie's for a sum so large that I hardly dare to mention it. It was done in an afternoon.

Sometimes on a rainy day, when it was decided they should dine at home, she would fetch the food and cook

it, and lay the cloth, and even make the salad.   She was
a better saladist than Taffy, a better cook than the Laird,
a better caterer than Little Billee.   And she would be
invited to take her share in the banquet.   And on these
occasions her tremulous happiness was so immense that
it would be quite pathetic to see—almost painful ; and
their three British hearts were touched by thoughts of
all the loneliness and homelessness, the expatriation, the
half-conscious loss of caste, that all this eager childish
clinging revealed.

And that is why (no doubt) that with all this familiar
intimacy there was never any hint of gallantry or flirta-
tion in any shape or form whatever—*bonne camaraderie
voilà tout.*   Had she been Little Billee's sister she could
not have been treated with more real respect.   And her
deep gratitude for this unwonted compliment transcended
any passion she had ever felt.   As the good Lafontaine
so prettily says—

> ' Ces animaux vivaient entre eux comme cousins ;
> Cette union si douce, et presque fraternelle,
> Edifiait tous les voisins ! '

And then their talk !   It was to her as the talk of
the gods in Olympus, save that it was easier to understand, and she could always understand it.   For she was
a very intelligent person, in spite of her wofully neglected
education, and most ambitious to learn—a new ambition
for her.

So they lent her books—English books : Dickens,
Thackeray, Walter Scott—which she devoured in the
silence of the night, the solitude of her little attic in the
Rue des Pousse-Cailloux, and new worlds were revealed to

CUISINE BOURGEOISE EN BOHÊME

her. She grew more English every day ; and that was a
good thing.

Trilby speaking English and Trilby speaking French
were two different beings. Trilby's English was more or
less that of her father, a highly-educated man ; her
mother, who was a Scotchwoman, although an uneducated
one, had none of the ungainliness that mars the speech
of so many Englishwomen in that humble rank—no
droppings of the *h*, no broadening of the *o*'s and *a*'s.

Trilby's French was that of the Quartier Latin—droll,
slangy, piquant, quaint, picturesque—quite the reverse of
ungainly, but in which there was scarcely a turn of phrase
that would not stamp the speaker as being hopelessly,
emphatically 'no lady!' Though it was funny without
being vulgar, it was perhaps a little *too* funny!

And she handled her knife and fork in the dainty
English way, as no doubt her father had done—and his ;
and, indeed, when alone with them she was so absolutely
'like a lady' that it seemed quite odd (though very
seductive) to see her in a grisette's cap and dress and apron.
So much for her English training.

But enter a Frenchman or two, and a transformation
effected itself immediately—a new incarnation of Trilbyness—so droll and amusing that it was difficult to decide
which of her two incarnations was the more attractive.

It must be admitted that she had her faults—like
Little Billee.

For instance, she would be miserably jealous of any
other woman who came to the studio, to sit or scrub or
sweep or do anything else, even of the dirty tipsy old hag
who sat for Taffy's 'Found drowned'—'as if she couldn't
have sat for it herself!'

And then she would be cross and sulky, but not for long—an injured martyr, soon ready to forgive and be forgiven.

She would give up any sitting to come and sit to her three English friends. Even Durien had serious cause for complaint.

Then her affection was exacting : she always wanted to be told one was fond of her, and she dearly loved her own way, even in the sewing on of buttons and the darning of socks, which was innocent enough. But when it came to the cutting and fashioning of garments for a toreador's bride, it was a nuisance not to be borne !

'What could *she* know of toreadors' brides and their wedding-dresses ? ' the Laird would indignantly ask—as if he were a toreador himself ; and this was the aggravating side of her irrepressible Trilbyness.

In the caressing, demonstrative tenderness of her friendship she ' made the soft eyes ' at all three indiscriminately. But sometimes Little Billee would look up from his work as she was sitting to Taffy or the Laird, and find her gray eyes fixed on him with an all-enfolding gaze, so piercingly, penetratingly, unutterably sweet and kind and tender, such a brooding, dovelike look of soft and warm solicitude, that he would feel a flutter at his heart, and his hand would shake so that he could not paint ; and in a waking dream he would remember that his mother had often looked at him like that when he was a small boy, and she a beautiful young woman untouched by care or sorrow ; and the tear that always lay in readiness so close to the corner of Little Billee's eye would find it very difficult to keep itself in its proper place—unshed.

And at such moments the thought that Trilby sat for the figure would go through him like a knife.

She did not sit promiscuously to anybody who asked, it is true. But she still sat to Durien; to the great Gérôme; to M. Carrel, who scarcely used any other model.

It was poor Trilby's sad distinction that she

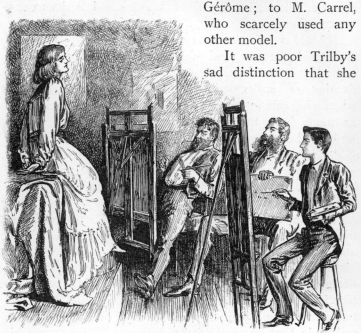

'THE SOFT EYES'

surpassed all other models as Calypso surpassed her nymphs; and whether by long habit, or through some obtuseness in her nature, or lack of imagination, she was equally unconscious of self with her clothes on or without! Truly, she could be naked and unashamed—in this respect an absolute savage.

She would have ridden through Coventry, like Lady
Godiva—but without giving it a thought beyond wondering why the streets were empty and the shops closed and
the blinds pulled down—would even have looked up to
Peeping Tom's shutter with a friendly nod, had she known
he was behind it.

In fact, she was absolutely without that kind of shame,
as she was without any kind of fear. But she was
destined soon to know both fear and shame.

And here it would not be amiss for me to state a fact
well known to all painters and sculptors who have used
the nude model (except a few shady pretenders, whose
purity, not being of the right sort, has gone rank from
too much watching), namely, that nothing is so chaste as
nudity. Venus herself, as she drops her garments and
steps on to the model-throne, leaves behind her on the floor
every weapon in her armoury by which she can pierce to
the grosser passions of man. The more perfect her un-
veiled beauty, the more keenly it appeals to his higher
instincts. And where her beauty fails (as it almost
always does somewhere in the Venuses who sit for hire),
the failure is so lamentably conspicuous in the studio
light—the fierce light that beats on this particular throne
—that Don Juan himself, who has not got to paint, were
fain to hide his eyes in sorrow and disenchantment, and
fly to other climes.

All beauty is sexless in the eyes of the artist at his
work—the beauty of man, the beauty of woman, the
heavenly beauty of the child, which is the sweetest and
best of all.

Indeed it is woman, lovely woman, whose beauty falls
the shortest, for sheer lack of proper physical training.

As for Trilby, G——, to whom she sat for his Phryne, once told me that the sight of her thus was a thing to melt Sir Galahad, yet sober Silenus, and chasten Jove himself—a thing to Quixotise a modern French masher! I can well believe him. For myself, I only speak of Trilby as I have seen her—clothed and in her right mind. She never sat to me for any Phryne, never bared herself to me, nor did I ever dream of asking her. I would as soon have asked the Queen of Spain to let me paint her legs! But I have worked from many female models in many countries, some of them the best of their kind. I have also, like Svengali, seen Taffy 'trying to get himself clean,' either at home or in the swimming-baths of the Seine ; and never a sitting woman among them all who could match for grace or finish or splendour of outward form that mighty Yorkshireman sitting in his tub, or sunning himself, like Ilyssus, at the Bains Henri Quatre, or taking his running header *à la hussarde*, off the spring-board at the Bains Deligny, with a group of wondering Frenchmen gathered round.

Up he shot himself into mid-air with a sounding double downward kick, parabolically ; then, turning a splendid semi-demi-somersault against the sky, down he came headlong, his body straight and stiff as an arrow, and made his clean hole in the water without splash or sound, to reappear a hundred yards farther on !

'Sac à papier ! quel gaillard que cet Anglais, hein ? '

'A-t-on jamais vu un torse pareil ! '

'Et les bras, donc ! '

'Et les jambes, nom d'un tonnerre ! '

'Mâtin ! J'aimerais mieux être en colère contre lui qu'il ne soit en colère contre moi ! ' etc. etc. etc.

Omne ignotum pro magnifico !

If our climate were such that we could go about without any clothes on, we probably should ; in which case,
although we should still murder and lie and steal and bear
false witness against our neighbour, and break the Sabbath

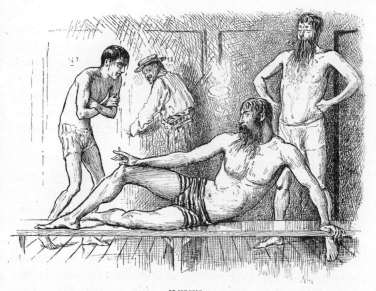

ILYSSUS

Day, and take the Lord's name in vain, much deplorable
wickedness of another kind would cease to exist for sheer
lack of mystery ; and Christianity would be relieved of its
hardest task in this sinful world, and Venus Aphrodite
(*alias* Aselgeia) would have to go a-begging along with
the tailors and dressmakers and bootmakers, and perhaps
our bodies and limbs would be as those of the Theseus

H

and Venus of Milo ; who was no Venus, except in good looks !

At all events, there would be no cunning, cruel deceptions, no artful taking in of artless inexperience, no unduly hurried waking-up from Love's young dream, no handing down to posterity of hidden uglinesses and weaknesses, and worse !

And also many a flower, now born to blush unseen, would be reclaimed from its desert, and suffered to hold its own, and flaunt away with the best in the inner garden of roses ! And poor Miss Gale, the figure-model, would be permitted to eke out her slender earnings by teaching calisthenics and deportment to the daughters of the British upper middle-class at Miss Pinkerton's academy for young ladies, The Mall, Chiswick.

And here let me humbly apologise to the casual reader for the length and possible irrelevancy of this digression, and for its subject. To those who may find matter for sincere disapprobation or even grave offence in a thing that has always seemed to me so simple, so commonplace, as to be hardly worth talking or writing about, I can only plead a sincerity equal to theirs, and as deep a love and reverence for the gracious, goodly shape that God is said to have made after His own image for inscrutable purposes of His own.

Nor, indeed, am I pleading for such a subversive and revolutionary measure as the wholesale abolition of clothes, being the chilliest of mortals, and quite unlike Mr. Theseus or Mr. Ilyssus either.

Sometimes Trilby would bring her little brother to the studio in the Place St. Anatole des Arts, in his *beaux habits de Pâques,* his hair well curled and pomatumed, his hands and face well washed.

He was a very engaging little mortal. The Laird would fill his pockets full of Scotch goodies, and paint him as a little Spaniard in ' Le Fils du Toréador,' a sweet little Spaniard with blue eyes, and curly locks as light as tow, and a complexion of milk and roses, in singular and piquant contrast to his swarthy progenitors.

Taffy would use him as an Indian club or a dumb-bell, to the child's infinite delight, and swing him on the trapeze, and teach him *la boxe.*

And the sweetness and fun of his shrill, happy, infantile laughter (which was like an echo of Trilby's, only an octave higher) so moved and touched and tickled one that Taffy had to look quite fierce, so he might hide the strange delight of tenderness that somehow filled his manly bosom at the mere sound of it (lest Little Billee and the Laird should think him goody-goody); and the fiercer Taffy looked, the less this small mite was afraid of him.

Little Billee made a beautiful water-colour sketch of him, just as he was, and gave it to Trilby, who gave it to le père Martin, who gave it to his wife with strict injunctions not to sell it as an old master. Alas! it *is* an old master now, and Heaven only knows who has got it!

Those were happy days for Trilby's little brother, happy days for Trilby, who was immensely fond of him, and very proud. And the happiest day of all was when the *trois* Angliches took Trilby and Jeannot (for so the mite was called) to spend the Sunday in the woods at Meudon, and breakfast and dine at the *garde champêtre's.* Swings, peep-shows, donkey-rides ; shooting at a mark with cross-bows and little pellets of clay, and

smashing little plaster figures and winning macaroons ;
losing one's self in the beautiful forest ; catching newts
and tadpoles and young frogs ; making music on *mirlitons*.
Trilby singing 'Ben Bolt' into a *mirliton* was a thing to
be remembered, whether one would or no!

Trilby on this occasion came out in a new character, *en
demoiselle*, with a little black bonnet, and a gray jacket of
her own making.

To look at (but for her loose, square-toed, heel-less silk
boots laced up the inner side), she might have been the
daughter of an English dean—until she undertook to
teach the Laird some favourite cancan steps. And then
the Laird himself, it must be admitted, no longer looked
like the son of a worthy, God-fearing, Sabbath-keeping
Scotch solicitor.

This was after dinner, in the garden, at *la loge du
garde champêtre*. Taffy and Jeannot and Little Billee
made the necessary music on their *mirlitons*, and the
dancing soon became general, with plenty also to look on,
for the *garde* had many customers who dined there on
summer Sundays.

It is no exaggeration to say that Trilby was far and
away the belle of that particular ball, and there have been
worse balls in much finer company, and far plainer
women!

Trilby lightly dancing the cancan (there are cancans
and cancans) was a singularly gainly and seductive person
—*et vera incessu patuit dea !* Here, again, she was funny
without being vulgar. And for mere grace (even in the
cancan), she was the forerunner of Miss Kate Vaughan ;
and for sheer fun, the precursor of Miss Nelly Farren !

And the Laird, trying to dance after her ('dongsong

le konkong,' as he called it), was too funny for words ;
and if genuine popular success is a true test of humour,
no greater humorist ever danced a *pas seul.*

' "VOILÀ L'ESPAYCE DE HOM KER JER SWEE !" '

What Englishmen could do in France during the fifties,
and yet manage to preserve their self-respect, and even
the respect of their respectable French friends !

'Voilà l'espayce de hom ker jer swee !' said the Laird,
every time he bowed in acknowledgment of the applause

that greeted his performance of various solo steps of his own—Scotch reels and sword-dances that came in admirably. . . .

Then, one fine day (as a judgment on him, no doubt), the Laird fell ill, and the doctor had to be sent for, and he ordered a nurse. But Trilby would hear of no nurses, not even a Sister of Charity! She did all the nursing herself, and never slept a wink for three successive days and nights.

On the third day the Laird was out of all danger, the delirium was past, and the doctor found poor Trilby fast asleep by the bedside.

Madame Vinard, at the bedroom door, put her finger to her lips, and whispered : ' Quel bonheur ! il est sauvé, M. le Docteur ; écoutez ! il dit ses prières en Anglais, ce brave garçon !'

The good old doctor, who didn't understand a word of English, listened, and heard the Laird's voice, weak and low, but quite clear, and full of heartfelt fervour, intoning, solemnly :

> ' " Green herbs, red peppers, mussels, saffron,
> Soles, onions, garlic, roach, and dace—
> All these you eat at Terré's Tavern
> In that one dish of bouillabaisse ! " '

' Ah ! mais c'est très bien de sa part, ce brave jeune homme ! rendre grâces au ciel comme cela, quand le danger est passé ! très bien, très bien !'

Sceptic and Voltairian as he was, and not the friend of prayer, the good doctor was touched, for he was old, and therefore kind and tolerant, and made allowances.

And afterwards he said such sweet things to Trilby about it all, and about her admirable care of his patient,

that she positively wept with delight—like sweet Alice
with hair so brown, whenever Ben Bolt gave her a smile.

All this sounds very goody-goody, but it's true.

So it will be easily understood how the *trois* Angliches
came in time to feel for Trilby quite a peculiar regard,
and looked forward with sorrowful forebodings to the day
when this singular and pleasant little quartet would have
to be broken up, each of them to spread his wings and
fly away on his own account, and poor Trilby to be left
behind all by herself. They would even frame little plans
whereby she might better herself in life, and avoid the
many snares and pitfalls that would beset her lonely path
in the Quartier Latin when they were gone.

Trilby never thought of such things as these; she took
short views of life, and troubled herself about no morrows.

There was, however, one jarring figure in her little
fool's paradise, a baleful and most ominous figure that
constantly crossed her path, and came between her and
the sun, and threw its shadow over her, and that was
Svengali.

He also was a frequent visitor at the studio in the
Place St. Anatole, where much was forgiven him for the
sake of his music, especially when he came with Gecko
and they made music together. But it soon became
apparent that they did not come there to play to the three
Angliches; it was to see Trilby, whom they both had
taken it into their heads to adore, each in a different
fashion :

Gecko, with a humble, doglike worship that expressed
itself in mute, pathetic deference and looks of lowly self-
depreciation, of apology for his own unworthy existence,
as though the only requital he would ever dare to dream

of were a word of decent politeness, a glance of tolerance or good-will—a mere bone to a dog.

Svengali was a bolder wooer. When he cringed, it was with a mock humility full of sardonic threats ; when he was playful, it was with a terrible playfulness, like that of a cat with a mouse—a weird, ungainly cat, and most unclean ; a sticky, haunting, long, lean, uncanny, black spider-cat, if there is such an animal outside a bad dream.

It was a great grievance to him that she had suffered from no more pains in her eyes. She had ; but preferred to endure them rather than seek relief from *him.*

So he would playfully try to mesmerise her with his glance, and sidle up nearer and nearer to her, making passes and counter-passes, with stern command in his eyes, till she would shake and shiver and almost sicken with fear, and all but feel the spell come over her, as in a nightmare, and rouse herself with a great effort and escape.

If Taffy were there he would interfere with a friendly ' Now then, old fellow, none of that ! ' and a jolly slap on the back, which would make Svengali cough for an hour, and paralyse his mesmeric powers for a week.

Svengali had a stroke of good-fortune. He played at three grand concerts with Gecko, and had a well-deserved success. He even gave a concert of his own, which made a furore, and blossomed out into beautiful and costly clothes of quite original colour and shape and pattern, so that people would turn round and stare at him in the street—a thing he loved. He felt his fortune was secure, and ran into debt with tailors, hatters, shoe-makers, jewellers, but paid none of his old debts to his friends. His pockets were always full of printed slips—

things that had been written about him in the papers—
and he would read them aloud to everybody he knew,
especially to Trilby, as she sat darning socks on the
model-throne while the fencing and boxing were in train.
And he would lay his fame and his fortune at her feet,
on condition that she should share her life with him.

'Ach, himmel, Drilpy!' he would say, 'you don't
know what it is to be a great pianist like me—*hein?*
What is your Little Billee, with his stinking oil-bladders,
sitting mum in his corner, his mahlstick and his palette
in one hand, and his twiddling little footle pig's-hair brush
in the other! What noise does *he* make? When his
little fool of a picture is finished he will send it to
London, and they will hang it on a wall with a lot of
others, all in a line, like recruits called out for inspection,
and the yawning public will walk by in procession and
inspect, and say "damn!" Svengali will go to London
himself. Ha! ha! He will be all alone on a platform,
and play as nobody else can play; and hundreds of
beautiful Engländerinnen will see and hear and go mad
with love for him—Prinzessen, Comtessen, Serene English
Altessen. They will soon lose their Serenity and their
Highness when they hear Svengali! They will invite
him to their palaces, and pay him a thousand francs to
play for them; and after, he will loll in the best arm-
chair, and they will sit all round him on footstools, and
bring him tea and gin and *küchen* and *marrons glacés*,
and lean over him and fan him—for he is tired after
playing them for a thousand francs of Chopin! Ha, ha!
I know all about it—*hein?*

'And he will not look at them, even! He will look
inward, at his own dream—and his dream will be about

Drilpy—to lay his talent, his glory, his thousand francs at her beautiful white feet!

'Their stupid, big, fat, tow-headed, putty-nosed husbands will be mad with jealousy, and long to box him, but they will be afraid. Ach! those beautiful Anclaises! they will think it an honour to mend his shirts, to sew buttons on his pantaloons; to darn his socks, as you are doing now for that sacred imbecile of a Scotchman who is always trying to paint toréadors, or that sweating, pig-headed bullock of an Englander who is always trying to get himself dirty and then to get himself clean again!—*e da capo!*

'Himmel! what big socks are those! what potato-sacks!

'Look at your Taffy! what is he good for but to bang great musicians on the back with his big bear's paw! He finds that droll, the bullock! . . .

'Look at your Frenchmen there—your damned conceited *verfluchte* pig-dogs of Frenchmen—Durien, Barizel, Bouchardy! What can a Frenchman talk of, *hein?* Only himself, and run down everybody else! His vanity makes me sick! He always thinks the world is talking about *him*, the fool! He forgets that there is a fellow called *Svengali* for the world to talk about! I tell you, Drilpy, it is about *me* the world is talking—me and nobody else—me, me, me!

'Listen what they say in the *Figaro* (reads it).

'What do you think of that, *hein?* What would your Durien say if people wrote of *him* like that?

'But you are not listening, sapperment! great big she-fool that you are — sheep's-head! Dummkopf! Donnerwetter! you are looking at the chimney-pots

when Svengali talks! Look a little lower down between
the houses, on the other side of the river! There is a
little ugly gray building there, and inside are eight
slanting slabs of brass, all of a row, like beds in a school
dormitory, and one fine day you shall lie asleep on one
of those slabs—you, Drilpy, who would not listen to
Svengali, and therefore lost him! . . . And over the
middle of you will be a little leather apron, and over
your head a little brass tap, and all day long and all
night the cold water shall trickle, trickle, trickle all the
way down your beautiful white body to your beautiful
white feet till they turn green, and your poor, damp,
draggled, muddy rags will hang above you from the
ceiling for your friends to know you by; drip, drip, drip!
But you will have no friends. . . .

'And people of all sorts, strangers, will stare at you
through the big plate-glass window—Englanders, chiffon-
niers, painters and sculptors, workmen, piou-pious, old
hags of washerwomen—and say, "Ah! what a beautiful
woman was that! Look at her! She ought to be
rolling in her carriage and pair!" And just then who
should come by, rolling in his carriage and pair,
smothered in furs, and smoking a big cigar of the
Havana, but Svengali, who will jump out, and push the
canaille aside, and say, "Ha! ha! that is la grande
Drilpy, who would not listen to Svengali, but looked at
the chimney-pots when he told her of his manly love,
and——"'

'Hi! damn it, Svengali, what the devil are you
talking to Trilby about? You're making her sick;
can't you see? Leave off, and go to the piano, man, or
I'll come and slap you on the back again!'

Thus would that sweating, pig-headed bullock of an Englander stop Svengali's love-making and release Trilby from bad quarters of an hour.

Then Svengali, who had a wholesome dread of the pig-headed bullock, would go to the piano and make impossible discords, and say: 'Dear Drilpy, come and sing "Pen Polt!" I am thirsting for those so beautiful chest notes! Come!'

Poor Trilby needed little pressing when she was asked to sing, and would go through her lamentable performance, to the great discomfort of Little Billee. It lost nothing of its grotesqueness from Svengali's accompaniment, which was a triumph of cacophony, and he would encourage her—*Très pien, très pien, ça y est!*

When it was over, Svengali would test her ear, as he called it, and strike the C in the middle and then the F just above, and ask which was the highest; and she would declare they were both exactly the same. It was only when he struck a note in the bass and another in the treble that she could perceive any difference, and said that the first sounded like Père Martin blowing up his wife, and the second like her little godson trying to make the peace between them.

She was quite tone-deaf, and didn't know it; and he would pay her extravagant compliments on her musical talent, till Taffy would say: 'Look here, Svengali, let's hear *you* sing a song!'

And he would tickle him so masterfully under the ribs that the creature howled and became quite hysterical.

Then Svengali would vent his love of teasing on Little Billee, and pin his arms behind his back and swing him

TIT FOR TAT

round, saying : ' Himmel ! what's this for an arm ?   It's
like a girl's ! '

    ' It's strong enough to paint ! ' said Little Billee.

    ' And what's this for a leg ?   It's like a mahlstick ! '

    ' It's strong enough to kick, if you don't leave off ! '

    And Little Billee, the young and tender, would let out
his little heel and kick the German's shins ; and just as
the German was going to retaliate, big Taffy would pin
his arms and make him sing another song, more dis-
cordant than Trilby's—for he didn't dream of kicking
Taffy : of that you may be sure !

    Such was Svengali—only to be endured for the sake
of his music—always ready to vex, frighten, bully, or
torment anybody or anything smaller and weaker than
himself—from a woman or a child to a mouse or a fly

PART THIRD

' Par deçà, ne dela la mer
  Ne sçay dame ni damoiselle
  Qui soit en tous biens parfaits telle —
  C'est un songe que d'y penser :
  Dieu ! qu'il fait bon la regarder !'

ONE lovely Monday morning in late September, at about eleven or so, Taffy and the Laird sat in the studio —each opposite his picture, smoking, nursing his knee, and saying nothing. The heaviness of Monday weighed on their spirits more than usual, for the three friends had returned late on the previous night from a week spent at Barbizon and in the forest of Fontainebleau—a heavenly week among the painters ; Rousseau, Millet, Corot, Daubigny, let us suppose, and others less known to fame this day. Little Billee, especially, had been fascinated by all this artistic life in blouses and sabots and immense straw hats and panamas, and had sworn to himself and to his friends that he would some day live and die there— painting the forest as it is, and peopling it with beautiful people out of his own fancy—leading a healthy outdoor life of simple wants and lofty aspirations.

At length Taffy said ; 'Bother work this morning ! I feel much more like a stroll in the Luxembourg Gardens and lunch at the Café de l'Odéon, where the omelets are

THE HAPPY LIFE

good and the wine isn't blue.'

'The very thing I was thinking of myself,' said the Laird.

So Taffy slipped on his old shooting-jacket and his old Harrow cricket cap, with the peak turned the wrong way, and the Laird put on an old greatcoat of Taffy's that reached to his heels, and a battered straw hat they had found in the studio when they took it; and both sallied forth into the mellow sunshine on the way to Carrel's. For they meant to seduce Little Billee from his work, that he might share in their laziness, greediness, and general demoralisation.

And whom should they meet coming down the narrow turreted Rue Vielle des Trois Mauvais Ladres but Little Billee himself, with an air of general demoralisation so tragic that they were quite alarmed. He had his paint-box and field-easel in one hand and his little valise in the other. He was pale, his hat on the back of his head, his hair staring all at sixes and sevens, like a sick Scotch terrier's.

'Good Lord! what's the matter?' said Taffy.

'Oh! oh! oh! she's sitting at Carrel's!'

'Who's sitting at Carrel's?'

'Trilby! sitting to all those ruffians! There she was, just as I opened the door; I saw her, I tell you! The sight of her was like a blow between the eyes, and I bolted! I shall never go back to that beastly hole again! I'm off to Barbizon, to paint the forest; I was coming round to tell you. Good-bye! . . .'

'Stop a minute—are you mad?' said Taffy, collaring him.

'Let me go, Taffy—let me go, damn it! I'll come back in a week—but I'm going now! Let me go; do you hear?'

'But look here—I'll go with you.'

'No; I want to be alone—quite alone. Let me go, I tell you!'

'I shan't let you go unless you swear to me, on your honour, that you'll write directly you get there, and every day till you come back. Swear!'

'All right; I swear—honour bright! Now there! Good-bye — good-bye; back on Sunday — good-bye!' And he was off.

'Now, what the devil does all that mean?' asked Taffy, much perturbed.

'I suppose he's shocked at seeing Trilby in that guise, or disguise, or unguise, sitting at Carrel's—he's such an odd little chap. And I must say, I'm surprised at Trilby. It's a bad thing for her when we're away. What could

I

have induced her? She never sat in a studio of that kind before. I thought she only sat to Durien and old Carrel.'

They walked for a while in silence.

' Do you know, I've got a horrid idea that the little fool's in love with her!'

' I've long had a horrid idea that *she's* in love with *him.*'

' That would be a very stupid business,' said Taffy.

They walked on, brooding over those two horrid ideas, and the more they brooded, considered, and remembered, the more convinced they became that both were right.

' Here's a pretty kettle of fish!' said the Laird—' and talking of fish, let's go and lunch.'

And so demoralised were they that Taffy ate three omelets without thinking, and the Laird drank two half-bottles of wine, and Taffy three, and they walked about the whole of that afternoon for fear Trilby should come to the studio—and were very unhappy.

This is how Trilby came to sit at Carrel's studio :

Carrel had suddenly taken it into his head that he would spend a week there, and paint a figure among his pupils, that they might see and paint with—and if possible like—him. And he had asked Trilby as a great favour to be the model, and Trilby was so devoted to the great Carrel that she readily consented. So that Monday morning found her there, and Carrel posed her as Ingres's famous figure in his picture called ' La Source,' holding an earthenware pitcher on her shoulder.

And the work began in religious silence. Then in five minutes or so Little Billee came bursting in, and as

"'LET ME GO, TAFFY ...'"

soon as he caught sight of her he stopped and stood as
one petrified, his shoulders up, his eyes staring.   Then
lifting his arms, he turned and fled.

'Qu'est ce qu'il a donc, ce Litrebili?' exclaimed one
or two students (for they had turned his English nickname into French).

'Perhaps he's forgotten something,' said another.
'Perhaps he's forgotten to brush his teeth and part his
hair!'

'Perhaps he's forgotten to say his prayers!' said
Barizel.

'He'll come back, I hope!' exclaimed the master.

And the incident gave rise to no further comment.

But Trilby was much disquieted, and fell to wondering
what on earth was the matter.

At first she wondered in French: French of the
Quartier Latin.   She had not seen Little Billee for a
week, and wondered if he were ill.   She had looked
forward so much to his painting her—painting her beautifully—and hoped he would soon come back, and lose no
time.

Then she began to wonder in English—nice clean
English of the studio in the Place St. Anatole des Arts—
her father's English—and suddenly a quick thought
pierced her through and through, and made the flesh
tingle on her insteps and the backs of her hands, and
bathed her brow and temples with sweat.

She had good eyes, and Little Billee had a singularly
expressive face.

Could it possibly be that he was *shocked* at seeing her
sitting there?

She knew that he was peculiar in many ways.   She

remembered that neither he nor Taffy nor the Laird had ever asked her to sit for the figure, though she would have been only too delighted to do so for them. She also remembered how Little Billee had always been silent whenever she alluded to her posing for the 'altogether,' as she called it, and had sometimes looked pained and always very grave.

She turned alternately pale and red, pale and red all over, again and again, as the thought grew up in her —and soon the growing thought became a torment.

This new-born feeling of shame was unendurable—its birth a travail that racked and rent every fibre of her moral being, and she suffered agonies beyond anything she had ever felt in her life.

'What is the matter with you, my child? Are you ill?' asked Carrel, who, like every one else, was very fond of her, and to whom she had sat as a child

' "QU'EST CE QU'IL A DONC, CE LITREBILI?" '

('L'Enfance de Psyché,' now in the Luxembourg Gallery, was painted from her).

She shook her head, and the work went on.

Presently she dropped her pitcher, that broke into bits ;

and putting her two hands to her face she burst into tears and sobs—and there, to the amazement of everybody, she stood crying like a big baby—*La source aux larmes?*

'What *is* the matter, my poor dear child?' said Carrel, jumping up and helping her off the throne.

'Oh, I don't know—I don't know—I'm ill—very ill— let me go home!'

And with kind solicitude and despatch they helped her on with her clothes, and Carrel sent for a cab and took her home.

And on the way she dropped her head on his shoulder, and wept, and told him all about it as well as she could, and Monsieur Carrel had tears in his eyes too, and wished to Heaven he had never induced her to sit for the figure, either then or at any other time. And pondering deeply and sorrowfully on such terrible responsibility (he had grown-up daughters of his own), he went back to the studio; and in an hour's time they got another model and another pitcher, and went to work again. So the pitcher went to the well once more.

And Trilby, as she lay disconsolate on her bed all that day and all the next, and all the next again, thought of her past life with agonies of shame and remorse that made the pain in her eyes seem as a light and welcome relief. For it came, and tortured worse and lasted longer than it had ever done before. But she soon found, to her miserable bewilderment, that mind-aches are the worst of all.

Then she decided that she must write to one of the *trois* Angliches, and chose the Laird.

She was more familiar with him than with the other

REPENTANCE

two : it was impossible not to be familiar with the Laird
if he liked one, as he was so easy-going and demonstrative,
for all that he was such a canny Scot! Then she had
nursed him through his illness ; she had often hugged
and kissed him before the whole studio full of people—
and even when alone with him it had always seemed
quite natural for her to do so. It was like a child caressing a favourite young uncle or elder brother. And though
the good Laird was the least susceptible of mortals, he
would often find these innocent blandishments a somewhat trying ordeal! She had never taken such a liberty
with Taffy ; and as for Little Billee, she would sooner
have died !

So she wrote to the Laird. I give her letter without
the spelling, which was often faulty, although her nightly
readings had much improved it :

'My dear Friend—I am very unhappy. I was
sitting at Carrel's, in the Rue des Potirons, and Little
Billee came in, and was so shocked and disgusted that he
ran away and never came back.

'I saw it all in his face.

'I sat there because M. Carrel asked me to. He has
always been very kind to me—M. Carrel—ever since I
was a child ; and I would do anything to please him, but
never *that* again.

'He was there too.

'I never thought anything about sitting before. I sat
first as a child to M. Carrel. Mamma made me, and made
me promise not to tell papa, and so I didn't. It soon
seemed as natural to sit for people as to run errands for
them, or wash and mend their clothes. Papa wouldn't

have liked my doing that either, though we wanted the money badly. And so he never knew.

'I have sat for the "altogether" to several other people besides—M. Gérôme, Durien, the two Hennequins, and Émile Baratier ; and for the head and hands to lots of people, and for the feet only to Charles Faure, André Besson, Mathieu Dumoulin, and Collinet. Nobody else.

'It seemed as natural for me to sit as for a man. Now I see the awful difference.

'And I have done dreadful things besides, as you must know—as all the Quartier knows. Baratier and Besson ; but not Durien, though people think so. Nobody else, I swear—except old Monsieur Penque at the beginning, who was mamma's friend.

'It makes me almost die of shame and misery to think of it ; for that's not like sitting. I knew how wrong it was all along—and there's no excuse for me, none. Though lots of people do as bad, and nobody in the Quartier seems to think any the worse of them.

'If you and Taffy and Little Billee cut me, I really think I shall go mad and die. Without your friendship I shouldn't care to live a bit. Dear Sandy, I love your little finger better than any man or woman I ever met ; and Taffy's and Little Billee's little fingers too.

'What shall I do ? I daren't go out for fear of meeting one of you. Will you come and see me ?

'I am never going to sit again, not even for the face and hands. I am going back to be a *blanchisseuse de fin* with my old friend Angèle Boisse, who is getting on very well indeed, in the Rue des Cloîtres Ste. Pétronille.

'You *will* come and see me, won't you ? I shall be in all day till you do. Or else I will meet you somewhere,

if you will tell me where and when ; or else I will go and
see you in the studio, if you are sure to be alone.   Please
don't keep me waiting long for an answer.

'You don't know what I'm suffering.

'Your ever loving, faithful friend,

'TRILBY O'FERRALL.'

She sent this letter by hand, and the Laird came in
less than ten minutes after she had sent it ; and she
hugged and kissed and cried over him so that he was
almost ready to cry himself ; but he burst out laughing
instead—which was better and more in his line, and very
much more comforting—and talked to her so nicely and
kindly and naturally that by the time he left her humble
attic in the Rue des Pousse-Cailloux her very aspect,
which had quite shocked him when he first saw her, had
almost become what it usually was.

The little room under the leads, with its sloping roof
and mansard window, was as scrupulously neat and clean
as if its tenant had been a holy sister who taught the
noble daughters of France at some Convent of the Sacred
Heart.   There were nasturtiums and mignonette on the
outer window-sill, and convolvulus was trained to climb
round the window.

As she sat by his side on the narrow white bed, clasping and stroking his painty, turpentiny hand, and kissing
it every five minutes, he talked to her like a father—as he
told Taffy afterwards—and scolded her for having been so
silly as not to send for him directly, or come to the studio.
He said how glad he was, how glad they would all be,
that she was going to give up sitting for the figure—not,
of course, that there was any real harm in it, but it was

CONFESSION

better not—and especially how happy it would make them
to feel she intended to live straight for the future.   Little
Billee was to remain at Barbizon for a little while ; but
she must promise to come and dine with Taffy and himself that very day, and cook the dinner ; and when he
went back to his picture, 'Les Noces du Toréador '—
saying to her as he left, 'à ce soir donc, mille sacrés
tonnerres de nong de Dew ! '—he left the happiest woman
in the whole Latin Quarter behind him : she had confessed
and been forgiven.

And with shame and repentance and confession and
forgiveness had come a strange new feeling—that of a
dawning self-respect.

Hitherto, for Trilby, self-respect had meant little more
than the mere cleanliness of her body, in which she had
always revelled ; alas ! it was one of the conditions of her
humble calling.   It now meant another kind of cleanliness,
and she would luxuriate in it for evermore ; and the
dreadful past—never to be forgotten by her—should be so
lived down as in time, perhaps, to be forgotten by others.

The dinner that evening was a memorable one for
Trilby.   After she had washed up the knives and forks
and plates and dishes, and put them by, she sat and sewed.
She wouldn't even smoke her cigarette, it reminded her so
of things and scenes she now hated.   No more cigarettes
for Trilby O'Ferrall.

They all talked of Little Billee.   She heard about the
way he had been brought up, about his mother and sister,
the people he had always lived among.   She also heard
(and her heart alternately rose and sank as she listened)
what his future was likely to be, and how rare his genius
was, and how great—if his friends were to be trusted.

Fame and fortune would soon be his—such fame and fortune as fall to the lot of very few—unless anything should happen to spoil his promise and mar his prospects in life, and ruin a splendid career ; and the rising of the heart was all for him, the sinking for herself. How could she ever hope to be even the friend of such a man? Might she ever hope to be his servant—his faithful, humble servant?

Little Billee spent a month at Barbizon, and when he came back it was with such a brown face that his friends hardly knew him ; and he brought with him such studies as made his friends 'sit up.'

The crushing sense of their own hopeless inferiority was lost in wonder at his work, in love and enthusiasm for the workman.

Their Little Billee, so young and tender, so weak of body, so strong of purpose, so warm of heart, so light of hand, so keen and quick and piercing of brain and eye, was their master, to be stuck on a pedestal and looked up to and bowed down to, to be watched and warded and worshipped for evermore.

When Trilby came in from her work at six, and he shook hands with her and said ' Hullo, Trilby!' her face turned pale to the lips, her under lip quivered, and she gazed down at him (for she was among the tallest of her sex) with such a moist, hungry, wide-eyed look of humble craving adoration that the Laird felt his worst fears were realised : and the look Little Billee sent up in return filled the manly bosom of Taffy with an equal apprehension.

Then they all four went and dined together at le père Trin's, and Trilby went back to her *blanchisserie de fin*.

Next day Little Billee took his work to show Carrel, and Carrel invited him to come and finish his picture 'The Pitcher Goes to the Well' at his own private studio —an unheard-of favour, which the boy accepted with a thrill of proud gratitude and affectionate reverence.

So little was seen for some time of Little Billee at the studio in the Place St. Anatole des Arts, and little of Trilby; a *blanchisseuse de fin* has not many minutes to spare from her irons. But they often met at dinner. And on Sunday mornings Trilby came to repair the Laird's linen and darn his socks and look after his little comforts, as usual, and spend a happy day. And on Sunday afternoons the studio would be as lively as ever, with the fencing and boxing, the piano-playing and fiddling—all as it used to be.

And week by week the friends noticed a gradual and subtle change in Trilby. She was no longer slangy in French, unless it were now and then by a slip of the tongue, no longer so facetious and droll, and yet she seemed even happier than she had ever seemed before.

Also, she grew thinner, especially in the face, where the bones of her cheeks and jaws began to show themselves, and these bones were constructed on such right principles (as were those of her brow and chin and the bridge of her nose) that the improvement was astonishing, almost inexplicable.

Also, she lost her freckles as the summer waned and she herself went less into the open air. And she let her hair grow, and made of it a small knot at the back of her head, and showed her little flat ears, which were charming, and just in the right place, very far back and rather high; Little Billee could not have placed them

"ALL AS IT USED TO BE"

better himself. Also, her mouth, always too large, took on a firmer and sweeter outline, and her big British teeth were so white and regular that even Frenchmen forgave them their British bigness. And a new soft brightness came into her eyes that no one had ever seen there before. They were stars, just twin gray stars—or rather planets just thrown off by some new sun, for the steady mellow light they gave out was not entirely their own.

Favourite types of beauty change with each succeeding generation. These were the days of Buckner's aristocratic Album beauties, with lofty foreheads, oval faces, little aquiline noses, heart-shaped little mouths, soft dimpled chins, drooping shoulders, and long side ringlets that fell over them—the Lady Arabellas and the Lady Clementinas, Musidoras and Medoras! A type that will perhaps come back to us some day.

May the present scribe be dead!

Trilby's type would be infinitely more admired now than in the fifties. Her photograph would be in the shop-windows. Sir Edward Burne-Jones—if I may make so bold as to say so—would perhaps have marked her for his own, in spite of her almost too exuberant joyousness and irrepressible vitality. Rossetti might have evolved another new formula from her; Sir John Millais another old one of the kind that is always new and never sates or palls—like Clytie, let us say—ever old and ever new as love itself!

Trilby's type was in singular contrast to the type Gavarni had made so popular in the Latin Quarter at the period we are writing of, so that those who fell so readily under her charm were rather apt to wonder why. Moreover, she was thought much too tall for her sex, and her day, and her station in life, and especially for the country she lived in. She hardly looked up to a bold gendarme! and a bold gendarme was nearly as tall as a *dragon de la garde*, who was nearly as tall as an average English policeman. Not that she was a giantess, by any means. She was about as tall as Miss Ellen Terry—and that is a charming height, *I* think.

One day Taffy remarked to the Laird: 'Hang it! I'm blest if Trilby isn't the handsomest woman I know! She looks like a grande dame masquerading as a grisette— almost like a joyful saint at times. She's lovely! By Jove! I couldn't stand her hugging me as she does you! There'd be a tragedy—say the slaughter of Little Billee.'

'TWIN GRAY STARS'

'Ah! Taffy, my boy,' rejoined the Laird, 'when those long sisterly arms are round my neck it isn't *me* she's hugging.'

'And then,' said Taffy, 'what a trump she is! Why, she's as upright and straight and honourable as a man! And what she says to one about one's self is always so pleasant to hear! That's Irish, I suppose. And, what's more, it's always true.'

'Ah, that's Scotch!' said the Laird, and tried to wink at Little Billee, but Little Billee wasn't there.

Even Svengali perceived the strange metamorphosis. 'Ach, Drilpy,' he would say, on a Sunday afternoon,

K

'how beautiful you are! It drives me mad! I adore you. I like you thinner; you have such beautiful bones! Why do you not answer my letters? What! you do not *read* them? You *burn* them? And yet I—— Donner-wetter! I forgot! The grisettes of the Quartier Latin have not learned how to read or write; they have only learned how to dance the cancan with the dirty little pig-dog monkeys they call men. Sacrement! *We* will teach the little pig-dog monkeys to dance something else some day, we Germans. We will make music for them to dance to! Boum! boum! Better than the waiter at the Café de la Rotonde, *hein?* And the grisettes of the Quartier Latin shall pour us out your little white wine— *fotre betit fin planc,* as your pig-dog monkey of a poet says, your rotten *verfluchter* De Musset, "who has got such a splendid future behind him!" Bah! What do *you* know of Monsieur Alfred de Musset? We have got a poet too, my Drilpy. His name is Heinrich Heine. If he's still alive, he lives in Paris, in a little street off the Champs Élysées. He lies in bed all day long, and only sees out of one eye, like the Countess Hahn-Hahn, ha! ha! He adores French grisettes. He married one. Her name is Mathilde, and she has got *süssen füssen,* like you. He would adore you too, for your beautiful bones; he would like to count them one by one, for he is very playful, like me. And, ach! what a beautiful skeleton you will make! And very soon, too, because you do not smile on your madly-loving Svengali. You burn his letters without reading them! You shall have a nice little mahogany glass case all to yourself in the museum of the École de Médecine, and Svengali shall come in his new fur-lined coat, smoking his big cigar of the Havana,

and push the dirty carabins out of the way, and look
through the holes of your eyes into your stupid empty
skull, and up the nostrils of your high, bony sounding-
board of a nose without either a tip or a lip to it, and
into the roof of your big mouth, with your thirty-two big
English teeth, and between your big ribs into your big
chest, where the big leather lungs used to be, and say,
" Ach ! what a pity she had no more music in her than a
big tom-cat ! " And then he will look all down your
bones to your poor crumbling feet, and say, " Ach ! what
a fool she was not to answer Svengali's letters ! " and the
dirty carabins shall———'

' Shut up, you
sacred fool, or I'll
precious soon spoil
your skeleton for you.'

Thus the short-
tempered Taffy, who
had been listening.

Then Svengali,
scowling, would play
Chopin's funeral
march more divinely
than ever ; and where
the pretty soft part
comes in, he would
whisper to Trilby,
' That is Svengali
coming to look at you
in your little mahogany glass case ! '

' AN INCUBUS '

And here let me say that these vicious imaginations of
Svengali's, which look so tame in English print, sounded

much more ghastly in French, pronounced with a Hebrew-German accent, and uttered in his hoarse, rasping, nasal, throaty rook's caw, his big yellow teeth baring themselves in a mongrel canine snarl, his heavy upper eyelids drooping over his insolent black eyes.

Besides which, as he played the lovely melody he would go through a ghoulish pantomime, as though he were taking stock of the different bones in her skeleton with greedy but discriminating approval. And when he came down to the feet, he was almost droll in the intensity of his terrible realism. But Trilby did not appreciate this exquisite fooling, and felt cold all over.

He seemed to her a dread powerful demon, who, but for Taffy (who alone could hold him in check), oppressed and weighed on her like an incubus—and she dreamed of him oftener than she dreamed of Taffy, the Laird, or even Little Billee!

Thus pleasantly and smoothly, and without much change or adventure, things went on till Christmas-time.

Little Billee seldom spoke of Trilby, or Trilby of him. Work went on every morning at the studio in the Place St. Anatole des Arts, and pictures were begun and finished —little pictures that didn't take long to paint—the Laird's Spanish bull-fighting scenes, in which the bull never appeared, and which he sent to his native Dundee and sold there; Taffy's tragic little dramas of life in the slums of Paris—starvings, drownings—suicides by charcoal and poison—which he sent everywhere, but did not sell.

Little Billee was painting all this time at Carrel's studio —his private one—and seemed preoccupied and happy when they all met at meal-time, and less talkative even than usual.

He had always been the least talkative of the three ; more prone to listen, and no doubt to think the more.

In the afternoon people came and went as usual, and boxed and fenced and did gymnastic feats, and felt Taffy's biceps, which by this time equalled Mr. Sandow's !

Some of these people were very pleasant and remarkable, and have become famous since then in England, France, America—or have died, or married, and come to grief or glory in other ways. It is the Ballad of the Bouillabaisse all over again !

It might be worth while my trying to sketch some of the more noteworthy, now that my story is slowing for a while like a French train when the engine-driver sees a long curved tunnel in front of him, as I do—and no light at the other end !

My humble attempts at characterisation might be useful as *mémoires pour servir* to future biographers. Besides, there are other reasons, as the reader will soon discover.

There was Durien, for instance — Trilby's especial French adorer, *pour le bon motif !* a son of the people, a splendid sculptor, a very fine character in every way—so perfect, indeed, that there is less to say about him than any of the others—modest, earnest, simple, frugal, chaste, and of untiring industry ; living for his art, and perhaps also a little for Trilby, whom he would have been only too glad to marry. He was Pygmalion ; she was his Galatea —a Galatea whose marble heart would never beat for *him !*

Durien's house is now the finest in the Parc Monceau ; his wife and daughters are the best-dressed women in

Paris, and he one of the happiest of men ; but he will never quite forget poor Galatea :

'La belle aux pieds d'albâtre—aux deux talons de rose!'

Then there was Vincent, a Yankee medical student, who could both work and play.

He is now one of the greatest oculists in the world, and Europeans cross the Atlantic to consult him. He can still play, and when he crosses the Atlantic himself for that purpose he has to travel incognito like a royalty, lest his play should be marred by work. And his daughters are so beautiful and accomplished that British dukes have sighed after them in vain. Indeed, these fair young ladies spend their autumn holiday in refusing the British aristocracy. We are told so in the society papers, and I can quite believe it. Love is not always blind ; and if he is, Vincent is the man to cure him.

In those days he prescribed for us all round, and punched and stethoscoped us, and looked at our tongues for love, and told us what to eat, drink, and avoid, and even where to go for it.

For instance : late one night Little Billee woke up in a cold sweat, and thought himself a dying man—he had felt seedy all day and taken no food ; so he dressed and dragged himself to Vincent's hotel, and woke him up, and said, 'Oh, Vincent, Vincent! I'm a dying man!' and all but fainted on his bed. Vincent felt him all over with the greatest care, and asked him many questions. Then, looking at his watch, he delivered himself thus : 'Humph! 3.30! rather late—but still—look here, Little Billee—do you know the Halle, on the other side of the water, where they sell vegetables?'

'Oh yes! yes! What vegetable shall I——'

'Listen! On the north side are two restaurants—Bordier and Baratte. They remain open all night. Now go straight off to one of those tuck shops, and tuck in as big a supper as you possibly can. Some people prefer Baratte. I prefer Bordier myself. Perhaps you'd better try Bordier first and Baratte after. At all events, lose no time; so off you go!'

Thus he saved Little Billee from an early grave.

Then there was the Greek, a boy of only sixteen, but six feet high, and looking ten years older than he was, and able to smoke even stronger tobacco than Taffy himself, and colour pipes divinely; he was a great favourite in the Place St. Anatole, for his *bonhomie*, his niceness, his warm geniality. He was the capitalist of this select circle (and nobly lavish of his capital). He went by the name of Poluphloisboiospaleapologos Petrilopetrolico-conose—for so he was christened by the Laird—because his real name was thought much too long; and much too lovely for the Quartier Latin, and reminded one too much of the Isles of Greece—where burning Sappho loved and sang.

What was he learning in the Latin Quarter? French? He spoke French like a native! Nobody knows. But when his Paris friends transferred their Bohemia to London, where were they ever made happier and more at home than in his lordly parental abode—or fed with nicer things?

That abode is now his, and lordlier than ever, as becomes the dwelling of a millionaire and city magnate; and its gray-bearded owner is as genial, as jolly, and as hospitable as in the old Paris days, but he no longer colours pipes.

Then there was Carnegie, fresh from Balliol, redolent of the 'varsity. He intended himself then for the diplomatic service, and came to Paris to learn French as it is spoke ; and spent most of his time with his fashionable English friends on the right side of the river, and the rest with Taffy, the Laird, and Little Billee on the left. Perhaps that is why he has not become an ambassador. He is now only a rural dean, and speaks the worst French I know, and speaks it wherever and whenever he can.

It serves him right, I think.

He was fond of lords, and knew some (at least, he gave one that impression), and often talked of them, and dressed so beautifully that even Little Billee was abashed in his presence. Only Taffy, in his threadbare, out-at-elbow shooting-jacket and cricket-cap, and the Laird, in his tattered straw hat and Taffy's old overcoat down to his heels, dared to walk arm-in-arm with him—nay, insisted on doing so—as they listened to the band in the Luxembourg Gardens.

And his whiskers were even longer and thicker and more golden than Taffy's own. But the mere sight of a boxing-glove made him sick.

Then there was the yellow-haired Antony, a Swiss—the idle apprentice, *le roi des truands*, as we called him—to whom everything was forgiven, as to François Villon, *à cause de ses gentillesses*—surely, for all his reprehensible pranks, the gentlest and most lovable creature that ever lived in Bohemia, or out of it,

THE CAPITALIST AND THE SWELL

Always in debt, like Svengali, for he had no more notion of the value of money than a humming-bird, and gave away in reckless generosity to friends what in strictness belonged to his endless creditors; like Svengali, humorous, witty, and a most exquisite and original artist, and also somewhat eccentric in his attire (though scrupulously clean), so that people would stare at him as he walked along—a thing that always gave him dire offence! But, unlike Svengali, full of delicacy, refinement, and distinction of mind and manner, void of any self-conceit; and, in spite of the irregularities of his life, the very soul of truth and honour, as gentle as he was chivalrous and brave; the warmest, staunchest, sincerest, most unselfish friend in the world; and, as long as his purse was full, the best and drollest boon companion in the world—but that was not for ever!

When the money was gone, then would Antony hie him to some beggarly attic in some lost Parisian slum, and write his own epitaph in lovely French or German verse—or even English (for he was an astounding linguist); and telling himself that he was forsaken by family, friends, and mistress alike, look out of his casement over the Paris chimney-pots for the last time, and listen once more to 'the harmonies of nature,' as he called it, and 'aspire towards the infinite,' and bewail 'the cruel deceptions of his life,' and finally lay himself down to die of sheer starvation.

And as he lay and waited for his release, that was so long in coming, he would beguile the weary hours by mumbling a crust 'watered with his own salt tears,' and decorating his epitaph with fanciful designs of the most exquisite humour, pathos, and beauty; these early illustrated epitaphs of the young Antony, of which there still exist a goodly number, are now priceless, as all collectors know all over the world.

Fainter and fainter would he grow, and finally, on the third day or thereabouts, a remittance would reach him from some long-suffering sister or aunt in far Lausanne ; or else the fickle mistress or faithless friend (who had been looking for him all over Paris) would discover his hiding-place, the beautiful epitaph would be walked off in triumph to le père Marcas in the Rue du Ghette and sold for twenty, fifty, a hundred francs ; and then *vogue la galère !* and back again to Bohemia, dear Bohemia and all its joys, as long as the money lasted . . . *e poi, da capo !*

And now that his name is a household word in two hemispheres, and he himself an honour and a glory to the land he has adopted as his own, he loves to remember all this, and look back from the lofty pinnacle on which he sits perched up aloft to the impecunious days of his idle apprenticeship—*le bon temps où l'on était si malheureux !*

And with all that Quixotic dignity of his, so famous is he as a wit that when he jokes (and he is always joking), people laugh first, and then ask what he was joking about, and you can even make your own mild funniments raise a roar by merely prefacing them ' as Antony once said ! '

The present scribe has often done so. And if by a happy fluke you should some day hit upon a really good thing of your own—good enough to be quoted—be sure it will come back to you after many days prefaced ' as Antony once said ! '

And these jokes are so good-natured that you almost

resent their being made at anybody's expense but your
own !　Never from Antony :

> ' The aimless jest that striking has caused pain,
> The idle word that he'd wish back again ! '

Indeed, in spite of his success, I don't suppose he ever
made an enemy in his life.

And here let me add (lest there be any doubt as to
his identity) that he is now tall and stout and strikingly
handsome, though rather bald ; and such an aristocrat in
bearing, aspect, and manner, that you would take him for
a blue-blooded descendant of the Crusaders instead of the
son of a respectable burgher in Lausanne.

Then there was Lorrimer, the industrious apprentice,
who is now also well pinnacled on high ; himself a pillar
of the Royal Academy— probably, if he lives long enough,
its future president—the duly knighted or baroneted
Lord Mayor of 'all the plastic arts' (except one or two
perhaps, here and there, that are not altogether without
some importance).

May this not be for many, many years !　Lorrimer
himself would be the first to say so !

Tall, thin, red-haired, and well-favoured, he was a most
eager, earnest, and painstaking young enthusiast, of pre-
cocious culture, who read improving books, and did not
share in the amusements of the Quartier Latin, but spent
his evenings at home with Handel, Michael Angelo, and
Dante, on the respectable side of the river.　Also, he
went into good society sometimes, with a dress-coat on,
and a white tie, and his hair parted in the middle !

But in spite of these blemishes on his otherwise
exemplary record as an art student, he was the most

delightful companion—the most affectionate, helpful, and sympathetic of friends. May he live long and prosper!

Enthusiast as he was, he could only worship one god at a time. It was either Michael Angelo, Phidias, Paul Veronese, Tintoret, Raphael, or Titian—never a modern —moderns didn't exist! And so thoroughgoing was he in his worship, and so persistent in voicing it, that he made those immortals quite unpopular in the Place St. Anatole des Arts. We grew to dread their very names. Each of them would last him a couple of months or so; then he would give us a month's holiday, and take up another.

Antony did not think much of Lorrimer in those days, nor Lorrimer of him, for all they were such good friends. And neither of them thought much of Little Billee, whose pinnacle (of pure unadulterated fame) is now the highest of all—the highest probably that can be for a mere painter of pictures!

And what is so nice about Lorrimer, now that he is a graybeard, an Academician, an accomplished man of the world and society, is that he admires Antony's genius more than he can say—and reads Mr. Rudyard Kipling's delightful stories as well as Dante's *Inferno*—and can listen with delight to the lovely songs of Signor Tosti, who has not precisely founded himself on Handel—can even scream with laughter at a comic song—even a nigger melody—so, at least, that it but be sung in well-bred and distinguished company—for Lorrimer is no Bohemian.

'Shoo, fly! don'tcher bother me!
For I belong to the Comp'ny G!'

Both these famous men are happily (and most beautifully) married—grandfathers for all I know—and 'move

in the very best society' (Lorrimer always, I'm told;
Antony now and then); *la haute*, as it used to be called
in French Bohemia—meaning dukes and lords and even
royalties, I suppose, and those who love them, and whom
they love!

That *is* the best society, isn't it?   At all events, we
are assured it used to be; but that must have been before
the present scribe (a meek and somewhat innocent outsider) had been privileged to see it with his own little
eye.

And when they happen to meet there (Antony and
Lorrimer, I mean), I don't expect they rush very wildly
into each other's arms, or talk very fluently about old
times.   Nor do I suppose their wives are very intimate.
None of our wives are.   Not even Taffy's and the Laird's.

Oh, Orestes!   Oh, Pylades!

Oh, ye impecunious, unpinnacled young inseparables
of eighteen, nineteen, twenty, even twenty-five, who share
each other's thoughts and purses, and wear each other's
clothes, and swear each other's oaths, and smoke each
other's pipes, and respect each other's lights o' love, and
keep each other's secrets, and tell each other's jokes, and
pawn each other's watches and merrymake together on
the proceeds, and sit all night by each other's bedsides in
sickness, and comfort each other in sorrow and disappoint-
ment with silent, manly sympathy—'wait till you get to
forty year!'

Wait even till each or either of you gets himself a little
pinnacle of his own—be it ever so humble!

Nay, wait till either or each of you gets himself a
wife!

History goes on repeating itself, and so do novels,

and this is a platitude, and there's nothing new under the sun.

May too cecee (as the idiomatic Laird would say in the language he adores)—may too cecee ay nee eecee nee lâh !

Then there was Dodor, the handsome young *dragon de la garde*—a full private, if you please, with a beardless face, and damask-rosy cheeks, and a small waist, and narrow feet like a lady's, and who, strange to say, spoke English just like an Englishman.

And his friend Gontran, *alias* l'Zouzou—a corporal in the Zouaves.

Both of these worthies had met Taffy in the Crimea, and frequented the studios in the Quartier Latin, where they adored (and were adored by) the grisettes and models, especially Trilby.

Both of them were distinguished for being the worst subjects (*les plus mauvais garnements*) of their respective regiments ; yet both were special favourites not only with their fellow-rankers, but with those in command, from their colonels downward.

Both were in the habit of being promoted to the rank of corporal or brigadier, and degraded to the rank of private next day for general misconduct, the result of a too exuberant delight in their promotion.

Neither of them knew fear, envy, malice, temper, or low spirits ; ever said or did an ill-natured thing ; ever even thought one ; ever had an enemy but himself. Both had the best or the worst manners going, according to their company, whose manners they reflected ; they were true chameleons !

Both were always ready to share their last ten-sou

piece (not that they ever seemed to have one) with each
other or anybody else, or anybody else's last ten-sou
piece with you ; to offer you a friend's cigar ; to invite
you to dine with any friend they had ; to fight with you,
or for you, at a moment's notice.   And they made up for
all the anxiety, tribulation, and sorrow they caused at
home by the endless fun and amusement they gave to
all outside.

It was a pretty dance they led ; but our three friends
of the Place St. Anatole (who hadn't got to pay the
pipers) loved them both, especially Dodor.

One fine Sunday afternoon Little Billee found himself
studying life and character in that most delightful and
festive scene la Fête de St. Cloud, and met Dodor and
l'Zouzou there, who hailed him with delight, saying :

' Nous allons joliment jubiler, nom d'une pipe ! ' and
insisted on his joining in their amusements and paying
for them—round-abouts, swings, the giant, the dwarf, the
strong man, the fat woman—to whom they made love
and were taken too seriously, and turned out—the
menagerie of wild beasts, whom they teased and aggravated
till the police had to interfere.   Also *al fresco* dances, where
their cancan step was of the wildest and most unbridled
character, till a *sous-officier* or a gendarme came in sight, and
then they danced quite mincingly and demurely, *en maître
d'école*, as they called it, to the huge delight of an immense
and ever-increasing crowd, and the disgust of all truly
respectable men.

They also insisted on Little Billee's walking between
them, arm-in-arm, and talking to them in English whenever they saw coming towards them a respectable English
family with daughters.   It was the dragoon's delight to

"'I WILL NOT! I WILL NOT!'"

L

get himself stared at by fair daughters of Albion for
speaking as good English as themselves—a rare accomplishment in a French trooper—and Zouzou's happiness to be thought English too, though the only English
he knew was the phrase, ' I will not !   I will not !' which
he had picked up in the Crimea, and repeated over and
over again when he came within ear-shot of a pretty
English girl.

Little Billee was not happy in these circumstances.
He was no snob.   But he was a respectably-brought-up
young Briton of the higher middle class, and it was not
quite pleasant for him to be seen (by fair country-women
of his own) walking arm-in-arm on a Sunday afternoon
with a couple of French private soldiers, and uncommonly
rowdy ones at that.

Later, they came back to Paris together on the top of
an omnibus, among a very proletarian crowd ; and there
the two facetious warriors immediately made themselves
pleasant all round and became very popular, especially
with the women and children ; but not, I regret to say,
through the propriety, refinement, and discretion of their
behaviour.   Little Billee resolved that he would not go
a-pleasuring with them any more.

However, they stuck to him through thick and thin,
and insisted on escorting him all the way back to the
Quartier Latin by the Pont de la Concorde and the Rue
de Lille in the Faubourg St. Germain.

Little Billee loved the Faubourg St. Germain, especially
the Rue de Lille.   He was fond of gazing at the magnificent old mansions, the *hôtels* of the old French noblesse,
or rather the outside walls thereof, the grand sculptured
portals with the armorial bearings and the splendid old

historic names above them——Hôtel de This, Hôtel de
That, Rohan-Chabot, Montmorency, La Rochefoucauld-
Liancourt, La Tour d'Auvergne.

He would forget himself in romantic dreams of past
and forgotten French chivalry which these glorious names
called up; for he knew a little of French history, loving
to read Froissart and Saint Simon and the genial
Brantôme.

Halting opposite one
of the finest and oldest
of all these gateways, his
especial favourite, labelled

DODOR IN HIS GLORY

'Hôtel de la Rochemartel' in letters of faded gold over a ducal coronet and a huge escutcheon of stone, he began to descant upon its architectural beauties and noble proportions to l'Zouzou.

'*Parbleu!*' said l'Zouzou, '*connu, farceur!* why, I was *born* there, on the 6th of March 1834, at 5.30 in the morning. Lucky day for France—*hein?*'

'Born there? what do you mean—in the porter's lodge?'

At this juncture the two great gates rolled back, a liveried *Suisse* appeared, and an open carriage and pair came out, and in it were two elderly ladies and a younger one.

To Little Billee's indignation, the two incorrigible warriors made the military salute, and the three ladies bowed stiffly and gravely.

And then (to Little Billee's horror this time) one of them happened to look back, and Zouzou actually kissed his hand to her.

'Do you *know* that lady?' asked Little Billee, very sternly.

'*Parbleu! si je la connais!* Why, it's my mother! Isn't she nice? She's rather cross with me just now.'

'Your *mother!* Why, what do you mean? What on earth would your mother be doing in that big carriage and at that big house?'

'*Parbleu, farceur!* She lives there!'

'*Lives* there? Why, who and what is she, your mother?

'The Duchesse de la Rochemartel, *parbleu!* and that's my sister; and that's my aunt, Princesse de Chevagné-Bauffremont! She's the "*patronne*" of that *chic* equipage. She's a millionaire, my aunt Chevagné!'

HÔTEL DE LA ROCHEMARTEL

'Well, I never!   What's *your* name, then?'

'Oh, *my* name!   Hang it—let me see!   Well—
Gontran—Xavier—François—Marie—Joseph d'Amaury
de Brissac de Roncesvaulx de la Rochemartel-Boisségur,
at your service!'

'Quite correct!' said Dodor; '*l'enfant dit vrai!*'

'Well—I—never!   And what's *your* name, Dodor?'

'Oh!   I'm only a humble individual, and answer to
the one-horse name of Théodore Rigolot de Lafarce.
But Zouzou's an awful swell, you know—his brother's the
Duke!'

Little Billee was no snob.   But he was a respectably-
brought-up young Briton of the higher middle class, and
these revelations, which he could not but believe,
astounded him so that he could hardly speak.   Much as
he flattered himself that he scorned the bloated aristocracy, titles are titles—even French titles!—and when it
comes to dukes and princesses who live in houses like
the Hôtel de la Rochemartel . . . !

It's enough to take a respectably-brought-up young
Briton's breath away.

When he saw Taffy that evening, he exclaimed: 'I
say, Zouzou's mother's a duchess!'

'Yes—the Duchesse de la Rochemartel-Boisségur.'

'You never told me!'

'You never asked me.   It's one of the greatest names
in France.   They're very poor, I believe.'

'Poor!   You should see the house they live in!'

'I've been there, to dinner; and the dinner wasn't
very good.   They let a great part of it, and live mostly
in the country.   The Duke is Zouzou's brother; very
unlike Zouzou; he's consumptive and unmarried, and the

most respectable man in Paris.   Zouzou will be the Duke
some day.'

'And Dodor—he's a swell, too, I suppose—he says
he's *de* something or other ! '

'Yes—Rigolot de Lafarce.   I've no doubt he descends
from the Crusaders too ; the name seems to favour it,
anyhow ; and such lots of them do in this country.   His
mother was English, and bore the worthy name of Brown.
He was at school in England ; that's why he speaks
English so well—and behaves so badly, perhaps !   He's
got a very beautiful sister, married to a man in the 60th
Rifles—Jack Reeve, a son of Lord Reevely's ; a selfish
sort of chap.   I don't suppose he gets on very well with
his brother-in-law.   Poor Dodor !   His sister's about the
only living thing he cares for—except Zouzou.'

I wonder if the bland and genial Monsieur Théodore
—'notre Sieur Théodore'—now junior partner in the
great haberdashery firm of ' Passefil et Rigolot,' on the
Boulevard des Capucines, and a pillar of the English
chapel in the Rue Marbœuf, is very hard on his
employés and employées if they are a little late at their
counters on a Monday morning?

I wonder if that stuck-up, stingy, stodgy, communard-
shooting, church-going, time-serving, place-hunting, pious-
eyed, pompous old prig, martinet, and philistine, Monsieur
le Maréchal-Duc de la Rochemartel-Boisségur, ever tells
Madame la Maréchale-Duchesse (*née* Hunks, of Chicago)
how once upon a time Dodor and he—

We will tell no tales out of school.

The present scribe is no snob.   He is a respectably-
brought-up old Briton of the higher middle class—at

least, he flatters himself so. And he writes for just such
old philistines as himself, who date from a time when
titles were not thought so cheap as to-day. Alas! all
reverence for all that is high and time-honoured and
beautiful seems at a discount.

So he has kept his blackguard ducal Zouave for the
bouquet of this little show—the final *bonne bouche* in his
Bohemian *menu*—that he may make it palatable to those
who only look upon the good old Quartier Latin (now no
more to speak of) as a very low, common, vulgar quarter indeed, deservedly swept away, where misters the students
(shocking bounders and cads) had nothing better to do,
day and night, than mount up to a horrid place called the
thatched house—*la chaumière*—

> ' Pour y danser le cancan
> Ou le Robert Macaire—
> Toujours—toujours—toujours—
> La nuit comme le jour . . .
> Et youp! youp! youp!
> Tra la la la la . . . la la la!'

Christmas was drawing near.

There were days when the whole Quartier Latin would
veil its iniquities under fogs almost worthy of the Thames
Valley between London Bridge and Westminster, and out
of the studio window the prospect was a dreary blank.
No Morgue! no towers of Notre Dame! not even the
chimney-pots over the way—not even the little mediæval
toy turret at the corner of the Rue Vieille des Trois
Mauvais Ladres, Little Billee's delight!

The stove had to be crammed till its sides grew a
dull deep red before one's fingers could hold a brush or
squeeze a bladder; one had to box or fence at nine in

the morning, that one might recover from the cold bath, and get warm for the rest of the day!

Taffy and the Laird grew pensive and dreamy, child-like and bland; and when they talked it was generally about Christmas at home in Merry England and the distant Land of Cakes, and how good it was to be there at such a time—hunting, shooting, curling, and endless carouse!

It was Ho! for the jolly West Riding, and Hey! for the bonnets of Bonnie Dundee, till they grew quite homesick, and wanted to start by the very next train.

They didn't do anything so foolish. They wrote over to friends in London for the biggest turkey, the biggest plum-pudding, that could be got for love or money, with mince-pies, and holly and mistletoe, and sturdy, short, thick English sausages; half a Stilton cheese, and a sirloin of beef—two sirloins, in case one should not be enough.

For they meant to have a Homeric feast in the studio on Christmas Day—Taffy, the Laird, and Little Billee—and invite all the delightful chums I have been trying to describe; and that is just why I tried to describe them—Durien, Vincent, Antony, Lorrimer, Carnegie, Petrolicoconose, l'Zouzou, and Dodor!

The cooking and waiting should be done by Trilby, her friend Angèle Boisse, M. et Mme. Vinard, and such little Vinards as could be trusted with glass and crockery and mince-pies; and if that was not enough, they would also cook themselves, and wait upon each other.

When dinner should be over, supper was to follow with scarcely any interval to speak of; and to partake of this other guests should be bidden—Svengali and Gecko, and perhaps one or two more. No ladies!

For, as the unsusceptible Laird expressed it, in the language of a gillie he had once met at a servant's dance in a Highland country-house, ' Them wimmen spiles the ball ! '

Elaborate cards of invitation were sent out, in the designing and ornamentation of which the Laird and Taffy exhausted all their fancy (Little Billee had no time).

Wines and spirits and English beers were procured at great cost from M. E. Delevingne's, in the Rue St. Honoré, and liqueurs of every description—chartreuse, curaçoa, *ratafia de cassis*, and anisette ; no expense was spared.

Also, truffled galantines of turkey, tongues, hams, *rillettes de Tours*, *pâtés de foie gras*, *fromage d'Italie* (which has nothing to do with cheese), *saucissons d'Arles et de Lyon*, with and without garlic, cold jellies peppery and salt—everything that French *charcutiers* and their wives can make out of French pigs, or any other animal whatever, beast, bird, or fowl (even cats and rats), for the supper ; and sweet jellies, and cakes, and sweetmeats, and confections of all kinds, from the famous pastry-cook at the corner of the Rue Castiglione.

Mouths went watering all day long in joyful anticipation. They water somewhat sadly now at the mere remembrance of these delicious things—the mere immediate sight or scent of which in these degenerate latter days would no longer avail to promote any such delectable secretion. *Hélas ! ahimè ! ach weh ! ay de mi ! eheu !* οἴμοι—in point of fact, *alas !*

That is the very exclamation I wanted.

Christmas Eve came round. The pieces of resistance

CHRISTMAS EVE

and plum-pudding and mince-pies had not yet arrived from London—but there was plenty of time.

Les trois Angliches dined at le père Trin's, as usual, and played billiards and dominoes at the Café du Luxembourg, and possessed their souls in patience till it was time to go and hear the midnight mass at the Madeleine, where Roucouly, the great barytone of the Opéra Comique, was retained to sing Adam's famous Noël.

The whole Quartier seemed alive with the *réveillon*. It was a clear, frosty night, with a splendid moon just past the full, and most exhilarating was the walk along the quays on the Rive Gauche, over the Pont de la Concorde and across the Place thereof, and up the thronged Rue de la Madeleine to the massive Parthenaic place of worship that always has such a pagan, worldly look of smug and prosperous modernity.

They struggled manfully, and found standing and kneeling room among that fervent crowd, and heard the impressive service with mixed feelings, as became true Britons of very advanced liberal and religious opinions; not with the unmixed contempt of the proper British Orthodox (who were there in full force, one may be sure).

But their susceptible hearts soon melted at the beautiful music, and in mere sensuous *attendrissement* they were quickly in unison with all the rest.

For as the clock struck twelve out pealed the organ, and up rose the finest voice in France :

> 'Minuit, Chrétiens ! c'est l'heure solennelle
> Où l'Homme-Dieu descendit parmi nous !'

And a wave of religious emotion rolled over Little Billee and submerged him ; swept him off his little legs, swept him out of his little self, drowned him in a great seething surge of love—love of his kind, love of love, love of life, love of death, love of all that is and ever was and ever will be—a very large order indeed, even for Little Billee.

' "ALLONS, GLYCÈRE! ROUGIS MON VERRE. . . ."

And it seemed to him that he stretched out his arms for love to one figure especially beloved beyond all the rest—one figure erect on high with arms outstretched to him, in more than common fellowship of need; not the sorrowful figure crowned with thorns, for it was in the likeness of a woman; but never that of the Virgin Mother of Our Lord.

It was Trilby, Trilby, Trilby! a poor fallen sinner and waif all but lost amid the scum of the most corrupt city on earth. Trilby weak and mortal like himself, and in woful want of pardon! and in her gray dove-like eyes he saw the shining of so great a love that he was abashed; for well he knew that all that love was his, and would be his for ever, come what would or could.

'Peuple, debout! Chante ta délivrance!
Noël! Noël! Voici le Rédempteur!'

So sang and rang and pealed and echoed the big, deep, metallic barytone bass—above the organ, above the incense, above everything else in the world—till the very universe seemed to shake with the rolling thunder of that great message of love and forgiveness!

Thus at least felt Little Billee, whose way it was to magnify and exaggerate all things under the subtle stimulus of sound, and the singing human voice had especially strange power to penetrate into his inmost depths—even the voice of man!

And what voice but the deepest and gravest and grandest there is can give worthy utterance to such a message as that, the epitome, the abstract, the very essence of all collective humanity's wisdom at its best!

Little Billee reached the Hôtel Corneille that night in a very exalted frame of mind indeed; the loftiest, lowliest mood of all.

Now see what sport we are of trivial, base, ignoble earthly things!

Sitting on the doorstep, and smoking two cigars at

once he found Ribot, one of his fellow-lodgers, whose room was just under his own. Ribot was so tipsy that he could not ring. But he could still sing, and did so at the top of his voice. It was not the Noël of Adam that he sang. He had not spent his *réveillon* in any church.

With the help of a sleepy waiter, Little Billee got the bacchanalian into his room and lit his candle for him, and, disengaging himself from his maudlin embraces, left him to wallow in solitude.

As he lay awake in his bed, trying to recall the deep and high emotions of the evening, he heard the tipsy hog below tumbling about his room and still trying to sing his senseless ditty :

> ' Allons, Glycère !
> Rougis mon verre
> Du jus divin dont mon cœur est toujours jaloux . . .
> Et puis à table,
> Bacchante aimable !
> Enivrons-nous (hic) Les g-glougloux sont des rendez-vous !' . . .

Then the song ceased for a while, and soon there were other sounds, as on a Channel steamer. Glougloux indeed !

Then the fear arose in Little Billee's mind lest the drunken beast should set fire to his bedroom curtains. All heavenly visions were chased away for the night. . . .

Our hero, half crazed with fear, disgust, and irritation, lay wide awake, his nostrils on the watch for the smell of burning chintz or muslin, and wondered how an educated man—for Ribot was a law-student—could ever make such a filthy beast of himself as that ! It was a scandal —a disgrace ; it was not to be borne ; there should be no forgiveness for such as Ribot—not even on Christmas Day ! He would complain to Madame Paul, the *patronne;* he would have Ribot turned out into the street; he would leave the hotel himself the very next morning! At last he fell asleep, thinking of all he would do; and thus, ridiculously and ignominiously for Little Billee, ended the *réveillon.*

Next morning he complained to Madame Paul; and though he did not give her warning, nor even insist on the expulsion of Ribot (who, as he heard with a hard heart, was *bien malade ce matin*), he expressed himself very severely on the conduct of that gentleman, and on the dangers from fire that might arise from a tipsy man being trusted alone in a small bedroom with chintz curtains and a lighted candle. If it hadn't been for himself, he told her, Ribot would have slept on the door-step, and serve him right! He was really grand in his virtuous indignation, in spite of his imperfect French; and Madame Paul was deeply contrite for her peccant lodger, and profuse in her apologies; and Little Billee began his twenty-first Christmas Day like a Pharisee, thanking his star that he was not as Ribot!

PART FOURTH

'Félicité passée
Qui ne peux revenir,
Tourment de ma pensée,
Que n'ay-je, en te perdant, perdu le souvenir !'

MID-DAY had struck. The expected hamper had not turned up in the Place St. Anatole des Arts.

All Madame Vinard's kitchen battery was in readiness ; Trilby and Madame Angèle Boisse were in the studio, their sleeves turned up, and ready to begin.

At twelve the *trois* Angliches and the two fair *blanchisseuses* sat down to lunch in a very anxious frame of mind, and finished a *pâté de foie gras* and two bottles of Burgundy between them, such was their disquietude.

The guests had been invited for six o'clock.

Most elaborately they laid the cloth on the table they had borrowed from the Hôtel de Seine, and settled who was to sit next to whom, and then unsettled it, and quarrelled over it—Trilby, as was her wont in such matters, assuming an authority that did not rightly belong to her, and of course getting her own way in the end.

And that, as the Laird remarked, was her confounded Trilbyness.

Two o'clock—three—four—but no hamper ! Darkness had almost set in. It was simply maddening.

M

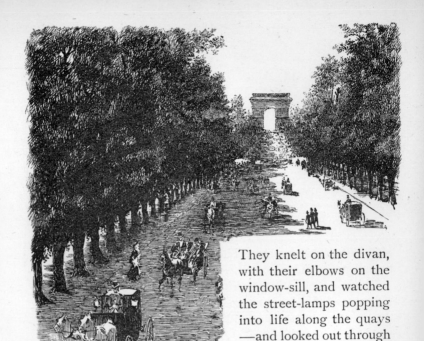

SOUVENIR

They knelt on the divan, with their elbows on the window-sill, and watched the street-lamps popping into life along the quays —and looked out through the gathering dusk for the van from the Chemin de Fer du Nord—and gloomily thought of the Morgue, which they could still make out across the river.

At length the Laird and Trilby went off in a cab to the station—a long drive—and, lo! before they came back the long-expected hamper arrived, at six o'clock.

And with it Durien, Vincent, Antony, Lorrimer, Carnegie, Petrolicoconose, Dodor, and l'Zouzou—the last two in uniform, as usual.

And suddenly the studio, which had been so silent, dark, and dull, with Taffy and Little Billee sitting hopeless and despondent round the stove, became a scene of the noisiest, busiest, and cheerfullest animation. The three big lamps were lit, and all the Chinese lanterns. The pieces of resistance and the pudding were whisked off by Trilby, Angèle, and Madame Vinard to other regions —the porter's lodge and Durien's studio (which had been lent for the purpose); and every one was pressed into the preparations for the banquet. There was plenty for idle hands to do. Sausages to be fried for the turkey, stuffing made, and sauces, salads mixed, and punch—holly hung in festoons all round and about—a thousand things. Everybody was so clever and good-humoured that nobody got in anybody's way—not even Carnegie, who was in evening dress (to the Laird's delight). So they made him do the scullion's work—cleaning, rinsing, peeling, etc.

The cooking of the dinner was almost better fun than the eating of it. And though there were so many cooks, not even the broth was spoiled (cockaleekie, from a receipt of the Laird's).

It was ten o'clock before they sat down to that most memorable repast.

Zouzou and Dodor, who had been the most useful and energetic of all its cooks, apparently quite forgot they were due at their respective barracks at that very moment; they had only been able to obtain *la permission de dix heures*. If they remembered it, the certainty that next day Zouzou would be reduced to the ranks for the fifth time, and Dodor confined to his barracks for a month, did not trouble them in the least.

The waiting was as good as the cooking. The handsome, quick, authoritative Madame Vinard was in a dozen places at once, and openly prompted, rebuked, and bully-ragged her husband into a proper smartness. The pretty little Madame Angèle moved about as deftly and as quietly as a mouse ; which of course did not prevent them both from genially joining in the general conversation whenever it wandered into French.

Trilby, tall, graceful, and stately, and also swift of action, though more like Juno or Diana than Hebe, devoted herself more especially to her own particular favourites— Durien, Taffy, the Laird, Little Billee—and Dodor and Zouzou, whom she loved, and *tutoyé'd en bonne camarade* as she served them with all there was of the choicest.

The two little Vinards did their little best—they scrupulously respected the mince-pies, and only broke two bottles of oil and one of Harvey sauce, which made their mother furious.   To console them, the Laird took one of them on each knee and gave them of his share of plum-pudding and many other unaccustomed good things, so bad for their little French tumtums.

The genteel Carnegie had never been at such a queer scene in his life.   It opened his mind—and Dodor and Zouzou, between whom he sat (the Laird thought it would do him good to sit between a private soldier and a humble corporal), taught him more French than he had learned during the three months he had spent in Paris.   It was a specialty of theirs.   It was more colloquial than what is generally used in diplomatic circles, and stuck longer in the memory ; but it hasn't interfered with his preferment in the Church.

He quite unbent.   He was the first to volunteer a song (without being asked) when the pipes and cigars were lit, and after the usual toasts had been drunk—Her Majesty's health, Tennyson, Thackeray, and Dickens ; and John Leech.

He sang, with a very cracked and rather hiccupy voice, his only song (it seems)—an English one, of which the burden, he explained, was French :

> 'Veeverler veeverler veeverler vee
> Veeverler companyee !'

And Zouzou and Dodor complimented him so profusely on his French accent that he was with difficulty prevented from singing it all over again.

Then everybody sang in rotation.

The Laird, with a capital barytone, sang

> 'Hie diddle dee for the Lowlands low,'

which was encored.

Little Billee sang 'Little Billee.'

Vincent sang.

> 'Old Joe kicking up behind and afore,
> And the yaller gal a-kicking up behind old Joe.'

A capital song, with words of quite a masterly scansion.

Antony sang 'Le Sire de Framboisy.' Enthusiastic encore.

Lorrimer, inspired no doubt by the occasion, sang the 'Hallelujah Chorus,' and accompanied himself on the piano, but failed to obtain an encore.

Durien sang

> 'Plaisir d'amour ne dure qu'un moment ;
> Chagrin d'amour dure toute la vie. . . .'

It was his favourite song, and is one of the beautiful songs of the world, and he sang it very well—and it became popular in the Quartier Latin ever after.

The Greek couldn't sing, and very wisely didn't.

Zouzou sang capitally a capital song in praise of *le vin à quat' sous !*

Taffy, in a voice like a high wind (and with a very good imitation of the Yorkshire brogue), sang a Somersetshire hunting ditty, ending :

> ' Of this 'ere song should I be axed the reason for to show,
> I don't exactly know, I don't exactly know !
> But all my fancy dwells upon Nancy,
> And I sing Tally-ho ! '

It is a quite superexcellent ditty, and haunts my memory to this day ; and one felt sure that Nancy was a dear and a sweet, wherever she lived, and when. So Taffy was encored twice—once for her sake, once for his own.

And finally, to the surprise of all, the bold dragoon sang (in English) ' My Sister Dear,' out of *Masaniello*, with such pathos, and in a voice so sweet and high and well in tune, that his audience felt almost weepy in the midst of their jollification ; and grew quite sentimental, as Englishmen abroad are apt to do when they are rather tipsy and hear pretty music, and think of their dear sisters across the sea, or their friends' dear sisters.

Madame Vinard interrupted her Christmas dinner on the model-throne to listen, and wept and wiped her eyes quite openly, and remarked to Madame Boisse, who stood modestly close by : ' Il est gentil tout plein, ce dragon ! Mon Dieu ! comme il chante bien ! Il est Angliche aussi, il paraît. Ils sont joliment bien élevés, tous ces Angliches—tous plus gentils les uns que les autres ! et quant à Monsieur Litrebili, on lui donnerait le bon Dieu sans confession ! '

And Madame Boisse agreed.

Then Svengali and Gecko came, and the table had to be laid and decorated anew, for it was supper-time.

"MY SISTER DEAR"

Supper was even jollier than dinner, which had taken off the keen edge of the appetites, so that every one talked at once—the true test of a successful supper—except when Antony told some of his experiences of Bohemia ; for instance, how, after staying at home all day for a month to avoid his creditors, he became reckless one Sunday morning, and went to the Bains Deligny, and jumped into a deep part by mistake, and was saved from a watery grave by a bold swimmer, who turned out to be his bootmaker, Satory, to whom he owed sixty francs—of all his duns the one he dreaded the most, and who didn't let him go in a hurry.

Whereupon Svengali remarked that he also owed sixty francs to Satory—' Mais comme che ne me baigne chamais, che n'ai rien à craindre !'

Whereupon there was such a laugh that Svengali felt he had scored off Antony at last, and had a prettier wit. He flattered himself that he'd got the laugh of Antony *this* time.

And after supper Svengali and Gecko made such lovely music that everybody was sobered and athirst again, and the punch-bowl, wreathed with holly and mistletoe, was placed in the middle of the table, and clean glasses set all round it.

Then Dodor and l'Zouzou stood up to dance with Trilby and Madame Angèle, and executed a series of cancan steps, which, though they were so inimitably droll that they had each and all to be encored, were such that not one of them need have brought the blush of shame to the cheek of modesty.

Then the Laird danced a sword-dance over two T-squares and broke them both. And Taffy, baring his

mighty arms to the admiring gaze of all, did dumb-bell
exercises, with Little Billee for a dumb-bell, and all but
dropped him into the punch-bowl; and tried to cut a
pewter ladle in two with Dodor's sabre, and sent it
through the window; and this made him cross, so that he
abused French sabres, and said they were made of worse
pewter than even French ladles; and the Laird sententiously opined that they managed these things better
in England, and winked at Little Billee.

A DUCAL FRENCH FIGHTING COCK

Then they played at 'cock-fighting,' with their wrists
tied across their shins, and a broomstick thrust in between; thus manacled, you are placed opposite your
antagonist, and try to upset him with your feet, and he
you. It is a very good game. The cuirassier and the

Zouave playing at this got so angry, and were so irresistibly funny a sight, that the shouts of laughter could be
heard on the other side of the river, so that a *sergent-de-
ville* came in and civilly requested them not to make so
much noise. They were disturbing the whole Quartier,
he said, and there was quite a *rassemblement* outside. So
they made him tipsy, and also another policeman, who
came to look after his comrade, and yet another; and
these guardians of the peace of Paris were trussed and
made to play at cock-fighting, and were still funnier than
the two soldiers, and laughed louder and made more
noise than any one else, so that Madame Vinard had to
remonstrate with them, till they got too tipsy to speak,
and fell fast asleep, and were laid next to each other
behind the stove.

The *fin de-siècle* reader, disgusted at the thought of
such an orgy as I have been trying to describe, must
remember that it happened in the fifties, when men calling themselves gentlemen, and being called so, still
wrenched off door-knockers and came back drunk from
the Derby, and even drank too much after dinner before
joining the ladies, as is all duly chronicled and set down
in John Leech's immortal pictures of life and character
out of *Punch*.

Then M. and Mme. Vinard and Trilby and Angèle
Boisse bade the company good-night, Trilby being the
last of them to leave.

Little Billee took her to the top of the staircase, and
there he said to her :

'Trilby, I have asked you nineteen times, and you
have refused. Trilby, once more, on Christmas night, for

"'ANSWER ME, TRILBY!'"

the twentieth time—*will* you marry me? If not, I leave Paris to-morrow morning, and never come back. I swear it on my word of honour!'

Trilby turned very pale, and leaned her back against the wall, and covered her face with her hands.

Little Billee pulled them away.

'Answer me, Trilby!'

'God forgive me, *yes!*' said Trilby, and she ran down-stairs, weeping.

It was now very late.

It soon became evident that Little Billee was in extraordinarily high spirits—in an abnormal state of excitement.

He challenged Svengali to spar, and made his nose bleed, and frightened him out of his sardonic wits. He performed wonderful and quite unsuspected feats of strength. He swore eternal friendship to Dodor and

A CARY*HA*TIDE

Zouzou, and filled their glasses again and again, and also (in his innocence) his own, and *trinquéd* with them many times running. They were the last to leave (except the three helpless policemen) ; and at about five or six in the morning, to his surprise, he found himself walking between Dodor and Zouzou by a late windy moonlight in the Rue Vieille des Trois Mauvais Ladres, now on one side of the frozen gutter, now on the other, now in the middle of it, stopping them now and then to tell them how jolly they were and how dearly he loved them.

Presently his hat flew away, and went rolling and skipping and bounding up the narrow street, and they discovered that as soon as they let each other go to run after it, they all three sat down.

So Dodor and Little Billee remained sitting, with their arms round each other's necks and their feet in the gutter, while Zouzou went after the hat on all fours, and caught it, and brought it back in his mouth like a tipsy retriever. Little Billee wept for sheer love and gratitude, and called him a cary*hat*ide (in English), and laughed loudly at his own wit, which was quite thrown away on Zouzou ! ' No man ever *had* such dear, dear frenge ! no man ever *was* s'happy !'

After sitting for a while in love and amity, they managed to get up on their feet again, each helping the other ; and in some never-to-be-remembered way they reached the Hôtel Corneille.

There they sat Little Billee on the door-step and rang the bell, and seeing some one coming up the Place de l'Odéon, and fearing he might be a *sergent-de-ville*, they bid Little Billee a most affectionate but hasty farewell, kissing him on both cheeks in French fashion, and contrived to get themselves round the corner and out of sight.

Little Billee tried to sing Zouzou's drinking-song :

' Quoi de plus doux
    Que les glougloux—
Les glougloux du vin à quat' sous. . . .'

The stranger came up.   Fortunately, it was no *sergent-de-ville*, but Ribot, just back from a Christmas-tree and a little family dance at his aunt's, Madame Kolb (the Alsatian banker's wife, in the Rue de la Chaussée d'Antin).

Next morning poor Little Billee was dreadfully ill.

He had passed a terrible night.   His bed had heaved like the ocean, with oceanic results.   He had forgotten to put out his candle, but fortunately Ribot had blown it out for him, after putting him to bed and tucking him up like a real good Samaritan.

And next morning, when Madame Paul brought him a cup of *tisane de chiendent* (which does not happen to mean a hair of the dog that bit him), she was kind, but very severe on the dangers and disgrace of intoxication, and talked to him like a mother.

' If it had not been for kind Monsieur Ribot ' (she told him), ' the doorstep would have been his portion ; and who could say he didn't deserve it ?   And then think of the danger of fire from a tipsy man all alone in a small bed-room with chintz curtains and a lighted candle !'

' Ribot was kind enough to blow out my candle,' said Little Billee, humbly.

' Ah, Dame !' said Madame Paul, with much meaning —' au moins il a *bon cœur*, Monsieur Ribot !'

And the cruellest sting of all was when the good-natured and incorrigibly festive Ribot came and sat by his bedside, and was kind and tenderly sympathetic, and got him a pick-me-up from the chemist's (unbeknown to Madame Paul).

'Credieu! vous vous êtes crânement bien amusé, hier soir! quelle bosse, hein! je parie que c'était plus drôle que chez ma tante Kolb!'

' "LES GLOUGLOUX DU VIN À QUAT' SOUS. . . ." '

All of which, of course, it is unnecessary to translate; except, perhaps, the word *bosse*, which stands for *noce*, which stands for a 'jolly good spree.'

In all his innocent little life Little Billee had never dreamed of such humiliation as this—such ignominious depths of shame and misery and remorse! He did not care to live. He had but one longing : that Trilby, dear Trilby, kind Trilby, would come and pillow his head on her beautiful white English bosom, and lay her soft, cool, tender hand on his aching brow, and there let him go to sleep, and sleeping, die !

He slept and slept, with no better rest for his aching brow than the pillow of his bed in the Hôtel Corneille, and failed to die this time. And when, after some forty-eight hours or so, he had quite slept off the fumes of that memorable Christmas debauch, he found that a sad thing had happened to him, and a strange !

It was as though a tarnishing breath had swept over the reminiscent mirror of his mind and left a little film behind it, so that no past thing he wished to see therein was reflected with quite the old pristine clearness. As though the keen, quick, razor-like edge of his power to reach and re-evoke the bygone charm and glamour and essence of things had been blunted and coarsened. As though the bloom of that special joy, the gift he unconsciously had of recalling past emotions and sensations and situations, and making them actual once more by a mere effort of the will, had been brushed away.

And he never recovered the full use of that most precious faculty, the boon of youth and happy childhood, and which he had once possessed, without knowing it, in such singular and exceptional completeness. He was to lose other precious faculties of his over-rich and complex nature—to be pruned and clipped and thinned—that his one supreme faculty of painting might have elbow-room to reach its fullest, or else you could never have seen the wood for the trees (or *vice versa*—which is it?)

On New Year's Day Taffy and the Laird were at their work in the studio, when there was a knock at the door, and Monsieur Vinard, cap in hand, respectfully introduced a pair of visitors, an English lady and gentleman.

The gentleman was a clergyman, small, thin, round-shouldered, with a long neck; weak-eyed and dryly polite. The lady was middle-aged, though still young-looking; very pretty, with gray hair; very well dressed; very small, full of nervous energy, with tiny hands and feet. It was Little Billee's mother; and the clergyman, the Rev. Thomas Bagot, was her brother-in-law.

Their faces were full of trouble—so much so that the two painters did not even apologise for the carelessness of their attire, or for the odour of tobacco that filled the room. Little Billee's mother recognised the two painters at a glance, from the sketches and descriptions of which her son's letters were always full.

They all sat down.

After a moment's embarrassed silence, Mrs. Bagot exclaimed, addressing Taffy: 'Mr. Wynne, we are in terrible distress of mind. I don't know if my son has told you, but on Christmas day he engaged himself to be married!'

'To—be—*married!*' exclaimed Taffy and the Laird, for whom this was news indeed.

'Yes—to be married to a Miss Trilby O'Ferrall, who, from what he implies, is in quite a different position in life from himself. Do you know the lady, Mr. Wynne?'

'Oh yes! I know her very well indeed; we *all* know her.'

N

' Is she English ? '

' She's an English subject, I believe.'

' Is she a Protestant or a Roman Catholic ? ' inquired the clergyman.

' A—a—upon my word, I really don't know ! '

' You know her very well indeed, and you *don't— know—that*, Mr. Wynne ! ' exclaimed Mr. Bagot.

' Is she a *lady*, Mr. Wynne ? ' asked Mrs. Bagot, somewhat impatiently, as if that were a much more important matter.

By this time the Laird had managed to basely desert his friend ; had got himself into his bedroom, and from thence, by another door, into the street and away.

' A lady ? ' said Taffy ; ' a—it so much depends upon what that word exactly means, you know ; things are so —a—so different here. Her father was a gentleman, I believe—a Fellow of Trinity, Cambridge—and a clergyman, if *that* means anything ! . . . he was unfortunate and all that—a—intemperate, I fear, and not successful in life. He has been dead six or seven years.'

' And her mother ? '

' I really know very little about her mother, except that she was very handsome, I believe, and of inferior social rank to her husband. She's also dead ; she died soon after him.'

' What is the young lady, then ? An English governess, or something of that sort ? '

' Oh no, no—a—nothing of *that* sort,' said Taffy (and inwardly, ' You coward—you cad of a Scotch thief of a sneak of a Laird—to leave all this to me ! ')

' What ? Has she independent means of her own, then ? '

'A—not that I know of; I should even say, decidedly not!'

'What *is* she, then? She's at least respectable, I hope?'

'"IS SHE A *LADY*, MR. WYNNE?"'

'At present she's a—a *blanchisseuse de fin*—that is considered respectable here.'

'Why, that's a washerwoman, isn't it?'

'Well—rather better than that, perhaps—*de fin*, you know!—things are so different in Paris! I don't think you'd say she was very much like a washerwoman—to look at!'

'Is she so good-looking, then?'

'Oh yes; extremely so. You may well say that—very beautiful, indeed—about that, at least, there is no doubt whatever!'

'And of unblemished character?'

Taffy, red and perspiring as if he were going through his Indian-club exercise, was silent—and his face expressed a miserable perplexity. But nothing could equal the anxious misery of those two maternal eyes, so wistfully fixed on his.

After some seconds of a most painful stillness, the lady said, 'Can't you—oh, *can't* you give me an answer, Mr. Wynne?'

'Oh, Mrs. Bagot, you have placed me in a terrible position! I—I love your son just as if he were my own brother! This engagement is a complete surprise to me —a most painful surprise! I'd thought of many possible things, but never of *that!* I cannot—I really *must* not conceal from you that it would be an unfortunate marriage for your son—from a—a worldly point of view, you know —although both I and M'Allister have a very deep and warm regard for poor Trilby O'Ferrall—indeed, a great admiration and affection and respect. She was once a model.'

'A *model*, Mr. Wynne? What *sort* of a model—there are models and models, of course.'

'Well, a model of every sort, in every possible sense of the word—head, hands, feet, everything!'

'A model for the *figure?*'

'Well—yes!'

'Oh, my God! my God! my God!' cried Mrs. Bagot
—and she got up and walked up and down the studio in
a most terrible state of agitation, her brother-in-law
following her and begging her to control herself. Her
exclamations seemed to shock him, and she didn't seem
to care.

'Oh! Mr. Wynne! Mr. Wynne! If you only *knew*
what my son is to me—to all of us—always has been!
He has been with us all his life, till he came to this
wicked, accursed city! My poor husband would never
hear of his going to any school, for fear of all the harm
he might learn there. My son was as innocent and pure-
minded as any girl, Mr. Wynne—I could have trusted
him anywhere—and that's why I gave way and allowed
him to come *here*, of all places in the world—all alone.
Oh! I should have come with him! Fool—fool—fool
that I was! . . .

'Oh, Mr. Wynne, he won't see either his mother or
his uncle! I found a letter from him at the hotel, saying
he'd left Paris—and I don't even know where he's gone!
. . . Can't *you*, can't Mr. M'Allister do *anything* to
avert this miserable disaster? You don't know how he
loves you both—you should see his letters to me and to
his sister! they are always full of you!'

'Indeed, Mrs. Bagot—you can count on M'Allister
and me for doing everything in our power! But it is of
no use our trying to influence your son—I feel quite sure
of *that!* It is to *her* we must make our appeal.'

'Oh, Mr. Wynne! to a washerwoman—a figure model
—and Heaven knows what besides! and with such a
chance as this!'

'Mrs. Bagot, you don't know her! She may have

been all that.   But strange as it may seem to you—and
seems to me, for that matter—she's a—she's—upon my
word of honour, I really think she's about the best woman
I ever met—the most unselfish—the most——'

'Ah !   She's a *beautiful* woman—I can well see *that !* '

'She has a beautiful nature, Mrs. Bagot—you may
believe me or not as you like—and it is to that I shall
make my appeal, as your son's friend, who has his interests
at heart.   And let me tell you that deeply as I grieve for
you in your present distress, my grief and concern for her
are far greater ! '

'What ! grief for her if she marries my son ! '

'No, indeed—but if she refuses to marry him.   She
may not do so, of course—but my instinct tells me she
will ! '

'Oh ! Mr. Wynne, is that likely ? '

'I will do my best to make it so—with such an utter
trust in her unselfish goodness of heart and her passionate
affection for your son as——'

'How do you know she has all this passionate
affection for him ? '

'Oh, M'Allister and I have long guessed it—though
we never thought this particular thing would come of it.
I think, perhaps, that first of all you ought to see her
yourself—you would get quite a new idea of what she
really is—you would be surprised, I assure you.'

Mrs. Bagot shrugged her shoulders impatiently, and
there was silence for a minute or two.

And then, just as in a play, Trilby's 'Milk below ! '
was sounded at the door, and Trilby came into the little
antechamber, and seeing strangers, was about to turn back.
She was dressed as a grisette, in her Sunday gown and

pretty white cap (for it was New Year's Day), and looking her very best.

Taffy called out, 'Come in, Trilby!'

And Trilby came into the studio.

As soon as she saw Mrs. Bagot's face she stopped short—erect, her shoulders a little high, her mouth a little open, her eyes wide with fright—and pale to the lips—a pathetic, yet commanding, magnificent, and most distinguished apparition, in spite of her humble attire.

The little lady got up and walked straight to her, and looked up into her face, that seemed to tower so. Trilby breathed hard.

At length Mrs. Bagot said, in her high accents, 'You are Miss Trilby O'Ferrall?'

'Oh yes yes I am Trilby O'Ferrall, and you are Mrs. Bagot; I can see that!'

A new tone had come into her large, deep, soft voice, so tragic, so touching, so strangely in accord with her whole aspect just then—so strangely in accord with the whole situation—that Taffy felt his cheeks and lips turn cold, and his big spine thrill and tickle all down his back.

'Oh yes; you are very, very beautiful—there's no doubt about *that!* You wish to marry my son?'

'I've refused to marry him nineteen times—for his own sake; he will tell you so himself. I am not the right person for him to marry. I know that. On Christmas night he asked me for the twentieth time; he swore he would leave Paris next day for ever if I refused him. I hadn't the courage. I was weak, you see! It was a dreadful mistake.'

'Are you so fond of him?'

'*Fond* of him? Aren't *you?*'

'I'm his mother, my good girl!'

To this Trilby seemed to have nothing to say.

'You have just said yourself you are not a fit wife for

'"*FOND* OF HIM? AREN'T *YOU?*"'

him. If you are so *fond* of him, will you ruin him by marrying him; drag him down; prevent him from getting on in life; separate him from his sister, his family, his friends?'

Trilby turned her miserable eyes to Taffy's miserable face, and said, ' Will it really be all that, Taffy ? '

' Oh, Trilby, things have got all wrong, and can't be righted ! I'm afraid it might be so. Dear Trilby—I can't tell you what I feel—but I can't tell you lies, you know ! '

' Oh no—Taffy—you don't tell lies ! '

Then Trilby began to tremble very much, and Taffy tried to make her sit down, but she wouldn't. Mrs. Bagot looked up into her face, herself breathless with keen suspense and cruel anxiety—almost imploring.

Trilby looked down at Mrs. Bagot very kindly, put out her shaking hand, and said : ' Good-bye, Mrs. Bagot. I will not marry your son. I *promise* you. I will never see him again.'

Mrs. Bagot caught and clasped her hand and tried to kiss it, and said : ' Don't go yet, my dear good girl. I want to talk to you. I want to tell you how deeply I ——'

' Good-bye, Mrs. Bagot,' said Trilby, once more ; and disengaging her hand, she walked swiftly out of the room.

Mrs. Bagot seemed stupefied, and only half content with her quick triumph.

' She will not marry your son, Mrs. Bagot. I only wish to God she'd marry *me !* '

' Oh, Mr. Wynne ! ' said Mrs. Bagot, and burst into tears.

' Ah ! ' exclaimed the clergyman, with a feebly satirical smile and a little cough and sniff that were not sympathetic, ' now if *that* could be arranged—and I've no doubt there wouldn't be much opposition on the part of the lady' (here he made a little complimentary bow), 'it would be a very desirable thing all round!'

'It's tremendously good of you, I'm sure—to interest yourself in *my* humble affairs,' said Taffy. 'Look here, sir—I'm not a great genius like your nephew—and it doesn't much matter to any one but myself what I make of my life—but I can assure you that if Trilby's heart were set on me as it is on him, I would gladly cast in my lot with hers for life. She's one in a thousand. She's the one sinner that repenteth, you know?'

'Ah, yes—to be sure!—to be sure! I know all about that; still, facts are facts, and the world is the world, and we've got to live in it,' said Mr. Bagot, whose satirical smile had died away under the gleam of Taffy's choleric blue eye.

Then said the good Taffy, frowning down on the parson (who looked mean and foolish, as people can sometimes do even with right on their side): 'And now, Mr. Bagot—I can't tell you how very keenly I have suffered during this— a—this most painful interview—on account of my very deep regard for Trilby O'Ferrall. I congratulate you and your sister-in-law on its complete success. I also feel very deeply for your nephew. I'm not sure that he has not lost more than he will gain by—a—by the—a—the success of this—a—this interview, in short!'

Taffy's eloquence was exhausted, and his quick temper was getting the better of him.

Then Mrs. Bagot, drying her eyes, came and took his hand in a very charming and simple manner, and said: 'Mr. Wynne, I think I know what you are feeling just now. You must try and make some allowance for us. You will, I am sure, when we are gone, and you have had

time to think a little. As for that noble and beautiful
girl, I only wish that she were such that my son *could*
marry her—in her past life, I mean. It is not her
humble rank that would frighten me ; *pray* believe that I
am quite sincere in this—and don't think too hardly of
your friend's mother. Think of all I shall have to go
through with my poor son—who is deeply in love—and
no wonder ! and who has won the love of such a woman
as that ! and who cannot see at present how fatal to him
such a marriage would be. I can see all the charm and
believe in all the goodness, in spite of all. And, oh, how
beautiful she is, and what a voice ! All that counts for so
much, doesn't it ? I cannot tell you how I grieve for her.
I can make no amends—who could, for such a thing ?
There are no amends, and I shall not even try. I will
only write and tell her all I think and feel. You will
forgive us, won't you ? '

And in the quick, impulsive warmth and grace and
sincerity of her manner as she said all this, Mrs. Bagot was
so absurdly like Little Billee that it touched big Taffy's
heart, and he would have forgiven anything, and there
was nothing to forgive.

'Oh, Mrs. Bagot, there's no question of forgiveness.
Good heavens ! it is all so unfortunate, you know ! Nobody's to blame, that I can see. Good-bye, Mrs. Bagot ;
good-bye, sir,' and so saying, he saw them down to their
remise, in which sat a singularly pretty young lady of
seventeen or so, pale and anxious, and so like Little Billee
that it was quite funny, and touched big Taffy's heart
again.

When Trilby went out into the courtyard in the Place

St. Anatole des Arts, she saw Miss Bagot looking out of
the carriage window, and in the young lady's face, as she
caught her eye, an expression of sweet surprise and sympathetic admiration, with lifted eyebrows and parted lips
—just such a look as she had often got from Little Billee!
She knew her for his sister at once.   It was a sharp
pang.

She turned away, saying to herself: 'Oh no; I will
not separate him from his sister, his family, his friends!
That would *never* do!   *That's* settled, anyhow!'

Feeling a little dazed, and wishing to think, she
turned up the Rue Vieille des Mauvais Ladres, which was
always deserted at this hour.   It was empty, but for a
solitary figure sitting on a post, with its legs dangling,
its hands in its trousers-pockets, an inverted pipe in its
mouth, a tattered straw hat on the back of its head, and
a long gray coat down to its heels.   It was the Laird.

As soon as he saw her he jumped off his post and
came to her, saying: 'Oh, Trilby—what's it all about?
I couldn't stand it!   I ran away!   Little Billee's mother's
there!'

'Yes, Sandy dear, I've just seen her.'

'Well, what's up?'

'I've promised her never to see Little Billee any
more.   I was foolish enough to promise to marry him.
I refused many times these last three months, and then
he said he'd leave Paris and never come back, and so,
like a fool, I gave way.   I've offered to live with him
and take care of him and be his servant—to be everything he wished but his wife!   But he wouldn't hear of
it.   Dear, dear Little Billee! he's an angel—and I'll
take precious good care no harm shall ever come to him

through me ! I shall leave this hateful place and go and
live in the country : I suppose I must manage to get
through life somehow. . . . Days are so long—*aren't*
they ! and there's *such* a lot of 'em ! I know of some
poor people who were once very fond of me, and I could
live with them and help them and keep myself. The
difficulty is about Jeannot. I thought it all out before it
came to this. I was well prepared, you see.'

' SO LIKE LITTLE BILLEE '

She smiled in a forlorn sort of way, with her upper
lip drawn tight against her teeth, as if some one were
pulling her back by the lobes of her ears.

'Oh ! but, Trilby—what shall we do without you ?
Taffy and I, you know ! You've become one of us !'

'Now, how good and kind of you to say that !'
exclaimed poor Trilby, her eyes filling. 'Why, that's
just all I lived for, till all this happened. But it can't

be any more now, can it? Everything is changed for
me—the very sky seems different. Ah! Durien's little
song—" *Plaisir d'amour—chagrin d'amour !* " it's all quite
true, isn't it? I shall start immediately, and take
Jeannot with me, I think.'

'But where do you think of going?'

'Ah! I mayn't tell you that, Sandy dear—not for a
long time! Think of all the trouble there'd be. Well,
there's no time to be lost. I must take the bull by the
horns.'

She tried to laugh, and took him by his big side
whiskers and kissed him on the eyes and mouth, and her
tears fell on his face.

Then, feeling unable to speak, she nodded farewell,
and walked quickly up the narrow winding street. When
she came to the first bend she turned round and waved
her hand, and kissed it two or three times, and then
disappeared.

The Laird stared for several minutes up the empty
thoroughfare—wretched, full of sorrow and compassion.
Then he filled himself another pipe and lit it, and hitched
himself on to another post, and sat there dangling his
legs and kicking his heels, and waited for the Bagots'
cab to depart, that he might go up and face the righteous
wrath of Taffy like a man, and bear up against his bitter
reproaches for cowardice and desertion before the foe.

Next morning Taffy received two letters : one, a very
long one, was from Mrs. Bagot. He read it twice over,
and was forced to acknowledge that it was a very good
letter—the letter of a clever, warm-hearted woman, but a
woman also whose son was to her as the very apple of

"'I MUST TAKE THE BULL BY THE HORNS'"

her eye. One felt she was ready to flay her dearest
friend alive in order to make Little Billee a pair of
gloves out of the skin, if he wanted a pair ; but one also
felt she would be genuinely sorry for the friend. Taffy's
own mother had been a little like that, and he missed
her every day of his life.

Full justice was done by Mrs. Bagot to all Trilby's
qualities of head and heart and person ; but at the same
time she pointed out, with all the cunning and ingeniously
casuistic logic of her sex, when it takes to special
pleading (even when it has right on its side), what the
consequences of such a marriage must inevitably be in a
few years—even sooner ! The quick disenchantment,
the lifelong regret, on both sides !

He could not have found a word to controvert her
arguments, save perhaps in his own private belief that
Trilby and Little Billee were both exceptional people ;
and how could he hope to know Little Billee's nature
better than the boy's own mother !

And if he had been the boy's elder brother in blood,
as he already was in heart and affection, would he, should
he, could he have given his fraternal sanction to such a
match ?

Both as his friend and his brother he felt it was out
of the question.

The other letter was from Trilby, in her bold, careless
handwriting, that sprawled all over the page, and her
occasionally imperfect spelling. It ran thus :—

'My dear, dear Taffy—This is to say good-bye.
I'm going away, to put an end to all this misery, for
which nobody's to blame but myself.

'The very moment after I'd said *yes* to Little Billee I knew perfectly well what a stupid fool I was, and I've been ashamed of myself ever since. I had a miserable week, I can tell you. I knew how it would all turn out.

'I am dreadfully unhappy, but not half so unhappy as if I married him and he were ever to regret it and be ashamed of me; and of course he would, really, even if he didn't show it—good and kind as he is—an angel!

'Besides—of course I could never be a lady—how could I?—though I ought to have been one, I suppose. But everything seems to have gone wrong with me, though I never found it out before—and it can't be righted!

'Poor papa!

'I am going away with Jeannot. I've been neglecting him shamefully. I mean to make up for it all now.

'You mustn't try and find out where I am going; I know you won't if I beg you, nor any one else. It would make everything so much harder for me.

'Angèle knows; she has promised me not to tell. I should like to have a line from you very much. If you send it to her she will send it on to me.

'Dear Taffy, next to Little Billee, I love you and the Laird better than any one else in the whole world. I've never known real happiness till I met you. You have changed me into another person—you and Sandy and Little Billee.

'Oh, it *has* been a jolly time, though it didn't last long. It will have to do for me for life. So good-bye. I shall never, never forget; and remain, with dearest love, your ever faithful and most affectionate friend,

TRILBY O'FERRALL.

O

'*P.S.*—When it has all blown over and settled again, if it ever does, I shall come back to Paris, perhaps, and see you again some day.'

The good Taffy pondered deeply over this letter— read it half a dozen times at least ; and then he kissed it, and put it back into its envelope and locked it up.

He knew what very deep anguish underlay this some-what trivial expression of her sorrow.

He guessed how Trilby, so childishly impulsive and de-monstrative in the ordinary intercourse of friendship, would be more reticent than most women in such a case as this.

He wrote to her warmly, affectionately, at great length, and sent the letter as she had told him.

The Laird also wrote a long letter full of tenderly-worded friendship and sincere regard. Both expressed their hope and belief that they would soon see her again, when the first bitterness of her grief would be over, and that the old pleasant relations would be renewed.

And then, feeling wretched, they went and silently lunched together at the Café de l'Odéon, where the omelets were good and the wine wasn't blue.

Late that evening they sat together in the studio, reading. They found they could not talk to each other very readily without Little Billee to listen—three's company sometimes and two's none !

Suddenly there was a tremendous getting up the dark stairs outside in a violent hurry, and Little Billee burst into the room like a small whirlwind—haggard, out of breath, almost speechless at first with excitement.

' Trilby ! where is she ? . . . what's become of her ? . . . She's run away . . . oh ! She's written me such a

letter! . . . We were to have been married . . . at the
Embassy . . . my mother . . . she's been meddling ; and
that cursed old ass . . . that beast . . . my uncle ! . . .
They've been here ! I know all about it. . . . Why didn't
you stick up for her ? . . .'

' "TRILBY ! WHERE IS SHE ?" '

'I did . . . as well as I could. Sandy couldn't stand
it, and cut.'

'*You* stuck up for her . . . *you*—why, you agreed
with my mother that she oughtn't to marry me—you—
you false friend—*you* ! . . . Why, she's an angel—far too
good for the likes of *me* . . . you know she is. As . . .

as for her social position and all that, what degrading rot !
Her father was as much a gentleman as mine . . . besides
. . . what the devil do I care for her father ? . . . it's
her I want—*her*—*her*—*her*, I tell you . . . I can't *live*
without her . . . I must have her *back*—I must have her
back . . . do you *hear ?*   We were to have lived together at
Barbizon . . . all our lives—and I was to have painted
stunning pictures . . . like those other fellows there.
Who cares for *their* social position, I should like to know
. . . or that of their wives ?   *Damn* social position ! . . .
we've often said so—over and over again.   An artist's
life should be *away* from the world—above all that mean-
ness and paltriness . . . all in his work.   Social position,
indeed !   Over and over again we've said what fetid,
bestial rot it all was—a thing to make one sick and shut
one's self away from the world. . . . Why say one thing
and act another ? . . . Love comes before all—love levels
all—love and art . . . and beauty—before such beauty
as Trilby's rank doesn't exist.   Such rank as mine, too !
Good God ! I'll never paint another stroke till I've got
her back . . . never, never, never, I tell you—I can't—
I won't ! . . .'

And so the poor boy went on, tearing and raving
about in his rampage, knocking over chairs and easels,
stammering and shrieking, mad with excitement.

They tried to reason with him, to make him listen, to
point out that it was not her social position alone that un-
fitted her to be his wife and the mother of his children, etc.

It was no good.   He grew more and more uncontrollable, became almost unintelligible, he stammered so—a
pitiable sight and pitiable to hear.

'Oh ! oh ! good heavens ! are you so precious

immaculate, you two, that you should throw stones at poor Trilby! What a shame, what a hideous shame it is that there should be one law for the woman and another for the man! . . . poor weak women—poor, soft, affectionate things that beasts of men are always running after, and pestering, and ruining, and trampling under foot. . . . Oh! oh! it makes me sick — it makes me sick!' And finally he gasped and screamed and fell down in a fit on the floor.

The doctor was sent for; Taffy went in a cab to the Hôtel de Lille et d'Albion to fetch his mother; and poor Little Billee, quite unconscious, was undressed by Sandy and Madame Vinard and put into the Laird's bed.

The doctor came, and not long after Mrs. Bagot and her daughter. It was

LA SŒUR DE LITREBILI

a serious case. Another doctor was called in. Beds were got and made up in the studio for the two grief-stricken ladies, and thus closed the eve of what was to have been poor Little Billee's wedding-day, it seems.

Little Billee's attack appears to have been a kind of epileptic seizure. It ended in brain fever and other complications—a long and tedious illness. It was many

weeks before he was out of danger, and his convalescence
was long and tedious too.

His nature seemed changed. He lay languid and
listless—never even mentioned Trilby, except once to ask
if she had come back, and if any one knew where she was,
and if she had been written to.

She had not, it appears. Mrs. Bagot had thought it
was better not, and Taffy and the Laird agreed with her
that no good could come of writing.

Mrs. Bagot felt bitterly against the woman who had been
the cause of all this trouble, and bitterly against herself
for her injustice. It was an unhappy time for everybody.

There was more unhappiness still to come.

One day in February Madame Angèle Boisse called
on Taffy and the Laird in the temporary studio where
they worked. She was in terrible tribulation.

Trilby's little brother had died of scarlet fever and was
buried, and Trilby had left her hiding-place the day after
the funeral and had never come back, and this was a week
ago. She and Jeannot had been living at a village called
Vibraye, in La Sarthe, lodging with some poor people
she knew—she washing and working with her needle till
her brother fell ill.

She had never left his bedside for a moment, night or
day, and when he died her grief was so terrible that
people thought she would go out of her mind; and the
day after he was buried she was not to be found anywhere—she had disappeared, taking nothing with her, not
even her clothes—simply vanished and left no sign, no
message of any kind.

All the ponds had been searched—all the wells, and the small stream that flows through Vibraye—and the old forest.

Taffy went to Vibraye, cross-examined everybody he could, communicated with the Paris police, but with no result ; and every afternoon, with a beating heart, he went to the Morgue. . . .

The news was of course kept from Little Billee. There was no difficulty about this. He never asked a question, hardly ever spoke.

When he first got up and was carried into the studio he asked for his picture 'The Pitcher Goes to the Well,' and looked at it for a while, and then shrugged his shoulders and laughed —a miserable sort of laugh, painful to hear and see—the laugh of a cold old man, who laughs so as not to cry ! Then he looked at his mother and sister, and saw the sad havoc that grief and anxiety had wrought in them.

It seemed to him, as in a bad dream, that he had been mad for many years—a cause of endless sickening terror and distress ; and that his poor weak wandering wits had come back at last, bringing in their train cruel remorse, and the remembrance of all the patient love and kindness that had been lavished on him ; for many, many years ! His sweet sister—his dear, long-suffering mother ! what had really happened to make them look like this ?

And taking them both in his feeble arms, he fell a-weeping, quite desperately and for a long time.

And when his weeping-fit was over, when he had quite wept himself out, he fell asleep.

And when he awoke he was conscious that another sad thing had happened to him, and that for some

mysterious cause his power of loving had not come back
with his wandering wits—had been left behind—and it
seemed to him that it was gone for ever and ever—would
never come back again—not even his love for his mother

'HE FELL A-WEEPING, QUITE DESPERATELY'

and sister, not even his love for Trilby—where all *that*
had once been was a void, a gap, a blankness. . . .

Truly, if Trilby had suffered much, she had also been
the innocent cause of terrible suffering. Poor Mrs.
Bagot, in her heart, could not forgive her.

I feel this is getting to be quite a sad story, and that it is high time to cut this part of it short.

As the warmer weather came, and Little Billee got stronger, the studio became more lively. The ladies' beds were removed to another studio on the next landing, which was vacant, and the friends came to see Little Billee, and make life more easy for him and his mother and sister.

As for Taffy and the Laird, they had already long been to Mrs. Bagot as a pair of crutches, without whose invaluable help she could never have held herself upright to pick her way in all this maze of trouble.

Then M. Carrel came every day to chat with his favourite pupil and gladden Mrs. Bagot's heart. And also Durien, Carnegie, Petrolicoconose, Vincent, Antony, Lorrimer, Dodor, and l'Zouzou ; Mrs. Bagot thought the last two irresistible, when she had once been satisfied that they were 'gentlemen,' in spite of appearances. And, indeed, they showed themselves to great advantage ; and though they were so much the opposite to Little Billee in everything, she felt almost maternal towards them, and gave them innocent, good, motherly advice, which they swallowed *avec attendrissement,* not even stealing a look at each other. And they held Mrs. Bagot's wool, and listened to Miss Bagot's sacred music with upturned pious eyes, and mealy mouths that butter wouldn't melt in !

It is good to be a soldier and a detrimental ; you touch the hearts of women and charm them—old and young, high or low (excepting, perhaps, a few worldly mothers of marriageable daughters). They take the sticking of your tongue in the cheek for the wearing of your heart on the sleeve.

Indeed, good women all over the world, and ever since it began, have loved to be bamboozled by these genial, roistering dare-devils, who haven't got a penny to bless themselves with (which is so touching), and are supposed to carry their lives in their hands, even in piping times of peace. Nay, even a few rare *bad* women sometimes; such women as the best and wisest of us are often ready to sell our souls for!

> ' A lightsome eye, a soldier's mien,
>   A feather of the blue,
>   A doublet of the Lincoln green—
>   No more of me you knew,
>   My love !
>   No more of me you knew. . . .'

As if that wasn't enough, and to spare!

Little Billee could hardly realise that these two polite and gentle and sympathetic sons of Mars were the lively grigs who had made themselves so pleasant all round, and in such a singular manner, on the top of that St. Cloud omnibus; and he admired how they added hypocrisy to their other crimes!

Svengali had gone back to Germany, it seemed, with his pockets full of napoleons and big Havana cigars, and wrapped in an immense fur-lined coat, which he meant to wear all through the summer. But little Gecko often came with his violin and made lovely music, and that seemed to do Little Billee more good than anything else.

It made him realise in his brain all the love he could no longer feel in his heart. The sweet melodic phrase, rendered by a master, was as wholesome, refreshing balm to him while it lasted—as manna in the wilderness. It was the one good thing within his reach, never to be

"THE SWEET MELODIC PHRASE"

taken from him as long as his ear-drums remained and he could hear a master play.

Poor Gecko treated the two English ladies *de bas en haut* as if they had been goddesses, even when they accompanied him on the piano! He begged their pardon for every wrong note they struck, and adopted their 'tempi'—that is the proper technical term, I believe— and turned scherzos and allegrettos into funeral dirges to please them; and agreed with them, poor little traitor, that it all sounded much better like that!

O Beethoven! O Mozart! did you turn in your graves?

Then, on fine afternoons, Little Billee was taken for drives to the Bois de Boulogne with his mother and sister in an open fly, and generally Taffy as a fourth; to Passy, Auteuil, Boulogne, St. Cloud, Meudon—there are many charming places within an easy drive of Paris.

And sometimes Taffy or the Laird would escort Mrs. and Miss Bagot to the Luxembourg Gallery, the Louvre, the Palais Royal; to the Comédie Française once or twice; and on Sundays, now and then, to the English chapel in the Rue Marbœuf. It was all very pleasant; and Miss Bagot looks back on the days of her brother's convalescence as among the happiest in her life.

And they would all five dine together in the studio, with Madame Vinard to wait, and her mother (a cordon bleu) for cook; and the whole aspect of the place was changed and made fragrant, sweet, and charming by all this new feminine invasion and occupation.

And what is sweeter to watch than the dawn and growth of love's young dream, when strength and beauty meet together by the couch of a beloved invalid?

Of course the sympathetic reader will foresee how readily the stalwart Taffy fell a victim to the charms of his friend's sweet sister, and how she grew to return his more than brotherly regard! and how, one lovely evening, just as March was going out like a lamb (to make room for the first of April), Little Billee joined their hands together, and gave them his brotherly blessing!

As a matter of fact, however, nothing of this kind happened. Nothing ever happens but the *un*foreseen. Pazienza!

Then at length one day—it was a fine, sunny, showery day in April, by the bye, and the big studio window was open at the top and let in a pleasant breeze from the north-west, just as when our little story began—a railway omnibus drew up at the porte cochère in the Place St. Anatole des Arts, and carried away to the station of the Chemin de Fer du Nord Little Billee and his mother and sister, and all their belongings (the famous picture had gone before); and Taffy and the Laird rode with them, their faces very long, to see the last of the dear people, and of the train that was to bear them away from Paris, and Little Billee, with his quick, prehensile, æsthetic eye, took many a long and wistful parting gaze at many a French thing he loved, from the gray towers of Notre Dame downward—Heaven only knew when he might see them again!—so he tried to get their aspect well by heart, that he might have the better store of beloved shape and colour memories to chew the cud of when his lost powers of loving and remembering clearly should come back, and he lay awake at night and listened to the wash of the Atlantic along the beautiful red sandstone coast at home.

He had a faint hope that he should feel sorry at parting with Taffy and the Laird.

But when the time came for saying good-bye he couldn't feel sorry in the least, for all he tried and strained so hard !

So he thanked them so earnestly and profusely for all their kindness and patience and sympathy (as did also his mother and sister) that their hearts were too full to speak, and their manner was quite gruff—it was a way they had when they were deeply moved and didn't want to show it.

And as he gazed out of the carriage window at their two forlorn figures looking after him when the train steamed out of the station, his sorrow at not feeling sorry made him look so haggard and so woe-begone that they could scarcely bear the sight of him departing without them, and almost felt as if they must follow by the next train, and go and cheer him up in Devonshire, and themselves too.

They did not yield to this amiable weakness. Sorrowfully, arm-in-arm, with trailing umbrellas, they recrossed the river, and found their way to the Café de l'Odéon, where they ate many omelets in silence, and dejectedly drank of the best they could get, and were very sad indeed.

.   .   .   .   .   .

Nearly five years have elapsed since we bade farewell and *au revoir* to Taffy and the Laird at the Paris station of the Chemin de Fer du Nord, and wished Little Billee and his mother and sister Godspeed on their way to Devonshire, where the poor sufferer was to rest and lie fallow for a few months, and recruit his lost strength and

"SORROWFULLY. ARM IN ARM"

energy, that he might follow up his first and well-deserved success, which perhaps contributed just a little to his recovery.

Many of my readers will remember his splendid *début* at the Royal Academy in Trafalgar Square with that now so famous canvas 'The Pitcher Goes to the Well,' and how it was sold three times over on the morning of the private view, the third time for a thousand pounds—just five times what he got for it himself. And that was thought a large sum in those days for a beginner's picture two feet by four.

I am well aware that such a vulgar test is no criterion whatever of a picture's real merit. But this picture is well known to all the world by this time, and sold only last year at Christie's (more than thirty-six years after it was painted) for three thousand pounds.

Thirty-six years! That goes a long way to redeem even three thousand pounds of all their cumulative vulgarity.

'The Pitcher' is now in the National Gallery, with that other canvas by the same hand, 'The Moon-Dial.' There they hang together for all who care to see them, his first and his last—the blossom and the fruit.

He had not long to live himself, and it was his good fortune, so rare among those whose work is probably destined to live for ever, that he succeeded at his first go off.

And his success was of the best and most flattering kind.

It began high up, where it should, among the masters of his own craft. But his fame filtered quickly down to those immediately beneath, and through these to wider circles. And there was quite enough of opposition and vilification and coarse abuse of him to clear it of any suspicion of cheapness or evanescence. What better antiseptic can there be than the philistine's deep hate? what sweeter, fresher, wholesomer music than the sound of his voice when he doth so furiously rage?

Yes! That is 'good production'—as Svengali would have said—' C'est un cri du cœur.'

And then, when popular acclaim brings the great dealers and the big cheques, up rises the printed howl of the duffer, the disappointed one, the 'wounded thing with an angry cry'—the prosperous and happy bagman that *should* have been, who has given up all for art, and finds he can't paint and make himself a name, after all, and never will, so falls to writing about those who can—and what writing!

To write in hissing dispraise of our more successful fellow-craftsman, and of those who admire him—that is not a clean or pretty trade. It seems, alas! an easy one, and it gives pleasure to so many. It does not even want good grammar. But it pays—well enough even to start and run a magazine with, instead of scholarship, and taste, and talent! humour, sense, wit, and wisdom! It is something like the purveying of pornographic pictures: some of us look at them and laugh, and even buy. To be a purchaser is bad enough; but to be the purveyor thereof—ugh!

A poor devil of a cracked soprano (are there such people still?) who has been turned out of the Pope's choir because he can't sing in tune, *after all!*—think of him yelling and squeaking his treble rage at Santley—Sims Reeves—Lablache!

Poor, lost, beardless nondescript! why not fly to other climes, where at least thou might'st hide from us thy woful crack, and keep thy miserable secret to thyself! Are there no harems still left in Stamboul for the likes of thee to sweep and clean, no women's beds to make and slops to empty, and doors and windows to bar—and tales to carry, and the pasha's confidence and favour and protection to win? Even *that* is a better trade than pandering for hire to the basest instinct of all—the dirty pleasure we feel (some of us) in seeing mud and dead cats and rotten eggs flung at those we cannot but admire —and secretly envy!

All of which eloquence means that Little Billee was pitched into right and left, as well as overpraised. And it all rolled off him like water off a duck's back, both praise and blame.

It was a happy summer for Mrs. Bagot, a sweet compensation for all the anguish of the winter that had gone before, with her two beloved children together under her wing, and all the world (for her) ringing with the praise of her boy, the apple of her eye, so providentially rescued from the very jaws of death, and from other dangers almost as terrible to her fiercely-jealous maternal heart.

And his affection for her *seemed* to grow with his returning health; but, alas! he was never again to be quite the same light-hearted, innocent, expansive lad he had been before that fatal year spent in Paris.

One chapter of his life was closed, never to be reopened, never to be spoken of again by him to her, by her to him. She could neither forgive nor forget. She could but be silent.

Otherwise he was pleasant and sweet to live with, and everything was done to make his life at home as sweet and pleasant as a loving mother could—as could a most charming sister—and others' sisters who were charming too, and much disposed to worship at the shrine of this young celebrity, who woke up one morning in their little village to find himself famous, and bore his blushing honours so meekly. And among them the vicar's daughter, his sister's friend and co-teacher at the Sunday-school, 'a simple, pure, and pious maiden of gentle birth,' everything he once thought a young lady should be ; and her name it was Alice, and she was sweet, and her hair was brown —as brown ! . . .

And if he no longer found the simple country pleasures, the junketings and pic-nics, the garden-parties and innocent little musical evenings, quite so exciting as of old, he never showed it.

Indeed, there was much that he did not show, and that his mother and sister tried in vain to guess—many things.

And among them one thing that constantly preoccupied and distressed him—the numbness of his affections. He could be as easily demonstrative to his mother and sister as though nothing had ever happened to him— from the mere force of a sweet old habit—even more so, out of sheer gratitude and compunction.

But alas ! he felt that in his heart he could no longer care for them in the least !—nor for Taffy, nor the Laird, nor for himself; not even for Trilby, of whom he constantly thought, but without emotion ; and of whose strange disappearance he had been told, and the story had been confirmed in all its details by Angèle Boisse, to whom he had written.

It was as though some part of his brain where his affections were seated had been paralysed, while all the rest of it was as keen and as active as ever. He felt like some poor live bird or beast or reptile, a part of whose cerebrum (or cerebellum, or whatever it is) had been dug out by the vivisector for experimental purposes ; and the strongest emotional feeling he seemed capable of was his anxiety and alarm about this curious symptom, and his concern as to whether he ought to mention it or not.

He did not do so, for fear of causing distress, hoping that it would pass away in time, and redoubled his caresses to his mother and sister, and clung to them more than ever ; and became more considerate of others in thought and manner, word, and deed than he had ever been before, as though by constantly assuming the virtue he had no longer he would gradually coax it back again. There was no trouble he would not take to give pleasure to the humblest.

Also, his vanity about himself had become as nothing, and he missed it almost as much as his affection.

Yet he told himself over and over again that he was a great artist, and that he would spare no pains to make himself a greater. But that was no merit of his own.

$2 + 2 = 4$, also $2 \times 2 = 4$: that peculiarity was no reason why 4 should be conceited ; for what was 4 but a result, either way ?

Well, he was like 4—just an inevitable result of circumstances over which he had no control—a mere product or sum ; and though he meant to make himself as big a 4 as he could (to cultivate his peculiar *fourness*), he could no longer feel the old conceit and self-complacency; and they had been a joy, and it was hard to do without them.

At the bottom of it all was a vague, disquieting unhappiness, a constant fidget.

And it seemed to him, and much to his distress, that such mild unhappiness would be the greatest he could ever feel henceforward—but that, such as it was, it would never leave him, and that his moral existence would be for evermore one long gray gloomy blank—the glimmer of twilight—never glad, confident morning again!

So much for Little Billee's convalescence.

Then one day in the late autumn he spread his wings and flew away to London, which was very ready with open arms to welcome William Bagot, the already famous painter, *alias* Little Billee!

PART FIFTH

LITTLE BILLEE

An Interlude

Then the mortal coldness of the soul like death itself comes down ;
It cannot feel for others' woes, it dare not dream its own ;
That heavy chill has frozen o'er the fountain of our tears,
And, though the eye may sparkle yet, 'tis where the ice appears.

'Though wit may flash from fluent lips, and mirth distract the breast,
Through midnight hours that yield no more their former hope of rest :
'Tis but as ivy leaves around a ruined turret wreathe,
All green and wildly fresh without, but worn and gray beneath.'

WHEN Taffy and the Laird went back to the studio in the Place St. Anatole des Arts, and resumed their ordinary life there, it was with a sense of desolation and dull bereavement beyond anything they could have imagined ; and this did not seem to lessen as the time wore on.

They realised for the first time how keen and penetrating and unintermittent had been the charm of those two central figures—Trilby and Little Billee—and how hard it was to live without them, after such intimacy as had been theirs.

'Oh, it *has* been a jolly time, though it didn't last long !' So Trilby had written in her farewell letter to

Taffy; and these words were true for Taffy and the Laird as well as for her.

And that is the worst of those dear people who have charm : they are so terrible to do without, when once you have got accustomed to them and all their ways.

And when, besides being charming, they are simple, clever, affectionate, constant, and sincere, like Trilby and Little Billee! Then the lamentable hole their disappearance makes is not to be filled up! And when they are full of genius, like Little Billee—and like Trilby, funny without being vulgar! For so she always seemed to the Laird and Taffy, even in French (in spite of her Gallic audacities of thought, speech, and gesture).

All seemed to have suffered change. The very boxing and fencing were gone through perfunctorily, for mere health's sake ; and a thin layer of adipose deposit began to soften the outlines of the hills and dales on Taffy's mighty forearm.

Dodor and l'Zouzou no longer came so often, now that the charming Little Billee and his charming mother and still more charming sister had gone away—nor Carnegie, nor Antony, nor Lorrimer, nor Vincent, nor the Greek. Gecko never came at all. Even Svengali was missed, little as he had been liked. It is a dismal and sulky-looking piece of furniture, a grand piano that nobody ever plays—with all its sound and its souvenirs locked up inside—a kind of mausoleum! a lop-sided coffin, trestles and all! So it went back to London by the 'little quickness,' just as it had come!

Thus Taffy and the Laird grew quite sad and mopy, and lunched at the Café de l'Odéon every day—till the goodness of the omelets palled, and the redness of the

wine there got on their nerves and into their heads and
faces, and made them sleepy till dinner-time.   And then,
waking up, they dressed respectably, and dined expensively,
'like gentlemen,' in the Palais Royal, or the Passage
Choiseul, or the Passage des Panoramas—for three francs,
three francs fifty, even five francs a head, and half a franc
to the waiter !—and went to the theatre almost every
night, on that side of the water—and more often than not
they took a cab home, each smoking a Panatellas, which
costs twenty-five centimes—five sous—2½d. !

Then they feebly drifted into quite decent society—
like Lorrimer and Carnegie—with dress-coats and white
ties on, and their hair parted in the middle and down the
back of the head, and brought over the ears in a bunch at
each side, as was the English fashion in those days ; and
subscribed to *Galignani's Messenger ;* and had themselves
proposed and seconded for the Cercle Anglais in the Rue
Sainte-n'y Touche, a circle of British philistines of the
very deepest dye ; and went to hear divine service on
Sunday mornings in Rue Marbœuf !

Indeed, by the end of the summer they had sunk into
such depths of demoralisation that they felt they must
really have a change ; and decided on giving up the
studio in the Place St. Anatole des Arts, and leaving Paris
for good ; and going to settle for the winter in Düsseldorf,
which is a very pleasant place for English painters who do
not wish to overwork themselves—as the Laird well knew,
having spent a year there.

It ended in Taffy's going to Antwerp for the Kermesse,
to paint the Flemish drunkard of our time just as he
really is ; and the Laird's going to Spain, so that he
might study toreadors from the life.

DEMORALISATION

I may as well state here that the Laird's toreador pictures, which had had quite a vogue in Scotland as long as he had been content to paint them in the Place St. Anatole des Arts, quite ceased to please (or sell) after he had been to Seville and Madrid; so he took to painting Roman cardinals and Neapolitan pifferari from the depths of his consciousness—and was so successful that he made up his mind he would never spoil his market by going to Italy!

So he went and painted his cardinals and his pifferari in Algiers, and Taffy joined him there, and painted Algerian Jews—just as they really are (and didn't sell them) ; and then they spent a year in Munich, and then a year in Düsseldorf, and a winter in Cairo, and so on.

And all this time, Taffy, who took everything *au grand sérieux*—especially the claims and obligations of friendship—corresponded regularly with Little Billee, who wrote him long and amusing letters back again, and had plenty to say about his life in London—which was a series of triumphs, artistic and social—and you would have thought from his letters, modest though they were, that no happier young man, or more elate, was to be found anywhere in the world.

It was a good time in England, just then, for young artists of promise ; a time of evolution, revolution, change, and development—of the founding of new schools and the crumbling away of old ones—a keen struggle for existence—a surviving of the fit—a preparation, let us hope, for the ultimate survival of the fittest.

And among the many glories of this particular period two names stand out very conspicuously—for the immediate and (so far) lasting fame their bearers achieved, and the wide influence they exerted, and continue to exert still.

The world will not easily forget Frederic Walker and William Bagot, those two singularly gifted boys, whom it soon became the fashion to bracket together, to compare and to contrast, as one compares and contrasts Thackeray and Dickens, Carlyle and Macaulay, Tennyson and Browning—a futile though pleasant practice, of which the temptations seem irresistible !

Yet why compare the lily and the rose ?

These two young masters had the genius and the luck to be the progenitors of much of the best art work that has been done in England during the last thirty years, in oils, in water colour, in black and white.

They were both essentially English and of their own time ; both absolutely original, receiving their impressions straight from nature itself ; uninfluenced by any school, ancient or modern, they founded schools instead of following any, and each was a law unto himself, and a law-giver unto many others. Both were equally great in whatever they attempted— landscape, figures, birds, beasts, or fishes. Who does not remember the fish- monger's shop, by F. Walker, or W. Bagot's little piebald piglings, and their venerable black mother, and their im- mense fat wallowing pink papa ? An ineffable charm of poetry and refinement, of pathos and sympathy and delicate humour combined, an incomparable ease and grace and felicity of workmanship belong to each ; and yet in

FRED WALKER

their work are they not as wide apart as the poles ; each complete in himself and yet a complement to the other ?

And, oddly enough, they were both singularly alike in aspect—both small and slight, though beautifully made, with tiny hands and feet ; always arrayed as the lilies of the field, for all they toiled and spun so arduously ; both had regularly-featured faces of a noble cast and most winning character ; both had the best and simplest manners in the world, and a way of getting themselves much and quickly and permanently liked. . . .

Que la terre leur soit légère!

And who can say that the fame of one is greater than the other's!

Their pinnacles are twin, I venture to believe—of just an equal height and width and thickness, like their bodies in this life; but unlike their frail bodies in one respect: no taller pinnacles are to be seen, methinks, in all the garden of the deathless dead painters of our time, and none more built to last!

But it is not with the art of Little Billee, nor with his fame as a painter, that we are chiefly concerned in this unpretending little tale, except in so far as they have some bearing on his character and his fate.

'I should like to know the detailed history of the Englishman's first love, and how he lost his innocence!'

'Ask him!'

'Ask him yourself!'

Thus Papelard and Bouchardy, on the morning of Little Billee's first appearance at Carrel's studio, in the Rue des Potirons St. Michel.

And that is the question the present scribe is doing his little best to answer.

A good-looking, famous, well-bred, and well-dressed youth finds that London society opens its doors very readily; he hasn't long to knock; and it would be difficult to find a youth more fortunately situated, handsomer, more famous, better dressed or better bred, more seemingly happy and successful, with more attractive qualities and more condonable faults, than Little

Billee, as Taffy and the Laird found him when they came to London after their four or five years in foreign parts—their Wanderjahr.

He had a fine studio and a handsome suite of rooms in Fitzroy Square. Beautiful specimens of his unfinished work, endless studies, hung on his studio walls. Everything else was as nice as it could be—the furniture, the bibelots, and bric-à-brac, the artistic foreign and Eastern knick-knacks and draperies and hangings and curtains and rugs—the semi-grand piano by Collard and Collard.

That immortal canvas, the ' Moon-Dial ' (just begun, and already commissioned by Moses Lyon, the famous picture-dealer), lay on his easel.

No man worked harder and with teeth more clinched than Little Billee when he was at work—none rested or played more discreetly when it was time to rest or play.

The glass on his mantelpiece was full of cards of invitation, reminders, pretty mauve and pink and lilac scented notes ; nor were coronets wanting on many of these hospitable little missives. He had quite overcome his fancied aversion for bloated dukes and lords and the rest (we all do sooner or later, if things go well with us) ; especially for their wives and sisters and daughters and female cousins ; even their mothers and aunts. In point of fact, and in spite of his tender years, he was in some danger (for his art) of developing into that type so adored by sympathetic women who haven't got much to do : the friend, the tame cat, the platonic lover (with many loves) —the squire of dames, the trusty one, of whom husbands and brothers have no fear !—the delicate, harmless dilettante of Eros—the dainty shepherd who dwells ' dans le pays du tendre ! '—and stops there !

The woman flatters and the man confides—and there is no danger whatever, I'm told—and I'm glad !

PLATONIC LOVE

One man loves his fiddle (or, alas ! his neighbour's sometimes) for all the melodies he can wake from it— it is but a selfish love !

Another, who is no fiddler, may love a fiddle too; for its symmetry, its neatness, its colour — its delicate grainings, the lovely lines and curves of its back and front—for its own sake, so to speak. He may have a whole galleryful of fiddles to love in this innocent way—a harem!—and yet not know a single note of music, or even care to hear one. He will dust them and stroke them, and take them down and try to put them in tune—*pizzicato !*—and put them back again, and call them ever such sweet little pet exotic names :

viol, viola, viola d' amore, viol di gamba, violino mio!
and breathe his little troubles into them, and they will give
back inaudible little murmurs in sympathetic response,
like a damp Æolian harp ; but he will never draw a bow
across the strings, nor wake a single chord—or discord!

And who shall say he is not wise in his generation ?
It is but an old-fashioned philistine notion that fiddles
were only made to be played on—the fiddles themselves
are beginning to resent it ; and rightly, I wot!

In this harmless fashion Little Billee was friends with
more than one fine lady *de par le monde.*

Indeed, he had been reproached by his more bohemian
brothers of the brush for being something of a tuft-hunter
—most unjustly. But nothing gives such keen offence
to our unsuccessful brother, bohemian or bourgeois, as our
sudden intimacy with the so-called great, the little lords
and ladies of this little world! Not even our fame and
success, and all the joy and pride they bring us, are so
hard to condone—so embittering, so humiliating, to the
jealous fraternal heart.

Alas! poor humanity—that the mere countenance of
our betters (if they *are* our betters!) should be thought so
priceless a boon, so consummate an achievement, so
crowning a glory, as all that!

> ' A dirty bit of orange-peel,
> The stump of a cigar—
> Once trod on by a princely heel,
> How beautiful they are ! '

Little Billee was no tuft-hunter—he was the tuft-hunted,
or had been. No one of his kind was ever more persist-
ently, resolutely, hospitably harried than this young 'hare
with many friends' by people of rank and fashion.

And at first he thought them most charming ; as they so often are, these graceful, gracious, gay, good-natured stoics and barbarians, whose manners are as easy and simple as their morals—but how much better !—and who, at least, have this charm, that they can wallow in untold gold (when they happen to possess it) without ever seeming to stink of the same : yes, they bear wealth gracefully—and the want of it more gracefully still ! and these are pretty accomplishments that have yet to be learned by our new aristocracy of the shop and counting-house, Jew or Gentile, which is everywhere elbowing its irresistible way to the top and front of everything, both here and abroad.

Then he discovered that, much as you might be with them, you could never be *of* them, unless perchance you managed to hook on by marrying one of their ugly ducklings—their failures—their remnants ! and even then life isn't all beer and skittles for a rank outsider, I'm told ! Then he discovered that he didn't want to be *of* them in the least ; especially at such a cost as that ! and that to be very much *with* them was apt to pall, like everything else !

Also, he found that they were very mixed—good, bad, and indifferent ; and not always very dainty or select in their predilections, since they took unto their bosoms such queer outsiders (just for the sake of being amused a little while) that their capricious favour ceased to be an honour and a glory—if it ever was ! And then, their fickleness !

Indeed, he found, or thought he found, that they could be just as clever, as liberal, as polite or refined—as narrow, insolent, swaggering, coarse, and vulgar—as handsome, as ugly—as graceful, as ungainly—as modest

or conceited, as any other upper class of the community
—and indeed some lower ones !

Beautiful young women, who had been taught how to
paint pretty little landscapes (with an ivy-mantled ruin in
the middle distance), talked technically of painting to
him, *de pair à pair*, as though they were quite on the
same artistic level, and didn't mind admitting it, in spite
of the social gulf between.

Hideous old frumps (osseous or obese, yet with
unduly bared necks and shoulders that made him sick)
patronised him and gave him good advice, and told him
to emulate Mr. Buckner both in his genius and his
manners—since Mr. Buckner was the only 'gentleman'
who ever painted for hire ; and they promised him, in
time, an equal success !

Here and there some sweet old darling specially
enslaved him by her kindness, grace, knowledge of life,
and tender womanly sympathy, like the dowager Lady
Chiselhurst—or some sweet young one, like the lovely
Duchess of Towers, by her beauty, wit, good-humour, and
sisterly interest in all he did, and who in some vague,
distant manner constantly reminded him of Trilby,
although she was such a great and fashionable lady !

But just such darlings, old or young, were to be
found, with still higher ideals, in less exalted spheres ;
and were easier of access, with no impassable gulf between
—spheres where there was no patronising, nothing but
deference and warm appreciation and delicate flattery,
from men and women alike—and where the aged
Venuses, whose prime was of the days of Waterloo, went
with their historical remains duly shrouded, like ivy-
mantled ruins (and in the middle distance !).

"DARLINGS, OLD OR YOUNG"

So he actually grew tired of the great before they had time to tire of him—incredible as it may seem, and against nature; and this saved him many a heart-burning; and he ceased to be seen at fashionable drums or gatherings of any kind, except in one or two houses where he was especially liked and made welcome for his own sake; such as Lord Chiselhurst's in Piccadilly, where the 'Moon-Dial' found a home for a few years before going to its last home and final resting-place in the National Gallery (*R.I.P.*); or Baron Stoppenheim's in Cavendish Square, where many lovely little water-colours signed W. B. occupied places of honour on gorgeously-gilded walls; or the gorgeously-gilded bachelor rooms of Mr. Moses Lyon, the picture-dealer in Upper Conduit Street—for Little Billee (I much grieve to say it of a hero of romance) was an excellent man of business. That infinitesimal dose of the good old Oriental blood kept him straight, and not only made him stick to his last through thick and thin, but also to those whose foot his last was found to match (for he couldn't or wouldn't alter his last).

He loved to make as much money as he could, that he might spend it royally in pretty gifts to his mother and sister, whom it was his pleasure to load in this way, and whose circumstances had been very much altered by his quick success. There was never a more generous son or brother than Little Billee of the clouded heart, that couldn't love any longer!

As a set-off to all these splendours, it was also his pleasure now and again to study London life at its lower den—the eastest end of all. Whitechapel, the Minories,

the Docks, Ratcliffe Highway, Rotherhithe, soon got to
know him well, and he found much to interest him and
much to like among their denizens, and made as many
friends there among ship-carpenters, excisemen, longshoremen, jack-tars, and what not, as in Bayswater and
Belgravia (or Bloomsbury).

'THE MOON-DIAL'

He was especially fond of frequenting sing-songs, or
'free-and-easies,' where good hard-working fellows met of
an evening to relax and smoke and drink and sing, round
a table well loaded with steaming tumblers and pewter
pots, at one end of which sits Mr. Chairman in all his
glory, and at the other 'Mr. Vice.' They are open

to any one who can afford a pipe, a screw of tobacco,
and a pint of beer, and who is willing to do his best and
sing a song.

No introduction is needed ; as soon as any one has
seated himself and made himself comfortable, Mr. Chairman taps the table with his long clay pipe, begs for
silence, and says to his vis-à-vis : 'Mr. Vice, it strikes me
as the gen'l'man as is just come in 'as got a singing face.
Per'aps, Mr. Vice, you'll be so very kind as juster harsk
the aforesaid gentl'man to oblige us with a 'armony.'

Mr. Vice then puts it to the new-comer, who, thus
appealed to, simulates a modest surprise, and finally
professes his willingness, like Mr. Barkis ; then, clearing
his throat a good many times, looks up to the ceiling,
and after one or two unsuccessful starts in different keys,
bravely sings 'Kathleen Mavourneen,' let us say—perhaps
in a touchingly sweet tenor voice :

> 'Kathleen Mavourneen, the gry dawn is brykin,
> The 'orn of the 'unter is 'eard on the 'ill . . .'

And Little Billee didn't mind the dropping of all these
aitches if the voice was sympathetic and well in tune,
and the sentiment simple, tender, and sincere.

Or else, with a good rolling jingo bass, it was,

> ' 'Earts o' hoak are our ships ; 'earts o' hoak are our men ;
> And we'll fight and we'll conkwer agen and agen !'

And no imperfection of accent, in Little Billee's estima-
tion, subtracted one jot from the manly British pluck
that found expression in these noble sentiments, nor
added one tittle to their swaggering, blatant, and idiotically
aggressive vulgarity !

Well, the song finishes with general applause all

round.   Then the chairman says, 'Your 'ealth and song,
sir!'   And drinks, and all do the same.

Then Mr. Vice asks, 'What shall we ave the pleasure
of saying, sir, after that very nice 'armony?'

And the blushing vocalist, if he knows the ropes,
replies, 'A roast leg o' mutton in Newgate, and nobody to
eat it!'   Or else, 'May 'im as is going up the 'ill o'
prosperity never meet a friend coming down!'   Or else,
' 'Ere's to 'er as shares our sorrers and doubles our joys!'
Or else, ' 'Ere's to 'er as shares our joys and doubles our
expenses!' and so forth.

More drink, more applause, and many 'ear 'ear's.
And Mr. Vice says to the singer: 'You call, sir.   Will
you be so good as to call on some other gen'l'man for a
'armony?'   And so the evening goes on.

And nobody was more quickly popular at such
gatherings, or sang better songs, or proposed more
touching sentiments, or filled either chair or vice-chair
with more grace and dignity than Little Billee.   Not
even Dodor or l'Zouzou could have beaten him at that.

And he was as happy, as genial, and polite, as much at
his ease, in these humble gatherings as in the gilded
saloons of the great, where grand-pianos are, and hired
accompanists, and highly paid singers, and a good deal of
talk while they sing.

So his powers of quick, wide, universal sympathy grew
and grew, and made up to him a little for his lost power
of being specially fond of special individuals.   For he
made no close friends among men, and ruthlessly snubbed
all attempts at intimacy—all advances towards an affection
which he felt he could not return; and more than one
enthusiastic admirer of his talent and his charm was

THE CHAIRMAN

forced to acknowledge that, with all his gifts, he seemed
heartless and capricious ; as ready to drop you as he had
been to take you up.

He loved to be wherever he could meet his kind, high
or low ; and felt as happy on a penny steamer as on the
yacht of a millionaire—on the crowded knifeboard of an
omnibus as on the box-seat of a nobleman's drag—
happier ; he liked to feel the warm contact of his
fellow-man at either shoulder and at his back, and didn't
object to a little honest grime !   And I think all this
genial caressing love of his kind, this depth and breadth
of human sympathy, are patent in all his work.

On the whole, however, he came to prefer for society
that of the best and cleverest of his own class—those
who live and prevail by the professional exercise of their
own specially-trained and highly-educated wits, the skilled
workmen of the brain—from the Lord Chief-Justice of
England downward—the salt of the earth, in his opinion ;
and stuck to them.

There is no class so genial and sympathetic as *our
own*, in the long run—even if it be but the criminal class !
none where the welcome is likely to be so genuine and
sincere, so easy to win, so difficult to outstay, if we be but
decently pleasant and successful ; none where the memory
of us will be kept so green (if we leave any memory at
all !).

So Little Billee found it expedient, when he wanted
rest and play, to seek them at the houses of those whose
rest and play were like his own—little halts in a seeming
happy life-journey, full of toil and strain and endeavour ;
oases of sweet water and cooling shade, where the food
was good and plentiful, though the tents might not be of

cloth of gold ; where the talk was of something more to
his taste than court or sport or narrow party politics ;
the new beauty ; the coming match of the season ; the
coming ducal conversion to Rome ; the last elopement in
high life—the next! and where the music was that of
the greatest music-makers that can be, who found rest
and play in making better music for love than they ever
made for hire—and were listened to as they should be,
with understanding and religious silence, and all the
fervent gratitude they deserved.

There were several such houses in London then—and
are still—thank Heaven! And Little Billee had his
little billet there—and there he was wont to drown
himself in waves of lovely sound, or streams of clever
talk, or rivers of sweet feminine adulation, seas ! oceans !—
a somewhat relaxing bath !—and forget for a while his
everlasting chronic plague of heart-insensibility, which no
doctor could explain or cure, and to which he was
becoming gradually resigned—as one does to deafness or
blindness or locomotor ataxia—for it had lasted nearly
five years ! But now and again, during sleep, and in a
blissful dream, the lost power of loving—of loving mother,
sister, friend—would be restored to him, just as with a
blind man who sometimes dreams he has recovered his
sight ; and the joy of it would wake him to the sad
reality : till he got to know, even in his dream, that he
was only dreaming after all, whenever that priceless boon
seemed to be his own once more—and did his utmost
not to wake. And these were nights to be marked with
a white stone, and remembered !

And nowhere was he happier than at the houses of
the great surgeons and physicians who interested them-

selves in his strange disease.   When the Little Billees of
this world fall ill, the great surgeons and physicians (like
the great singers and musicians) do better for them, out
of mere love and kindness, than for the princes of the
earth, who pay them thousand-guinea fees and load them
with honours.

And of all these notable London houses none was
pleasanter than that of Cornelys, the great sculptor, and
Little Billee was such a favourite in that house that he
was able to take his friends Taffy and the Laird there the
very day they came to London.

First of all they dined together at a delightful little
Franco-Italian pothouse near Leicester Square, where
they had *bouillabaisse* (imagine the Laird's delight), and
spaghetti, and a *poulet rôti*, which is *such* a different affair
from a roast fowl ! and salad, which Taffy was allowed to
make and mix himself ; and they all smoked just where
they sat, the moment they had swallowed their food—as
had been their way in the good old Paris days.

That dinner was a happy one for Taffy and the Laird,
with their Little Billee apparently unchanged—as demonstrative, as genial and caressing as ever, and with no
swagger to speak of ; and with so many things to talk
about that were new to them, and of such delightful
interest !   They also had much to say—but they didn't
say very much about Paris, for fear of waking up Heaven
knows what sleeping dogs !

And every now and again, in the midst of all this
pleasant forgathering and communion of long-parted
friends, the pangs of Little Billee's miserable mind-malady
would shoot through him like poisoned arrows.

A HAPPY DINNER

He would catch himself thinking how fat and fussy and serious about trifles Taffy had become ; and what a shiftless, feckless, futile duffer was the Laird ; and how greedy they both were, and how red and coarse their ears and gills and cheeks grew as they fed, and how shiny their faces ; and how little he would care, try as he might, if they both fell down dead under the table ! And this would make him behave more caressingly to them, more genially and demonstratively than ever—for he knew it was all a grewsome physical ailment of his own, which he could no more help than a cataract in his eye !

Then, catching sight of his own face and form in a mirror, he would curse himself for a puny, misbegotten shrimp, an imp—an abortion—no bigger, by the side of the herculean Taffy or the burly Laird of Cockpen, than sixpennorth o' halfpence : a wretched little overrated follower of a poor trivial craft—a mere light amuser ! For what did pictures matter, or whether they were good or bad, except to the triflers who painted them, the dealers who sold them, the idle, uneducated, purse-proud fools who bought them and stuck them up on their walls because they were told !

And he felt that if a dynamite shell were beneath the table where they sat, and its fuse were smoking under their very noses, he would neither wish to warn his friends nor move himself. He didn't care a d——— !

And all this made him so lively and brilliant in his talk, so fascinating and droll and witty, that Taffy and the Laird wondered at the improvement success and the experience of life had wrought in him, and marvelled at the happiness of his lot, and almost found it in their warm affectionate hearts to feel a touch of envy !

Oddly enough, in a brief flash of silence, 'entre la poire et le fromage,' they heard a foreigner at an adjoining table (one of a very noisy group) exclaim : ' Mais quand je vous dis que j'l'ai entendue, moi, La Svengali ! et même qu'elle a chanté l'Impromptu de Chopin absolument comme si c'était un piano qu'on jouait ! voyons ! . . .'

' Farceur ! la bonne blague !' said another—and then the conversation became so noisily general it was no good listening any more.

' Svengali ! how funny that name should turn up ! I wonder what's become of *our* Svengali, by the way ? ' observed Taffy.

' I remember *his* playing Chopin's Impromptu,' said Little Billee ; ' what a singular coincidence ! '

There were to be more coincidences that night ; it never rains them but it pours !

So our three friends finished their coffee and liqueured up, and went to Cornelys's three in a hansom—

' Like Mars,
A smokin' their poipes and cigyars.'

Sir Louis Cornelys, as everybody knows, lives in a palace on Campden Hill, a house of many windows ; and whichever window he looks out of, he sees his own garden and very little else. In spite of his eighty years, he works as hard as ever, and his hand has lost but little of its cunning. But he no longer gives those splendid parties that made him almost as famous a host as he was an artist.

When his beautiful wife died he shut himself up from the world ; and now he never stirs out of his house and

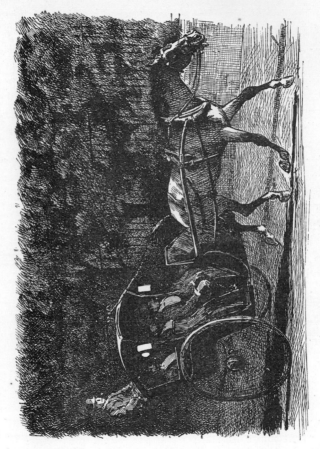

"A-SMOKIN' THEIR POIPES AND CIGYARS"

grounds except to fulfil his duties at the Royal Academy, and dine once a year with the Queen.

It was very different in the early sixties. There was no pleasanter or more festive house than his in London, winter or summer—no lordlier host than he—no more irresistible hostesses than Lady Cornelys and her lovely daughters ; and if ever music had a right to call itself divine, it was there you heard it—on late Saturday nights during the London season—when the foreign birds of song come over to reap their harvest in London Town.

It was on one of the most brilliant of these Saturday nights that Taffy and the Laird, chaperoned by Little Billee, made their *début* at Mechelen Lodge, and were received at the door of the immense music-room by a tall, powerful man with splendid eyes and a gray beard, and a small velvet cap on his head—and by a Greek matron so beautiful and stately and magnificently attired that they felt inclined to sink them on their bended knees as in the presence of some overwhelming Eastern royalty—and were only prevented from doing so, perhaps, by the simple, sweet, and cordial graciousness of her welcome.

And whom should they be shaking hands with next but Antony, Lorrimer, and the Greek—with each a beard and moustache of nearly five years' growth !

But they had no time for much exuberant greeting, for there was a sudden piano crash—and then an immediate silence, as though for pins to drop—and Signor Giuglini and the wondrous maiden Adelina Patti sang the 'Miserere' out of Signor Verdi's most famous opera—to the delight of all but a few very superior ones who had just read Mendelssohn's letters (or misread them) and despised Italian music, and thought cheaply of 'mere virtuosity,' either vocal or instrumental.

When this was over, Little Billee pointed out all the lions to his friends—from the Prime Minister down to the present scribe—who was right glad to meet them again and talk of auld lang syne, and present them to the daughters of the house and other charming ladies.

Then Roucouly, the great French barytone, sang Durien's favourite song—

> ' Plaisir d'amour ne dure qu'un moment ;
> Chagrin d'amour dure toute la vie . . .'

with quite a little drawing-room voice—but quite as divinely as he had sung ' Noël, noël,' at the Madeleine in full blast one certain Christmas Eve our three friends remembered well.

Then there was a violin solo by young Joachim, then as now the greatest violinist of his time ; and a solo on the pianoforte by Madame Schumann, his only peeress ! and these came as a wholesome check to the levity of those for whom all music is but an agreeable pastime, a mere emotional delight, in which the intellect has no part ; and also as a well-deserved humiliation to all virtuosi who play so charmingly that they make their listeners forget the master who invented the music in the lesser master who interprets it !

For these two—man and woman—the highest of their kind, never let you forget it was Sebastian Bach they were playing—playing in absolute perfection, in absolute forgetfulness of themselves—so that if you weren't up to Bach, you didn't have a very good time !

But if you were (or wished it to be understood or thought you were), you seized your opportunity and you scored; and by the earnestness of your rapt and tranced immobility, and the stony, gorgon-like intensity of your gaze, you rebuked the frivolous—as you had rebuked them before by the listlessness and carelessness of your bored resignation to the Signorina Patti's trills and fioritures, or M. Roucouly's pretty little French mannerisms.

And what added so much to the charm of this delightful concert was that the guests were not packed together sardine-wise, as they are at most concerts; they were comparatively few and well chosen, and could get up and walk about and talk to their friends between the pieces, and wander off into other rooms and look at endless beautiful things, and stroll in the lovely grounds, by moon or star or Chinese-lantern light

And there the frivolous could sit and chat and laugh and flirt when Bach was being played inside; and the earnest wander up and down together in soul-communion, through darkened walks and groves and alleys where the sound of French or Italian warblings could not reach them, and talk in earnest tones of the great Zola, or Guy de Maupassant and Pierre Loti, and exult in beautiful English over the inferiority of English literature, English art, English music, English everything else.

For these high-minded ones who can only bear the sight of classical pictures and the sound of classical music do not necessarily read classical books in any language— no Shakespeares or Dantes or Molières or Goethes for *them*. They know a trick worth two of that!

And the mere fact that these three immortal French writers of light books I have just named had never been heard of at this particular period doesn't very much matter; they had cognate predecessors whose names I happen to forget. Any stick will do to beat a dog with, and history is always repeating itself.

Feydeau, or Flaubert, let us say—or for those who don't know French and cultivate an innocent mind, Miss Austen (for to be dead and buried is almost as good as to be French and immoral!)—and Sebastian Bach, and Sandro Botticelli—that all the arts should be represented. These names are rather discrepant, but they make very good sticks for dog-beating; and with a thorough knowledge and appreciation of these (or the semblance thereof), you were well equipped in those days to hold your own among the elect of intellectual London circles, and snub the philistine to rights.

Then, very late, a tall, good-looking, swarthy foreigner came in, with a roll of music in his hands, and his entrance made quite a stir; you heard all round, 'Here's Glorioli,' or 'Ecco Glorioli,' or 'Voici Glorioli,' till Glorioli got on your nerves. And beautiful ladies, ambassadresses, female celebrities of all kinds, fluttered up to him and cajoled and fawned;—as Svengali would have said, 'Prinzessen, Comtessen, Serene English Altessen!'—and they soon forgot their Highness and their Serenity!

For with very little pressing Glorioli stood up on the platform, with his accompanist by his side at the piano, and in his hands a sheet of music, at which he never looked. He looked at the beautiful ladies, and ogled and smiled; and from his scarcely-parted, moist, thick, bearded lips, which he always licked before singing, there issued the most ravishing sounds that had ever been heard from throat of man or woman or boy! He could sing both high and low and soft and loud, and the frivolous were bewitched, as was only to be expected;

but even the earnestest of all, caught, surprised, rapt, astounded, shaken, tickled, teased, harrowed, tortured, tantalised, aggravated, seduced, demoralised, degraded, corrupted into mere naturalness, forgot to dissemble their delight.

And Sebastian Bach (the especially adored of all really great musicians, and also, alas! of many priggish outsiders who don't know a single note and can't remember a single tune) was well forgotten for the night; and who were more enthusiastic than the two great players who had been playing Bach that evening? For these, at all events, were broad and catholic and sincere, and knew what was beautiful, whatever its kind.

It was but a simple little song that Glorioli sang, as light and pretty as it could well be, almost worthy of the words it was written to, and the words are De Musset's; and I love them so much I cannot resist the temptation of setting them down here, for the mere sensuous delight of writing them, as though I had just composed them myself:

> ‘ Bonjour, Suzon, ma fleur des bois !
>   Es-tu toujours la plus jolie ?
> Je reviens, tel que tu me vois,
>   D'un grand voyage en Italie !
>   Du paradis j'ai fait le tour—
> J'ai fait des vers—j'ai fait l'amour. . . .
>   Mais que t'importe !
> Je passe devant ta maison :
>   Ouvre ta porte !
>   Bonjour, Suzon !

> ‘ Je t'ai vue au temps des lilas.
>   Ton cœur joyeux venait d'éclore,
> Et tu disais : “ Je ne veux pas,
>   Je ne veux pas qu'on m'aime encore.”
> Qu'as-tu fait depuis mon départ ?

Qui part trop tôt revient trop tard.
Mais que m'importe?
Je passe devant ta maison :
Ouvre ta porte !
Bonjour, Suzon !'

And when it began, and while it lasted, and after it was over, one felt really sorry for all the other singers. And nobody sang any more that night ; for Glorioli was tired, and wouldn't sing again, and none were bold enough or disinterested enough to sing after him.

Some of my readers may remember that meteoric bird of song, who, though a mere amateur, would condescend to sing for a hundred guineas in the saloons of the great (as Monsieur Jourdain sold cloth); who would sing still better for love and glory in the studios of his friends.

For Glorioli—the biggest, handsomest, and most distinguished-looking Jew that ever was—one of the Sephardim (one of the Seraphim!)—hailed from Spain, where he was junior partner in the great firm of Moralés, Peralés, Gonzalés, and Glorioli, wine merchants, Malaga. He travelled for his own firm ; his wine was good, and he sold much of it in England. But his voice would bring him far more gold in the month he spent here ; for his wines have been equalled—if it be not libellous to say so —but there was no voice like his anywhere in the world, and no more finished singer.

Anyhow his voice got into Little Billee's head more than any wine, and the boy could talk of nothing else for days and weeks ; and was so exuberant in his expressions of delight and gratitude that the great singer took a real fancy to him (especially when he was told that this fervent boyish admirer was one of the greatest of English

"BONJOUR, SUZON !"

painters); and as a mark of his esteem, privately con-
fided to him after supper that every century two human
nightingales were born—only two! a male and a female;
and that he, Glorioli, was the representative 'male
rossignol of this soi-disant dix-neuvième siècle.'

'I can well believe that! And the female, your mate
that should be—*la rossignolle*, if there is such a word?'
inquired Little Billee.

'Ah! mon ami . . . it was Alboni, till la petite
Adelina Patti came out a year or two ago; and now it
is *La Svengali.*'

'La Svengali?'

'Oui, mon fy! You will hear her some day—et vous
m'en direz des nouvelles!'

'Why, you don't mean to say that she's got a better
voice than Madame Alboni?'

'Mon ami, an apple is an excellent thing—until you
have tried a peach! Her voice to that of Alboni is as a
peach to an apple— I give you my word of honour! but
bah! the voice is a detail. It's what she does with it—
it's incredible! it gives one cold all down the back! it
drives you mad! it makes you weep hot tears by the
spoonful! Ah! the tear, mon fy! tenez! I can draw
everything but *that!* Ça n'est pas dans mes cordes! *I*
can only madden with *love!* But La Svengali! . . .
And then, in the middle of it all, prrrout! . . . she makes
you laugh! Ah! le beau rire! faire rire avec des larmes
plein les yeux—voilà qui me passe! . . . Mon ami,
when I heard her it made me swear that even *I* would
never try to sing any more—it seemed *too* absurd! and I
kept my word for a month at least—and you know, je
sais ce que je vaux, moi!'

A HUMAN NIGHTINGALE

'You are talking of La Svengali, I bet,' said Signor Spartia.

'Oui, parbleu! You have heard her?'

'Yes—at Vienna last winter,' rejoined the greatest singing-master in the world. 'J'en suis fou! hélas! I thought *I* could teach a woman how to sing, till I heard that blackguard Svengali's pupil. He has married her, they say?'

'That *blackguard* Svengali·!' exclaimed Little Billee . . . 'why, that must be a Svengali I knew in Paris—a famous pianist! a friend of mine!'

'That's the man! also une fameuse crapule (sauf vot' respect); his real name is Adler; his mother was a Polish singer; and he was a pupil at the Leipsic Conservatorio. But he's an immense artist, and a great singing-master, to teach a woman like that! and such a woman! belle comme un ange—mais bête comme un pot. I tried to talk to her—all she can say is 'ja wohl,' or 'doch,' or 'nein,' or 'soh!' not a word of English or French or Italian, though she sings them, oh! but *divinely!* It is '*il bel canto*' come back to the world after a hundred years. . . .'

'But what voice is it?' asked Little Billee.

'Every voice a mortal woman can have—three octaves —four! and of such a quality that people who can't tell one tune from another cry with pleasure at the mere sound of it directly they hear her; just like anybody else. Everything that Paganini could do with his violin, she does with her voice—only better—and what a voice! un vrai baume!'

'Now I don't mind petting zat you are schbeaking of La Sfencali,' said Herr Kreutzer, the famous composer, joining in. 'Quelle merfeille, hein? I heard her in St. Betersburg, at ze Vinter Balace. Ze vomen all vent mat, and pulled off zeir bearls and tiamonts and kave zem to her—vent town on zeir knees and gried and gissed her hants. She tit not say vun vort! She tit not efen schmile! Ze men schnifelled in ze gorners, and looked at ze bictures, and tissempled—efen I, Johann Kreutzer! efen ze Emperor?'

'You're joking,' said Little Billee.

'My vrent, I neffer choke ven I talk apout zinging. You vill hear her zum tay yourzellof, and you vill acree viz me zat zere are two classes of beoble who zing. In ze vun class, La Sfencali; in ze ozzer, all ze ozzer zingers!'

'And does she sing good music?'

'I ton't know. *All* music is koot ven *she* zings it. I forket ze zong; I can only sink of ze zinger. Any koot zinger can zing a peautiful zong and kif bleasure, I zubboce! But I voot zooner hear La Sfencali zing a scale zan anypotty else zing ze most peautiful zong in ze vorldt—efen vun of my own! Zat is berhaps how zung ze crate Italian zingers of ze last century. It vas a lost art, and she has found it; and she must haf pecun to zing pefore she pecan to schpeak—or else she voot not haf hat ze time to learn all zat she knows, for she is not yet zirty! She zings in Paris in Ogdoper, Gott sei dank! and gums here after Christmas to zing at Trury Lane. Chullien kifs her ten sousand bounts!'

'I wonder, now? Why, that must be the woman I heard at Warsaw two years ago—or three,' said young Lord Witlow. 'It was at Count Siloszech's. He'd heard her sing in the streets, with a tall black-bearded

ruffian, who accompanied her on a guitar, and a little
fiddling gypsy fellow.   She was a handsome woman, with
hair down to her knees, but stupid as an owl.   She sang
at Siloszech's, and all the fellows went mad and gave
her their watches and diamond studs and gold scarf-pins.
By gad !   I never heard or saw anything like it.   I don't
know much about music myself—couldn't tell " God save
the Queen" from 'Pop goes the Weasel," if the people didn't
get up and stand and take their hats off; but I was as mad as
the rest—why, I gave her a little German-silver vinaigrette
I'd just bought for my wife ; hanged if I didn't—and I
was only just married, you know !   It's the peculiar twang
of her voice, I suppose ! '

And hearing all this, Little Billee made up his mind
that life had still something in store for him, since he
would some day hear La Svengali.   Anyhow, he wouldn't
shoot himself till then !

Thus the night wore itself away.   The Prinzessen,
Comtessen, and Serene English Altessen (and other ladies
of less exalted rank) departed home in cabs and carriages ;
and hostess and daughters went to bed.   Late sitters of
the ruder sex supped again, and smoked and chatted and
listened to comic songs and recitations by celebrated
actors.   Noble dukes hobnobbed with low comedians ;
world-famous painters and sculptors sat at the feet of
Hebrew capitalists and aitchless millionaires.   Judges,
cabinet ministers, eminent physicians and warriors and
philosophers saw Sunday morning steal over Campden
Hill and through the many windows of Mechelen Lodge,
and listened to the pipe of half-awakened birds, and
smelt the freshness of the dark summer dawn.   And as

Taffy and the Laird walked home to the Old Hummums by daylight, they felt that last night was ages ago, and that since then they had forgathered with 'much there was of the best in London.' And then they reflected that 'much there was of the best in London' were still strangers to them—except by reputation—for there had not been time for many introductions : and this had made them feel a little out of it ; and they found they hadn't had such a very good time after all. And there were no cabs. And they were tired, and their boots were tight.

And the last they had seen of Little Billee before leaving was a glimpse of their old friend in a corner of Lady Cornelys's boudoir, gravely playing cup and ball with Fred Walker for sixpences—both so rapt in the game that they were unconscious of anything else, and both playing so well (with either hand) that they might have been professional champions !

And that saturnine young sawbones, Jakes Talboys (now Sir Jakes, and one of the most genial of Her Majesty's physicians), who, sometimes after supper and champagne, was given to thoughtful, sympathetic, and acute observation of his fellow-men, remarked to the Laird in a whisper that was almost convivial :—

'Rather an enviable pair ! Their united ages amount to forty-eight or so, their united weights to about fifteen stone, and they couldn't carry you or me between them. But if you were to roll all the other brains that have been under this roof to-night into one, you wouldn't reach the sum of their united genius. . . . I wonder which of the two is the most unhappy ! '

CUP-AND-BALL

The season over, the song-birds flown, summer on the wane, his picture, the 'Moon-Dial,' sent to Moses Lyon's (the picture-dealer in Conduit Street), Little Billee felt the time had come to go and see his mother and sister in Devonshire, and make the sun shine twice as brightly for them during a month or so, and the dew fall softer!

So one fine August morning found him at the Great Western Station—the nicest station in all London, I think—except the stations that book you to France and far away.

It always seems so pleasant to be going west! Little Billee loved that station, and often went there for a mere stroll, to watch the people starting on their westward way, following the sun towards Heaven knows what joys or sorrows, and envy them their sorrows or their joys—any sorrows or joys that were not merely physical, like a chocolate drop or a pretty tune, a bad smell or a toothache.

And as he took a seat in a second-class carriage (it would be third in these democratic days), south corner, back to the engine, with *Silas Marner*, and Darwin's *Origin of Species* (which he was reading for the third time), and *Punch* and other literature of a lighter kind to beguile him on his journey, he felt rather bitterly how happy he could be if the little spot, or knot, or blot, or clot which paralysed that convolution of his brain where he kept his affections could but be conjured away!

The dearest mother, the dearest sister in the world, in the dearest little seaside village (or town) that ever was! and other dear people—especially Alice, sweet Alice with hair so brown, his sister's friend, the simple, pure, and pious maiden of his boyish dreams: and himself, but for that wretched little kill-joy cerebral occlusion, as sound, as healthy, as full of life and energy, as he had ever been!

And when he wasn't reading _Silas Marner_, or looking out of window at the flying landscape, and watching it revolve round its middle distance (as it always seems to do), he was sympathetically taking stock of his fellow-passengers, and mildly envying them, one after another, indiscriminately!

A fat, old, wheezy philistine, with a bulbous nose and only one eye, who had a plain, sickly daughter, to whom he seemed devoted, body and soul; an old lady, who still wept furtively at recollections of the parting with her grandchildren, which had taken place at the station (they had borne up wonderfully, as grandchildren do); a consumptive curate, on the opposite corner seat by the window, whose tender, anxious wife (sitting by his side) seemed to have no thoughts in the whole world but for him; and her patient eyes were his stars of consolation, since he turned to look into them almost every minute, and always seemed a little the happier for doing so. There is no better star-gazing than that!

So Little Billee gave her up _his_ corner seat, that the poor sufferer might have those stars where he could look into them comfortably without turning his head.

Indeed (as was his wont with everybody), Little Billee made himself useful and pleasant to his fellow-travellers in many ways—so many that long before they had reached their respective journeys' ends they had almost grown to love him as an old friend, and longed to know who this singularly attractive and brilliant youth, this genial, dainty, benevolent little princekin could possibly be, who was dressed so fashionably, and yet went second class, and took such kind thought of others ; and they wondered at the happiness that must be his at merely being alive, and told him more of their troubles in six hours than they told many an old friend in a year.

But he told them nothing about himself—that self he was so sick of—and left them to wonder.

And at his own journey's end, the farthest end of all, he found his mother and sister waiting for him, in a beautiful little pony-carriage—his last gift—and with them sweet Alice, and in her eyes, for one brief moment, that unconscious look of love surprised which is not to be forgotten for years and years and years—which can only be seen by the eyes that meet it, and which, for the time it lasts (just a flash), makes all women's eyes look exactly the same (I'm told) : and it seemed to Little Billee that, for the twentieth part of a second, Alice had looked at him with Trilby's eyes ; or his mother's, when that he was a little tiny boy.

It all but gave him the thrill he thirsted for ! Another twentieth part of a second, perhaps, and his brain-trouble would have melted away ; and Little Billee would have come into his own again—the kingdom of love !

A beautiful human eye ! *Any* beautiful eye—a dog's, a deer's, a donkey's, an owl's even ! To think of all that it can look, and all that it can see ! all that it can even *seem*, sometimes ! What a prince among gems ! what a star !

But a beautiful eye that lets the broad white light of infinite space (so bewildering and garish and diffused) into one pure virgin heart, to be filtered there ! and lets it out again, duly warmed, softened, concentrated, subli-

mated, focused to a point as in a precious stone, that it
may shed itself (a love-laden effulgence) into some stray
fellow-heart close by—through pupil and iris, entre quatre-
z-yeux—the very elixir of life !

Alas ! that such a crown-jewel should ever lose its
lustre and go blind !

Not so blind or dim, however, but it can still see well
enough to look before and after, and inward and upward,
and drown itself in tears, and yet not die ! And that's
the dreadful pity of it. And this is a quite uncalled-for
digression ; and I can't think why I should have gone out
of my way (at considerable pains) to invent it ! In
fact—

> ' Of this 'ere song, should I be axed the reason for to show,
> I don't exactly know, I don't exactly know !
> *But all my fancy dwells upon Nancy.*'

'How pretty Alice has grown, mother ! quite lovely,
I think ! and so nice ; but she was always as nice as she
could be ! '

So observed Little Billee to his mother that evening
as they sat in the garden and watched the crescent moon
sink to the Atlantic.

'Ah ! my darling Willie ! If you *could* only guess
how happy you would make your poor old mammy by
growing fond of Alice. . . . And Blanche, too ! what a
joy for *her !* '

'Good heavens ! mother . . . Alice is not for the like
of *me !* She's for some splendid young Devon squire,
six foot high, and acred and whiskered within an inch of
his life ! . . .'

'Ah, my darling Willie ! you are not of those who ask

for love in vain. . . . If you only *knew* how she believes in you! She almost beats your poor old mammy at *that!*'

And that night he dreamed of Alice—that he loved her as a sweet good woman should be loved ; and knew, even in his dream, that it was but a dream ; but, oh! it was good! and he managed not to wake ; and it was a night to be marked with a white stone! And (still in his dream) she had kissed him, and healed him of his brain-trouble for ever. But when he woke next morning, alas! his brain-trouble was with him still, and he felt that no dream kiss would ever cure it—nothing but a real kiss from Alice's own pure lips!

SWEET ALICE

And he rose thinking of Alice, and dressed and breakfasted thinking of her—and how fair she was, and how innocent, and how well and carefully trained up the way she should go—the beau ideal of a wife. . . . Could she possibly care for a shrimp like himself?

For in his love of outward form he could not understand that any woman who had eyes to see should ever quite condone the signs of physical weakness in man, in favour of any mental gifts or graces whatsoever.

Little Greek that he was, he worshipped the athlete, and opined that all women without exception—all

S

English women especially—must see with the same eyes
as himself.

He had once been vain and weak enough to believe in
Trilby's love (with a Taffy standing by—a careless,
unsusceptible Taffy, who was like unto the gods of
Olympus!)—and Trilby had given him up at a word, a
hint—for all his frantic clinging.

She would not have given up Taffy *pour si peu*, had
Taffy but lifted a little finger! It is always 'just whistle,
and I'll come to you, my lad!' with the likes of
Taffy . . . but Taffy hadn't even whistled! Yet still he
kept thinking of Alice—and he felt he couldn't think of
her well enough till he went out for a stroll by himself on
a sheep-trimmed down. So he took his pipe and his
Darwin, and out he strolled into the early sunshine—up
the green Red Lane, past the pretty church, Alice's
father's church—and there, at the gate, patiently waiting
for his mistress, sat Alice's dog—an old friend of his,
whose welcome was a very warm one.

Little Billee thought of Thackeray's lovely poem in
Pendennis :

> ' She comes—she's here—she's past !
> May heaven go with her ! . . . '

Then he and the dog went on together to a little bench
on the edge of the cliff—within sight of Alice's bedroom
window. It was called 'the Honeymooners' Bench.'

' That look—that look—that look! Ah—but Trilby
had looked like that, too! And there are many Taffys
in Devon!'

He sat himself down and smoked and gazed at the
sea below, which the sun (still in the east) had not yet
filled with glare and robbed of the lovely sapphire-blue,

shot with purple and dark green, that comes over it now and again of a morning on that most beautiful coast.

There was a fresh breeze from the west, and the long, slow billows broke into creamier foam than ever, which reflected itself as a tender white gleam in the blue concavities of their shining shoreward curves as they came rolling in. The sky was all of turquoise but for the smoke of a distant steamer—a long thin horizontal streak of dun—and there were little brown or white sails here and there, dotting ; and the stately ships went on. . . .

Little Billee tried hard to feel all this beauty with his heart as well as his brain—as he had so often done when a boy—and cursed his insensibility out loud for at least the thousand-and-first time.

Why couldn't these waves of air and water be turned into equivalent waves of sound, that he might feel them through the only channel that reached his emotions! That one joy was still left to him—but, alas ! alas ! he was only a painter of pictures—and not a maker of music !

He recited 'Break, break, break,' to Alice's dog, who loved him and looked up into his face with sapient, affectionate eyes—and whose name, like that of so many dogs in fiction and so few in fact, was simply Tray. For Little Billee was much given to monologues out loud, and profuse quotations from his favourite bards.

Everybody quoted that particular poem either mentally or aloud when they sat on that particular bench—except a few old-fashioned people, who still said,

'Roll on, thou deep and dark blue ocean, roll !'

or people of the very highest culture, who only quoted

the nascent (and crescent) Robert Browning ; or people
of no culture at all, who simply held their tongues—and
only felt the more !

　　Tray listened silently.

　　'Ah, Tray, the best thing but one to do with the sea
is to paint it.　The next best thing to that is to bathe in
it.　The best of all is to lie asleep at the bottom.　How
would *you* like that ?

> ' " And on thy ribs the limpet sticks,
> And in thy heart the scrawl shall play. . . ." '

Tray's tail became as a wagging point of interrogation,
and he turned his head first on one side and then on the
other—his eyes fixed on Little Billee's, his face irresistible
in its genial doggy wistfulness.

　　'Tray, what a singularly good listener you are—and
therefore what singularly good manners you've got !　I
suppose all dogs have !' said Little Billee ; and then, in a
very tender voice, he exclaimed,

　　'Alice, Alice, Alice !'

　　And Tray uttered a soft, cooing, nasal croon in his
head register, though he was a barytone dog by nature,
with portentous, warlike chest-notes of the jingo order.

　　'Tray, your mistress is a parson's daughter, and
therefore twice as much of a mystery as any other
woman in this puzzling world !

　　'Tray, if my heart weren't stopped with wax, like the
ears of the companions of Ulysses when they rowed past
the sirens—you've heard of Ulysses, Tray ? he loved a
dog—if my heart weren't stopped with wax, I should be
deeply in love with your mistress ; perhaps she would
marry me if I asked her—there's no accounting for
tastes !—and I know enough of myself to know that I

should make her a good husband—that I should make her happy—and I should make two other women happy besides.

'As for myself personally, Tray, it doesn't very much matter. One good woman would do as well as another, if she's equally good-looking. You doubt it? Wait till you get a pimple inside your bump of—your bump of—wherever you keep your fondnesses, Tray.

'For that's what's the matter with me—a pimple—just a little clot of blood at the root of a nerve, and no bigger than a pin's point!

'That's a small thing to cause such a lot of wretchedness, and wreck a fellow's life, isn't it? Oh, curse it, curse it, curse it—every day and all day long.

'And just as small a thing will take it away, I'm told!

'Ah! grains of sand are small things—and so are diamonds! But diamond or grain of sand, only Alice has got that small thing! Alice alone, in all the world, has got the healing touch for me now; the hands, the lips, the eyes! I know it—I feel it! I dreamed it last night! She looked me well in the face, and took my hand — both hands— and kissed me, eyes and mouth, and told me how she loved me. Ah! what a dream it was! And my little clot melted away like a snowflake on the lips, and I was

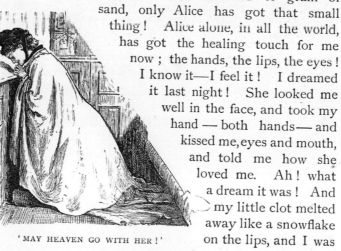

'MAY HEAVEN GO WITH HER!'

my old self again, after many years—and all through that kiss of a pure woman.

'I've never been kissed by a pure woman in my life—never! except by my dear mother and sister; and mothers and sisters don't count, when it comes to kissing.

'Ah! sweet physician that she is, and better than all! It will all come back again with a rush, just as I dreamed, and we will have a good time together, we three! . . .

'But your mistress is a parson's daughter, and believes everything she's been taught from a child, just as you do—at least, I hope so. And I like her for it—and you too.

'She has believed her father—will she ever believe me, who think so differently? And if she does, will it be good for her?—and then, where will her father come in?

'Oh! it's a bad thing to live and no longer believe and trust in your father, Tray! to doubt either his honesty or his intelligence. For he (with your mother to help) has taught you all the best he knows, if he has been a good father—till some one else comes and teaches you better—or worse!

'And then, what are you to believe of what good still remains of all that early teaching—and how are you to sift the wheat from the chaff? . . .

'Kneel undisturbed, fair saint! I, for one, will never seek to undermine thy faith in any father, on earth or above it!

'Yes, there she kneels in her father's church, her pretty head bowed over her clasped hands, her cloak and skirts falling in happy folds about her: I see it all!

'And underneath, that poor, sweet, soft, pathetic thing of flesh and blood, the eternal woman—great heart and slender brain—for ever enslaved or enslaving, never self-

sufficing, never free . . . that dear, weak, delicate shape,
so cherishable, so perishable, that I've had to paint so
often, and know so well by heart! and love . . . ah,
how I love it! Only painter-fellows and sculptor-fellows
can ever quite know the fulness of that pure love.

'There she kneels and pours forth her praise or plaint,
meekly and duly. Perhaps it's for me she's praying.

'" Leave thou thy sister when she prays."

'She believes her poor little prayer will be heard and
answered somewhere up aloft. The impossible will be
done. She wants what she wants so badly, and prays
for it so hard.

'She believes—she believes—what *doesn't* she believe,
Tray?

'The world was made in six days. It is just six
thousand years old. Once it all lay smothered under
rain-water for many weeks, miles deep, because there were
so many wicked people about somewhere down in Judee,
where they didn't know everything! A costly kind of
clearance! And then there was Noah, who *wasn't* wicked,
and his most respectable family, and his ark—and Jonah
and his whale—and Joshua and the sun, and what not.
I remember it all, you see, and, oh! such wonderful
things that have happened since! And there's everlasting
agony for those who don't believe as she does; and yet
she is happy; and good, and very kind; for the mere
thought of any live creature in pain makes her wretched!

'After all, if she believes in me, she'll believe in anything; let her!

'Indeed, I'm not sure that it's not rather ungainly for
a pretty woman *not* to believe in all these good old cosmic

taradiddles, as it is for a pretty child not to believe in
Little Red Riding-hood, and Jack and the Beanstalk, and
Morgiana and the Forty Thieves ; we learn them at our
mother's knee, and how nice they are ! Let us go on
believing them as long as we can, till the child grows up
and the woman dies and it's all found out.

'Yes, Tray, I will be dishonest for her dear sake. I
will kneel by her side if ever I have the happy chance,
and ever after, night and morning, and all day long on
Sundays if she wants me to ! What will I *not* do for
that one pretty woman who believes in *me ?* I will
respect even *that* belief, and do my little best to keep it
alive for ever. It is much too precious an earthly boon
for *me* to play ducks and drakes with. . . .

'So much for Alice, Tray—your sweet mistress and
mine.

'But then, there's Alice's papa—and that's another
pair of sleeves, as we say in France.

'Ought one ever to play at make-believe with a full-
grown man for any consideration whatever—even though
he be a parson, and a possible father-in-law ? *There's* a
case of conscience for you !

'When I ask him for his daughter, as I must, and he
asks me for my profession of faith, as he will, what can I
tell him ? The truth ?

(And now, I regret to say, the reticent Little Billee is
going to show his trusty four-footed friend the least
attractive side of his many-sided nature, its modernity,
its dreary scepticism—his own unhappy portion of *la
maladie du siècle*). . . .

'But then, what will *he* say ? What allowances will
he make for a poor little weak-kneed, well-meaning waif

'"SO MUCH FOR ALICE, TRAY"'

of a painter-fellow like me, whose only choice lay between
Mr. Darwin and the Pope of Rome, and who has chosen
once and for ever—and that long ago—before he'd ever
even heard of Mr. Darwin's name.

'Besides, why should he make allowances for me?   I
don't for him.   I think no more of a parson than he does
of a painter-fellow—and that's precious little, I'm afraid.

'What will he think of a man who says :

'"Look here! the God of your belief isn't mine and
never will be—but I love your daughter, and she loves
me, and I'm the only man to make her happy!"

'He's no Jephthah; he's made of flesh and blood, although he's a parson—and loves his daughter as much as Shylock loved his.

'Tell me, Tray—thou that livest among parsons—what man, not being a parson himself, can guess how a parson would think, an average parson, confronted by such a poser as that?

'Does he, dare he, *can* he ever think straight or simply on any subject as any other man thinks, hedged in as he is by so many limitations?

'He is as shrewd, vain, worldly, self-seeking, ambitious, jealous, censorious, and all the rest, as you or I, Tray—for all his Christian profession—and just as fond of his kith and kin!

'He is considered a gentleman—which perhaps you and I are not—unless we happen to behave as such; it is a condition of his noble calling. Perhaps it's in order to become a gentleman that he's become a parson! It's about as short a royal road as any to that enviable distinction—as short almost as Her Majesty's commission, and much safer, and much less expensive—within reach of the sons of most fairly successful butchers and bakers and candlestick-makers.

'While still a boy he has bound himself irrevocably to certain beliefs, which he will be paid to preserve and preach and enforce through life, and act up to through thick and thin—at all events in the eyes of others—even his nearest and dearest—even the wife of his bosom.

'They are his bread and butter, these beliefs—and a man mustn't quarrel with his bread and butter. But a parson must quarrel with those who don't believe as he tells them!

'Yet a few years' thinking and reading and experience of life, one would suppose, might possibly just shake his faith a little (just as though, instead of being parson, he had been tinker, tailor, soldier, sailor, gentleman, apothecary, ploughboy, thief), and teach him that many of these beliefs are simply childish—and some of them very wicked indeed—and most immoral.

'It is very wicked and most immoral to believe, or affect to believe, and tell others to believe, that the unseen, unspeakable, unthinkable Immensity we're all part and parcel of, source of eternal, infinite, indestructible life and light and might, is a kind of wrathful, glorified, and self-glorifying ogre in human shape, with human passions, and most inhuman hates—who suddenly made us out of nothing, one fine day—just for a freak—and made us so badly that we fell the next—and turned us adrift the day after—damned us from the very beginning—*ab ovo* —*ab ovo usque ad malum*—ha, ha!—and ever since! never gave us a chance!

'All-merciful Father, indeed! Why, the Prince of Darkness was an angel in comparison (and a gentleman into the bargain).

'Just think of it, Tray—a finger in every little paltry pie—an eye and an ear at every keyhole, even that of the larder, to catch us tripping, and find out if we're praising loud enough, or grovelling low enough, or fasting hard enough—poor God-forsaken worms!

'And if we're naughty and disobedient, everlasting torment for us; torture of so hideous a kind that *we* wouldn't inflict it on the basest criminal, not for one single moment!

'Or else, if we're good and do as we are bid, an

eternity of bliss so futile, so idle, and so tame that we
couldn't stand it for a week, but for thinking of its one
horrible alternative, and of our poor brother for ever and
ever roasting away, and howling for the drop of water he
never gets.

'Everlasting flame, or everlasting dishonour—nothing
between!

'Isn't it ludicrous as well as pitiful—a thing to make
one snigger through one's tears? Isn't it a grievous sin
to believe in such things as these, and go about teaching
and preaching them, and being paid for it—a sin to be
heavily chastised, and a shame? What a legacy!

'They were shocking bad artists, those conceited,
narrow-minded Jews, those poor old doting monks and
priests and bigots of the grewsome, dark age of faith!
They couldn't draw a bit—no perspective, no anatomy,
no chiaro-oscuro; and it's a woful image they managed to
evolve for us out of the depths of their fathomless
ignorance, in their zeal to keep us off all the forbidden
fruit we're all so fond of, because we were built like that!
And by whom? By our Maker, I suppose (who also
made the forbidden fruit, and made it very nice—and put
it so conveniently for you and me to see and smell and
reach, Tray—and sometimes even pick, alas!).

'And even at that it's a failure, this precious image!
Only the very foolish little birds are frightened into good
behaviour. The naughty ones laugh and wink at each
other, and pull out its hair and beard when nobody's
looking, and build their nests out of the straw it's stuffed
with (the naughty little birds in black, especially), and
pick up what they want under its very nose, and thrive
uncommonly well; and the good ones fly away out of

sight ; and some day, perhaps, find a home in some happy, useful fatherland far away where the Father isn't a bit like this. Who knows?

'And I'm one of the good little birds, Tray—at least, I hope so. And that unknown Father lives in me whether I will or no, and I love Him whether He be or not, just because I can't help it, and with the best and bravest love that can be—the perfect love that believeth no evil, and seeketh no reward, and casteth out fear. For I'm His father as much as He's mine, since I've conceived the thought of Him after my own fashion!

'And He lives in you too, Tray—you and all your kind. Yes, good dog, you king of beasts, I see it in your eyes. . . .

'Ah, bon Dieu Père, le Dieu des bonnes gens! Oh! if we only knew for *certain*, Tray! what martyrdom would we not endure, you and I, with a happy smile and a grateful heart—for sheer *love* of such a father! How little should *we* care for the things of this earth!

'But the poor parson?

'He must willy-nilly go on believing, or affecting to believe, just as he is told, *word for word*, or else good-bye to his wife and children's bread and butter, his own preferment, perhaps even his very gentility—that gentility of which his Master thought so little, and he and his are apt to think so much—with possibly the Archbishopric of Canterbury at the end of it, the *bâton de maréchal* that lies in every clerical knapsack.

'What a temptation! one is but human!

'So how can he be honest without believing certain things, to believe which (without shame) one must be as simple as a little child ; as, by the way, he is so cleverly

told to be in these matters, and so cleverly tells us—and
so seldom is himself on any other matter whatever—his
own interests, other people's affairs, the world, the flesh,
and the devil! And that's clever of him too. . . .

'And if he chooses to be as simple as a little child,
why shouldn't I treat him as a little child, for his own
good, and fool him to the top of his little bent for his dear
daughter's sake, that I may make her happy, and thereby
him too?

'And if he's *not* quite so simple as all that, and makes
artful little compromises with his conscience—for a good
purpose, of course—why shouldn't I make artful little
compromises with mine, and for a better purpose still, and
try to get what I want in the way *he* does? I want to
marry his daughter far worse than he can ever want to live
in a palace, and ride in a carriage and pair with a mitre
on the panels.

'If he *cheats*, why shouldn't I cheat too?

'If *he* cheats, he cheats everybody all round—the wide,
wide world, and something wider and higher still that
can't be measured, something in himself. *I* only cheat
him!

'*If* he cheats, he cheats for the sake of very worldly
things indeed—tithes, honours, influence, power, authority,
social consideration and respect—not to speak of bread
and butter! *I* only cheat for the love of a lady fair—
and cheating for cheating, I like my cheating best.

'So, whether he cheats or not, I'll—

'Confound it! what would old Taffy do in such a çase,
I wonder? . . .

'Oh, bother! it's no good wondering what old Taffy
would do.

'Taffy never wants to marry *anybody's* daughter ; he doesn't even want to paint her ! He only wants to paint his beastly ragamuffins and thieves and drunkards, and be left alone.

'Besides, Taffy's as simple as a little child himself, and couldn't fool any one, and wouldn't if he could—not even a parson. But if any one tries to fool *him*, my eyes ! don't he cut up rough, and call names, and kick up a shindy, and even knock people down ! That's the worst of fellows like Taffy. They're too good for this world and too solemn. They're impossible, and lack all sense of humour. In point of fact Taffy's a *gentleman*—poor fellow ! *et puis voilà !*

'I'm not simple—worse luck ; and I can't knock people down—I only wish I could ! I can only paint them ! and not even *that* "as they really are !" . . . Good old Taffy ! . . .

'Faint heart never won fair lady !

'Oh, happy, happy thought—I'll be brave and win !

'I can't knock people down, or do doughty deeds, but I'll be brave in my own little way—the only way I can. . . .

'I'll simply lie through thick and thin—I must—I will—nobody need ever be a bit the wiser ! I can do more good by lying than by telling the truth, and make more deserving people happy, including myself and the sweetest girl alive—the end shall justify the means : that's my excuse, my only excuse ! and this lie of mine is on so stupendous a scale that it will have to last me for life. It's my only one, but its name is *Lion !* and I'll never tell another as long as I live.

'And now that I know what temptation really is, I'll

never think any harm of any parson any more . . . never, never, never!'

So the little man went on, as if he knew all about it, had found it all out for himself, and nobody else had ever found it out before! and I am not responsible for his ways of thinking (which are not necessarily my own).

It must be remembered, in extenuation, that he was very young, and not very wise: no philosopher, no scholar—just a painter of lovely pictures; only that and nothing more. Also, that he was reading Mr. Darwin's immortal book for the third time, and it was a little too strong for him; also, that all this happened in the early sixties, long ere Religion had made up her mind to meet Science half-way, and hobnob and kiss and be friends. Alas! before such a lying down of the lion and the lamb can ever come to pass, Religion will have to perform a larger share of the journey than half, I fear!

Then, still carried away by the flood of his own eloquence (for he had never had such an innings as this, nor such a listener), he again apostrophised the dog Tray, who had been growing somewhat inattentive (like the reader, perhaps), in language more beautiful than ever:

'Oh, to be like you, Tray—and secrete love and good-will from morn till night, from night till morning—like saliva, without effort! with never a moment's cessation of flow, even in disgrace and humiliation! How much better to love than to be loved—to love as you do, my Tray—so warmly, so easily, so unremittingly—to forgive all wrongs and neglect and injustice so quickly and so well—and forget a kindness never! Lucky dog that you are!

‘ “ Oh ! could I feel as I have felt, or be as I have been,
    Or weep as I could once have wept, o’er many a vanished scene,
    As springs in deserts found seem sweet, all brackish tho’ they be,
    So ’midst this withered waste of life those tears would flow to me ! ”

‘ What do you think of those lines, Tray ? I *love* them, because my mother taught them to me when I was about your age—six years old, or seven ! and before the bard who wrote them had fallen ; like Lucifer, son of the morning ! Have you ever heard of Lord Byron, Tray ? He too, like Ulysses, loved a dog, and many people think that’s about the best there is to be said of him nowadays ! Poor Humpty Dumpty ! Such a swell as he once was ! Not all the king’s horses, nor all the——’

Here Tray jumped up suddenly and bolted—he saw some one else he was fond of, and ran to meet him. It was the vicar, coming out of his vicarage.

A very nice-looking vicar—fresh, clean, alert, well tanned by sun and wind and weather—a youngish vicar still ; tall, stout, gentlemanlike, shrewd, kindly, worldly, a trifle pompous, and authoritative more than a trifle ; not much given to abstract speculation, and thinking fifty times more of any sporting and orthodox young country squire, well-inched and well-acred (and well-whiskered), than of all the painters in Christendom.

‘ “ When Greeks joined Greeks, then was the tug of war,” ’ thought Little Billee ; and he felt a little uncomfortable. Alice’s father had never loomed so big and impressive before, or so distressingly nice to look at.

‘ Welcome, my Apelles, to your ain countree, which is growing quite proud of you, I declare ! Young Lord Archie Waring was saying only last night that he wished he had half your talent ! He’s *crazed* about painting, you

know, and actually wants to be a painter himself! The
poor dear old marquis is quite sore about it!'

With this happy exordium the parson stopped and
shook hands ; and they both stood for a while, looking
seaward. The parson said the usual things about the sea
—its blueness, its grayness, its greenness, its beauty, its
sadness, its treachery.

> ' " Who shall put forth on thee,
> Unfathomable sea ! " '

'Who indeed!' answered Little Billee, quite agreeing.
' I vote *we* don't, at all events.' So they turned inland.

The parson said the usual things about the land (from
the country-gentleman's point of view), and the talk began
to flow quite pleasantly, with quoting of the usual poets,
and capping of quotations in the usual way—for they
had known each other many years, both here and in
London. Indeed, the vicar had once been Little Billee's
tutor.

And thus, amicably, they entered a small wooded
hollow. Then the vicar, turning of a sudden his full blue
gaze on the painter, asked, sternly—

'What book's that you've got in your hand, Willie?'

' A—a—it's the *Origin of Species*, by Charles Darwin.
I'm very f-f-fond of it. I'm reading it for the third time.
. . . It's very g-g-good. It *accounts* for things, you know.'

Then, after a pause, and still more sternly—

'What place of worship do you most attend in London
—especially of an evening, William?'

Then stammered Little Billee, all self-control forsaking
him—

'I d-d-don't attend any place of worship at all—
morning, afternoon, or evening. I've long given up going

to church altogether.   I can only be frank with you ; I'll
tell you why. . . .'

And as they walked along the talk drifted on to very
momentous subjects indeed, and led, unfortunately, to a
serious falling out—for which probably both were to
blame—and closed in a distressful way at the other end
of the little wooded hollow—a way most sudden and
unexpected, and quite grievous to relate.   When they
emerged into the open, the parson was quite white, and
the painter crimson.

'Sir,' said the parson, squaring himself up to more
than his full height and breadth and dignity, his face big
with righteous wrath, his voice full of strong menace—
'sir, you're—you're a—you're a *thief,* sir, a *thief!*   You're
trying to *rob me of my Saviour!*   Never you dare to
darken *my* door-step again !'

'Sir,' said Little Billee, with a bow, 'if it comes to
calling names, you're—you're a—no ; you're Alice's
father ; and whatever else you are besides, I'm another
for trying to be honest with a parson ; so good-morning
to you.'

And each walked off in an opposite direction, stiff as
pokers ; and Tray stood between, looking first at one
receding figure, then at the other, disconsolate.

And thus Little Billee found out that he could no
more lie than he could fly.   And so he did not marry
sweet Alice after all, and no doubt it was ordered for her
good and his.   But there was tribulation for many days
in the house of Bagot, and for many months in one
tender, pure, and pious bosom.

And the best and the worst of it all is that, not very
many years after, the good vicar—more fortunate than

"'YOU'RE A *THIEF*, SIR!'"

most clergymen who dabble in stocks and shares—grew suddenly very rich through a lucky speculation in Irish beer, and suddenly, also, took to thinking seriously about things (as a man of business should)—more seriously than he had ever thought before. So at least the story goes in North Devon, and it is not so new as to be incredible. Little doubts grew into big ones—big doubts resolved themselves into downright negations. He quarrelled with his bishop; he quarrelled with his dean; he even quarrelled with his 'poor dear old marquis,' who died before there was time to make it up again. And finally he felt it his duty, in conscience, to secede from a Church which had become too narrow to hold him, and took himself and his belongings to London, where at least he could breathe. But there he fell into a great disquiet, for the long habit of feeling himself always *en évidence*— of being looked up to and listened to without contradiction; of exercising influence and authority in spiritual matters (and even temporal); of impressing women, especially, with his commanding presence, his fine sonorous voice, his lofty brow, so serious and smooth, his soft, big, waving hands, which soon lost their country tan—all this had grown as a second nature to him, the breath of his nostrils, a necessity of his life. So he rose to be the most popular Positivist preacher of his day, and pretty broad at that.

But his dear daughter Alice, she stuck to the old faith, and married a venerable High-Church archdeacon, who very cleverly clutched at and caught her and saved her for himself just as she stood shivering on the very brink of Rome; and they were neither happy nor unhappy together—*un ménage bourgeois, ni beau ni laid, ni bon ni mauvais.* And thus, alas! the bond of religious sympathy, that counts for so much in united families, no longer existed between father and daughter, and the heart's division divided them. *Ce que c'est que de nous!* . . . The pity of it!

And so no more of sweet Alice with hair so brown.

PART SIXTH

'Vraiment, la reine auprès d'elle était laide
    Quand, vers le soir,
Elle passait sur le pont de Tolède
    En corset noir !
Un chapelet du temps de Charlemagne
    Ornait son cou. . . .
Le vent qui vient à travers la montagne
    Me rendra fou !

'Dansez, chantez, villageois ! la nuit tombe. . . .
    Sabine, un jour,
A tout donné—sa beauté de colombe,
    Et son amour—
Pour un anneau du Comte de Saldagne,
    Pour un bijou. . . .
Le vent qui vient à travers la montagne
    M'a rendu fou !'

BEHOLD our three musketeers of the brush once more reunited in Paris, famous, after long years.

In emulation of the good Dumas, we will call it 'cinq ans après.' It was a little more.

Taffy stands for Porthos and Athos rolled into one, since he is big and good-natured, and strong enough to 'assommer un homme d'un coup de poing,' and also stately and solemn, of aristocratic and romantic appearance, and not too fat—not too much ongbongpwang, as the Laird called it—and also he does not dislike a bottle of wine, or even two, and looks as if he had a history.

The Laird, of course, is D'Artagnan, since he sells his pictures well, and by the time we are writing of has already become an Associate of the Royal Academy; like Quentin Durward, this D'Artagnan was a Scotsman:

'Ah, wasna he a Roguey, this piper of Dundee!'

And Little Billee, the dainty friend of duchesses, must stand for Aramis, I fear! It will not do to push the simile too far; besides, unlike the good Dumas, one has a conscience. One does not play ducks and drakes with historical facts, or tamper with historical personages. And if Athos, Porthos, and Co. are not historical by this time, I should like to know who are!

Well, so are Taffy, the Laird, and Little Billee—*tout ce qu'il y a de plus historique!*

Our three friends, well groomed, frock-coated, shirt-collared within an inch of their lives, duly scarfed and scarf-pinned, chimney-pot-hatted, and most beautifully trousered, and balmorally booted, or neatly spatted (or whatever was most correct at the time), are breakfasting together on coffee, rolls, and butter at a little round table in the huge courtyard of an immense caravansérai, paved with asphalt, and covered in at the top with a glazed roof that admits the sun and keeps out the rain—and the air.

A magnificent old man as big as Taffy, in black cloth coat and breeches and black silk stockings, and a large metal chain round his neck and chest, looks down like Jove from a broad flight of marble steps—as though to welcome the coming guests, who arrive in cabs and railway omnibuses through a huge archway on the boulevard; or to speed those who part through a lesser archway opening on to a side street.

'Bon voyage, messieurs et dames!'

At countless other little tables other voyagers are breakfasting or ordering breakfast; or, having breakfasted, are smoking and chatting and looking about. It is a babel of tongues—the cheerfullest, busiest, merriest scene in the world, apparently the costly place of rendezvous for all wealthy Europe and America; an atmosphere of bank-notes and gold.

Already Taffy has recognised (and been recognised by) half a dozen old fellow-Crimeans, of unmistakable military aspect like himself; and three canny Scotsmen have discreetly greeted the Laird; and as for Little Billee, he is constantly jumping up from his breakfast and running to this table or that, drawn by some irresistible British smile of surprised and delighted female recognition: 'What, *you* here? How nice! Come over to hear La Svengali, I suppose?'

At the top of the marble steps is a long terrace, with seats and people sitting, from which tall glazed doors, elaborately carved and gilded, give access to luxurious drawing-rooms, dining-rooms, reading-rooms, lavatories, postal and telegraph offices; and all round and about are huge square green boxes, out of which grow tropical and exotic evergreens all the year round—with beautiful names that I have forgotten. And leaning against these boxes are placards announcing what theatrical or musical entertainments will take place in Paris that day or night; and the biggest of these placards (and the most fantastically decorated) informs the cosmopolite world that Madame Svengali intends to make her first appearance in Paris that very evening, at nine punctually, in the Cirque des Bashibazoucks, Rue St. Honoré!

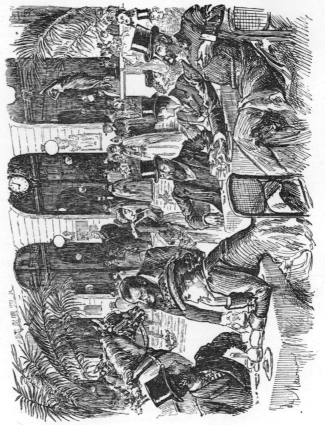

"AN ATMOSPHERE OF BANK-NOTES AND GOLD"

Our friends had only arrived the previous night, but they had managed to secure stalls a week beforehand. No places were any longer to be got for love or money. Many people had come to Paris on purpose to hear La Svengali—many famous musicians from England and everywhere else—but they would have to wait many days.

The fame of her was like a rolling snow-ball that had been rolling all over Europe for the last two years—wherever there was snow to be picked up in the shape of golden ducats.

Their breakfast over, Taffy, the Laird, and Little Billee, cigar in mouth, arm-in-arm, the huge Taffy in the middle (*comme autrefois*), crossed the sunshiny boulevard into the shade, and went down the Rue de la Paix, through the Place Vendôme and the Rue Castiglione to the Rue de Rivoli—quite leisurely, and with a tender midriff-warming sensation of freedom and delight at almost every step.

Arrived at the corner pastrycook's, they finished the stumps of their cigars as they looked at the well-remembered show in the window; then they went in and had, Taffy a Madeleine, the Laird a Baba, and Little Billee a Savarin—and each, I regret to say, a liqueur-glass of *rhum de la Jamaïque.*

After this they sauntered through the Tuileries Gardens, and by the quay to their favourite Pont des Arts, and looked up and down the river—*comme autrefois !*

It is an enchanting prospect at any time and under any circumstances ; but on a beautiful morning in mid-October, when you haven't seen it for five years, and are still young ! and almost every stock and stone that meets your eye, every sound, every scent, has some sweet and subtle reminder for you——

Let the reader have no fear.   I will not attempt to describe it.   I shouldn't know where to begin (nor when to leave off!).

Not but what many changes had been wrought ; many old landmarks were missing.   And among them, as they found out a few minutes later, and much to their chagrin, the good old Morgue !

They inquired of a *gardien de la paix*, who told them that a new Morgue—'une bien jolie Morgue, ma foi !'—and much more commodious and comfortable than the old one, had been built beyond Notre Dame, a little to the right.

'Messieurs devraient voir ça—on y est très bien !'

But Notre Dame herself was still there, and La Sainte Chapelle and Le Pont Neuf, and the equestrian statue of Henri IV.   *C'est toujours ça !*

'A LITTLE PICTURE OF THE THAMES'

And as they gazed and gazed, each framed unto himself, mentally, a little picture of the Thames they had just left—and thought of Waterloo Bridge, and St. Paul's, and

London—but felt no home-sickness whatever, no desire to go back in a hurry!

And looking down the river westward there was but little change.

On the left-hand side the terraces and garden of the Hôtel de la Rochemartel (the sculptured entrance of which was in the Rue de Lille) still overtopped the neighbouring houses and shaded the quay with tall trees, whose lightly-falling leaves yellowed the pavement for at least a hundred yards of frontage—or backage, rather; for this was but the rear of that stately palace.

'I wonder if l'Zouzou has come into his dukedom yet?' said Taffy.

And Taffy the realist, Taffy the modern of moderns, also said many beautiful things about old historical French dukedoms; which, in spite of their plentifulness, were so much more picturesque than English ones, and constituted a far more poetical and romantic link with the past; partly on account of their beautiful, high-sounding names!

'Amaury de Brissac de Roncesvaulx de la Rochemartel-Boisségur! what a generous mouthful! Why, the very sound of it is redolent of the twelfth century! Not even Howard of Norfolk can beat that!'

For Taffy was getting sick of 'this ghastly thin-faced time of ours,' as he sadly called it (quoting from a strange and very beautiful poem called 'Faustine,' which had just appeared in the *Spectator*—and which our three enthusiasts already knew by heart), and beginning to love all things that were old and regal and rotten and forgotten and of bad repute, and to long to paint them just as they really were.

'Ah! they managed these things better in France, especially in the twelfth century, and even the thirteenth!' said the Laird. 'Still, Howard of Norfolk isn't bad at a pinch—*fote de myoo!*' he continued, winking at Little Billee. And they promised themselves that they would leave cards on Zouzou, and if he wasn't a duke, invite him to dinner; and also Dodor, if they could manage to find him.

Then along the quay and up the Rue de Seine, and by well-remembered little mystic ways to the old studio in the Place St. Anatole des Arts.

Here they found many changes. A row of new houses on the north side, by Baron Haussmann—the well-named—a boulevard was being constructed right through the place. But the old house had been respected; and looking up, they saw the big north window of their good old abode blindless and blank and black, but for a white placard in the middle of it with the words: 'À louer. Un atelier, et une chambre à coucher.'

They entered the courtyard through the little door in the porte cochère, and beheld Madame Vinard standing on the step of her loge, her arms akimbo, giving orders to her husband—who was sawing logs for firewood, as usual at that time of the year—and telling him he was the most helpless log of the lot.

She gave them one look, threw up her arms, and rushed at them, saying, 'Ah, mon Dieu! les trois Angliches!'

And they could not have complained of any lack of warmth in her greeting, or in Monsieur Vinard's.

'Ah! mais quel bonheur de vous revoir! Et comme vous avez bonne mine, tous! Et Monsieur Litrebili, donc ! il a grandi !' etc., etc. 'Mais vous allez boire la goutte avant tout—vite, Vinard ! Le ratafia de cassis que Monsieur Durien nous a envoyé la semaine dernière !'

And they were taken into the loge and made free of it—welcomed like prodigal sons ; a fresh bottle of black-currant brandy was tapped, and did duty for the fatted calf. It was an ovation, and made quite a stir in the Quartier.

Le Retour des trois Angliches—cinq ans après !

She told them all the news : about Bouchardy ; Papelard ; Jules Guinot, who was now in the Ministère de la Guerre ; Barizel, who had given up the arts and gone into his father's business (umbrellas) ; Durien, who had married six months ago, and had a superb atelier in the Rue Taitbout, and was coining money ; about her own family—Aglaë, who was going to be married to the son of the charbonnier at the corner of the Rue de la Canicule—' un bon mariage ; bien solide !' Niniche, who was studying the piano at the Conservatoire, and had won the silver medal ; Isidore, who, alas ! had gone to the bad—'perdu par les femmes ! un si joli garçon, vous concevez ! ça ne lui a pas porté bonheur, par exemple !' And yet she was proud ! and said his father would never have had the pluck !

'A dix-huit ans, pensez donc !'

'And that good Monsieur Carrel ; he is dead, you know ! Ah, messieurs savaient ça ? Yes, he died at Dieppe, his natal town, during the winter, from the consequences of an indigestion—que voulez-vous ! He always had the stomach so feeble ! . . . Ah, the beautiful interment, messieurs ! Five thousand people, in spite of the rain ! Car il pleuvait averse ! And M. le Maire and

his adjunct walking behind the hearse, and the gendarmerie
and the douaniers, and a bataillon of the douzième
chasseurs-à-pied, with their music, and all the sapper-
pumpers, en grande tenue with their beautiful brass
helmets! All the town was there, following: so there
was nobody left to see the procession go by! q'c'était
beau! Mon Dieu, q'c'était beau! c'que j'ai pleuré, d'voir
ça! n'est-ce-pas, Vinard?'

'Dame, oui, ma biche! j'crois bien! It might have
been Monsieur le Maire himself that one was interring in
person!'

'Ah, ça! voyons, Vinard; thou'rt not going to
compare the Maire of Dieppe to a painter like Monsieur
Carrel?'

'Certainly not, ma biche! But still, M. Carrel was a
great man all the same, in his way. Besides, I wasn't
there—nor thou either, as to that!'

'Mon Dieu! comme il est idiot, ce Vinard—of a
stupidity to cut with a knife! Why, thou might'st
almost be a Mayor thyself, sacred imbecile that thou
art!'

And an animated discussion arose between husband
and wife as to the respective merits of a country mayor
on one side and a famous painter and a member of the
Institute on the other, during which *les trois Angliches*
were left out in the cold. When Madame Vinard had
sufficiently routed her husband, which did not take very
long, she turned to them again, and told them that she
had started a *magasin de bric-à-brac*, 'vous verrez ça!'

Yes, the studio had been to let for three months.
Would they like to see it? Here were the keys. They
would, of course, prefer to see it by themselves, alone;

"'AH! THE BEAUTIFUL INTERMENT, MESSIEURS!'"

U

'je comprends ça! et vous verrez ce que vous verrez!' Then they must come and drink once more again the drop, and inspect her *magasin de bric-à-brac.*

So they went up, all three, and let themselves into the old place where they had been so happy—and one of them for a while so miserable!

It was changed indeed.

Bare of all furniture, for one thing; shabby and unswept, with a pathetic air of dilapidation, spoliation, desecration, and a musty, shut-up smell; the window so dirty you could hardly see the new houses opposite; the floor a disgrace!

All over the walls were caricatures in charcoal and white chalk, with more or less incomprehensible legends; very vulgar and trivial and coarse, some of them, and pointless for *trois Angliches.*

But among these (touching to relate) they found, under a square of plate-glass that had been fixed on the wall by means of an oak frame, Little Billee's old black-and-white-and-red chalk sketch of Trilby's left foot, as fresh as if it had been done only yesterday! Over it was written: 'Souvenir de la Grande Trilby, par W. B. (Litrebili).' And beneath, carefully engrossed on imperishable parchment, and pasted on the glass, the following stanzas :—

> 'Pauvre Trilby—la belle et bonne et chère!
> Je suis son pied.   Devine qui voudra
> Quel tendre ami, la chérissant naguère,
> Encadra d'elle (et d'un amour sincère)
> Ce souvenir charmant qu'un caprice inspira—
>   Qu'un souffle emportera!
>
> 'J'étais jumeau : qu'est devenu mon frère?
>   Hélas!   Hélas!   L'Amour nous égara.

"PAUVRE TRILBY"

L'Éternité nous unira, j'espère ;
Et nous ferons comme autrefois la paire
Au fond d'un lit bien chaste où nul ne troublera
    Trilby—qui dormira.

' Ô tendre ami, sans nous qu'allez-vous faire ?
La porte est close où Trilby demeura.
Le Paradis est loin . . . et sur la terre
(Qui nous fut douce et lui sera légère)
Pour trouver nos pareils, si bien qu'on cherchera—
    Beau chercher l'on aura ! '

Taffy drew a long breath into his manly bosom, and kept it there as he read this characteristic French doggerel (for so he chose to call this touching little symphony in *ère* and *ra*). His huge frame thrilled with tenderness and pity and fond remembrance, and he said to himself (letting out his breath): ' Dear, dear Trilby ! Ah ! if you had only cared for *me*, *I* wouldn't have let you give me up—not for any one on earth. *You* were the mate for *me !* '

And that, as the reader has guessed long ago, was big Taffy's ' history.'

The Laird was also deeply touched, and could not speak. Had he been in love with Trilby, too ? Had he ever been in love with any one ?

He couldn't say. But he thought of Trilby's sweetness and unselfishness, her gaiety, her innocent kissings and caressings, her drollery and frolicsome grace, her way of filling whatever place she was in with her presence, the charming sight and the genial sound of her ; and felt that no girl, no woman, no lady he had ever seen yet was a match for this poor waif and stray, this long-legged, cancan-dancing, Quartier Latin grisette, blanchisseuse de fin, ' and Heaven knows what besides ! '

'Hang it all!' he mentally ejaculated, 'I wish to goodness I'd married her *myself!*'

Little Billee said nothing either. He felt unhappier than he had ever once felt for five long years—to think that he could gaze on such a memento as this, a thing so strongly personal to himself, with dry eyes and a quiet pulse! and he unemotionally, dispassionately, wished himself dead and buried for at least the thousand-and-first time!

All three possessed casts of Trilby's hands and feet, and photographs of herself. But nothing so charmingly suggestive of Trilby as this little masterpiece of a true artist, this happy fluke of a happy moment. It was Trilbyness itself, as the Laird thought, and should not be suffered to perish.

They took the keys back to Madame Vinard in silence.

She said : 'Vous avez vu—n'est-ce pas, messieurs ?— le pied de Trilby! c'est bien gentil! C'est Monsieur Durien qui a fait mettre le verre, quand vous êtes partis ; et Monsieur Guinot qui a composé *l'épitaphe.* Pauvre Trilby! qu'est-ce qu'elle est devenue! comme elle était bonne fille, hein ? et si belle! et comme elle était vive elle était vive elle était vive! Et comme elle vous aimait tous bien—et surtout Monsieur Litrebili—n'est-ce pas ?'

Then she insisted on giving them each another liqueur-glass of Durien's ratafia de cassis, and took them to see her collection of *bric-à-brac* across the yard, a gorgeous show, and explained everything about it—how she had begun in quite a small way, but was making it a big business.

'Voyez cette pendule! It is of the time of Louis

Onze, who gave it with his own hands to Madame de Pompadour (!). I bought it at a sale in——'

'Combiang?' said the Laird.

'C'est cent-cinquante francs, monsieur—c'est bien bon marché—une véritable occasion, et——'

'Je prong!' said the Laird, meaning 'I take it!'

Then she showed them a beautiful brocade gown 'which she had picked up a bargain at——'

'Combiang?' said the Laird.

'Ah, ça, c'est trois cents francs, monsieur. Mais——'

'Je prong!' said the Laird.

'Et voici les souliers qui vont avec, et que——'

'Je pr——'

But here Taffy took the Laird by the arm and dragged him by force out of this too seductive siren's cave.

The Laird told her where to send his purchases, and with many expressions of love and good-will on both sides, they tore themselves away from Monsieur et Madame Vinard.

The Laird, however, rushed back for a minute, and hurriedly whispered to Madame Vinard: 'Oh—er—le piay de Trilby—sur le mure, vous savvy—avec le verre et toot le reste—coopy le mure—comprenny? . . . Combiang?'

'Ah, monsieur!' said Madame Vinard—'c'est un peu difficile, vous savez—couper un mur comme ça! On parlera au propriétaire si vous voulez, et ça pourrait peut-être s'arranger, si c'est en bois! seulement il fau——'

'Je prong!' said the Laird, and waved his hand in farewell.

They went up the Rue Vieille des Trois Mauvais Ladres, and found that about twenty yards of a high wall had been pulled down—just at the bend where the Laird had seen the last of Trilby, as she turned round and kissed her hand to him—and they beheld, within, a quaint and ancient long-neglected garden; a gray old garden,

' "JE PRONG!" '

with tall, warty, black-boled trees, and damp, green, mossy paths that lost themselves under the brown and yellow leaves and mould and muck which had drifted into heaps here and there, the accumulation of years—a queer old

faded pleasance, with wasted bowers and dilapidated
carved stone benches and weather-beaten discoloured
marble statues—noseless, armless, earless fauns and
hamadryads! And at the end of it, in a tumble-down
state of utter ruin, a still inhabited little house, with
shabby blinds and window-curtains, and broken window-
panes mended with brown paper—a Pavillon de Flore,
that must have been quite beautiful a hundred years ago
—the once mysterious love-resort of long-buried abbés
with light hearts, and well-forgotten lords and ladies gay
—red-heeled, patched, powdered, frivolous, and shameless,
but, oh! how charming to the imagination of the
nineteenth century! And right through the ragged lawn
(where lay, upset in the long dewy grass, a broken doll's
perambulator by a tattered Polichinelle) went a desecrat-
ing track made by cart-wheels and horses' hoofs; and
this, no doubt, was to be a new street—perhaps, as Taffy
suggested, 'La Rue *Neuve* des Trois Mauvais Ladres!'
(The *new* street of the three bad lepers!)

'Ah, Taffy!' sententiously opined the Laird, with his
usual wink at Little Billee—'I've no doubt the *old* lepers
were the best, bad as they were!'

'I'm quite *sure* of it!' said Taffy, with sad and sober
conviction and a long-drawn sigh. 'I only wish I had a
chance of painting one—just as he really was!'

How often they had speculated on what lay hidden
behind that lofty old brick wall! and now this melancholy
little peep into the once festive past, the touching sight of
this odd old poverty-stricken abode of Heaven knows
what present grief and desolation, which a few strokes of
the pickaxe had laid bare, seemed to chime in with their
own gray mood that had been so bright and sunny an

hour ago ; and they went on their way quite dejectedly, for a stroll through the Luxembourg Gallery and Gardens.

The same people seemed to be still copying the same pictures in the long, quiet, genial room, so pleasantly smell- ing of oil-paint—Rosa Bonheur's ' Labourage Nivernais,' Hébert's ' Malaria,' Couture's ' Decadent Romans.'

And in the formal dusty gardens were the same pioupious and zouzous still walking with the same nounous, or sitting by their sides on benches by formal ponds with gold and silver fish in them—and just the same old couples petting the same toutous and loulous ! [1]

Then they thought they would go and lunch at le père Trin's—the Restaurant de la Couronne, in the Rue du Luxembourg—for the sake of auld lang syne ! But when they got there, the well-remembered fumes of that humble refectory, which had once seemed not unappetis- ing, turned their stomachs. So they contented them- selves with warmly greeting le père Trin, who was quite overjoyed to see them again, and anxious to turn the whole establishment topsy-turvy that he might entertain such guests as they deserved.

Then the Laird suggested an omelet at the Café de l'Odéon. But Taffy said, in his masterful way, ' Damn the Café de l'Odéon ! '

And hailing a little open fly, they drove to Ledoyen's, or some such place, in the Champs Élysées, where they feasted as became three prosperous Britons out for a holiday in Paris—three irresponsible musketeers, lords of

---

[1] *Glossary.*—Pioupiou (*alias* pousse-caillou, *alias* tourlourou)—a private soldier of the line.   Zouzou—a Zouave.   Nounou—a wet-nurse with a pretty ribboned cap and long streamers.   Toutou—a nondescript French lapdog, of no breed known to Englishmen (a regular little beast !)   Loulou—a Pomeranian dog—not much better.

themselves and Lutetia, *beati possidentes !*—and afterwards
had themselves driven in an open carriage and pair
through the Bois de Boulogne to the fête de St. Cloud (or
what still remained of it, for it lasts six weeks), the scene
of so many of Dodor's and Zouzou's exploits in past years,
and found it more amusing than the Luxembourg Gardens ;
the lively and irrepressible spirit of Dodor seemed to per-
vade it still.

But it doesn't want the presence of a Dodor to make
the blue-bloused sons of the Gallic people (and its neatly-
shod, white-capped daughters) delightful to watch as they
take their pleasure.   And the Laird (thinking perhaps of
Hampstead Heath on an Easter Monday) must not be
blamed for once more quoting his favourite phrase—the
pretty little phrase with which the most humorous and
least exemplary of British parsons began his famous
journey to France.

When they came back to the hotel to dress and dine,
the Laird found he wanted a pair of white gloves for the
concert—' Oon pair de gong blong,' as he called it—and
they walked along the boulevards till they came to a
haberdasher's shop of very good and prosperous appearance, and, going in, were received graciously by the
' patron,' a portly little bourgeois, who waved them to a
tall and aristocratic and very well-dressed young commis
behind the counter, saying, ' Une paire de gants blancs
pour monsieur.'

And what was the surprise of our three friends in
recognising Dodor !

The gay Dodor, Dodor *l'irrésistible*, quite unembarrassed
by his position, was exuberant in his delight at seeing
them again, and introduced them to the patron and his

"'OON PAIR DE GONG BLONG'"

wife and daughter, Monsieur, Madame, and Mademoiselle
Passefil.　And it soon became pretty evident that, in spite
of his humble employment in that house, he was a great
favourite in that family, and especially with mademoiselle.

Indeed, Monsieur Passefil invited our three heroes to
stay and dine then and there; but they compromised
matters by asking Dodor to come and dine with *them* at
the hotel, and he accepted with alacrity.

Thanks to Dodor, the dinner was a very lively one, and
they soon forgot the regretful impressions of the day.

They learned that he hadn't got a penny in the world,
and had left the army, and had for two years kept the
books at le père Passefil's and served his customers, and
won his good opinion and his wife's, and especially his
daughter's; and that soon he was to be not only his
employer's partner, but his son-in-law; and that, in spite
of his impecuniosity, he had managed to impress them
with the fact that in marrying a Rigolot de Lafarce she
was making a very splendid match indeed!

His brother-in-law, the Honourable Jack Reeve, had
long cut him for a bad lot.　But his sister, after a while,
had made up her mind that to marry Mlle. Passefil wasn't
the worst he could do; at all events, it would keep him
out of England, and *that* was a comfort!　And passing
through Paris, she had actually called on the Passefil
family, and they had fallen prostrate before such splendour; and no wonder, for Mrs. Jack Reeve was one of the
most beautiful, elegant, and fashionable women in London,
the smartest of the smart.

'And how about l'Zouzou?' asked Little Billee.

'Ah, old Gontran!　I don't see much of him.　We no
longer quite move in the same circles, you know; not

that he's proud, or me either! but he's a sub-lieutenant in
the Guides—an officer! Besides, his brother's dead, and
he's the Duc de la Rochemartel, and a special pet of the
Empress; he makes her laugh more than anybody!
He's looking out for the biggest heiress he can find, and
he's pretty safe to catch her, with such a name as that!
In fact, they say he's caught her already—Miss Lavinia
Hunks, of Chicago. Twenty million dollars!—at least,
so the *Figaro* says!'

Then he gave them news of other old friends; and
they did not part till it was time for them to go to the
Cirque des Bashibazoucks, and after they had arranged to
dine with his future family on the following day.

In the Rue St. Honoré was a long double file of cabs
and carriages slowly moving along to the portals of that
huge hall, Le Cirque des Bashibazoucks. Is it there still,
I wonder? I don't mind betting not! Just at this period
of the Second Empire there was a mania for demolition
and remolition (if there is such a word), and I have no
doubt my Parisian readers would scarch the Rue St.
Honoré for the Salle des Bashibazoucks in vain!

Our friends were shown to their stalls, and looked
round in surprise. This was before the days of the
Albert Hall, and they had never been in such a big place
of the kind before, or one so regal in aspect, so gorgeously
imperial with white and gold and crimson velvet, so
dazzling with light, so crammed with people from floor
to roof, and cramming itself still.

A platform carpeted with crimson cloth had been
erected in front of the gates where the horses had once
used to come in, and their fair riders, and the two jolly

English clowns; and the beautiful nobleman with the long frock-coat and brass buttons, and soft high boots, and four-in-hand whip—*la chambrière.*

In front of this was a lower stand for the orchestra. The circus itself was filled with stalls—*stalles d'orchestre.* A pair of crimson curtains hid the entrance to the platform at the back, and by each of these stood a small page, ready to draw it aside and admit the diva.

The entrance to the orchestra was by a small door under the platform, and some thirty or forty chairs and music-stands, grouped around the conductor's *estrade,* were waiting for the band.

Little Billee looked round, and recognised many countrymen and countrywomen of his own—many great musical celebrities especially, whom he had often met in London. Tiers upon tiers of people rose up all round in a widening circle, and lost themselves in a dazy mist of light at the top—it was like a picture by Martin! In the imperial box were the English ambassador and his family, with an august British personage sitting in the middle, in front, his broad blue ribbon across his breast and his opera-glass to his royal eyes.

Little Billee had never felt so excited, so exhilarated by such a show before, nor so full of eager anticipation. He looked at his programme, and saw that the Hungarian band (the first that had yet appeared in Western Europe, I believe) would play an overture of gypsy dances. Then Madame Svengali would sing 'un air connu, sans accompagnement,' and afterwards other airs, including the 'Nussbaum' of Schumann (for the first time in Paris, it seemed). Then a rest of ten minutes; then more *csárdás ;* then the diva would sing 'Malbrouck s'en va-t'en guerre,' of all things in the world! and finish up with 'un impromptu de Chopin, sans paroles.'

Truly a somewhat incongruous bill of fare.

Close on the stroke of nine the musicians came in and took their seats. They were dressed in the foreign hussar uniform that has now become so familiar. The first violin had scarcely sat down before our friends recognised in him their old friend Gecko.

Just as the clock struck, Svengali, in irreproachable evening dress, tall and stout and quite splendid in appearance, notwithstanding his long black mane (which had been curled), took his place at his desk. Our friends would have known him at a glance, in spite of the wonderful alteration time and prosperity had wrought in his outward man.

He bowed right and left to the thunderous applause that greeted him, gave his three little bâton-taps, and the lovely music

GECKO

began at once. We have grown accustomed to strains of this kind during the last twenty years, but they were new then, and their strange seduction was a surprise as well as an enchantment.

Besides, no such band as Svengali's had ever been heard; and in listening to this overture the immense crowd almost forgot that it was a mere preparation for a great musical event, and tried to encore it. But Svengali merely turned round and bowed—there were to be no encores that night.

Then a moment of silence and breathless suspense— curiosity on tiptoe !

Then the two little page-boys each drew a silken rope, and the curtains parted and looped themselves up on each side symmetrically ; and a tall female figure appeared, clad in what seemed like a classical dress of cloth of gold, embroidered with garnets and beetles' wings ; her snowy arms and shoulders bare, a gold coronet of stars on her head, her thick light brown hair tied behind and flowing all down her back to nearly her knees, like those ladies in hair-dressers' shops who sit with their backs to the plate - glass window to advertise the merits of some particular hair-wash.

She walked slowly down to the front, her hands hanging at her sides in quite a simple fashion, and made a slight inclination of her head and body towards the imperial box, and then to right and left. Her lips and cheeks were rouged ; her dark level eye-brows nearly met at the bridge of her short high nose. Through her parted lips you could see her large glistening white teeth ; her gray eyes looked straight at Svengali.

Her face was thin, and had a rather haggard expression, in spite of its artificial freshness ; but its contour was divine, and its character so tender, so humble, so touch- ingly simple and sweet, that one melted at the sight of her. No such magnificent or seductive apparition has ever been seen before or since on any stage or platform—not even Miss Ellen Terry as the priestess of Artemis in the late laureate's play, *The Cup*.

The house rose at her as she came down to the front ;

and she bowed again to right and left, and put her hand to her heart quite simply and with a most winning natural gesture, an adorable *gaucherie*—like a graceful and unconscious school-girl, quite innocent of stage deportment.

It was Trilby!

Trilby the tone-deaf, who couldn't sing one single note in tune! Trilby, who couldn't tell a C from an F!!

What was going to happen?

Our three friends were almost turned to stone in the immensity of their surprise.

Yet the big Taffy was trembling all over; the Laird's jaw had all but fallen on to his chest; Little Billee was staring, staring his eyes almost out of his head. There was something, to them, so strange and uncanny about it all; so oppressive, so anxious, so momentous!

The applause had at last subsided. Trilby stood with her hands behind her, one foot (the left one) on a little stool that had been left there on purpose, her lips parted, her eyes on Svengali's, ready to begin.

He gave his three beats, and the band struck a chord. Then, at another beat from him, but in her direction, she began, without the slightest appearance of effort, without any accompaniment whatever, he still beating time—conducting her, in fact, just as if she had been an orchestra herself:

> ' Au clair de la lune,
>   Mon ami Pierrot !
>   Prête-moi ta plume
>   Pour écrire un mot.
>   Ma chandelle est morte . . .
>   Je n'ai plus de feu !
>   Ouvre-moi ta porte
>   Pour l'amour de Dieu !'

X

"AU CLAIR DE LA LUNE"

This was the absurd old nursery rhyme with which La Svengali chose to make her *début* before the most critical audience in the world! She sang it three times over—the same verse. There is but one.

The first time she sang it without any expression whatever—not the slightest. Just the words and the tune; in the middle of her voice, and not loud at all; just as a child sings who is thinking of something else; or just as a young French mother sings who is darning socks by a cradle, and rocking her baby to sleep with her foot.

But her voice was so immense in its softness, richness, freshness, that it seemed to be pouring itself out from all round; its intonation absolutely, mathematically pure; one felt it to be not only faultless, but infallible; and the seduction, the novelty of it, the strangely sympathetic quality! How can one describe the quality of a peach or a nectarine to those who have only known apples?

Until La Svengali appeared, the world had only known apples—Catalanis, Jenny Linds, Grisis, Albonis, Pattis! The best apples that can be, for sure—but still only apples!

If she had spread a pair of large white wings and gracefully fluttered up to the roof and perched upon the chandelier, she could not have produced a greater sensation. The like of that voice has never been heard, nor ever will be again. A woman archangel might sing like that, or some enchanted princess out of a fairy tale.

Little Billee had already dropped his face into his hands and hid his eyes in his pocket-handkerchief; a big tear had fallen on to Taffy's left whisker; the Laird was trying hard to keep his tears back.

She sang the verse a second time, with but little added

expression and no louder; but with a sort of breathy widening of her voice that made it like a broad heavenly smile of universal motherhood turned into sound.   One

'OUVRE-MOI TA PORTE
POUR L'AMOUR DE DIEU!'

felt all the genial gaiety and grace of impishness of Pierrot and Columbine idealised into frolicsome beauty and holy innocence, as though they were performing for the saints in Paradise—a baby Columbine, with a cherub for clown! The dream of it all came over you for a second or two— a revelation of some impossible golden age—priceless— never to be forgotten! How on earth did she do it?

Little Billee had lost all control over himself, and was shaking with his suppressed sobs — Little Billee, who hadn't shed a single tear for five long years! Half the people in the house were in tears, but tears of sheer delight, of delicate inner laughter.

Then she came back to earth, and saddened and veiled and darkened her voice as she sang the verse for the third time; and it was a great and sombre tragedy, too deep for any more tears; and somehow or other poor Columbine, forlorn and betrayed and dying, out in the cold at midnight—sinking down to hell, perhaps—was making her last frantic appeal! It was no longer Pierrot and Columbine—it was Marguerite —it was Faust! It was the most terrible and pathetic of all possible human tragedies, but expressed with no dramatic or histrionic exaggeration of any sort; by mere tone, slight, subtle changes in the quality of the sound— too quick and elusive to be taken count of, but to be felt with, oh, what poignant sympathy!

When the song was over, the applause did not come immediately, and she waited with her kind wide smile, as if she were well accustomed to wait like this; and then the storm began, and grew and spread and rattled and echoed—voice, hands, feet, sticks, umbrellas!—and down came the bouquets, which the little page-boys picked up; and Trilby bowed to front and right and left in her simple *débonnaire* fashion. It was her usual triumph. It had never failed, whatever the audience, whatever the country, whatever the song.

Little Billee didn't applaud. He sat with his head in his hands, his shoulders still heaving. He believed himself to be fast asleep and in a dream, and was trying his utmost not to wake; for a great happiness was his. It was one of those nights to be marked with a white stone!

As the first bars of the song came pouring out of her parted lips (whose shape he so well remembered), and her dove-like eyes looked straight over Svengali's head, straight in his own direction—nay, *at* him—something melted in his brain, and all his long-lost power of loving came back with a rush.

It was like the sudden curing of a deafness that has been lasting for years. The doctor blows through your nose into your Eustachian tube with a little india-rubber machine; some obstacle gives way, there is a snap in your head, and straightway you hear better than you had ever heard in all your life, almost too well; and all your life is once more changed for you!

At length he sat up again, in the middle of La Svengali's singing of the 'Nussbaum,' and saw her; and saw the Laird sitting by him, and Taffy, their eyes riveted on Trilby, and knew for certain that it was *no* dream this time, and his joy was almost a pain!

She sang the 'Nussbaum' (to its heavenly accompaniment) as simply as she had sung the previous song. Every separate note was a highly-finished gem of sound, linked to the next by a magic bond. You did not require to be a lover of music to fall beneath the spell of such a voice as that; the mere melodic phrase had all but ceased to matter. Her phrasing, consummate as it was, was as simple as a child's.

It was as if she said: 'See! what does the composer count for? Here is about as beautiful a song as was ever written, with beautiful words to match, and the words have been made French for you by one of your smartest poets! But what do the words signify, any more than the tune, or even the language? The "Nussbaum" is neither better nor worse than "Mon ami Pierrot" when I am the singer; for I am *Svengali;* and you shall hear nothing, see nothing, think of nothing, but *Svengali, Svengali, Svengali !'*

It was the apotheosis of voice and virtuosity! It was 'il bel canto' come back to earth after a hundred years

—the bel canto of Vivarelli, let us say, who sang the
same song every night to the same King of Spain for a
quarter of a century, and was rewarded with a dukedom,
and wealth beyond the dreams of avarice.

And, indeed, here was this immense audience, made
up of the most cynically critical people in the world, and
the most anti-German, assisting with rapt ears and streaming eyes at the imagined spectacle of a simple German
damsel, a Mädchen, a Fräulein, just *verlobte*—a future
Hausfrau—sitting under a walnut-tree in some suburban
garden—à Berlin !—and around her, her family and her
friends, probably drinking beer and smoking long porcelain pipes, and talking politics or business, and cracking
innocent elaborate old German jokes ; with bated breath,
lest they should disturb her maiden dream of love ! And
all as though it were a scene in Elysium, and the Fräulein
a nymph of many-fountained Ida, and her people
Olympian gods and goddesses.

And such, indeed, they were when Trilby sang of
them !

After this, when the long, frantic applause had subsided, she made a gracious bow to the royal British opera-
glass (which had never left her face), and sang 'Ben Bolt'
in English !

And then Little Billee remembered there was such a
person as Svengali in the world, and recalled his little
flexible flageolet !

'That is how I teach Gecko ; that is how I teach la
bedite Honorine ; that is how I teach il bel canto. . . .
It was lost, il bel canto—and I found it in a dream—I,
Svengali !'

And his old cosmic vision of the beauty and sadness

of things, the very heart of them, and their pathetic evanescence, came back with a tenfold clearness—that heavenly glimpse beyond the veil! And with it a crushing sense of his own infinitesimal significance by the side of this glorious pair of artists, one of whom had been his friend and the other his love—a love who had offered to be his humble mistress and slave, not feeling herself good enough to be his wife!

It made him sick and faint to remember, and filled him with hot shame, and then and there his love for Trilby became as that of a dog for its master!

She sang once more—'Chanson de Printemps,' by Gounod (who was present, and seemed very hysterical), and the first part of the concert was over, and people had time to draw breath and talk over this new wonder, this revelation of what the human voice could achieve; and an immense hum filled the hall—astonishment, enthusiasm, ecstatic delight!

But our three friends found little to say—for what *they* felt there were as yet no words!

Taffy and the Laird looked at Little Billee, who seemed to be looking inward at some transcendent dream of his own; with red eyes, and his face all pale and drawn, and his nose very pink, and rather thicker than usual; and the dream appeared to be out of the common blissful, though his eyes were swimming still, for his smile was almost idiotic in its rapture!

The second part of the concert was still shorter than the first, and created, if possible, a wilder enthusiasm.

Trilby only sang twice.

Her first song was 'Malbrouck s'en va-t'en guerre.'

She began it quite lightly and merrily, like a jolly

march ; in the middle of her voice, which had not as yet
revealed any exceptional compass or range.   People
laughed quite frankly at the first verse :—

' Malbrouck s'en va-t'en guerre—
   Mironton, mironton, mirontaine !
Malbrouck s'en va-t'en guerre. . . .
      Ne sais quand reviendra !
      Ne sais quand reviendra !
      Ne sais quand reviendra !'

The *mironton, mirontaine*
was the very essence of high

'MALBROUCK S'EN VA-T'EN GUERRE'

martial resolve and
heroic self - confi-
dence ; one would
have led a forlorn
hope after hearing
it once !

' Il reviendra-z à Pâques—
   Mironton, mironton, mirontaine !
Il reviendra-z à Pâques. . . .
      Ou . . . à la Trinité !'

People still laughed, though the *mironton, mirontaine,* betrayed an uncomfortable sense of the dawning of doubts and fears—vague forebodings!

> ' La Trinité se passe—
>   *Mironton, mironton, mirontaine!*
> La Trinité se passe. . . .
>   Malbrouck ne revient pas !'

And here, especially in the *mironton, mirontaine,* a note of anxiety revealed itself—so poignant, so acutely natural and human, that it became a personal anxiety of one's own, causing the heart to beat, and one's breath was short.

> ' Madame à sa tour monte—
>   *Mironton, mironton, mirontaine!*
> Madame à sa tour monte,
>   Si haut qu'elle peut monter !'

Oh!　How one's heart went with her!　Anne!　Sister Anne!　Do you see anything?

> ' Elle voit de loin son page—
>   *Mironton, mironton, mirontaine!*
> Elle voit de loin son page,
>   Tout de noir habillé !'

One is almost sick with the sense of impending calamity —it is all but unbearable!

> ' Mon page—mon beau page !—
>   *Mironton, mironton, mirontaine!*
> Mon page—mon beau page !
>   Quelle nouvelles apportez ?'

And here Little Billee begins to weep again, and so does everybody else!　The *mironton, mirontaine,* is an agonised wail of suspense—poor bereaved duchess !—poor Sarah Jennings!　Did it all announce itself to you just like that?

All this while the accompaniment had been quite simple—just a few obvious ordinary chords.

But now, quite suddenly, without a single modulation or note of warning, down goes the tune a full major third, from E to C—into the graver depths of Trilby's great contralto—so solemn and ominous that there is no more weeping, but the flesh creeps ; the accompaniment slows and elaborates itself ; the march becomes a funeral march, with muted strings, and quite slowly :

> ' Aux nouvelles que j'apporte—
> *Mironton, mironton, mirontaine !*
> Aux nouvelles que j'apporte,
> Vos beaux yeux vont pleurer ! '

Richer and richer grows the accompaniment. The *mironton, mirontaine,* becomes a dirge !

> ' Quittez vos habits roses—
> *Mironton, mironton, mirontaine !*
> Quittez vos habits roses,
> Et vos satins brochés ! '

Here the ding-donging of a big bell seems to mingle with the score ; . . . and very slowly, and so impressively that the news will ring for ever in the ears and hearts of those who hear it from La Svengali's lips :

> ' Le Sieur Malbrouck est mort—
> *Mironton, mironton, mirontaine !*
> Le Sieur—Malbrouck—est—mort !
> Est mort—et enterré ! '

And thus it ends quite abruptly !

And this heartrending tragedy, this great historical epic in two dozen lines, at which some five or six thousand gay French people are sniffling and mopping their eyes like so many Niobes, is just a common old French comic

'AUX NOUVELLES QUE J'APPORTE,
VOS BEAUX YEUX VONT PLEURER !'

song—a mere nursery ditty, like 'Little Bo-peep'—to the
tune,

' We won't go home till morning,
Till daylight doth appear.'

And after a second or two of silence (oppressive and impressive as that which occurs at a burial when the handful of earth is being dropped on the coffin lid) the audience
bursts once more into madness ; and La Svengali, who
accepts no encores, has to bow for nearly five minutes,
standing amid a sea of flowers. . . .

Then comes her great and final performance.   The

orchestra swiftly plays the first four bars of the bass in Chopin's Impromptu (A flat); and suddenly, without words, as a light nymph catching the whirl of a double skipping-rope, La Svengali breaks in, and vocalises that astounding piece of music that so few pianists can even play; but no pianist has ever played it like this; no piano has ever given out such notes as these!

Every single phrase is a string of perfect gems, of purest ray serene, strung together on a loose golden thread! The higher and shriller she sings, the sweeter it is; higher and shriller than any woman had ever sung before.

Waves of sweet and tender laughter, the very heart and essence of innocent, high-spirited girlhood, alive to all that is simple and joyous and elementary in nature—the freshness of the morning, the ripple of the stream, the click of the mill, the lisp of the wind in the trees, the song of the lark in the cloudless sky—the sun and the dew, the scent of early flowers and summer woods and meadows—the sight of birds and bees and butterflies and frolicsome young animals at play—all the sights and scents and sounds that are the birthright of happy children, happy savages in favoured climes—things within the remembrance and the reach of most of us! All this, the memory and the feel of it, are in Trilby's voice as she warbles that long, smooth, lilting, dancing laugh, that shower of linked sweetness, that wondrous song without words; and those who hear feel it all, and remember it with her. It is irresistible; it forces itself on you; no words, no pictures, could ever do the like! So that the tears that are shed out of all these many French eyes are tears of pure, unmixed delight in happy remi-

niscence! (Chopin, it is true, may have meant something quite different—a hot-house, perhaps, with orchids
and arum lilies and tuberoses and hydrangeas—but all
this is neither here nor there, as the Laird would say in
French.)

Then comes the slow movement, the sudden adagio,
with its capricious ornaments—the waking of the virgin
heart, the stirring of the sap, the dawn of love ; its doubts
and fears and questionings ; and the mellow, powerful,
deep chest notes are like the pealing of great golden bells,
with a light little pearl shower tinkling round—drops
from the upper fringe of her grand voice as she
shakes it. . . .

Then back again the quick part, childhood once more,
da capo, only quicker! hurry, hurry! but distinct as ever.
Loud and shrill and sweet beyond compare—drowning
the orchestra ; of a piercing quality quite ineffable ; a joy
there is no telling ; a clear, purling, crystal stream that
gurgles and foams and bubbles along over sunlit stones ;
a wonder, a world's delight!

And there is not a sign of effort, of difficulty overcome.
All through, Trilby smiles her broad, angelic smile ; her
lips well parted, her big white teeth glistening as she
gently jerks her head from side to side in time to
Svengali's bâton, as if to shake the willing notes out
quicker and higher and shriller. . . .

And in a minute or two it is all over, like the lovely
bouquet of fireworks at the end of the show, and she lets
what remains of it die out and away like the afterglow of
fading Bengal fires— her voice receding into the distance
—coming back to you like an echo from all round, from
anywhere you please—quite soft—hardly more than a

UN IMPROMPTU DE CHOPIN

breath ; but *such* a breath !   Then one last chromatically
ascending rocket, *pianissimo*, up to E in alt, and then
darkness and silence !

And after a little pause the many-headed rises as one,
and waves its hats and sticks and handkerchiefs, and
stamps and shouts . . . 'Vive La Svengali ! Vive La
Svengali !'

Svengali steps on to the platform by his wife's side
and kisses her hand ; and they both bow themselves
backward through the curtains, which fall, to rise again
and again and again on this astounding pair !

Such was La Svengali's *début* in Paris.

It had lasted little over an hour, one quarter of which,
at least, had been spent in plaudits and courtesies !

The writer is no musician, alas ! (as, no doubt, his
musical readers have found out by this) save in his
thraldom to music of not too severe a kind, and laments
the clumsiness and inadequacy of this wild (though
somewhat ambitious) attempt to recall an impression
received more than thirty years ago ; to revive the ever-
blessed memory of that unforgettable first night at the
Cirque des Bashibazoucks.

Would that I could transcribe here Berlioz's famous
series of twelve articles, entitled 'La Svengali,' which
were republished from *La Lyre Éolienne,* and are now out
of print !

Or Théophile Gautier's elaborate rhapsody, ' Madame
Svengali—*Ange ou Femme ?* ' in which he proves that
one need not have a musical ear (he hadn't) to be enslaved
by such a voice as hers, any more than the eye for beauty
(this he *had*) to fall the victim of ' her celestial form and
face.'   It is enough, he says, to be simply human !   I

forget in which journal this eloquent tribute appeared ;
it is not to be found in his collected works.

Or the intemperate diatribe by Herr Blagner (as I
will christen him) on the tyranny of the prima donna
called 'Svengalismus'; in which he attempts to show
that mere virtuosity carried to such a pitch is mere
viciosity——base acrobatismus of the vocal chords, a
hysteric appeal to morbid Gallic 'sentimentalismus'; and
that this monstrous development of a phenomenal larynx,
this degrading cultivation and practice of the abnormal-
ismus of a mere physical peculiarity, are death and
destruction to all true music ; since they place Mozart
and Beethoven, and even *himself,* on a level with Bellini,
Donizetti, Offenbach——any Italian tune-tinkler, any
ballad-monger of the hated Paris pavement! and can
make the highest music of all (even *his own*) go down
with the common French herd at the very first hearing,
just as if it were some idiotic refrain of the *café chantant!*

So much for Blagnerismus *v.* Svengalismus.

But I fear there is no space within the limits of this
humble tale for these masterpieces of technical musical
criticism.

Besides, there are other reasons.

Our three heroes walked back to the boulevards, the
only silent ones amid the throng that poured through
the Rue St. Honoré, as the Cirque des Bashibazoucks
emptied itself of its over-excited audience.

They went arm-in-arm, as usual ; but this time Little
Billee was in the middle. He wished to feel on each
side of him the warm and genial contact of his two beloved
old friends. It seemed as if they had suddenly been

restored to him, after five long years of separation; his heart was overflowing with affection for them, too full to speak just yet! Overflowing, indeed, with the love of love, the love of life, the love of death—the love of all that is, and ever was, and ever will be! just as in his old way.

He could have hugged them both in the open street, before the whole world; and the delight of it was that this was no dream; about that there was no mistake. He was himself again at last, after five years, and wide awake; and he owed it all to Trilby!

And what did he feel for Trilby? He couldn't tell yet. It was too vast as yet to be measured; and, alas! it was weighted with such a burden of sorrow and regret that he might well put off the thought of it a little while longer, and gather in what bliss he might: like the man whose hearing has been restored after long years, he would revel in the mere physical delight of hearing for a space, and not go out of his way as yet to listen for the bad news that was already in the air, and would come to roost quite soon enough.

Taffy and the Laird were silent also; Trilby's voice was still in their ears and hearts, her image in their eyes, and utter bewilderment still oppressed them and kept them dumb.

It was a warm and balmy night, almost like mid-summer; and they stopped at the first café they met on the Boulevard de la Madeleine (*comme autrefois*), and ordered bocks of beer, and sat at a little table on the pavement, the only one unoccupied; for the café was already crowded, the hum of lively talk was great, and 'La Svengali' was in every mouth.

The Laird was the first to speak. He emptied his bock at a draught, and called for another, and lit a cigar, and said, 'I don't believe it was Trilby, after all!' It was the first time her name had been mentioned between them that evening—and for five years!

'Good heavens!' said Taffy. 'Can you doubt it?'

'Oh yes! that was Trilby,' said Little Billee.

Then the Laird proceeded to explain that, putting aside the impossibility of Trilby's ever being taught to sing in tune, and her well-remembered loathing for Svengali, he had narrowly scanned her face through his opera-glass, and found that in spite of a likeness quite marvellous there were well-marked differences. Her face was narrower and longer, her eyes larger, and their expression not the same; then she seemed taller and stouter, and her shoulders broader and more drooping, and so forth.

But the others wouldn't hear of it, and voted him cracked, and declared they even recognised the peculiar twang of her old speaking voice in the voice she now sang with, especially when she sang low down. And they all three fell to discussing the wonders of her performance like everybody else all round; Little Billee leading, with an eloquence and a seeming of technical musical knowledge that quite impressed them, and made them feel happy and at ease; for they were anxious for his sake about the effect this sudden and so unexpected sight of her would have upon him after all that had passed.

He seemed transcendently happy and elate—incomprehensibly so, in fact—and looked at them both with quite a new light in his eyes, as if all the music he had heard had trebled not only his joy in being alive, but his

pleasure at being with them. Evidently he had quite
outgrown his old passion for her, and that was a comfort
indeed!

But Little Billee knew better.

He knew that his old passion for her had all come
back, and was so overwhelming and immense that he
could not feel it just yet, nor yet the hideous pangs of a
jealousy so consuming that it would burn up his life.
He gave himself another twenty-four hours.

But he had not to wait so long. He woke up after
a short, uneasy sleep that very night, to find that the
flood was over him; and he realised how hopelessly,
desperately, wickedly, insanely he loved this woman, who
might have been his, but was now the wife of another
man; a greater than he, and one to whom she owed it
that she was more glorious than any other woman on
earth—a queen among queens—a goddess! for what was
any earthly throne compared to that she established in
the hearts and souls of all who came within the sight and
hearing of her; beautiful as she was besides—beautiful,
beautiful! And what must be her love for the man who
had taught her and trained her, and revealed her towering
genius to herself and to the world!—a man resplendent
also, handsome and tall and commanding—a great artist
from the crown of his head to the sole of his foot!

And the remembrance of them—hand in hand, master
and pupil, husband and wife—smiling and bowing in the
face of all that splendid tumult they had called forth and
could not quell, stung and tortured and maddened him so
that he could not lie still, but got up and raged and
rampaged up and down his hot, narrow, stuffy bedroom,
and longed for his old familiar brain-disease to come back

and narcotise his trouble, and be his friend, and stay with him till he died !

Where was he to fly for relief from such new memories as these, which would never cease ; and the old memories,

'AND THE REMEMBRANCE OF THEM—HAND IN HAND'

and all the glamour and grace of them that had been so suddenly called out of the grave? And how could he escape, now that he felt the sight of her face and the sound of her voice would be a craving—a daily want— like that of some poor starving outcast for warmth and meat and drink?

And little innocent, pathetic, ineffable, well-remembered

sweetnesses of her changing face kept painting themselves
on his retina ; and incomparable tones of this new thing,
her voice, her infinite voice, went ringing in his head, till
he all but shrieked aloud in his agony.

And then the poisoned and delirious sweetness of those
mad kisses,

> ' by hopeless fancy feigned
> On lips that are for others ' !

And then the grewsome physical jealousy, that
miserable inheritance of all artistic sons of Adam, that
plague and torment of the dramatic, plastic imagination,
which can idealise so well, and yet realise, alas ! so keenly.
After three or four hours spent like this, he could stand
it no longer ; madness was lying his way.   So he hurried
on a garment, and went and knocked at Taffy's door.

' Good God ! what's the matter with you ? ' exclaimed
the good Taffy, as Little Billee tumbled into his room,
calling out :

' Oh, Taffy, Taffy, I've g-g-gone mad, I think ! '   And
then, shivering all over, and stammering incoherently, he
tried to tell his friend what was the matter with him, with
great simplicity.

Taffy, in much alarm, slipped on his trousers and made
Little Billee get into his bed, and sat by his side holding
his hand.   He was greatly perplexed, fearing the re-
currence of another attack like that of five years back.
He didn't dare leave him for an instant to wake the Laird
and send for a doctor.

Suddenly Little Billee buried his face in the pillow
and began to sob, and some instinct told Taffy this was
the best thing that could happen.   The boy had always
been a highly-strung, emotional, over-excitable, over-

sensitive, and quite uncontrolled mammy's-darling, a cry-baby sort of chap, who had never been to school. It was all a part of his genius, and also a part of his charm. It would do him good once more to have a good blub after five years! After a while Little Billee grew quieter, and then suddenly he said : ' What a miserable ass you must think me, what an unmanly duffer!'

' Why, my friend ?'

' Why, for going on in this idiotic way. I really couldn't help it. I went mad, I tell you. I've been walking up and down my room all night, till everything seemed to go round.'

' So have I.'

' You ? What for ?'

' The very same reason.'

' *What!*'

' I was just as fond of Trilby as you were. Only she happened to prefer *you.*'

' *What!*' cried Little Billee again ' *You* were fond of Trilby ?'

' I believe you, my boy !'

' In *love* with her ?'

' I believe you, my boy !'

' She never knew it, then !'

' Oh yes, she did.'

' She never told me, then !'

' Didn't she ? That's like her. *I* told *her*, at all events. I asked her to marry me.'

' Well—I *am* damned ! When ?'

' That day we took her to Meudon, with Jeannot, and dined at the garde champêtre's, and she danced the cancan with Sandy.'

' Well—I *am* ——   And she *refused* you ? '

' Apparently so.'

' Well, I——   Why on earth did she refuse you ? '

' Oh, I suppose she'd already begun to fancy *you*, my friend.   *Il y en a toujours un autre !* '

' " ' I BELIEVE YOU, MY BOY ! " '

' Fancy *me*—prefer *me*—to *you* ? '

' Well, yes.   It *does* seem odd—eh, old fellow ?   But there's no accounting for tastes, you know.   She's built on such an ample scale herself, I suppose, that she likes little 'uns—contrast, you see.   She's very maternal, I think. Besides, you're a smart little chap ; and you ain't half bad ; and you've got brains and talent, and lots of cheek, and all that. I'm rather a *ponderous* kind of party.'

' Well—I *am* damned !'

' *C'est comme ça !* I took it lying down you see.'

' Does the Laird know ? '

' No ; and I don't want him to—nor anybody else.'

' Taffy, what a regular downright old trump you are ! '

' Glad you think so ; anyhow, we're both in the same boat, and we've got to make the best of it. She's another man's wife, and probably she's very fond of him. I'm sure she ought to be, cad as he is, after all he's done for her. So there's an end of it.'

' Ah ! there'll never be an end of it for *me*—never—never—oh, never, my God ! She would have married me but for my mother's meddling, and that stupid old ass, my uncle. What a wife ! Think of all she must have in her heart and brain, only to *sing* like that ! And, O Lord ! how beautiful she is—a goddess ! Oh, the brow and cheek and chin, and the way her head's put on ! did you *ever* see anything like it ? Oh, if only I hadn't written and told my mother I was going to marry her ! why, we should have been man and wife for five years by this time—living at Barbizon—painting away like mad ! Oh, what a heavenly life ! Oh, curse all officious meddling with other people's affairs ! Oh ! oh ! . . .'

' There you go again ! What's the good ? And where do *I* come in, my friend ? *I* should have been no better off, old fellow—worse than ever, I think.'

Then there was a long silence.

At length Little Billee said :

' Taffy, I can't tell you what a trump you are. All

I've ever thought of you—and God knows that's enough
—will be nothing to what I shall always think of you
after this.'

'All right, old chap!'

'And now I think *I'm* all right again, for a time—and
I shall cut back to bed. Good night! Thanks more
than I can ever express!' And Little Billee, restored to
his balance, cut back to his own bed just as the day was
breaking.

PART SEVENTH

'The moon made thy lips pale, beloved,
  The wind made thy bosom chill;
    The night did shed
    On thy dear head
  Its frozen dew, and thou didst lie
Where the bitter breath of the naked sky
  Might visit thee at will.'

NEXT morning our three friends lay late abed, and breakfasted in their rooms.

They had all three passed 'white nights'—even the Laird, who had tossed about and pressed a sleepless pillow till dawn, so excited had he been by the wonder of Trilby's reincarnation, so perplexed by his own doubts as to whether it was really Trilby or not.

And certain haunting tones of her voice, that voice so cruelly sweet (which clove the stillness with a clang so utterly new, so strangely heart-piercing and seductive, that the desire to hear it once more became nostalgic— almost an ache!), certain bits and bars and phrases of the music she had sung, unspeakable felicities and facilities of execution; sudden exotic warmths, fragrances, tendernesses, graces, depths, and breadths; quick changes from grave to gay, from rough to smooth, from great metallic brazen clangours to soft golden suavities; all the varied

modes of sound we try so vainly to borrow from vocal
nature by means of wind and reed and string—all this
new 'Trilbyness' kept echoing in his brain all night (for
he was of a nature deeply musical), and sleep had been
impossible to him.

> 'As when we dwell upon a word we know,
> Repeating, till the word we know so well
> Becomes a wonder, and we know not why,'

so dwelt the Laird upon the poor old tune 'Ben Bolt,'
which kept singing itself over and over again in his tired
consciousness, and maddened him with novel, strange, unhackneyed, unsuspected beauties such as he had never
dreamed of in any earthly music.

It had become a wonder, and he knew not why!

They spent what was left of the morning at the
Louvre, and tried to interest themselves in the 'Marriage
of Cana,' and the 'Woman at the Well,' and Vandyck's
man with the glove, and the little Princess of Velasquez,
and Lisa Gioconda's smile: it was of no use trying.
There was no sight worth looking at in all Paris but
Trilby in her golden raiment; no other princess in the
world; no smile but hers, when through her parted lips
came bubbling Chopin's Impromptu. They had not long
to stay in Paris, and they must drink of that bubbling
fountain once more—*coûte que coûte!* They went to the
Salle des Bashibazoucks, and found that all seats all over
the house had been taken for days and weeks; and the
'queue' at the door had already begun! and they had
to give up all hopes of slaking this particular thirst.

Then they went and lunched perfunctorily, and talked
desultorily over lunch, and read criticisms of La Svengali's
début in the morning papers—a chorus of journalistic

acclamation gone mad, a frenzied eulogy in every key—
but nothing was good enough for them! Brand-new
words were wanted—another language!

Then they wanted a long walk, and could think of
nowhere to go in all Paris—that immense Paris, where
they had promised themselves to see so much that the
week they were to spend there had seemed too short!

Looking in a paper, they saw it announced that the
band of the Imperial Guides would play that afternoon in
the Pré Catelan, Bois de Boulogne, and thought they
might as well walk there as anywhere else, and walk back
again in time to dine with the Passefils—a prandial
function which did not promise to be very amusing ; but
still it was something to kill the evening with, since they
couldn't go and hear Trilby again.

Outside the Pré Catelan they found a crowd of cabs
and carriages, saddle-horses and grooms. One might
have thought one's self in the height of the Paris season.
They went in, and strolled about here and there, and
listened to the band, which was famous (it has performed
in London at the Crystal Palace), and they looked about
and studied life, or tried to.

Suddenly they saw, sitting with three ladies (one of
whom, the eldest, was in black), a very smart young
officer, a Guide, all red and green and gold, and recognised their old friend Zouzou. They bowed, and he
knew them at once, and jumped up and came to them
and greeted them warmly, especially his old friend Taffy,
whom he took to his mother—the lady in black—and
introduced to the other ladies, the younger of whom
(strangely unlike the rest of her countrywomen) was so
lamentably, so pathetically plain that it would be brutal

to attempt the cheap and easy task of describing her. It was Miss Lavinia Hunks, the famous American million-airess, and her mother. Then the good Zouzou came back and talked to the Laird and Little Billee.

Zouzou, in some subtle and indescribable way, had become very ducal indeed.

He looked extremely distinguished, for one thing, in his beautiful Guides' uniform, and was most gracefully and winningly polite. He inquired warmly after Mrs. and Miss Bagot, and begged Little Billee would recall him to their amiable remembrance when he saw them again. He expressed most sympathetically his delight to see Little Billee looking so strong and so well (Little Billee looked like a pallid little washed-out ghost, after his white night).

They talked of Dodor. He said how attached he was to Dodor, and always should be; but Dodor, it seemed, had made a great mistake in leaving the army and going into a retail business (*petit commerce*). He had done for himself—*dégringolé!* He should have stuck to the *dragons* —with a little patience and good conduct he would have 'won his epaulet'—and then one might have arranged for him a good little marriage—*un parti convenable*—for he was 'très joli garçon, Dodor! bonne tournure—et très gentiment né! C'est très ancien, les Rigolot—dans le Poitou, je crois—Lafarce, et tout ça; tout à fait bien!'

It was difficult to realise that this polished and discreet and somewhat patronising young man of the world was the jolly dog who had gone after Little Billee's hat on all fours in the Rue Vieille des Trois Mauvais Ladres and brought it back in his mouth—the Caryhatide!

Little Billee little knew that Monsieur le Duc de la

Rochemartel-Boisségur had quite recently delighted a very small and select and most august imperial supper-party at Compiègne with this very story, not blinking a single detail of his own share in it—and had given a most touching and sympathetic description of 'le joli petit peintre anglais qui s'appelait Litrebili, et ne pouvait pas se tenir sur ses jambes—et qui pleurait d'amour fraternel dans les bras de mon copain Dodor!'

'Ah! Monsieur Gontran, ce que je donnerais pour avoir vu ça!' had said the greatest lady in France; 'un de mes zouaves—à quatre pattes—dans la rue—un chapeau dans la bouche—oh—c'est impayable!'

Zouzou kept these blackguard bohemian reminiscences for the imperial circle alone—to which it was suspected that he was secretly rallying himself. Among all outsiders—especially within the narrow precincts of the cream of the noble Faubourg (which remained aloof from the Tuileries)—he was a very proper and gentlemanlike person indeed, as his brother had been— and, in his mother's fond belief, 'très bien pensant, très bien vu, à Frohsdorf et à Rome.'

On lui aurait donné le bon Dieu sans confession—as Madame Vinard had said of Little Billee—they would have shriven him at sight, and admitted him to the holy communion on trust!

He did not present Little Billee and the Laird to his mother, nor to Mrs. and Miss Hunks; that honour was reserved for 'the Man of Blood' alone; nor did he ask where they were staying, nor invite them to call on him. But in parting he expressed the immense pleasure it had given him to meet them again, and the hope he had of some day shaking their hands in London.

As the friends walked back to Paris together, it tran-
spired that 'the Man of Blood' had been invited by
Madame Duchesse Mère (Maman Duchesse, as Zouzou
called her) to dine with her next day, and meet the
Hunkses at a furnished apartment she had taken in the
Place Vendôme ; for they had let (to the Hunkses) the
Hôtel de la Rochemartel in the Rue de Lille ; they had
also been obliged to let their place in the country, le
château de Boisségur (to Monsieur Despoires, or 'des
Poires,' as he chose to spell himself on his visiting
cards—the famous soap manufacturer—'Un très brave
homme, à ce qu'on dit!' and whose only son, by the
way, soon after married Mademoiselle Jeanne-Adélaïde
d'Amaury-Brissac de Roncesvaulx de Boisségur de la
Rochemartel).

'Il ne fait pas gras chez nous à présent—je vous
assure!' Madame Duchesse Mère had pathetically said
to Taffy—but had given him to understand that things
would be very much better for her son in the event of his
marriage with Miss Hunks.

'Good heavens!' said Little Billee, on hearing this ;
'that grotesque little bogy in blue? Why, she's deformed
—she squints—she's a dwarf, and looks like an idiot!
Millions or no millions, the man who marries her is a
felon! As long as there are stones to break and a road
to break them on, the able-bodied man who marries a
woman like that for anything but pity and kindness—and
even then—dishonours himself, insults his ancestry, and
inflicts on his descendants a wrong that nothing will ever
redeem—he nips them in the bud—he blasts them for
ever! He ought to be cut by his fellow-men—sent to
Coventry—to jail—to penal servitude for life! He ought

"MAMAN DUCHESSE"

Z

to have a separate hell to himself when he dies—he ought
to——'

'Shut up, you little blaspheming ruffian!' said the
Laird. 'Where do *you* expect to go to, yourself, with
such frightful sentiments? And what would become of
your beautiful old twelfth-century dukedoms, with a
hundred yards of back frontage opposite the Louvre, on a
beautiful historic river, and a dozen beautiful historic
names, and no money—if *you* had your way?' and the
Laird wunk his historic wink.

'Twelfth-century dukedoms be damned!' said Taffy,
au grand sérieux, as usual. 'Little Billee's quite right,
and Zouzou makes me sick! Besides, what does she
marry *him* for—not for his beauty either, I guess! She's
his fellow-criminal, his deliberate accomplice, *particeps
delicti*, accessory before the act and after! She has no
right to marry at all! tar and feathers and a rail for both
of them—and for Maman Duchesse too—and I suppose
that's why I refused her invitation to dinner! and now
let's go and dine with Dodor— . . . anyhow Dodor's
young woman doesn't marry him for a dukedom—or even
his 'de'—*mais bien pour ses beaux yeux!* and if the
Rigolots of the future turn out less nice to look at than
their sire, and not quite so amusing, they will probably be
a great improvement on him in many other ways. There's
room enough—and to spare!'

''Ear! 'ear!' said Little Billee (who always grew
flippant when Taffy got on his high horse). 'Your 'ealth
and song, sir—them's my sentiments to a T! What shall
we 'ave the pleasure of drinkin', after that wery nice
'armony?'

After which they walked on in silence, each, no doubt,

musing on the general contrariness of things, and imagining what splendid little Wynnes, or Bagots, or M'Allisters might have been ushered into a decadent world for its regeneration if fate had so willed it that a certain magnificent and singularly gifted grisette, etc. etc. etc. . . .

Mrs. and Miss Hunks passed them as they walked along, in a beautiful blue barouche with C-springs—*un 'huit-ressorts'*; Maman Duchesse passed them in a hired fly; Zouzou passed them on horseback; 'tout Paris' passed them; but they were none the wiser, and agreed that the show was not a patch on that in Hyde Park during the London season.

When they reached the Place de la Concorde it was that lovely hour of a fine autumn day in beautiful bright cities when all the lamps are lit in the shops and streets and under the trees, and it is still daylight—a quickly fleeting joy; and as a special treat on this particular occasion the sun set, and up rose the yellow moon over eastern Paris, and floated above the chimney-pots of the Tuileries.

They stopped to gaze at the homeward procession of cabs and carriages, as they used to do in the old times. Tout Paris was still passing; tout Paris is very long.

They stood among a little crowd of sightseers like themselves, Little Billee right in front—in the road.

Presently a magnificent open carriage came by—more magnificent than even the Hunkses', with liveries and harness quite vulgarly resplendent—almost Napoleonic.

Lolling back in it lay Monsieur et Madame Svengali—he with his broad-brimmed felt sombrero over his long black curls, wrapped in costly furs, smoking his big cigar of the Havana.

By his side La Svengali—also in sables—with a large
black velvet hat on, her light brown hair done up in a
huge knot on the nape of her neck. She was rouged
and pearl-powdered, and
her eyes were blackened
beneath, and thus made to

THE CUT DIRECT

look twice their size ; but in spite of all such disfigurements
she was a most splendid vision, and caused quite a little
sensation in the crowd as she came slowly by.

Little Billee's heart was in his mouth. He caught
Svengali's eye, and saw him speak to her. She turned
her head and looked at him standing there—they both
did. Little Billee bowed. She stared at him with a cold
stare of disdain, and cut him dead—so did Svengali.

And as they passed he heard them both snigger—she with a little high-pitched flippant snigger worthy of a London barmaid.

Little Billee was utterly crushed, and everything seemed turning round.

The Laird and Taffy had seen it all without losing a detail. The Svengalis had not even looked their way. The Laird said :

'It's not Trilby—I swear! She could *never* have done that—it's not *in* her! and it's another face altogether—I'm sure of it!'

Taffy was also staggered and in doubt. They caught hold of Little Billee, each by an arm, and walked him off to the boulevards. He was quite demoralised, and wanted not to dine at Passefil's. He wanted to go straight home at once. He longed for his mother as he used to long for her when he was in trouble as a small boy and she was away from home—longed for her desperately—to hug her and hold her and fondle her, and be fondled, for his own sake and hers ; all his old love for her had come back in full—with what arrears ! all his old love for his sister, for his old home.

When they went back to the hotel to dress (for Dodor had begged them to put on their best evening war-paint, so as to impress his future mother-in-law), Little Billee became fractious and intractable. And it was only on Taffy's promising that he would go all the way to Devonshire with him on the morrow, and stay with him there, that he could be got to dress and dine.

The huge Taffy lived entirely by his affections, and he hadn't many to live by—the Laird, Trilby, and Little Billee.

Trilby was unattainable, the Laird was quite strong and independent enough to get on by himself, and Taffy had concentrated all his faculties of protection and affection on Little Billee, and was equal to any burden or responsibility all this instinctive young fathering might involve.

In the first place, Little Billee had always been able to do quite easily, and better than any one else in the world, the very things Taffy most longed to do himself and couldn't, and this inspired the good Taffy with a chronic reverence and wonder he could not have expressed in words.

Then Little Billee was physically small and weak, and incapable of self-control. Then he was generous, amiable, affectionate, transparent as crystal, without an atom of either egotism or conceit : and had a gift of amusing you and interesting you by his talk (and its complete sincerity) that never palled ; and even his silence was charming—one felt so sure of him—so there was hardly any sacrifice, little or big, that big Taffy was not ready and glad to make for Little Billee. On the other hand, there lay deep down under Taffy's surface irascibility and earnestness about trifles (and beneath his harmless vanity of the strong man), a long-suffering patience, a real humility, a robustness of judgment, a sincerity and all-roundness, a completeness of sympathy, that made him very good to trust and safe to lean upon. Then his powerful, impressive aspect, his great stature, the gladiator-like poise of his small round head on his big neck and shoulders, his huge deltoids and deep chest and slender loins, his clean-cut ankles and wrists, all the long and bold and highly-finished athletic shapes of him, that

easy grace of strength that made all his movements a
pleasure to watch, and any garment look well when he
wore it—all this was a perpetual feast to the quick,
prehensile, æsthetic eye. And then he had such a solemn,
earnest, lovable way of bending pokers round his neck,
and breaking them on his arm, and jumping his own
height (or near it), and lifting up arm-chairs by one leg
with one hand, and what not else!

So that there was hardly any sacrifice, little or big,
that Little Billee would not accept from big Taffy as a
mere matter of course—a fitting and proper tribute
rendered by bodily strength to genius.

Par nobile fratrum—well met and well mated for fast
and long-enduring friendship.

.   .   .   .   .   .

The family banquet at Monsieur Passefil's would have
been dull but for the irrepressible Dodor, and still more
for the Laird of Cockpen, who rose to the occasion, and
surpassed himself in geniality, drollery, and eccentricity of
French grammar and accent. Monsieur Passefil was also
a droll in his way, and had the quickly familiar, jocose
facetiousness that seems to belong to the successful
middle-aged bourgeois all over the world, when he's not
pompous instead (he can even be both sometimes).

Madame Passefil was not jocose. She was much
impressed by the aristocratic splendour of Taffy, the
romantic melancholy and refinement of Little Billee, and
their quiet and dignified politeness. She always spoke of
Dodor as Monsieur de Lafarce, though the rest of the
family (and one or two friends who had been invited)
always called him Monsieur Théodore, and he was officially known as Monsieur Rigolot.

Whenever Madame Passefil addressed him or spoke of him in this aristocratic manner (which happened very often), Dodor would wink at his friends, with his tongue in his cheek. It seemed to amuse him beyond measure.

Mademoiselle Ernestine was evidently too much in love to say anything, and seldom took her eyes off Monsieur Théodore, whom she had never seen in evening dress before. It must be owned that he looked very nice —more ducal than even Zouzou — and to be Madame de Lafarce *en perspective*, and the future owner of such a brilliant husband as Dodor, was

'PETIT ENFANT, J'AIMAIS D'UN AMOUR TENDRE
MA MÈRE ET DIEU—SAINTES AFFECTIONS!
PUIS MON AMOUR AUX FLEURS SE FIT ENTENDRE,
PUIS AUX OISEAUX, ET PUIS AUX PAPILLONS!

enough to turn a stronger little bourgeois head than Mademoiselle Ernestine's.

She was not beautiful, but healthy, well grown, well brought up, and presumably of a sweet, kind, and amiable disposition—an *ingénue* fresh from her convent—innocent as a child, no doubt ; and it was felt that Dodor had done better for himself (and for his race) than Monsieur le Duc. Little Dodors need have no fear.

After dinner the ladies and gentlemen left the dining-room together, and sat in a pretty salon overlooking the boulevard, where cigarettes were allowed, and there was music. Mademoiselle Ernestine laboriously played 'Les Cloches du Monastère' (by Monsieur Lefébure-Wély, if I'm not mistaken). It's the most bourgeois piece of music I know.

Then Dodor, with his sweet high voice, so strangely pathetic and true, sang goody-goody little French songs of innocence (of which he seemed to have an endless *répertoire*) to his future wife's conscientious accompaniment—to the immense delight, also, of all his future family, who were almost in tears—and to the great amusement of the Laird, at whom he winked in the most pathetic parts, putting his forefinger to the side of his nose, like Noah Claypole in *Oliver Twist*.

The wonder of the hour, La Svengali, was discussed, of course ; it was unavoidable. But our friends did not think it necessary to reveal that she was 'la grande Trilby.' That would soon transpire by itself.

And, indeed, before the month was a week older the papers were full of nothing else.

Madame Svengali—'la grande Trilby,'—was the only

daughter of the honourable and reverend Sir Lord O'Ferrall.

She had run away from the primeval forests and lonely marshes of le Dublin, to lead a free-and-easy life among the artists of the Quartier Latin of Paris—*une vie de bohème !*

She was the Venus Anadyomene from top to toe.

She was *blanche comme neige, avec un volcan dans le cœur.*

Casts of her alabaster feet could be had at Brucciani's, in the Rue de la Souricière St. Denis. (He made a fortune.)

Monsieur Ingres had painted her left foot on the wall of a studio in the Place St. Anatole des Arts ; and an eccentric Scotch milord (le Comte de Pencock) had bought the house containing the flat containing the studio containing the wall on which it was painted, had had the house pulled down, and the wall framed and glazed and sent to his castle of Édimbourg.

(This, unfortunately, was in excess of the truth. It was found impossible to execute the Laird's wish, on account of the material the wall was made of. So the Lord Count of Pencock—such was Madame Vinard's version of Sandy's nickname—had to forego his purchase.)

Next morning our friends were in readiness to leave Paris ; even the Laird had had enough of it, and longed to get back to his work again—a ' Hari-Kari in Yokohama.' (He had never been to Japan ; but no more had any one else in those early days.)

They had just finished breakfast, and were sitting in the courtyard of the hotel, which was crowded, as usual.

Little Billee went into the hotel post-office to despatch a note to his mother. Sitting sideways there at a small table and reading letters was Svengali—of all people in the world. But for these two and a couple of clerks the room was empty.

Svengali looked up; they were quite close together.

Little Billee, in his nervousness, began to shake, and half put out his hand, and drew it back again, seeing the look of hate on Svengali's face.

Svengali jumped up, put his letters together, and passing by Little Billee on his way to the door, called him 'verfluchter Schweinhund,' and deliberately spat in his face.

Little Billee was paralysed for a second or two; then he ran after Svengali, and caught him just at the top of the marble stairs, and kicked him, and knocked off his hat, and made him drop all his letters. Svengali turned round and struck him over the mouth and made it bleed, and Little Billee hit out like a fury, but with no effect : he couldn't reach high enough, for Svengali was well over six feet.

There was a crowd round them in a minute, including the beautiful old man in the court suit and gold chain, who called out :

'Vite! vite! un commissaire de police!'—a cry that was echoed all over the place.

Taffy saw the row, and shouted, 'Bravo, little 'un!' and jumping up from his table, jostled his way through the crowd ; and Little Billee, bleeding and gasping and perspiring and stammering said :

'He spat in my face, Taffy—damn him! I'd never even spoken to him—not a word, I swear!'

Svengali had not reckoned on Taffy's being there ; he recognised him at once, and turned white.

Taffy, who had dogskin gloves on, put out his right hand, and deftly seized Svengali's nose between his fore and middle fingers and nearly pulled it off, and swung his head two or three times backward and forward by it, and then from side to side, Svengali holding on to his wrist ; and then, letting him go, gave him a sounding open-handed smack on his right cheek—and a smack on the face from Taffy (even in play) was no joke, I'm told ; it made one smell brimstone, and see and hear things that didn't exist.

Svengali gasped worse than Little Billee, and couldn't speak for a while. Then he said :

' Lâche—grand lâche ! che fous enferrai mes témoins ! '

' At your orders ! ' said Taffy, in beautiful French, and drew out his card-case, and gave him his card in quite the orthodox French manner, adding : ' I shall be here till to-morrow at twelve—but that is my London address, in case I don't hear from you before I leave. I'm sorry, but you really mustn't spit, you know—it's not done. I will come to you whenever you send for me—even if I have to come from the end of the world.'

' Très bien ! très bien ! ' said a military-looking old gentleman close by, who gave Taffy *his* card, in case he might be of any service—and who seemed quite delighted at the row—and indeed it was really pleasant to note with what a smooth, flowing, rhythmical spontaneity the good Taffy could always improvise these swift little acts of summary retributive justice : no hurry or scurry or flurry whatever—not an inharmonious gesture, not an infelicitous line—the very poetry of violence, and almost its only excuse !

"VITE! VITE! UN COMMISSAIRE DE POLICE!"

Whatever it was worth, this was Taffy's special gift, and it never failed him at a pinch.

When the commissaire de police arrived, all was over. Svengali had gone away in a cab, and Taffy put himself at the disposition of the commissaire.

They went into the post-office and discussed it all with the old military gentleman, and the majordome in velvet, and the two clerks who had seen the original insult.   And all that was required of Taffy and his friends for the present was 'their names, prenames, titles, qualities, age, address, nationality, occupation,' etc.

' C'est une affaire qui s'arrangera autrement, et autre part !' had said the military gentleman—monsieur le général Comte de la Tour-aux-Loups.

So it blew over quite simply, and all that day a fierce unholy joy burned in Taffy's choleric blue eye.

Not, indeed, that he had any wish to injure Trilby's husband, or meant to do him any grievous bodily harm, whatever happened.   But he was glad to have given Svengali a lesson in manners.

That Svengali should injure *him* never entered into his calculations for a moment.   Besides, he didn't believe Svengali would show fight; and in this he was not mistaken.

But he had, for hours, the feel of that long, thick, shapely Hebrew nose being kneaded between his gloved knuckles, and a pleasing sense of the effectiveness of the tweak he had given it.   So he went about chewing the cud of that heavenly remembrance all day, till reflection brought remorse, and he felt sorry ; for he was really the mildest-mannered man that ever broke a head !

Only the sight of Little Billee's blood (which had been

made to flow by such an unequal antagonist) had roused the old Adam.

No message came from Svengali to ask for the names and addresses of Taffy's seconds ; so Dodor and Zouzou (not to mention Mister the general Count of the Tooral-oorals, as the Laird called him) were left undisturbed ; and our three musketeers went back to London clean of blood, whole of limb, and heartily sick of Paris.

Little Billee stayed with his mother and sister in Devonshire till Christmas, Taffy staying at the village inn.

It was Taffy who told Mrs. Bagot about La Svengali's all but certain identity with Trilby, after Little Billee had gone to bed, tired and worn out, the night of their arrival.

' Good heavens ! ' said poor Mrs. Bagot. ' Why, that's the new singing woman who's coming over here ! There's an article about her in to-day's *Times*. It says she's a wonder, and that there's no one like her ! Surely, that can't be the Miss O'Ferrall I saw in Paris ! '

' It seems impossible—but I'm almost certain it is— and Willy has no doubts in the matter. On the other hand, M'Allister declares it isn't.'

' Oh, what trouble ! So *that's* why poor Willy looks so ill and miserable ! It's all come back again. Could she sing at all then, when you knew her in Paris ? '

' Not a note—her attempts at singing were quite grotesque.'

' Is she still very beautiful ? '

' Oh yes ; there's no doubt about that ; more than ever ! '

' And her singing—is that so very wonderful ? I remember that she had a beautiful voice in speaking.'

' Wonderful ? Ah, yes ; I never heard or dreamed
the like of it. Grisi, Alboni, Patti—not one of them to
be mentioned in the same breath ! '

' Good heavens ! Why, she must be simply irresistible !
I wonder you're not in love with her yourself. How
dreadful these sirens are, wrecking the peace of families ! '

' You mustn't forget that she gave way at once at a
word from you, Mrs. Bagot ; and she was very fond of
Willy. She wasn't a siren then.'

' Oh yes—oh yes ! that's true—she behaved very well
—she did her duty—I can't deny that ! You must try
and forgive me, Mr. Wynne—although I can't forgive
her !—that dreadful illness of poor Willy's—that bitter
time in Paris——'

And Mrs. Bagot began to cry, and Taffy forgave.
' Oh, Mr. Wynne, let us still hope that there's some
mistake—that it's only somebody like her ! Why, she's
coming to sing in London after Christmas ! My poor
boy's infatuation will only increase. What *shall* I do ? '

' Well—she's another man's wife, you see. So Willy's
infatuation is bound to burn itself out as soon as he fully
recognises that important fact. Besides, she cut him dead
in the Champs Élysées—and her husband and Willy had
a row next day at the hotel, and cuffed and kicked each
other—that's rather a bar to any future intimacy, I
think.'

' Oh, Mr. Wynne ! my son cuffing and kicking a man
whose wife he's in love with ! Good heavens ! '

' Oh, it was all right—the man had grossly insulted
him ; and Willy behaved like a brick, and got the best of
it in the end, and nothing came of it. I saw it all.'

' Oh, Mr. Wynne—and you didn't interfere ? '

'I SUPPOSE YOU DO ALL THIS KIND OF THING FOR MERE
AMUSEMENT, MR. WYNNE?'

'Oh yes, I interfered—everybody interfered! It was
all right, I assure you. No bones were broken on either
side, and there was no nonsense about calling out, or
swords or pistols, and all that.'

'Thank Heaven!'

In a week or two Little Billee grew more like himself
again, and painted endless studies of rocks and cliffs and
sea—and Taffy painted with him, and was very content.

The vicar and Little Billee patched up their feud.   The
vicar also took an immense fancy to Taffy, whose cousin,
Sir Oscar Wynne, he had known at college, and lost no
opportunity of being hospitable and civil to him. · And
his daughter was away in Algiers.

And all ' the nobility and gentry ' of the neighbourhood, including ' the poor dear marquis ' (one of whose
sons was in Taffy's old regiment), were civil and hospitable also to the two painters—and Taffy got as much
sport as he wanted, and became immensely popular.
And they had, on the whole, a very good time till
Christmas, and a very pleasant Christmas, if not an ex-
uberantly merry one.

After Christmas Little Billee insisted on going back
to London—to paint a picture for the Royal Academy ;
and Taffy went with him ; and there was dulness in the
house of Bagot—and many misgivings in the maternal
heart of its mistress.

And people of all kinds, high and low, from the
family at the Court to the fishermen on the little pier
and their wives and children, missed the two genial
painters, who were the friends of everybody, and made
such beautiful sketches of their beautiful coast.

.   .   .   .   .   .

La Svengali has arrived in London.   Her name is in
every mouth.   Her photograph is in the shop-windows.
She is to sing at J——'s monster concerts next week.
She was to have sung sooner, but it seems some hitch has
occurred—a quarrel between Monsieur Svengali and his
first violin, who is a very important person.

A crowd of people as usual, only bigger, is assembled
in front of the windows of the Stereoscopic Company in

Regent Street, gazing at presentments of Madame Svengali in all sizes and costumes. She is very beautiful—there is no doubt of that ; and the expression of her face is sweet and kind and sad, and of such a distinction that one feels an imperial crown would become her even better than her modest little coronet of golden stars. One of the photographs represents her in classical dress, with her left foot on a little stool, in something of the attitude of the Venus of Milo, except that her hands are clasped behind her back ; and the foot is bare but for a Greek sandal, and so smooth and delicate and charming, and with so rhythmical a set and curl of the five slender toes (the big one slightly tip-tilted and well apart from its longer and slighter and more aquiline neighbour), that this presentment of her sells quicker than all the rest.

And a little man who, with two bigger men, has just forced his way in front says to one of his friends : ' Look, Sandy, look—*the foot ! Now* have you got any doubts ? '

'Oh yes—those are Trilby's toes, sure enough ! ' says Sandy. And they all go in and purchase largely.

As far as I have been able to discover, the row between Svengali and his first violin had occurred at a rehearsal in Drury Lane Theatre.

Svengali, it seems, had never been quite the same since the 15th of October previous, and that was the day he had got his face slapped and his nose tweaked by Taffy in Paris. He had become short-tempered and irritable, especially with his wife (if she *was* his wife). Svengali, it seems, had reasons for passionately hating Little Billee.

He had not seen him for five years—not since the

Christmas festivity in the Place St. Anatole, when they
had sparred together after supper, and Svengali's nose
had got in the way on this occasion, and had been made
to bleed ; but that was not why he hated Little Billee.

When he caught sight of him standing on the curb in
the Place de la Concorde and watching the procession of
' tout Paris,' he knew him directly, and all his hate flared
up ; he cut him dead, and made his wife do the same.

Next morning he saw him again in the hotel post-
office, looking small and weak and flurried, and apparently
alone ; and being an Oriental Israelite Hebrew Jew, he
had not been able to resist the temptation of spitting in
his face, since he must not throttle him to death.

The minute he had done this he had regretted the
folly of it. Little Billee had run after him, and kicked
and struck him, and he had returned the blow and drawn
blood ; and then, suddenly and quite unexpectedly, had
come upon the scene that apparition so loathed and
dreaded of old—the pig-headed Yorkshireman—the huge
British philistine, the irresponsible bull, the junker, the
ex-Crimean, Front-de-Bœuf, who had always reminded
him of the brutal and contemptuous sword-clanking, spur-
jingling aristocrats of his own country—ruffians that
treated Jews like dogs. Callous as he was to the woes of
others, the self-indulgent and highly-strung musician was
extra sensitive about himself—a very bundle of nerves—
and especially sensitive to pain and rough usage, and by
no means physically brave. The stern, choleric, invincible
blue eye of the hated northern Gentile had cowed him at
once. And that violent tweaking of his nose, that heavy
open-handed blow on his face, had so shaken and
demoralised him that he had never recovered from it.

He was thinking about it always—night and day—
and constantly dreaming at night that he was being
tweaked and slapped over again by a colossal nightmare
Taffy, and waking up in agonies of terror, rage, and
shame.   All healthy sleep had forsaken him.

Moreover, he was much older than he looked—nearly
fifty—and far from sound.   His life had been a long,
hard struggle.

He had for his wife, slave, and pupil a fierce, jealous
kind of affection that was a source of endless torment to
him ; for indelibly graven in her heart, which he wished
to occupy alone, was the never-fading image of the little
English painter, and of this she made no secret.

Gecko no longer cared for the master.   All Gecko's
doglike devotion was concentrated on the slave and pupil,
whom he worshipped with a fierce but pure and unselfish
passion.   The only living soul that Svengali could trust was
the old Jewess who lived with them—his relative—but even
she had come to love the pupil as much as the master.

On the occasion of this rehearsal at Drury Lane he
(Svengali) was conducting and Madame Svengali was
singing.   He interrupted her several times, angrily and
most unjustly, and told her she was singing out of tune,
' like a verfluchter tomcat,' which was quite untrue.   She
was singing beautifully, ' Home, Sweet Home.'

Finally he struck her two or three smart blows on her
knuckles with his little bâton, and she fell on her knees,
weeping and crying out :

' Oh ! oh ! Svengali ! ne me battez pas, mon ami—je
fais tout ce que je peux ! '

On which little Gecko had suddenly jumped up and
struck Svengali on the neck near the collar-bone, and

then it was seen that he had a little bloody knife in his hand, and blood flowed from Svengali's neck, and at the sight of it Svengali had fainted ; and Madame Svengali had taken his head on her lap, looking dazed and stupefied, as in a waking dream.

Gecko had been disarmed, but as Svengali recovered from his faint and was taken home, the police had not been sent for, and the affair was hushed up, and a public scandal avoided. But La Svengali's first appearance, to Monsieur J——'s despair, had to be put off for a week. For Svengali would not allow her to sing without him ; nor, indeed, would he be parted from her for a minute, or trust her out of his sight.

The wound was a slight one. The doctor who attended Svengali described the wife as being quite imbecile, no doubt from grief and anxiety. But she never left her husband's bedside for a moment, and had the obedience and devotion of a dog.

When the night came round for the postponed *début*, Svengali was allowed by the doctor to go to the theatre, but he was absolutely forbidden to conduct. His grief and anxiety at this were uncontrollable ; he raved like a madman ; and Monsieur J—— was almost as bad.

Monsieur J—— had been conducting the Svengali band at rehearsals during the week, in the absence of its master—an easy task. It had been so thoroughly drilled and knew its business so well that it could almost conduct itself, and it had played all the music it had to play (much of which consisted of accompaniments to La Svengali's songs) many times before. Her *répertoire* was immense, and Svengali had written these orchestral scores with great care and felicity.

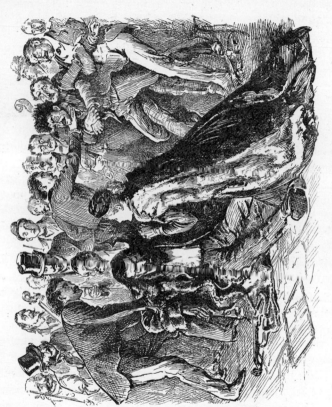

THE FIRST VIOLIN LOSES HIS TEMPER

On the famous night it was arranged that Svengali should sit in a box alone, exactly opposite his wife's place on the platform, where she could see him well ; and a code of simple signals was arranged between him and Monsieur J —— and the band, so that virtually he might conduct, himself, from his box, should any hesitation or hitch occur. This arrangement was rehearsed the day before (a Sunday) and had turned out quite successfully, and La Svengali had sung in perfection in the empty theatre.

When Monday evening arrived everything seemed to be going smoothly ; the house was soon crammed to suffocation, all but the middle box on the grand tier. It was not a promenade concert, and the pit was turned into guinea stalls (the promenade concerts were to begin a week later).

Right in the middle of these stalls sat the Laird and Taffy and Little Billee.

The band came in by degrees and tuned their instruments.

Eyes were constantly being turned to the empty box, and people wondered what royal personages would appear.

Monsieur J —— took his place amid immense applause, and bowed in his inimitable way, looking often at the empty box.

Then he tapped and waved his bâton, and the band played its Hungarian dance music with immense success ; when this was over there was a pause, and soon some signs of impatience from the gallery. Monsieur J —— had disappeared.

Taffy stood up, his back to the orchestra, looking round.

Some one came into the empty box, and stood for a moment in front, gazing at the house. A tall man, deathly pale, with long black hair and a beard.

It was Svengali.

He caught sight of Taffy and met his eyes, and Taffy said : ' Good God ! Look ! look ! '

' HAST THOU FOUND ME, O MINE ENEMY ? '

Then Little Billee and the Laird got up and looked.

And Svengali for a moment glared at them. And the expression of his face was so terrible with wonder, rage, and fear that they were quite appalled—and then he sat down, still glaring at Taffy, the whites of his eyes showing at the top, and his teeth bared in a spasmodic grin of hate.

Then thunders of applause filled the house, and turning round and seating themselves, Taffy and Little Billee and the Laird saw Trilby being led by J—— down the platform, between the players, to the front, her face smiling rather vacantly, her eyes anxiously intent on Svengali in his box.

She made her bows to right and left just as she had done in Paris.

The band struck up the opening bars of 'Ben Bolt,' with which she was announced to make her *début.*

She still stared—but she didn't sing—and they played the little symphony three times.

One could hear Monsieur J—— in a hoarse, anxious whisper saying,

' Mais chantez donc, madame—pour l'amour de Dieu, commencez donc—commencez ! '

She turned round with an extraordinary expression of face, and said,

' Chanter ? pourquoi donc voulez-vous que je chante, moi ? chanter quoi, alors ? '

' Mais " Ben Bolt," parbleu—chantez ! '

' Ah—" Ben Bolt ! " oui—je connais ça ! '

Then the band began again.

And she tried, but failed to begin herself.   She turned round and said,

' Comment diable voulez-vous que je chante avec tout ce train qu'ils font, ces diables de musiciens ! '

' Mais, mon Dieu, madame—qu'est-ce que vous avez donc ? ' cried Monsieur J——.

' J'ai que j'aime mieux chanter sans toute cette satanée musique, parbleu !   J'aime mieux chanter toute seule ! '

' Sans musique, alors—mais chantez—chantez ! '

The band was stopped—the house was in a state of indescribable wonder and suspense.

"'OH, DON'T YOU REMEMBER SWEET ALICE, BEN BOLT?'"

She looked all round, and down at herself, and fingered her dress. Then she looked up to the chandelier with a tender, sentimental smile and began—

> ' Oh, don't you remember sweet Alice, Ben Bolt?
>   Sweet Alice with hair so brown,
>   Who wept with delight when you gave her a smile—'

She had not got further than this when the whole house was in an uproar—shouts from the gallery—shouts of laughter, hoots, hisses, cat-calls, cock-crows.

She stopped and glared like a brave lioness, and called out—

' Qu'est-ce que vous avez donc, tous! tas de vieilles pommes cuites que vous êtes! Est-ce qu'on a peur de vous?' and then, suddenly—

' Why, you're all English, aren't you?—what's all the row about?—what have you brought me here for?—what have *I* done, I should like to know?'

And in asking these questions the depth and splendour of her voice were so extraordinary—its tone so pathetic-ally feminine, yet so full of hurt and indignant command, that the tumult was stilled for a moment.

It was the voice of some being from another world—some insulted daughter of a race more puissant and nobler than ours ; a voice that seemed as if it could never utter a false note.

Then came a voice from the gods in answer—

' Oh, ye're Henglish, har yer?   Why don't yer sing as yer *hought* to sing—yer've got *voice* enough, any'ow! why don't yer sing in *tune?*'

' Sing in *tune!*' cried Trilby.   ' I didn't want to sing at all—I only sang because I was asked to sing—that gentleman asked me—that French gentleman with the white waistcoat! I won't sing another note!'

'Oh, yer won't, won't yer! then let us 'ave our money back, or we'll know what for!'

And again the din broke out, and the uproar was frightful.

Monsieur J——— screamed out across the theatre: 'Svengali! Svengali! qu'est-ce qu'elle a donc, votre femme? . . . Elle est devenue folle!'

Indeed she had tried to sing 'Ben Bolt,' but had sung it in her old way—as she used to sing it in the Quartier Latin—the most lamentably grotesque performance ever heard out of a human throat!

'Svengali! Svengali!' shrieked poor Monsieur J——— , gesticulating towards the box where Svengali was sitting, quite impassible, gazing at Monsieur J———, and smiling a ghastly, sardonic smile, a *rictus* of hate and triumphant revenge—as if he were saying—

'I've got the laugh of you *all*, this time!'

Taffy, the Laird, Little Billee, the whole house, were now staring at Svengali, and his wife was forgotten.

She stood vacantly looking at everybody and everything—the chandelier, Monsieur J———, Svengali in his box, the people in the stalls, in the gallery—and smiling as if the noisy scene amused and excited her.

'Svengali! Svengali! Svengali!'

The whole house took up the cry, derisively. Monsieur J——— led Madame Svengali away; she seemed quite passive. That terrible figure of Svengali still sat, immovable, watching his wife's retreat—still smiling his ghastly smile. All eyes were now turned on him once more.

Monsieur J——— was then seen to enter his box with

a policeman and two or three other men, one of them in
evening dress. He quickly drew the curtains to ; then, a
minute or two after, he reappeared on the platform, bowing and scraping to the audience, as pale as death, and
called for silence, the gentleman in evening dress by his
side ; and this person explained that a very dreadful
thing had happened—that Monsieur Svengali had suddenly
died in that box—of apoplexy or heart disease ; that his
wife had seen it from her place on the stage, and had
apparently gone out of her senses, which accounted for
her extraordinary behaviour.

He added that the money would be returned at the
doors, and begged the audience to disperse quietly.

Taffy, with his two friends behind him, forced his way
to a stage door he knew. The Laird had no longer any
doubts on the score of Trilby's identity—*this* Trilby, at
all events.

Taffy knocked and thumped till the door was opened,
and gave his card to the man who opened it, stating that
he and his friends were old friends of Madame Svengali,
and must see her at once.

The man tried to slam the door in his face, but Taffy
pushed through, and shut it on the crowd outside, and
insisted on being taken to Monsieur J—— immediately ;
and was so authoritative and big, and looked such a swell,
that the man was cowed, and led him.

They passed an open door, through which they had a
glimpse of a prostrate form on a table—a man partially
undressed, and some men bending over him, doctors
probably.

That was the last they saw of Svengali.

Then they were taken to another door, and Monsieur

"THE LAST THEY SAW OF SVENGALI"

J——— came out, and Taffy explained who they were, and they were admitted.

La Svengali was there, sitting in an armchair by the fire, while several of the band stood round gesticulating, and talking German or Polish or Yiddish. Gecko, on his knees, was alternately chafing her hands and feet. She seemed quite dazed.

But at the sight of Taffy she jumped up and rushed at him, saying : ' Oh, Taffy dear—oh, Taffy ! what's it all about ?   Where on earth am I ?   What an age since we met ! '

Then she caught sight of the Laird, and kissed him ; and then she recognised Little Billee.

She looked at him for a long while in great surprise, and then shook hands with him.

' How pale you are ! and so changed—you've got a moustache !   What's the matter ?   Why are you all dressed in black, with white cravats, as if you were going to a funeral ?   Where's Svengali ?   I should like to go home ! '

' Where—what do you call—home, I mean—where is it ? ' asked Taffy.

' C'est à l'Hôtel de Normandie, dans le Haymarket. On va vous y conduire, madame ! ' said Monsieur J———.

' Oui—c'est ça ! ' said Trilby—' Hôtel de Normandie —mais Svengali—où est-ce qu'il est ? '

' Hélas ! madame—il est très malade ! '

' Malade ?   Qu'est-ce qu'il a ?   How funny you look, with your moustache, Little Billee ! dear, *dear* Little Billee ! so pale, so very pale !   Are you ill too ?   Oh, I hope not !   How *glad* I am to see you again—you can't tell ! though I promised your mother I wouldn't

— never, never! Where are we now, dear Little Billee?'

Monsieur J—— seemed to have lost his head. He was constantly running in and out of the room, distracted. The bandsmen began to talk and try to explain, in incomprehensible French, to Taffy. Gecko seemed to have disappeared. It was a bewildering business—noises from outside, the tramp and bustle and shouts of the departing crowd, people running in and out and asking for Monsieur J——, policemen, firemen, and what not!

Then Little Billee, who had been exerting the most heroic self-control, suggested that Trilby should come to his house in Fitzroy Square, first of all, and be taken out of all this—and the idea struck Taffy as a happy one— and it was proposed to Monsieur J——, who saw that our three friends were old friends of Madame Svengali's, and people to be trusted; and he was only too glad to be relieved of her, and gave his consent.

Little Billee and Taffy drove to Fitzroy Square to prepare Little Billee's landlady, who was much put out at first at having such a novel and unexpected charge imposed on her. It was all explained to her that it must be so. That Madame Svengali, the greatest singer in Europe and an old friend of her tenant's, had suddenly gone out of her mind from grief at the tragic death of her husband, and that for this night at least the unhappy lady must sleep under that roof—indeed, in Little Billee's own bed, and that he would sleep at a hotel; and that a nurse would be provided at once—it might be only for that one night; and that the lady was as quiet as a lamb, and would probably recover her faculties after a night's rest. A doctor was sent for from close by, and soon

2 B

Trilby appeared, with the Laird, and her appearance and her magnificent sables impressed Mrs. Godwin, the landlady—brought her figuratively on her knees. Then Taffy, the Laird, and Little Billee departed again and dispersed—to procure a nurse for the night, to find Gecko, to fetch some of Trilby's belongings from the Hôtel de Normandie, and her maid.

The maid (the old German Jewess and Svengali's relative), distracted by the news of her master's death, had gone to the theatre. Gecko was in the hands of the police. Things had got to a terrible pass. But our three friends did their best, and were up most of the night.

So much for La Svengali's *début* in London.

The present scribe was not present on that memorable occasion, and has written this inadequate and most incomplete description partly from hearsay and private information, partly from the reports in the contemporary newspapers.

Should any surviving eye-witness of that lamentable fiasco read these pages, and see any gross inaccuracy in this bald account of it, the P. S. will feel deeply obliged to the same for any corrections or additions, and these will be duly acted upon and gratefully acknowledged in all subsequent editions; which will be numerous, no doubt, on account of the great interest still felt in 'La Svengali,' even by those who never saw or heard her (and they are many), and also because the present scribe is better qualified (by his opportunities) for the compiling of this brief biographical sketch than any person now living, with the exception, of course, of 'Taffy' and 'the Laird,' to whose kindness, even more than to his own personal recollections, he owes whatever it may contain of serious historical value.

Next morning they all three went to Fitzroy Square. Little Billee had slept at Taffy's rooms in Jermyn Street.

Trilby seemed quite pathetically glad to see them again. She was dressed simply and plainly—in black ; her trunks had been sent from the hotel.

The hospital nurse was with her ; the doctor had just left. He had said that she was suffering from some great nervous shock—a pretty safe diagnosis !

Her wits had apparently not come back, and she seemed in no way to realise her position.

'Ah! what it is to see you again, all three ! It makes one feel glad to be alive ! I've thought of many things, but never of this—never ! Three nice clean Englishmen, all speaking English—and *such* dear old friends ! Ah ! j'aime tant ça—c'est le ciel ! I wonder I've got a word of English left !'

Her voice was so soft and sweet and low that these ingenuous remarks sounded like a beautiful song. And she 'made the soft eyes' at them all three, one after another, in her old way ; and the soft eyes quickly filled with tears.

She seemed ill and weak and worn out, and insisted on keeping the Laird's hand in hers.

'What's the matter with Svengali ? He must be dead !'

They all three looked at each other, perplexed.

'Ah ! he's dead ! I can see it in your faces. He'd got heart disease. I'm sorry ! oh, very sorry indeed ! He was always very kind, poor Svengali !'

'"THREE NICE CLEAN ENGLISHMEN"'

'Yes. He's dead,' said Taffy.

'And Gecko—dear little Gecko—is he dead too? I saw him last night—he warmed my hands and feet: where were we?'

'No. Gecko's not dead. But he's had to be locked up for a little while. He struck Svengali, you know. You saw it all.'

'I? No! I never saw it. But I *dreamt* something like it! Gecko with a knife, and people holding him, and Svengali bleeding on the ground. That was just before Svengali's illness. He'd cut himself in the neck, you know—with a rusty nail, he told me. I wonder

how? . . . But it was wrong of Gecko to strike him.
They were such friends. Why did he?'

'Well—it was because Svengali struck you with his
conductor's wand when you were rehearsing. Struck you
on the fingers and made you cry! don't you remember?'

'Struck *me! rehearsing?*—made me *cry!* what *are*
you talking about, dear Taffy? Svengali never *struck* me!
He was kindness itself—always! and what should *I*
rehearse?'

'Well, the songs you were to sing at the theatre in the
evening.'

'Sing at the theatre! *I* never sang at any theatre—
except last night, if that big place was a theatre! and
they didn't seem to like it! I'll take precious good care
never to sing in a theatre again! How they howled!
and there was Svengali in the box opposite, laughing at
me. Why was I taken there? and why did that funny
little Frenchman in the white waistcoat ask me to sing?
I know very well I can't sing well enough to sing in a
place like that! What a fool I was! It all seems like
a bad dream! What was it all about? *Was* it a dream,
I wonder!'

'Well—but don't you remember singing at Paris, in
the Salle des Bashibazoucks—and at Vienna—St. Petersburg—lots of places?'

'What nonsense, dear—you're thinking of some one
else! *I* never sang anywhere! I've been to Vienna and
St. Petersburg—but I never *sang* there—good heavens!'

Then there was a pause, and our three friends looked
at her helplessly.

Little Billee said: 'Tell me, Trilby—what made you
cut me dead when I bowed to you in the Place de la

Concorde, and you were riding with Svengali in that swell carriage?'

'*I* never rode in a swell carriage with Svengali! Omnibuses were more in *our* line! You're dreaming, dear Little Billee—you're taking me for somebody else; and as for my cutting *you*—why, I'd sooner cut myself—into little pieces!'

'*Where* were you staying with Svengali in Paris?'

'I really forget. *Were* we in Paris? Oh yes, of course. Hôtel Bertrand, Place Notre Dame des Victoires.'

'How long have you been going about with Svengali?'

'Oh, months, years—I forget. I was very ill. He cured me.'

'Ill! What was the matter?'

'Oh! I was mad with grief, and pain in my eyes, and wanted to kill myself, when I lost my dear little Jeannot, at Vibraye. I fancied I hadn't been careful enough with him. I was crazed! Don't you remember writing to me there, Taffy—through Angèle Boisse? Such a sweet letter you wrote! I know it by heart! And you too, Sandy'; and she kissed him. 'I wonder where they are, your letters? I've got nothing of my own in the world—not even your dear letters—nor Little Billee's—such lots of them!

'Well, Svengali used to write to me too—and then he got my address from Angèle. . . .

'When Jeannot died, I felt I must kill myself or get away from Vibraye—get away from the people there; so when he was buried I cut my hair short and got a workman's cap and blouse and trousers and walked all the way to Paris without saying anything to anybody. I didn't want anybody to know; I wanted to escape from

Svengali, who wrote that he was coming there to fetch
me.   I wanted to hide in Paris.   When I got there at
last it was two o'clock in
the morning, and I was in
dreadful pain—and I'd lost
all my money—thirty francs
— through a hole in my
trousers' pocket.   Besides,
I had a row with a carter in
the Halle.   He thought I
was a man, and hit me and
gave me a black eye, just
because I patted his horse
and fed it with a carrot I'd
been trying to eat myself.
He was tipsy, I think.   Well,
I looked over the bridge
at the river—just by the
Morgue — and wanted to
jump in.   But the Morgue
sickened me, so I hadn't the
pluck.   Svengali used to be
always talking about the
Morgue, and my going there
some day.   He used to say
he'd come and look at me

'POENA PEDE CLAUDO'

there, and the idea made me so sick I couldn't.   I got
bewildered and quite stupid.

   'Then I went to Angèle's, in the Rue des Cloîtres Ste.
Pétronille, and waited about ; but I hadn't the courage to
ring, so I went to the Place St. Anatole des Arts, and
looked up at the old studio window, and thought how

comfortable it was in there, with the big settee near the stove, and all that, and felt inclined to ring up Madame Vinard ; and then I remembered Little Billee was ill there, and his mother and sister were with him. Angèle had written me, you know. Poor Little Billee! There he was, very ill!

'So I walked about the place, and up and down the Rue des Trois Mauvais Ladres. Then I went down the Rue de Seine to the river again, and again I hadn't the pluck to jump in. Besides, there was a *sergent-de-ville* who followed and watched me. And the fun of it was that I knew him quite well, and he didn't know me a bit. It was Célestin Beaumollet, who got so tipsy on Christmas night. Don't you remember ? The tall one, who was pitted with the small-pox.

'Then I walked about till near daylight. Then I could stand it no longer, and went to Svengali's, in the Rue Tireliard, but he'd moved to the Rue des Saints Pères ; and I went there and found him. I didn't want to a bit, but I couldn't help myself. It was fate, I suppose! He was very kind, and cured me almost directly, and got me coffee and bread and butter—the best I ever tasted—and a warm bath from Bidet Frères, in the Rue Savonarole. It was heavenly! And I slept for two days and two nights! And then he told me how fond he was of me, and how he would always cure me, and take care of me, and marry me, if I would go away with him. He said he would devote his whole life to me, and took a small room for me, next to his.

'I stayed with him there a week, never going out or seeing any one, mostly asleep. I'd caught a chill.

'He played in two concerts and made a lot of money ;

and then we went away to Germany together ; and no one was a bit the wiser.'

'And *did* he marry you ?'

'Well—no. He couldn't, poor fellow ! He'd already got a wife living, and three children, which he declared were not his. They live in Elberfeld in Prussia ; she keeps a small sweet-stuff shop there. He behaved very badly to them. But it was not through me ! He'd deserted them long before ; but he used to send them plenty of money when he'd got any ; I made him, for I was very sorry for her. He was always talking about her, and what she said and what she did, and imitating her saying her prayers and eating pickled cucumber with one hand and drinking schnapps with the other, so as not to lose any time ; till he made me die of laughing. He could be very funny, Svengali, though he *was* German, poor dear ! And then Gecko joined us, and Marta.'

'Who's Marta ?'

'THE OLD STUDIO'

'His aunt. She cooked for us, and all that. She's coming here presently; she sent word from the hotel; she's very fond of him. Poor Marta! Poor Gecko! What *will* they ever do without Svengali?'

'Then what did he do to live?'

'Oh! he played at concerts, I suppose—and all that.'

'Did you ever hear him?'

'Yes. Sometimes Marta took me; at the beginning, you know. He was always very much applauded. He plays beautifully. Everybody said so.'

'Did he never try and teach you to sing?'

'Oh, maïe aïe! not he! Why, he always laughed when I tried to sing; and so did Marta; and so did Gecko! It made them roar! I used to sing "Ben Bolt." They used to make me, just for fun—and go into fits. *I* didn't mind a scrap. I'd had no training, you know!'

'Was there anybody else he knew — any other woman?'

'Not that *I* know of! He always made out he was so fond of me that he couldn't even *look* at another woman. Poor Svengali!' (Here her eyes filled with tears again.) 'He was always very kind! But I never could be fond of him in the way he wished—never! It made me sick even to think of! Once I used to hate him—in Paris—in the studio; don't you remember?

'He hardly ever left me; and then Marta looked after me—for I've always been weak and ill, and often so languid that I could hardly walk across the room. It was that three days' walk from Vibraye to Paris. I never got over it.

'I used to try and do all I could—be a daughter to him, as I couldn't be anything else—mend his things, and all that, and cook him little French dishes. I fancy he was very poor at one time ; we were always moving from place to place. But I always had the best of everything. He insisted on that—even if he had to go without himself. It made him quite unhappy when I wouldn't eat, so I used to force myself.

'Then, as soon as I felt uneasy about things, or had any pain, he would say, "Dors, ma mignonne!" and I would sleep at once—for hours, I think—and wake up oh, so tired! and find him kneeling by me, always so anxious and kind—and Marta and Gecko! and sometimes we had the doctor, and I was ill in bed.

'Gecko used to dine and breakfast with us—you've no idea what an angel he is, poor little Gecko! But what a dreadful thing to strike Svengali! *Why* did he? Svengali taught him all he knows!'

'And you knew no one else—no other woman?'

'No one that I can remember—except Marta—not a soul!'

'And that beautiful dress you had on last night?'

'It isn't mine. It's on the bed upstairs, and so's the fur cloak. They belong to Marta. She's got lots of them, lovely things—silk, satin, velvet—and lots of beautiful jewels. Marta deals in them, and makes lots of money.

'I've often tried them on; I'm very easy to fit,' she said, ' being so tall and thin. And poor Svengali would kneel down and cry, and kiss my hands and feet, and tell me I was his goddess and empress, and all that, which I hate. And Marta used to cry, too. And then he would say—

'"Et maintenant dors, ma mignonne!"

'And when I woke up I was so tired that I went to sleep again on my own account.

'But he was very patient. Oh, dear me! I've always been a poor, helpless, useless log and burden to him!

'Once I actually walked in my sleep—and woke up in the market-place at Prague—and found an immense crowd, and poor Svengali bleeding from the forehead, in a faint on the ground. He'd been knocked down by a horse and cart, he told me. He'd got his guitar with him. I suppose he and Gecko had been playing somewhere, for Gecko had his fiddle. If Gecko hadn't been there, I don't know what we should have done. You never saw such queer people as they were—such crowds—you'd think they'd never seen an Englishwoman before. The noise they made, and the things they gave me . . . some of them went down on their knees, and kissed my hands and the skirts of my gown.

'He was ill in bed for a week after that, and I nursed him, and he was very grateful. Poor Svengali! God knows *I* felt grateful to *him* for many things! Tell me how he died! I hope he hadn't much pain.'

They told her it was quite sudden, from heart disease.

'Ah! I knew he had that; he wasn't a healthy man; he used to smoke too much. Marta used always to be very anxious.'

Just then Marta came in.

Marta was a fat elderly Jewess of rather a grotesque and ignoble type. She seemed overcome with grief—all but prostrate.

Trilby hugged and kissed her, and took off her bonnet and shawl, and made her sit down in a big arm-chair, and got her a foot-stool.

"'ET MAINTENANT DORS, MA MIGNONNE!'"

She couldn't speak a word of anything but Polish and a little German. Trilby had also picked up a little German, and with this and by means of signs, and no doubt through a long intimacy with each other's ways, they understood each other very well. She seemed a very good old creature, and very fond of Trilby, but in mortal terror of the three Englishmen.

Lunch was brought up for the two women and the nurse, and our friends left them, promising to come again that day.

They were utterly bewildered ; and the Laird would have it that there was another Madame Svengali somewhere, the real one, and that Trilby was a fraud—self-deceived and self-deceiving—quite unconsciously so, of course.

Truth looked out of her eyes, as it always had done—truth was in every line of her face.

The truth only—nothing but the truth could ever be told in that ' voice of velvet,' which rang as true when she spoke as that of any thrush or nightingale, however rebellious it might be now (and for ever perhaps) to artificial melodic laws and limitations and restraints. The long training it had been subjected to had made it ' a wonder, a world's delight,' and though she might never sing another note, her mere speech would always be more golden than any silence, whatever she might say.

Except on the one particular point of her singing, she had seemed absolutely sane—so, at least, thought Taffy, the Laird, and Little Billee. And each thought to himself, besides, that this last incarnation of Trilbyness was quite the sweetest, most touching, most endearing of all.

They had not failed to note how rapidly she had aged,

now that they had seen her without her rouge and pearl-powder ; she looked thirty at least—she was only twenty-three.

Her hands were almost transparent in their waxen whiteness ; delicate little frosty wrinkles had gathered round her eyes ; there were gray streaks in her hair ; all strength and straightness and elasticity seemed to have gone out of her with the memory of her endless triumphs (if she really *was* La Svengali), and of her many wanderings from city to city all over Europe.

It was evident enough that the sudden stroke which had destroyed her power of singing had left her physically a wreck.

But she was one of those rarely-gifted beings who cannot look or speak or even stir without waking up (and satisfying) some vague longing that lies dormant in the hearts of most of us, men and women alike ; grace, charm, magnetism—whatever the nameless seduction should be called that she possessed to such an unusual degree—she had lost none of it when she lost her high spirits, her buoyant health and energy, her wits !

Tuneless and insane, she was more of a siren than ever —a quite unconscious siren—without any guile, who appealed to the heart all the more directly and irresistibly that she could no longer stir the passions.

All this was keenly felt by all three—each in his different way—by Taffy and Little Billee especially.

All her past life was forgiven—her sins of omission and commission ! And whatever might be her fate—recovery, madness, disease, or death—the care of her till she died or recovered should be the principal business of their lives.

Both had loved her. All three, perhaps. One had

been loved by her as passionately, as purely, as unselfishly, as any man could wish to be loved, and in some extra-ordinary manner had recovered, after many years, at the mere sudden sight and sound of her, his lost share in our common inheritance—the power to love, and all its joy and sorrow ; without which he had found life not worth living, though he had possessed every other gift and blessing in such abundance.

'Oh, Circe, poor Circe, dear Circe, divine enchantress that you were !' he said to himself, in his excitable way. 'A mere look from your eyes, a mere note of your heavenly voice, has turned a poor, miserable, callous brute back into a man again ! and I will never forget it— never ! And now that a still worse trouble than mine has befallen you, you shall always be first in my thoughts till the end !'

And Taffy felt pretty much the same, though he was not by way of talking to himself so eloquently about things as Little Billee.

As they lunched, they read the accounts of the previous evening's events in different papers, three or four of which (including the *Times*) had already got leaders about the famous but unhappy singer who had been so suddenly widowed and struck down in the midst of her glory. All these accounts were more or less correct. In one paper it was mentioned that Madame Svengali was under the roof and care of Mr. William Bagot, the painter, in Fitzroy Square.

The inquest on Svengali was to take place that after-noon, and also Gecko's examination at the Bow Street Police Court, for his assault.

Taffy was allowed to see Gecko, who was remanded till the result of the *post-mortem* should be made public. But beyond inquiring most anxiously and minutely after Trilby, and betraying the most passionate concern for her, he would say nothing, and seemed indifferent as to his own fate.

'TAFFY WAS ALLOWED TO SEE GECKO'

When they went to Fitzroy Square, late in the afternoon, they found that many people, musical, literary, fashionable, and otherwise (and many foreigners), had called to inquire after Madame Svengali, but no one had

2 C

been admitted to see her. Mrs. Godwin was much elated by the importance of her new lodger.

Trilby had been writing to Angèle Boisse, at her old address in the Rue des Cloîtres Ste. Pétronille, in the hope that this letter would find her still there. She was anxious to go back and be a *blanchisseuse de fin* with her friend. It was a kind of nostalgia for Paris, the Quartier Latin, her clean old trade.

This project our three heroes did not think it necessary to discuss with her just yet ; she seemed quite unfit for work of any kind.

The doctor, who had seen her again, had been puzzled by her strange physical weakness, and wished for a consultation with some special authority ; Little Billee, who was intimate with most of the great physicians, wrote about her to Sir Oliver Calthorpe.

She seemed to find a deep happiness in being with her three old friends, and talked and listened with all her old eagerness and geniality, and much of her old gaiety, in spite of her strange and sorrowful position. But for this it was impossible to realise that her brain was affected in the slightest degree, except when some reference was made to her singing, and this seemed to annoy and irritate her, as though she were being made fun of. The whole of her marvellous musical career, and everything connected with it, had been clean wiped out of her recollection.

She was very anxious to get into other quarters, that Little Billee should suffer no inconvenience, and they promised to take rooms for her and Marta on the morrow.

They told her cautiously all about Svengali and

Gecko ; she was deeply concerned, but betrayed no such poignant anguish as might have been expected. The thought of Gecko troubled her most, and she showed much anxiety as to what might befall him.

Next day she moved with Marta to some lodgings in Charlotte Street, where everything was made as comfortable for them as possible.

Sir Oliver saw her with Dr. Thorne (the doctor who was attending her) and Dr. Jakes Talboys.

Sir Oliver took the greatest interest in her case, both for her sake and his friend Little Billee's. Also his own, for he was charmed with her. He saw her three times in the course of the week, but could not say for certain what was the matter with her, beyond taking the very gravest view of her condition. For all he could advise or prescribe, her weakness and physical prostration increased rapidly, through no cause he could discover. Her insanity was not enough to account for it. She lost weight daily ; she seemed to be wasting and fading away from sheer general atrophy.

Two or three times he took her and Marta for a drive.

On one of these occasions, as they went down Charlotte Street, she saw a shop with transparent French blinds in the window, and through them some Frenchwomen, with neat white caps, ironing. It was a French *blanchisserie de fin,* and the sight of it interested and excited her so much that she must needs insist on being put down and on going into it.

' Je voudrais bien parler à la patronne, si ça ne la dérange pas,' she said.

The *patronne,* a genial Parisian, was much astonished

to hear a great French lady, in costly garments, evidently
a person of fashion and importance, applying to her
rather humbly for employment in the business, and showing a thorough knowledge of the work (and of the

A FAIR BLANCHISSEUSE DE FIN

Parisian work woman's colloquial dialect).   Marta managed
to catch the *patronne's* eye, and tapped her own forehead
significantly, and Sir Oliver nodded.   So the good woman
humoured the great lady's fancy, and promised her
abundance of employment whenever she should want it.

Employment! Poor Trilby was hardly strong enough to walk back to the carriage; and this was her last outing.

But this little adventure had filled her with hope and good spirits—for she had as yet received no answer from Angèle Boisse (who was in Marseilles), and had begun to realise how dreary the Quartier Latin would be without Jeannot, without Angèle, without the *trois Angliches* in the Place St. Anatole des Arts.

She was not allowed to see any of the strangers who came and made kind inquiries. This her doctors had strictly forbidden. Any reference to music or singing irritated her beyond measure. She would say to Marta, in bad German—

'Tell them, Marta—what nonsense it is! They are taking me for another—they are mad. They are trying to make a fool of me!'

And Marta would betray great uneasiness—almost terror—when she was appealed to in this way.

PART EIGHTH

'La vie est vaine :
   Un peu d'amour,
Un peu de haine. . . .
   Et puis—bonjour !

'La vie est brève :
   Un peu d'espoir,
Un peu de rêve. . . .
   Et puis—bonsoir.'

SVENGALI had died from heart disease. The cut he had received from Gecko had not apparently (as far as the verdict of a coroner's inquest could be trusted) had any effect in aggravating his malady or hastening his death.

But Gecko was sent for trial at the Old Bailey, and sentenced to hard labour for six months (a sentence which, if I remember aright, gave rise to much comment at the time). Taffy saw him again, but with no better result than before. He chose to preserve an obstinate silence on his relations with the Svengalis and their relations with each other.

When he was told how hopelessly ill and insane Madame Svengali was, he shed a few tears, and said: 'Ah, pauvrette, pauvrette—ah ! monsieur—je l'aimais tant, je l'aimais tant ! il n'y en a pas beaucoup comme elle, Dieu de misère ! C'est un ange du Paradis ! '

And not another word was to be got out of him.

It took some time to settle Svengali's affairs after his death. No will was found. His old mother came over from Germany, and two of his sisters, but no wife. The comic wife and the three children, and the sweet-stuff shop in Elberfeld, had been humorous inventions of his own—a kind of Mrs. Harris!

He left three thousand pounds, every penny of which (and of far larger sums that he had spent) had been earned by 'La Svengali,' but nothing came to Trilby of this; nothing but the clothes and jewels he had given her, and in this respect he had been lavish enough; and there were countless costly gifts from emperors, kings, great people of all kinds. Trilby was under the impression that all these belonged to Marta. Marta behaved admirably; she seemed bound hand and foot to Trilby by a kind of slavish adoration, as that of a plain old mother for a brilliant and beautiful but dying child.

It soon became evident that, whatever her disease might be, Trilby had but a very short time to live.

She was soon too weak even to be taken out in a Bath chair, and remained all day in her large sitting-room with Marta; and there, to her great and only joy, she received her three old friends every afternoon, and gave them coffee, and made them smoke cigarettes of caporal as of old; and their hearts were daily harrowed as they watched her rapid decline.

Day by day she grew more beautiful in their eyes, in spite of her increasing pallor and emaciation—her skin was so pure and white and delicate, and the bones of her face so admirable!

Her eyes recovered all their old humorous brightness

when *les trois Angliches* were with her, and the expression
of her face was so wistful and tender for all her playfulness, so full of eager clinging to existence and to them, that
they felt the memory of it would haunt them for ever,
and be the sweetest and saddest memory of their lives.

Her quick, though feeble gestures, full of reminiscences
of the vigorous and lively girl they had known a few
years back, sent waves of pity through them and pure
brotherly love ; and the incomparable tones and changes
and modulations of her voice, as she chatted and laughed,
bewitched them almost as much as when she had sung the
' Nussbaum ' of Schumann in the Salle des Bashibazoucks.

Sometimes Lorrimer came, and Antony, and the
Greek. It was like a genial little court of bohemia.
And Lorrimer, Antony, the Laird, and Little Billee made
those beautiful chalk and pencil studies of her head which
are now so well known—all so singularly like her, and so
singularly unlike each other ! *Trilby vue à travers
quatre tempéraments !*

These afternoons were probably the happiest poor
Trilby had ever spent in her life—with these dear people
round her, speaking the language she loved ; talking of
old times and jolly Paris days, she never thought of the
morrow.

But later—at night, in the small hours—she would
wake up with a start from some dream full of tender and
blissful recollection, and suddenly realise her own mischance, and feel the icy hand of that which was to come
before many morrows were over ; and taste the bitterness
of death so keenly that she longed to scream out loud,
and get up, and walk up and down, and wring her hands
at the dreadful thought of parting for ever !

A THRONE IN BOHEMIA

But she lay motionless and mum as a poor little frightened mouse in a trap, for fear of waking up the good old tired Marta, who was snoring at her side.

And in an hour or two the bitterness would pass away, the creeps and the horrors; and the stoical spirit of resignation would steal over her—the balm, the blessed calm! and all her old bravery would come back.

And then she would sink into sleep again, and dream more blissfully than ever, till the good Marta woke her with a motherly kiss and a fragrant cup of coffee; and she would find, feeble as she was, and doomed as she felt herself to be, that joy cometh of a morning; and life was still sweet for her, with yet a whole day to look forward to.

One day she was deeply moved at receiving a visit from Mrs. Bagot, who, at Little Billee's earnest desire, had come all the way from Devonshire to see her.

As the graceful little lady came in, pale and trembling all over, Trilby rose from her chair to receive her, and rather timidly put out her hand, and smiled in a frightened manner. Neither could speak for a second. Mrs. Bagot stood stock-still by the door gazing (with all her heart in her eyes) at the so terribly altered Trilby—the girl she had once so dreaded.

Trilby, who seemed also bereft of motion, and whose face and lips were ashen, exclaimed, 'I'm afraid I haven't quite kept my promise to you, after all! but things have turned out so differently! anyhow, you needn't have any fear of me *now*.'

At the mere sound of that voice, Mrs. Bagot, who was as impulsive, emotional, and unregulated as her son, rushed forward, crying, 'Oh, my poor girl, my poor girl!'

and caught her in her arms, and kissed and caressed her,
and burst into a flood of tears, and forced her back into
her chair, hugging her as if she were a long-lost child.

'I love you now as much as I always admired you—
pray believe it!'

'"OH, MY POOR GIRL! MY POOR GIRL!"'

'Oh, how kind of you to say that!' said Trilby, her
own eyes filling. 'I'm not at all the dangerous or
designing person you thought. I knew quite well I
wasn't a proper person to marry your son all the time;
and told him so again and again. It was very stupid of

me to say yes at last.   I was miserable directly after, I assure you.   Somehow I couldn't help myself—I was driven.'

'Oh, don't talk of that! don't talk of that!   You've never been to blame in any way—I've long known it— I've been full of remorse!   You've been in my thoughts always, night and day.   Forgive a poor jealous mother. As if *any* man could help loving you—or any woman either.   Forgive me!'

'Oh, Mrs. Bagot—forgive *you*!   What a funny idea! But, anyhow, you have forgiven *me*, and that's all I care for now.   I was very fond of your son—as fond as could be.   I am now, but in quite a different sort of way, you know—the sort of way *you* must be, I fancy!   There was never another like him that I ever met—anywhere! You *must* be so proud of him; who wouldn't?   *Nobody's* good enough for him.   I would have been only too glad to be his servant, his humble servant!   I used to tell him so—but he wouldn't hear of it—he was much too kind! He always thought of others before himself.   And, oh! how rich and famous he's become!   I've heard all about it, and it did me good.   It does me more good to think of than anything else; far more than if I were to be ever so rich and famous myself, I can tell you!'

This from La Svengali, whose overpowering fame, so utterly forgotten by herself, was still ringing all over Europe; whose lamentable illness and approaching death were being mourned and discussed and commented upon in every capital of the civilised world, as one distressing bulletin appeared after another.   She might have been a royal personage!

Mrs. Bagot knew, of course, the strange form her

insanity had taken, and made no allusion to the flood of
thoughts that rushed through her own brain as she
listened to this towering goddess of song, this poor mad
queen of the nightingales, humbly gloating over her son's
success . . .

Poor Mrs. Bagot had just come from Little Billee's, in
Fitzroy Square, close by. There she had seen Taffy, in a
corner of Little Billee's studio, laboriously answering
endless letters and telegrams from all parts of Europe—
for the good Taffy had constituted himself Trilby's
secretary and *homme d'affaires*—unknown to her, of
course. And this was no sinecure (though he liked it):
putting aside the numerous people he had to see and be
interviewed by, there were kind inquiries and messages of
condolence and sympathy from nearly all the crowned
heads of Europe, through their chamberlains ; applications
for help from unsuccessful musical strugglers all over the
world to the pre-eminently successful one ; beautiful letters
from great and famous people, musical or otherwise ;
disinterested offers of service ; interested proposals for
engagements when the present trouble should be over ;
beggings for an interview from famous *impresarios,* to
obtain which no distance would be thought too great, etc.
etc. etc. It was endless, in English, French, German,
Italian—in languages quite incomprehensible (many letters
had to remain unanswered)—Taffy took an almost
malicious pleasure in explaining all this to Mrs. Bagot.

Then there was a constant rolling of carriages up to
the door, and a thundering of Little Billee's knocker :
Lord and Lady Palmerston wish to know—the Lord
Chief Justice wishes to know—the Dean of Westminster
wishes to know—the Marchioness of Westminster wishes

to know—everybody wishes to know if there is any
better news of Madame Svengali!

These were small things, truly; but Mrs. Bagot was a
small person from a small village in Devonshire, and one
whose heart and eye had hitherto been filled by no larger
image than that of Little Billee; and Little Billee's fame,
as she now discovered for the first time, did not quite fill
the entire universe.

And she mustn't be too much blamed if all these
obvious signs of a world-wide colossal celebrity impressed
and even awed her a little.

Madame Svengali! Why, this was the beautiful girl
whom she remembered so well, whom she had so grandly
discarded with a word, and who had accepted her *congé*
so meekly in a minute; whom, indeed, she had been
cursing in her heart for years, because—because what?

Poor Mrs. Bagot felt herself turn hot and red all
over, and humbled herself to the very dust, and almost
forgot that she had been in the right, after all, and
that 'la grande Trilby' was certainly no fit match for her
son!

So she went quite humbly to see Trilby, and found a
poor pathetic mad creature still more humble than herself,
who still apologised for—for what?

A poor, pathetic, mad creature who had clean forgotten
that she was the greatest singer in all the world—one of
the greatest artists that had ever lived; but who remembered with shame and contrition that she had once taken
the liberty of yielding (after endless pressure and repeated
disinterested refusals of her own, and out of sheer irresistible
affection) to the passionate pleadings of a little obscure
art student, a mere boy—no better off than herself—just

as penniless and insignificant a nobody ; but—the son of
Mrs. Bagot !

All due sense of proportion died out of the poor lady
as she remembered and realised all this !

And then Trilby's pathetic beauty, so touching, so
winning, in its rapid decay ; the nameless charm of look
and voice and manner that was her special appanage, and
which her malady and singular madness had only
increased ; her childlike simplicity, her transparent forgetfulness of self—all these so fascinated and entranced
Mrs. Bagot, whose quick susceptibility to such impressions
was just as keen as her son's, that she very soon found
herself all but worshipping this fast-fading lily—for so
she called her in her own mind—quite forgetting (or
affecting to forget) on what very questionable soil the lily
had been reared, and through what strange vicissitudes of
evil and corruption it had managed to grow so tall and
white and fragrant !

Oh, strange compelling power of weakness and grace
and prettiness combined, and sweet, sincere unconscious
natural manners ! not to speak of world-wide fame !

For Mrs. Bagot was just a shrewd little conventional
British country matron of the good upper middle-class
type, bristling all over with provincial proprieties and
respectabilities, a philistine of the philistines, in spite of
her artistic instincts ; one who for years had (rather
unjustly) thought of Trilby as a wanton and perilous
siren, an unchaste and unprincipled and most dangerous
daughter of Heth, and the special enemy of her house.

And here she was—like all the rest of us monads
and nomads and bohemians—just sitting at Trilby's feet.
. . . 'A washerwoman ! a figure model ! and Heaven

knows what besides!' and she had never even heard her sing!

It was truly comical to see and hear!

Mrs. Bagot did not go back to Devonshire. She remained in Fitzroy Square, at her son's, and spent most of her time with Trilby, doing and devising all kinds of things to distract and amuse her, and lead her thoughts gently to heaven, and soften for her the coming end of all.

Trilby had a way of saying, and especially of looking, 'Thank you' that made one wish to do as many things for her as one could, if only to make her say and look it again.

And she had retained much of her old, quaint, and amusing manner of telling things, and had much to tell still left of her wandering life, although there were so many strange lapses in her powers of memory—gaps— which, if they could only have been filled up, would have been full of such surpassing interest!

Then she was never tired of talking and hearing of Little Billee ; and that was a subject of which Mrs. Bagot could never tire either!

Then there were the recollections of her childhood. One day, in a drawer, Mrs. Bagot came upon a faded daguerreotype of a woman in a Tam o' Shanter, with a face so sweet and beautiful and saint-like that it almost took her breath away. It was Trilby's mother.

'Who and what was your mother, Trilby?'

'Ah, poor mamma!' said Trilby, and she looked at the portrait a long time. 'Ah, she was ever so much prettier than that! Mamma was once a *demoiselle de comptoir*— that's a barmaid, you know— at the Montagnards Écossais, in the Rue du Paradis Poissonnière—a place where men used to drink and smoke without sitting down. That was unfortunate, wasn't it?

'Papa loved her with all his heart, although, of course, she wasn't his equal. They were married at the Embassy, in the Rue du Faubourg St.-Honoré.

'*Her* parents weren't married at all. Her mother was the daughter of a boatman on Loch Ness, near a place called Drumnadrochit; but her father was the Honourable Colonel Desmond. He was related to all sorts of great people in England and Ireland. He behaved very badly to my grandmother and to poor mamma—his own

' " AH, POOR MAMMA ! SHE WAS EVER SO MUCH PRETTIER THAN THAT ! " '

daughter! deserted them both! Not very *honourable* of him, *was* it? And that's all I know about him.'

And then she went on to tell of the home in Paris that might have been so happy but for her father's passion for drink ; of her parents' deaths, and little Jeannot, and so forth. And Mrs. Bagot was much moved and interested by these naive revelations, which accounted in a measure for so much that seemed unaccountable in this extraordinary woman ; who thus turned out to be a kind of cousin (though on the wrong side of the blanket) to no less a person than the famous Duchess of Towers.

With what joy would that ever kind and gracious lady have taken poor Trilby to her bosom had she only known ! She had once been all the way from Paris to Vienna merely to hear her sing. But, unfortunately, the Svengalis had just left for St. Petersburg, and she had her long journey for nothing !

Mrs. Bagot brought her many good books, and read them to her—Dr. Cumming's on the approaching end of the world, and other works of a like comforting tendency for those who are just about to leave it ; the *Pilgrim's Progress*, sweet little tracts, and what not.

Trilby was so grateful that she listened with much patient attention. Only now and then a faint gleam of amusement would steal over her face, and her lips would almost form themselves to ejaculate, ' Oh, maïe, aïe ! '

Then Mrs. Bagot, as a reward for such winning docility, would read her *David Copperfield*, and that was heavenly indeed !

But the best of all was for Trilby to look over John Leech's *Pictures of Life and Character*, just out. She had never seen any drawings of Leech before, except now and then in an occasional *Punch* that turned up in the studio in Paris. And they never palled upon her, and taught her more of the aspect of English life (the life she loved) than any book she had ever read. She laughed and laughed ; and it was almost as sweet to listen to as if she were vocalising the quick part in Chopin's Impromptu.

One day she said, her lips trembling: ' I can't make out why you're so wonderfully kind to me, Mrs. Bagot. I hope you have not forgotten who and what I am, and what my story is. I hope you haven't forgotten that I'm not a respectable woman ? '

' Oh, my dear child—don't ask me. . . . I only know that you are you ! . . . and I am I ! and that is enough for me . . . you're my poor, gentle, patient, suffering daughter, whatever else you are—more sinned against than sinning, I feel sure ! But there . . . I've misjudged you so, and been so unjust, that I would give worlds to make you some amends . . . besides, I should be just as fond of you if you'd committed a murder, I really believe —you're so strange ! you're irresistible ! Did you ever, in all your life, meet anybody that *wasn't* fond of you ? '

Trilby's eyes moistened with tender pleasure at such a pretty compliment. Then, after a few minutes' thought, she said, with engaging candour and quite simply : ' No, I can't say I ever did, that I can think of just now. But I've forgotten such lots of people ! '

One day Mrs. Bagot told Trilby that her brother-in-law, Mr. Thomas Bagot, would much like to come and talk to her.

' Was that the gentleman who came with you to the studio in Paris ? '

' Yes.'

' Why, he's a clergyman, isn't he ? What does he want to come and talk to *me* about ? '

' Ah ! my dear child . . .' said Mrs. Bagot, her eyes filling.

Trilby was thoughtful for a while, and then said : ' I'm

going to die, I suppose. Oh yes! oh yes! There's no mistake about that!'

'Dear Trilby, we are all in the hands of an Almighty Merciful God!' And the tears rolled down Mrs. Bagot's cheeks.

After a long pause, during which she gazed out of the window, Trilby said, in an abstracted kind of way, as though she were talking to herself: 'Après tout, c'est pas déjà si raide, de claquer! J'en ai tant vus, qui ont passé par la! Au bout du fossé la culbute, ma foi!'

'What are you saying to yourself in French, Trilby? Your French is so difficult to understand!'

'Oh, I beg your pardon! I was thinking it's not so difficult to die, after all! I've seen such lots of people do it. I've nursed them, you know—papa and mamma and Jeannot, and Angèle Boisse's mother-in-law, and a poor *casseur de pierres*, Colin Maigret, who lived in the Impasse des Taupes St. Germain. He'd been run over by an omnibus in the Rue Vaugirard, and had to have both his legs cut off just above the knee. They none of them seemed to mind dying a bit. They weren't a bit afraid! *I'm* not!

'Poor people don't think much of death. Rich people shouldn't either. They should be taught when they're quite young to laugh at it and despise it, like the Chinese. The Chinese die of laughing just as their heads are being cut off, and cheat the executioner! It's all in the day's work, and we're all in the same boat—so who's afraid!'

'Dying is not all, my poor child! Are you prepared to meet your Maker face to face? Have you ever thought about God, and the possible wrath to come if you should die unrepentant?'

'Oh, but I sha'n't! I've been repenting all my life! Besides, there'll be no wrath for any of us—not even the worst! *Il y aura amnistie générale!* Papa told me so, and he'd been a clergyman, like Mr. Thomas Bagot. I often think about God. I'm very fond of Him. One *must* have something perfect to look up to and be fond of—even if it's only an idea! even if it's too good to be true!

'Though some people don't even believe He exists! Le père Martin didn't—but, of course, *he* was only a *chiffonnier*, and doesn't count.

'One day, though, Durien, the sculptor, who's very clever, and a very good fellow indeed, said:

'"Vois-tu, Trilby—I'm very much afraid He doesn't really exist, le bon Dieu! most unfortunately for *me*, for I *adore* Him! I never do a piece of work without thinking how nice it would be if I could only please *Him* with it!"

'And I've often thought, myself, how heavenly it must be to be able to paint, or sculpt, or make music, or write beautiful poetry, for that very reason!

'Why, once on a very hot afternoon we were sitting, a lot of us, in the court-yard outside la mère Martin's shop, drinking coffee with an old Invalide called Bastide Lendormi, one of the Vieille Garde, who'd only got one leg and one arm and one eye, and everybody was very fond of him. Well, a model called Mimi la Salope came out of the Mont-de-piété opposite, and Père Martin called out to her to come and sit down, and gave her a cup of coffee, and asked her to sing.

'She sang a song of Béranger's, about Napoleon the Great, in which it says—

‘ “ Parlez-nous de lui, grandmère !
 Grandmère, parlez-nous de lui ! ”

I suppose she sang it very well, for it made old Bastide
Lendormi cry ; and when Père Martin *blagué'd* him about
it, he said—

 ‘ “ C'est égal, voyez-vous ! to sing like that is *to pray !* ”

‘ “TO SING LIKE THAT IS *TO PRAY !*”

 ‘ And then I thought how lovely it would be if *I* could
only sing like Mimi la Salope, and I've thought so ever
since—just to *pray !* ’

 ‘ *What !* Trilby ? if *you* could only sing like—— Oh,

but never mind, I forgot! Tell me, Trilby—do you ever pray to Him, as other people pray?'

'Pray to Him? Well, no—not often—not in words and on my knees and with my hands together, you know! *Thinking's* praying, very often—don't you think so? And so's being sorry and ashamed when one's done a mean thing, and glad when one's resisted a temptation, and grateful when it's a fine day and one's enjoying one's self without hurting any one else! What is it but praying when you try and bear up after losing all you cared to live for? And very good praying too! There can be prayers without words just as well as songs, I suppose; and Svengali used to say that songs without words are the best!

'And then it seems mean to be always asking for things. Besides, you don't get them any the faster that way, and that shows!

'La mère Martin used to be always praying. And Père Martin used always to laugh at her; yet he always seemed to get the things *he* wanted oftenest!

'*I* prayed once, very hard indeed! I prayed for Jeannot not to die!'

'Well—but how do you *repent*, Trilby, if you do not humble yourself, and pray for forgiveness on your knees?'

'Oh, well—I don't exactly know! Look here, Mrs. Bagot, I'll tell you the lowest and meanest thing I ever did. . . .'

(Mrs. Bagot felt a little nervous.)

'I'd promised to take Jeannot on Palm-Sunday to St. Philippe du Roule, to hear l'abbé Bergamot. But Durien (that's the sculptor, you know) asked me to go with him to St. Germain, where there was a fair, or something; and with

Mathieu, who was a student in law; and a certain Victorine Letellier, who—who was Mathieu's mistress, in fact—a lace-mender in the Rue Ste. Maritorne la Pocharde. And so I went on Sunday morning to tell Jeannot that I couldn't take him.

'He cried so dreadfully that I thought I'd give up the others and take him to St. Philippe, as I'd promised. But then Durien and Mathieu and Victorine drove up and waited outside, and so I *didn't* take him, and went with them, and I didn't enjoy anything all day, and was miserable.

'They were in an open carriage with two horses; it was Mathieu's treat, and Jeannot might have ridden on the box by the coachman without being in anybody's way. But I was afraid they didn't want him, as they didn't say anything, and so I didn't dare ask—and Jeannot saw us drive away, and I *couldn't* look back! And the worst of it is that when we were half-way to St. Germain, Durien said, "What a pity you didn't bring Jeannot!" and they were all sorry I hadn't.

'It was six or seven years ago, and I really believe I've thought of it every day, and sometimes in the middle of the night!

'Ah! and when Jeannot was dying! and when he was dead—the remembrance of that Palm-Sunday!

'And if *that's* not repenting, I don't know what is!'

'Oh, Trilby, what nonsense! *that's* nothing; good heavens!—putting off a small child! I'm thinking of far worse things—when you were in the Quartier Latin, you know—sitting to painters and sculptors. . . . Surely, so attractive as you are. . . .'

'Oh yes. . . . I know what you mean—it was horrid,

and I was frightfully ashamed of myself; and it wasn't amusing a bit; *nothing* was, till I met your son and Taffy and dear Sandy M'Allister! But then it wasn't deceiving

'THE REMEMBRANCE OF THAT PALM-SUNDAY!'

or disappointing anybody, or hurting their feelings—it was only hurting myself!

'Besides, all that sort of thing, in women, is punished severely enough down here, God knows! unless one's a Russian empress like Catherine the Great, or a grande dame like lots of them, or a great genius like Madame Rachel or Georges Sand !

'Why, if it hadn't been for that, and sitting for the figure, I should have felt myself good enough to marry your son, *although* I was only a *blanchisseuse de fin*—you've said so yourself!

'And I should have made him a good wife—of that feel sure. He wanted to live all his life at Barbizon, and paint, you know ; and didn't care for society in the least. Anyhow, I should have been equal to such a life as that ! Lots of their wives are *blanchisseuses* over there, or people of that sort ; and they get on very well indeed, and nobody troubles about it !

'So I think I've been pretty well punished—richly as I've deserved to !'

'Trilby, have you ever been confirmed ? '

'I forget. I fancy not !'

'Oh dear, oh dear ! And do you know about our blessed Saviour, and the Atonement and the Incarnation and the Resurrection. . . .'

'Oh yes—I *used* to, at least. I used to have to learn the Catechism on Sundays—mamma made me. Whatever her faults and mistakes were, poor mamma was always very particular about *that!* It all seemed very complicated. But papa told me not to bother too much about it, but to be good. He said that God would make it all right for us somehow, in the end—all of us. And that seems sensible, *doesn't* it ?

'He told me to be good, and not to mind what priests and clergymen tell us. He'd been a clergyman himself, and knew all about it, he said.

'I haven't been very good—there's not much doubt

about that, I'm afraid! But God knows I've repented often enough and sore enough; I do now! But I'm rather glad to die, I think; and not a bit afraid—not a scrap! I believe in poor papa, though he *was* so unfortunate! He was the cleverest man I ever knew, and the best—except Taffy and the Laird and your dear son!

'There'll be no hell for any of us—he told me so—except what we make for ourselves and each other down here; and that's bad enough for anything. He told me that *he* was responsible for me—he often said so—and that mamma was too, and his parents for *him*, and his grandfathers and grandmothers for *them*, and so on up to Noah and ever so far beyond, and God for us all!

'He told me always to think of other people before myself; as Taffy does, and your son; and never to tell lies or be afraid, and keep away from drink, and I should be all right. But I've sometimes been all wrong, all the same; and it wasn't papa's fault, but poor mamma's and mine; and I've known it, and been miserable at the time, and after! and I'm sure to be forgiven—perfectly certain—and so will everybody else, even the wickedest that ever lived! Why, just give them sense enough in the next world to understand all their wickedness in this, and that'll punish them enough for anything, I think! That's simple enough, *isn't* it? Besides, there may be *no* next world—that's on the cards too, you know!—and that will be simpler still!

'Not all the clergymen in all the world, not even the Pope of Rome, will ever make me doubt papa, or believe in any punishment after what we've all got to go through here. *Ce serait trop bête!*

'So that if you don't want me to very much, and he won't think it unkind, I'd rather not talk to Mr. Thomas Bagot about it. I'd rather talk to Taffy if I *must.* He's very clever, Taffy, though he doesn't often say such clever things as your son does, or paint nearly so well ; and I'm sure he'll think papa was right.'

And as a matter of fact the good Taffy, in his opinion on this solemn subject, was found to be at one with the late Reverend Patrick Michael O'Ferrall—and so was the Laird—and so (to his mother's shocked and pained surprise) was Little Billee.

And so were Sir Oliver Calthorpe and Sir Jakes (then Mr.) Talboys and Doctor Thorne and Antony and Lorrimer and the Greek !

And so—in after-years, when grief had well pierced and torn and riddled her through and through, and time and age had healed the wounds, and nothing remained but the consciousness of great inward scars of recollection to remind her how deep and jagged and wide the wounds had once been—did Mrs. Bagot herself!

Late on one memorable Saturday afternoon, just as it was getting dusk in Charlotte Street, Trilby, in her pretty blue dressing-gown, lay on the sofa by the fire—her head well propped, her knees drawn up—looking very placid and content.

She had spent the early part of the day dictating her will to the conscientious Taffy.

It was a simple document, although she was not without many valuable trinkets to leave : quite a fortune ! Souvenirs from many men and women she had charmed by her singing, from royalties downward.

She had been looking them over with the faithful
Marta, to whom she had always thought they belonged.
It was explained to her that they were gifts of Svengali's ;
since she did not remember when and where and by
whom they were presented to her, except a few that
Svengali had given her himself, with many passionate
expressions of his love, which seems to have been deep
and constant and sincere ; none the less so, perhaps, that
she could never return it !

She had left the bulk of these to the faithful Marta.

But to each of the *trois Angliches* she had bequeathed
a beautiful ring, which was to be worn by their brides if
they ever married, and the brides didn't object.

To Mrs. Bagot she left a pearl necklace, to Miss Bagot
her gold coronet of stars ; and pretty (and most costly)
gifts to each of the three doctors who had attended her
and been so assiduous in their care ; and who, as she was
told, would make no charge for attending on Madame
Svengali. And studs and scarf-pins to Antony, Lorrimer,
the Greek, Dodor, and Zouzou ; and to Carnegie a little
German silver vinaigrette which had once belonged to
Lord Witlow ; and pretty souvenirs to the Vinards,
Angèle Boisse, Durien, and others.

And she left a magnificent gold watch and chain to
Gecko, with a most affectionate letter and a hundred
pounds—which was all she had in money of her own.

She had taken great interest in discussing with Taffy
the particular kind of trinket which would best suit the
idiosyncrasy of each particular legatee, and derived great
comfort from the business-like and sympathetic con-
scientiousness with which the good Taffy entered upon all
these minutiæ—he was so solemn and serious about it,

FOR GECKO

and took such pains. She little guessed how his dumb but deeply feeling heart was harrowed !

This document had been duly signed and witnessed and entrusted to his care ; and Trilby lay tranquil and happy, and with a sense that nothing remained for her but to enjoy the fleeting hour, and make the most of each precious moment as it went by.

She was quite without pain of either mind or body, and surrounded by the people she adored—Taffy, the Laird, and Little Billee, and Mrs. Bagot, and Marta, who sat knitting in a corner with her black mittens on, and her brass spectacles.

She listened to the chat and joined in it, laughing as usual ; 'love in her eyes sat playing' as she looked from one to another, for she loved them all beyond expression. 'Love on her lips was straying, and warbling in her breath,' whenever she spoke ; and her weakened voice was still larger, fuller, softer than any other voice in the room, in the world—of another kind, from another sphere.

A cart drove up, there was a ring at the door, and presently a wooden packing-case was brought into the room.

At Trilby's request it was opened, and found to contain a large photograph, framed and glazed, of Svengali, in the military uniform of his own Hungarian band (which he had always worn until he came to Paris and London, where he conducted in ordinary evening dress), and looking straight out of the picture, straight at you. He was standing by his desk with his left hand turning over a leaf of music, and waving his bâton with his right. It was a splendid photograph, by a Viennese photographer, and a most speaking likeness ; and Svengali

looked truly fine—all made up of importance and
authority, and his big black eyes were full of stern
command.

Marta trembled as she looked. It was handed to
Trilby, who exclaimed in surprise. She had never seen
it. She had no photograph
of him, and had never possessed one.

No message of any kind,
no letter of explanation, accompanied this unexpected
present, which, from the post-
marks on the case, seemed to
have travelled all over Europe
to London, out of some remote
province in eastern Russia—
out of the mysterious East!
The poisonous East—birth-
place and home of an ill
wind that blows nobody good.

Trilby laid it against her
legs as on a lectern, and lay
gazing at it with close attention for a long time, making
a casual remark now and

'OUT OF THE MYSTERIOUS EAST'

then, as, 'He was very handsome, I think'; or, 'That
uniform becomes him very well. Why has he got it on,
I wonder?'

The others went on talking, and Mrs. Bagot made
coffee.

Presently Mrs. Bagot took a cup of coffee to Trilby,

and found her still staring intently at the portrait, but with her eyes dilated, and quite a strange light in them.

'Trilby, Trilby, your coffee! What is the matter, Trilby?'

Trilby was smiling, with fixed eyes, and made no answer.

The others got up and gathered round her in some alarm. Marta seemed terror-stricken, and wished to snatch the photograph away, but was prevented from doing so; one didn't know what the consequences might be.

Taffy rang the bell, and sent a servant for Dr. Thorne, who lived close by, in Fitzroy Square.

Presently Trilby began to speak, quite softly, in French: 'Encore une fois? bon! je veux bien! avec la voix blanche alors, n'est-ce pas? et puis foncer au milieu. Et pas trop vite en commençant! Battez bien la mesure, Svengali—que je puisse bien voir—car il fait déjà nuit! c'est ça! Allons, Gecko—donne-moi le ton!'

Then she smiled, and seemed to beat time softly by moving her head a little from side to side, her eyes intent on Svengali's in the portrait, and suddenly she began to sing Chopin's Impromptu in A flat.

She hardly seemed to breathe as the notes came pouring out, without words—mere vocalising. It was as if breath were unnecessary for so little voice as she was using, though there was enough of it to fill the room—to fill the house—to drown her small audience in holy, heavenly sweetness.

She was a consummate mistress of her art. How that could be seen! And also how splendid had been her training. It all seemed as easy to her as opening and shutting her eyes, and yet how utterly impossible to anybody else!

Between wonder, enchantment, and alarm they were frozen to statues—all except Marta, who ran out of the room crying, 'Gott im Himmel! wieder zurück! wieder zurück!'

She sang it just as she had sung it at the Salle des Bashibazoucks, only it sounded still more ineffably seductive, as she was using less voice—using the essence of her voice in fact—the pure spirit, the very cream of it.

There can be little doubt that these four watchers by that enchanted couch were listening to not only the most divinely beautiful, but also the most astounding feat of musical utterance ever heard out of a human throat.

The usual effect was produced. Tears were streaming down the cheeks of Mrs. Bagot and Little Billee. Tears were in the Laird's eyes, a tear on one of Taffy's whiskers —tears of sheer delight.

When she came back to the quick movement again, after the adagio, her voice grew louder and shriller, and sweet with a sweetness not of this earth ; and went on increasing in volume as she quickened the time, nearing the end ; and then came the dying away into all but nothing—a mere melodic breath ; and then the little soft chromatic ascending rocket, up to E in alt, the last parting caress (which Svengali had introduced as a finale, for it does not exist in the piano score).

When it was over, she said : ' Ça y est-il, cette fois, Svengali ? Ah! tant mieux, à la fin! c'est pas malheureux ! Et maintenant, mon ami, *je suis fatiguée—bon soir !* '

Her head fell back on the pillow, and she lay fast asleep.

"'SVENGALI!... SVENGALI!... SVENGALI!...'"

Mrs. Bagot took the portrait away gently. Little Billee knelt down and held Trilby's hand in his and felt for her pulse, and could not find it.

He said, 'Trilby! Trilby!' and put his ear to her mouth to hear her breathe. Her breath was inaudible.

But soon she folded her hands across her breast, and uttered a little short sigh, and in a weak voice said: '*Svengali . . . Svengali . . . Svengali . . .*'

They remained in silence round her for several minutes, terror-stricken.

The doctor came; he put his hand to her heart, his ear to her lips. He turned up one of her eyelids and looked at her eye. And then, his voice quivering with strong emotion, he stood up and said, 'Madame Svengali's trials and sufferings are all over!'

'Oh, good God! is she *dead?*' cried Mrs. Bagot.

'Yes, Mrs. Bagot. She has been dead several minutes —perhaps a quarter of an hour.'

VINGT ANS APRÈS

Porthos-Athos, *alias* Taffy Wynne, is sitting to breakfast (opposite his wife) at a little table in the courtyard of that huge caravansérai on the Boulevard des Capucines, Paris, where he had sat more than twenty years ago with the Laird and Little Billee; where, in fact, he had pulled Svengali's nose.

Little is changed in the aspect of the place: the same cosmopolite company, with more of the American element, perhaps; the same arrivals and departures in railway omnibuses, cabs, hired carriages; and, airing his calves on the marble steps, stood just such another colossal and beautiful old man in black cloth coat and knee-breeches and silk stockings as of yore, with probably the very same pinchbeck chain. Where do they breed these magnificent old Frenchmen? In Germany, perhaps, 'where all the good big waiters come from!'

And also the same fine weather. It is always fine weather in the courtyard of the Grand Hôtel. As the Laird would say, they manage these things better there!

Taffy wears a short beard, which is turning gray. His kind blue eye is no longer choleric, but mild and friendly —as frank as ever; and full of humorous patience. He has grown stouter; he is very big indeed, in all three dimensions, but the symmetry and the gainliness of the athlete belong to him still in movement and repose; and his clothes fit him beautifully, though they are not new, and show careful beating and brushing and ironing, and even a faint suspicion of all but imperceptible fine-drawing here and there.

What a magnificent old man *he* will make some day, should the Grand Hôtel ever run short of them! He looks as if he could be trusted down to the ground—in all things, little or big; as if his word were as good as his bond, and even better; his wink as good as his word, his nod as good as his wink; and, in truth, as he looks, so he is.

The most cynical disbeliever in 'the grand old name of gentleman,' and its virtues as a noun of definition, would almost be justified in quite dogmatically asserting at sight, and without even being introduced, that, at all events, Taffy is a 'gentleman,' inside and out, up and down—from the crown of his head (which is getting rather bald) to the sole of his foot (by no means a small one, or a lightly shod—*ex pede Herculem*)!

Indeed, this is always the first thing people say of Taffy—and the last. It means, perhaps, that he may be a trifle dull. Well, one can't be everything!

Porthos was a trifle dull—and so was Athos, I think; and likewise his son, the faithful Viscount of Bragelonne —*bon chien chasse de race!* And so was Wilfred of Ivanhoe, the disinherited; and Edgar, the Lord of Ravenswood! and so, for that matter, was Colonel Newcome, of immortal memory!

Yet who does not love them—who would not wish to be like them, for better, for worse!

Taffy's wife is unlike Taffy in many ways; but (fortunately for both) very like him in some. She is a little woman, very well shaped, very dark, with black, wavy hair, and very small hands and feet; a very graceful, handsome, and vivacious person; by no means dull; full, indeed, of quick perceptions and intuitions; deeply interested in all that is going on about and around her, and with always lots to say about it, but not too much.

She distinctly belongs to the rare, and ever-blessed, and most precious race of charmers.

She had fallen in love with the stalwart Taffy more than a quarter of a century ago in the Place St. Anatole des Arts, where he and she and her mother had tended the sick couch of Little Billee—but she had never told her love. *Tout vient à point, à qui sait attendre!*

That is a capital proverb, and sometimes even a true one. Blanche Bagot had found it to be both!

One terrible night, never to be forgotten, Taffy lay fast

'TOUT VIENT À POINT, À QUI SAIT ATTENDRE'

asleep in bed, at his rooms in Jermyn Street, for he was
very tired; grief tires more than anything, and brings a
deeper slumber.

That day he had followed Trilby to her last home in
Kensal Green, with Little Billee, Mrs. Bagot, the Laird,
Antony, the Greek, and Durien (who had come over from
Paris on purpose) as chief mourners; and very many
other people, noble, famous, or otherwise, English and
foreign; a splendid and most representative gathering,
as was duly chronicled in all the newspapers here and

abroad ; a fitting ceremony to close the brief but splendid career of the greatest pleasure-giver of our time.

He was awakened by a tremendous ringing at the street-door bell, as if the house were on fire; and then there was a hurried scrambling up in the dark, a tumbling over stairs and kicking against banisters, and Little Billee had burst into his room, calling out : 'Oh! Taffy, Taffy! I'm g-going mad—I'm g-going m-mad! I'm d-d-done for. . . .'

' All right, old fellow—just wait till I strike a light!'

'Oh, Taffy! I haven't slept for four nights—not a wink! She d-d-died with Sv—Sv—Sv . . . damn it, I can't get it out! that ruffian's name on her lips! . . . it was just as if he were calling her from the t-t-tomb! She recovered her senses the very minute she saw his photograph—she was so f-fond of him she f-forgot everybody else! She's gone straight to him, after all—in some other life! . . . to slave for him, and sing for him, and help him to make better music than ever! Oh, T—T—oh—oh! Taffy—oh! oh! oh! catch hold! c-c-catch. . . .' And Little Billee had all but fallen on the floor in a fit.

And all the old miserable business of five years before had begun over again!

There has been too much sickness in this story, so I will tell as little as possible of poor Little Billee's long illness, his slow and only partial recovery, the paralysis of his powers as a painter, his quick decline, his early death, his manly, calm, and most beautiful surrender—the wedding of the moth with the star, of the night with the morrow!

For all but blameless as his short life had been, and so

full of splendid promise and performance, nothing ever became him better than the way he left it. It was as if he were starting on some distant holy quest, like some gallant knight of old—'A Bagot to the rescue!' in another life. It shook the infallibility of a certain vicar down to its very founda-tions, and made him think more deeply about things than he had ever thought yet. It gave him pause! . . . and so

'I, PETE COELESTES. . . .

wrung his heart that when, at the last, he stooped to kiss his poor young dead friend's pure white forehead, he dropped a bigger tear on it than Little Billee (once so given to the dropping of big tears) had ever dropped in his life.

But it is all too sad to write about.

It was by Little Billee's bedside, in Devonshire, that Taffy had grown to love Blanche Bagot, and not very many weeks after it was all over that Taffy had asked her to be his wife ; and in a year they were married, and a very happy marriage it turned out—the one thing that poor Mrs. Bagot still looks upon as a compensation for all the griefs and troubles of her life.

During the first year or two Blanche had perhaps been the more ardently loving of this well-assorted pair. That beautiful look of love surprised (which makes all women's eyes look the same) came into hers whenever she looked at Taffy, and filled his heart with tender compunction, and a queer sense of his own unworthiness.

Then a boy was born to them, and that look fell on the boy, and the good Taffy caught it as it passed him by, and he felt a helpless, absurd jealousy, that was none the less painful for being so ridiculous ! and then that look fell on another boy, and yet another, so that it was through these boys that she looked at their father. Then *his* eyes caught the look, and kept it for their own use ; and he grew never to look at his wife without it ; and as no daughter came, she retained for life the monopoly of that most sweet and expressive regard.

They are not very rich. He is a far better sportsman than he will ever be a painter ; and if he doesn't sell his pictures, it is not because they are too good for the public taste : indeed, he has no illusions on that score himself, even if his wife has ! He is quite the least conceited art-duffer I ever met—and I have met many far worse duffers than Taffy.

Would only that I might kill off his cousin Sir Oscar, and Sir Oscar's five sons (the Wynnes are good at sons), and his seventeen grandsons, and the fourteen cousins (and their numerous male progeny), that stand between Taffy and the baronetcy, and whatever property goes with it ; so that he might be Sir Taffy, and dear Blanche Bagot (that was) might be called ' my lady ' ! This Shakes-pearian holocaust would scarcely cost me a pang !

It is a great temptation, when you have duly slain your first hero, to enrich hero number two beyond the dreams of avarice, and provide him with a title and a castle and park, as well as a handsome wife and a nice family ! But truth is inexorable—and, besides, they are just as happy as they are.

They are well off enough, anyhow, to spend a week in Paris at last, and even to stop at the Grand Hôtel ! now that two of their sons are at Harrow (where their father was before them), and the third is safe at a preparatory school at Elstree, Herts.

It is their first outing since the honeymoon and the Laird should have come with them.

But the good Laird of Cockpen (who is now a famous Royal Academician) is preparing for a honeymoon of his own. He has gone to Scotland to be married himself— to wed a fair and clever countrywoman of just a suitable age, for he has known her ever since she was a bright little lassie in short frocks, and he a promising A.R.A. (the pride of his native Dundee)—a marriage of reason, and well-seasoned affection, and mutual esteem—and therefore sure to turn out a happy one! and in another fortnight or so the pair of them will very possibly be sitting to break-fast opposite each other at that very corner table in the courtyard of the Grand Hôtel! and she will laugh at every-thing he says—and they will live happily ever after.

So much for hero number three—D'Artagnan? Here's to you, Sandy M'Allister, canniest, genialest, and most humorous of Scots? most delicate, and dainty, and fanciful of British painters? ' I trink your health, mit your family's —may you lif long—and brosper! '

So Taffy and his wife have come for their second honeymoon, their Indian-summer honeymoon, alone ; and are well content that it should be so. Two's always company for such a pair—the amusing one and the amusable !—and they are making the most of it !

They have been all over the Quartier Latin, and revisited the well-remembered spots ; and even been allowed to enter the old studio, through the kindness of the *concierge* (who is no longer Madame Vinard). It is tenanted by two American painters, who are coldly civil on being thus disturbed in the middle of their work.

The studio is very spick and span, and most respect-able. Trilby's foot, and the poem, and the sheet of plate-glass have been improved away, and a bookshelf put in their place. The new *concierge* (who has only been there a year) knows nothing of Trilby ; and of the Vinards, only that they are rich and prosperous, and live somewhere in the south of France, and that Monsieur Vinard is mayor of his commune. *Que le bon Dieu les bénisse ! c'étaient de bien braves gens.*

Then Mr. and Mrs. Taffy have also been driven (in an
open *calèche* with two horses) through the Bois de Boulogne
to St. Cloud ; and to Versailles, where they lunched at the
Hôtel des Réservoirs—*parlez-moi de ça !* and to St.
Germain, and to Meudon (where they lunched at *la loge du
garde champêtre*—a new one) ; they have visited the
Salon, the Louvre, the porcelain manufactory at Sèvres,
the Gobelins, the Hôtel Cluny, the Invalides, with
Napoleon's tomb ; and seen half a dozen churches, including Notre Dame and the Sainte Chapelle ; and dined with
the Dodors at their charming villa near Asnières, and with
the Zouzous at the splendid Hôtel de la Rochemartel, and
with the Duriens in the Parc Monceau (Dodor's food was
best and Zouzou's worst ; and at Durien's the company
and talk were so good that one forgot to notice the food—
and that was a pity). And the young Dodors are all
right—and so are the young Duriens. As for the young
Zouzous, there aren't any—and *that's* a weight off one's
mind !

And they've been to the Variétés and seen Madame
Chaumont, and to the Français and seen Sarah Bernhardt
and Coquelin and Delaunay, and to the Opéra and heard
Monsieur Lassalle.

And to-day being their last day, they are going to
laze and flane about the boulevards, and buy things, and
lunch anywhere, *sur le pouce*, and do the Bois once more
and see *tout* Paris, and dine early at Durand's, or Bignon's
(or else the Café des Ambassadeurs), and finish up the
well-spent day at the ' Mouches d'Espagne '—the new
theatre in the Boulevard Poissonnière—to see Madame
Cantharidi in ' Petits Bonheurs de Contrebande,' which
they are told is immensely droll and quite proper—funny

without being vulgar!   Dodor was their informant—he
had taken Madame Dodor to see it three or four times.

Madame Cantharidi, as everybody knows, is a very
clever but extremely plain old woman with a cracked
voice—of spotless reputation, and the irreproachable
mother of a grown-up family whom she has brought up
in perfection.   They have never been allowed to see their
mother (and grandmother) act—not even the sons.   Their
excellent father (who adores both them and her) has drawn
the line at that!

'PETITS BONHEURS DE CONTREBANDE'

In private life she is 'quite the lady,' but on the stage
—well, go and see her, and you will understand how she
comes to be the idol of the Parisian public.   For she is
the true and liberal dispenser to them of that modern
esprit gaulois which would make the good Rabelais turn
uneasily in his grave and blush there like a Benedictine
Sister.

And truly she deserves the reverential love and gratitude of her *chers Parisiens !*   She amused them all through
the Empire ; during the *année terrible* she was their only
stay and comfort, and has been their chief delight ever
since, and is now.

When they come back from *La Revanche*, may Madame
Cantharidi be still at her post, ' Les mouches d'Espagne,'
to welcome the returning heroes, and exult and crow with
them in her funny cracked old voice ; or, haply, even
console them once more, as the case may be.

' Victors or vanquished, they will laugh the same ! '

Mrs. Taffy is a poor French scholar.   One must know
French very well indeed (and many other things besides)
to seize the subtle points of Madame Cantharidi's play
(and by-play) !

But Madame Cantharidi has so droll a face and voice,
and such very droll, odd movements, that Mrs. Taffy goes
into fits of laughter as soon as the quaint little old lady
comes on the stage.   So heartily does she laugh that a
good Parisian bourgeois turns round and remarks to his
wife : ' V'là une jolie p'tite Anglaise qui n'est pas bégueule,
au moins !   Et l' gros bœuf avec les yeux bleus en boules
de loto—c'est son mari, sans doute ! il n'a pas l'air trop
content par exemple, celui-là ! '

The fact is that the good Taffy (who knows French
very well indeed) is quite scandalised, and very angry
with Dodor for sending them there ; and as soon as the
first act is finished he means, without any fuss, to take his
wife away.

As he sits patiently, too indignant to laugh at what is
really funny in the piece (much of it is vulgar *without*

being funny), he finds himself watching a little white-haired man in the orchestra, a fiddler, the shape of whose back seems somehow familiar, as he plays an *obbligato* accompaniment to a very broadly comic song of Madame Cantharidi's. He plays beautifully—like a master—and the loud applause is as much for him as for the vocalist.

Presently this fiddler turns his head so that his profile can be seen, and Taffy recognises him.

After five minutes' thought, Taffy takes a leaf out of his pocket-book and writes (in perfectly grammatical French) :—

'DEAR GECKO—You have not forgotten Taffy Wynne, I hope ; and Litrebili, and Litrebili's sister, who is now Mrs. Taffy Wynne. We leave Paris to-morrow, and would like very much to see you once more. Will you, after the play, come and sup with us at the Café Anglais ? If so, look up and make "yes" with the head, and enchant— Your well-devoted   TAFFY WYNNE.'

He gives this, folded, to an attendant—for 'le premier violon—celui qui a des cheveux blancs.'

Presently he sees Gecko receive the note and read it and ponder for a while.

Then Gecko looks round the theatre, and Taffy waves his handkerchief and catches the eye of the premier violon, who 'makes "yes" with the head.'

And then, the first act over, Mr. and Mrs. Wynne leave the theatre ; Mr. explaining why, and Mrs. very ready to go, as she was beginning to feel strangely uncomfortable without quite realising as yet what was amiss with the lively Madame Cantharidi.

They went to the Café Anglais and bespoke a nice little room on the *entresol* overlooking the boulevard, and ordered a nice little supper ; salmi of something very good, mayonnaise of lobster, and one or two other dishes better still—and chambertin of the best. Taffy was particular about these things on a holiday, and regardless of expense. Porthos was very hospitable, and liked good food and plenty of it ; and Athos dearly loved good wine !

And then they went and sat at a little round table outside the Café de la Paix on the boulevard, near the Grand Opéra, where it is always very gay, and studied Paris life, and nursed their appetites till supper-time.

At half-past eleven Gecko made his appearance—very meek and humble. He looked old—ten years older than he really was—much bowed down, and as if he had roughed it all his life, and had found living a desperate long, hard grind.

He kissed Mrs. Taffy's hand, and seemed half inclined to kiss Taffy's too, and was almost tearful in his pleasure at meeting them again, and his gratitude at being asked to sup with them. He had soft, clinging, caressing manners, like a nice dog's, that made you his friend at once. He was obviously genuine and sincere, and quite pathetically simple, as he always had been.

At first he could scarcely eat for nervous excitement ; but Taffy's fine example and Mrs. Taffy's genial, easy-going cordiality (and a couple of glasses of chambertin) soon put him at his ease and woke up his dormant appetite, which was a very large one, poor fellow !

He was told all about Little Billee's death, and deeply moved to hear the cause which had brought it about, and then they talked of Trilby.

2 F

ENTER GECKO

He pulled her watch out of his waistcoat-pocket and reverently kissed it, exclaiming: 'Ah! c'était un ange! un ange du Paradis! when I tell you I lived with them for five years! Oh! her kindness, Dio, Dio Maria! It was "Gecko this!" and "Gecko that!" and "Poor Gecko, your toothache, how it worries me!" and "Gecko, how tired and pale you look—you distress me so, looking like that! Shall I mix you a maitrank?" And "Gecko, you love artichokes à la Barigoule; they remind you of Paris—I have heard you say so. Well, I have found out where to get artichokes, and I know how to do them à la Barigoule, and you shall have them for dinner to-day and to-morrow and all the week after!" and we did!

'Ach! dear kind one—what did I really care for artichokes à la Barigoule? . . .

'And it was always like that—always—and to Svengali and old Marta just the same! and she was never well—never! *toujours souffrante!*

'And it was she who supported us all—in luxury and splendour sometimes!'

'And *what* an artist!' said Taffy.

'Ah, yes! but all that was Svengali, you know. Svengali was the greatest artist I ever met! Monsieur, Svengali was a demon, a magician! I used to think him a god! He found me playing in the streets for copper coins, and took me by the hand, and was my only friend, and taught me all I ever knew—and yet he could not play my instrument!

'And now he is dead, I have forgotten how to play it myself! That English jail! it demoralised me, ruined me for ever! ach! quel enfer, nom de Dieu (pardon, madame)! I am just good enough to play the *obbligato* at the Mouches d'Espagne, when the old Cantharidi sings,

> ' " V'là mon mari qui r'garde !
> Prends garde—ne m'chatouille plus ! " '

'It does not want much of an *obbligato, hein,* a song so noble and so beautiful as that !

'And that song, monsieur, all Paris is singing it now. And that is the Paris that went mad when Trilby sang the "Nussbaum" of Schumann at the Salle des Bashi-bazoucks. You heard her ? Well ! '

And here poor Gecko tried to laugh a little sardonic laugh in falsetto, like Svengali's, full of scorn and bitterness—and very nearly succeeded.

'But what made you strike him with—with that knife, you know ? '

'Ah, monsieur, it had been coming on for a long time. He used to work Trilby too hard ; it was killing her—it killed her at last ! And then at the end he was unkind to her and scolded her and called her names—horrid names—and then one day in London he struck her. He struck her on the fingers with his bâton, and she fell down on her knees and cried. . . .

'Monsieur, I would have defended Trilby against a locomotive going *grande vitesse !* against my own father—against the Emperor of Austria—against the Pope ! and I am a good Catholic, monsieur ! I would have gone to the scaffold for her, and to the devil after ! '

And he piously crossed himself.

'But, Svengali—wasn't *he* very fond of her ? '

'Oh yes, monsieur ! *quant à ça,* passionately ! But she did not love him as he wished to be loved. She loved Litrebili, monsieur ! Litrebili, the brother of madame. And I suppose that Svengali grew angry and jealous at last. He changed as soon as he came to Paris. Perhaps Paris reminded him of Litrebili—and reminded Trilby, too!'

'But how on earth did Svengali ever manage to teach her how to sing like that? She had no ear for music whatever when *we* knew her!'

Gecko was silent for a while, and Taffy filled his glass, and gave him a cigar, and lit one himself.

'Monsieur, no—that is true. She had not much ear. But she had such a voice as had never been heard. Svengali knew that. He had found it out long ago. Litolff had found it out, too. One day Svengali heard Litolff tell Meyerbeer that the most beautiful female voice in Europe belonged to an English grisette who sat as a model to sculptors in the Quartier Latin, but that unfortunately she was quite tone-deaf, and couldn't sing one single note in tune. Imagine how Svengali chuckled! I see it from here!

'Well, we both taught her together—for three years— morning, noon, and night—six—eight hours a day. It used to split me the heart to see her worked like that! We took her voice note by note—there was no end to her notes, each more beautiful than the other—velvet and gold, beautiful flowers, pearls, diamonds, rubies—drops of dew and honey ; peaches, oranges, and lemons! *en veux- tu en voilà !*—all the perfumes and spices of the Garden of Eden! Svengali with his little flexible flageolet, I with my violin—that is how we taught her to make the sounds—and then how to use them. She was a *phénomène* monsieur! She could keep on one note and make it go through all the colours in the rainbow—according to the

way Svengali looked at her. It would make you laugh
—it would make you cry—but, cry or laugh, it was the
sweetest, the most touching, the most beautiful note you
ever heard—except all her others! and each had as

' "WE TOOK HER VOICE NOTE BY NOTE" '

many overtones as the bells in the Carillon de Notre
Dame. She could run up and down the scales, chromatic
scales, quicker and better and smoother than Svengali on
the piano, and more in tune than any piano! and her
shake—*ach!* twin stars, monsieur! She was the greatest

contralto, the greatest soprano the world has ever known! the like of her has never been! the like of her will never be again! and yet she only sang in public for two years!

'*Ach!* those breaks and runs and sudden leaps from darkness into light and back again—from earth to heaven!... those slurs and swoops and slides à la Paganini from one note to another, like a swallow flying! ... or a gull! Do you remember them? how they drove you mad? Let any other singer in the world try to imitate them—they would make you sick! That was Svengali ... he was a magician!

'And how she looked, singing! do you remember? her hands behind her—her dear, sweet, slender foot on a little stool—her thick hair lying down all along her back! And that good smile like the Madonna's, so soft and bright and kind! *Ach! Bel ucel di Dio!* it was to make you weep for love, merely to see her (*c'était à vous faire pleurer d'amour, rien que de la voir*)! That was Trilby! Nightingale and bird of paradise in one!

'*Enfin* she could do anything—utter any sound she liked, when once Svengali had shown her how—and he was the greatest master that ever lived! and when once she knew a thing, she knew it. *Et voilà!*'

'How strange,' said Taffy, 'that she should have suddenly gone out of her senses that night at Drury Lane, and so completely forgotten it all! I suppose she saw Svengali die in the box opposite, and that drove her mad!'

And then Taffy told the little fiddler about Trilby's death-song, like a swan's, and Svengali's photograph. But Gecko had heard it all from Marta, who was now dead.

Gecko sat and smoked and pondered for a while, and

looked from one to the other. Then he pulled himself together with an effort, so to speak, and said, 'Monsieur, she never went mad—not for one moment!'

'What? Do you mean to say she *deceived* us all ?'

'Non, monsieur! She could never deceive anybody, and never would. *She had forgotten—voilà tout !*'

'But hang it all, my friend, one doesn't *forget* such a——'

'Monsieur, listen! She is dead. And Svengali is dead —and Marta also. And I have a good little malady that will kill me soon, *Gott sei dank*—and without much pain.

'I will tell you a secret.

'*There were two Trilbys.* There was the Trilby you knew, who could not sing one single note in tune. She was an angel of paradise. She is now! But she had no more idea of singing than I have of winning a steeple-chase at the croix de Berny. She could no more sing than a fiddle can play itself! She could never tell one tune from another—one note from the next. Do you remember how she tried to sing "Ben Bolt" that day when she first came to the studio in the Place St. Anatole des Arts? It was droll, *hein ? à se boucher les oreilles !* Well, that was Trilby, your Trilby! that was my Trilby too—and I loved her as one loves an only love, an only sister, an only child—a gentle martyr on earth, a blessed saint in heaven! And that Trilby was enough for *me !*

'And that was the Trilby that loved your brother, madame—oh! but with all the love that was in her! He did not know what he had lost, your brother! Her love, it was immense, like her voice, and just as full of celestial sweetness and sympathy! She told me every-thing! *ce pauvre Litrebili, ce qu'il a perdu !*

'But all at once—pr-r-r-out! presto! *augenblick!* . . . with one wave of his hand over her—with one look of his eye—with a word—Svengali could turn her into the other Trilby, *his* Trilby—and make her do whatever he liked . . . you might have run a red-hot needle into her and she would not have felt it. . . .

'He had but to say "*Dors!*" and she suddenly became an unconscious Trilby of marble, who could produce wonderful sounds—just the sounds he wanted, and nothing else—and think his thoughts and wish his wishes—and love him at his bidding with a strange, unreal, factitious love . . . just his own love for himself turned inside out —*à l'envers*—and reflected back on him, as from a mirror . . . *un écho, un simulacre, quoi! pas autre chose!* . . . It was not worth having! I was not even jealous!

'Well, that was the Trilby he taught how to sing— and—and I helped him, God of heaven forgive me! That Trilby was just a singing-machine—an organ to play upon—an instrument of music—a Stradivarius—a flexible flageolet of flesh and blood—a voice, and nothing more—just the unconscious voice that Svengali sang with —for it takes two to sing like La Svengali, monsieur— the one who has got the voice, and the one who knows what to do with it. . . . So that when you heard her sing the "Nussbaum," the "Impromptu," you heard Svengali singing with her voice, just as you hear Joachim play a *chaconne* of Bach with his fiddle! . . . Herr Joachim's fiddle . . . what does it know of Sebastian Bach? and as for *chaconnes* . . . *il s'en moque pas mal, ce fameux violon!* . . .

'And *our* Trilby . . . what did she know of Schumann, Chopin?—nothing at all! She mocked herself not badly

of Nussbaums and Impromptus . . . they would make
her yawn to demantibulate her jaws! . . . When Svengali's
Trilby was being taught to sing . . . when Svengali's
Trilby was singing—or seemed to *you* as if she were sing-

THE NIGHTINGALE'S FIRST SONG

ing—*our* Trilby had ceased to exist . . . *our* Trilby was
fast asleep . . . in fact, *our* Trilby was *dead*. . . .

'Ah, monsieur . . . that Trilby of Svengali's! I
have heard her sing to kings and queens in royal palaces!

. . . as no woman has ever sung before or since. . . . I have seen emperors and grand-dukes kiss her hand, monsieur—and their wives and daughters kiss her lips, and weep. . . .

'I have seen the horses taken out of her sledge and the pick of the nobility drag her home to the hotel . . . with torchlights and choruses and shoutings of glory and long life to her! . . . and serenades all night, under her window! . . . *she* never knew! she heard nothing—felt nothing—saw nothing! and she bowed to them, right and left, like a queen!

'I have played the fiddle for her while she sang in the streets, at fairs and festas and Kermessen . . . and seen the people go mad to hear her . . . and once, at Prague, Svengali fell down in a fit from sheer excitement! and then, suddenly, *our* Trilby woke up and wondered what it was all about . . . and we took him home and put him to bed and left him with Marta—and Trilby and I went together arm-in-arm all over the town to fetch a doctor and buy things for supper and that was the happiest hour in all my life!

'*Ach!* what an existence! what travels! what triumphs! what adventures! Things to fill a book—a dozen books— Those five happy years—with those two Trilbys! what recollections! . . . I think of nothing else, night or day . . . even as I play the fiddle for old Cantharidi. *Ach!* . . . To think how often I have played the fiddle for La Svengali . . . to have done that is to have lived . . . and then to come home to Trilby . . . *our* Trilby . . . the *real* Trilby! . . . Gott sei dank! Ich habe *geliebt und gelebet! geliebt und gelebet! geliebt und gelebet!* Cristo di Dio . . . Sweet sister in heaven . . . Ô Dieu de Misère, ayez pitié de nous. . . .'

His eyes were red, and his voice was high and shrill and tremulous and full of tears ; these remembrances were too much for him ; and perhaps also the chambertin ! He put his elbows on the table and hid his face in his hands and wept, muttering to himself in his own language (whatever that might have been—Polish, probably) as if he were praying.

Taffy and his wife got up and leaned on the window-bar and looked out on the deserted boulevards, where an army of scavengers, noiseless and taciturn, was cleansing the asphalt roadway. The night above was dark, but 'star-dials hinted of morn,' and a fresh breeze had sprung up, making the leaves dance and rustle on the sycamore trees along the boulevard—a nice little breeze ; just the sort of little breeze to do Paris good. A four-wheel cab came by at a foot pace, the driver humming a tune ; Taffy hailed him ; he said, 'V'là, m'sieur !' and drew up.

Taffy rang the bell, and asked for the bill, and paid it, Gecko had apparently fallen asleep. Taffy gently woke him up and told him how late it was. The poor little man seemed dazed and rather tipsy, and looked older than ever ; sixty, seventy—any age you like. Taffy helped him on with his great-coat, and taking him by the arm, led him downstairs, giving him his card, and telling him how glad he was to have seen him, and that he would write to him from England—a promise that was kept, one may be sure.

Gecko uncovered his fuzzy white head, and took Mrs.

Taffy's hand and kissed it, and thanked her warmly for her 'si bon et sympathique accueil.'

Then Taffy all but lifted him into the cab, the jolly cabman saying—

'Ah! bon—connais bien, celui là ; vous savez—c'est lui qui joue du violon aux Mouches d'Espagne ! Il a soupé, l'bourgeois ; n'est-ce pas, m'sieur ? "petits bonheurs de contrebande," hein ? . . . ayez pas peur ! on vous aura soin de lui ! il joue joliment bien, m'sieur ; n'est-ce pas ? '

Taffy shook Gecko's hand and asked,

'Où restez - vous, Gecko ? '

"'ICH HABE *GELIEBT UND GELEBET!*'"

' Quarante-huit Rue des Pousse-cailloux, au cinquième.'

' How strange ! ' said Taffy to his wife—' how touching ! why, that's where Trilby used to live—the very number ! the very floor ! '

' Oui, oui,' said Gecko, waking up ; ' c'est l'ancienne mansarde à Trilby—j'y suis depuis douze ans—*j'y suis, j'y reste. . . .*'

And he laughed feebly at his mild little joke.

Taffy told the address to the cabman, and gave him five francs.

' Merci, m'sieur ! C'est de l'aut' côté de l'eau—près de la Sorbonne, s'pas ? On vous aura soin du bourgeois ; soyez tranquille—ayez pas peur ! quarante-huit ; on y va. Bonsoir, monsieur et dame ! ' And he clacked his whip and rattled away, singing :—

> ' V'là mon mari qui r'garde—
> Prends garde !
> Ne m'chatouill' plus ! '

Mr. and Mrs. Wynne walked back to the hotel, which was not far. She hung on to his big arm and crept close to him, and shivered a little. It was quite chilly. Their footsteps were very audible in the stillness; 'pit-pat, floppety-clop,' otherwise they were both silent. They were tired, yawny, sleepy, and very sad ; and each was thinking (and knew the other was thinking) that a week in Paris was just enough—and how nice it would be, in just a few hours more, to hear the rooks cawing round their own quiet little English country home—where three jolly boys would soon be coming for the holidays.

And there we will leave them to their useful, humdrum, happy domestic existence—than which there is no better that I know of, at their time of life—and no better time of life than theirs!

' Où peut-on être mieux qu'au sein de sa famille?'

That blessed harbour of refuge well within our reach, and having really cut our wisdom teeth at last, and learned the ropes, and left off hankering after the moon— we can do with so little down here. . . .

> A little work, a little play
> To keep us going—and so, good-day!
>
> A little warmth, a little light
> Of love's bestowing—and so, good-night!
>
> A little fun, to match the sorrow
> Of each day's growing—and so, good-morrow!
>
> A little trust that when we die
> We reap our sowing! And so—good-bye!

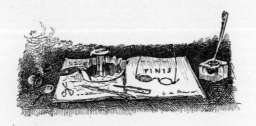

Printed by R. & R. CLARK, LIMITED, *Edinburgh.*

MISCELLANEOUS WORKS.

MEMOIRS OF BARRAS, Member of the Directorate. Edited with a General Introduction, Prefaces, and Appendices, by GEORGE DURUY. Translated by C. E. ROCHE. With seven Portraits in Heliogravure, two Facsimiles, and two Plans. In four volumes. The first two will be published 15th May 1895, the last two February 1896. Large demy 8vo, handsomely bound in buckram, gilt top. 16s. per vol.

" For more than half a century students and writers of history have been expecting the publication of the Memoirs of the Vicomte Paul Barras. After many curious adventures, the Memoirs have fallen into the hands of M. George Duruy, the eminent historian. M. Duruy has edited them for publication, and written a remarkable preface to each of the first two volumes.

" In these Memoirs, Barras spares nobody. Carnot, the 'Organiser of Victory,' appears under a new aspect. Cochon, the Minister of Police, is shown up. The quarrels, ambitions, and rascalities of the Directors are all recorded by the Memoirist. Tallyrand, Fouché, Danton, Robespierre, Marat, Fouquier-Tinville, Madame de Stael, Madame Tallien, Benjamin Constant, are all described and criticised. But—need it be said—the most interesting of all Barras' pen-and-ink portraits is that of Napoleon. If any mortal could be said to have 'made' Napoleon, it was Barras. To Barras, more than to any man, the friendless, almost despairing young Corsican interloper owed his first chance. Barras was the first to detect genius in the sallow, lanky, underfed, silent, and rather morose, lieutenant of artillery. In the end, as all men know, Barras became one of Napoleon's bitterest enemies.

" We understand that 'the connection between Josephine de Beauharnais, Barras, and Bonaparte is at last told by Barras, with particulars of a piquant order.' One of the curiosities among the illustrations is Robespierre's signature, which he had only partly written when he was shot down by the gendarme Méda."—*From the* DAILY NEWS, *30th March* 1895.

THE LIFE OF MARIE ANTOINETTE. By MAXIME DE LA ROCHETERIE. With Twenty-seven Portraits. Two vols. Cloth extra. 21s.

" No life of Marie Antoinette that has yet been published is as good as that of M. de la Rocheterie."—*Spectator.*

DUC DE LAUZUN: The Private Court Life of Louis XV. Translated from the French of GASTON MAUGRAS. With Portrait. Demy 8vo, cloth extra. 12s. 6d.

Extract from the Preface :—

" It was from a copy of the copy preserved by Queen Hortense that the first edition of the *Mémoires de Lauzun* was printed, and published in 1821 by Barrois *ainé.* It produced great excitement in society, for several persons to whom it alluded in no discreet terms were then still living. Indignant protests arose on all sides, the edition was confiscated, and it was declared to be a forgery."—GASTON MAUGRAS.

THE EMPRESS EUGÉNIE: or The Secret of an Empire. By PIERRE DE LANO. Crown 8vo, cloth extra. 6s.

LONDON : OSGOOD, McILVAINE & CO., 45 ALBEMARLE STREET, W.

FICTION.

NEW BOOKS.

A DAUGHTER OF THE SOIL. A Novel. By M. E.
FRANCIS, Author of "The Story of Dan," and "In a North-Country
Village." Crown 8vo, cloth extra. **6s.**

THE LIGHT OF SCARTHEY. By EGERTON CASTLE,
Author of "Schools and Masters of Fence from the Middle Ages,"
"Consequences," "La Bella," etc. Crown 8vo, cloth extra. **6s.**

COMRADES IN ARMS. A Military Romance. By
ARTHUR AMYAND, Author of "Only a Drummer Boy" and "With
Rank and File." Crown 8vo, cloth extra. **6s.**

A PLIABLE MARRIAGE. A Novel. By PERCIVAL
PICKERING. Crown 8vo, cloth. **3s. 6d.**

LORD STIRLING'S SON. A Novel. By A. H. MARSHALL.
Crown 8vo, cloth. **3s. 6d.**

THE JUDGMENT BOOKS. By E. F. BENSON, Author
of "Dodo," "Six Common Things," etc. Crown 8vo, cloth extra. **3s. 6d.**

THE CRUCIFIX. By LAURENCE ALMA-TADEMA, Author of
"The Wings of Icarus." Crown 8vo, cloth extra. **3s. 6d.**

WITH RANK AND FILE: Sidelights on Soldier Life. By
ARTHUR AMYAND (Captain A. HAGGARD), Author of "Only a Drummer
Boy." Crown 8vo, cloth. **3s. 6d.**

"Mr. Amyand seems to have derived his inspiration to some extent from Mr. Kipling.
All the stories in the book are admirably told. They are full of sympathetic insight, and
without exception leave a vivid impression on the imagination of the reader. Cannot fail to
be read with pleasure by all whose tastes include military fiction."—*Glasgow Herald.*

LONDON: OSGOOD, McILVAINE & CO., 45 ALBEMARLE STREET, W.

FICTION.

SOME EVERY-DAY FOLKS. By EDEN PHILLPOTTS

Crown 8vo, cloth extra. 6s.

"There is wherewithal to suit all tastes and temperaments. Modern fictional literature cannot boast of an abler or more entertaining work."—*Daily Telegraph.*

PEMBROKE. By MARY E. WILKINS, Author of "A New

England Nun," "Jane Field," "Young Lucretia," etc. Crown 8vo, cloth extra. 6s.

"Miss Mary Wilkins has fairly surpassed her predecessors in this kind of fiction."—*The Times.*

"This is the gem of Miss Wilkins's very remarkable productions."—*The Spectator.*

THE MAIDEN'S PROGRESS. A Novel in Dialogue.

By VIOLET HUNT. Crown 8vo, cloth extra. 6s.

"A cleverly written satire upon modern young-lady society, free from the indelicacies to be found in some 'modern women' novels, and shows a deeper insight into human nature."—*Christian World.*

"That Miss Hunt's is among the most brilliant of the successes of the day no one who reads her *Maiden's Progress* will deny."—*Literary World.*

A WARD IN CHANCERY. By Mrs. ALEXANDER. Crown

8vo, cloth extra. 6s.

"Mrs. Alexander's skill in drawing a charming heroine is almost unrivalled. Her style keeps its easy fluency."—*Daily Chronicle.*

LENA'S PICTURE. By Mrs. RUSSELL BARRINGTON. Crown

8vo, cloth. 5s.

"The story is told from the realistic point of view; but whereas most realism sounds the note of hopelessness, often of despair, Mrs. Barrington's, for all its sadness, is full of hope and faith. And in this she sounds a truer note than do most of the other realists."—*Pall Mall Gazette.*

LONDON: OSGOOD, McILVAINE & CO., 45 ALBEMARLE STREET, W.

FICTION.

THE TWO LANCROFTS. By C. F. KEARY. Crown 8vo, cloth extra. 6s.

"One of the most striking and original novels which have appeared for a very long time."—*Saturday Review*.

HELEN'S ORDEAL. By Mrs. RUSSELL BARRINGTON, Author of "Lena's Picture." Crown 8vo, cloth. 6s.

"A very delightful tale—delightful because the subject is so fresh and original, and so full of a noble idealism."—*Spectator*.

LOVE ON A MORTAL LEASE. By O. SHAKESPEAR. Crown 8vo, cloth. 6s.

"A strong and clever story."—*Morning Post*.
"Exceedingly well told."—*Pall Mall Gazette*.

FOR HONOUR AND LIFE. By WILLIAM WESTALL. Crown 8vo, cloth extra. 6s.

"An excellent tale of adventure, with an abundance of hairbreadth escapes and thrilling episodes."—*The Speaker*.

THE GOLDEN HOUSE. By CHARLES DUDLEY WARNER. Crown 8vo, cloth extra. 6s. Second Edition.

"Fresh, racy, clever sketches of society and scenes in New York."—*Spectator*.

THE STORY OF DAN. A Romance of Irish Peasant Life. By M. E. FRANCIS, Author of "In a North-Country Village." Crown 8vo, cloth. 3s. 6d.

"It is, so far, Mrs. Francis' best achievement . . . 'a village tragedy' at once powerful and persuasive."—*Freeman's Journal*.

ONLY A DRUMMER BOY. A Realistic Tale of Regimental Life. By ARTHUR AMYAND. Crown 8vo, cloth. 3s. 6d.

"Deals with the adventures of a drummer-boy who is 'really and truly' the heir to a baronetcy."—*Scottish Leader*.

"Presents the army and the British soldier in an attractive light."—*Public Opinion*.

LONDON : OSGOOD, McILVAINE & CO., 45 ALBEMARLE STREET, W.